Physical Geography

The Global Environment

Physical Geography

H.J. de Blij • Peter O. Muller • Richard S. Williams, Jr.
Cathy T. Conrad • Peter Long

Physical Geography
The Global Environment

Second Canadian Edition

OXFORD
UNIVERSITY PRESS

OXFORD

UNIVERSITY PRESS

8 Sampson Mews, Suite 204, Don Mills, Ontario M3C 0H5
www.oupcanada.com

Oxford University Press is a department of the University of Oxford.
It furthers the University's objective of excellence in research, scholarship,
and education by publishing worldwide in

Oxford New York
Auckland Cape Town Dar es Salaam Hong Kong Karachi
Kuala Lumpur Madrid Melbourne Mexico City Nairobi
New Delhi Shanghai Taipei Toronto

With offices in
Argentina Austria Brazil Chile Czech Republic France Greece
Guatemala Hungary Italy Japan Poland Portugal Singapore
South Korea Switzerland Thailand Turkey Ukraine Vietnam

Oxford is a trade mark of Oxford University Press
in the UK and in certain other countries

Published in Canada
by Oxford University Press

Copyright © Oxford University Press Canada 2009

The moral rights of the author have been asserted

Database right Oxford University Press (maker)

First published 2009

Library and Archives Canada Cataloguing in Publication

Physical geography : the global environment / H.J. de
Blij ... [et al.]. – 2nd Canadian ed.

Includes bibliographical references and index.
ISBN 978-0-19-542897-1

1. Physical geography–Textbooks. I. De Blij, Harm J.

GB55.P49 2009   910'.02   C2008-908019-X

Cover Image: Ethan Melag/Getty Images

4 5 6 - 18 17 16
Printed in the United States of America

Contents Overview

PART THREE   The Restless Crust

PART FOUR   Sculpting the Surface

PART FIVE   The Biosphere

Detailed Contents

(Each unit includes Objectives, Key Terms, Review Questions, References and Further Readings, and Web Resources.)

PART ONE A Global Perspective

PART TWO Atmosphere and Hydrosphere

PART THREE   The Restless Crust

PART FOUR   Sculpting the Surface

PART FIVE The Biosphere

Perspectives on the Human Environment

Boxes by Unit

Content Correlation Guide

In *Physical Geography* you will find marginal icons that highlight key themes and topics that recur throughout the text. We've developed the following guide to help you trace the major topics of physical geography through the different units.

Page References by Topic

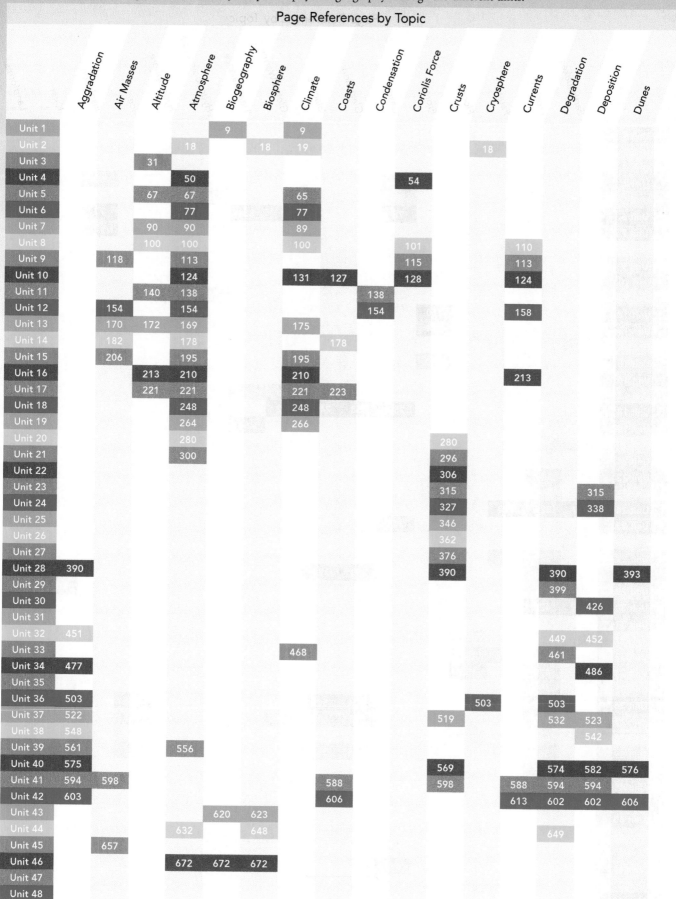

	Aggradation	Air Masses	Altitude	Atmosphere	Biogeography	Biosphere	Climate	Coasts	Condensation	Coriolis Force	Crusts	Cryosphere	Currents	Degradation	Deposition	Dunes
Unit 1					9		9									
Unit 2				18		18	19					18				
Unit 3			31													
Unit 4				50						54						
Unit 5			67	67			65									
Unit 6				77			77									
Unit 7			90	90			89									
Unit 8			100	100			100		101				110			
Unit 9		118		113					115				113			
Unit 10				124			131	127	128				124			
Unit 11		140		138						138						
Unit 12		154		154						154			158			
Unit 13		172	170	169			175									
Unit 14			182	178				178								
Unit 15			206	195			195									
Unit 16			213	210			210						213			
Unit 17			221	221			221	223								
Unit 18				248			248									
Unit 19				264			266									
Unit 20				280						280						
Unit 21				300						296						
Unit 22										306						
Unit 23										315					315	
Unit 24										327					338	
Unit 25										346						
Unit 26										362						
Unit 27										376						
Unit 28	390									390				390		393
Unit 29														399		
Unit 30															426	
Unit 31																
Unit 32	451													449	452	
Unit 33						468								461		
Unit 34	477														486	
Unit 35																
Unit 36	503											503		503		
Unit 37	522										519			532	523	
Unit 38	548														542	
Unit 39	561			556												
Unit 40	575									569				574	582	576
Unit 41	594	598						588		598			588	594	594	
Unit 42	603						606						613	602	602	606
Unit 43					620	623										
Unit 44			632			648									649	
Unit 45		657														
Unit 46				672	672	672										
Unit 47																
Unit 48																

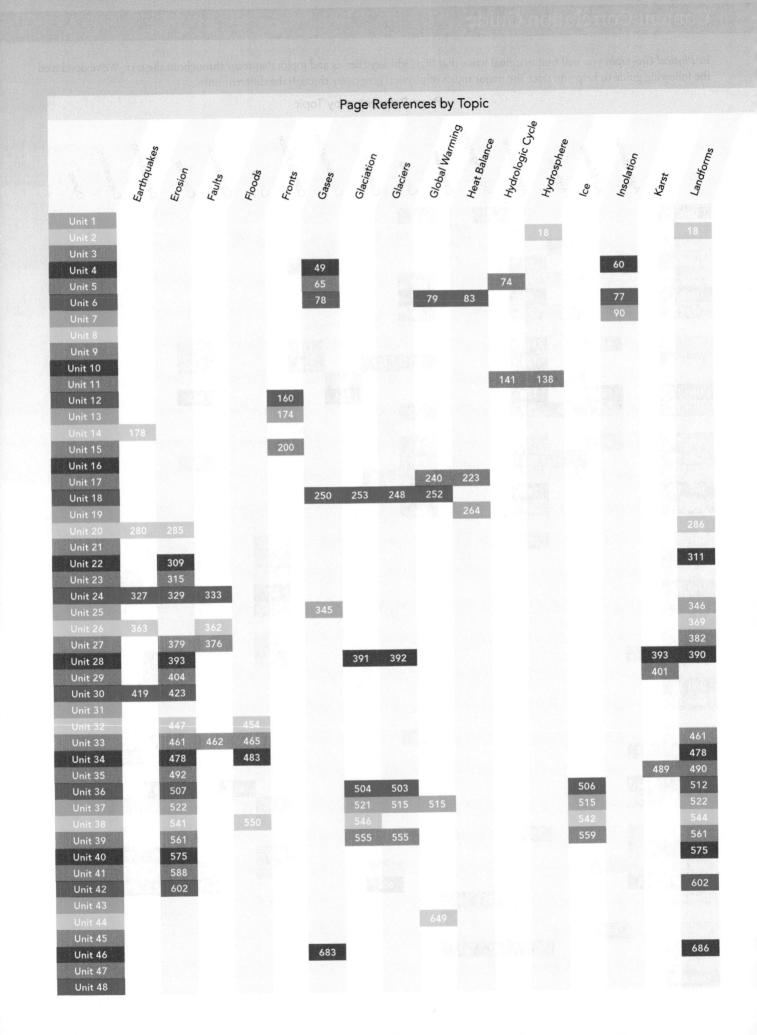

Page References by Topic

Page References by Topic

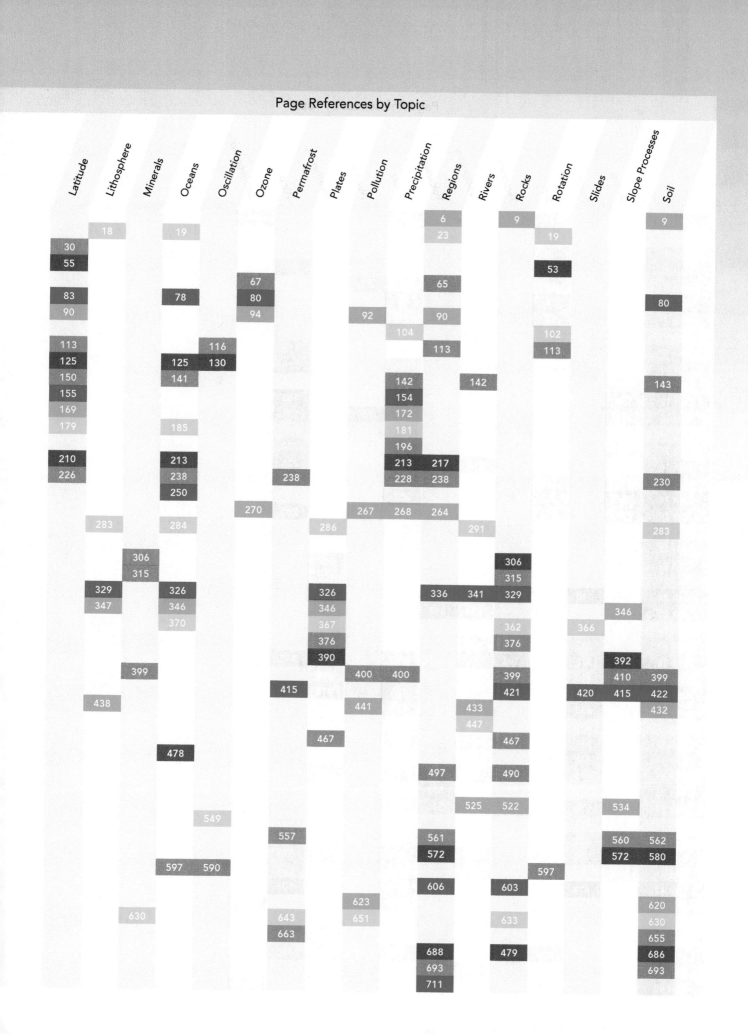

Page References by Topic

	Storms	Streams	Sun	Tectonics	Topography	Volcanism	Water	Weather	Weathering	Wind	Zoogeography
Unit 1			7				9				9
Unit 2						25	20				
Unit 3			30								
Unit 4			48							50	
Unit 5			69				67	65			
Unit 6			77				80				
Unit 7			97				91				
Unit 8					106		106			100	
Unit 9			116							115	
Unit 10							124			126	
Unit 11		148					144				
Unit 12		156					155			163	
Unit 13		169						169		171	
Unit 14		178						178		179	
Unit 15		203								200	
Unit 16					213					213	
Unit 17		240	224								
Unit 18		258	255				257				
Unit 19		272	264					266		265	
Unit 20					287				285		
Unit 21											
Unit 22									307		
Unit 23									320		
Unit 24			340	326	329	328			338		
Unit 25					354	345					
Unit 26											
Unit 27			382	377	380				377		
Unit 28			392	393	390		392		391	393	
Unit 29			410				399		399		
Unit 30			426				426		418		
Unit 31			433				438				
Unit 32			450				450		250		
Unit 33			461	467	461		465				
Unit 34			478								
Unit 35			495		489		492		493		
Unit 36						505					
Unit 37			533	519	516	516	535				
Unit 38			541				542				
Unit 39			560				559		559	561	
Unit 40	573		570		578		568		569	573	
Unit 41	598				588		596			588	
Unit 42			613				602			606	
Unit 43							620				623
Unit 44					636		650		630	630	
Unit 45									666		
Unit 46			676	680			685		678	685	
Unit 47					693						
Unit 48											706

Preface to the Second Canadian Edition

Building on the foundation provided by the first Canadian edition of *Physical Geography: The Global Environment*, this new edition retains the international scope of the American original but takes advantage of Canada's exceptional physical diversity to add a wealth of new material that Canadian students can relate to, on topics ranging from wind patterns to geomorphological processes, from soil classification to hurricanes, from permafrost to drought, from avalanches to mega-volcanoes, from water use to flooding, and from air pollution to weather analysis—to name only a few.

New additions to the second Canadian edition include:

- More details on Canadian contributions to mapping and technology, including Geographic Information Systems.
- Reorganization of former units to better reflect modern teaching themes in introductory physical geography courses.
- Enhanced content related to weather and climate, with the inclusion of fundamental mathematical concepts on those topics.
- New material on wind systems and the Coriolis force.
- Inclusion of content on the Pacific Decadal Oscillation and Arctic Oscillation, which, with the North Atlantic Oscillation, are increasingly understood to drive decadal-scale fluctuations in global climate.
- More content on precipitation processes.
- New and updated 'Perspectives on the Human Environment' boxes, including fog as a particularly Canadian hazard, Mount Everest and the jet stream, carbon footprints, near-Earth objects and the movies, the Northwest Passage, the significance of Iceland as a living laboratory for physical geographical research, and dunes and the growth of the game of golf.
- New and updated information on humans, climate change, and weather, including sections on smog, green technologies, and weather modification.
- New units on severe weather, impact cratering, and fluvioglacial processes and landforms.
- Expanded coverage on all aspects of soils and vegetation, and on human impacts on soils.
- Added material on lakes, biogeochemical cycling, and arid environments and aeolian processes.
- New end-of-book student exercises.
- New links to other units.
- A completely revised Glossary.

In addition, the second Canadian edition of *Physical Geography* includes many new photographs and diagrams, and updated readings and online resources at the end of each unit.

The result, we hope, is a book that will engage Canadian students and provide a solid base for lifelong exploration of the physical world in all its variety, whether in Canada or around the globe.

Acknowledgements

Cathy Conrad thanks her colleagues and students in the Department of Geography at Saint Mary's University. She would also like to thank the cartographer at SMU, Don Bonner, for his research and his preparation of some of the maps in the earlier units. Thanks to Anne Baker for ongoing support and assistance in administrative matters. Finally, she thanks her husband, Scott, and sons, Jakob and Sam. It is wonderful to enjoy this amazing environment we live in with all of you. It is my hope that it will be preserved and protected for future generations to come.

Peter Long would like to thank his friends (faculty, staff, graduate and undergraduate students) in the Department of Geography at York University; the staff of the Scott Map Library (especially Mary McDowell and Dana Craig) and the Geography Department's Geographic Resources Centre (Mike Flosznik and Rita Parente) for helping to find maps and other resources on some fairly arcane subjects; and John Radford, the former chair of the Department, for permission to reprint some exceptional images from the Hans Carol slide collection. He is grateful to Professor Osamu Oshima of the University of Tokyo at Komaba, Japan, for information about earthquake and volcanic preparedness and hazards, and to Dr Catherine Hickson of the Geological Survey of Canada in Vancouver, who provided information about the Anahim Volcanic Belt in BC. He would also like to express his thanks to Dr Christopher Green, FRGS, FGS (Honorary Research Fellow, Centre for Quaternary Research, Department of Geography, Royal Holloway, University of London), for instilling in him a deep appreciation for geomorphology and Pleistocene studies when he was a callow student during the early and mid-1970s. Dr Green remains a constant inspiration. Finally, Peter thanks his wife, Christine, and son, Adam, who remain a continued source of love and much support.

In addition, we are both very grateful to our colleagues Roger Phillips (Aquafor Beech Ltd.), Gita Laidler (Carleton University), John Menzies (Brock University), Philip Giles (Saint Mary's University), Norm Catto (Memorial University of Newfoundland), and Blair Hrabi (SRK Consulting Engineers & Scientists) for their contributions to the 'Canadian Geographers in the Field' sections. We would also like to thank the wonderful editorial staff at Oxford University Press Canada, including Katherine Skene, Jennifer Charlton, and Phyllis Wilson, and our copy editor, Richard Tallman.

We would like to thank the following reviewers, whose thoughtful comments and suggestions helped to shape the first and second edition.

Claire Beaney, University College of the Fraser Valley
Norm Catto, Memorial University of Newfoundland
Daryl Dagesse, Brock University
Philip Giles, Saint Mary's University
John Iacozza, University of Manitoba
Matthew Letts, University of Lethbridge
John Lindsay, University of Guelph
John Maclachlan, McMaster University
Anne Marie Ryan, Dalhousie University
Susan Smythe, Douglas College

Cathy Conrad
Peter Long

From the Publisher

Few subjects have been more central to human beings than the study of the physical world. Yet it is only in the past five hundred years—and particularly the last hundred and fifty—that we have begun to have any scientific understanding of the Earth and the processes that continue to shape it.

Today we are becoming aware that the most crucial social and political issues are often inextricably linked to geographic realities: from the finite nature of the world's water supplies and the location of its oil reserves to the massive changes that are already underway as a result of global warming. A basic understanding of our physical environment—its nature, history, and limitations—has never been more vital to the average citizen. And as the present century progresses, environmental issues will undoubtedly come to play an ever more central role in shaping the fate not just of nations but of every individual on Earth.

With these considerations in mind, Oxford University Press is proud to publish the second Canadian edition of *Physical Geography: The Global Environment*. Of course there is nothing uniquely Canadian about the subject of physical geography; it would be hard to imagine a more international discipline. But under its broad umbrella there are distinctive contributions made by Canadian scholars, as well as topics of special interest to students living in a country whose physical geography is one of the most diverse anywhere on the Earth. This text provides the most authoritative introduction to physical geography now available, in a way that is accessible and engaging for Canadian students.

Special Features of This Text

Physical Geography: The Global Environment includes numerous features designed to make its subject matter accessible and interesting to students. Among them are the following:

- *A stunning new four-colour design.* Physical geography is by nature one of the most visually oriented of all the sciences. *Physical Geography* presents:

▶ Visually appealing charts and diagrams that are clear and easy to interpret.

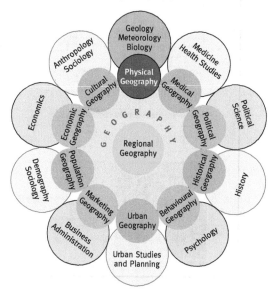

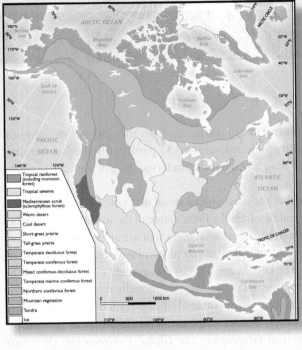

▶ **Attractive maps that are informative and effortless to read.**

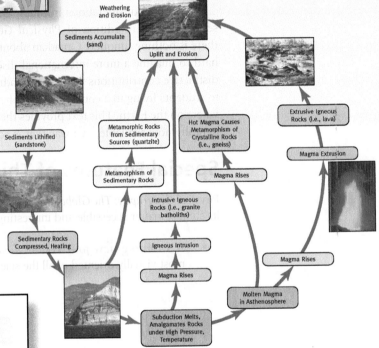

▶ **Illustrations that show features of the natural world as realistically as possible.**

▶ **A text that is straightforward to navigate and inviting to read.**

- *Student-centred learning resources.* A good textbook is not the final word on its subject but an invitation to further learning. At the end of each chapter are several pedagogical features designed with this purpose in mind, including:

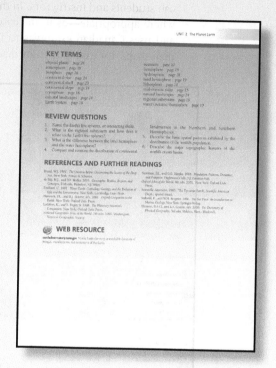

  ▶ *Key Terms* listed with page references;

  ▶ *Review Questions* focusing on major themes and topics of the chapter;

  ▶ *References and Further Readings* intended to direct students to useful print resources; and

  ▶ *Web Resources* annotated by the authors to highlight their potential value for further research.

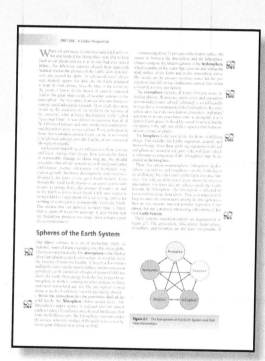

  ▶ *Links to other Units.* Marginal icons highlight key themes and topics that occur throughout the text. A Content Correlation Guide at the start of the book summarizes the cross-references so that students can make important linkages between core concepts.

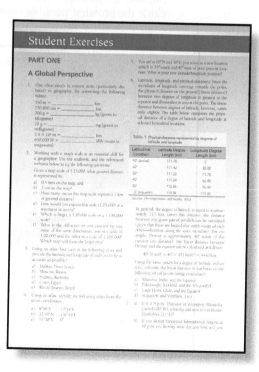

  ▶ *End-of-book Student Exercises* introduce students to the practical side of physical geography;

- *Canadian content where appropriate.* It's true that astronauts looking at the Earth from space see no national boundaries. But imaginary lines can still have real effects. Texts published for the US market naturally reflect the needs and interests of American students and instructors. In the same way, this text highlights Canadian content where appropriate—as in the case of the Canadian System of Soil Classification—and uses Canadian examples to illustrate fundamental concepts—featuring Canadian maps, for example, in its discussion of standard cartographic symbols.

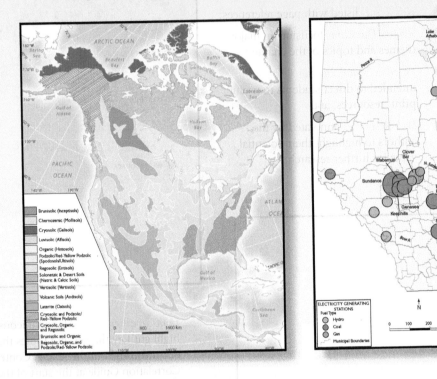

- *International coverage.* At the same time—as the book's subtitle reminds us—physical geography is a global discipline. Hence every effort has been made to include the broadest possible range of international examples and research.

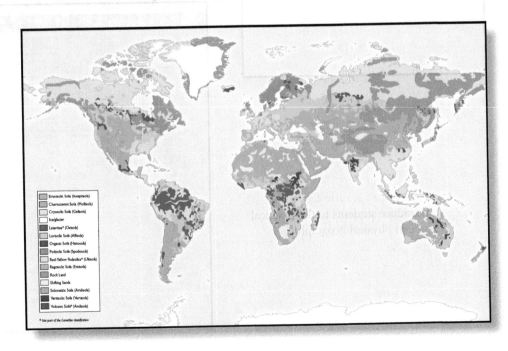

- *Canadian Geographers in the Field.* Drawn from the notebooks of practising geographers, these boxes offer students direct insight into the research process.

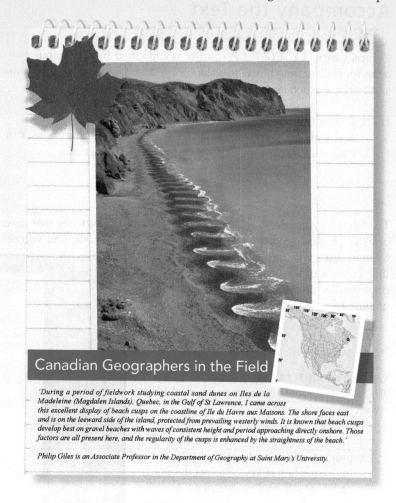

Canadian Geographers in the Field

'During a period of fieldwork studying coastal sand dunes on Iles de la Madeleine (Magdalen Islands), Quebec, in the Gulf of St Lawrence, I came across this excellent display of beach cusps on the coastline of Ile du Havre aux Maisons. The shore faces east and is on the leeward side of the island, protected from prevailing westerly winds. It is known that beach cusps develop best on gravel beaches with waves of consistent height and period approaching directly onshore. Those factors are all present here, and the regularity of the cusps is enhanced by the straightness of the beach.'

Philip Giles is an Associate Professor in the Department of Geography at Saint Mary's University.

- *Perspectives on the Human Environment.* These special boxed features provide additional insight into important and interesting issues, beyond the coverage included in the body of the text. For instance, 'Sliding Scale' places humans in the broad context of the physical world.

Perspectives on the Human Environment

Sliding Scale

Imagine a couple sun bathing on Cavendish Beach. We can photograph them occupying a square of sand about 1 m on a side. If we move the camera higher, a square of 10 (10^1) m reveals their companions. When we focus on a 100 (10^2) m area, we can see a crowd of people on the beach. A picture of 1000 (10^3) m includes the beach, some sea, and some land (as in Figure 1.6). One with an edge of 10,000 (10^4) m captures most of Prince Edward Island National Park and parts of the neighbouring north shore of Prince Edward Island.

Moving the camera still farther, we shoot a picture of a 100,000 (10^5) m square. It encompasses most of the central PEI region. The next step is 1,000,000 (10^6) m. This snapshot takes in the entire province of PEI, some neighbouring provinces, and parts of the Atlantic Ocean, the Gulf of St Lawrence, and the Bay of Fundy. A photo at the next level of generalization, showing a square of 10,000,000 (10^7) m, covers most of the visible Earth. And if the camera is far enough away in outer space to focus on a square of 100,000,000 (10^8) m, we see Planet Earth as a small globe. Somewhere on it is that couple lying on a square of Cavendish Beach's seaside sand.

Instructors' and Students' Supplements to Accompany the Text

Physical Geography: A Global Perspective is supported by a wide range of supplementary items for students and instructors alike, all designed to enhance and complete the learning and teaching experience.

Included in the book:

- An exciting new *DVD-ROM*, with visual models and animations, that allows students to explore the key concepts of physical geography.

Lab Manual

The laboratory manual contains over 20 hands-on lab exercises that cover the core concepts of physical geography—climate, geomorphology, soils, and vegetation & animals, to name just a few. Each lab relates to a particular unit or units of the textbook, using maps, aerial photographs, or data to highlight Canadian geographical features and localities.

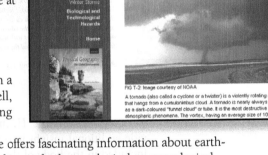

For Students

Online Resources:

The following student resources are available at www.oupcanada.com/deblij2

- *Student study guide.* This interactive program allows students to test their understanding of key concepts through a variety of self-grading questions. As well, the site offers links to additional learning resources; and
- *Natural Hazards website.* This website offers fascinating information about earthquakes, hurricanes, floods, winter weather, and other geological, meteorological, and biological hazards.

For Instructors

The following instructors' resources are available online to qualifying adopters. Please contact your OUP Canada sales representative for more information.

- *Instructors' manual.* A comprehensive resource package featuring lecture outlines, teaching objectives, media resources, small group and project ideas, and review questions.
- *PowerPoint slides.* Dozens of images, including maps, charts, and diagrams, digitized for classroom use.
- *Computerized Test Item File.* Fully interactive testing software not only provides hundreds of multiple choice, true/false, and short answer questions but makes it possible to customize exams; add new questions and modify existing ones; and publish tests to a variety of media, including print and the Web.

Physical Geography

The Global Environment

PART ONE
A Global Perspective

Units

PART ONE A Global Perspective

Relationships among the Five Spheres of the Earth System

Modern physical geographers view the Earth as the manifestation of a set of interconnected, interactive, interlocking systems that generate the forces, processes, and landscapes with which we are familiar. These geochemical, geophysical, and biological systems, propelled by innumerable subsidiary systems in which energy and matter are transported, stored, and redeployed, forge the Earth as we know it. Thus, the planet may be viewed in terms of five gigantic open (interacting) systems represented as *spheres* of which the oldest is the lithosphere, the sphere of rocks (and earthquakes and volcanoes), and the youngest is the biosphere, the realm of plants and animals. We experience the atmosphere and its weather subsystems; know the Earth as the 'blue planet' because the waters of the hydrosphere cover about 70 per cent of its surface; and are reminded by the ice of the cryosphere in polar and high-mountain areas that ice-age conditions, once much more extensive, still persist over parts of the globe. Dominant systems produce these discrete earthly spheres, but interactive processes prevail, and the borders among them, transitional in nature, vary in space and time.

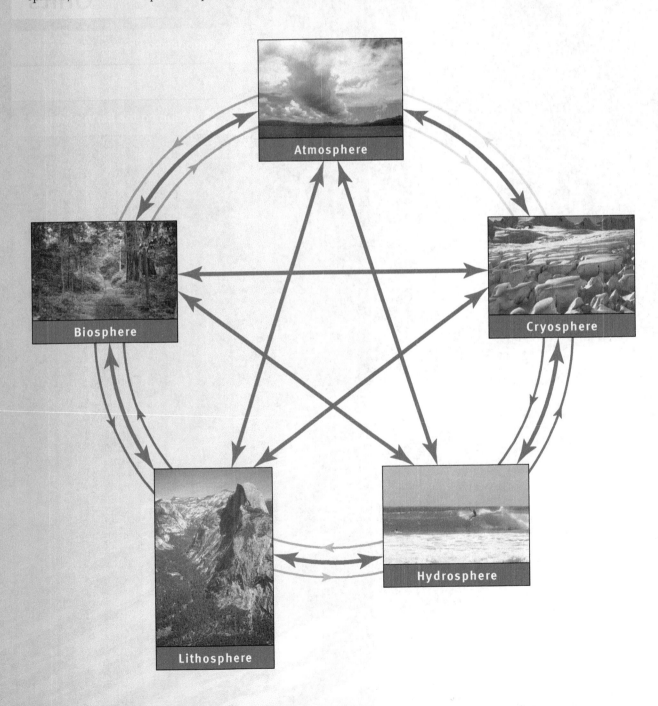

Introducing Physical Geography

Objectives

- To introduce and discuss the contemporary focus of physical geography.

- To relate physical geography to the other natural and physical sciences.

- To introduce the systems and modelling approaches to physical geography.

This is a book about the Earth's natural environments. Its title, *Physical Geography: The Global Environment*, suggests the unifying perspective. Earth's human habitat will be examined, with a focus on the fragile layer of life that sustains humanity along with millions of species of animals and plants. Features of the natural world—such as erupting volcanoes, winding rivers, advancing deserts, and changing shorelines—are examined not only as physical phenomena, but also in terms of their relation to human societies and communities.

Physical geography is a broad discipline, with physical geographers working on a great variety of research topics. The Earth will be discussed, therefore, from various vantage points. It will be studied in space and from space, from mountaintops and in underground shafts, from clouds and ocean waves to rocks and minerals, from fertile soils and verdant forests to arid deserts and icy wastelands.

Geography

Geographers, of course, are not the only researchers studying the Earth's surface. Geologists, meteorologists, biologists, hydrologists, and scientists from many other disciplines also study aspects of the planetary surface and what lies above and below it. But only geography combines and integrates, and *synthesizes* knowledge from all these other fields as it makes its own research contributions. Time and again in this book you will become aware of connections among physical phenomena and between natural phenomena and human activities of which you might not have become aware in another course.

Although geography is a modern discipline in which scientists increasingly use high-technology research equipment, its roots extend to the very dawn of scholarly inquiry. When the ancient Greeks realized the need to organize the knowledge they were gathering, they divided it all into two areas: geography (the study of the terrestrial world) and cosmography (the study of the skies, stars, and the universe beyond). A follower of Aristotle, a scholar named Eratosthenes (c. 275–c. 195 BCE), coined the term **geography** in the third century BCE. To him, geography was the accurate description of the Earth (*geo*, meaning Earth; *graphia*, meaning description), and during his lifetime volumes were written about rocks, soils, and plants. A magnificent library in Alexandria (in what is now Egypt) came to contain the greatest collection of existing geographical studies.

Soon the mass of information (i.e., the database) concerning terrestrial geography became so large that the rubric lost its usefulness. Scientific specialization began. Some scholars concentrated on the rocks that make up the hard surface of the Earth, and geology emerged. Others studied living organisms, and biology grew into a separate discipline. Eventually even these specializations became too comprehensive. Biologists, for example, focused on plants (botany) or animals (zoology). The range of scientific disciplines expanded—and continues to do so today.

This, however, did not mean that geography itself lost its identity or relevance. As science became more compartmentalized, geographers realized that they could contribute in several ways, not only by conducting basic research, but also by maintaining that connective, integrative perspective that links knowledge from different disciplines. One aspect of this perspective relates to the 'where' with which geography is popularly associated. The location or position of features on the surface of the Earth (or above or below it) may well be one of the most significant things about them. Thus, geographers seek to learn not only about the features themselves, but also about their spatial relationships. The word **spatial** comes from the noun 'space'—not the outer space surrounding our planet, but earthly, terrestrial space.

The question is not only *where* things are located, but also *why* they are positioned where they are and *how* they came to occupy that position. To use more technical language: What is the cause of the variations in the distribution of phenomena we observe to exist in geographic space? What are the dynamics that shape the spatial organization of each part of the Earth's surface? These are among the central questions that geographers have asked for centuries and continue to pose today.

In some ways, geography is similar to history: both are broad, *holistic* (all-inclusive), integrating disciplines. Historians are interested in questions concerning time and chronology, whereas geographers analyze problems involving space and place. Thus geography's scope is even broader than that of history. As we will see later, historical and chronological matters concern us in physical as well as human geography. But no body of facts or data belongs exclusively to geography. To that extent, at least, geography lost the pre-eminence it enjoyed in the days of the ancient Greeks.

It is useful to divide modern approaches to geography into four traditions or schools of thought. These are: area studies, earth science, human–land relations, and spatial organization. Area study is often referred to as regional geography, earth science is traditional physical geography, human–land relationships are environmental geography, and spatial organization is concerned with the distribution of features, people, activities, and processes over the Earth's surface (where?), and in providing explanations for these distributions (why there?). Thoughtful geographers still employ a blend of the four approaches outlined above, although usually with an emphasis on one particular tradition. All four traditions, too, share a core set of geographic concepts. These may be grouped under the five themes of location, place, movement, region, and human–environment interaction. Once items are mapped by absolute location, we can then examine their location relative to other items (site and situation), and such secondary concepts as size, direction, and distribution. Each *place* has a unique set of characteristics, and its own special character. Groups of similar places may form districts, and groups of similar districts may form *regions*. The regions themselves may be natural, cultural, functional, and each will have its distinct landscapes.

LINK

Fields of Geography

Specialization has also developed within geography. Although all geographers share an interest in spatial arrangements, distribution, and organization, some geographers are more interested in physical features or natural phenomena, whereas others concentrate on people and their activities. That is why reference is made in the previous paragraphs to *physical* and *human* geography, the broadest possible division of the discipline. But even within these broad areas there are subdivisions. For example, a physical geographer may work on shorelines and beaches, on soil erosion, or on climate change. A human geographer may be interested in urban problems, in geopolitical trends, or in health issues. As a result, geography today consists of a cluster of fields, many of which are shown in Figure 1.1. Note that each of the geographic fields included (such as cultural geography, political geography, and population geography) is closely related to what is sometimes called a cognate (common-source) discipline. Thus, cultural geography relates closely to anthropology, political geography to political science, population geography to demography, and so forth. In turn, all the fields of geography are related to each other through the spatial perspective that is geography's common bond.

Figure 1.1 is actually a simplification of the real situation in geography. Each of the fields shown consists of a combination of subfields. Cultural geography, for example, encompasses several subfields, including studies of the cultural landscape (the imprint of a culture upon the land),

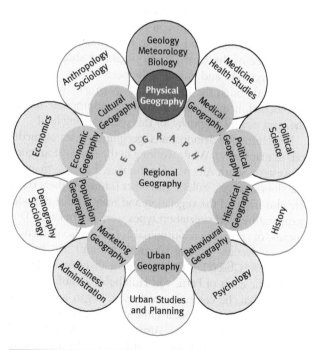

Figure 1.1 Schematic representation of the modern discipline of geography—physical geography highlighted—and its cognate fields.

cultural ecology (the interrelationships between culture and nature), culture hearths (the source areas of civilizations), and cultural diffusion (the movement of innovations and ideas from place to place). Physical geography, too, is an umbrella term for an even larger number of subfields. These subfields will be examined in the units that follow. But first let us examine physical geography as a field of geography.

Physical Geography

Physical geography is the geography of the physical world. This field, like the entire discipline, is an old one. Eratosthenes was a pioneer in physical geography at a time when scholars still were unsure about the size or shape of our planet. Eratosthenes's name is permanently enshrined in physical geography's 'hall of fame' because of his remarkably accurate calculation of the circumference of the Earth, a measurement he based on observations of the angle of the Sun at various locations in Egypt, where he worked. This was the beginning of research in a field now known as *geodesy*: the study of the size and shape of the Earth, but for Eratosthenes it was just one of several geographic pursuits. He realized the importance of mapping his observations, and trained himself to become a skilled *cartographer* (mapmaker and/or analyst). Having concluded that the Earth was spherical (and not flat, as many of his colleagues believed) and that parts of it were better warmed by the Sun than others, Eratosthenes drew maps of the Earth's environmental zones. He concluded—without ever having been anywhere near most of them—that the spherical Earth would have a hot equatorial zone, two cold polar zones, and two temperate zones lying between these. Centuries after Eratosthenes's death there still were scholars who did not believe that his ideas were essentially accurate. He was a geographer way ahead of his time.

Other Greek geographers, and later Roman geographers, studied such physical features as mountains (including the Mediterranean region's volcanoes), rivers, coasts, and islands. Some of them were excellent observers and recorders, and what they wrote about the Mediterranean basin continues to be of interest to scientists today. A scholar named Pliny the Younger (nephew of Pliny the Elder, a scientist) witnessed the eruption of Mount Vesuvius in CE 79 from a boat in the nearby Bay of Naples (Figure 1.2). He described the mushroom cloud rising above the mountain and the burial of such towns as Pompeii and Herculaneum. What he did not know, as he chronicled the disaster from a safe distance, was that his uncle, who had rushed to the scene to help the stricken, died in Vesuvius's poisonous fumes.

Sadly, much of what those ancient geographers wrote has been lost over time; what has survived is of enormous interest. From fragments of Greek and Roman writing we know about how wide and fast-flowing the rivers were, about the activity of some now-quiet volcanoes, and about the density of vegetation in places where there is none today. Worse, after the Romans carried geography so far forward, Europe descended into the Dark Ages, and

LINK

Figure 1.2   A computer-generated image of how the eruption of Mount Vesuvius in CE 79 would have appeared to the citizens of Herculaneum and Pompeii.

Figure 1.3   A painter's depiction of the expedition of Alexander von Humboldt (standing in boat) making its way through the lowland tropics of northern South America shortly after the turn of the nineteenth century.

geography (along with science in general) stagnated. For a thousand years, geographic learning in the Arab realm of North Africa/Southwest Asia and in China advanced far beyond that of Europe. Little of what was achieved by Arab or Chinese scholars was added to the European inventory, however. In addition, many records, maps, and books were lost as a result of wars, fires, and neglect.

Physical geography revived when the age of exploration and discovery dawned around 1500. Portuguese navigators skirted the African coast; Columbus crossed the Atlantic Ocean and returned with reports of new lands in the West. Cartographers recorded the accumulating knowledge on increasingly accurate maps. In European cities the news circulated of great rivers, snowcapped mountains, wild coasts, vast plains, forbidding escarpments, dense forests with taller trees than ever had been seen, strange and fearful animals, and alien peoples. Explorers and fortune hunters brought back hoards of gold and other valuables. For some explorers and their patrons, geographic knowledge became the means to wealth.

While Europeans rushed to the new lands, scientists tried to find some order in the mass of new information that confronted them. One of the greatest of these scholars was Alexander von Humboldt (1769–1859), who travelled to the New World not for wealth but for knowledge (Figure 1.3). He managed to travel 3000 km up the uncharted Orinoco River in northern South America, did fieldwork in Ecuador and Peru, crossed what is now Mexico, and visited Cuba before reaching the United States in 1804. Later he traversed Russia, including remote Siberia. He collected thousands of rock samples and plant specimens and made hundreds of drawings of the animals he observed. After settling down in Paris, he wrote 30 books on his American travels and later produced his famous six-volume series *Cosmos*, one of the gigantic scientific achievements of the nineteenth century.

From von Humboldt's writings we can learn about the state of physical geography in his time. It is evident that physical geography had become more than the study of the surface of the Earth. It also included studies of the soils, vegetation and animals, the oceans, and the atmosphere. Although the term *physical geography* was firmly entrenched, it might have been more appropriate to use the term *natural geography* for this wide-ranging field.

Von Humboldt demonstrated geographic research methods in many ways. While working in the Andes Mountains of western South America, for instance, he made maps of the slopes, ranges, valleys, and other features of the terrain. He also mapped the vegetation and realized that altitude, temperature, and vegetation types were interrelated. This means, of course, that altitudinal zonation also influences crop cultivation, linking physical (natural) and human geography. Observing the movement of ocean water off the Pacific coast of Peru, von Humboldt identified a cold current that, he correctly concluded, began in Antarctic waters and carried a polar chill to the western shores of equatorial South America. Again, he correctly connected this cold water and prevailing onshore wind patterns with the resulting desert conditions along the narrow Peruvian coastal plain. This ocean current, in fact, was for a long time named the Humboldt Current in his honour (more recently it has become known as the Peru Current).

Subfields of Physical Geography

The stage was now set for the development of specializations within the field of physical geography, and soon these subfields began to take shape. Over the past century, physical geography has evolved into a cluster of research foci, the most important of which are diagrammed in Figure 1.4. Remember that the entire field of physical geography is only one of those illustrated in Figure 1.1.

The geography of landscape, **geomorphology** (1), remains one of the most productive subfields of physical geography. As the term suggests (*geo,* meaning Earth; *morph,* meaning shape or form), this area of research focuses on the structuring of the Earth's surface. Geomorphologists seek to understand the evolution of slopes, the development of plains and plateaus, and the processes shaping dunes and caves and cliffs—the elements of the physical landscape. Often geomorphology has far-reaching implications. From the study of landscape it is possible to prove the former presence of ice sheets and mountain glaciers, rivers, and deserts. *Geology* is geomorphology's closest ally, but the study of geomorphology can involve far more than rocks. The work of running water, moving ice, surging waves, and restless air all contribute to landscape genesis. And while these forces shape the surface above, geologic forces modify it from below.

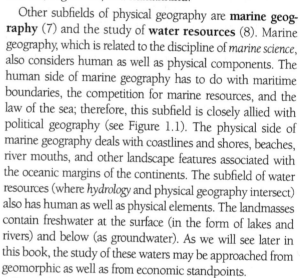

Proceeding clockwise from the top of Figure 1.4, we observe that *meteorology* (the branch of physics that deals with atmospheric phenomena) and physical geography combine to form **climatology** (2), the study of climates and their spatial distribution. Climatology involves not only the classification of climates and the analysis of their distribution, but also broader environmental questions, including climatic change, vegetation patterns, soil formation, and the relationships between human societies and climate.

As Figure 1.4 indicates, the next three subfields relate physical geography to aspects of *biology.* Where biology and physical geography overlap is the broad subfield of **biogeography** (3–5), but there are specializations within biogeography itself. Physical geography combined with botany forms **phytogeography** (3), and combined with zoology it becomes **zoogeography** (5). Note that biogeography (4), itself linked to *ecology,* lies between these two subfields; in fact, both zoogeography and phytogeography are parts of biogeography. The next subfield of physical geography is related to soil science, or *pedology.* Pedologists' research tends to focus on the internal properties of soils and the processes that go on during soil development. In **soil geography** (6), research centres on the spatial patterns of soils, their distribution, and their relationships to climate, vegetation, and humankind.

Other subfields of physical geography are **marine geography** (7) and the study of **water resources** (8). Marine geography, which is related to the discipline of *marine science,* also considers human as well as physical components. The human side of marine geography has to do with maritime boundaries, the competition for marine resources, and the law of the sea; therefore, this subfield is closely allied with political geography (see Figure 1.1). The physical side of marine geography deals with coastlines and shores, beaches, river mouths, and other landscape features associated with the oceanic margins of the continents. The subfield of water resources (where *hydrology* and physical geography intersect) also has human as well as physical elements. The landmasses contain freshwater at the surface (in the form of lakes and rivers) and below (as groundwater). As we will see later in this book, the study of these waters may be approached from geomorphic as well as from economic standpoints.

Recent interest in global change and environmental issues and sustainability have advanced the environmental tradition in physical geography and provided further linkages between physical and human geography. Environmental geography is not an entirely new concept, however. Geography's origins lie in the linkages between human and natural systems. New developments in physical geography coupled with the increasingly interconnected human and physical world indicate increased prospects for a more explicit geographical environmental field of study. Because both social and natural aspects of environmental problems coexist, the separation of human and physical geography is artificial in the context of better understanding global and regional components of the Earth. In its simplest sense, environmental geography can be understood to be the geographical study of environmental problems. The twenty-first century is remarkable for the renewed study of nature with respect to society.

In the 47 units that follow, various subfields of physical geography will be examined in some detail, and the connections between physical and human geography also will be revealed.

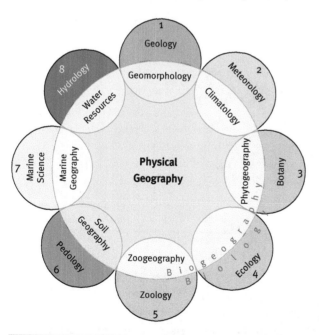

Figure 1.4 Schematic representation of the specialized subfields that constitute physical geography.

As you will see, we must go beyond the confines of Figure 1.4 to put our work in proper perspective. To understand the basics of physical geography, we must comprehend the general properties of our planet, not only deep below its surface, but also in relation to its cosmological orientation as it orbits the Sun as part of the solar system in our tiny corner of the vast universe. Comprehending general properties will be among our first tasks and constitute much of the remainder of Part One.

A Century of Physical Geography

During the past century, physical geographers have made many noteworthy contributions to science. Over time, the nature of these contributions has changed. Just 100 years ago, for example, the map of the physical geography of North America was still being filled in, and physical geographers such as John Wesley Powell and Grove Karl Gilbert reported on the spectacular scenery they studied in the western United States. Through sketches and cross-sectional profiles, Powell described his journeys down the Colorado River and told the story of one of the Earth's greatest natural features, the Grand Canyon. The 1814 map of western Canada by David Thompson (1770–1857), an explorer and geographer in the employ of the North West Company, was a milestone in the development of physical geography in Canada (Figure 1.5). The John Franklin expeditions (from 1819 to 1822) to the Arctic also led to advances in early northern studies. Geological and physiographic interpretations of the Mackenzie River Valley and the Arctic coast of Canada were among the first such studies. Over two decades later, Franklin's fatal 1845–7 expedition resulted in numerous private and government-sponsored search parties over the next dozen years and the mapping of much of the Canadian Arctic.

Other physical geographers, explorer-scientists all, fired the imaginations of their colleagues and students. Some of their names became permanently associated with the landscapes or physical features they studied: Louis Agassiz and glaciers, William Libbey and ocean currents, Arnold Guyot and ocean-floor topography. But perhaps the most important scholar between the 1880s and 1930s was William Morris Davis (1850–1934), who taught physical geography at Harvard and several other universities. Davis was less the explorer and more the theoretician (although he travelled worldwide in pursuit of his ideas), and in a series of significant papers he published the first comprehensive theory concerning the way rocks and geologic structures are worn down by the force of running (stream) water. He coined many terms we still use today, and he moved physical geography into the modern scientific era. In Unit 33 we look at Davis's theories and see how others built upon (or countered) them.

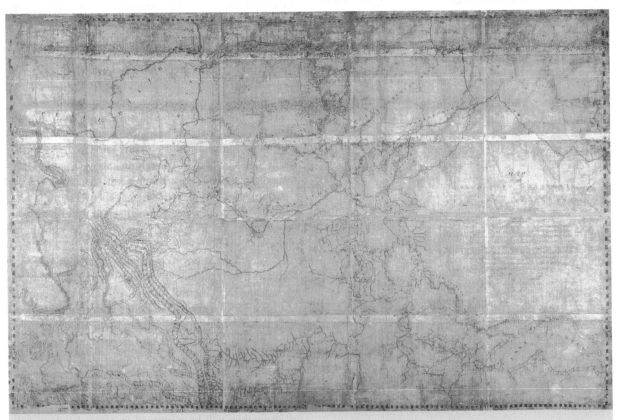

Figure 1.5   Map of the North-West Territory of the Province of Canada by David Thompson, 1814, commonly known as Thompson's 'Great Map'.

Following Davis, specialization in physical geography proliferated, and the subfields shown in Figure 1.4 gained recognition. In the United States, Wallace Atwood took the field in a more physiographic (regional), less geomorphic direction at Harvard University, where he succeeded Davis. In Canada the geomorphic tradition remained strong, well into the twentieth century and continues today, with a very active group of internationally recognized geomorphologists. Climatologists such as C. Warren Thornthwaite and Wladimir P. Köppen advanced this field of physical geography, and Canadians like F. Kenneth Hare, Timothy Oke, and Marie Sanderson more recently have made important contributions to our knowledge of Canadian geography. Griffith Taylor, an Antarctic scientist who contributed to Scott's Antarctic expedition and to the development of geography in Canada, Australia, and the United States, has described the evolution of the discipline and its philosophical basis (see reference list at the end of this unit).

Many other scholars, too numerous to mention here, have contributed to the recent development of physical geography in North America. You will find much of their work cited in the end-of-unit references throughout this book. Physical geographers still are working on large, theoretical questions as Davis did, but now with the aid of sophisticated quantitative techniques and computer-based approaches. Others work on highly specialized, very specific questions. These days, when you ask a physical geographer what his or her specialty is, you frequently hear such answers as hydroclimatology, periglacial processes, paleogeography, or wetland ecosystems. The wide range of material you encounter in this book provides an overview of a broad field encompassing many topics.

Recently, geographic information systems (GIS) and new geostatistical procedures have further enabled locational analysis. GIS in particular is much used by physical geographers, biologists, and social scientists, and by government agencies, environmental consultants, planners, land developers, and forestry companies, among many other practitioners.

Systems and Models in Physical Geography

Physical geography is a multi-faceted science that seeks to understand major elements of our complex world. In order to deal with this complexity, physical geographers employ numerous concepts and specialized methods, many of which will emerge in the units that follow. This section provides an introduction to that analysis by considering two general approaches to the subject: systems and models.

Systems

In recent years, many physical geographers have found it convenient to organize their approach to the field within a systems framework of thinking. A **system** may be regarded as any set of related events or objects and their interactions. A city could be described as a large and elaborate system.

Each day the system receives an inflow of energy, food, water, and vast quantities of consumer goods. Most of this energy and matter is used and changed in form by the various populations that reside in the urban centre. At the same time, huge amounts of energy, manufactured goods, and services, along with sewage and other waste products, are produced in and exported from the city. Note that energy and matter freely transfer across the city's boundaries, making it an **open system** and underscoring its relationships with surrounding systems, such as the agricultural and energy-producing systems of the region of which it is a part. There are many examples of open systems throughout this book, such as a weather system or a river drainage basin. Indeed, in terms of energy flows, the Earth itself is an enormous open system that comprises several interconnected lesser systems. Although it is difficult to find one on the Earth's surface, we should also know what is meant by the term **closed system**: a self-contained system exhibiting no exchange of energy or matter across its boundaries. (One example of a closed system, when the entire Earth is considered, is the carbon cycle, which is discussed in Unit 6.)

An important property of a system is its organization as an integrated whole. Accordingly, systems often contain one or more subsystems. A **subsystem** is a component of a larger system. A subsystem can act independently, but it operates within, and is linked to, the larger system. The food distribution, manufacturing, and sewage systems are subsystems of the total city system described in the preceding paragraph. Systems and subsystems have boundaries, called *interfaces*. The transfer or exchange of energy and matter takes place at these interfaces (which may also be regarded as surfaces). Sometimes interfaces are visible: you can see where sunlight strikes the roof of a building. But often they are not visible: you cannot see the movement of groundwater, a part of the global water system, as it flows through the subterranean rocks of the geologic system. Many geographers focus their attention on these interfaces, visible or invisible, particularly when they coincide with the Earth's surface. It is here that we find the greatest activity of our dynamic world.

Two other ideas commonly used in systems approaches are those of dynamic equilibrium and feedback. A system is in **dynamic equilibrium** when it is neither growing nor getting smaller but continues to be in balance and complete operation. **Feedback** occurs when a change in one part of the system causes a change in another part of the system. Let us consider two examples. If you were to look at the sand in a specific area of Miami Beach (Figure 1.6), you would barely perceive that the currents moving along the shore are taking away some sand and bringing in a replacement supply. There is continual movement, yet over a period of weeks the beach apparently stays the same. The beach, thus, can be said to be in a state of dynamic equilibrium.

An example of feedback, or a *feedback mechanism*, would be the case of solar radiation being reflected from a Toronto sidewalk. The sidewalk's surface receives energy from the Sun, but it also reflects and radiates (emits absorbed radiation) some of that energy back into the atmosphere as

From the Fieldnotes

Figure 1.6 *'South Florida's Atlantic coast, looking northward beyond Miami Beach. At present the beach seen in this photograph represents a system in dynamic equilibrium, with currents flowing parallel to the coast, continuously removing sand and at the same time depositing a replacement supply.'*

well as losing it in other ways. The more energy the sidewalk receives, the more it reflects and re-radiates. Because of the reflection and re-radiation, the sidewalk does not become increasingly hotter. Without the feedback mechanisms of reflection and re-radiation, it would certainly be impossible to walk on that surface at midday during summer.

A feedback mechanism that operates to keep a system in its original condition, such as the reflection or radiation from the sidewalk, is called a *negative feedback mechanism*. The opposite case, in which a feedback mechanism induces a progressively greater change from the original condition of a system, is called a *positive feedback mechanism*. In a later unit it is explained why the growth of a metropolitan area leads to higher average air temperatures. A change of this kind is an example of positive feedback.

Models

Another way that physical geographers approach the study of the Earth's phenomena is to make models of them. In his landmark book on geographic analysis, Peter Haggett defined a **model** as *the creation of an idealized representation of reality in order to demonstrate its most important properties*. Model-building, therefore, is a complementary way of thinking about the world. It entails the controlled simplification of a complex reality, filtering out the essential forces and patterns from the myriad details with which they are embedded in a complicated world. Such abstractions, which convey not the entire truth but a valid and

reasonable part of it, are highly useful because they facilitate the development of generalizations. We saw this in the preceding discussion of the city system, which underscored some universal attributes concerning the spatial interaction between cities and the surrounding regions they serve. Systems, therefore, may also be regarded as models.

Physical geographers undertake digital elevation models to model hydrological systems, catchment models, prediction models of cycles and flows of energy, water, sediment, nutrients, and contaminants, to name a few examples. Computer models simulate complex Earth systems in selective, mathematical, and visual ways (alexandria.sdc.ucsb.edu/~acoleman/amodels3.html). Models will be used frequently in this book because they allow us to penetrate a complex subject quickly and highlight its most essential aspects.

Geographic Magnitude

In approaching the real world, we must also consider the size of the subjects and phenomena that interest us. Even speeding at 1000 km per hour, one may become uncomfortable on a 16-hour flight from Vancouver to Sydney, Australia, because, in human terms, the world is such a big place. But in studying our planet, we must not think of distance and magnitude in purely human terms.

Let us consider different sizes, or **orders of magnitude**. Figure 1.7 shows the various orders of magnitude with which we must become familiar. The scale in this figure

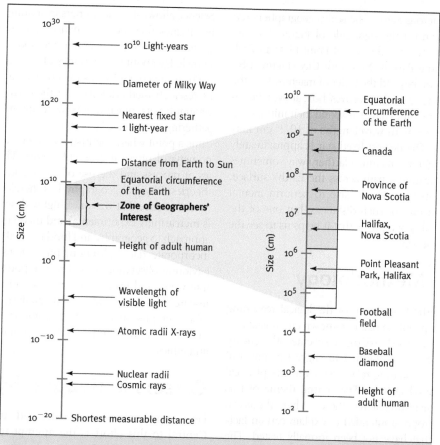

Figure 1.7 Orders of geographic magnitude. Geographers mostly operate in the context of the scales shown on the right, but sometimes they must think in much smaller or larger terms, as indicated at left.

Perspectives on the Human Environment

Sliding Scale

Imagine a couple sunbathing on Cavendish Beach. We can photograph them occupying a square of sand about 1 m on a side. If we move the camera higher, a square of 10 (10^1) m reveals their companions. When we focus on a 100 (10^2) m area, we can see a crowd of people on the beach. A picture of 1000 (10^3) m includes the beach, some sea, and some land (as in Figure 1.6). One with an edge of 10,000 (10^4) m captures most of Prince Edward Island National Park and parts of the neighbouring north shore of Prince Edward Island.

Moving the camera still farther, we shoot a picture of a 100,000 (10^5) m square. It encompasses most of the central PEI region. The next step is 1,000,000 (10^6) m. This snapshot takes in the entire province of PEI, some neighbouring provinces, and parts of the Atlantic Ocean, the Gulf of St Lawrence, and the Bay of Fundy. A photo at the next level of generalization, showing a square of 10,000,000 (10^7) m, covers most of the visible Earth. And if the camera is far enough away in outer space to focus on a square of 100,000,000 (10^8) m, we see Planet Earth as a small globe. Somewhere on it is that couple lying on a square of Cavendish Beach's seaside sand.

is written in *exponential* notation. This means that 100 is written as 10^2 (10×10), 1000 is 10^3 ($10 \times 10 \times 10$), 0.01 is 10^{-2} (1/100), and so forth. This notation saves us from writing numerous zeros. The scales geographers use most often—shown on the right side of Figure 1.7—go from about 10^5 or 10^6 cm, the size of Point Pleasant Park in Halifax or Central Park in New York City (Figure 1.8), up to about 10^{10} cm, beyond the order of magnitude of the Earth's circumference (see 'Perspectives' box, above). Physical geographers sometimes have to expand their minds even further. Cosmic rays with wavelengths of 10^{-16} cm may affect our climate. The nearest fixed star is approximately 10^{18} cm away. Brighter stars much farther away sometimes help persons navigating a path across the Earth's surface. Occasionally (as in Unit 4) we have to perform mental gymnastics to conceive of such distances, but one of the beauties of physical geography is that it helps us to see the world in a different way.

Scientific Methodology

The scientific method is a term for the logical reasoning process by which people explain unknown circumstances. Sir Francis Bacon (1561–1626), a seventeenth-century English philosopher, was the first to suggest a universal methodology for explaining relationships in the physical world in an ordered fashion. The central theme of this methodology is the testing of hypotheses. A hypothesis can be defined as a proposal intended to explain certain facts or observations that have not been formally tested. The primary goal of science is to better comprehend the world around us. A variety of disciplines, including physics, chemistry, biology, medicine, and the earth sciences, have used science exclusively to expand their knowledge base. Science allows its practitioners to acquire knowledge using techniques that are both neutral and unbiased. Physical geographers use the scientific method as a tool to gather knowledge about the workings of our natural world.

Physical geography has experienced a radical change in its research methodologies. In the early years of physical geography, its practitioners were interested primarily in gathering descriptive facts about the world. However, there came a point when scientists wanted to know *why* the phenomena of physical geography exist. This involved studies of process and the use of the scientific method to test theories. Physical geography has therefore been changing from a science that was once highly descriptive to one that is increasingly experimental and theoretical. The scientific approach to geography and fundamental research concepts incorporate data collection, physical measurements, behavioural observations, archives, reports such as surveys, interviews and tests, experimental and non-experimental research design, sampling, data analysis, displays such as tables, graphs, maps, and illustrations, geographic information techniques in research, scientific communication, and ethics.

Careers in Geography

Let us now embark on our detailed study of the Earth. Central to this effort is the attempt to understand the environment at the Earth's surface, a habitat we must

Figure 1.8 Central Park really does occupy a central location on the totally built up island of Manhattan. This north-looking view of the 340-hectare green space shows the park, first laid out in 1856, flanked by tall buildings in all directions. Central Park for many years has been the subject of geographic studies, ranging from biogeography (the survival of plants and animals in this unique setting) to human geography (the behaviour of people as they use the park for purposes ranging from open-air symphony concerts to skateboarding).

all live with in a one-to-one relationship. Nobody who has become acquainted with physical geography is ever likely to forget that, and many people go on from this awareness of a personal relationship with the planet to lifelong careers related to physical geography. The variety and diversity of potential careers in geography are staggering. A strong background in physical geography may lead to careers directly concerned with the environment, among them: environmental manager, forestry technician, park ranger, outdoor guide, coastal zone manager, soil conservation specialist, hydrologist, park warden, ecotourism planner, or cartographer. In combination with other specialization, students of physical geography may become: hazardous-waste planners, emergency managers, environmental impact analysts, environmental lawyers, meteorologists, climatologists, geographic information systems specialists, remote sensing analysts, and surveyors.

KEY TERMS

biogeography   *page 9*
climatology   *page 9*
closed system   *page 11*
dynamic equilibrium   *page 11*
feedback   *page 11*
geography   *page 6*
geomorphology   *page 9*
marine geography   *page 9*
model   *page 13*
open system   *page 11*

orders of magnitude   *page 13*
physical geography   *page 7*
phytogeography   *page 9*
soil geography   *page 9*
spatial   *page 6*
subsystem   *page 11*
system   *page 11*
water resources   *page 9*
zoogeography   *page 9*

REVIEW QUESTIONS

1. Define the term *spatial* and show how it is central to the study of geography.
2. What contributions did the Greeks and Romans make to the early evolution of physical geography?
3. What is physical geography? How does it differ from other sciences?
4. Define the eight major subfields of physical geography. What are their major foci of study? How do

these differ from other fields in the natural and social sciences?

5. Define the terms *system, subsystem, open system, dynamic equilibrium,* and *feedback.*
6. Define the term *model*, and describe how models can help us understand our complex physical world.

REFERENCES AND FURTHER READINGS

Atwood, W.W. 1940. *The Physiographic Provinces of North America.* New York: Ginn.

Bouwer, K. 1985. 'Ecological and Spatial Traditions in Geography, and the Study of Environmental Problems', *GeoJournal* 11, 4: 307–12.

Castree, N. 2005. *Nature.* New York/London: Routledge.

Chorley, R.J., et al. 1973. *The History of the Study of Landforms, or the Development of Geomorphology. Vol. 2: The Life and Work of William Morris Davis.* New York: Wiley.

Draper, D. 2002. *Our Environment: A Canadian Perspective.* Scarborough, Ont.: Thompson Canada.

Gaile, G.L., and C.J. Willmot, eds. 1989. *Geography in America.* Columbus, Ohio: Merrill, 28–94, 112–46.

Goudie, A.S., et al., eds. 1994. *The Encyclopedic Dictionary of Physical Geography,* 3rd edn. Cambridge, Mass.: Blackwell.

Gregory, K.J. 2000. *The Changing Nature of Physical Geography.* New York: Oxford Univ. Press.

Haggett, P. 1965. *Locational Analysis in Human Geography.* London: Edward Arnold.

Hancock, P.L., and B.J. Skinner, eds. 2001. *Oxford Companion to the Earth.* New York: Oxford Univ. Press.

Holt-Jensen, A. 1999. *Geography: Its History and Concepts,* 3rd edn. Thousand Oaks, Calif.: Sage.

Inkpen, R. 2005. *Science, Philosophy, and Physical Geography.* London/New York: Routledge.

James, P.E., and G.J. Martin. 1993. *All Possible Worlds: A History of Geographical Ideas,* 3rd edn. New York: Wiley.

Marcus, M.G. 1979. 'Coming Full Circle: Physical Geography in the Twentieth Century', *Annals, Association of American Geographers* 69: 521–32.

Marsh, W.M., and J. Grossa Jr. 2005. *Environmental Geography: Science, Land Use, and Earth Systems,* 3rd edn. New York: Wiley.

Montello, D.R., and P.C. Sutton. 2006. *An Introduction to Scientific Research Methods in Geography.* Thousand Oaks, Calif.: Sage.

National Research Council. 1997. *Rediscovering Geography: New Relevance for Science and Society.* Washington: National Academy Press.

Orme, A.R., ed. 2001. *The Physical Geography of North America.* New York: Oxford Univ. Press.

Pattison, W.D. 1964. 'The Four Traditions of Geography', *Journal of Geography* 63: 211–16.

Sanderson, M. 1988. *Griffith Taylor: Antarctic Scientist and Pioneer Geographer.* Ottawa: Carleton Univ. Press.

Taylor, G., ed. 1951. *Geography in the Twentieth Century.* London: Methuen.

Thomas, D., and A.S. Goudie, eds. 2000. *The Dictionary of Physical Geography,* 3rd edn. Malden, Mass.: Blackwell.

Tinkler, K. 1985. *A Short History of Geomorphology.* London: Croom Helm.

Wolman, M.G. 1992. 'Contemporary Value of Geography: Applied Physical Geography and the Environmental Sciences', in A. Rogers et al., eds. *The Student's Companion to Geography.* Cambridge, Mass.: Blackwell, 3–7.

 # WEB RESOURCES

www.aag.org A general introduction to the field of geography from the Association of American Geographers (AAG), which includes specialty groups in physical geography.

www.cag-acg.ca The Canadian Association of Geographers (CAG). The CAG is the national organization representing practising geographers from public and private sectors and from universities.

The Planet Earth

Objectives

- To define and highlight the five spheres of the Earth System.

- To highlight the general characteristics of the Earth's continents.

- To introduce the world's ocean basins and the topographic characteristics of the seafloor.

When US astronauts for the first time left Earth's orbit and reached the Moon, they were able to look back at our planet and see it as no one had ever seen it before. The television cameras aboard their spacecraft beamed spectacular pictures of the Earth, seen on television sets around the globe. As colour-enhanced photos later showed, against the dark sky the Earth displayed a range of vivid colours, from the blue of the oceans to the green of forests to the brown of sparsely vegetated land to the great white swirls of weather systems in the atmosphere. The astronauts, however, also saw things no camera could adequately transmit. Most of all, they were struck by the smallness of our world in the vastness of the universe, what architect Buckminster Fuller called 'Spaceship Earth'. It was difficult to conceive that all of the billions of humans and their works were confined to, and dependent upon, so tiny a planet. Every participant in those Moon missions returned with a sense of awe—and a heightened concern over the fragility of our terrestrial life-support systems.

In the units that follow, we will examine these systems and learn, among other things, how serious the threat of irreversible damage to them may be. We should remember that all the systems we will study—weather and climate, oceanic circulation, soil formation, vegetation growth, landform development, and erosion—ultimately are parts of one great Earth System. Even though this total Earth System is an open system with respect to energy flows, the amount of matter on and in the Earth is pretty much fixed. Little new matter is being added to supplement what we use up, and so far nothing of consequence permanently leaves the Earth. This means that our material resource base is finite; that is, parts of it can be used up. It also means that any hazardous products we create must remain a part of our environment.

Spheres of the Earth System

Our planet consists of a set of interacting shells, or 'spheres', some of them extending over the entire globe, others covering it partially. The **atmosphere** is the blanket 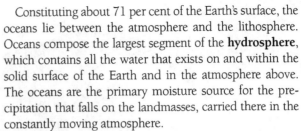 of air that adheres to the Earth's surface. It is our life layer, the mixture of gases we breathe. It begins a few metres within the soil or on the water's surface, and its outermost periphery can be tracked to a height of about 60,000 km above the Earth. Heat energy from the Sun keeps the atmosphere in motion, causing weather systems to form and travel across land and sea. The atmosphere is most dense at sea level and thins out with increasing altitude.

Below the atmosphere lies the outermost shell of the solid Earth, the **lithosphere** (*lithos* means rock). The lithosphere's upper surface is sculpted into the almost endless variety of landforms and physical landscapes that form the Earth's scenery. The lithosphere continues under the oceans, where the surface of the seafloor is created by forces quite different from those on land.

Constituting about 71 per cent of the Earth's surface, the oceans lie between the atmosphere and the lithosphere. Oceans compose the largest segment of the **hydrosphere**, which contains all the water that exists on and within the solid surface of the Earth and in the atmosphere above. The oceans are the primary moisture source for the precipitation that falls on the landmasses, carried there in the constantly moving atmosphere.

The **cryosphere** includes all forms of frozen water, including glaciers, floating ice, snow cover, and permafrost (permanently frozen subsoil). Although it could logically be regarded as a component of the hydrosphere, the cryosphere does have its own distinct properties, and many scientists in recent years have come to recognize it as a distinct Earth sphere. It should be noted, however, that the cryosphere is the only one of these spheres that is discontinuous across our planet.

The **biosphere** is the zone of life, the home of all living things. This includes the Earth's vegetation, animals, and human beings. Since there are living organisms in the soil and plants are rooted in soil, part of the soil layer (which is otherwise a component of the lithosphere) may be included in the biosphere.

These five spheres—atmosphere, lithosphere, hydrosphere, cryosphere, and biosphere—are the Earth layers we shall study; but other shells of the Earth also play their roles. Not only are there outer layers above the effective atmosphere, but there also are spheres inside the Earth, beneath the lithosphere. The lithosphere is affected by forces and processes from above. Thus, it is important to keep in mind the interactions among the five spheres—they are not separate and independent segments of our planet, but are constantly interacting subsystems of the total **Earth System**.

These systemic interrelationships are diagrammed in Figure 2.1. The atmosphere, lithosphere, hydrosphere, cryosphere, and biosphere are the main components of

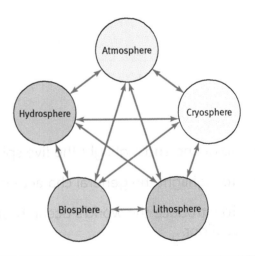

Figure 2.1   The five spheres of the Earth System and their interrelationships.

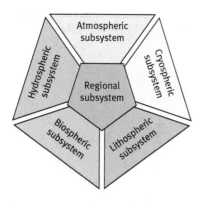

Figure 2.2 The Earth System and its subsystems. A regional subsystem encompasses parts of the other five subsystems.

the physical world. They are linked together in any one place an[d over the Earth as a whole. As the diagram dem]onstrate[s ...] within th[...] them. W[...] subsyste[...] a **region**[...] in the s[...] work to [...] each reg[...] similarit[...] produce[...] types of[...] groupin[...] eral uni[...]

> *Earth can be broken not only into spheres but into hemispheres*
> *└ Northern, Southern, Eastern, Western.*
>
> *6 continents, 7 seas.*

Hem[...]

In addi[tion ...] lithosphere, hydrosphere, cryosphere, and biosphere), the Earth also can be divided into **hemispheres** (from the ancient Greek, *hemi*, meaning half; *sphaira*, meaning sphere). The northern half of the globe, from the Equator to the North Pole, is the Northern Hemisphere; the southern half is the Southern Hemisphere. There are many differences between the two hemispheres, which will be seen in later units that treat patterns of seasonality, planetary rotational effects, and the regionalization of climates.

Perhaps the most obvious difference concerns the distribution of land and sea (Figure 2.3). The Earth's continental landmasses are far more heavily concentrated in the Northern Hemisphere (which contains about 70 per cent of the total land area); the Southern Hemisphere has much less land and much more water than the Northern Hemisphere. Moreover, the polar areas of each hemisphere differ considerably. The Northern Hemisphere polar zone—the *Arctic*—consists of peripheral islands covered mostly by thick ice and a central mass of sea ice floating atop the Arctic Ocean

(Figure 2.3, inset map A). The Southern Hemisphere polar zone—the *Antarctic*—is dominated by a large continental landmass covered with the world's largest continuous ice sheet (inset map B).

The Earth can be further divided into Eastern and Western Hemispheres. Technically, the Eastern Hemisphere lies to the east of an imaginary line drawn from pole to pole through the Royal Observatory in Greenwich, England (part of the city of London), and on through the middle of the Pacific Ocean on the opposite side of the world. In practice, however, the Western Hemisphere consists of the half of the Earth centred on the Americas, and the Eastern Hemisphere contains all of Eurasia and Africa. So, there is a precise use, based on a grid drawn on the globe (which is elaborated in Unit 3), and a more general use of this hemispheric division.

A look at any globe representing the Earth suggests yet another pair of hemispheres: a **land hemisphere** and a **water (oceanic) hemisphere**. The landmasses are concen[tr]ated on one side of the Earth to such a degree that it is [ap]propriate to refer to that half of the Earth as the land [he]misphere (Figure 2.4). This hemisphere is centred on [Af]rica, which lies surrounded by the other continents: the [A]mericas to the west, Eurasia to the north and northeast, [A]ustralia to the southeast, and Antarctica to the south. The [op]posite hemisphere, the water hemisphere, is dominated [by] the Earth's greatest ocean, the Pacific. When you look [at] a globe from above the centre of the Pacific Ocean, only [th]e fringes of the landmasses appear along the margins of [th]is huge body of water.

[C]ontinents and Oceans

[T]here is an old saying to the effect that 'the Earth has six [c]ontinents and seven seas'. In fact, that generalization is [n]ot too far off the mark (see Figure 2.3). The Earth does [h]ave six continental landmasses: Africa, South America, North America, Eurasia (Europe and Asia occupy a single large landmass), Australia, and Antarctica. As for the seven seas, there are five great oceanic bodies of water and several smaller seas. The Pacific Ocean is the largest of all. The Indian Ocean lies between Africa and Australia. The North Atlantic Ocean and the South Atlantic Ocean may be regarded as two discrete oceans that are dissimilar in a number of ways. Encircling Antarctica is the Southern Ocean. Sixth, and largest of the smaller seas, is the Arctic Ocean, which lies beneath the floating Arctic icecap.

The seventh body of water often identified with these oceans is the Mediterranean Sea, which lies between Europe and Africa and is connected to the interior sea of Eurasia, the Black Sea. The Mediterranean is not of oceanic dimensions, but unlike the Caribbean or the Arabian Sea, it also is not merely an extension of an ocean. The Mediterranean is very nearly landlocked and has only one narrow natural outlet, through the Strait of Gibraltar between Spain and Morocco.

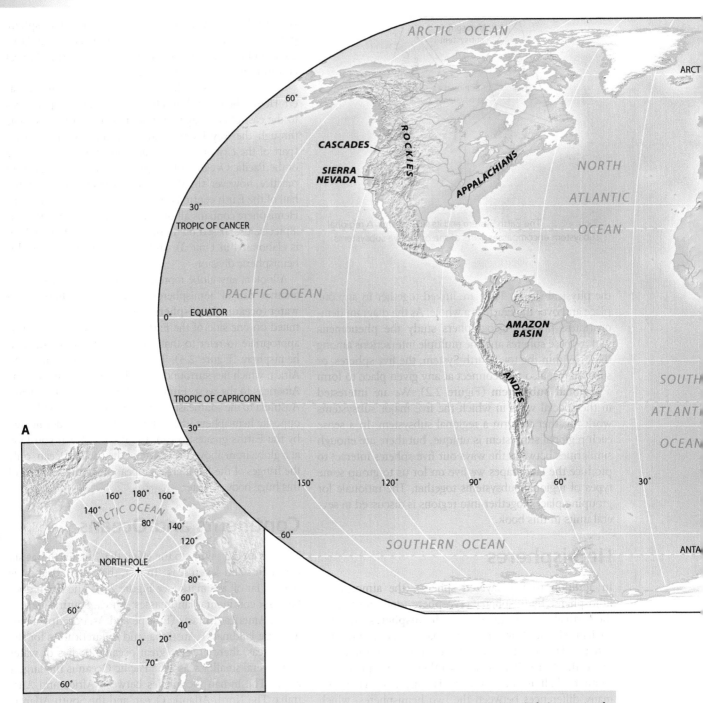

Figure 2.3 Distribution of land and sea on the Earth's surface. The continents are shown in topographic relief; the terrain of the ocean floor is shown in Figure 2.6.

In our study of weather and climate, the relative location, general dimensions, and the topography of the landmasses are important, because these influence the movement of moisture-carrying air.

The Landmasses

Only about 29 per cent of the surface of the Earth is constituted by land; 71 per cent is water or ice. Thus,

less than one-third of our planet is habitable by human beings, but much of this area is too dry, too cold, or too rugged to allow large concentrations of settlement. Our livable world where permanent settlement is possible—known as the **ecumene**—is small indeed (see 'Perspectives' box).

Each of the six continental landmasses possesses unique physical properties. *Africa*, which accounts for just over 20 per cent of the total land area, is at the

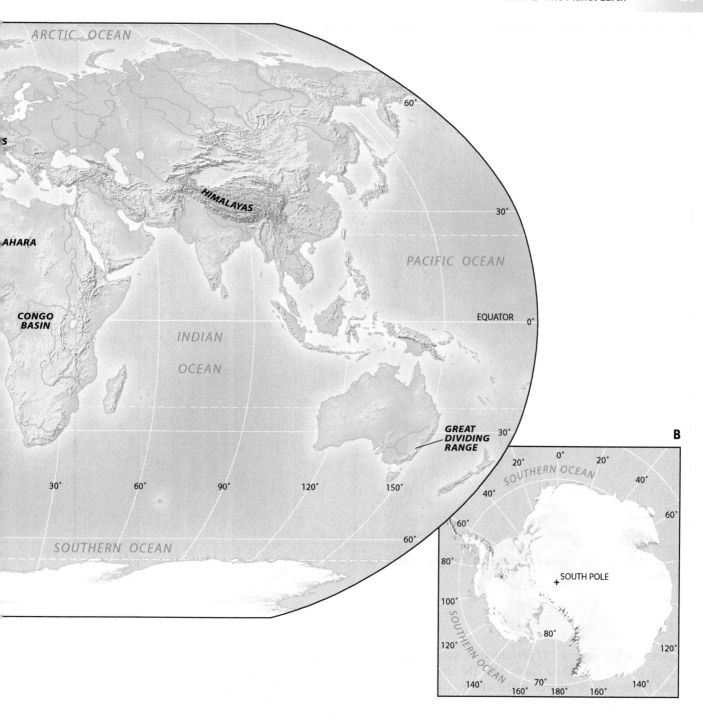

heart of the land hemisphere. Of all the landmasses, Africa alone lies astride the Equator in such a way that large segments of it occupy the Northern as well as the Southern Hemisphere. Africa often is called the plateau continent, because much of its landmass lies above 1000 m in elevation, and coastal plains are relatively narrow. As Figure 2.3 reveals, a fairly steep escarpment rises near the coast in many parts of Africa, leading rapidly up to the plateau surface of the interior. African rivers that rise in the interior plunge over falls and rapids before reaching the coast, limiting their navigability. Furthermore, Africa lacks a physical feature seen on all the other landmasses: a linear mountain range comparable to South America's Andes, North America's Rocky Mountains, Eurasia's Himalayas, or Australia's Great Dividing Range. The reason for this will become clear when the geomorphic history of that continent is discussed.

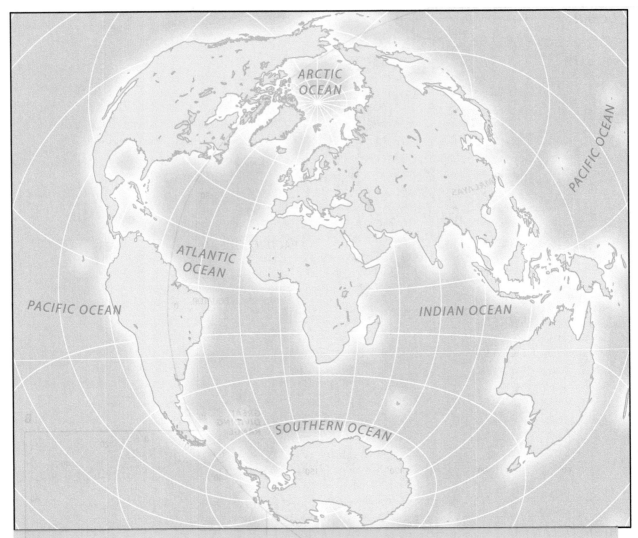

Figure 2.4   Land Hemisphere. This is the half of the globe that contains most of the world's landmasses, which surround the African continent.

South America, occupying 12 per cent of the world's land, is much smaller than Africa (Table 2.1). The topography of this landmass is dominated in the west by the gigantic Andes Mountains, which exceed 6000 m in height in many places. East of the mountains, the surface becomes a plateau interrupted by the basins of major rivers, among which the Amazon is by far the largest. The Andes constitute a formidable barrier to the cross-continental movement of air, which has a major impact on the distribution of South America's climates.

North America, with one-sixth of the total land area, is substantially larger than South America. This landmass extends from Arctic to tropical environments. Western North America is mainly mountainous; the great Rocky Mountains stretch from Alaska to Mexico. West of the Rockies are other major mountain ranges, such as the Sierra Nevada and the Cascades. East of the Rocky

Mountains are extensive plains covering a vast area from Hudson Bay south to the Gulf of Mexico and curving up along the Atlantic seaboard as far north as New York City. Another north–south-trending mountain range, the Appalachians, rises between the coastal and interior lowlands of the East. Thus, the continental topography is somewhat funnel-shaped. This means that air from both polar and tropical areas can penetrate the heart of the continent, without topographic obstruction, from north and south. As a result, summer weather there can be tropical, whereas winter weather exhibits Arctic-like extremes.

Eurasia (covering 36.5 per cent of the land surface) is by far the largest landmass on Earth, and all of it lies in the Northern Hemisphere. The topography of Europe and Asia is dominated by a huge mountain chain that extends from west to east across the hybrid continent. It has many

Table 2.1 Dimensions of the Landmasses

Landmass	Area (km²)	Percentage of Land Surface	Highest Mountain	Elevation (m)
Africa	30,300	20.2	Kilimanjaro	5,861
South America	17,870	11.9	Aconcagua	6,919
North America	24,350	16.3	McKinley	6,158
Eurasia	54,650	36.5	Everest	8,848
Australia	8,290	5.6	Kosciusko	2,217
Antarctica	13,990	9.3	Vinson Massif	5,110

names according to the various countries containing some part of it; the most familiar of which are the Alps in Central Europe and the Himalayas in South Asia. In Europe, the Alps lie between the densely populated North European Lowland to the north and the subtropical Mediterranean lands to the south. In Asia, the Himalayas form but one of many great mountain ranges that emanate from Central Asia northeastward into Russia's Siberia, eastward into China, and southeastward into South and Southeast Asia. Between and below these ranges lie several of the world's most densely populated river plains, including China's Huang He (Yellow) and Chang Jiang (Yangzi) and India's Ganges.

Australia is the world's smallest continent (constituting less than 6 per cent of the total land area) and is its lowest continent topographically. The Great Dividing Range lies near the continent's eastern coast, and its highest peak reaches a mere 2217 m. Australia's northern areas lie in the tropics, but its southern coasts are washed by the outer fringes of Antarctic waters.

Antarctica, the 'frozen continent', lies almost entirely buried by the world's largest and thickest ice sheet. Beneath the ice, Antarctica—constituting the remaining 9.3 per cent of the world's land area—has a varied topography that includes the southernmost link in the Andean mountain chain (the backbone of the Antarctic Peninsula). Currently very little of this underlying landscape is exposed, but Antarctica was not always a frigid polar landmass. As will be discussed in more detail later, the Antarctic ice, the air above it, and the waters around it are critically important in the global functioning of the atmosphere, hydrosphere, and biosphere.

The Ocean Basins

Before the twentieth century, the ocean basins were unknown territory. Only the tidal fringes of the continents and the shores of deep-sea islands revealed glimpses of what might lie below the vast world ocean. Then, sounding devices were developed, and some of the ocean-floor topography became apparent, at least in cross-sectional profile. Next, equipment was built that permitted the collection of rock samples from the seabed. And now, marine scientists are venturing down to deep areas of the ocean floor and can watch volcanic eruptions in progress through the portholes of deep-sea submersibles. The secrets of the submerged 71 per cent of the lithosphere finally are being revealed.

When the seafloors were mapped and the composition and age of rock samples were determined, a remarkable discovery was made: the deep ocean floors are geologically different from the continental landmasses. The ocean floors have a varied topography, but this topography is not simply an extension of what we see on land. There are ridges and valleys and mountains and plains, but these are not comparable to the Appalachians or to the Amazon Basin. We return to this topic in Part Three.

For the present we should acquaint ourselves with the main features of the ocean basins. If all the water were removed from the ocean basins, they would reveal the topography shown in Figure 2.6. The map reveals that the ocean basins can be divided into three regions: (1) the margins of the continents, (2) the abyssal zones—extensive, mound-studded plains at great depth, and (3) a system of ridges flanked by elaborate fractures and associated relief.

The continental margin consists of the continental shelf, continental slope, and continental rise. The **continental shelf** is the very gently sloping, relatively shallow, submerged plain at the edge of the continent. The map shows the continental shelves to be continuations of the continental landmasses (see especially the areas off eastern North America, southeastern South America, and northwestern Europe). Generally these shelves extend no deeper than 180 m. Their average width is about 80 km, but some are as wide as 1000 km. Because the continental shelves are extensions of the landmasses, the continental geologic structure continues to their edges. During the most recent ice age, when much ocean water was taken up by the ice sheets, sea levels dropped enough to expose most of these continental shelves. Rivers flowed across them and carved valleys that can still be seen on detailed maps. The oceans

LINK

today are fuller than in the past, and they have flooded the extensive plains at the margins of the continents.

At a depth of about 180 m, the continental shelf ends at a break in slope that is quite marked in some places and less steep in others. At this discontinuity the **continental slope** begins and plunges steeply downward. Often at the foot of the continental slope there is a transitional **continental rise** of gently downward sloping seafloor (Figure 2.6). The continental rise leads into the abyssal zone. This zone consists mainly of the **abyssal plains**, large expanses of lower-relief ocean floor. The abyssal plains form the floors of the deepest areas of each ocean, except for even deeper *trenches*, which occur at the foot of some continental slopes (as along the Pacific margin of Asia). The abyssal zone is not featureless, however, and the extensive plains are diversified by numerous hills and seamounts, all of which are of volcanic origin. (*Seamounts* are volcanic mountains reaching over 1000 m above the seafloor.) There also are lengthy valleys, as though rivers had carved them here more than 1800 m below the water surface. The origin of these valleys remains uncertain.

Perspectives on the Human Environment

Human Population and Natural Processes

This book focuses on the physical systems, forces, and processes that modify natural landscapes, but at this early stage we should take note of the human factor and its impact on the natural world. As we will note later, animals, from worms to wallabies, play their roles in modifying landscapes in burrowing, digging, grazing, browsing, and even, by beavers, in felling trees and building dams. But no species in the history of this planet has transformed natural landscapes to the degree humans have. We have converted entire regions to irrigated agriculture, terraced cultivable hillslopes, confined and controlled whole river systems, and reconstructed shorelines. We are also deforesting vast areas, destroying soil cover, gouging huge open-pit mines, and building and paving once-natural surfaces into megacities so large that they become global-scale landscape features in themselves. In the first half of the twentieth century, geographers began to distinguish between **natural landscapes**, those areas of the planet still essentially subject to the physical processes we discuss here, and **cultural landscapes**, in which human intervention dominates to such an extent that physical processes have been subordinated. As the human population has grown, the cultural has gained and the natural has receded.

Population grew explosively during the twentieth century, from 1.5 billion in 1900 to more than 6 billion in 2000. Although the overall rate of growth has been declining in recent decades, the world still is adding about 75 million people per year to a total that already exceeded 6.3 billion in 2003. And while population in some areas of the world has begun to stabilize and even decline (Russia, Japan, most of Europe), it continues to mushroom elsewhere, notably in South and Southwest Asia. But sheer numbers are no guide to a population's impact on the natural world. Highly developed, rich societies place demands on the resources of our planet that translate into massive intervention (in the United States, think of the Tennessee Valley Authority, the Colorado and Mississippi Rivers, the agricultural Midwest, the northeastern seaboard's Megalopolis that stretches from north of Boston to south of Washington, DC). More populous but less-developed and less-demanding societies cannot afford to bend nature to their needs and tend to live subject to its uncertainties, as do the vast majority of the people in Bangladesh.

It is nevertheless useful to have a sense of the spatial distribution of the world's population (Figure 2.5). Our technological, environment-controlling capacities notwithstanding, this map still represents the historic accommodation

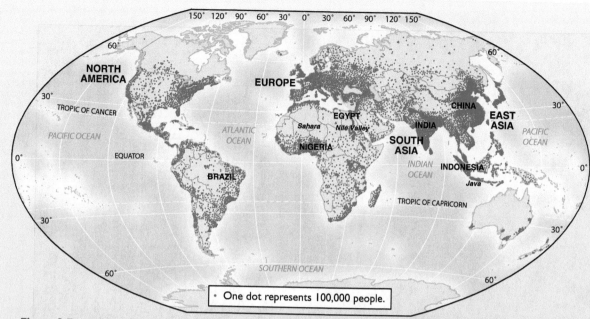

Figure 2.5 Spatial distribution of the world's population in 2003. The way people have arranged themselves in geographic space represents the totality of their adjustments to the environments that are capable of supporting human settlement.

humans made as populations entered and adjusted to habitats capable of supporting them. Two of the three great clusters—East Asia and South Asia—still represent dominantly rural, agricultural populations, despite what is happening on Asia's Pacific Rim. The third and smallest of the major clusters, Europe, is the most modernized, industrialized, and urbanized of the three, but this population's impact on the region's natural environments is greater by many measures than that of the other two.

As Figure 2.5 shows, about 90 per cent of the world's people live on a relatively small fraction (about one-fifth) of the land. Fertile river lowlands and deltas still contain the highest regional densities; altitudinally, more than three-quarters of all humankind resides below 500 m; and nearly 70 per cent live within 500 km of a seacoast. This leaves large parts of the planet with sparse human populations, including deserts such as the Sahara, high-latitude regions such as Siberia, and mountains such as the Himalayas. But even there, as we will see, humans make their impact. To the atmosphere, biosphere, lithosphere, hydrosphere, and cryosphere, should we add the demosphere?

LINK

The third major ocean-floor feature is a global system of **mid-oceanic ridges**. These ridges are high, submarine, volcanic mountain ranges. The existence of one such ridge, the Mid-Atlantic Ridge, was long known to scientists. But its properties were not understood until quite recently, when it became clear that mid-oceanic ridges also extend across the Indian, Pacific, and Southern Ocean floors (Figure 2.6). As is noted in Part Three, these mid-oceanic ridges are the scenes of active submarine volcanism and major movements of the Earth's crust. When scientists were able to observe them for the first time, they brought back dramatic records of violent eruptions, superheated water, and exotic marine life forms populating these active ridges that had never been seen before.

The active character of the mid-oceanic ridges and the geologic properties of the ocean floor become important to us when we study their implications in geomorphology. But the configuration of the ocean floors affects the movement of ocean water just as the topography on land influences the movement of air. The ocean basins are filled with water that, like the air, is in constant motion. Great, permanent circulation systems have developed in the oceans, and these systems affect the weather and climate on neighbouring continents. Our water-dominated planet is finally yielding secrets it has held for eons.

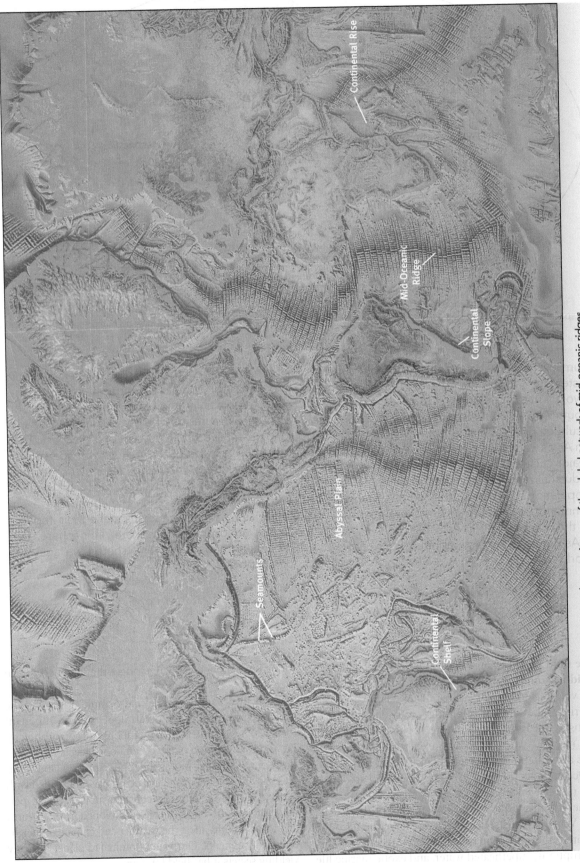

Figure 2.6   World ocean-floor map, underscoring the prominence of the global network of mid-oceanic ridges.

KEY TERMS

abyssal plains *page 24*
atmosphere *page 18*
biosphere *page 18*
continental rise *page 24*
continental shelf *page 23*
continental slope *page 24*
cryosphere *page 18*
cultural landscapes *page 24*
Earth System *page 18*

ecumene *page 20*
hemisphere *page 19*
hydrosphere *page 18*
land hemisphere *page 19*
lithosphere *page 18*
mid-oceanic ridge *page 25*
natural landscapes *page 24*
regional subsystem *page 19*
water (oceanic) hemisphere *page 19*

REVIEW QUESTIONS

1. Name the Earth's five spheres, or interacting shells.
2. What is the regional subsystem and how does it relate to the Earth's five spheres?
3. What is the difference between the land hemisphere and the water hemisphere?
4. Compare and contrast the distribution of continental landmasses in the Northern and Southern Hemispheres.
5. Describe the basic spatial patterns exhibited by the distribution of the world's population.
6. Describe the major topographic features of the world's ocean basins.

REFERENCES AND FURTHER READINGS

Broad, W.J. 1997. *The Universe Below: Discovering the Secrets of the Deep Sea*. New York: Simon & Schuster.

de Blij, H.J., and P.O. Muller. 2004. *Geography: Realms, Regions, and Concepts*, 11th edn. Hoboken, NJ: Wiley.

Emiliani, C. 1992. *Planet Earth: Cosmology, Geology, and the Evolution of Life and the Environment*. New York: Cambridge Univ. Press.

Hancock, P.L., and B.J. Skinner, eds. 2001. *Oxford Companion to the Earth*. New York: Oxford Univ. Press.

Lodders, K., and B. Fegley Jr. 1998. *The Planetary Scientist's Companion*. New York: Oxford Univ. Press.

National Geographic Atlas of the World, 7th edn. 1999. Washington: National Geographic Society.

Newman, J.L., and G.E. Matzke. 1984. *Population: Patterns, Dynamics, and Prospects*. Englewood Cliffs, NJ: Prentice-Hall.

Oxford Atlas of the World, 9th edn. 2001. New York: Oxford Univ. Press.

Scientific American. 1983. 'The Dynamic Earth', *Scientific American* (Sept.; special issue).

Seibold, E., and W.H. Bergerer. 1996. *The Sea Floor: An Introduction to Marine Geology*. New York: Springer-Verlag.

Thomas, D.S.G., and A.S. Goudie, eds. 2000. *The Dictionary of Physical Geography*, 3rd edn. Malden, Mass.: Blackwell.

 ## WEB RESOURCE

earthobservatory.nasa.gov Visible Earth directory, a searchable directory of images, visualizations, and animations of the Earth.

Unit 3

Mapping the Earth's Surface

Objectives

- To introduce the reference system for locations on the Earth's surface.

- To describe the most important characteristics of maps and the features of common classes of map projections.

- To discuss the elements of map interpretation and contemporary cartographic techniques.

When you go to a new city, your process of learning about it begins at the hotel where you stay or in your new home. You then locate the nearest important service facilities, such as supermarkets and shopping centres. Gradually your knowledge of the city, and your activity space within it, expands. This slow pace of learning about the space you live in repeats the experience of every human society as it learned about the Earth. Early in the learning process, directions concerning the location of a particular place have to be taken from or given to someone. The most common form of conveying such information is the **map**, which Phillip Muehrcke has defined as *any geographical image of the environment*. All of us have seen sketch maps directing us to a place for a social gathering. The earliest maps were of a similar nature, beginning with maps scratched in the dust or sand.

Although humans have been drawing maps throughout most of their history, the oldest surviving maps date from only about 2500 BCE. They were drawn on clay tablets in Mesopotamia (modern-day Iraq) and represented individual towns, the entire known country, and the early Mesopotamian view of the world (Figure 3.1). The religious and astrological text above the map (Figure 3.1A) indicates that the Mesopotamian idea of space was linked to ideas about humankind's place in the universe. This is a common theme in **cartography**—the science, art, and technology of mapmaking and map use. Even today, maps of newly discovered space, such as star charts, raise questions in our minds of where we, as humans, fit into the overall scheme of things.

The Spherical Earth

If you look out your window, there is no immediate reason for you to suppose that the Earth's surface is anything but flat. It takes a considerable amount of travelling and observation to reach any other conclusion. Yet, the notion of the Earth as a sphere is a longstanding one and was accepted by several Greek philosophers as far back as 350 BCE. By 200 BCE the Earth's circumference (approximately 40,000 km) had been accurately estimated by Eratosthenes to within a few percentage points of its actual size. The idea of a spherical Earth continued to be challenged, however, and was not universally accepted until the Magellan expedition successfully circumnavigated the globe in the early sixteenth century.

Dividing the Earth

When a sphere is cut into two parts, the edges of the cut form circles. Once the Earth was conceived of as spherical, it was logical to divide it by means of circles. Sometime

A

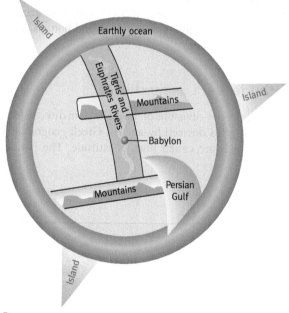

B

Figure 3.1 Mesopotamian world map. The original (A) was drawn in clay about 4500 years ago, with an explanatory text (top). An interpretive diagram (B) indicates its principal features.

between the development of the wheel and the measurement of the planet's circumference, mathematicians had decided that the circle should be divided into 360 parts by means of 360 straight lines radiating from the centre of the circle. The angle between two of these lines was called a **degree**. For such a large circle as the Earth's circumference, further subdivisions became necessary. Each degree was divided into 60 *minutes*, and each minute was further subdivided into 60 *seconds*.

With a system for dividing the curved surface of the Earth, the problem became the origin and layout of these circles. Two sets of information could be used to tackle this problem. First, a sense of direction had been gained by studying the movements of the Sun, Moon, and stars. In particular, the Sun at midday was always located in the same direction, which was designated as *south*. Knowing this, it was easy to arrive at the concepts of *north, east,* and *west*. The division of the circle could refine these directional concepts. The second piece of information was that some geographical locations in the Mediterranean region, fixed by star measurements, could be used as reference points for the division of the Earth.

Using this knowledge, it was possible to imagine a series of 'lines' on the Earth's surface (actually, circles around the spherical Earth), some running north–south and some running east–west, which together form a grid. The east–west lines of this grid are still called **parallels**, the name the Greeks gave them; the north–south lines are called **meridians**. As we can see in Figure 3.2, the two sets of lines differ. Parallels never intersect with one another, whereas meridians intersect at the top and bottom points (poles) of the sphere.

Latitude and Longitude

The present-day divisions of the globe stem directly from the Earth grids devised by ancient Greek geographers. The parallels are called lines of latitude. The parallel

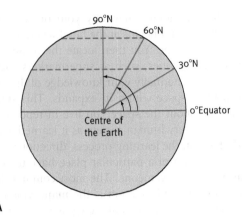

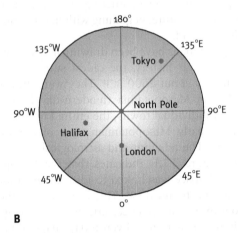

Figure 3.3 Latitude and longitude. Viewed from the side (A), lines of latitude (including the Equator) are horizontal parallels. Lines of longitude, the meridians, appear to radiate from a centre point when viewed from above the North Pole (B); they converge again at the South Pole.

running around the middle of the globe, the **Equator**, is defined as zero degrees latitude. As Figure 3.3A illustrates, **latitude** is the angular distance, measured in degrees north or south, of a point along a parallel from the Equator. Lines of latitude in both the Northern and Southern Hemispheres are defined this way. Thus, Vancouver has a latitude of 49 degrees, 15 minutes north of the Equator (49°15'N), and Sydney, Australia, a latitude of 33 degrees, 55 minutes south (33°55'S). The 'top' of the Earth, the *North Pole*, is at latitude 90°N; the 'bottom', the *South Pole*, is at 90°S.

The meridians are called lines of longitude. In 1884, the meridian that passes through the Royal Observatory at Greenwich in London, England, was established as the global starting point for measuring longitude. This north–south line is called the **Prime Meridian** and is defined as having a longitude of zero degrees. **Longitude** is the angular distance, measured in degrees east or west, of a point along a meridian from the Prime Meridian. The other

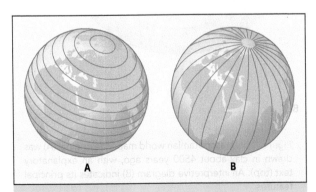

Figure 3.2 Parallels (A) and meridians (B) on a globe. Parallels run east–west; meridians run north–south.

meridians are ascertained as if we were looking down on the Earth from above the North Pole, as Figure 3.3B indicates. Measurements are taken both east and west from the Prime Meridian. Therefore, Vancouver has a longitude of 123 degrees, 04 minutes west of the Greenwich meridian (123°04'W), and Sydney has a longitude of 151 degrees, 17 minutes east (151°17'E).

Because meridians converge at the North and South Poles, the actual distance contained in one degree of longitude varies from 111 km at the Equator to zero at the poles. In contrast, the length of a degree of latitude is about 111 km anywhere between 0° and 90°N or S. We say 'about' because the Earth is not a perfect sphere—it bulges slightly at the Equator and is flattened at the poles. The Greek geographers, however, knew nothing of this. They had a more immediate and difficult problem to confront: how could they represent the three-dimensional Earth on a flat chart?

Today, for an increasingly large number of people, measurement of latitude and longitude has become a routine daily experience thanks to **global positioning system (GPS)** technology. With the aid of a relatively inexpensive GPS receiver, anyone can now determine his or her exact geographic position. The GPS was developed by the US Department of Defense for a variety of military applications, but its use by scientists, private industry, and the public at large continues to expand. The GPS involves a constellation of more than two dozen satellites that orbit the Earth at an altitude of 20,000 km. A GPS receiver, either handheld or mounted in a vehicle, detects signals simultaneously from several satellites to precisely calculate its latitude and longitude (and even its elevation). Over the past few years, that capability quickly resulted in widespread applications of GPS technology, not only for on-board navigational purposes in ships, aircraft, cars, and trucks, but also to locate and monitor the movements of such vehicles (and even of individuals).

LINK

UTM

The Universal Transverse Mercator (or UTM) spatial co-ordinate system was developed in the mid-twentieth century as a result of the need for an internationally recognized co-ordinate system. After World War II, all of the nations in NATO (the North Atlantic Treaty Organization, the group of Western nations organized to oppose the Soviet Union and its allies) agreed that a standard was needed. As long as each nation's military used its own, it would be impossible to precisely co-ordinate military movements between nations. A standard would eliminate this problem.

The UTM system is a grid-based system for specifying locations on the surface of the Earth. It differs from traditional latitude and longitude in several respects. First and foremost, the UTM system is not a single map projection (see below). The UTM system divides the surface of the Earth between 80°S latitude and 84°N latitude into 60 zones, each of which is 6° of longitude in width and centered over a meridian of longitude. Zones are numbered from 1 through 60. Zone 1 is bounded by longitude 180° to 174° W and is centred on the 177th West meridian. Zone numbering increases in an easterly direction. Figure 3.4 illustrates how Canada is divided into 16 zones (from 7 through 22) on the UTM system. The UTM system further subdivides the longitude zones into 20 latitude zones. Each latitude zone spans 8° and is lettered, starting with a 'C' at 80°S latitude, proceeding through the English alphabet to Z (the letters 'I' and 'O' are omitted due to their similarity to numerals one and zero). A convenient way to remember where the letters reside in terms of the locations on the Earth is that the letter 'N' is the first letter in the Northern Hemisphere, so any territory designated by a letter before 'N' in the alphabet resides in the Southern Hemisphere and any territory designated by a letter after 'N' is in the Northern Hemisphere.

Each grid square is referenced as its longitude zone number and the latitude zone letter. The UTM for a position in Toronto, Canada, would be located in longitude zone 17 and latitude zone 'T', for a full reference of '17T'. A full reference using the UTM system includes the UTM longitude zone as a so-called easting and northing co-ordinate pair. The easting is the distance of the position from the central meridian, while the northing is the distance of the point from the equator.

Map Projections

If you have ever tried to cut the skin from an orange or any other spherical surface and then lay it flat, you realize that this is not an easy task. At least some part of the skin must be stretched to make it completely flat. Cylinders or cones may be cut easily to be laid out flat without distortion, but not a sphere, which in geometric and cartographic terms is an *undevelopable* surface, incapable of being flattened. Once the ancient Greeks had accepted the idea that the Earth was a sphere, they had to determine how best to represent the round Earth on a flat surface. There is no totally satisfactory solution to this problem, but the early mapmakers soon invented many of the partial solutions that still are used commonly today.

The Greeks had noted that a light placed at the centre of a globe casts shadows along the meridians and parallels. These shadows, which form lines, can be 'projected' outward onto some surface that can later be cut and laid out flat. The resulting series of projected lines on the new surface is called a **map projection**, which may be defined as an orderly arrangement of meridians and parallels—produced by any systematic method—that can be used for drawing a map of the spherical Earth on a flat surface. All modern map projections, it should be added, are constructed mathematically.

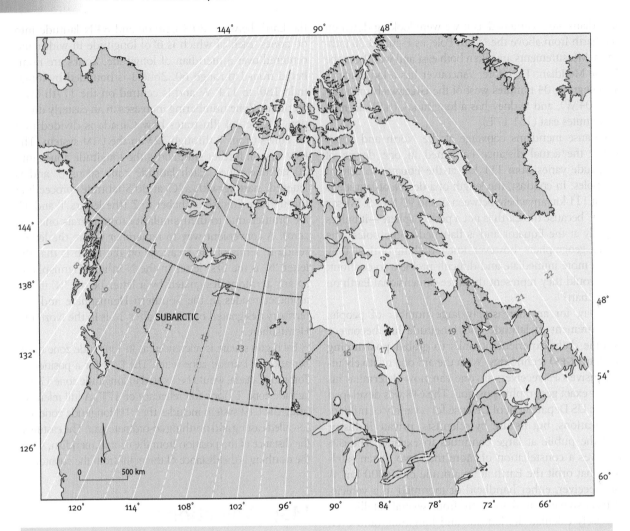

Figure 3.4   Canada divided by the UTM—spatial co-ordinate—zones.

Properties of Map Projections

Any map projection has three variable properties: scale, area, and shape. **Scale** is the ra[...]
the map to the actual size of th[...]
ample, consider a model globe [...]
It represents the real Earth, w[...]
Therefore, 1 cm of the globe re[...]
divided by 25 km), or 51,600,([...]
we say that the scale of the mo[...]
or 1:51,600,000. Why must [...]
instead of saying 1 (cm) to 516[...]
of fractions is that the numerat[...]
always be given in the same ma[...]

The *area* of a section of the [...]
multiplying its east–west dista[...]
tance. This calculation is simp[...]
land, but tedious for territori[...]
shapes. In many map proje[...]
can be well represented simp[...]
(scaling down the distances). [...]

relative to other Canadian provinces on a model globe as in the real world. The only difference is that the scale has changed.

[...] When a map projection preserves [...]a, it is said to be 'conformal'. Shape [...]n map projections—but not always. [...]shape of Saskatchewan is almost a [...]ith a scale of 1:50,000 for north–[...]cale of 1:200,000 for east–west dis-[...]squeezed in the east–west direction [...]th–south direction.

[...]jection from a globe, we can pre-[...]s two, of the properties of scale, [...]s not possible to preserve all three [...]of the map. Try it for yourself by [...]astic ball and then cutting the ball [...]ensional map. You will be forced [...]mize this problem, the Greeks fol-[...]hers still use: select the map pro-[...]e particular geographical purpose

Handwritten note: Scale: the ratio of the size of an object on the map to the actual size of the object it represents.

Types of Map Projections

Since the time of the pioneering Greeks, mapmakers have devised hundreds of projections to flatten the globe so that all of it is visible at once. Indeed, mathematically it is possible to create an infinite number of map projections. In practice, however, these cartographic transformations of the three-dimensional, spherical surface of the Earth have tended to fall into a small number of categories. The four most common classes of map projections are considered here: cylindrical, conic, plane, and equal-area.

A **cylindrical projection** involves the transfer of the Earth's latitude/longitude grid from the globe to a cylinder, which is then cut and laid flat. When this operation is completed, the parallels and the meridians appear on the opened cylinder as straight lines intersecting at right angles. On any map projection, the least distortion occurs where the globe touches, or is *tangent* to, the geometric object it is projected onto; the greatest distortion occurs farthest from this place of contact. In Figure 3.5A we observe in the left-hand diagram that the globe and the cylinder are tangent along the parallel of the Equator. The parallel of tangency between a globe and the surface onto which it is projected is called the **standard parallel**. The right-hand diagram of Figure 3.5A shows a globe larger than the cylinder, and two standard parallels result. This projection reduces distortion throughout the map, and is particularly useful for representing the low-latitude zone straddling the Equator between the pair of standard parallels.

Mathematical modifications have increased the utility of cylindrical projections, the best known of which was devised in 1569 by the Flemish cartographer Gerhardus Mercator. In a **Mercator projection** (Figure 3.6), the spacing of parallels increases toward the poles. This increase is in direct proportion to the false widening between normally convergent meridians that is necessary to draw those meridians as parallel lines. Although this technique produced extreme distortion in the area of the polar latitudes, it provided a tremendously important service for navigators using the newly perfected magnetic compass. Unlike any other map projection, a straight line drawn on this one is a line of true and constant compass bearing. Such lines are called **rhumb lines**. Once a navigator has determined from the Mercator map of the world the compass direction to be travelled, the ship can be locked onto this course.

Cones can be cut and laid out flat as easily as cylinders, and the **conic projection** has been in use almost as long as the cylindrical. A conic projection involves the transfer of the Earth's latitude/longitude grid from a globe to a cone, which is then cut and laid flat. Figure 3.5B shows the derivation of the two most common conic projections, the one- and two-standard-parallel cases. On a conic projection, meridians are shown as straight lines that converge towards the (North) Pole. Parallels appear as arcs of concentric circles with the same centre point that shorten as the latitude increases. This projection is best suited for the middle latitudes, such as the United States and Europe,

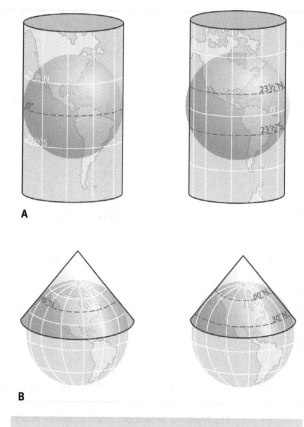

A

B

Figure 3.5 Construction of cylindrical (A) and conic (B) projections with one and two standard parallels.

where distortion is minimal if the apex of the imaginary cone is positioned directly above the North Pole.

Planar projections, in which an imaginary plane touches the globe at a single point, exhibit a wheel-like symmetry around the point of tangency between the plane and the sphere. Planar projections were the first map projections developed by the ancient Greeks. Today they are most frequently used to represent the polar regions (Figure 3.7). One type of planar projection, the *gnomonic*, possesses an especially useful property: a straight line on this projection is the shortest route between two points on the Earth's surface. This has vital implications in this age of intercontinental jet travel. Long international flights seek to follow the shortest routes, and these are found on the spherical Earth by imagining the globe to be cut exactly in half along a straight line running through the origin and destination cities. When a sphere is cut in half, the circle formed along the edge of the cut is called a *great circle*. (*Small circles* are the edges of all other cuts when a sphere is divided into two unequal portions.) Long-distance air traffic usually follows great-circle routes, such as the one shown between New York and London in Figure 3.7.

Through the mathematical manipulation of projective geometry, it is possible to derive an unlimited number of map projections that go beyond the convenience and simplicity of the cylinder, cone, and plane. Among these

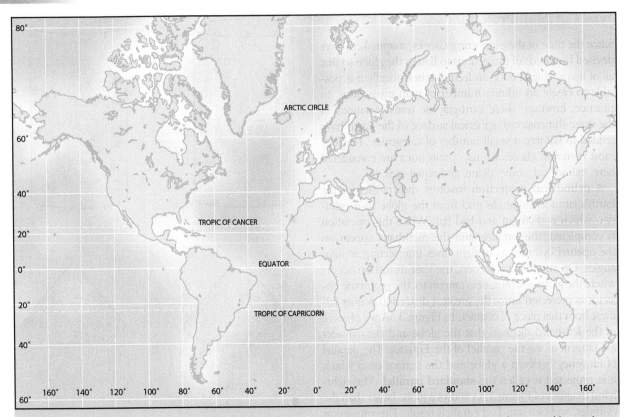

Figure 3.6 The Mercator projection, which produces straight parallels and meridians. Any straight line drawn on this map is a (rhumb) line of constant compass bearing, a tremendous advantage for long-distance navigation.

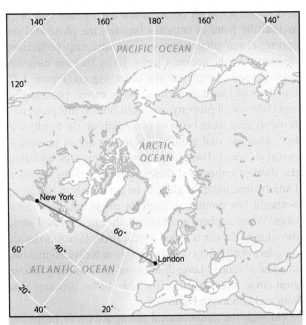

Figure 3.7 The great-circle route from New York to London, which becomes a straight line on this polar gnomonic projection.

other types of map projections, **equal-area projections** rank among the most important. An equal-area projection is one in which all the areas mapped are represented in correct proportion to one another. Thus, on a world map of this type, the relative areal sizes of the continents are preserved. True shape, however, must be sacrificed. Nonetheless, good equal-area projections attempt to limit the distortion of shape so that the continental landmasses are still easily recognizable. This should be carefully noted in Figure 3.8, which displays the flat polar quartic projection. Because they maintain the areal relationships of every part of the globe, equal-area projections are particularly useful for mapping the worldwide spatial distributions of land-based phenomena. The map in Figure 3.8 possesses another feature you have undoubtedly observed by now: it is not a continuous representation but is *interrupted*. This device helps the cartographer minimize distortion, devote most of the projection to the parts that project best, and de-emphasize areas of the globe that are not essential to the distribution at hand (such as omitting large parts of the oceans in mappings of land-based phenomena).

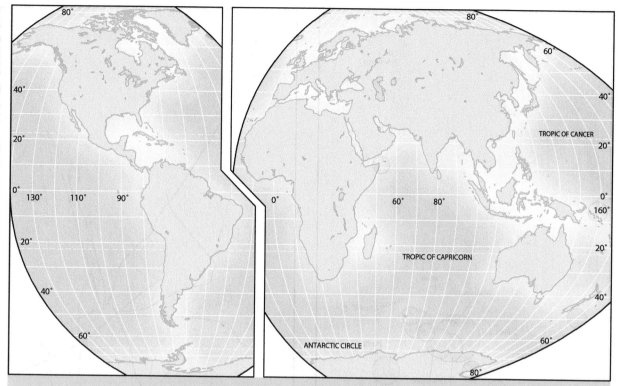

Figure 3.8 Equal-area projection. All areas mapped are represented in their correct relative sizes. This flat polar quartic equal-area projection—in interrupted form—was developed in 1949 for the US Coast and Geodetic Survey by F.W. McBryde and P.D. Thomas.

Map Interpretation

One of the most important functions of maps is to communicate their content effectively and efficiently. Because so much spatial information exists in the real world, cartographers must first carefully choose the information to be included and deleted in order to avoid cluttering the map with less-relevant data. Thus *maps are models*: their compilers simplify the complexity of the real world, filtering out all but the most essential information. Even so, a considerable amount of information remains, and all of it must be compressed into the small confines of the final map. To facilitate that task, cartographers have learned to encode their spatial messages through the use of symbolization. Decoding this cartographic shorthand is not a difficult task, and the place to begin is the map's key or **legend** (or sometimes its written caption), in which symbols and colours are identified. These symbols usually correspond to the different categories of geographic data: dimensionless *points*, one-dimensional *lines*, two-dimensional *areas*, and three-dimensional *volumes* or *surfaces*.

Point symbols tell us the location of each occurrence of the phenomenon being mapped and, frequently, its quantity. This is illustrated in Figure 3.9, which is a map of electrical generating stations in Alberta. A dot or circle marks the location of each station, whose generating capacity can be ascertained in the legend. Taken together, all these point symbols exhibit the provincial distribution of this phenomenon.

Line symbols represent linkages and/or flows that exist between places. The map in Figure 3.10 shows the pattern of crude oil and gas pipelines in the province of Alberta.

Area symbols portray two-dimensional spaces, with colours representing specific quantitative ranges. An example is seen in Figure 3.11, which maps population density (persons/km^2) by census division in Alberta in 1996. The northern part of the province is representative of a relatively low population density, as indicated by the light shading, whereas the areas around Edmonton, Red Deer, and Calgary have higher population densities, as represented with darker shading.

Volume symbols describe *surfaces* that can be generalizations of real surfaces (such as the world topographic relief map in Figure 2.3) or representations of conceptual surfaces. An example of the latter is provided in Figure 3.12, which shows Alberta's January daily mean temperatures (1971 to 2000). Bands of 'warmer'

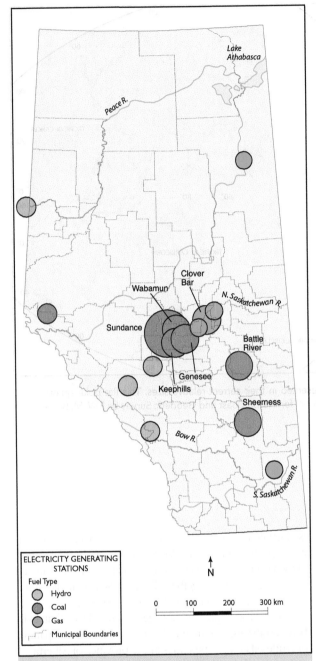

Figure 3.9 Alberta's electrical generating stations (fuel type and capacity), an example of a proportional symbol map.

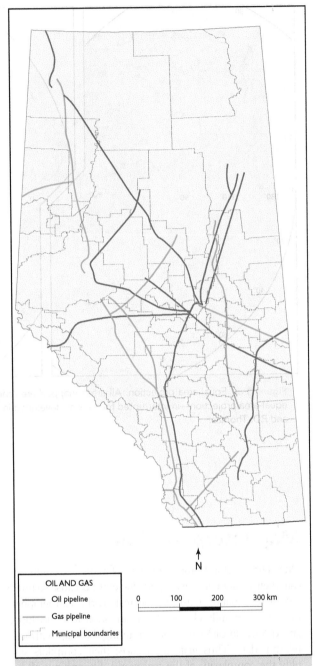

Figure 3.10 Alberta's oil and gas pipelines, demonstrating a line-mapping technique.

temperatures can be seen to the southwest corner, with bands of progressively colder temperatures toward the north. This mapping technique is known as **isarithmic (isoline) mapping** and consists of numerous **isolines** that connect all places possessing the same value of a given phenomenon or 'height' above the flat base of the surface. In Figure 3.12 the boundary lines between colour zones, as the legend indicates, connect all points reporting that particular temperature.

Perhaps the best-known use of isolines in physical geography is the representation of surface relief by **contouring**. As Figure 3.13 demonstrates, each contour line represents a specific and constant elevation, and all the contours together provide a useful generalization of the surface being mapped. A more practical example of contouring is shown in Figure 3.14, where the landscape portrayed in Figure 3.14A corresponds to the *topographic map* of that terrain in Figure 3.14B. By comparing the two

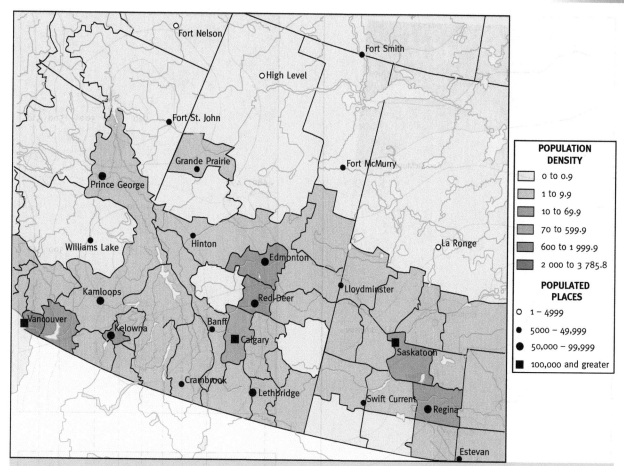

Figure 3.11 Population density by census division (persons/km²), 1996, Alberta and portions of BC and Saskatchewan. This is an example of a choropleth map (area symbol mapping technique).

it is easy to read the contour map and understand how this cartographic technique portrays the configuration of the Earth's surface relief accurately. The land surface of the United States, except for Alaska, has been completely mapped at the fairly detailed scale of 1:24,000. Approximately 55,000 topographic quadrangle maps at this scale have been published by the US Geological Survey and can now be purchased in both printed and digital formats. The latter is fully computer-accessible, and its recent availability is but one product of the technological revolution that is transforming cartography in the twenty-first century.

Evolving Cartographic Technology

The late twentieth century saw rapid advances in computer power and speed. Cartographers quickly applied the new technology to mapmaking, and today virtually all maps are compiled digitally. As sophisticated mapping software was being pioneered, closely related breakthroughs were simultaneously occurring in airborne and satellite remote sensing cartography (see 'Perspectives' box). This led to an explosion of new data about the Earth's surface, and propelled the rapid development of geographic information systems to analyze and interpret them.

A **geographic information system**—GIS for short—is an assemblage of computer hardware and software that enables spatial data to be collected, recorded, stored, retrieved, manipulated, analyzed, and displayed to the user. Especially when linked to remotely sensed data from high-altitude observation platforms, this approach allows for the simultaneous collection of several layers of information pertaining to the same study area. These layers can then be integrated by multiple map overlays (Figure 3.15) in order to assemble the components of the complex real-world pattern, a powerful analytical tool.

For cartographers, GIS technology is particularly valuable because all digital data are geo-referenced with respect to the Earth's latitude/longitude grid. This enables

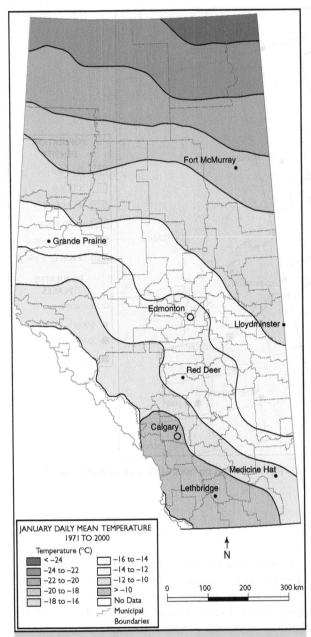

Figure 3.12   January daily mean temperature in Alberta (1971–2000), showing the use of an isarithmic mapping technique.

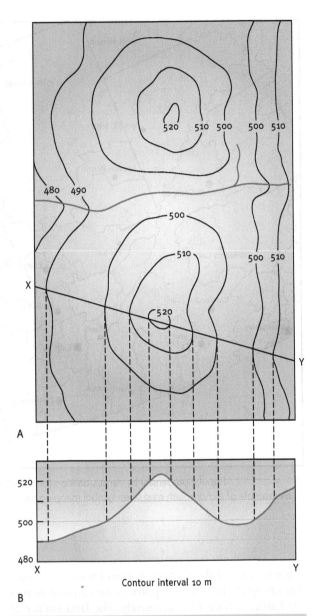

Figure 3.13   In topographic contouring, each contour line's points have the identical height above sea level. The surface relief described by the contour map (A) can be linked to a cross-sectional profile of the terrain. (In diagram B this is done for line X–Y on map A.) Note how contour spacing corresponds to slope patterns: the wider the spacing, the gentler the slope, and vice versa.

the data to be mapped within the framework of any map projection, and to move easily from one projection to another. It also allows the collating of digital data from diverse sources, even if the original source material exists in different map projections and/or at different scales. Another highly advantageous capability is the conversion of digital data from point-based format to line- or area-based formats, and vice versa.

Perhaps the most revolutionary aspect of GIS cartography is its break with the static map of the past. The use of GIS methodology involves a constant dialogue, via computer commands and feedback to queries, between the map and the map user. This instantaneous two-way communication is known as **interactive mapping**, and it is expected to become the cornerstone of cartography in the future. Just one of the many possibilities of this technique is the use of video-disk maps displayed on automobile dashboards, allowing the driver to ask questions that elicit immediate map directions showing the best route to the desired destination.

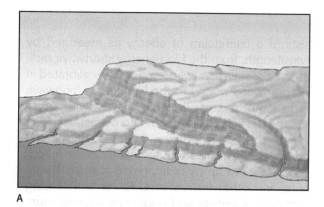

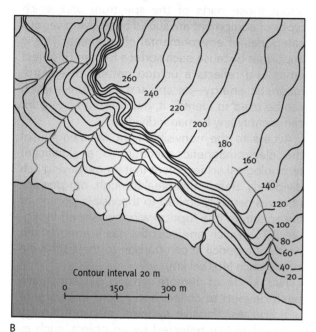

B

Contour interval 20 m

0   150   300 m

Figure 3.14 Perspective sketch of a coastal landscape (A) and its corresponding topographic map (B), adapted from US Geological Survey sources. Note that the contour interval—most appropriate for this map—is 20 m.

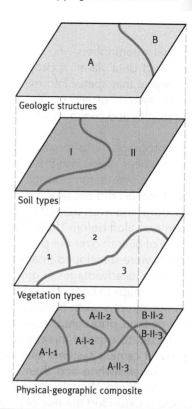

Geologic structures

Soil types

Vegetation types

Physical-geographic composite

Figure 3.15 GIS processing of overlays to produce map composite.

GIS is a Canadian invention, stemming from the early work undertaken by Roger Tomlinson, who was just a young geographer in the 1960s. While Tomlinson was working with the federal government he initiated, planned, and directed the development of the first computerized GIS in the world. The GIS in the discipline of geography can be compared to the microscope in biology; it has substantially advanced our ability to analyze geographical information.

Perspectives on the Human Environment

Remote Sensing of the Environment

Maps have been used for centuries to graphically communicate information about the Earth's surface. The Greek legend of Icarus, who flew too close to the Sun and melted his wax-and-feather wings, shows how intensely the scientific ancestors of modern geographers wanted to view the Earth from the sky. Today such views are possible, and the work of mapmakers and spatial analysts is greatly facilitated and enhanced by powerful new tools and techniques. The most important of these is remote-sensing technology, the ability to scan the Earth from airborne and satellite observation platforms.

Remote sensing has been defined by Benjamin Richason as any technique of imaging objects without the sensor being in direct contact with the object or scene itself. He goes on to point out that geographers who use this method normally collect data via an appropriate imaging system, interpret that spatial information (which is stored in the system, usually on film or computer tape), and display and communicate the results on a map.

Aerial photography is a remote-sensing technique that has been used since the advent of cameras early in the nineteenth century. Even though the Wright brothers did not take flight until 1903, hot-air balloons and even trained birds were able to carry cameras aloft before 1850. With the rapid proliferation of aircraft over the past century, several methods were developed (many by the military to improve its advantages in ground warfare) that permitted maps to be produced directly from series of photographs taken from survey aircraft.

At the same time, photographic technology was being perfected to expand this capability. Along with improved camera systems came ever more sensitive black-and-white and then colour films. Moreover, by World War II, ultrasensitive film breakthroughs extended the use of photography into the infrared radiation (IR) range beyond the visible capacities of the human eye. By directly 'seeing' reflected and radiated solar energy, aerial infrared photography could, for the first time, penetrate clouds, haze, and smoke—and obtain clear images of the ground even at night. The US Air Force further pioneered the use of IR colour imagery, although the 'colours' obtained—known as false-colour images—bore no resemblance to the natural colours of the objects photographed, but could readily be decoded by analysts.

During the late twentieth century, non-photographic remote sensing developed swiftly as new techniques and instruments opened up a much wider portion of the electromagnetic spectrum. This spectrum, diagrammed in Figure 3.16, consists of a continuum of energy as measured by wavelength, from the high-energy shortwave radiation of cosmic rays (whose waves are calibrated in billionths of a metre) to the low-energy longwave radiation of radio and electric power (with waves measured in units as large as kilometres).

Figure 3.16 also shows the discrete spectral bands within the electromagnetic spectrum, which can be picked up by radio, radar, thermal IR sensors, and other instruments. As remote sensing matured, scientists and engineers learned more about those parts of the spectrum and which types of equipment are suited to studying various categories of environmental phenomena. This is important because each surface feature or object emits and reflects a unique pattern of electromagnetic energy—its spectral signature—which can be used to identify it, much like a fingerprint can identify any human individual.

Access to the nonvisible-light wavelengths of the electromagnetic spectrum is a significant technological achievement that is now paying rich dividends. Before this breakthrough, our perception was narrowly limited to the visible portion of the spectrum (the 'optical window' shown in Figure 3.16), which one scientist has likened to the width of a pencil in comparison to the Earth's circumference (40,000 km).

Two kinds of remote-sensing systems have been devised to collect and record electromagnetic pulses. 'Passive systems' measure energy radiated and/or reflected by an object, such as the IR photography method . Also common today are so-called 'active systems', which transmit their own pulsations of energy, thereby 'illuminating' target objects that 'backscatter', or reflect, some of that energy to receiving sensors that 'see' the image (radar is a good example of such a system). Many remote-sensing platforms now employ

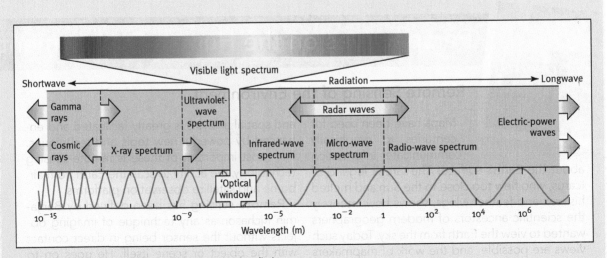

Figure 3.16   The complete (electromagnetic) radiation spectrum.

both active and passive systems. In fact, they increasingly utilize multispectral systems, arrays of scanners attuned simultaneously to several different spectral bands, which greatly enhances the quality of observations and their interpretations.

Although remote sensors can be ground-based, most systems that facilitate our understanding of physical geography need to collect data at high altitudes. Aircraft have been and continue to be useful, but they are limited by how high they can fly (approximately 20 km) and the weather conditions in which they can operate. With planes unable to reach the very high altitudes required to obtain the small-scale imagery for seeing large areas of the surface in a single view, the opening of the space age in 1957 soon provided the needed alternative in Earth-orbiting satellites.

By the 1980s, dozens of special-purpose satellites were circling the Earth at appropriate altitudes and providing remotely sensed data to aid in assembling the 'big picture'. Canada has played an important role in the development and application of aerial photography and photogrammetry. Originating from strategic and military uses and applications, the field of remote sensing in Canada evolved to focus on applications in the Canadian Arctic. Examples include the study of floating ice and information in aid of safe surface navigation through the North West Passage. Among the most important satellites in operation in Canada today is the RADARSAT series. In 1979 the Canadian Interagency Committee on Remote Sensing approved the development of Canada's first radar satellite. RADARSAT-1 was successfully launched in November 1995 (Figure 3.17). Since then there have been numerous Canadian applications, including studies of glacier motion, oil-spill detection, snow mapping, forestlands management, ice-type identification and reconnaissance, geological mapping, and flood monitoring.

RADARSAT-2 was launched on 14 December 2007 and is expected to remain operational for seven years, although the hope is that it will extend beyond this period. RADARSAT-1, which had a design lifespan of 5 years has remained fully operational after 11 years. RADARSAT-2 has been designed with significant and powerful technical advancements from the first RADARSAT. Some of the applications for which RADARSAT-2 has been implemented include the early detection of ice break-up, such as the new 18 kilometre-long network of cracks running from the southern edge of the Ward Hunt Ice Shelf to the Arctic Ocean.

RADARSAT-2 is an invaluable resource in agricultural applications (e.g., crop conditions), disaster management (e.g., disaster assessments), and forestry, geology, and hydrology applications. The comprehensive RADARSAT-2 website (www.radarsat2.info) provides an enormous amount of information and imagery.

RADARSAT-2 is the result of a unique collaboration between government—the Canadian Space Agency—and industry—MacDonald, Dettwiler, and Associates Ltd (MDA). Concern was raised early in 2008 when a proposal by MDA to sell the RADARSAT-2 to a US firm was made public. Critics of the sale questioned whether or not Canada's access to that data would continue if the satellite were sold to a US-based firm. Ultimately, the federal government blocked the $1.3 billion sale.

Figure 3.17 The first RADARSAT image ever produced was of the Cape Breton Highlands of Nova Scotia. The fact that the image was acquired through darkness, cloudy skies, rain, and strong winds (5:41 p.m. AST on the evening of 28 November 1995) illustrates the advantages of the Synthetic Aperture Radar (SAR).

KEY TERMS

cartography   *page 29*
conic projection   *page 33*
contouring   *page 36*
cylindrical projection   *page 33*
degree   *page 30*
equal-area projection   *page 34*
Equator   *page 30*
geographic information system (GIS)   *page 37*
global positioning system (GPS)   *page 31*
interactive mapping   *page 38*
isarithmic (isoline) mapping   *page 36*
isoline   *page 36*
latitude   *page 30*

legend   *page 35*
longitude   *page 30*
map   *page 29*
map projection   *page 31*
Mercator projection   *page 33*
meridians   *page 30*
parallels   *page 30*
planar projection   *page 33*
Prime Meridian   *page 30*
remote sensing   *page 39*
rhumb lines   *page 33*
scale   *page 32*
standard parallel   *page 33*

REVIEW QUESTIONS

1. What is the difference between latitude and longitude? What are the reference lines and/or points for each measurement system?

2. Describe how the properties of *scale, area,* and *shape* relate to a map projection.

3. What are the differences between cylindrical, conical, and planar map projections?

4. What is an equal-area projection, and what mapping task(s) is it well suited to?

5. Define and give examples of point, line, area, and volume map symbols.

6. What are the distinguishing features of the geographic information system (GIS) and remote-sensing techniques?

REFERENCES AND FURTHER READINGS

Campbell, J.B. 1998. *Map Use and Analysis,* 3rd edn. Dubuque, Iowa: WCB/McGraw-Hill.

———. 2002. *Introduction to Remote Sensing,* 3rd edn. New York: Guilford Press.

Chrisman, N. 2002. *Exploring Geographic Information Systems,* 3rd edn. New York: Wiley.

Dent, B.D. 1996. *Cartography: Thematic Map Design, with USGS Map Projection Poster,* 4th edn. Dubuque, Iowa: WCB/McGraw-Hill.

Goodchild, M.F. 1997. 'Geographic Information Systems', in Susan Hanson, ed. *Ten Geographic Ideas That Changed the World.* New Brunswick, NJ: Rutgers Univ. Press, 60–83.

Greenhood, D. 1964. *Mapping.* Chicago: Univ. of Chicago Press.

Jensen, J.R. 2000. *Remote Sensing of the Environment: An Earth Resource Perspective.* Englewood Cliffs, NJ: Prentice-Hall.

Jones, C.B. 1997. *Geographical Information Systems and Computer Cartography.* London/New York: Longman.

Keates, J.S. 1996. *Understanding Maps,* 2nd edn. London/New York: Longman.

Lillesand, T.M., R.W. Kiefer, and J.W. Chipman. 2004. *Remote Sensing and Image Interpretation,* 5th edn. New York: Wiley.

Longley, P.A., M.F. Goodchild, D.J. Maguire, and D.W. Rhind. 2001. *Geographic Information Systems and Science.* New York: Wiley.

Muehrcke, P.C., and J.O. Muehrcke. 1997. *Map Use: Reading—Analysis—Interpretation,* 4th edn. Madison, Wis.: JP Publ.

Parkinson, C.L. 1997. *Earth from Above: Using Color-Coded Satellite Images to Examine the Global Environment.* New York: University Science Press.

Richason, B.F., Jr. 1983. 'Remote Sensing: An Overview', in B.F. Richason, Jr, ed., *Introduction to Remote Sensing of the Environment,* 2nd edn. Dubuque, Iowa: Kendall/Hunt, 3–15.

Robinson, A.H., J.L. Morrison, P.C. Muehrcke, A.J. Kimerling, and S.C. Guptill. 1995. *Elements of Cartography,* 6th edn. New York: Wiley.

Snyder, J.P. 1993. *Flattening the Earth: Two Thousand Years of Map Projections.* Chicago: Univ. of Chicago Press.

Thrower, N.J.W. 1996. *Maps and Civilization: Cartography in Culture and Society.* Chicago: Univ. of Chicago Press.

WEB RESOURCES

atlas.gc.ca The Atlas of Canada site includes many examples of thematic Canadian maps.

ess.nrcan.gc.ca/mapcar/index_e.php Natural Resources Canada's guide to mapping, including links to a variety of Canadian mapping organizations.

geogratis.cgdi.gc.ca/CLI/frames.html The Canada Land Inventory is a comprehensive multi-disciplinary land inventory of rural Canada, covering over 2.5 million km² of land and water. Over 1000 map sheets at the 1:250,000 scale are available on this site for online mapmaking and download for desktop publishing, or in GIS formats.

www.ccrs.nrcan.gc.ca The Canada Centre for Remote Sensing provides historical and contemporary perspectives on remote sensing in Canada with many examples of research applications.

www.geo.hunter.cuny.edu/mp/ Background information and detailed graphics of map projections, as well as how cartographers choose an appropriate projection.

www.laurentian.ca/Laurentian/Home/Departments/Geography/link_pages/ A useful set of links to GIS job search engines, as well as general job search engines.

www.rsi.ca The official RADARSAT International website.

www.sfei.org/ecoatlas/GIS/MapInterpretation/MapsandScales.html A guide to calculating map scales and mapping techniques.

PART TWO
Atmosphere and Hydrosphere

PART TWO Atmosphere and Hydrosphere

Circulation Systems in Air and Ocean

The Sun's energy, combined with forces arising from the Earth's rotation, drives the hydrosphere and atmosphere into giant circulation systems that carry warmth from equatorial latitudes towards the poles and from sea level to high continental interiors. Giant cells of circular movement occupy entire ocean basins as water moves in slow drifts and faster currents from warm tropical environs to cooler mid-latitudes and beyond, returning towards the tropics with infusions of polar cold. In the atmosphere, equatorial warmth moves upward by convection, generating a set of sub-systems that move air vertically as well as horizontally. At and near the surface, huge air-circulation cells are the scenes of competition between low-latitude warmth and high-latitude cold, producing weather-making collisions that can spawn storms and tornadoes. Embedded in these systems are other, powerful subsystems ranging from hurricanes (see bottom photograph) to blizzards. The Earth's rotation influences the direction of circulation in water and in air, the movement of weather systems, and the prevalence of persistent winds. Remember the interaction principle: conditions in the hydrosphere (warmth) under certain circumstances can promote the formation of hurricanes in the atmosphere; when a hurricane strikes land, it has an impact on the lithosphere (erosion) as well as the biosphere (destruction of natural vegetation and wildlife). Environmental systems are open systems.

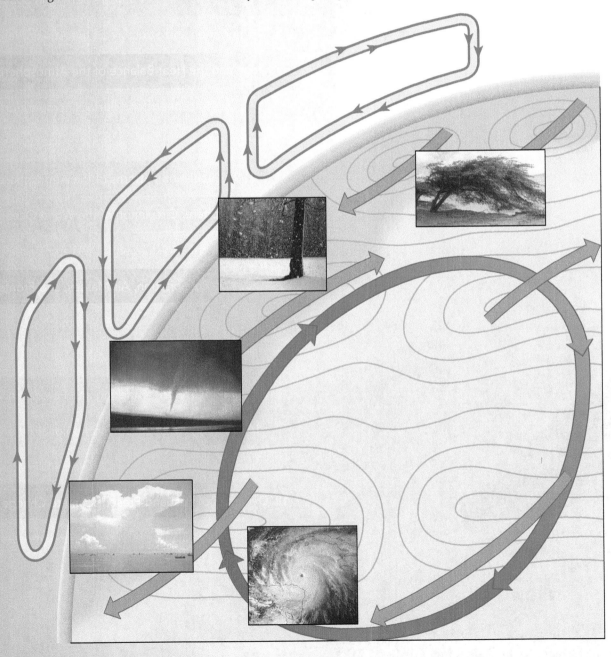

Earth's Setting in Space

Objectives

- To introduce the basic structure of the universe, speculations about its origin, and the position of our home galaxy and star within it.

- To describe the functions of the Sun as the dominant body of the solar system.

- To examine the Earth's motions relative to the Sun.

- To demonstrate the consequences of the Earth's axis tilt for the annual march of the seasons.

- To introduce the time and spatial variations in solar radiation received at surface locations.

LINK

It was pointed out in Unit 2 that we live on a small, fragile planet. Even from the vantage point of the Moon—our nearest neighbour in outer space, only 390,000 km away—the Earth appears greatly shrunken in size. If we were to view the Earth from the vicinity of the Sun, from a distance of 150 million km, it would be only a tiny speck. But these perspectives do not begin to suggest the unimaginable vastness of the universe. How big is the universe? What is its structure? How do our Sun and its family of planets (including Earth) fit into the overall scheme of things? These are some of the key questions to be considered in this unit.

The Universe

The **universe** may be defined as the entity that contains all of the matter and energy that exists anywhere in space and time. As for its size, to understand the enormity of the universe it must be considered in both space and time. The fastest thing that moves in the universe is light, a form of radiant energy that travels at a speed of 300,000 km per second. Thus, in a single second, a ray of light travels a distance equal to 7½ times the Earth's circumference. Even at this speed, however, it takes about eight minutes for light to travel from the Sun to the Earth. Light from the next nearest star takes *more than four years* to get here. If that star exploded today, we would not know it for another four-plus years; our telescopes, therefore, show us only history.

Given the untold billions of stars that populate the universe (Figure 4.1) and the fact that years are required for

the light to reach us even from the nearest star beyond our own Sun, astronomers calibrate interstellar distances in light-years. A **light-year** is the distance travelled by a pulse of light in one year: 9.46 trillion (9.46×10^{12}) km. To travel that distance aboard an airplane moving at 800 km per hour would require a journey of almost 1,350,000 years.

In terms of 'deep space', our planetary system belongs to a **galaxy** (an organized, disk-like assemblage of billions of stars) called the *Milky Way*, which is about 120,000 light-years in diameter. As recently as the 1920s, this was believed to be the entire universe, but newer astronomical discoveries have drastically transformed that perception. We now know that the Milky Way galaxy is merely one of about 30 loosely bound galaxies that have clustered to form what astronomers call the *local galaxy group*, which measures about 4 million light-years across its longest dimension. This local group, in turn, is but a small component of the *local supercluster* (a supercluster is a conglomeration of galaxies, comprising the largest of all celestial formations), measuring approximately 100 million light-years in diameter.

To this point three time–space levels have been discussed—galaxy, galaxy cluster, galaxy supercluster—but only now are we ready to tackle the full dimensions of the known universe. That ultimate level is now under intense investigation by astrophysicists around the world, and research frontiers continue to expand. Today astronomers record images from the Hubble Space Telescope that have travelled almost 13 billion light-years from what are believed to be the outer edges of the universe. Since our local supercluster lies near the universe's centre, the *radius* of the universe is now estimated to be 13.7 billion light-years, and the *diameter* should be no less than 27.4 billion light-years.

The hierarchical organization of the universe's various time–space levels is seen in the 'cones of resolution' diagrammed in Figure 4.2. Each level is highly complex in its internal structure. For instance, the Milky Way galaxy alone consists of more than 100 billion stars, of which our Sun is a middle-sized one. In all, there are billions of galaxies. Their sheer numbers are beyond our comprehension, and most lie beyond the view of our most powerful telescopes. Then how many of those huge balls of glowing gas that we call stars does the total universe actually contain? The current estimate is more than 200 *billion-billion* (200×10^{18}), about 50 billion stars for every human now alive. Where did all these celestial bodies and the other diverse matter and energy of the universe come from, and how was everything scattered across such an immense space?

The answers to these questions rest with theories concerning the origin of the universe, which a consensus of scientists believes to be the result of the so-called *Big Bang*. The Big Bang was a massive explosion of truly cosmic proportions, in which all the primordial matter and energy that existed before the formation of the universe was compressed together at almost infinite density, heated to trillions of degrees, and blown apart. This stupendous blast propelled matter and energy outward in a rapidly expanding fireball,

Figure 4.1   A tiny slice of the nighttime sky (featuring the constellation Orion near the centre of the photo), which can only suggest the enormous number of stars contained in the universe.

Figure 4.2 Spatial structure of the universe—and our place within it. All dimensions shown are radial measurements with respect to the centre of each disk.

which has been cooling and slowing ever since. In the wake of this violent advancing wave lay an amorphous cloud of debris, from which the contents of the universe gradually formed. Galaxies and larger star clusters slowly took shape from the condensation and consolidation of cooling gas and dust clouds. A key force binding them together was **gravity**, the force of attraction acting among all physical objects due to their *mass*, the quantity of material of which they are composed. Indeed, gravitational forces shape the structure of every one of the universe's time–space levels, bonding enormous interstellar clusters as well as the superheated gases of individual stars.

The Big Bang, which is based on Albert Einstein's general theory of relativity, took place approximately 13.7 billion years ago. As was noted, the farthest objects in the universe appear to be located at a distance of about 13 billion light-years from Earth. If the universe still is expanding in the wake of the Big Bang, then the matter and energy at the outermost extremities of the universe represent the leading edge of that advance. The matter that exists at these extremities has been formed into mysterious, star-like objects; these brightly glowing masses are called *quasars*, shorthand for 'quasi-stellar objects'. Quasars are embedded in a uniform glow of radio-wave-frequency radiation, an energy environment consistent with the hypothesis that this cosmic radiation (confirmed to exist everywhere in space) is the faint 'echo' of the Big Bang that occurred so long ago.

Many scientists also are studying the consequences of these recent revelations for the future evolution of the universe. If the universe should turn out to be a finite or closed system, then gravity will inevitably reverse the expanding edge, force an implosion leading to another Big Bang, and spawn infinite expansion–contraction cycles beyond it. However, should the universe prove to be an open system, then it may end with a whimper rather than a bang as galaxies inexorably overcome the pull of gravity and eventually drift away from one another. In the search for answers, some researchers now subscribe to even more complex outcomes.

The Solar System

Our home galaxy, the Milky Way, began to form more than 12 billion years ago. The star we know as the Sun, however, was a relatively late addition and did not appear until about 4.6 billion years ago. The processes that formed the Sun mirrored the forces at work throughout the universe. One particular rotating cloud of gas and dust began to cool, and soon its centre condensed to form a star. Simultaneously, the remaining materials in the swirling cloud around this new star formed a disk and began to sort themselves out as the consolidating mass of the Sun exerted an ever stronger gravitational pull. Millions of eddies within this disk now began to condense as well and formed sizeable conglomerations of solid matter called *planetesimals*. As these objects grew in mass, gravity began to draw them together. Soon these planetesimals were travelling in swarms, and it was not long before they were compressed together to form nine planets that began to circle the Sun in regular orbits. (**Planets** are dark solid or gaseous bodies, much smaller in size than stars, whose movements are controlled by the gravitational effects of nearby stars.)

Most of the larger residual planetesimals were captured by the gravitational fields of the evolving planets and began to orbit them as satellites or **moons**. A large belt of smaller planetesimal-like materials (known as *asteroids*) congregated between the fourth and fifth planets, and remain in orbit today. The Sun's gravitational field also contains small bodies of frozen gases and related materials called *comets*, tiny clusters of rock known as *meteoroids*, and vast quantities of dust that may be remnants of the system's formation.

The Sun, its eight planets, and related residual materials were born together some 4.6 billion years ago and collectively constitute the **solar system** (Figure 4.3A). The Sun is located at the centre of the solar system and is the source of light, heat, and the overall gravitational field that sustains the planets. The eight planets may be grouped as follows. Mercury, Venus, Earth, and Mars comprise the four *inner* (terrestrial) *planets*, which are rather small in size (see Figure 4.3B). The next four—Jupiter, Saturn, Uranus,

and Neptune—constitute the *outer* (major) *planets* and are much larger in size. The outermost 'ninth planet', Pluto, was discovered in 1930. Although it seemed to be more like the inner planets, astronomers knew so little about it that Pluto was not classified within either group. About 2500 member scientists of the International Astronomical Union (IAU) voted in 2006 to remove Pluto's 'Planet' status since evidence showed that Pluto failed to dominate its orbit around the Sun in the same way as the other planets. Let us now examine the major components of the solar system.

The Sun

The Sun is the dominant body of the solar system. Its size relative to the planets and lesser orbiting materials is so great that the Sun accounts for 99.8 per cent of the mass of the entire solar system, more than 750 times the mass of all the planets combined. (The Sun's diameter alone is 109 times larger than the Earth's.) This, of course, enables the Sun to extend its gravitational field far out into space. The effect of that gravity on the planets does weaken with distance, but at a rather slow rate. Earth, the third planet, is located at an average distance of 150 million km. The orbit of outermost Pluto, however, is about 40 times that distance from the centre of the solar system, demonstrating that the Sun's gravitational pull is powerful enough to control the movements of a planet nearly 6 billion km away. Remember, too, that the largest planets are the fifth through eighth, located in a zone roughly 1 to 5 billion km distant from the Sun.

As with most stars, the Sun is a churning thermonuclear furnace, composed mainly of superheated hydrogen and helium gases mixed in a ratio of approximately 3:1. Surface temperatures average 6900°C. The enormous quantities of light and heat given off by the Sun, in the form of a stream of rapidly moving atomic particles, come from its surface and atmosphere (Figure 4.4). Most of that gaseous flow of energy, which radiates outward in every direction and is known as the *solar wind*, is lost in space. (The Earth receives less than one-billionth of the light and heat expelled by the Sun.) Although the solar wind 'blows' at a fairly steady speed, disturbances originating deep inside the Sun occasionally rise to the surface and modify the outflow of solar energy. Solar scientists are particularly familiar with an 11-year cycle of magnetic storm-like activity associated with large, dark 'spots' on the Sun's surface (see photo, p. 256). At their peak, *sunspots* can affect the Earth by triggering magnetic storms here that interfere with radio communications, cause powerline surges, and produce especially brilliant auroras in the night skies of the polar and subpolar regions. The last sunspot activity cycle peaked in 2001; the next mid-cycle minimum occurred in 2006.

The Planets

All the planets except Neptune are bright enough to be seen in the night skies without a telescope, and they have been observed by humans for thousands of years. The ancient

LINK

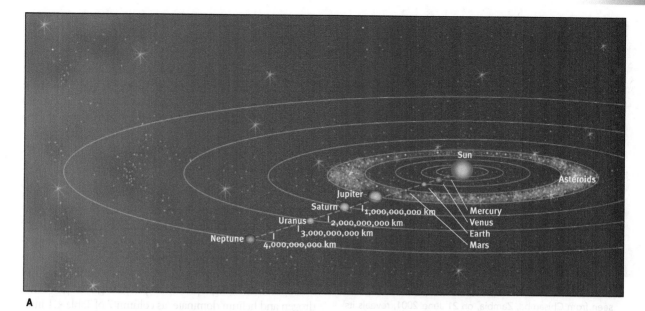

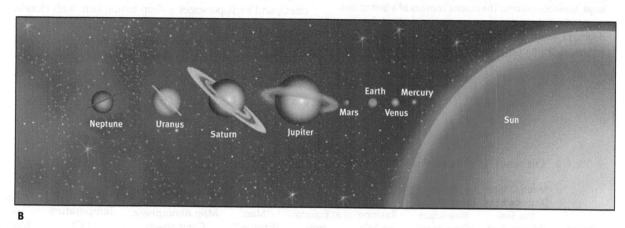

Figure 4.3 Solar system (A) and the relative sizes of the eight planets with respect to one another and the Sun (B). In diagram A the planets are aligned for demonstration purposes only; distances are given in millions of kilometres.

Greeks were particularly fascinated by these moving celestial bodies and coined the word *planet* (meaning 'wanderer'). The arrangement of the nine planets in the solar system is shown in Figure 4.3, which highlights their concentric orbits. The farther a planet is located from the Sun, the greater the length of its orbit. One complete circling of the Sun within such an orbital path is called a **revolution**. The closest planet to the Sun, Mercury, needs only 88 Earth-days to complete one revolution. The Earth, of course, requires exactly one year (365¼ days). The outer planets take far longer to revolve around the Sun. Saturn requires almost 30 years, whereas outermost Pluto requires more than 247 years. Information on revolution times is presented in column 3 of Table 4.1, which also displays seven other categories of planetary data.

The Inner Planets   The four planets nearest the Sun—Mercury, Venus, Earth, and Mars—are classified as *terrestrial*, or Earth-like. All are much smaller than the four outer planets (see columns 5 and 6 in Table 4.1). Each is a solid sphere, composed largely of iron and rock, built around a dense metallic core. The surface layer of each inner planet received vast quantities of gases that were exhaled by volcanoes as the planet gradually cooled. In each case an atmosphere formed. Only Mercury no longer possesses one; its atmospheric envelope quickly boiled away because of its proximity to the searing heat of the Sun. All of these planets experienced considerable volcanic and seismic (earthquake) activity. Again, only Mercury no longer exhibits those geologic disturbances, whereas the other three planets remain quite active. Another characteristic of the terrestrial planets is the paucity of moons. While the four outer planets claim a total of 90 moons, only three are found in the inner solar system. Earth's Moon is the largest of these, with the remaining two tiny moons in orbit around Mars.

Numerous objects, large and small, are known to have struck the Earth over its 4.6-billion-year history, as we shall

Figure 4.4 A total eclipse of the Sun, such as this one seen from Chisamba, Zambia, on 21 June 2001, reveals its large, luminous corona. The corona consists of a belt of fast-moving free electrons, at temperatures of about 2 million degrees Celsius, rising to about 75,000 km above the Sun's surface. A cloud of cosmic dust particles augments the corona far beyond.

see in Unit 21, on impact craters. The largest of all—it may have been the size of Mars—is believed to have struck at a low angle when our planet was only about 100 million years old, briefly burying itself in the molten mass of the Earth's primordial shell. So great was its speed, so huge the collision, that much of it bounced outward again into space, weighted down by a clump of earthly matter. Too heavy to escape the Earth's gravitational field, the slowed-down planetoid was trapped in Earth orbit. Our planet had acquired its Moon.

The Outer Planets   The outer planets—Jupiter, Saturn, Uranus, and Neptune—differ radically from their inner solar system counterparts. They are known as the *major planets* (or the *Jovian planets*—they all resemble giant, prototypical Jupiter) because they account for over 99 per cent of all the matter of the solar system exclusive of the Sun itself. Each of these planets is a huge sphere composed largely of gases (hydrogen and helium dominate, as column 7 of Table 4.1 indicates), and each possesses a deep atmosphere with clouds. All except Uranus give off more heat than they absorb from the distant Sun. This heat is a residue from the formation of these planets, a physical property that can be likened to still-warm pieces of coal long after their fires have gone out.

Table 4.1   Characteristics of the Planets of the Solar System

Planet	Mean Orbital Distance from the Sun (Millions km)	Period of One Revolution (Days/Years)	Period of Rotation on Axis	Diameter at Equator (km)	Mass (Earth = 1)	Main Atmospheric Components	Surface Temperature (°C)	Number of Moons
Mercury	57.9	88 (0.24 yrs)	58.7 days	4,879	0.06	Sodium Potassium Helium	−173 to 427	0
Venus	108.2	224.7 (0.62 yrs)	243 days	12,104	0.82	Carbon dioxide Carbon monoxide Hydrogen chloride	464	0
Earth	149.6	365.3 (1.0 yrs)	23 hrs, 56 mins	12,756	1.00	Nitrogen Oxygen Water vapour	−88 to 58	1
Mars	227.9	687 (1.9 yrs)	24 hrs, 37 mins	6,794	0.11	Carbon dioxide Carbon monoxide Water vapour	−63 to 27	2
Jupiter	778.6	4,331 (11.9 yrs)	9 hrs, 51 mins	142,984	317.8	Hydrogen Helium Methane	−163 to −123	28
Saturn	1,433.5	10,747 (29.5 yrs)	10 hrs, 14 mins	120,536	95.1	Hydrogen Helium Methane	−140	30
Uranus	2,872.5	30,589 (84.0 yrs)	17 hrs, 14 mins	51,118	14.54	Hydrogen Helium Methane	−195	21
Neptune	4,495.1	59,800 (164.8 yrs)	16 hrs, 3 mins	49,528	17.15	Hydrogen Helium Methane	−200	11

Perhaps the single most striking feature in this outer part of the solar system is the planet Saturn surrounded by its spectacular rings. Space scientists have recently discovered that Jupiter, Uranus, and Neptune also possess rings, but these are far less prominent and dramatic than Saturn's.

Earth–Sun Relationships

Earth is a small, fragile planet. As the third planet of the solar system it orbits the Sun—the source of light, heat, and the gravitational field that sustains all eight planets (see Figure 4.3). Among the planets, however, only the Earth exhibits the unique physical conditions essential for the support of life as we know it. Conceivably these conditions could exist on planets elsewhere in the vast universe. The Earth's natural environment, particularly its vital heating, is significantly shaped by the movements of our planet relative to the Sun. In this unit we explore basic Earth–Sun relationships and their profound consequences for the temperature patterns that occur on the Earth's surface.

Earth's Planetary Motions

There are two basic concepts of planetary motion—revolution and rotation. A revolution is one complete circling of the Sun by a planet within its orbital path. The Earth requires exactly one year to revolve around the Sun, which, in fact, is how we define our year. As it revolves, each planet also exhibits a second simultaneous motion—**rotation**, or spinning on its axis. It takes the Earth almost one calendar day to complete one full rotation on its **axis**, the imaginary line that extends from the North Pole to the South Pole through the centre of the Earth.

LINK

As the Earth revolves around the Sun and rotates on its axis, the Sun's most intense rays constantly strike a changing patch of its surface. Thus at any given moment, the Sun's heating (or solar energy) is unevenly distributed, always varying in geographic space and time. By 'time' we mean not only the hour of the day, but also the time of the year—the major rhythms of Earth time for all living things as measured in the annual march of the seasons. Before examining seasonality, we need to know more about the concepts of revolution and rotation.

Revolution

The Earth revolves around the Sun in an orbit that is almost circular. Its annual revolution around the Sun takes 365¼ days, which determines the length of our year. Rather than starting the New Year at a time other than midnight, one full day is added to the calendar every fourth year, when February has 29 days instead of 28. Such a year (occurring in 2004 and 2008, for example) is called a *leap year*.

Like the Earth itself, which is *nearly* a sphere, the Earth's orbital path is *nearly* circular around the Sun. In fact, the Earth is slightly closer to the Sun in early January than it is in early July. This makes its orbital trajectory slightly elliptical. The average distance from the Earth to the Sun is approximately 150 million km. But on 3 January, when the Earth is closest to the Sun, the distance is about 147.3 million km. This position is called the moment of **perihelion** (from the ancient Greek *peri*, meaning near; *helios*, meaning sun). From that time onward, the Earth–Sun distance increases slowly until 4 July, half a year later, when it reaches about 152.1 million km. This position is called **aphelion** (*ap* means away from). Thus, the Earth is farthest from the Sun during the Northern Hemisphere summer and closest during the northern winter (or Southern Hemisphere summer). But the total difference is only about 5 million km, not enough to produce a significant variation in the amount of solar energy received by our planet.

Rotation

Our planet ranks among the solar system's fast-spinning bodies, which produces equatorial bulging and polar-area flattening. Accordingly, geophysicists have discovered that the Earth's diameter when measured pole to pole (12,715 km) is slightly less than it is at the Equator (12,760 km). Thus, the Earth is not a perfect sphere; it is an *oblate spheroid*, the technical term used to describe the departure from a sphere that is induced by the bulging/flattening phenomenon just described. The Earth's deviation from a true sphere, however, is a minor one. In fact, the difference between the equatorial and polar diameters is so small (just 45 km, or 0.35 per cent) that it matters only to Earth scientists and other specialists involved in activities that demand exactness—for example, in space flight, detailed cartography, or *geodesy* (precise planetary measurement).

As the Earth rotates on its axis—which occurs in a west-to-east direction—this motion creates the alternations of day and night, as a constantly changing one-half of the planet is always turned towards the Sun whereas its other half always faces away. One complete rotation takes roughly 24 hours (23 hours, 56 minutes, to be exact), or one calendar day. During one full revolution around the Sun, the Earth makes 365¼ rotations. Consider this: the Earth's circumference at the Equator is slightly less than 40,000 km. Thus, a place on or near the Equator, say the city of Quito, Ecuador, rotates at a speed of 1666 km per hour—continuously! But the distance travelled during a complete rotation diminishes northward and southward from the Equator, until it becomes zero at the poles. A person standing on the North or South Pole would merely make one full turn in place every 24 hours. This contrast between the force of rotation at or near the poles (known as angular momentum) on the one hand, and at or near the Equator on the other, causes the Earth to develop that slight bulge at the Equator.

Actually, the person standing at the pole does not feel any effect different from someone standing on the Equator. We do not notice the effect of the Earth's rotation, because everything on the planet—land, water, air—moves along at the same rate of speed. And the rate of rotation does not vary, so no slowing down or speeding up is sensed. But look up into the sky and watch the stars or moon rise, and the reality of the Earth's rotation soon presents itself. This is especially true concerning the stationary Sun. To us, it appears to 'rise' in the east (the direction of rotation) as the leading edge of the unlit half of the Earth turns back toward the Sun. Similarly, the Sun appears to 'set' in the west as the trailing edge of the sunlit half of the Earth moves off toward the east.

Note that reference was made to a person *standing* at certain places on the Earth's surface. The fact is that a person or object not in motion does not experience any effect from our planet's rotation. But *moving* people and objects do. Moving currents of water and streams of air are affected by a force that tends to deflect them away from their original direction of movement. This force was not known until it was identified by the French scientist Gustave Gaspard de Coriolis in the 1830s. Everything that moves under the influence of our rotating Earth is affected by this force, which is appropriately named the *Coriolis force* after its discoverer. The Coriolis force is an important factor in the Earth's climate and weather, ocean currents, and related parts of other environmental systems (see Unit 8).

The Earth rotates eastward, so that sunrise is always observed on the eastern horizon. The Sun then traverses the sky to 'set' in the west. But, of course, it is not the Sun but the *Earth* whose movement causes this illusion. Looking down on a model globe, viewing it from directly above the North Pole (as in Figure 3.7), we see that rotation occurs in a counterclockwise direction. This might seem to be a rather simple exercise. But several years ago, in one of the great bloopers of television history, a major TV network opened its nightly national news program with a large model globe turning the wrong way!

Seasonality

If on a flat piece of paper you draw the orbital path of the Earth around the Sun, the paper could be described as a geometric plane. The actual plane in space, which contains the line traced by the Earth's slightly elliptical orbit and the stationary Sun, is called the **plane of the ecliptic**. The seasons occur because the Earth is *tilted* with respect to the plane of the ecliptic.

Axis Tilt

The Earth's axis is always tilted at an angle of 66½ degrees to the plane of the ecliptic and is always tilted in the same direction no matter where the Earth is in its orbit. The constant tilt of the axis is the key to these seasonal changes. Sometimes the term *parallelism* is used to describe this axial phenomenon, meaning that the Earth's axis remains parallel to itself at every position in its orbital revolution. Thus at one point in its revolution, around 22 June, the northern half of the Earth, the Northern Hemisphere, is maximally tilted towards the Sun. At this time, the Northern Hemisphere receives a much greater amount of solar energy than the Southern Hemisphere does. When the Earth has moved to the opposite point in its orbit six months later, around 22 December, the Northern Hemisphere is maximally tilted away from the Sun and receives the least energy. This accounts for the seasons of heat and cold, summer and winter. Figure 4.5 summarizes these Earth–Sun relationships and shows how these seasons occur at opposite times of the year in the Northern and Southern Hemispheres.

Now consider Figure 4.6, which shows that, on or about 22 June, parallel rays from the Sun fall vertically at noon on the Earth at latitude 23½°N. This latitude, where the Sun's rays strike the surface at an angle of 90 degrees, is given the name **Tropic of Cancer**—the most northerly latitude where the Sun's noontime rays strike vertically. All areas north of latitude 66½°N, which is called the **Arctic Circle**, remain totally in sunlight during the Earth's 24-hour rotation (Figure 4.7). If a vertical pole were placed at the Equator at noon on this day of the year, the Sun should appear to be northward of the pole, making an angle of 23½ degrees with the pole and an angle of 66½ degrees with the ground (Figure 4.8). Note that the summation of these two angles equals 90 degrees.

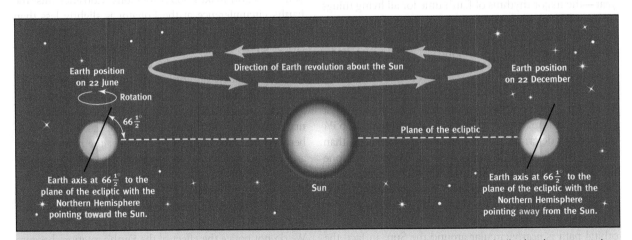

Figure 4.5 Extreme summer and winter positions of the Earth with regard to the Sun. The Earth's axis is tilted at the same angle to the plane of the ecliptic throughout the year.

Figure 4.6 Relative positions of Earth and Sun on 22 June and 22 December. Points on Earth receive the Sun's rays at different angles throughout the year.

Figure 4.7 The sky above the Canadian Arctic with the silhouette of an Inukshuk. In late July, just poleward of the Arctic Circle, the Sun never sets.

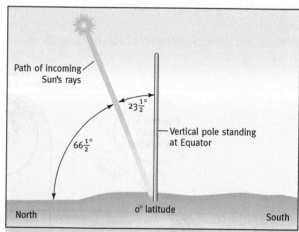

Figure 4.8 Angular relationships of incoming solar rays with the ground and a vertical pole standing at the Equator at noon on 22 June.

Precisely six months later, on 22 December, the position of the Earth relative to the Sun causes the Sun's rays to strike vertically at noon at 23½°S, the latitude called the **Tropic of Capricorn** (the southernmost latitude where the Sun's noon rays can strike the surface at 90 degrees). The other relationships between the Earth and the Sun for 22 June as described are exactly reversed (see Figure 4.6). Accordingly, the entire area south of the **Antarctic Circle**, located at latitude 66½°S, receives 24 hours of sunlight. Simultaneously, the area north of the Arctic Circle is in complete darkness. (Note that in Figure 4.6, the area south of the Antarctic Circle was similarly darkened on 22 June.)

LINK

Solstices and Equinoxes

To us on Earth it appears that the highest daily position of the Sun at noontime gets lower in the sky as the seasons progress from summer to fall to winter. If you were to plot the position of the noontime Sun throughout the year

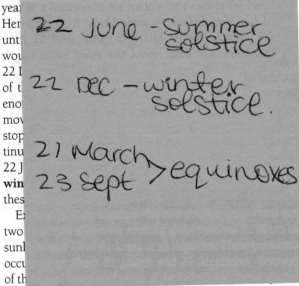

[handwritten note:]
22 June - Summer solstice
22 Dec - winter solstice.
21 March } equinoxes
23 Sept

positions are called **equinoxes**, which in Latin means equal nights. On these two occasions the Sun's rays fall vertically over the surface at the Equator, and the Sun rises and sets due east and west. The equinox of 21 March is known as the **spring (vernal) equinox**, and that of 23 September as the **fall (autumnal) equinox**.

The Four Seasons

You can achieve a clear idea of the causes of the seasons if you imagine you are looking down on the Earth's orbit around the Sun (the plane of the ecliptic) from a point high above the solar system, a perspective diagrammed in Figure 4.9. The North Pole always points to your right. At the summer solstice, the Arctic Circle receives sunlight during the entire daily rotation of the Earth, and all parts of the Northern Hemisphere have more than 12 hours of daylight. These areas receive a large amount of solar energy in the summer season. At the winter solstice, the area inside the Arctic Circle receives no sunlight at all, and every part of the Northern Hemisphere receives less than 12 hours of sunlight. Thus winter is a time of cooling, when solar energy levels are at a minimum. However, at both the spring and fall equinoxes, the Arctic Circle and the Equator are equally divided into day and night. Both hemispheres receive an equal amount of sunlight and darkness, and energy from the Sun is equally distributed.

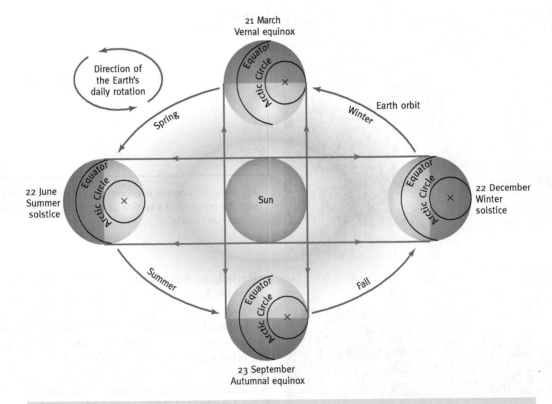

Figure 4.9 March of the seasons as viewed from a position above the solar system. Seasonal terminology here applies to the Northern Hemisphere. (The Southern Hemisphere seasonal cycle is the exact opposite.)

Perspectives on the Human Environment

Measuring Time on Our Rotating Earth

The measurement of time on the Earth's surface is important in the study of our planet. One of the most obvious ways to start dealing with time is to use the periods of light and darkness resulting from the daily rotation of the Earth. One rotation of the Earth, one cycle of daylight and nighttime hours, constitutes one full day. The idea of dividing the day into 24 equal hours dates from the fourteenth century.

With each place keeping track of its own time by the Sun, this system worked well as long as human movements were confined to local areas. But by the sixteenth century, when sailing ships began to undertake transoceanic voyages, problems arose because the sun is always rising in one part of the world as it sets in another. On a sea voyage, such as that of Columbus in the Santa Maria, it was always relatively simple to establish the latitude of the ship. Columbus's navigator had only to find the angle of the Sun at its highest point during the day. Then, by knowing what day of the year it was, he could calculate his latitude from a set of previously prepared tables giving the angle of the Sun at any latitude on a particular day.

It was impossible, however, for him to calculate his longitude. In order to do that, he would have to know precisely the difference between the time at some agreed meridian, such as the Prime Meridian (zero degrees longitude), and the time at the meridian where his ship was located. Until about 1750, no portable mechanical clock or chronometer was accurate enough to keep track of that time difference.

With the perfection of the chronometer in the late eighteenth century, the problem of timekeeping came under control. A new problem, however, emerged in the nineteenth century. A standardized time system became increasingly necessary as railway travel expanded, serving communities that used hundreds of different local times. Confused scheduling was the inevitable result. The need for a standard time was felt in Europe (with England adopting the first regional standard time) but even more so in North America, where railway routes passed through places that had several hours difference in local time. Sir Sandford Fleming, a Canadian civil and railway engineer, initiated efforts to establish time zones. He played an important role in the convening of an International Prime Meridian Conference in Washington, DC, in 1884, where 27 nations adopted the system of international standard time that is still in use today. The Earth was divided into the 24 time zones shown in Figure 4.10, each using the time at standard meridians located at intervals of 15 degrees of longitude with respect to the Prime Meridian (24 × 15° = 360°). Each time zone differs by one hour from the next, and the time within each zone can be related in one-hour units to the time at Greenwich. When the Sun rises at Greenwich, it has already risen in places east of the observatory. Thus the time zones to the east are designated as fast; time zones west of Greenwich are called slow.

This solution led to a peculiar problem. At noon at Greenwich on 2 January 2004, it is midnight on 2 January at 180°E longitude (12 time zones ahead) and midnight on January 1 at 180°W (12 time zones behind). However, 180°E and 180°W are the same line. This meridian was named the **international date line** by the Washington conference. It was agreed that travellers crossing the date line in an eastward direction, toward the Americas, should repeat a calendar day; those travelling west across it, toward Asia and Australia, should skip a day. The international date line did not pass through many land areas (it lies mainly in the middle of the Pacific Ocean), thereby avoiding severe date problems for people living near it. Where the 180th meridian did cross land, the date line was arbitrarily shifted to pass only over ocean areas.

Similarly, some flexibility is allowed in the boundaries of other time zones to allow for international borders and even for state borders in such countries as Australia and the United States (see Figure 4.10). Some countries, such as India, choose to have standard times differing by half or a quarter of an hour from the major time zones. Others, such as China, insist that the entire country adhere to a single time zone. In Canada, Newfoundland's standard time differs from that of its neighbours by a half hour.

A further arbitrary modification of time zones is the adoption in some areas of **daylight saving**

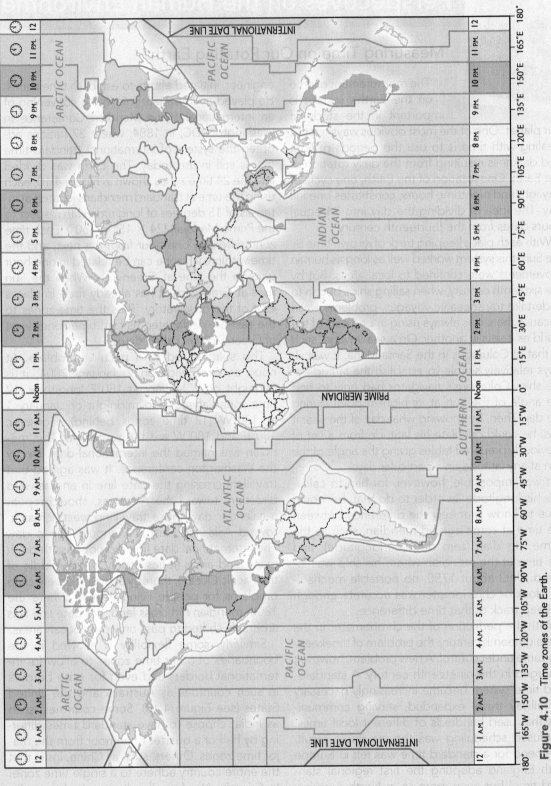

Figure 4.10   Time zones of the Earth.

time, whereby all clocks in a time zone are set forward by one hour from standard time for at least part of the year. The reason for this practice is that many human activities start well after sunrise and continue long after sunset, using considerable energy for lighting and heating.

Energy can be conserved by setting the clocks ahead of the standard time. In Canada today, most provinces (with the exception of Saskatchewan) begin daylight saving time during the first weekend in April and end it on the last weekend in October (Figure 4.11).

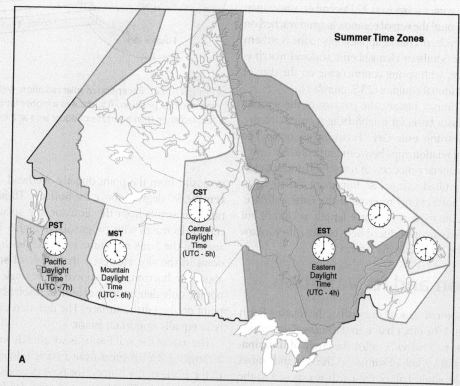

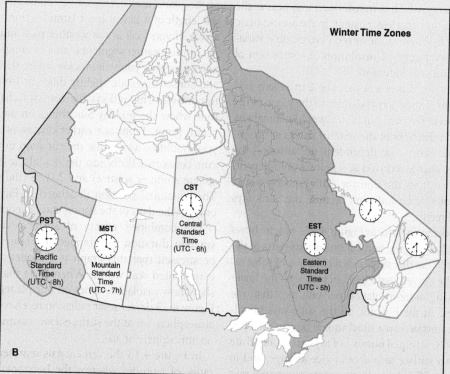

Figure 4.11 Canadian time zone maps—(A) summer and (B) winter.

The annual revolution of the Earth around the Sun and the constant tilt of its axis give our planet its different seasons of relative warmth and coldness. The yearly cycle of the four seasons may be traced using Figure 4.9. *Spring* begins at the vernal equinox on 21 March and ends at the summer solstice on 22 June; *summer* runs from that date through the autumnal equinox on 23 September; *autumn* occurs from then until the arrival of the winter solstice on 22 December; *winter* then follows and lasts until the vernal equinox is again reached on 21 March. This cycle, of course, applies only to the Northern Hemisphere; the Southern Hemisphere's seasonal march is the mirror image, with spring commencing on the date of the northern autumnal equinox (23 September).

Throughout human history, the passage of the seasons has been used as a basis for establishing secure reference points for measuring time (see 'Perspectives' box). The changing spatial relationships between Earth and Sun, produced by the planetary motions of revolution and rotation on a constantly tilted axis, cause important variations in the amount of solar energy received at the Earth's surface. Those patterns are explored at some length in Unit 6, but certain basic ideas are introduced here because they follow directly from the preceding discussion.

Insolation and Its Variation

At any given moment, exactly one-half of the rotating Earth is in sunlight and the other half is in darkness. The boundary between the two halves is called the **circle of illumination**, an ever-shifting line of sunrise in the east and sunset in the west. The sunlit half of the Earth is exposed to the Sun's radiant energy, which is transformed into heat at the planetary surface and, to a lesser extent, in the atmospheric envelope above it. There is, however, considerable variation in the surface receipt of **insolation** (a contraction of the term *incoming* solar *radiation*).

Let us imagine for a moment that the Earth's axis had no tilt, that it was always perpendicular to the plane of the ecliptic. If that were the case, our planet would maintain its equinox position throughout the year. In such a situation, insolation would strictly be dependent on latitude—the amount of solar energy received at a point would depend upon its distance from the Equator. The Equator would receive the greatest solar radiation because the Sun's rays strike it most directly.

This can be demonstrated in Figure 4.12, which shows how the parallel rays of the Sun fall on various parts of the spherical Earth. Note that three equal columns of solar radiation strike the curved surface differently, with the lower latitudes receiving more insolation per unit area than the higher latitudes. At the Equator, all the solar rays in column A are concentrated on a small square box; in the midlatitudes, at 35°N, an equal number of rays in column B are diffused across a surface area about twice as large; and in the polar zone, at 75°N latitude, that same number of rays in column C are scattered across an area more than three times the size of the box illuminated by column A.

In this particular instance, the Equator receives the most intense insolation because the midday Sun's rays strike it

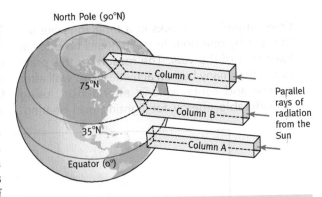

Figure 4.12   Reception of solar radiation, with the Earth in the equinox position. A surface at a higher latitude receives less radiation than a surface of equal area at a lower latitude.

vertically, from the point directly overhead (known as the **zenith**), 90 degrees above the horizon. Thus, if one travels north or south from the Equator, the solar radiation received decreases with progressively higher latitude as the angle of the Sun's noontime rays declines from the zenith point in the sky. However, that angle of **solar elevation** above the horizon, also known as the *angle of incidence*, is not the only determinant of annual insolation received at a point on the Earth's surface. The duration of daily sunlight is an equally important factor.

The axis of the real Earth, as we already know, is tilted at an angle of 23½ degrees from a straight line perpendicular to the plane of the ecliptic (or 66½ degrees with reference to the plane itself). This causes considerable variation in the length of a day at most latitudes during the course of a year. If you look at the weather page in today's newspaper or the weather segment of this evening's local television news program, you will quickly realize that today's sunrise and sunset times are slightly different from yesterday's or tomorrow's. This reflects the constant change of the latitude where the midday Sun shines on the Earth from the zenith point. From our earlier discussion of the seasons, you should be aware that the variation in this latitude occurs between 23½°N (on the day of the Northern Hemisphere summer solstice) and 23½°S (the winter solstice). The equatorial position illustrated in Figure 4.12 occurs only on the days of the spring and fall equinoxes.

The combined effects of solar elevation and daily sunlight duration are graphed in Figure 4.13. It should be stressed that this graph is a model of a much more complicated real world. Whereas its main purpose is to show how insolation varies on our planet, the patterns in Figure 4.13 depict solar radiation received at the top of the atmosphere (or at the surface if we assumed the Earth had no atmosphere at all).

In Figure 4.13 the vertical axis represents the complete range of latitudes whereas the horizontal axis represents the months of the calendar year, with the solstices and equinoxes specially drawn in. The units of solar radiation measurement are not important for understanding this graph (insolation here is calibrated in megajoules per

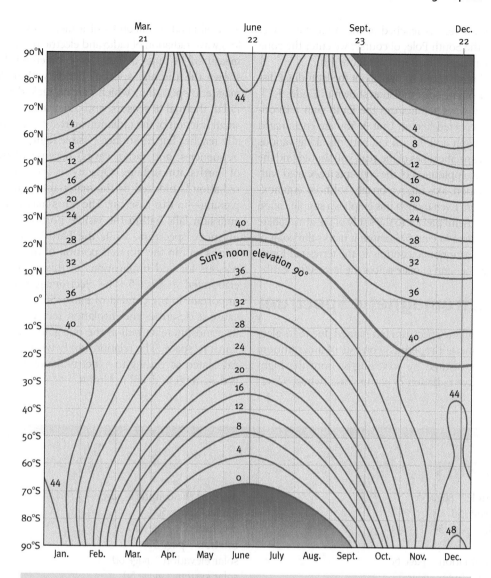

Figure 4.13 Spatial distribution of solar radiation falling on the top of the atmosphere (in megajoules per square metre per day). The annual variations you see are the result of the combined effects of solar elevation and the duration of daily sunlight.

square metre per day). However, variations of insolation can readily be interpreted by looking at the isoline pattern (isolines are explained on p. 36): the higher the value, the greater the amount of radiation received.

If we wanted to trace the global latitudinal profile of insolation for the summer solstice, we would follow the vertical line labelled June from pole to pole. Starting at the top at the North Pole, we begin with some of the highest recorded values on the graph (greater than 44), which are equalled or slightly surpassed only in the high latitudes of the Southern Hemisphere around the time of the winter solstice. Remember, that date is only 12 days before perihelion, when the Earth's orbit makes its closest approach to the Sun; hence the higher values at the start of the southern summer. The polar-area values on 22 June are high because the length of a day north of the Arctic Circle is 24 hours. Even though the Sun is at a fairly low angle there (23½ degrees or less above the horizon), the many extra

hours of sunlight are sufficient to raise the polar radiation-receipt level beyond the highest value ever recorded for the Equator (above 44, compared to an equatorial range of about 33 to 38).

As we descend in latitude from the Arctic Circle, the 22 June line does not fall but levels off across the middle latitudes all the way to near the Tropic of Cancer, where the value of 40 is reached. This high, stable radiation value is maintained because, despite the decrease in daylight length as we move south, insolation is increasingly reinforced by the rising angle of the Sun in the sky as we approach zenith at 23½°N latitude. (Note that the zenithal position of the Sun across the year is denoted by the bell-shaped curve drawn in red on Figure 4.13.) Once we proceed south of the Tropic of Cancer on the 22 June line, insolation values exhibit a very different trend: they begin to decline swiftly, and south of the Equator they also fall off regularly (about seven to eight units every 10 degrees of latitude) until zero is reached at the Antarctic Circle. From here to the South Pole, of course, we enter the zone of seasonal darkness, illustrated in Figure 4.6.

A great deal more could be said about the latitudinal distribution of incoming solar radiation shown in Figure 4.13, which in many ways summarizes the Earth–Sun relationships we have covered here in Unit 4. You are encouraged to study this graph and, by tracing patterns along various latitudes or for specific times of the year, you should find the exercise a useful application of the concepts associated with revolution, rotation, axis tilt, seasonality, solstices, equinoxes, and insolation. Even though this graph is a simplification of reality, it is a useful preface to the study of the atmosphere (which commences in Unit 5) because it marks the point of transition from astronomic controls to the terrestrial forces that shape weather and climate across the face of the Earth.

The Electromagnetic Spectrum

The electromagnetic spectrum (so-named due to its electrical and magnetic properties) consists of a continuum of energy, as measured by wavelength, from the high-energy shortwave radiation of cosmic rays (whose waves

are calibrated in billionths of a metre) to the low-energy longwave radiation of radio and electric power (with waves measured in units as large as kilometres). Figure 3.16 shows the discrete spectral bands within the electromagnetic spectrum, which can be picked up by radio, radar, thermal IR sensors, and other instruments. Only a small fraction of the radiation arriving at our planet actually reaches Earth's surface (visible light, certain infrared frequencies, and radio waves) because of the 'opacity' of Earth's atmosphere. 'Opacity' is the extent to which radiation is blocked by the material through which it is passing—in this case, air. The Sun's maximum radiation emission falls within the visible portion of the electromagnetic spectrum, while the Earth's maximum radiation is within the infrared portion of the spectrum. The reasons for and implications of this are explained and elaborated in Unit 5. The electromagnetic spectrum is important in the context of Earth–Sun relationships because it describes the insolation received by Earth and its atmosphere as well as the out-going energy from the Earth to space. The relationship between these often are calculated according to a 'net radiation balance', which is described in detail in Unit 6.

KEY TERMS

Antarctic Circle   *page 55*
aphelion   *page 53*
Arctic Circle   *page 54*
axis   *page 53*
circle of illumination   *page 60*
daylight saving time   *page 57*
equinox   *page 56*
fall (autumnal) equinox   *page 56*
galaxy   *page 48*
gravity   *page 49*
insolation   *page 60*
international date line   *page 57*
light-year   *page 48*
moon   *page 50*
perihelion   *page 53*

plane of the ecliptic   *page 54*
planet   *page 50*
revolution   *page 51*
rotation   *page 53*
solar elevation   *page 60*
solar system   *page 50*
solstices   *page 56*
spring (vernal) equinox   *page 56*
summer solstice   *page 56*
Tropic of Cancer   *page 54*
Tropic of Capricorn   *page 55*
universe   *page 48*
winter solstice   *page 56*
zenith   *page 60*

REVIEW QUESTIONS

1. Describe the hierarchical organization of the universe's time–space levels.
2. Define the term *planet* and describe how the solar system's planets formed.
3. Define the term *revolution* and discuss its application to the orbital patterns of the Sun's planets.
4. Describe the motions of the Earth in its revolution around the Sun and its rotation on its axis.
5. Describe the seasonal variation in the latitude of the vertical, noontime Sun during the course of the year.

6. Differentiate between the spring and autumnal equinoxes and between the summer and winter solstices.
7. What is an oblate spheroid, and why is the Earth an example of this phenomenon?
8. What is the international date line, and why is it a necessary part of the Earth's meridional system?
9. Why is insolation at the North Pole on the day of the summer solstice greater than that received at the Equator on the equinoxes?

REFERENCES AND FURTHER READINGS

Audouze, J., and G. Israel, eds. 1988. *The Cambridge Atlas of Astronomy*, 2nd edn. New York: Cambridge Univ. Press.

Bartyk, I.R., and E. Harrison. 1979. 'Standard and Daylight-Saving Time', *Scientific American* (May): 46–53.

Beatty, J.K., et al., eds. 1999. *The New Solar System*, 4th edn. New York: Cambridge Univ. Press.

Booth, N. 1996. *Exploring the Solar System*. New York: Cambridge Univ. Press.

Cloud, P. 1978. *Cosmos, Earth, and Man*. New Haven: Yale Univ. Press.

Gedzelman, S.D. 1980. *The Science and Wonders of the Atmosphere*. New York: Wiley.

Harrison, L.C. 1960. *Sun, Earth, Time and Man*. Chicago: Rand McNally.

Hawking, S.W. 1988. *A Brief History of Time: From the Big Bang to Black Holes*. New York: Bantam Books.

Hoyt, D.V., and K.H. Scatten. 1997. *The Role of the Sun in Climate Change*. New York: Oxford Univ. Press.

Johnson, W.E. 1907. *Mathematical Geography*. New York: American Book Co.

Lewis, J.S. 1996. *Rain of Iron and Ice: The Very Real Threat of Comet and Asteroid Bombardment*. Reading, Mass.: Addison-Wesley.

Lightman, A. 1993. *Ancient Light: Our Changing View of the Universe*. Cambridge, Mass.: Harvard Univ. Press.

Lodders, K., and B. Fegley, Jr. 1998. *The Planetary Scientist's Companion*. New York: Oxford Univ. Press.

McNab, D., and J. Younger. 1999. *The Planets*. New Haven: Yale Univ. Press.

Moore, P., ed. 2002. *Astronomy Encyclopedia: An A–Z Guide to the Universe*. New York: Oxford Univ. Press.

———. 1998. *Atlas of the Universe*. New York: Cambridge Univ. Press.

Neiburger, M., et al. 1982. *Understanding Our Atmospheric Environment*, 2nd edn. San Francisco: Freeman.

Sagan, C. 1980. *Cosmos*. New York: Random House.

Sobel, D. 1995. *Longitude: The True Story of a Lone Genius Who Solved the Greatest Scientific Problem of His Time*. New York: Walker.

Taylor, F.W. 2002. *The Cambridge Photographic Guide to the Planets*. New York: Cambridge Univ. Press.

US Naval Observatory. *The Air Almanac*. Washington: US Government Printing Office, annual.

Zeilik, M. 1997. *Astronomy: The Evolving Universe*, 8th edn. New York: Wiley.

 # WEB RESOURCES

hea-www.harvard.edu/~efortin/thesis/html/EMR_all.shtml A very useful interactive website on the electromagnetic spectrum prepared by Harvard University.

seds.lpl.arizona.edu/nineplanets/nineplanets/nineplanets.html An up-to-date multimedia presentation of the solar system, with links to more information.

ssd.jpl.nasa.gov A comprehensive guide to all planets, natural satellites, asteroids, and comets of the solar system, presented by NASA's Jet Propulsion Laboratory and Caltech.

vortex.plymouth.edu/sun.html Tutorial site covering insolation and seasonality.

www.canadiangeographic.ca/Magazine/SO98/geomap.asp An article from *Canadian Geographic* describing Canada's time zone irregularities.

www.canadiangeographic.ca/specialfeatures/Dst/dst.asp An article from *Canadian Geographic* describing the origin of Canada's legislated daylight savings time.

www.space.gc.ca The Canadian Space Agency includes details about the RADARSAT, the International Space Station, Canadian astronauts, and future Canadian missions.

www.windows.ucar.edu/tour/link=/earth/earth.html Explanation of Earth's planetary motions, Earth–Sun relationships, insolation, and seasonality; with three varying difficulty levels.

Unit 5

Composition and Structure of the Atmosphere

Objectives

- To describe the constituents of the atmosphere and their relative concentrations.

- To survey the four thermal layers of the atmosphere together with their major properties.

- To describe the functional properties of the atmosphere.

- To discuss the problem of ozone depletion and its consequences.

Our atmosphere, one of our most precious natural resources, constitutes a vital component in the systematic study of our planet. This thin, shell-like envelope of life-sustaining air that surrounds the Earth (see photo above) is a place of incredible activity—as the units of Part Two will demonstrate. It has been called the working fluid of our planetary heat engine, and its constant motions shape the course of environmental conditions at every moment in every locality on the surface. The short-term conditions of the restless atmospheric system that impinge on daily human activities are called **weather**; the long-term conditions of aggregate weather over a region, summarized by averages and measures of variability, constitute a region's **climate**.

The atmosphere extends from a few metres below the ground on land, or at the water's surface in oceanic areas, to its outermost edge at a height of about 60,000 km. Most of the mass of the atmosphere is concentrated near the planetary surface (see Figure 8.2). Physical geographers are especially interested in the lower parts of the atmosphere, those below 50 km and, in particular, below 10 km. Important flows of energy and matter occur within these

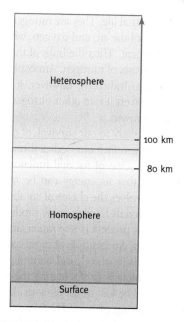

Heterosphere

100 km

80 km

Homosphere

Surface

Figure 5.1 Two main vertical regions of the atmosphere that can be distinguished on the basis of their chemical composition.

whose quantities also vary in time and space. Table 5.1 provides information on the relative components (by per cent volume) of both the constant and variable gases of Earth's atmosphere to a height of 25 km.

Constant Gases

Two major constant gases make up 99 per cent of the air by volume, and both are crucial to sustaining human and

Table 5.1 Average Composition of the Atmosphere up to an Altitude of 25 km.

Gas Name	Chemical Formula	Percent Volume
Nitrogen	N_2	78.08
Oxygen	O_2	20.95
Water*	H_2O	0 to 4
Argon	Ar	0.93
Carbon Dioxide*	CO_2	0.0360
Neon	Ne	0.0018
Helium	He	0.0005
Methane*	CH_4	0.00017
Hydrogen	H_2	0.00005
Nitrous Oxide*	N_2O	0.00003
Ozone*	O_3	0.000004

* variable gases
Source: Pidwirny, M. (2006). 'Atmospheric Composition', *Fundamentals of Physical Geography*, 2nd ed. At: <www.physicalgeography.net/fundamentals/7a.html>.

LINK

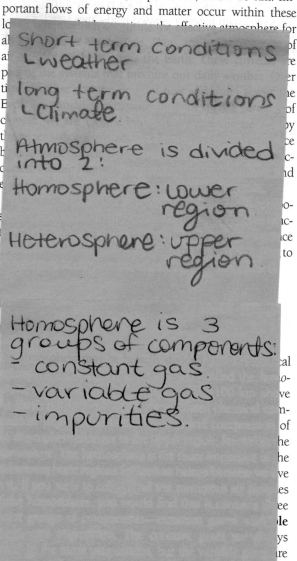

Short term conditions
└ weather

long term conditions
└ climate

Atmosphere is divided into 2:

Homosphere: lower region

Heterosphere: upper region

Homosphere is 3 groups of components:
- constant gas
- variable gas
- impurities.

other forms of terrestrial life. They are nitrogen, which constitutes 78 per cent of the air, and oxygen, which accounts for another 21 per cent. Thus the bulk of the atmosphere that we breathe consists of nitrogen. Atmospheric nitrogen is relatively inactive. Indirectly, however, it is important because bacteria convert it into other nitrogen compounds essential for plant growth.

Immediately necessary to our survival, of course, is oxygen. We absorb oxygen into our bodies through our lungs and into our blood. One of its vital functions there is to 'burn' our food so that its energy can be released. Such burning actually involves the chemical combination of oxygen and other materials to create new products. The biological name for this process is *respiration*, and the chemical name is *oxidation*. An example of rapid oxidation is the burning of *fossil fuels* (coal, oil, and natural gas). Without oxygen, this convenient way of releasing the energy stored in these fuels would be lost to us. Slow oxidation can also occur, as in the rusting of iron. Therefore, oxygen is essential not only for respiration but also for its role in many other chemical processes.

In 1894, when scientists first removed oxygen and nitrogen from a sample of air, they noticed that another gas remained that seemed completely inactive: it would not combine chemically with other compounds, thereby making it an *inert gas*. The discoverers named this gas argon and found that it makes up almost 1 per cent of the volume of dry air. Although this inert gas has some commercial uses (Figure 5.2), it plays only a very minor role in the workings of environmental systems.

Variable Gases

Although they collectively constitute only a tiny proportion of the air, we must also recognize the importance of certain atmospheric gases that are present in varying quan-

tities. Three of these variable gases are essential to human well-being—carbon dioxide, water vapour, and ozone.

Carbon Dioxide   Carbon dioxide (CO_2), which on average comprises only 0.04 per cent of dry air, is a significant constituent of the atmosphere in terms of its climatic influence. Despite the comparatively small amounts present, carbon dioxide fulfills two vital functions for the Earth. The first is in the process of *photosynthesis*, in which plants use carbon dioxide and other substances to form carbohydrates, which are an essential part of the food and tissue of both plants and animals. The second function of carbon dioxide is to absorb and re-emit some of the energy transferred to the atmosphere from the Earth's surface (a process discussed in Unit 6). Because most of the other atmospheric constituents are such poor absorbers of this energy, carbon dioxide helps to keep the atmosphere at temperatures that permit life (which now average globally just over 15°C).

Carbon dioxide plays still other environmental roles. It helps dissolve limestone, which leads to the intriguing features of certain limestone-based landscapes (see Unit 35). Furthermore, a number of scientists believe that carbon dioxide plays a role in both major and minor climatic change. It has been estimated that over the past two centuries the total quantity of this gas in the atmosphere has risen by as much as 25 per cent. The primary cause is believed to be increased industrialization and the associated burning of fossil fuels. The rise in the atmospheric carbon dioxide level since 1960 has occurred at a faster rate (Figure 5.3), accounting for just about half the total increase since the onset of the Industrial Revolution more than 200 years ago. Because carbon dioxide is a factor in the warming of the atmosphere, many researchers are concerned that its

Figure 5.2 Commercial use of atmospheric argon—the 'neon' lights of such places as Yonge Street in downtown Toronto, 1990s.

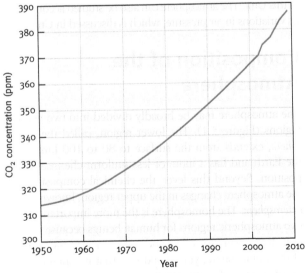

Figure 5.3 Changes in the carbon dioxide content of the Earth's atmosphere, 1950–2009. These data were collected at Mauna Loa Observatory on the island of Hawaii, far from the world's industrial and urban areas.

continued prodigious production could significantly affect the future climate of the Earth.

 Water Vapour The ability to absorb and re-emit energy from the Earth's surface and atmosphere also is found in the most widely distributed variable atmospheric gas—**water vapour**—the invisible gaseous form of water (H_2O).

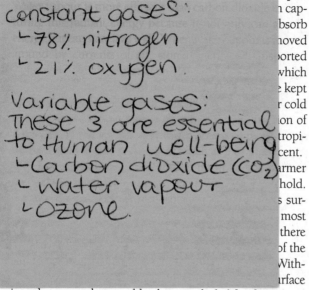

into the atmosphere and back again, little life of any kind would be found on our planet.

 Ozone The other variable gases in the lower parts of the atmosphere are found in much smaller quantities than water vapour. The most important of these is ozone, the rarer type of oxygen molecule composed of three oxygen atoms (O_3) instead of two (O_2). Ozone is confined mainly to the so-called **ozone layer** (or ozonosphere), which is described in detail in the section on functional

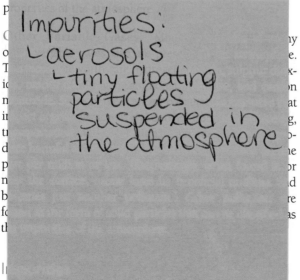

If you were to collect air samples, particularly near a city, they would likely contain a great number of impurities in the form of **aerosols** (tiny floating particles suspended in the atmosphere). Typical rural air might contain about four particles of dust per cubic millimetre, whereas city

parks often have four times that density. A business district in a metropolitan area might have 200 particles per cubic millimetre, and an industrial zone over 4000. Both smoke and dust particles are common in urban air, but dust particles are the most prevalent type in rural air. Bacteria and plant spores are found in all parts of the lower atmosphere. Salt crystals are another major impurity, with large quantities usually formed by evaporation above breaking ocean waves.

Collectively, the impurities play an active role in the atmosphere. Many of them help in the development of clouds and raindrops (see Unit 11). Moreover, the small particles can affect the colour of the sky. Air and the smallest impurities scatter more blue light from the Sun than any other colour. This is why the fair-weather sky looks blue. But when low-angle sunlight travels a longer distance through the atmosphere to the surface, as at sunrise or sundown, most of the blue light has been scattered. We see only the remaining yellow and red light, which, of course, produces colourful sunrises and sunsets. Occasionally, when there is an abnormally large amount of impurities in the atmosphere, such as after a major volcanic eruption, this process is carried to some spectacular extremes.

Thermal Properties of the Atmosphere

Earlier we noted that the atmosphere consists of two broad regions based on compositional characteristics: a lower homosphere and an upper heterosphere (Figure 5.1). A more detailed picture of the structure of the atmosphere emerges if we subdivide it into a number of vertical layers according to temperature characteristics. Altitude has a major influence on temperature, and the overall variation of atmospheric temperature with height above the surface is shown in Figure 5.5.

The bottom layer of the atmosphere, where temperature usually decreases with an increase in altitude, is called the **troposphere**. The rate of a decline in temperature is known as the **lapse rate**, and in the troposphere the average lapse rate is 6.5°C/1000 m. The upper boundary of the troposphere, at which temperatures stop decreasing with height, is called the **tropopause**.

Beyond this discontinuity, in a layer called the **stratosphere**, temperatures either stay the same or start increasing with altitude. Layers in which the temperature increases with altitude exhibit positive lapse rates. These are called **temperature inversions** because they invert or reverse what we on the surface believe to be the normal state of temperature change with elevation—a decrease with height.

As the top of the stratosphere is approached, beyond about 52 km above the Earth, temperatures remain constant with increasing altitude. This boundary zone is called the **stratopause**, and is topped by a layer known as the

From the Fieldnotes

Figure 5.4 *'The apartment in Honolulu, high on the slope of the Punch Bowl, afforded great daytime views over the city. But what was most remarkable, even here in the middle of the Pacific Ocean, was the daily vivid sunset, proof of the presence of volcanic and desert dust, high in the atmosphere.'*

mesosphere. In the mesosphere temperatures again fall with height, as they did in the troposphere. Eventually the decline in temperature stops, at a boundary you might rightly guess to be called the **mesopause**. This occurs at about 80 km above the Earth's surface. Not far beyond the mesopause, temperatures once more increase with height in a layer called the **thermosphere**.

The Troposphere

Because the troposphere is the atmospheric zone in which we live and the layer where almost all weather happens, we need to know quite a bit about it. That survey of its processes is undertaken in Units 6 through 9, with Unit 7 focusing on temperature relationships. Before that detailed treatment, let us summarize the most significant interactions across the tropopause and the nature of the layers that lie above it.

The tropopause, as Figure 5.5 indicates, is positioned at an average height of about 12 km. Actually, this altitude varies with latitude: it is lowest over the poles (about 8 km) and highest above the Equator (about 16 km). There are usually two distinct breaks in the tropopause, which are characterized by areas of variable lapse rates. These breaks generally are found at latitudes of about 25° and 50°N and S. The breaks, associated with fast-flowing winds in the upper atmosphere, are important because, through them, the troposphere and the stratosphere exchange materials and energy. Small amounts of water vapour may find their way up into the stratosphere at these breaks, whereas ozone-rich air may be carried downward into the troposphere through them.

The Stratosphere

Above the tropopause is the calmer, thinner, clear air of the stratosphere. The stratosphere is situated between about 10 km and 50 km above the surface at moderate latitudes, while at the poles it starts at about 8 km altitude. The positive relationship between increase in height and increasing

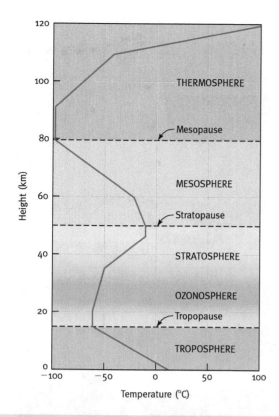

Figure 5.5 Variation of atmospheric temperature (red line) with

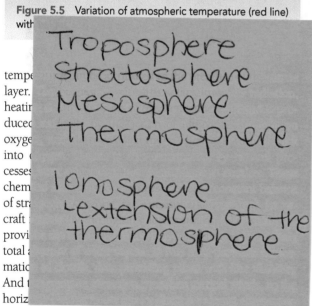

electrically charged particles called **ions** in a process known as *ionization*. Ionized particles concentrate in a zone called the **D**-layer, which reflects radio waves sent from the Earth's surface. 'Blackouts' in communications between the ground and astronauts occur as the **D**-layer is crossed by space vehicles during re-entry.

The Thermosphere

The thermosphere is found above 80 km and continues to the thermopause. The exact altitude varies by the energy inputs of location, time of day, solar flux, and season, and therefore ranges in height from 500–1000 km at a given place and time. The temperature rises sharply in this layer and likely reaches 900°C at 350 km. However, because the air molecules are so far apart at this altitude, these temperatures apply only to individual molecules and do not have the same kind of environmental significance they would have in the vicinity of the Earth's surface, meaning that the temperature felt by a human might actually be less than 0°C. The thermosphere has no definable outer boundary and gradually blends into interplanetary space.

Atmospheric Function

On the basis of *function*, the atmosphere has been organized into two regions: the *ionosphere* and the *ozonosphere*, both of which have been touched on, but which can be described in more detail on the basis of what functional processes occur in these atmospheric regions.

Ionosphere

Scientists call the **ionosphere** an extension of the thermosphere (www.windows.ucar.edu/tour/link=/earth_science/ Atm_Science/Temp_structure/structure_thermo.html), although it is classified on the basis of function rather than of temperature. Although the ionosphere represents less than 0.1 per cent of the total mass of the Earth's atmosphere, it is extremely important. Ionization takes place in this region of the atmosphere, producing two more belts (known as the **E**- and **F**-layers) that reflect radio waves (Figure 5.8).

The Sun's energy is so strong at this level that the ultraviolet light ionizes molecules and atoms, resulting in electrons floating around and molecules that have lost or gained electrons (www.windows.ucar.edu/tour/link=/ earth/Atmosphere/ion_solar_effect.html). Our society has learned to use the properties of the ionosphere in many beneficial ways over the last century (radio, television, and satellite communications, for example), but there is still a great deal to learn about its physics, its chemical makeup, and its everyday changes as a result of solar radiation. The upper parts of the ionosphere can be studied to some extent with satellites but the lower levels are below orbital altitudes while still too high to be studied using instruments carried by balloons or high-flying aircraft.

LINK

allel to the Earth's surface, ensuring smoother flights than in the troposphere.

The Mesosphere

Above the stratosphere, in the altitudinal zone between about 50 and 80 km, lies the layer of decreasing temperatures called the mesosphere. Over high latitudes in summer, the mesosphere at night sometimes displays high, wispy clouds, which are presumed to be sunlight reflected from meteoric dust particles that become coated with ice crystals. Another common phenomenon in this layer occurs when sunlight reduces molecules to individual

From the Fieldnotes

Figure 5.6 *'On my way to Los Angeles on a 707 (17 October 1962!). The advent of jet travel not only shortened flight times, it also allowed aircraft to fly near the stratosphere and thus avoid much of the bumpier air and obscuring cloud layers in the troposphere below.'*

Perspectives on the Human Environment

Ozone Holes in the Stratosphere

In 1982 a British environmental research team in Antarctica made a startling discovery: its instruments could not detect the ozone layer in the stratosphere overhead. Atmospheric scientists had never before encountered this phenomenon, but artificial satellites and high-flying aircraft by 1985 confirmed the readings of ground-based spectrophotometers and established that a large 'ozone hole' existed over most of the southern polar continent. Concerned investigators soon learned that this was a seasonal occurrence that peaked in the spring (Figure 5.7); but it was also clear that the overall level of ozone was declining.

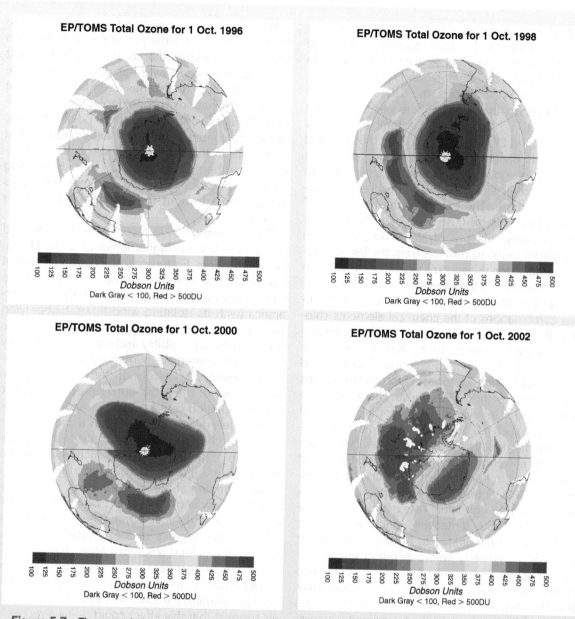

Figure 5.7 The ozone hole overlying Antarctica has been closely monitored since its detection in 1982. This sequence of remotely sensed satellite imagery, centred on the South Pole, shows the average distribution of ozone above the entire Southern Hemisphere for the same early spring month for the 1996–2002 period.

By the end of the 1980s, scientists had reached a consensus as to the causes of stratospheric ozone destruction. During the southern winter (late June through late September), Antarctic air is isolated from the rest of the Southern Hemisphere by a strong circumpolar wind flow above the surrounding Southern Ocean. With warmer air walled off and daylight reduced to a minimum (which inhibits the creation of ozone), the intense cold of Antarctica's surface gradually penetrates the overlying atmosphere. This supercooled air even affects the stratosphere, where icy cloud layers form.

The surfaces of the ice particles that constitute these clouds are sites of chemical reactions involving chlorine that are triggered by ultraviolet radia-

tion as soon as sunlight returns near the end of the long Antarctic winter. The chlorine atoms released by these reactions swiftly destroy ozone molecules by breaking them down into other forms of oxygen. Moreover, each single freed atom of chlorine can trigger hundreds of destructive ozone reactions. Thus, the ozone depletion process spreads rapidly, slowing only as rising temperatures evaporate the stratospheric clouds. By midsummer, ozone levels are again on the rise; they will peak in winter, but with the return of spring another cycle of destruction will be spawned.

This scenario should not necessarily suggest that the summer-through-winter buildup replenishes all the ozone lost in the spring. As Figure 5.7

indicates, large holes in the ozone layer—shown by the blue-to-black colour sequence—appeared above Antarctica in every year. According to NASA and National Oceanographic and Atmospheric Association (NOAA) scientists, the ozone hole above the Earth's Southern Hemisphere was the biggest on record in 2006. In late September, the new hole reached 27.5 million km². Even though most countries banned ozone-depleting chemicals many years ago, these chemicals are expected to continue their affect on the atmosphere for decades to come. The extent of the hole in 2007 was about average (just over 24 million km² or approximately the size of North America) when compared to measurements from the last few decades, although this was still significant, given that the ozone hole didn't even exist in the 1970s.

Ozone-depleting substances (ODS) include various combinations of the chemical elements chlorine, fluorine, bromine, carbon, and hydrogen and are generally referred to as 'halocarbons'. The compounds that contain chlorine, fluorine, and carbon are referred to as **chlorofluorocarbons (CFCs)**. Before the 1990s these chemicals were widely used in everyday life for a variety of purposes, such as coolants in refrigerators and air-conditioning systems, propellants in aerosol sprays, cleaning solvents for computer components, and plastic foam in hundreds of products. Vast quantities of CFCs entered the atmosphere for many years. Even though initial research on the ozone hole in the 1980s tentatively concluded that the phenomenon was limited to Antarctica, the world scientific community was concerned enough to call for action. That resulted in a 1987 conference in Montreal, where more than 30 countries took the first steps to limit their CFC production. The Montreal Protocol established a scientific assessment panel, whose recommendations would be followed as part of an ongoing process to counteract the depletion of atmospheric ozone. A second conference took place in 1990, at which nearly 100 countries agreed to phase out the manufacturing of CFCs by 2000. In 1991 that deadline was advanced to 1996 (developing countries have received dispensations to delay implementation), when the panel reported an intensification in global ozone loss; in 1992 additional CFC-type chemicals were added to the list of products to be phased out (by 2030). By the mid-1990s these measures appeared to have been rewarded because the annual rise in atmospheric CFC concentration was half of what it had been at the end of the 1980s. Moreover, the number of treaty signatories had risen to 132 countries, which contain almost 85 per cent of the world's population.

Nonetheless, new research findings underscore the environmental damage that has already taken place. We now know that as much as 10 per cent of the Earth's ozone layer has disappeared since 1970. A great deal also has been learned about the spatial variation of ozone depletion, which now extends far beyond the southern polar latitudes. Antarctica continues to be the leading region, but elsewhere in the Southern Hemisphere, particularly in southern South America, there is growing evidence of ozone depletion; and many scientists are concerned about the Northern Hemisphere as well.

Ozone destruction in recent years has reached serious levels in the higher latitudes of the Northern Hemisphere. Fortunately no ozone hole has yet opened above the northern polar region, whose winters are warmer and shorter than those of Antarctica (with its isolating wind flows, higher-lying terrain, and thick ice sheet). But an Arctic ozone hole remains a possibility and would undoubtedly have more immediate human consequences because almost 90 per cent of the world's population resides in the Northern Hemisphere. Arctic ozone depletion could be further enhanced over the next few decades, however, as a consequence of climatic changes resulting from increased accumulations of greenhouse gases such as CO^2 in the atmosphere. Although the buildup of these gases causes warming at the Earth's surface, it also contributes to cooling in the stratosphere. Since temperatures in the Arctic stratosphere often come within a few degrees of the threshold for polar stratospheric cloud (PSC) formation, further cooling of the stratosphere could cause PSCs to form more frequently and increase the severity of ozone losses. Preliminary studies with atmospheric models suggest that this effect could delay a recovery of the Arctic ozone layer by a decade or more.

Perhaps most sobering of all is the realization that humans have set off a sequence of atmospheric processes that cannot quickly be reversed. It takes about 10 years for rising CFC gases to reach the stratosphere; and when CFCs reach the ozone layer, they do not dissipate but remain in place as active chemicals for perhaps as long as another 140 years. The recently completed 2006 World Meteorological Organization/United Nations Environment Programme Scientific Assessment of Ozone Depletion concluded the ozone hole recovery would be masked by annual variability for the near future and the ozone hole would fully recover in approximately 2065.

The global depletion of atmospheric ozone ranks among the most serious problems of potential environmental change. In view of the current situation, predictions have been made that the quantity of ultraviolet radiation reaching the Earth's surface will increase 5 to 20 per cent over the next three decades. Even if the lower estimate is correct, at least 1 million new cases of skin cancer can be expected to materialize annually; other medical problems that would intensify include cataracts and the weakening of the immune system. Many animal and plant species would be threatened as well. One study has reported that a 10 per cent increase in ultraviolet radiation could eliminate most forms of plankton, the biological cornerstone of food chains in the oceans. Land plants would undoubtedly be adversely affected too, and crop yields could drop by as much as 25 per cent. This would present a disaster of unparalleled magnitude for a rapidly growing human population that can barely feed itself today.

Intermittently, ionized particles penetrate the ionosphere, creating vivid sheetlike displays of light, called the **aurora borealis** in the Northern Hemisphere and the **aurora australis** in the Southern Hemisphere (Figure 5.9). In the upper ionosphere there are further concentrations of ions, which comprise the Van Allen radiation belts.

Ozonosphere

The ozonosphere (more commonly referred to as the ozone layer) is situated between 15 and 50 km above the Earth, which is part of the vertically more extensive atmospheric layer known as the stratosphere. The greatest concentrations of ozone are found between about 20 and 25 km, although this gas usually is formed at higher levels and transported downward. Even where it is most highly concentrated, ozone often constitutes less than 6 parts per 100,000 of the atmosphere. But, like carbon dioxide, it is very important. It, too, has the ability to absorb radiant energy, in particular the **ultraviolet radiation** associated with incoming solar energy. Ultraviolet radiation can give us a suntan, but large doses cause severe sunburn, blindness, and skin cancers. The ozone layer shields us from excessive quantities of this high-energy radiation.

The critical importance of the ozone layer in shielding the surface of the Earth from ultraviolet radiation has already been noted. At the same time, the absorption of ultraviolet radiation heats the stratosphere, giving it the positive temperature lapse rate we noted earlier. Thus, it is vitally important to maintain the proper ozone balance. Not surprisingly, increasingly frequent reports of **ozone holes** in the atmosphere have raised concerns among environmental scientists (see 'Perspectives' box).

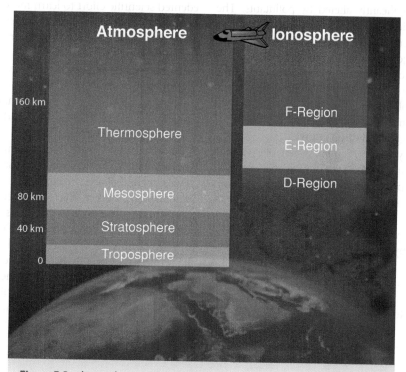

Figure 5.8 Atmosphere and ionosphere.

Figure 5.9   Aurora borealis ('northern lights') over snow and forest near Yellowknife, NWT. Such a curtain of light results from the collision of energy-charged particles from the Sun with gas molecules in the Earth's atmosphere near the poles.

Atmospheric Cycles

As the new planet Earth cooled following its birth about 4.6 billion years ago, the atmosphere was formed from gases expelled by volcanoes and the hot surface itself. During this formation, the atmospheric constituents achieved a state of dynamic equilibrium (a systems concept discussed in Unit 1), a condition that is maintained today—as long as the air is not significantly altered by pollutants. The prevailing composition of the atmosphere we have just described is not static but is the result of constant gains and losses of its major and minor components. A critical part of this component exchange takes place because the boundary or surface layer of the atmosphere adjoins the lithosphere, hydrosphere, and biosphere. Four vital cycles have developed at this interface, involving the transfer of water, oxygen, nitrogen, and carbon dioxide.

LINK

The **hydrologic cycle** is a complex system of exchange involving water as it circulates within and between the atmosphere, lithosphere, hydrosphere, and biosphere. This cycle is so important that much of Unit 11 is devoted to it.

In the **oxygen cycle**, oxygen is put back into the atmosphere as a by-product of photosynthesis. It is extracted from the atmosphere when it is inhaled by animals or chemically combined with other materials during oxidation.

The **nitrogen cycle** is maintained by plants, whose roots contain bacteria that can extract nitrogen from the air or soil. These *nitrogen-fixing bacteria* convert atmospheric nitrogen into the organic compounds of the plants, especially organic protein. Some of this organic material is transferred to animals, including human beings, when the plants are eaten. When the plants and animals die, the nitrogen is transformed by other bacteria and micro-organisms first into ammonia, urea, and nitrates, and then eventually back into the gaseous form of nitrogen, which returns to the atmosphere.

The **carbon dioxide cycle** is dominated by exchanges that occur between the air and the oceans. This atmospheric gas enters the sea by direct absorption from the air, by plant and animal respiration, and by the oxidation of organic matter. Alternatively, carbon dioxide is released from the ocean following the decomposition of countless millions of small organisms known as *plankton*. Another major carbon dioxide exchange takes place between the atmosphere and land plants of the biosphere, with the gas taken from the air by plants during photosynthesis and released by them during respiration and decay. In addition, carbon dioxide is released in the burning of fossil fuels, with possible consequences for climatic change.

Research Frontiers

Scientists still understand relatively little about the layers above the effective atmosphere. These outer regions beyond the troposphere, which consist of concentrated ozone, electrically charged particles, bitter cold and extreme heat, meteoric dust, and weirdly illuminated clouds, lie at the frontiers of our knowledge. The ozone-depletion crisis, however, is now unleashing an unprecedented scientific effort to learn more about these higher layers, because it is increasingly evident that what happens along the fragile outer fringes of our planetary domain is of significance to atmospheric and related processes in the surface layer. With human technology demonstrating a greater capacity to influence the chemistry of the air, much research is focusing on the nature of such change, its rates in various parts of the world, and the long-term consequences of its intensification.

As this work proceeds, a heightening sense of urgency prevails in certain quarters because climate and other environmental changes tend not to occur gradually and incrementally. Rather, they often seem to exhibit sharp jumps in response to the subtle but steady reorganization of the Earth's atmospheric system. The challenge lies not only in identifying the problems, but also in reversing the sequence of events that produce them (as in the attempt to halt human-induced ozone destruction). Such concerns—which also apply to the biosphere, the hydrosphere, and even the lithosphere—are becoming an integral part of physical geography through the twenty-first century.

KEY TERMS

aerosol   *page 67*
aurora australis   *page 73*
aurora borealis   *page 73*
carbon dioxide (CO_2) cycle   *page 74*
chlorofluorocarbons (CFCs)   *page 72*
climate   *page 65*
constant gases   *page 65*
hydrologic cycle   *page 74*
impurities   *page 65*
ion   *page 69*
ionosphere   *page 69*
lapse rate   *page 67*
mesopause   *page 68*
mesosphere   *page 68*

nitrogen cycle   *page 74*
oxygen cycle   *page 74*
ozone hole   *page 73*
ozone layer   *page 67*
stratopause   *page 67*
stratosphere   *page 67*
temperature inversion   *page 67*
thermosphere   *page 68*
tropopause   *page 67*
troposphere   *page 67*
ultraviolet radiation   *page 73*
variable gases   *page 65*
water vapour   *page 67*
weather   *page 65*

REVIEW QUESTIONS

1. What are the constituents of dry air in the atmosphere?
2. Discuss the role of ozone in absorbing incoming solar radiation. Where does this absorption take place?
3. Give the approximate altitudinal extents of each of the atmosphere's layers, and describe the temperature structure of each.
4. Define and describe the basic function of the oxygen, nitrogen, carbon dioxide, and hydrologic cycles.
5. What is the extent of the world's *ozone hole* problem, and what are its likely causes?

REFERENCES AND FURTHER READINGS

Amato, J.A. 2000. *Dust: A History of the Small and the Invisible*. Berkeley: Univ. of California Press.

Brimblecombe, P. 1995. *Air: Composition and Chemistry*, 2nd edn. New York: Cambridge Univ. Press.

Dameris, M., et al., 1998. 'Assessment of the Future Development of the Ozone Layer', *Geophysical Research Letters* 25: 3579–82.

Graedel, T.E., and P.J. Crutzen. 1989. 'The Changing Atmosphere', *Scientific American* (Sept.): 58–68.

Gribbin, J. 1988. 'The Ozone Layer', *New Scientist*, 'Inside-Science' Supplement 9 (5 May).

Ingersoll, A.P. 1983. 'The Atmosphere', *Scientific American* (Sept.): 162–74.

McElroy, M.B., and J.B. Salawitch. 1989. 'Changing Composition of the Global Stratosphere', *Science* 243 (10 Feb.): 763–70.

Meszaros, E. 1993. *Global and Regional Changes in Atmospheric Composition*. Boca Raton, Fla: CRC Press.

Minnaert, M. 1954. *The Nature of Light and Color in the Open Air*. New York: Dover.

Schaefer, V.J., and J. Day. 1981. *A Field Guide to the Atmosphere*. Boston: Houghton Mifflin.

Schneider, S.H., ed. 1996. *Encyclopedia of Climate and Weather*, 2 vols. New York: Oxford Univ. Press.

Stolarski, R.S. 1988. 'The Antarctic Ozone Hole', *Scientific American* (Jan.): 30–7.

Time Magazine. 1962. 'Vanishing Ozone: The Danger Moves Closer to Home', (17 Feb.): 60–8.

Toon, O.B., and R.P. Turco. 1991. 'Polar Stratosphere Clouds and Ozone Depletion', *Scientific American* (June): 68–74.

Young, L.B. 1979. *Earth's Aura*. New York: Avon.

———. 1990. *Sowing the Wind: Reflections on the Earth's Atmosphere*. Englewood Cliffs, NJ: Prentice-Hall.

WEB RESOURCES

jwocky.gsfc.nasa.gov Information about the ozone hole in the stratosphere.

www.ec.gc.ca/ozone/EN/index.cfm?intCat=158 Environment Canada's stratospheric ozone website.

www.infoplease.com/ce6/sci/A0856759.html Explanation of the structure of the atmosphere, as well as related links

to the role of the atmosphere and its components and characteristics.

www.nasa.gov/audience/forstudents/9-12/features/912_liftoff_atm. html Description of components and layering of the atmosphere.

Unit 6

Radiation and the Heat Balance of the Atmosphere

Objectives

- To understand the Sun-generated flows of energy affecting the Earth and its atmosphere.
- To link the greenhouse effect to the Earth's habitability and climatic variation.
- To introduce the Earth's heat flows and their spatial patterns.

To understand the workings of weather and climate, one needs to become familiar with the atmospheric processes that shape them. In Unit 5 the atmosphere is described as a dynamic, constantly churning component of a gigantic heat engine. In this unit, focus is placed on the functioning of that engine, which is fuelled by incoming solar radiation (*insolation*). Its main operations co-ordinate and distribute this radiant heat energy between the Earth's surface and the envelope of air that surrounds it. As the Earth is heated by the Sun's rays, the air in contact with the surface becomes warmer. That air begins to rise, cooler air descends to replace it, and the atmosphere has been set into motion. On a global scale, as insolation constantly changes, there is always considerable variation in heat energy across the planetary surface. To maintain equilibrium, large amounts of that energy must be moved from place to place to balance heat surpluses and deficits.

The Radiation Balance

The Sun provides 99.97 per cent of the energy required for all the physical processes that take place on the Earth and in its atmosphere. As a result of absorbed insolation, different types of radiant heat or radiation flow throughout the Earth's atmosphere system, and inputs and outputs of radiation are balanced at the planetary surface.

Radiation may be regarded as a transmission of energy in the form of electromagnetic waves. The *wavelength* of the radiation is the distance between two successive wave crests. This wavelength varies in different types of radiation and is inversely proportional to the temperature of the body that sent it out: the higher the temperature at which the radiation is emitted, the shorter the wavelength of the radiation. The Sun has a surface temperature of about 6900°C, whereas the average surface temperature of the Earth is approximately 15°C. Thus, radiation coming from the Sun is **shortwave radiation**, and that emitted from the Earth is **longwave radiation** (explained in further detail in the subsequent sections). There is, in fact, a wide spectrum of radiation of different wavelengths, which is depicted in Figure 3.16. This **electromagnetic spectrum** ranges from very short waves, such as cosmic rays and gamma rays, to very long waves, such as radio and electric-power waves.

Radiation from the Sun

Radiation from the Sun, or insolation, is referred to as shortwave radiation and can be explained by **Wien's Law**. Wien's Law identifies the wavelength at which maximum energy is emitted, on the basis of an object's temperature. Wien's Law can be stated as:

$$\lambda_{max} = \frac{2898 \; \mu mK}{T}$$

where the numerator (2898 μmK) is a constant, T is the absolute temperature of the radiating body, and λ_{max} is measured in μm. K is temperature measured in Kelvin (which can be converted to degrees Celsius by subtracting 273).

Wien's Law can be used to calculate the wavelength of maximum radiation emission for any object whose absolute temperature is known. Because the Sun's surface temperature is approximately 5770 K, and solving for Wien's Law, maximum radiation emission occurs near 0.5 μm (micrometres; 1000 μm = 1 mm). Looking at the electromagnetic spectrum (Figure 3.16), this wavelength resides within the visible portion, where wavelengths are relatively short compared to the longer infrared wavelengths.

While Wien's Law provides the wavelength of the peak of the radiation emission, the **Stefan-Boltzmann Law** gives the total energy being emitted at all wavelengths by the blackbody.* Wien's Law explains the shift of the peak to shorter wavelengths as the temperature increases, while the Stefan-Boltzmann Law explains the growth in the energy intensity as temperature increases. The Stefan-Boltzmann Law states that the total energy radiated by an object across all wavelengths (E) is proportional to the fourth power of its absolute temperature (T^4).

$$E = \sigma T^4$$

In the calculation, σ (Greek lower case letter *sigma*) is the Stefan-Boltzmann constant (5.67×10^{-8} Wm^{-2}K^{-4}), T is expressed in Kelvin, and E is expressed in Wm^{-2}. The Sun radiates at a much higher temperature than the Earth and therefore the energy output is also much higher: about 160,000 times that of the Earth's atmosphere system.

Measurements indicate that, on average, 1.95 calories** of energy per square centimetre are received every minute at the top of the Earth's atmosphere. This value, called the *solar constant*, would equal in one day all the world's industrial and domestic energy requirements for the next 100 years based on current rates of consumption.

Radiation from the Earth

The Earth does more than absorb or reflect shortwave insolation: it constantly gives off longwave radiation on its own. Again, using the radiation laws, we can better understand why Earth's radiation is referred to as *longwave*. Because Earth's average surface temperature is 288 K, when divided into the Wien's constant, the wavelength of maximum radiation emission is approximately 9.66 μm. Looking at the electromagnetic spectrum, this wavelength resides within the infrared (IR) portion of the electromagnetic spectrum,

---

*A blackbody is a physical body that absorbs all electromagnetic radiation that falls on it. No electromagnetic radiation passes through it and none is reflected. A blackbody is therefore a perfect absorber and a perfect emitter. Although neither the Sun nor the Earth is a perfect blackbody, they are so close to perfect radiators that blackbody radiation laws can be applied to them.

One **calorie is the amount of heat energy required to raise the temperature of 1 gram of water by 1°C. (This should not be confused with the calories associated with the energy value of food, which are 1000 times larger than the calories mentioned here.) Another metric unit used to measure energy is the joule (one calorie equals 4.184 joules); power, or energy per unit time, is often measured in watts (one watt equals one joule per second).

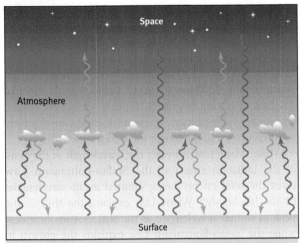

Figure 6.1 Longwave radiation emitted by the Earth (red arrows) and atmosphere (green arrows). Most of the terrestrial radiation is reflected back to the surface or absorbed by the atmosphere. The latter process simultaneously warms the atmosphere, which can now emit its own longwave radiation both downward towards the Earth (counterradiation, which is critically important in heating the planetary surface) and upward into space.

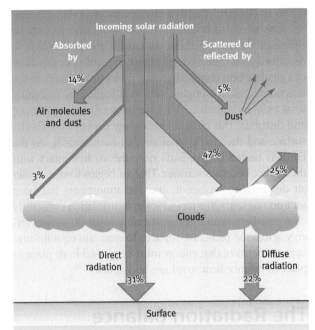

Figure 6.2 Solar radiation flows in the atmosphere.

where the individual wavelengths are relatively long compared to the shorter visible wavelengths. In addition, the amount of energy radiated from the Earth-atmosphere system is much smaller than that of the Sun (as explained by the Stefan-Boltzmann Law). When the Earth's landmasses and oceans absorb shortwave radiation from the Sun, it is transformed into longwave radiation. One of two things can happen to this radiation leaving the planetary surface: either it is absorbed by the atmosphere or it escapes into space (Figure 6.1).

Energy Transfer Mechanisms

When radiation travels through the atmosphere, several things can happen to it (Figure 6.2). According to estimates based on available data and global averages, of all the incoming solar energy only 31 per cent travels directly to the Earth's surface; this energy flow is called **direct radiation**. An almost equal amount, 30 per cent, is reflected and scattered back into space by clouds (25 per cent) and dust particles in the atmosphere (5 per cent). Another 17 per cent of the incoming solar rays is absorbed by clouds (3 per cent) and dust and other components of the atmosphere (14 per cent). Some of the scattered rays, 22 per cent in all, eventually find their way down to the Earth's surface and are collectively known as **diffuse radiation**. Altogether, just over half (53 per cent) of the solar energy arriving at the outer edge of the atmosphere reaches the surface as either direct or diffuse radiation. The rest is either absorbed by the atmosphere (17 per cent) or scattered and/or reflected back into space (30 per cent).

No matter where radiation strikes the Earth, one of two things can happen to it. It can either be *absorbed* by—and thereby heat—the Earth's surface, or it can be *reflected* by the surface, in which case there is no heating effect.

Scattering

In the course of penetration through the atmosphere, some of the incoming solar radiation is either absorbed or scattered in all directions by atmospheric gases, vapours, and dust particles. Two processes are known to be involved in atmospheric scattering of solar radiation. These are termed *selective scattering* and *non-selective scattering*. These two processes are determined by the different sizes of particles in the atmosphere. Selective scattering is so named because radiation of shorter wavelength is selectively scattered much more extensively than that of longer wavelength. Scattering takes place when atmospheric gases or particles that are smaller in dimension than the wavelength of a particular radiation are impacted by that radiation. Such scattering could be caused by gas molecules, smoke, fumes, and haze. Under clear atmospheric conditions, therefore, selective scattering would be much less severe than when the atmosphere is extensively polluted from anthropogenic sources. Non-selective scattering occurring in the lower atmosphere is caused by dust, fog, and clouds with particle sizes more than 10 times the wavelength of the components of solar radiation. Since the amount of scattering is equal for all wavelengths, clouds and fog appear white although their water particles are colourless. The scattering process is what causes our sky to look blue because this colour corresponds to those wavelengths that are best diffused. If scattering did not occur in our atmosphere the daylight sky would be black.

Albedo and Reflection

The amount of radiation reflected by a surface depends mainly on the colour, composition, and slope of the surface. A ray of solar energy falling on the Equator on the day of the equinox, because it strikes perpendicularly, is less likely to be reflected than one falling on the same day at 35°N (see Figure 4.12). And if the surface is a dark colour, such as black soil or asphalt, the energy is more likely to be absorbed than if the object has a light colour, such as a white building.

The proportion of incoming radiation that is reflected by a surface is called its **albedo**, a term derived from the Latin word *albus,* meaning white. The albedo of a snowy surface, which reflects most of the incoming radiation, might be 80 per cent, whereas the albedo of a dark-green rainforest, which reflects very little radiation, might be as low as 10 per cent (Figure 6.3). Consequently, albedo varies markedly from place to place. Of all the solar radiation entering the atmosphere, only about half is absorbed by the Earth's surface.

Absorption

If intercepted, some gases and particles in the atmosphere have the ability to absorb incoming insolation (www.physicalgeography.net/physgeoglos/a.html). Atmospheric absorption is defined as a process in which radiation is retained by a substance and converted into heat energy (www.physicalgeography.net/physgeoglos/h.html). The creation of heat energy also causes the substance to emit its own radiation. The major atmospheric constituents that absorb the Earth's longwave radiation are carbon dioxide, water vapour, and ozone (see Unit 5). Each of these variable gases absorbs radiation at certain wavelengths but allows other wavelengths to escape through an atmospheric 'window'. Up to 9 per cent of all terrestrial radiation is thereby lost to space, except when the window is shut by clouds.

Clouds absorb or re-radiate back to Earth almost all the outgoing longwave radiation. Therefore, a cloudy winter night is likely to be warmer than a clear one.

The atmosphere is heated by the longwave radiation it absorbs. Most of this radiation is absorbed at the lower, denser levels of the atmosphere, a fact that helps account for the air's higher temperatures near the Earth's surface. *Thus our atmosphere is actually heated from below, not directly by the Sun above.* The atmosphere itself, being warm, can also emit longwave radiation. Some goes off into space, but some, known as **counterradiation**, is re-radiated back to the Earth (Figure 6.1). Without this counterradiation from the atmosphere, the Earth's mean surface temperature would be about −20°C, 35°C colder than its current average of approximately 15°C. The atmosphere, therefore, acts as a blanket.

The blanket effect of the atmosphere is similar to the action of radiation and heat in a garden greenhouse. Shortwave radiation from the Sun is absorbed and transmitted through the greenhouse glass windows, strikes the interior surface, and is converted to heat energy. The longwave radiation generated by the surface heats the inside of the greenhouse. But the same glass that let the shortwave radiation in now acts as a trap to prevent that heat from being transmitted to the outside environment, thereby raising the temperature of the air inside the greenhouse. Another example of this same principle is the heating of a closed automobile parked in direct sunlight (Figure 6.4).

A similar process takes place on the Earth, with the atmosphere replacing the glass. Not surprisingly, we call this basic natural process of atmospheric heating the **greenhouse effect**. As explained in the discussion of ozone depletion in the stratosphere in Unit 5, human beings may be influencing the atmosphere's delicate natural processes. The greenhouse effect is now under intensive scrutiny because many scientists have voiced concern that human activities are triggering a sequence of events that could heighten a **global warming** trend, with possibly dire consequences for near-future environmental change (see 'Perspectives' box).

LINK

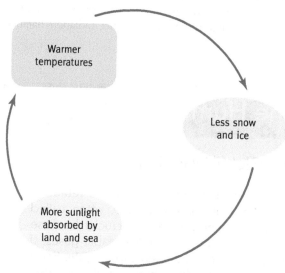

Figure 6.3 The albedo effect creates a feedback loop whereby, as the Earth warms up, there is less ice and snow cover on the Earth's surface to reflect solar radiation back into the atmosphere as it is absorbed by the darker land, vegetation, and sea surfaces. Consequently, as ice and snow cover disappears, the Earth continues to absorb even more solar radiation and continues to become warmer.

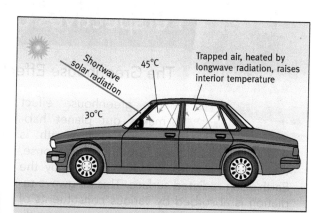

Figure 6.4 A parked automobile demonstrates the greenhouse effect. Shortwave radiation from the Sun enters through the glass windows and strikes interior surfaces. Now transformed into longwave radiation, that energy heats the interior air. But this air cannot pass through the glass and is trapped inside the car—at a temperature 15°C higher than the air outside.

Conduction, Convection, and Advection

The heat energy balance of the Earth's surface is composed, in its simplest form, of four different kinds of flows. One of these—the composite flows of *radiant heat*—makes up net radiation. The second—*latent heat* (which causes evaporating liquids to change into gases)—is treated in Unit 11. The remaining two—*sensible heat flow* and *ground heat flow*—are introduced here.

All air molecules contain heat energy, the heat that we feel on our skin, and this sensed heat is called **sensible heat flow**. Usually, during the day, the ground warms the air above it. Warmed air rises, and parcels of air move upward in a vertical heat-transfer process known as **convection**—thereby causing a sensible heat flow. We can occasionally see the results of this process, as in the case of shimmering air above pavement on a very hot day. Sometimes, when the ground surface is colder than the overlying air, sensible heat flows downward. This often happens at night or during the severe winters of cold climates.

Whereas sensible heat flow depends on convection, the heat that flows into and out of the ground depends on **conduction**, the transport of heat energy from one molecule to the next. The heat that is conducted into and out of the Earth's surface is collectively called **ground heat flow** or *soil heat flow*. These terms are used for convenience, even though this heat sometimes travels into plants, buildings, or the ocean. Ground heat flow is the smallest of the four heat balance components. Generally, the heat that passes into the ground during the day is approximately equal to that flowing out at night. Thus, over a 24-hour period, the balance of ground heat flow often is so small that it can be disregarded.

Except for the usually small amount of energy used by plants in photosynthesis, the total heat balance of any part

LINK

Table 6.1	Estimated Annual Radiation Balance (Net Radiation*) of the Earth's Surface
Incoming	
Shortwave radiation (insolation) reaching the top of the atmosphere	263
Longwave counterradiation from the atmosphere absorbed at the Earth's surface	206
	469
Outgoing	
Longwave radiation emitted by the Earth	258
Shortwave radiation reflected into space by the atmosphere and the Earth's surface	94
Shortwave radiation absorbed by the atmosphere	45
	397
Net Radiation Balance	
(incoming minus outgoing)	**72**

*In thousands of calories per square centimetre.
Source: Adapted from W.D. Sellers, *Physical Climatology* (Chicago: Univ. of Chicago Press, 1965), 32, 47.

of the Earth, say the part just outside your window, is made up of the flows of radiant heat (comprising net radiation), latent heat, sensible heat, and ground (soil) heat.

Net Radiation

The annual radiation balance for the Earth is given in Table 6.1. We can see that similar quantities of shortwave and longwave radiation arrive at our planet's surface, but that the outgoing radiation is dominated by the longwave radiation emitted by the Earth. The amount left over, when all the incoming and outgoing radiation flows have been tallied, is the **net radiation**. This net radiation balance

Perspectives on the Human Environment

The Greenhouse Effect and Global Warming

The greenhouse effect makes our planet habitable. Just as warmth is trapped beneath the glass of a greenhouse, the atmosphere retains heat emitted by the Earth's Sun-radiated surface. This longwave radiation is absorbed by various constituents of the atmosphere, chief among them carbon dioxide (CO_2), water vapour, and ozone. Without this absorption, the Earth's surface heat would escape into space and our planet would be frigid.

Water vapour is important in this retention of warmth, but carbon dioxide, often called the key 'greenhouse gas', is crucial because it is one of the atmosphere's variable gases. If there is more of it in the atmosphere, the Earth should warm up; when there is less, temperatures should cool down. The amount of CO_2 in the atmosphere is not constant. Carbon dioxide enters and leaves the atmosphere through several complex, interrelated cycles. Land plants remove CO_2 from the atmosphere during photosynthesis, but when they die and decay, the

LINK

LINK

gas is returned to the air. Carbon dioxide also is absorbed directly from the atmosphere by ocean water, to be used by plankton floating on the ocean surface. When plankton die, they sink to the ocean floor and release CO_2. That CO_2 eventually comes back to the surface and is released into the atmosphere. All this makes it difficult to assess long-term trends in the CO_2 content of the atmosphere.

Now the human factor enters. During the more than 200 years since the onset of the Industrial Revolution, the burning of coal, oil, and natural gas—the fossil fuels—has produced enormous quantities of carbon dioxide. As a result, the CO_2 content of the atmosphere has increased substantially. No reliable data exist to tell us what the atmosphere's CO_2 content was two centuries ago, but scientists report that its concentration has increased from about 315 parts per million (ppm) to almost 390 ppm over the past 60 years, an increase of approximately 15 per cent (see Figure 5.3).

Over the twentieth century the average temperature of the Earth increased 0.4–0.8°C. There are a number of possible factors influencing climate change, including the growing influence of anthropogenic factors. In the last 200 years, human activity has led to dramatic increases in the concentrations of a number of important greenhouse gases (GHGs): CO_2 is up by over 30 per cent, CH_4 is up by 150 per cent, and N_2O is up by 15 per cent in the Northern Hemisphere. The Intergovernmental Panel on Climate Change's (IPCC) Fourth Assessment Report (AR4) (2007: 4) stated that 'Atmospheric concentrations of CO_2 (379ppm) and CH_4 (1774 ppb) in 2005 far exceed the natural range over the last 650,000 years.'

According to the IPCC (2007) most of the observed warming over the last 50 years is *likely* (60–90 per cent chance) to have been due to the increase in anthropogenic GHG concentrations. The increase in CO_2 has had the largest contribution to the greenhouse effect, with annual emissions of CO_2 growing by about 80 per cent between 1970 and 2004. Global increases in CO_2 concentrations are primarily due to emissions from the combustion of fossil fuels and from deforesta-

tion in tropical countries. The observed increase in CH_4 concentration is due to emissions from a wide range of human activities, including agriculture, coal mining, and fossil fuel use. The increase in N_2O concentration is primarily due to agriculture. In addition, new artificial GHGs, such as chlorofluorocarbons (CFCs), hydrochlorofluorocarbons (HCFCs), and hydrofluorocarbons (HFCs) have been created and released into the atmosphere, and they also deplete the ozone layer.

The IPCC (2007) also concluded that world temperatures could rise by between 1.1 and 6.4°C during the twenty-first century. Along with a globally averaged temperature change, regional climates are subjected to change. Many natural systems in all continents and oceans are affected by such regional influences, for example:

- Sea levels will probably rise by 18 to 59 cm.
- There is a confidence level of > 90 per cent that there will be more frequent warm spells, heat waves, and heavy rainfall.
- There is a confidence level of > 66 per cent that there will be an increase in droughts, tropical cyclones, and extreme high tides.

At present, the shrinking Arctic ice cover and the collapse of Antarctic ice shelves are ominous signals of a warming planet. Recent heat waves have been signalled as indicators of what might become the norm. As for projected climate change and its impacts, the IPCC (2007: 6) indicated that 'There is *high agreement* and *much evidence* that with current climate change mitigation policies and related sustainable development practices, global GHG emissions will continue to grow over the next few decades.' The eventual scale and impact of climate change will depend on humanity's efforts to reduce GHG emissions through restructuring energy systems and land use practices.

The question is not whether the greenhouse effect waxes and wanes over time—it does. The crucial issue is the degree to which human intervention, through the emanation of artificial greenhouse-enhancing gases, is affecting the natural cycle currently in progress.

totals about one-fourth of the shortwave radiation that originally arrives at the atmosphere's uppermost layer.

The reflectivity (albedo) of the Earth's surface and its temperature play particularly important roles in determining the final value of global net radiation. For instance, there is usually a difference in albedo and surface temperature between areas of land and of sea at the same latitude (a topic treated

in Unit 7). As shown in Figure 6.5, these differences result in different net radiation values over the land and over the ocean (represented by the red and blue isolines, respectively). The amount of variance is greatest in the low latitudes and diminishes towards the poles. Overall, net radiation is greatest at low latitudes and smallest, or even negative (especially above ice-covered surfaces), at high latitudes.

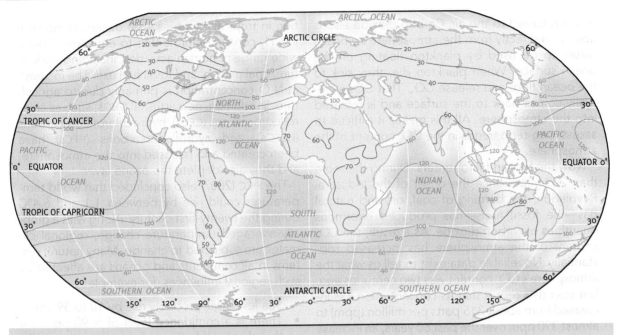

Figure 6.5   Annual distribution of net radiation at the surface of the Earth. Values are in thousands of calories per square centimetre. Red isolines show the pattern over land, blue isolines over the oceans.

Net radiation, moreover, may well be the single most important factor affecting the Earth's climates. Certainly, it is basic to the majority of physical processes that take place on the Earth because it provides their initial driving energy. For example, net radiation is by far the most significant factor determining the evaporation of water. The amount of water evaporated and the quantity of available net radiation taken together largely explains the distribution of vegetation across the land surfaces of the Earth, from the dense forests of the equatorial tropics to the sparse mosses and lichens of the Subarctic environmental zones. Furthermore, net radiation is vital in shaping the *heat energy balance* of the Earth.

Calculating the Surface Energy Balance

The components of the net radiation expressed in Table 6.1 can be explained with a simple equation:

$$Q = K\!\downarrow - K\!\uparrow + L\!\downarrow - L\!\uparrow$$

where Q is net radiation in Wm^{-2} (sometimes measured as Langleys per hour*), $K\!\downarrow$ is incoming solar radiation at Earth's surface, $K\!\uparrow$ is reflected solar radiation (a function of a surface's albedo), $L\!\downarrow$ is incoming longwave radiation

(primarily re-radiated from clouds), and $L\!\uparrow$ is outgoing longwave radiation. The surface radiation balance is made up, therefore, of both shortwave and longwave radiation. Depending on how large or small each of the components is, the net radiation will either be gained or lost at the surface.

Due to the fundamental importance of Earth's energy balance, it is necessary to be able to determine the amount of energy available at the surface of the Earth at any particular place and time. The following example will illustrate how the energy budget at a surface can be calculated with the use of the above equation.

It is a cloudless midday in July at Montreal. The surface being studied consists of a dry, sandy soil and the temperature is 35°C. The solar radiation at the surface ($K\!\downarrow$) has been measured as 72.0 ly hr^{-1}. The sky's radiation from CO_2 and water vapour is radiated at a temperature of 10°C. How might this information be utilized to calculate net radiation? We already know what $K\!\downarrow$ is. $K\!\uparrow$ would be the amount of reflectivity (the albedo) coming off the sandy soil surface. With an albedo of approximately 25 per cent, the solar radiation reflected from the surface can be calculated to be 18.0 ly hr^{-1} (25 per cent of the total 72.0 ly hr^{-1}). Using the Stefan-Boltzman equation, the incoming longwave radiation can be calculated as:

Intensity of Energy Emitted, $E = \sigma T^4$

where σ has a constant value of 4.9×10^{-9} and T is the temperature of the emitting surface in °K (°K = °C + 273). At a temperature of 10°C, the inward terrestrial (longwave) radiation ($L\!\downarrow$) can be calculated as 31.4 ly hr^{-1}. The final component to solve for the net radiation is outgoing

*When calculating the radiant energy, the unit that would be used is the calorie, and specifying the area of the surface (1 cm²), the basic working unit then becomes one calorie per cm² (a Langley). Since the amount of energy also depends on time, the energy receipts or losses based on the net radiation at the surface can best be expressed as Langleys per hour (ly hr⁻¹).

longwave terrestrial radiation (*L*↑), which can also be calculated with the Stefan-Boltzman equation. In this case, the temperature of the surface is 35°C, resulting in a value of 44 ly hr⁻¹.

Inserting all of these values into the net radiation equation:

$$Q = K{\downarrow} - K{\uparrow} + L{\downarrow} - L{\uparrow}$$
$$Q = 72.0 - 18.0 + 31.4 - 44.1 \text{ ly hr}^{-1} = 41.3 \text{ ly hr}^{-1}.$$

This would mean that there is a positive net radiation balance at this surface of Montreal on this particular date, providing energy to further heat the surface or provide a source of heat energy to be utilized for another process function.

Climates and the Heat Balance

At any location, the temperature of the atmosphere depends on how much heat is involved in local radiant, latent, and sensible (as well as ground) heat flows. Net radiation is usually a source of heat for the Earth, and the heat gained in this way is used mainly for evaporation (it is called *latent heat*) or in a sensible heat flow into the air. But there are significant variations on this theme across the Earth's surface, and these lead to significant variations in climate. With that in mind, let us examine and compare the heat balance characteristics of four locations at widely separated latitudes.

Deep in the equatorial rainforest of South America at latitude 3°S, 1100 km inland from the mouth of the Amazon River, lies the northern Brazilian city of Manaus. Its hot humid climate is explained by the high amount of net radiation it receives, which in turn evaporates much of its large annual quantity (1800 mm) of rainfall. If we examine the heat balance diagram for Manaus, shown in Figure 6.6A, we can see that most of the heat received in net radiation (**NR**) is lost through the latent (evaporative) heat flow (**LH**). A rather small amount is left over for the passage of sensible heat (**SH**) into the air. These conditions are almost constant throughout the year.

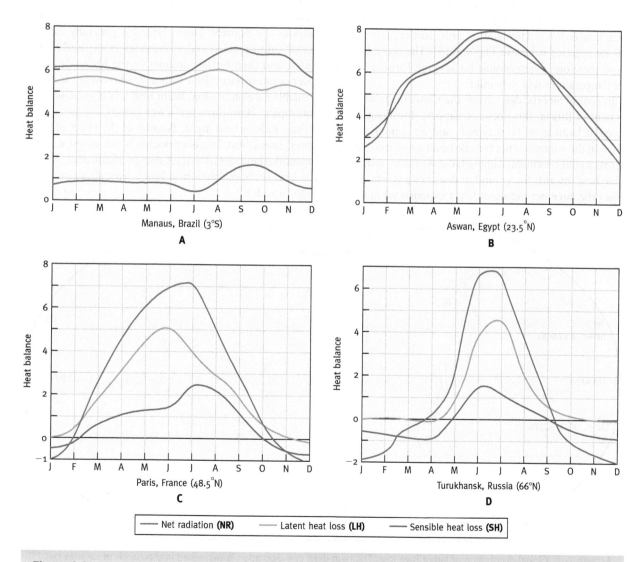

Figure 6.6 Heat balance at four contrasting locations. Values are in thousands of calories per square centimetre per month.

In contrast, at the subtropical latitude of Aswan, Egypt (located astride the Tropic of Cancer [23½°N]), net radiation varies with the season of the year, being highest in summer (Figure 6.6B). There is little surface water to be evaporated, so the loss by latent heat is virtually nil (**LH** values are too small to appear on the graph). But Aswan's scorching temperatures—it lies in the heart of the huge North African desert zone—would be even higher if most of the heat gained by net radiation did not pass, via sensible flow, higher into the atmosphere.

Paris, the capital of France, lies within the middle latitudes near 50°N and exhibits another type of heat balance, as Figure 6.6C indicates. The seasonal variation of net radiation is again a factor, but in Paris the loss of latent heat is only somewhat greater than the loss of sensible heat. However, a rather curious pattern occurs in Paris during the winter months. The net radiation becomes negative—more radiant heat is lost than is gained. Net radiation is no longer a heat source. Fortunately for the Parisians, this loss is offset: air that has been warmed in its journey across the North Atlantic Ocean can now provide heat to warm the Earth. Accordingly, during the winter months the sensible heat flow is directed toward the Earth's surface, as is shown by its negative values in Figure 6.6C. The sensible heat flow, therefore, is responsible for keeping Parisian winter air temperatures relatively mild.

In central Siberia, deep inside the northern Asian component of Russia, this does not happen. Turukhansk, located at latitude 66°N, is typical, and air coming to this town in the winter has not travelled over a warm ocean but across a cold continent. Although the air passes some sensible heat towards the ground, it does not pass enough to offset the large net radiation deficit experienced in winter near the Arctic Circle (Figure 6.6D). The result is bone-chilling temperatures. Yet here the seasonal change of climate is extreme. Paradoxically, the balance of heat in the summer months is rather like that in tropical Brazil! There are many such variations of heat balance across the ever-changing face of the Earth.

Global Distribution of Heat Flows

We have already examined the geographic variation of net radiation (Figure 6.5). Now we will consider the disposal of net radiation through latent and sensible heat, losses that are necessary to keep the totality of radiation in balance for the Earth's surface as a whole. To find the amount of heat lost as latent heat, we multiply the amount of water evaporated by the value of the *latent heat of vaporization* (the amount of energy required to evaporate water). The global distribution of latent heat loss is mapped in Figure 6.7. Over land surfaces (red isolines), the largest amount of latent heat loss occurs in the tropics on both sides of the Equator. Latent heat loss generally declines across subtropical latitudes, increases in the middle latitudes, and then further declines in the higher latitudes. Over ocean surfaces (blue isolines), where water is always available for evaporation, latent heat loss is greatest in the subtropics. Here there are fewer clouds, on average, to reduce radiant heat input. Because of the effect of cloud cover, latent heat loss over oceans is not as great in the equatorial latitudes as in the subtropical latitudes. As over the land surfaces, latent heat loss is least above oceans at high latitudes.

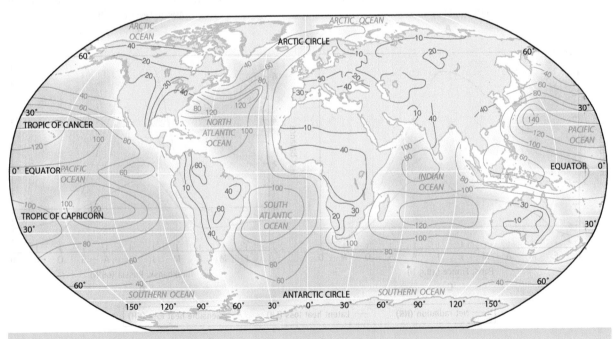

Figure 6.7 Global distribution of latent heat loss. The heat used in evaporation is expressed in thousands of calories per square centimetre per year. Red isolines show the pattern over land, blue isolines over the oceans.

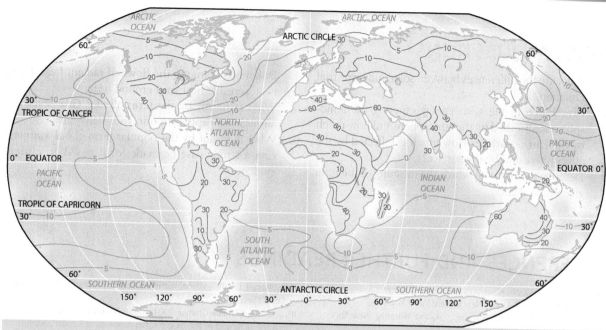

Figure 6.8 Global distribution of sensible heat loss. Values are in thousands of calories per square centimetre per year. Red isolines show the pattern over land, blue isolines over the oceans.

Sensible heat loss over the land surface is greatest in the subtropics; from there it decreases towards the poles and the Equator. This is shown by the red isolines in Figure 6.8, mapped in the same units as the world latent-heat-loss map (Figure 6.7). Above the oceans (blue isolines), however, the amount of sensible heat loss generally tends to increase with latitude.

Over the Earth's surface as a whole, the net radiation heat gain is itself balanced by 70 per cent of that heat being lost in the latent form and 30 per cent being used to heat the air as sensible heat. But at any single point on our planet's surface, there is a unique interaction between the values of net radiation and latent and sensible heat flows. Temperature is the result of these heat flows, and its properties and variations are the subject of Unit 7. In Unit 8, global heat flows are discussed further, especially their linkage to atmospheric circulation patterns.

KEY TERMS

albedo   *page 79*
calorie   *page 77*
conduction   *page 80*
convection   *page 80*
counterradiation   *page 79*
diffuse radiation   *page 78*
direct radiation   *page 78*
electromagnetic spectrum   *page 77*
global warming   *page 79*

greenhouse effect   *page 79*
ground heat flow   *page 80*
longwave radiation   *page 77*
net radiation   *page 80*
radiation   *page 77*
sensible heat flow   *page 80*
shortwave radiation   *page 77*
Stefan-Boltzman Law   *page 77*
Wien's Law   *page 77*

REVIEW QUESTIONS

1. What are the differences between solar and terrestrial radiation?
2. How much of the solar energy entering the atmosphere is absorbed by the atmosphere and how much by the Earth's surface? How much is reflected by the atmosphere and by the surface?
3. Describe in your own words the meaning of the term *greenhouse effect*.
4. Differentiate among the flows of radiant heat, latent heat, sensible heat, and ground heat.
5. What is meant by the term *albedo*? Give some examples of its application in your daily life.
6. What is meant by the popular term *global warming*? Can a strong case be made for it based on current evidence?

REFERENCES AND FURTHER READINGS

Abbasi, Daniel R. 2006. *Americans and Climate Change: Closing the Gap between Science and Action.* New Haven: Yale Univ. Press.

Benarde, M.A. 1992. *Global Warning . . . Global Warming.* New York: Wiley.

Collins, Editors of. 2006. *Fragile Earth: Views of a Changing World.* London: Collins.

Dow, Kirstin, and Thomas E. Downing. 2006. *The Atlas of Climate Change.* Berkeley: Univ. of California Press.

Drake, F. 2000. *Global Warming: The Science of Climate Change.* New York: Oxford Univ. Press.

Flannery, Tim. 2005. *The Weather Makers: How Man Is Changing the Climate and What It Means for Life on Earth.* Melbourne: Text Publishing Co.

Fröhlich, C., and J. London. 1985. *Radiation Manual.* Geneva: World Meteorological Organization.

Harvey L.D. 2004. 'Climatic Change: Addressing Complexity, Uncertainty, and Conflict', in B. Mitchell, ed., *Resource and Environmental Management in Canada.* Toronto: Oxford Univ. Press, 132–65.

Hengeveld, H., B. Whitewood, and A. Fergusson. 2005. *An Introduction to Climate Change: A Canadian Perspective.* Ottawa: Environment Canada.

Houghton, J.T. 1997. *Global Warming*, 2nd edn. New York: Cambridge Univ. Press.

IPCC. 2007. 'Climate Change 2007: Summary for Policymakers of the Synthesis Report of the IPCC Fourth Assessment Report', Subject to final copyedit. At: <www.ipcc.ch/pdf/assessment-report/ar4/syr/ar4_syr_spm.pdf>.

Joyce, T. 2002. 'The Heat before the Cold', *New York Times* (18 Apr.): A29.

Kondratyev, K. 1969. *Radiation in the Atmosphere.* New York: Academic Press.

Liou, K.-N. 1980. *An Introduction to Atmospheric Radiation.* New York: Academic Press.

MacCracken, Michael C., Frances Moore, and John C. Topping Jr, eds. 2008. *Sudden and Disruptive Climate Change: Exploring the Real Risks and How We Can Avoid Them.* London: Earthscan.

Schneider, D. 1997. 'Trends in Climate Research: The Rising Seas', *Scientific American* (Mar.): 112–17.

Time. 2001. 'Global Warming', (9 Apr.): 22–9.

WEB RESOURCES

icp.giss.nasa.gov/education/modules/eccm/model/ An interactive radiation-balance model from NASA.

ioc.unesco.org/iocweb/climateChange.php United Nations Educational, Scientific, and Cultural Organization portal to a huge amount of climate information.

lwf.ncdc.noaa.gov/oa/climate/globalwarming.html NOAA's guide to global warming and the greenhouse effect.

nsidc.org/sotc The National Snow and Ice Data Center in Colorado provides an overview of the status of snow and ice as indicators of climate change.

www.atmosphere.mpg.de/enid/1442 Espere (Environmental Science Published for Everybody Round the Earth) offers a 'Climate Encyclopedia' for non-scientists.

www.earthobservatory.nasa.gov/Observatory/Datasets/lwflux.erbe.html User can build false colour animations of longwave radiation emitted by Earth for any given month from 1990 to present, in order to compare heat received and transmitted for different time periods.

www.ec.gc.ca/climate/home-e.htm Environment Canada's climate change site, including action plans for Canada.

www.giss.nasa.gov/research/news Goddard Institute for Space Studies, NASA, offers research reports and news releases by James Hansen and his colleagues.

www.ipcc.ch The Intergovernmental Panel on Climate Change (IPCC) provides up-to-date reports.

www.nrdc.org/globalWarming/fgwscience.asp Natural Resources Defense Council, 'Global Warming Science: An Annotated Bibliography' includes seven years of peer-reviewed climate science.

www.ucsusa.org/global_warming/science Union of Concerned Scientists on climate change.

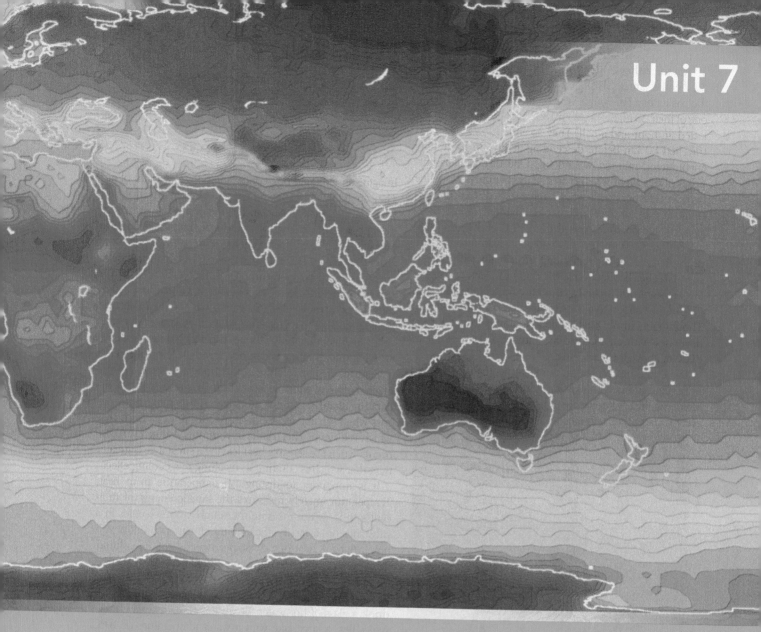

Atmospheric and Surface Temperature

Objectives

- To discuss the measurement and characteristics of temperature and heat.

- To explain the factors that control temperature.

- To discuss the global distribution of temperatures and their variation in time and space.

On the rather cloudy day of 26 June 1863, British scientist James Glaisher and his assistant climbed into the basket of a balloon in Wolverton, England. This flight, one of their 28 flights between 1862 and 1866 (Figure 7.1), lasted an hour and a half. They ascended to 7050 m and travelled 80 km before descending at Ely. En route they encountered rain, snow, and fog. One of the main purposes of this flight was to note the temperatures along the way. In Glaisher's own words, these varied from the 'extreme heat of summer' to the 'cold of winter'. In fact, however, the temperatures varied from 19°C at the ground to −8.3°C at 7050 m. The pair had good reason to be wary of the hazards of high altitudes: on a flight the previous year, Glaisher had fainted at 8700 m from lack of oxygen. His assistant, arms paralyzed with cold, climbed the rigging of the balloon to release the gas control with his teeth. Those flights firmly established that temperature typically decreases with an increase in altitude, at least as far as 8700 m above the surface.

These findings of vertical temperature changes were an important addition to existing knowledge. Together with what was already known about heating patterns of the planetary surface, they reinforced the notion that temperatures could be highly variable in any direction. Before we further examine those vertical and horizontal temperature relationships, we must briefly digress to inquire more explicitly about what is meant by the concept of temperature.

Temperature and Heat

Imagine an enclosed box containing only molecules of air. They are likely to be moving constantly in all directions, in what is called *random motion*. The molecules move because they possess the energy of movement, known as **kinetic energy**. The more kinetic energy molecules possess, the faster they move. The index we use to measure their kinetic energy is called **temperature**. Thus, temperature is an abstract term describing the energy, and therefore the speed of movement, of molecules. In a gas such as air, the molecules actually change their location when they move. But in a solid, like ice, they only vibrate in place. Nonetheless, the speed of this vibration is described by their temperature.

Changes in temperature result from a *flux convergence* or *divergence* of sensible heat (heat that results in a temperature change) through an object. A flux *convergence* occurs when sensible heat entering a substance exceeds that which is leaving. This results in warming. A flux *divergence* occurs when the sensible heat leaving a substance is greater than that which is entering it, resulting in a cooling effect.

It is important to distinguish temperature from heat. Temperature merely measures the kinetic energy of molecules. It does not measure the number of molecules in a substance or its *density* (the amount of mass per unit of volume). But the heat of a substance depends on its volume, its temperature, and its capacity to hold heat. Thus, a bowl of soup, with a high heat capacity, might burn your tongue at the same temperature at which you could comfortably drink a glass of hot water. Because it contains many more molecules, a large lake with a water temperature of 10°C contains much more heat than a cup of hot coffee at 70°C.

It is almost impossible to examine individual molecules, so we usually use an indirect method to measure temperature. We know that changes of temperature make gases, liquids, and solids expand and contract. Therefore, temperature is most commonly measured by observing the expansion and contraction of mercury in a glass tube. Such an instrument is called a **thermometer**, and you are probably familiar with the medical and weather varieties. The mercury thermometer is placed in the body, air, or some other medium where it can come into thermal equilibrium with the medium whose temperature it is measuring.

A thermometer is calibrated according to one of three scales. The metric scale used throughout most of the world (and in this book) is the **Celsius scale** (formerly centigrade scale). On this scale, the **boiling point** of water is set at 100°C and its **freezing point** at 0°C. Scientists also employ an *absolute scale*—the **Kelvin scale**—which is based on the temperature of *absolute zero* (−273°C). (Scientists theorize that a gas at absolute zero would have no volume, no molecular motion, and no pressure.) The

Figure 7.1 James Glaisher and his assistant, Coxwell, during a balloon flight on 5 September 1862.

Kelvin is identical in size to the Celsius degree, except that water freezes at 273°K and boils at 373°K. A third scale, Fahrenheit, has been largely replaced by the Celsius scale but is still in common use in the US and a few other countries, such as Belize. On the Fahrenheit scale, the boiling point of water is 212°F and the freezing point is 32°F.

LINK

Geographers often want to compare the climate characteristics from different regions of the world in an effort to understand and account for the variations. Some of the statistics that one would consider include the mean daily temperature, mean monthly temperature, and mean annual temperature. Let's consider what these values might be for Winnipeg and Vancouver.

The *mean daily temperature* is the mean of the maximum and minimum temperature for a given day:

$$\bar{T}_{daily} = \frac{T_{max} + T_{min}}{2}$$

where $\bar{T}_{daily}$ is the mean daily temperature in degrees Celsius, T_{max} is the maximum daily temperature in degrees Celsius, and T_{min} is the minimum daily temperature in degrees Celsius. On any given day in any part of Canada, the mean daily temperatures can have a large amount of variability and would not be used to describe the climatic conditions of that location. The mean daily temperature would be used instead to describe the weather conditions that might be prevailing on that particular day. For example, on 6 May 2008 the maximum temperature at Winnipeg was 15.6°C (at 3:00 p.m.) while the minimum was 4.1°C (at 2:00 a.m.). The mean temperature at Winnipeg for 8 May 2008 was therefore 9.85°C. This value masks the range of values as well as the fact that the daily mean temperature at Winnipeg would change considerably from year to year. Consider Vancouver on the same date; the maximum temperature on 6 May 2008 was 14.6°C (at 3:00 p.m.) and the minimum was 8.4°C (recorded for three hourly intervals in the very early morning hours of that date). The mean temperature for Vancouver on this date could therefore be recorded as 11.5°C. This might give one the impression that Vancouver was warmer on 6 May 2008 than Winnipeg, when in reality the maximum temperatures were very similar, but Vancouver wasn't as cold overnight as Winnipeg. A geographer would be interested in understanding why. Environment Canada's 'Climate Data Online' service provides current as well as archived weather station data for all of Canada, and is very useful for weather and climate analysis (www.climate.weatheroffice.ec.gc.ca/climateData/canada_e.html).

Now let's consider the *mean monthly temperature*, which is calculated as the mean of all mean daily temperatures for a given month:

$$\bar{T}_{monthly} = \frac{\Sigma \bar{T}_{daily}}{N}$$

where $\bar{T}_{monthly}$ is the mean monthly temperature in degrees Celsius for a given month, $\Sigma \bar{T}_{daily}$ is the sum of all mean daily temperatures in degrees Celsius for a given month, and N

is the total number of days in a given month. Based on this calculation, the mean monthly temperature for Winnipeg in May of 2007 was 12.2°C, and the mean monthly temperature for Vancouver in May 2007 was 12.8°C; very similar statistics. When considering the mean maximum and mean minimum temperatures for those locations, the results illustrate the highs and lows that are masked in the calculations of mean temperatures:

	Mean Min. Temp.	Mean Max. Temp
Winnipeg:	6.3°C	18.0°C
Vancouver	8.7°C	16.8°C

The *mean annual temperature* is derived from the mean of all mean monthly temperatures in a given year:

$$\bar{T}_{annual} = \frac{\Sigma \bar{T}_{monthly}}{12}$$

where $\bar{T}_{annual}$ is the mean annual temperature in degrees Celsius for a given year, $\Sigma \bar{T}_{monthly}$ is the sum of all mean monthly temperatures in degrees Celsius for a given year, and 12 is the number of months in any given year. The mean annual temperature for Winnipeg in 2007 was 4°C, while the mean annual temperature for Vancouver was 10.2°C. The lower average for Winnipeg is a result of the much colder winter months that are experienced there (in comparison to the milder winter temperatures in Vancouver).

Although two locations can have similar mean temperature values, they may sometimes show a completely different temperature range (the difference between the maximum and minimum daily, monthly, or annual temperatures). The *annual temperature range* is calculated as:

$$\Delta T = T_{annual\ max} - T_{annual\ min}$$

where ΔT is the annual temperature range, $T_{annual\ max}$ is the highest mean monthly temperature value in a given year, $T_{annual\ min}$ is the lowest mean monthly temperature value in the given year. The temperature range in Vancouver in 2007 was 15.8°C, while the temperature range in Winnipeg in 2007 was 40.1°C! Some of the factors that explain the variations in temperatures between these two Canadian cities can be found in the marine and continental effects discussed in this unit.

Daily and Yearly Temperature Cycles

The pattern of temperature change during a day is called the **diurnal temperature cycle**. Shortly after dawn, radiation from the Sun begins to exceed the radiant loss from the Earth's surface. The Earth begins to heat the air, so the air temperature rises. It continues to rise as the net radiation rises. But the heating of the ground and the flow of sensible heat take some time to develop fully. Thus, maximum air temperatures usually do not occur simultaneously with the maximum net radiation peaks at solar noon, but an hour or more later. In late afternoon, net radiation and sensible heat flow decline markedly, and temperatures begin to fall. After the Sun has set, more radiation leaves the Earth than arrives at the surface, which produces a negative net radiation. The surface and the air above it enter a cooling period that lasts all through the night. Temperatures are lowest near dawn; with sunrise, the diurnal cycle starts again.

The pattern of temperature change during a year is called the **annual temperature cycle**, which in the middle and high latitudes is rather similar to the diurnal cycle. In the spring, net radiation becomes positive and air temperatures begin to rise. The highest average temperatures do not occur at the time of the greatest net radiation, i.e., the summer solstice, but usually about a month later. In autumn, decreasing net radiation leads to progressively lower temperatures. The lowest winter temperatures occur towards the end of the period of lowest (and often negative) net radiation and when the ground has lost most of the heat it gained during summer. Then, it is spring again, and net radiation once more begins its cyclical increase.

Factors that Influence Temperature

The distribution of temperatures across the landmasses, oceans, and icecaps that constitute the Earth's surface represents the response to a number of factors. Certainly, insolation is one such factor, and the amount of solar radiation received depends on the length of daylight and the angle of the Sun's rays (both a function of the latitudinal position). But there are many additional factors that control Earth's surface temperatures. The following provides an explanation of how each of the factors (latitude, altitude, cloud cover, land–water heating differences, and marine or continental effects) influence surface temperatures on Earth.

Latitude

Temperatures on the Earth are largely dependent on how much energy is received from the Sun, which varies both with latitude on the Earth and the seasons. At present, the global average surface temperature is about 15°C. Regions nearer the Equator are much warmer than regions near the poles, with average surface temperatures near the Equator at 25°C or higher. In contrast, average temperatures on Antarctica are always well below freezing. This latitudinal temperature gradient generates a global transfer of heat from equatorial regions towards the poles via the circulation of air caused by wind, such that the Equator is kept cooler and the poles warmer than they would be if the Earth had no atmosphere. The equator, however, does not experience the highest temperatures on Earth. Here, rising air generates daily thunderstorms that consume considerable amounts of heat energy, suppressing the air temperature by several degrees Celsius.

The changing of the seasons also influences temperature. During the months of April to September, the Northern Hemisphere of the Earth is tilted towards the Sun, and consequently receives more sunlight, raising the surface temperatures. From October to March, the Southern Hemisphere receives more energy from the Sun. While it is winter in Canada it is summer in Australia. Differences between wintertime and summertime temperatures tend to be greatest in higher latitudes, and particularly in the interior of large landmasses such as North America and Asia far from the moderating influence of the oceans. Winter temperatures in Siberia and Canada, for example, can fall below −40°C, while in summer they may rise above 30°C. The British Isles, by contrast, have a more maritime climate and the yearly temperature range is only 10 to 15°C. The smallest annual temperature range occurs in the equatorial climate zone, where the changing angle of the Sun through the seasons has a proportionally smaller effect on the total amount of sunlight received.

Altitude

Glaisher's observations for the lower part of the atmosphere were indeed correct—temperature typically does decline with an increase in altitude. However, subsequent unmanned balloon observations showed that, above about 12 km, the temperature stops decreasing with height and begins to increase. Nobody believed this at first, and only after several hundred balloon ascents was it finally accepted. Later ascents during the twentieth century to still higher altitudes revealed an even more complex temperature pattern. These upper atmospheric layers are discussed in Unit 6, and their temperature characteristics are graphed in Figure 5.5. Our focus here is on the lowest atmospheric layer, the troposphere.

Since tropospheric temperatures usually decrease with an increase in altitude, places located at higher elevations tend to experience temperatures lower than those recorded at places closer to sea level. As shown in Figure 5.5, temperature typically decreases with increasing altitude until the tropopause is reached. The average tropospheric lapse rate (change in temperature with an increase in elevation) is approximately 6.5°C/1000 m of elevation. Therefore, for locations at the same latitude, having similar cloud cover, similar demographics, and similar proximity to a body of water, if one is at sea level and the other is at 1000 m above sea level, it would be expected that the one at a higher elevation would have temperatures that are on average 6.5°C cooler.

At Pincher Creek, Alberta (49°31'N latitude, 1190 m elevation), the average annual temperature is 5.8°C. At Penticton, BC (49°27'N latitude, 344 m elevation), although the latitude is very similar, the average annual temperature is almost twice that of Pincher Creek, at 10°C. The 846 m difference in elevation between the two locations has an influence on the temperatures experienced there (Figure 7.2).

Cloud Cover

Another moderator of surface temperatures is cloudiness, and places with more extensive cloud cover generally experience lower daytime high temperatures than similar places with clearer skies. (This may be true also in areas where

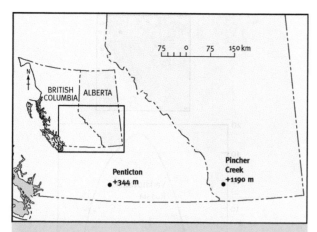

Figure 7.2 Penticton, BC, and Pincher Creek, Alberta, though situated at almost precisely the same latitude, have significantly different average annual temperatures. Pincher Creek, in the Rockies of southwestern Alberta, is much cooler than Penticton, at a lower elevation in southern BC at the southern end of Okanagan Lake.

pollution haze plays a role identical to that of clouds.) Some of the hottest places on Earth lie in the subtropical climate zone of high pressure patterns between latitudes 25° to 40°, where cloud cover is virtually non-existent and sunshine levels are very high throughout the year. Parts of the Sahara Desert, Saudi Arabia, California, and Australia can experience daytime temperatures of over 50°C, although during the winter months, severe radiation cooling under the clear skies at night can drop the air temperature close to or even below freezing.

Land–Water Heating Differences

Land heats and cools much more rapidly than water, and this strongly affects not only air temperatures directly above each type of surface, but also adjacent areas influenced by them. The time it takes to heat the surface at any particular location determines when the highest air temperatures will occur. The difference between land and ocean is particularly noteworthy. Dry land heats and cools relatively rapidly because radiation cannot penetrate the solid surface to any meaningful extent.

Unlike solid surfaces, water requires far more time to heat up and cool down. For one thing, compared to land, radiation can penetrate the surface layer of water to a relatively greater depth. There is also considerable vertical mixing—driven by waves, currents, and other water movements—that constantly takes place between newly warmed (or cooled) surface water and cooler (or warmer) layers below. Moreover, the energy required to raise the land temperature by a given number of degrees would have to be tripled in order to increase the surface temperature of a body of water by an equivalent amount.

Not surprisingly, the ocean surface exhibits a decidedly smaller annual temperature range—from −2°C to about 32°C, as opposed to the land-surface extremes of −88°C

and 58°C. In addition, seasonal ocean temperature change is particularly moderate. In the tropics this variation averages 1 to 4°C, and even the upper middle latitudes record only a modest 5 to 8°C swing between seasonal extremes. On a diurnal basis, the ocean-surface range is almost always less than 1°C.

Marine and Continental Effects

Coastal areas tend to have high mean temperatures but have relatively lower temperature ranges. Interior locations, however, tend to have lower mean annual temperatures (in high latitudes) with larger temperature ranges. As a consequence of the heating differences between land and water, the air above an ocean remains cooler in summer and warmer in winter than does the air over a land surface at the same latitude. This can be seen in Table 7.1, which displays data on the annual range of temperatures, at 15-degree latitudinal intervals, for each hemisphere. Note that the Southern Hemisphere, which is only about 20 per cent land, consistently exhibits smaller yearly temperature ranges than the Northern Hemisphere, whose surface is approximately 40 per cent land.

In places where the oceanic air is transported onto the continents (as in our discussion of Paris in Unit 6), air temperatures are ameliorated accordingly, that is, they do not become extremely hot or cold. As the distance from the coast increases, however, this moderating effect diminishes (it terminates more abruptly if high mountain ranges parallel to the shore block the inland movement of oceanic air). This is illustrated in Figure 7.3, which graphs the annual temperature regimes for Victoria, British Columbia, and Winnipeg, Manitoba, both located at approximately the same latitude. Interior Winnipeg, located in the heart of the North American continent, experiences both a warmer summer and a much colder winter, whereas Victoria, located on the Pacific coast, enjoys a temperature regime that is free of extremes in both summer and winter.

This moderating influence of the ocean on air temperatures is called the **maritime effect** on climate. In the

Table 7.1 Variation in Average Annual Temperature Range by Latitude, °C

Latitude	Northern Hemisphere	Southern Hemisphere
0	0	0
15	3	4
30	13	7
45	23	6
60	30	11
75	32	26
90	40	31

Source: Information from F.K. Lutgens and E.J. Tarbuck, *The Atmosphere: An Introduction to Meteorology*, 8th edn (Upper Saddle River, NJ: Prentice-Hall, 2001), 64.

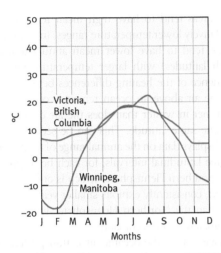

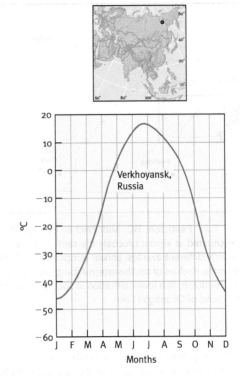

Figure 7.3 Annual temperature regimes in Victoria, British Columbia, and Winnipeg, Manitoba. Note the contrast between interior continental and coastal locations.

Figure 7.4 Annual temperature regime in Verkhoyansk (68°N, 133°E) in Russia's far northeastern Siberia, demonstrating the extremes of continentality.

opposite case, where the ocean has a minimal ameliorating influence on air temperatures well inland, there is a **continental effect.** This property of **continentality** is strongly suggested in the case of Winnipeg (Figure 7.3), but the most dramatic examples are found deep inside Eurasia, in the heart of the world's largest landmass. The Russian town of Verkhoyansk, located in far northeastern Siberia, is well known to climatologists in this regard, and its annual temperature regime is plotted in Figure 7.4.

Sometimes air from outside an area has more influence on air temperatures than do local radiation and sensible and latent heat flows. For instance, there might be quite a large amount of net radiation at midday during a Nebraska winter, but the air temperatures may still be very low. This is because the overlying air may have come from the Arctic, thousands of kilometres to the north, where a completely different heat balance prevailed. Thus, although the air temperature is a function of the amount of heat that makes up the local heat balance, it can also be affected by the **advection** (horizontal transport through the atmosphere via wind) of air from a region exhibiting a different heat energy balance. The results of different heat balances and the large-scale advection of air can be seen in the worldwide distribution of surface air temperatures.

Temperature Inversions and Air Pollution

In dealing with the **stability** of the troposphere, we really are considering the possibility—and vigour—of the vertical mixing of air within it. This has practical implications,

the most important of which is how well pollutants will disperse when released into the atmosphere. The initial vertical (and horizontal) distribution of pollutants depends on the location of their sources. Any further spread of air pollution is associated with two main factors: (1) the stability of the air and its propensity to allow vertical mixing, and (2) how well air stability combines with the flushing effect of horizontal winds. Both are related to the temperature structure of the lower troposphere, particularly the influence of temperature inversions.

Under usual conditions, the tropospheric temperature decreases with height as ground-warmed air rises, expands, and cools (see Figure 5.5). Thus, any pollutants contained in that surface layer of air would disperse along with it. At times, however, this vertical cleansing mechanism does not operate because the usual negative lapse rate is replaced by a positive one. Such an increase in temperature with height is defined in Unit 5 as a **temperature inversion** because it inverts what we, on the surface, believe to be the 'normal' behaviour of temperature change with altitude.

Because of the nightly cooling of the Earth's surface and the atmosphere near the ground, it is common for a temperature inversion—warm air lying above cold air—to develop in early morning over both city and countryside. These inversions, which form an atmospheric 'lid', can be broken down by rapid heating of the surface or by windy conditions. Without these conditions, air pollution is trapped and intensifies beneath the inversion layer (Figure 7.5). This is especially true in certain urban areas, where *dust domes* frequently build up (see 'Perspectives' box).

LINK

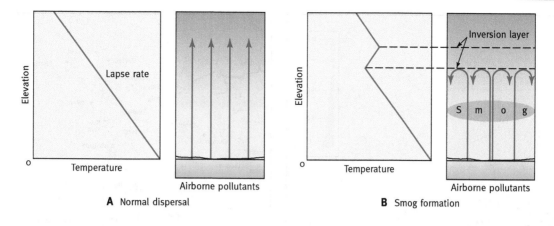

A Normal dispersal **B** Smog formation

Figure 7.5 Effect of a temperature inversion on the vertical dispersal of atmospheric pollutants. (A) Normal dispersal; (B) smog formation.

Figure 7.6 Downtown Toronto under a thick blanket of smog (7:08 a.m., 27 June 2001). The public has become increasingly aware of and concerned with high levels of ground-level ozone and inhalable particulates (the main ingredients of smog) in the city.

The **subsidence** (vertical downflow) of air from higher in the troposphere can also contribute to the trapping of pollutants, as residents of downtown Toronto know only too well (Figure 7.6). This airflow is usually quite cool and is reinforced by onshore surface winds that blow across the cold waters of the adjacent Pacific Ocean. Moreover, the cooling effect is heightened by the nighttime drainage of cold air into the Los Angeles Basin from the mountains that form its inland perimeter. These air movements often produce and sustain temperature inversions at an altitude of approximately 1000 m, resulting in poor-quality surface-level air that is popularly known as *smog* (a contraction of 'smoke' and 'fog').

Horizontal flushing by winds can help to relieve air pollution. Air pollution potential may be estimated by calculating the vertical range of well-mixed pollutants and the average wind speed through the mixing layer. Figure 7.7 shows the average number of days (between 1987 and

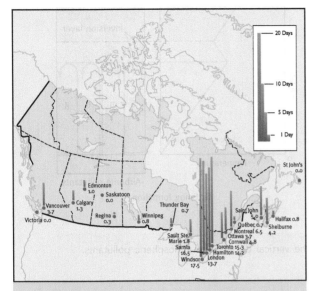

Figure 7.7 Average number of days when one-hour average concentrations of ozone surpassed 82 parts per billion (ppb). An excess of 65 ppb is indicative of relatively poor air-quality conditions.

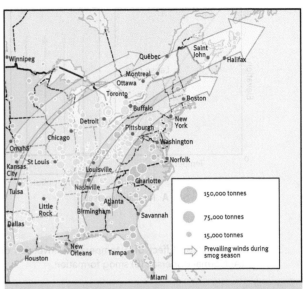

Figure 7.8 Annual emission of nitrogen oxides from electrical generating stations in eastern North America, indicating predominant flow of atmospheric transport of effluents.

1992) when ozone concentrations of 82 parts per billion (ppb) were exceeded. Levels above 65 ppb are considered poor air quality. On average it appears that air-quality and ventilation conditions are best in the northern, central, and western regions of Canada, with the poorest air-quality conditions occurring in southern Ontario and Atlantic Canada. The role of topographic factors is important in determining the fate of air pathways, a factor that does not show up at the scale of the map in Figure 7.7. The region from Windsor, Ontario, to Quebec City has the worst air quality in Canada. Approximately half of the smog in this region originates in the Ohio Valley and Cleveland and Detroit areas of the United States. Canada is now engaged in negotiations with the United States to reduce the trans-border issue of air pollution. The geographical location and tendency for hot, stagnant summer weather is the perfect scenario for the formation of ground-level ozone. In Atlantic Canada, 50 to 80 per cent of the smog originates in the United States or central Canada (see Figure 7.8).

Perspectives on the Human Environment

Urban Dust Domes and Heating Patterns

Many North American metropolitan areas lie beneath a dust dome. A high concentration of fuel combustion and heat from concrete can cause the air in **urban heat islands** to be warmer than surrounding areas (see urban heat islands, p. 267). This can result in **dust domes**, which trap particulates in a dome over a city, lowering air quality in those regions. The brownish haze of a dust dome can stand out against the blue sky (see Figure 7.6). This haze is often referred to as *smog*, a combination of 'smoke' and 'fog', referring to the brownish haze that can hang over cities. Ground level ozone (as opposed to the ozone layer found in the high atmosphere) is the main constituent of urban smog. Smog formation and ground level ozone buildup occur most often during hot and sunny afternoons of the summer months.

LINK

Canada's worst smog corridor extends from Windsor, Ontario, through to Montreal, Quebec, although smog days do occur in many other regions of the country. Around the Bay of Fundy in southern New Brunswick and parts of Nova Scotia, 50–80 per cent of the smog is caused by cross-border pollution from the northeastern United States and emissions from central Canada. As much as 80 per cent of the ground-level ozone and smog conditions in the Lower Fraser Valley in southern British Columbia (including Vancouver) come from local sources, particularly tailpipe emissions. 'Smog season' in Canada tends to last from May through September.

Torontonians have become increasingly concerned about the quality of their air. Ground-level ozone and inhalable particles (the main ingredients of smog) are believed to be leading to increased rates of respiratory and cardiovascular illness and even to premature death. Air temperatures have been rising and air quality has been declining over the past half-century. Lower temperatures and smog levels can be found only a short distance outside the urban core. The situation is similar in many other large cities in North America. Why don't these effluents simply just blow away?

Studies of the movement of dust and gaseous pollutants over cities show that heat generated in many urban areas forms a local circulation cell. Air currents capture the dust and mould it into a dome (Figure 7.9). Dust and pollution particles rise in air currents around the centre of the city where the temperature is warmest. As they move upward, the air cools and diverges. The particles gradually drift towards the edges of the city and settle downward. Near the ground they are drawn into the centre of the city to complete the circular motion. Frequent temperature inversions above the city prevent upward escape, and the particles

tend to remain trapped in this continuous cycle of air movement.

All parts of the radiation balance discussed in Unit 6 are altered in the urban environment. In London, England, researchers have discovered that the city centre has an average of 3.6 hours of sunshine per day. Outside the city, it is sunny an average of 4.3 hours per day because of the absence of a dust dome to intercept the incoming shortwave radiation.

The amount of insolation absorbed by a city's surface also depends on the albedo of that surface. This, in turn, depends on the actual materials used in construction and varies from city to city. Many cities are made of dark materials or materials that have been blackened by smoke (the industrial cities in Britain, for example). They have a lower albedo (17 per cent) than agricultural land does (approximately 23 per cent), and therefore they absorb more radiation. In contrast, some cities (for example, the central areas of Los Angeles) have construction materials with lighter colours and therefore exhibit a higher albedo than the more vegetated residential zones. Recent work on so-called 'green roofs' (roofs with a vegetated surface and substrate) has proved to be a promising mechanism to reduce the urban heat-island effect. During warm weather, green roofs reduce the amount of heat transferred through the roof, lowering the energy demands of the building air conditioning systems. In addition, the vegetated surfaces that replace dark and impervious surfaces act to increase the surface albedo (amount of solar radiation reflected back into the atmosphere). A study of Toronto indicated that if 50 per cent of the buildings had green roofs, the temperature reductions could be as great as 2°C in some areas.

Scientists know less about the behaviour of longwave radiation in cities, but many studies show increases in both upward and downward longwave radiation in urban areas. This increased radiation can offset the decreased shortwave radiation. The result is a net radiation that is not very different from that in surrounding rural areas. Some studies suggest that, of the net radiation arriving at the city surface, about 80 per cent is lost as sensible heat warming the city air and that the rest acts mainly as ground heat flow to warm the materials constituting the urban landscape. Very little heat appears to be used in evaporative cooling.

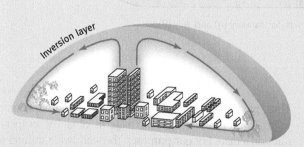

Figure 7.9 Air circulation within an urban dust dome.

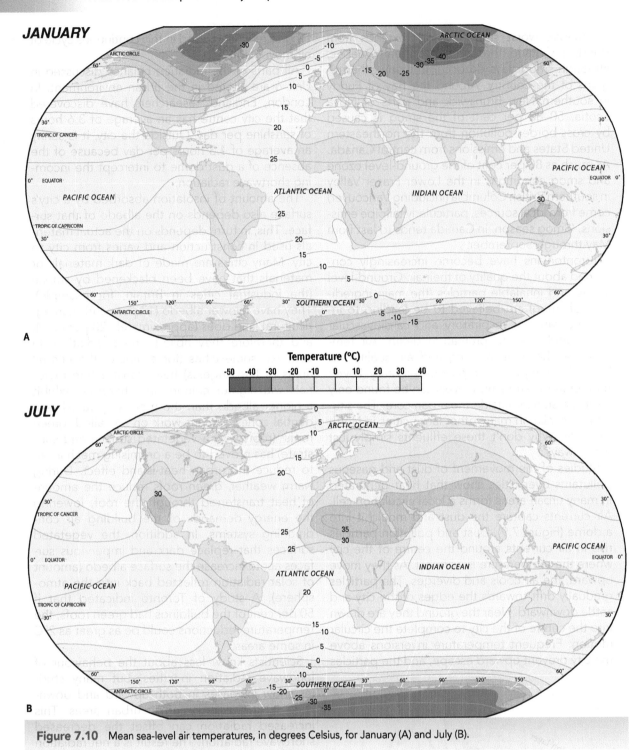

Figure 7.10   Mean sea-level air temperatures, in degrees Celsius, for January (A) and July (B).

Global Temperature Variations

The global distribution of air temperatures is mapped in Figure 7.10. In order to avoid the distorting effects of altitude, all temperatures have been converted to their averages at sea level. Insolation, which is determined by the angle of the Sun's rays striking the Earth and the length of daylight, can change significantly in most places over a period of weeks.

Thus, physical geographers have always faced a problem in trying to capture the dynamic patterns of global temperatures on a map. For our purposes, the worldwide shifting of air temperatures, or their *seasonal march*, is best visualized by comparing the patterns of the two extreme months of the year—January and July—which immediately follow the solstices. The cartographic technique of isarithmic mapping (defined in Unit 3) is used in Figure 7.10, where January and July distributions are shown by **isotherms**—lines connecting all points having the same temperature.

Both maps reveal a series of latitudinal temperature belts that are shifted towards the 'high-Sun' hemisphere (Northern Hemisphere in July, Southern Hemisphere in January). The tropical zone on both sides of the Equator experiences the least change between January and July, because higher total amounts of net radiation at low latitudes (see Figure 6.5) lead to higher air temperatures. The middle and upper latitudes, particularly in the hemisphere experiencing winter, exhibit quite a different pattern. Here the horizontal rate of temperature change over distance—or **temperature gradient**—is much more pronounced, as shown by the 'packing' or bunching of the isotherms. (Note that the isotherms are much farther apart in the tropical latitudes.)

Another major feature of Figure 7.10 is the contrast between temperatures overlying land and sea. There is no mistaking the effects of continentality on either map: the Northern Hemisphere landmasses vividly display their substantial interior annual temperature ranges. Clearly visible, too, are the moderating influence of the oceans and the maritime effect on the air temperatures over land

surfaces near them. Where warm ocean currents flow, as in the North Atlantic just west and northwest of Europe, the onshore movement of air across them can decidedly ameliorate winter temperatures; note that northern Britain, close to 60°N, lies on the 5°C January isotherm, the same isotherm that passes through North Carolina at about 35°N, the northern edge of the US Sunbelt! In general, we observe a bending of the isotherms over all the oceans towards the poles, an indicator of their relative warmth with respect to land at the same latitude. The only notable exceptions occur in conjunction with cold ocean currents, such as off the western coasts of Africa and South America south of the Equator, or off the northwestern coast of Africa north of the Equator.

The flow patterns associated with ocean currents and the movement of air above them remind us that the atmosphere and hydrosphere are highly dynamic entities. Indeed, both contain global-scale circulation systems that are vital to understanding weather and climate. Now that we are familiar with the temperature structure of the atmosphere, we are ready to examine the forces that shape these regularly recurring currents of air and water.

KEY TERMS

advection *page 92*
annual temperature cycle *page 90*
boiling point *page 88*
Celsius scale *page 88*
continental effect (continentality) *page 92*
diurnal temperature cycle *page 89*
dust dome *page 94*
freezing point *page 88*
isotherms *page 97*
Kelvin scale *page 88*

kinetic energy *page 88*
maritime effect *page 91*
stability *page 92*
subsidence *page 93*
temperature *page 88*
temperature gradient *page 97*
temperature inversion *page 92*
thermometer *page 88*
urban heat islands *page 94*

REVIEW QUESTIONS

1. Discuss the major differences between the Celsius and Kelvin temperature scales.
2. Calculate the difference between mean daily, mean monthly, and mean annual temperatures for two locations. What is the annual temperature range?
3. What is a *temperature inversion*, and what are the negative consequences for an urban area affected by

this atmospheric condition? How does it influence the ventilation of air pollution?
4. What are the factors that shape the spatial distribution of temperature across the Earth's surface?
5. What are the main differences in annual temperature regimes between maritime and interior continental locations?

REFERENCES AND FURTHER READINGS

Amato, J.A. 2000. *Dust: A History of the Small and the Invisible*. Berkeley: Univ. of California Press.

Bailey, W.G., T.R. Oke, and W.R. Rouse. 1997. *The Surface Climates of Canada*. Montreal and Kingston: McGill-Queen's Univ. Press.

Bass, B., E. Krayenhoof, A. Martilli, R. Stull, and H. Auld. 2003. 'The Impacts of Green Roofs on Toronto's Urban Heat Island', *Proceedings of the First North American Green Roof Conference: Greening Rooftops for Sustainable Communities*. Chicago: Cardinal Group, 292–304.

Elsom, D. 1992. *Atmospheric Pollution: A Global Problem*, 2nd edn. Cambridge, Mass.: Blackwell.

Geiger, R. 1965. *The Climate near the Ground*. Cambridge, Mass.: Harvard Univ. Press.

Goudie, A. 2000. *The Human Impact on the Natural Environment*, 5th edn. Cambridge, Mass.: MIT Press.

Henderson-Sellers, A., and P.J. Robinson. 1986. *Contemporary Climatology*. London/New York: Longman.

Kondratyev, K. 1969. *Radiation in the Atmosphere*. New York: Academic Press.

Mather, J.R. 1974. *Climatology: Fundamentals and Applications*. New York: McGraw-Hill.

Middleton, W. 1966. *A History of the Thermometer and Its Use in Meteorology*. Baltimore: Johns Hopkins Univ. Press.

Oke, T.R. 1987. *Boundary Layer Climates*, 2nd edn. New York: Methuen.

Thompson, R., and A. Perry, eds. 1997. *Applied Climatology: Principles and Practice*. London/New York: Routledge.

Trewartha, G.T., and L.H. Horn. 1980. *An Introduction to Climate*, 5th edn. New York: McGraw-Hill.

WEB RESOURCES

lavoieverte.qc.ec.gc.ca/atmos/smog/fiche_info_e.html Environment Canada's fact sheet on ground-level ozone.

www.ace.mmu.ac.uk/eae/english.html The Encyclopedia of the Atmospheric Environment, produced by the Atmosphere, Climate and Environment Information Programme in the UK, provides extensive introductory information on numerous environmental and climatological topics.

www.airnow.gov View an animation of current or previous levels of ozone in different regions of Canada.

www.atl.ec.gc.ca/airquality/query/ Atlantic Region interactive air-quality data (past 24 hours, daily, and monthly), indicating the type of pollutant.

www.climate.weatheroffice.ec.gc.ca/climateData/canada_e.html Climate data from across Canada.

www.cpc.ncep.noaa.gov/ NOAA's climate prediction centre displays daily US temperature analyses, as well as long-term temperature and precipitation plots for US cities.

www.ec.gc.ca/cleanair-airpur/ Environment Canada's air-quality and pollution website.

www.ec.gc.ca/cleanair-airpur/Pollution_Issues/Transboundary_Air/Canada_-_United_States_Air_Quality_Agreement-WS8390AC3-1_En.htm Canada–United States Air Quality Agreement, Ozone Annex.

www.greenontario.org/strategy/smog.html Information on smog.

www.toronto.ca/greenguide/cleaner_air.htm#aq_strategy Toronto's 'Moving towards Cleaner Air' reports on how the city can move forward in addressing air emissions.

Air Pressure and Winds

Objectives

- To explain atmospheric pressure and its altitudinal variation.

- To relate atmospheric pressure to windflow at the surface and aloft.

- To apply these relationships to the operation of local wind systems.

In our previous discussions, the atmosphere has been likened to a blanket and a protective shield. Another analogy is a surrounding ocean of air because the atmosphere resembles the world ocean in its circulation patterns. This unit is about atmospheric pressure and winds, the dynamic forces that shape the regularly recurring global movements of air (and water). Units 9 and 10 focus on the patterns that result—the atmospheric and oceanic currents that constitute the general circulation systems affecting our planetary surface and forming the framework for weather and climate.

The leading function of the general circulation of the atmosphere is to redistribute heat and moisture across the Earth's surface. Were it not for the transport of heat from the Equator to the poles, most of the Earth's surface would be uninhabitable because it would be too hot, too cold, or too dry. Atmospheric circulation accounts for approximately 87 per cent of this heat redistribution, and oceanic circulation accounts for the remainder. The atmosphere moves the way it does primarily because of the variation in the amount of net radiation received at the surface of the Earth. The resulting temperature differences produce the global wind system. We will begin to examine this system by detailing the relationships between air pressure, heat imbalances, winds, and the rotational effects of the Earth.

Atmospheric Pressure

Wind, the movement of air relative to the Earth's surface, is a response to an imbalance of forces acting on air molecules. This is true whether the air is moving horizontally or vertically, and indeed these two movement dimensions are related via the concept of atmospheric pressure. First we consider the concept of atmospheric pressure, its fundamental cause and the resultant vertical distribution produced. We then link atmospheric pressure to windflow by considering both the additional forces that come into play once motion begins and the patterns of air circulation within the atmosphere that result.

The Concept of Pressure

The primary force exerting an influence on air molecules is *gravity*. The atmosphere is 'held' against the Earth by gravitational attraction. The combined weight of all the air molecules in a column of atmosphere exerts a force on the surface of the Earth. Over a given area of the surface, say, 1 cm², this force produces a **pressure**. Although several different units are used to measure atmospheric pressure, the standard unit of pressure in atmospheric studies is the *millibar* (*mb*). The average weight of the atmospheric column pressing down on the Earth's surface (or *standard sea-level air pressure*) is 1013.25 mb.

Atmospheric pressure is commonly measured as the length of a column of liquid it will support. In 1643 the Italian scientist Evangelista Torricelli performed an

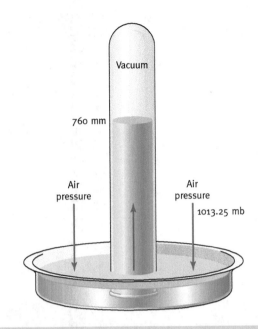

Figure 8.1   Mercury barometer invented by Torricelli. The greater the atmospheric pressure, the higher the column of mercury. These data exhibit the reading when standard sea-level pressure exists.

experiment in which he filled a glass tube with mercury and then placed the tube upside down in a dish of mercury. Figure 8.1 depicts his experiment. Instead of the mercury in the tube rushing out into the dish, the atmospheric pressure pushing down on the mercury in the surrounding dish supported the liquid still in the tube. The height of the column in the tube was directly proportional to the atmospheric pressure—the greater the pressure, the higher the column in the tube. (Note that standard sea-level air pressure produces a reading of 760 mm in the height of the mercury column.) Torricelli had invented the world's first pressure-measuring instrument, known as a **barometer**.

Atmospheric Pressure and Altitude

Once scientists found they could measure atmospheric pressure, they set about investigating its properties. They soon discovered that atmospheric pressure does not vary much horizontally but does decrease very rapidly with increasing altitude (about 1 kPa*) for every 100 m increase in elevation in the lower atmosphere). Measurements of atmospheric pressure from both higher land elevations and balloons show dramatic results. The standard pressure at sea level (1013 mb) decreases to about 848 mb at Banff, Alberta, elevation 1476 m. At the highest elevations at nearby Lake Louise, elevation 2637 m, the air pressure

---

*'Pa' is the abbreviation for 'Pascals'; 'kPa' is a measure of perpendicular force per unit area: (1 kPa = 1000 Pa) (1 kPa = 0.1 millibars [mb]).

is approximately 750 mb. On top of the world's tallest peak—Mount Everest in South Asia's Himalayas, elevation 8850 m, the pressure is only 320 mb. In order to have comparable readings of atmospheric pressure at different stations, the values are often 'corrected' to numbers as if all stations were at sea level.

Because air pressure depends on the number of molecules in motion and is highest in the lower atmospheric layers, we may deduce that most of the molecules are concentrated near the Earth's surface. This is confirmed in Figure 8.2, which graphs the percentage of the total mass of the atmosphere below certain elevations. For example, 50 per cent of the air of the atmosphere is found below 5 km, and 85 per cent lies within 16 km of the surface.

By definition, pressure is the amount of force exerted per unit of surface area. Atmospheric pressure is the weight of air applied onto the Earth's surface. Force is subsequently exerted by the mass of air that is pulled down to Earth by gravity. This relationship can be expressed as:

$$Pressure = \frac{Weight \times gravity}{Area} = \frac{Force}{Area}$$

This relationship can then be used to determine the units of pressure:

$$Units\ of\ Pressure = \frac{kg \times ms^{-2}}{m^2} = \frac{Newtons}{m^2} = Pascals\ (Pa)$$

Pressure depends in large part on the mass of the air, since gravity can be assumed to be a constant in the atmosphere.

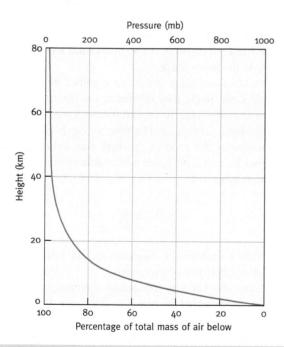

Figure 8.2 Mass of the atmosphere as a function of height. A greater proportion of the atmosphere is concentrated near the Earth's surface. Atmospheric pressure depends on mass, so it also decreases with altitude.

Air Movement in the Atmosphere

Since the days when it became common for sailing ships to make transoceanic voyages, people have known that the large-scale winds of the planet flow in certain generalized patterns. This information was vital in planning the routes of voyages that might take two or three years. However, it was often of little assistance in guiding the ships through the more localized, smaller-scale winds that fluctuate from day to day and place to place. It is therefore useful to separate large-scale air movement from smaller-scale movement, even though the two are related to the same phenomenon—atmospheric pressure. We begin by considering the causes, and resultant patterns, of the large-scale movement of air that is in contact with the surface of the Earth. Wind results from a horizontal difference in air pressure and since the sun heats different parts of the Earth differently, causing pressure differences, the Sun is the driving force for most winds. Each of the forces that collectively account for the *speed* and *direction* of winds will be explained: *gravitational force* (which we have already discussed), *pressure-gradient force*, *Coriolis force*, and *friction force*.

LINK

Pressure-Gradient Force

The **pressure-gradient force** is the trigger for the movement of air. Gravity causes the air to press down against the surface of the Earth; this is atmospheric pressure. The pressure, however, may be different at two locations. The difference in surface pressure over a given distance between two locations is called the *pressure gradient*. When there is a pressure gradient, it acts as a force that causes air to move from the place of higher pressure to that of lower pressure. This force, called the pressure-gradient force, increases as the difference in air pressure across a specified distance increases. The most common cause of the differences in air pressure is differences in air temperature, which, in turn, cause differences in air density. Warm air is less dense and tends to rise, lowering surface pressure as the inflow of air near the surface exceeds the outflow of air at higher altitudes. On the other hand, cold air tends to sink, reinforcing and raising surface pressure as the inflow aloft exceeds the outflow near the surface (Figure 8.3). On weather maps, a large pressure gradient is depicted by isobars that are spaced very close together. This indicates that pressure is changing rapidly over a short distance.

Coriolis Force

The simple rotation of the Earth influences the direction of atmospheric circulation (and large-scale wind

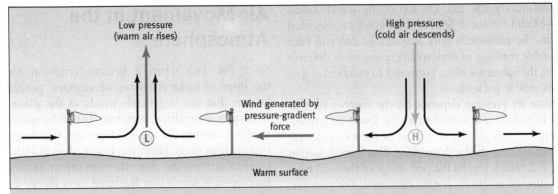

Figure 8.3   Air movement at the surface is always from areas of higher pressure (**H**) towards areas of lower pressure (**L**). The greater the pressure difference between **H** and **L**, the higher the pressure gradient and the stronger the wind.

systems). The most important effect is expressed as an apparent deflective force. An understanding of the nature of this force is best approached by an analogy.

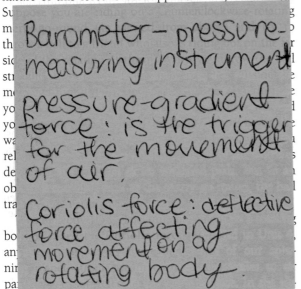

sence of any other forces, moving objects are deflected to their *right* in the Northern Hemisphere and to their *left* in the Southern Hemisphere. Thus, if a wind is blowing from the North Pole, it would be deflected to the right and become an easterly wind (Figure 8.4). (Note that this easterly wind blows towards the west: *winds are always named according to the direction from which they come.*) A little later we will see how the Coriolis force plays a major role in determining the general pattern of atmospheric circulation.

We are already familiar with the Coriolis force, which acts to deflect moving air to the right (Northern Hemisphere) or left (Southern Hemisphere). Here we need only to note two further observations. First, the Coriolis force is not constant, but is greatest at the poles and decreases as one approaches the Equator (Figure 8.5). Second, we can deduce that it will be significant only over

fairly large distances, since it is dependent on the rotation of the Earth.

Friction Force

Finally, some of the motion of the air in the atmosphere takes place very near the Earth's surface. Thus, the closer individual air molecules are to the surface, the more they are slowed by drag, or a **frictional force**. The magnitude of the frictional force depends primarily on the 'roughness' of the surface. There is less friction with movement across a smooth snow or water surface than across mountainous terrain or the ragged skyline of a metropolitan area. Friction is most important near the ground and less important higher in the atmosphere.

How do these three forces act together in the atmosphere? Collectively, they determine the pattern of windflow within any area. To explain the net force of the pressure gradient, Coriolis, and friction, we can begin with the calculation of the pressure gradient that exists between any two locations on Earth where atmospheric pressure has been measured:

$$PG = \frac{\Delta P}{\Delta D}$$

where ΔP is the pressure difference and ΔD is the horizontal distance between two locations.

Because the Earth is continually spinning on its axis, winds are deflected by the Coriolis force (C) (to the right in the Northern Hemisphere and to the left in the Southern Hemisphere). The deflection is larger if the wind speed is high. And due to the roughness of the Earth's surface, winds are slowed by the friction force (F), thus influencing the velocity and, in turn, the Coriolis force. The *surface wind* (W) is the result of the interaction of all these forces. The interaction of these forces is illustrated in Figure 8.6.

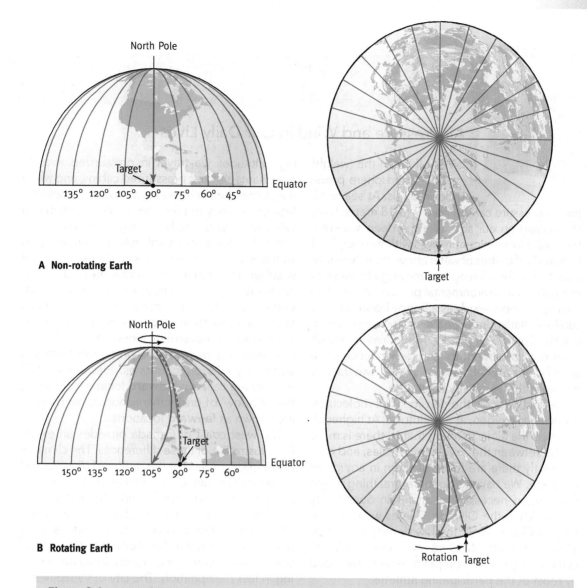

A Non-rotating Earth

B Rotating Earth

Figure 8.4 Coriolis force in action. A wind from the North Pole will blow towards the west because of the deflective force of the rotation of the Earth.

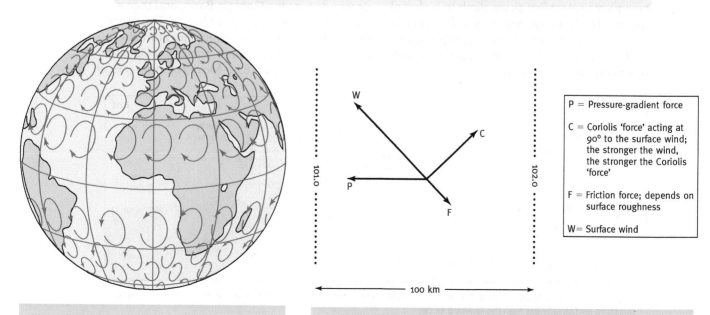

P = Pressure-gradient force

C = Coriolis 'force' acting at 90° to the surface wind; the stronger the wind, the stronger the Coriolis 'force'

F = Friction force; depends on surface roughness

W = Surface wind

Figure 8.5 The Coriolis force decreases towards the Equator and is greatest at the poles.

Figure 8.6 Wind flow in the area between two isobars in the Northern Hemisphere.

Perspectives on the Human Environment

Air Pressure and Wind in Our Daily Lives

We all bear the weight of the atmosphere pressing down on us. At sea level, the air pressure can be from 9 to 18 metric tons, depending on our size. Like the deep-sea creatures who live their entire lives with the weight of hundreds of metres of water above them, we have adapted to functioning and moving efficiently in our particular environmental pressure zone. Only a sharp change—such as a Prince Edward Island sea-level flatlander taking a vacation trip high in British Columbia's Rocky Mountains—reminds us of our adjustment to, and dependence on, a specific atmospheric environment. Two factors influence this sensitivity to altitude.

The first factor is the density of air molecules, particularly oxygen, at any altitude. At higher elevations the air is 'thinner'; that is, there is more space between the oxygen molecules, and consequently there are fewer of them in any given air space. We have to do more breathing to get the oxygen necessary to maintain our activity levels. When the Olympic Games were held in Mexico City in 1968, the low density of oxygen at that elevation (2240 m) was a decisive factor in the unimpressive competition times recorded by most of the participating athletes.

The second factor is the response of our internal organs to changes in atmospheric pressure. Our ears may react first as we climb to higher elevations. The 'pop' we hear is actually the clearing of a tiny tube that allows pressure between the inner and middle ear to equalize, thereby preventing our eardrums from rupturing. At very high altitudes we travel in pressurized aircraft. Astronauts also use pressurized cabins, and when they leave their vehicles for walks in atmosphere-less space, they require spacesuits to maintain a safe pressurized (and breathing) environment.

Winds play a constant role in our lives as well because they are a major element of local weather and climate. In coastal areas or on islands, atmospheric conditions can vary considerably over short distances. Oceanfront zones facing the direction of oncoming wind experience more air movement, cloudiness, and moisture than nearby locations protected from this airflow by hills or mountains. Places exposed to wind are called **windward** locations; areas in the 'shadow' of protective topographic barriers are known as **leeward** locations.

The west coast of Canada provides an excellent illustration of these differences. The climates of Vancouver Island in the region of Victoria and of the city of Vancouver are distinctly different. As wind rises over the Olympic Mountains and the ridge of hills and mountains over Vancouver Island, the air cools and moisture condenses. As the air descends on the leeward (east) side of the ranges, it warms and clouds dissipate, resulting in less precipitation. The city of Vancouver is located at the base of the Coast Range. Air flows over the Olympic Range and Vancouver Island, descends over the Georgia Basin, and then rises again to flow over the Coast Range. The second rise squeezes more precipitation from the air and gives Vancouver more annual precipitation than Victoria (Figure 8.7). Moving further inland

LINK

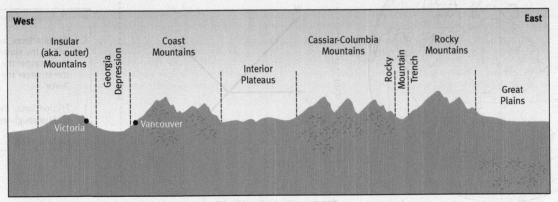

Figure 8.7   West coast of British Columbia, in profile. The windward slope facing the Pacific experiences more moisture and cloudiness than the leeward slope.

to Kamloops (258 km from the Pacific Ocean), one finds an even greater extreme. Movement over the Coastal Mountain barrier further condenses water vapour from the moist Westerlies, causing the area that extends up the Thompson River Valley to be one of the driest in southern Canada. The climate in this region is semi-arid, almost desert.

At another place and time, a similar windward/leeward relationship helped shape the locational pattern of the textile industry in nineteenth-century Britain. West of England's 'backbone' of the Pennine Mountains, in Lancashire, the humid air transported in from the Atlantic Ocean by westerly winds was ideal for cotton-textile manufacturing. Woollen-textile manufacturing, however, required a drier environment, which was readily available to the east in Yorkshire on the leeward side of the moisture-screening Pennines.

Countless other examples can be found of associations between wind and human activities. As we note in Unit 7, the horizontal flushing effects of wind are vital to maintaining acceptable air quality in urban areas, where large quantities of pollutants are dumped into the local atmosphere. Many outdoor sporting events are affected by wind conditions during games. For example, certain baseball stadiums are infamous for their unpredictable wind currents. San Francisco's now retired Candlestick Park (located in the lee of the peninsula alongside the Bay) was notorious in this regard; and in the 'Windy City' of Chicago, Cubs games are constantly subject to wind influences at venerable Wrigley Field. Canadian football fans will be aware of the potential problems at the Saskatchewan Roughriders' Taylor Field. Some CFL players say it is the worst place to kick because of the often strong and unpredictable winds.

The reinforcing effects of wind on cold winter temperatures continue to be an unpleasant fact of life. To give us a precise idea of how cold we would feel under given combinations of wind speed and air temperature, scientists have developed the **wind chill temperature (WCT) index**, which is displayed in Table 8.1. Although it does not take into account evaporative heat loss and the amount of protective clothing we wear, this index is closely related to the occurrence of frostbite. The WCT index, therefore, applies mainly to sensible heat loss. It is also based on the latest research findings and was introduced in late 2001 to replace an older, less precise index. The new wind-chill index approximates how the temperature of the human skin (especially the face) changes with various temperature and wind conditions. The index was verified at a Department

Table 8.1 Wind Chill Temperature Index

Temperature (°C)

T air	5	0	−5	−10	−15	−20	−25	−30	−35	−40	−45	−50
5	4	−2	−7	−13	−19	−24	−30	−36	−41	−47	−53	−58
10	3	−3	−9	−15	−21	−27	−33	−39	−45	−51	−57	−63
15	2	−4	−11	−17	−23	−29	−35	−41	−48	−54	−60	−66
20	1	−5	−12	−18	−24	−30	−37	−43	−49	−56	−62	−68
25	1	−6	−12	−19	−25	−32	−38	−44	−51	−57	−64	−70
30	0	−6	−13	−20	−26	−33	−39	−46	−52	−59	−65	−72
35	0	−7	−14	−20	−27	−33	−40	−47	−53	−60	−66	−73
40	−1	−7	−14	−21	−27	−34	−41	−48	−54	−61	−68	−74
45	−1	−8	−15	−21	−28	−35	−42	−48	−55	−62	−69	−75
50	−1	−8	−15	−22	−29	−35	−42	−49	−56	−63	−69	−76
55	−2	−8	−15	−22	−29	−36	−43	−50	−57	−63	−70	−77
60	−2	−9	−16	−23	−30	−36	−43	−50	−57	−64	−71	−78
65	−2	−9	−16	−23	−30	−37	−44	−51	−58	−65	−72	−79
70	−2	−9	−16	−23	−30	−37	−44	−51	−58	−65	−72	−80
75	−3	−10	−17	−24	−31	−38	−45	−52	−59	−66	−73	−80
80	−3	−10	−17	−24	−31	−38	−45	−52	−60	−67	−74	−81

V10 (km/h)

☐ Low risk of frostbite for most people

☐ Increasing risk of frostbite for most people in 10 to 30 minutes of exposure

☐ High risk for most people in 5 to 10 minutes of exposure

☐ High risk for most people in 2 to 5 minutes of exposure

☐ High risk for most people in 2 minutes of exposure or less

Frostbite Guide

Source: Environment Canada, 10 June 2004. (This website URL is given at end of this 'Perspectives' box).

of Defence lab in Toronto when 12 volunteers (six men and six women) underwent clinical trials in a refrigerated wind tunnel. Wind chill can have serious effects on the human body, especially as temperatures fall below approximately 17°C. According to Statistics Canada, 111 Canadians died in 1997 from the effects of cold weather. The coldest wind chill ever recorded in Canada was at Pelly Bay, Nunavut, on 13 January 1975. Fifty-six km/h winds made the temperature of –51°C feel closer to –92°C! Additional information, including a wind chill calculator for any given temperature and wind speed, can be found at <www.msc.ec.gc.ca/education/windchill/index_e.cfm>.

Large- and Smaller-Scale Wind Systems

Except for local winds (which affect only relatively small areas) and those near the Equator, the wind never blows in a straight path from an area of higher pressure to an area of lower pressure. Once motion begins, the pressure-gradient, Coriolis, and frictional forces come into play and heavily influence the direction of windflow.

Geostrophic Winds

Once a molecule of air starts moving under the influence of a pressure-gradient force, the Coriolis force deflects it to the right if it is in the Northern Hemisphere. Figure 8.8 diagrams the path that results: eventually, the pressure-gradient force and the Coriolis force acting on the wind balance each other out. The resultant wind, called a **geostrophic wind**, follows a relatively straight path that minimizes deflection. Geostrophic windflow is common in the 'free' atmosphere, that is, above the contact layer where friction with the surface occurs. Because of the balancing of forces, a geostrophic wind always flows *parallel* to the **isobars**—lines that join points of equal atmospheric pressure (Figure 8.8). If we have a map showing the distribution of atmospheric pressure well above the surface, we can get a rather good idea of where these winds are blowing (see Unit 15). We can, moreover, predict the wind speed if we also know the pressure-gradient force, the air density, and the latitude (which determines the strength of the Coriolis force; see Figures 8.4 and 8.5).

Frictional Surface Winds

Near the surface of the Earth, below an elevation of about 1000 m, frictional force comes into play and disrupts the balance represented by the geostrophic wind. Friction both reduces the speed and alters the direction of a geostrophic wind. The frictional force acts to cause the pressure-gradient force to overpower the Coriolis force, so that the (no-longer-geostrophic) wind at the surface blows *across* the isobars instead of parallel to them. This produces a flow of air out of high-pressure areas and into low-pressure areas, but at an angle to the isobars rather than straight across them.

Since surface pressure systems are often roughly circular when viewed from above, we can deduce the general circulation around cells of low and high pressure (Figure 8.9). Surface winds converge towards a **cyclone** (a low-pressure cell—**L** in Figure 8.9A); this converging air has to go somewhere, so it rises vertically in the centre of the low-pressure cell. The reverse is true in the centre of an **anticyclone** (a high-pressure cell—**H** in Figure 8.9B); diverging air moves outward and draws air down in the centre of the high-pressure cell (see also Figure 8.3). Thus, cyclones are associated with *rising air* at their centres, and anticyclones are associated with *subsiding air* at their centres. This simple vertical motion produces very different weather associated with each type of pressure system.

Local Wind Systems

Although one cannot overlook the forces outlined above, when attention is focused on small-scale airflows, local wind systems are often more significant in day-to-day weather because they respond to much more subtle variations in atmospheric pressure than are depicted in Figure 8.9. Moreover, because smaller distances are involved, the effect of the Coriolis force usually can be disregarded. A number of common local wind systems serve to illustrate how topography and surface type can influence the pressure gradient and its resultant windflow.

LINK

Sea/Land Breeze Systems

In coastal zones and on islands, two different surface types are in close proximity—land and water. As we have noted before, land surfaces and water bodies display sharply

LINK

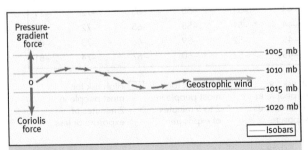

Figure 8.8 Formation of a geostrophic wind in the Northern Hemisphere, looking directly down towards the surface.

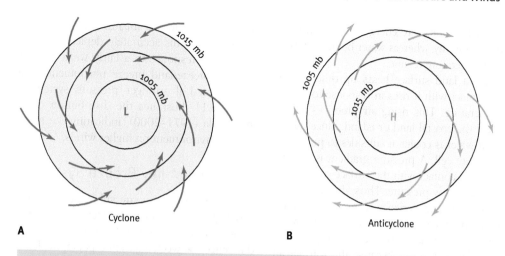

A   B

Figure 8.9 Air circulation patterns associated with a cyclonic low-pressure cell (A) and an anticyclon-ic high-pressure cell (B) in the Northern Hemisphere. In the Southern Hemisphere the windflows move in the opposite direction (clockwise toward cyclones and counterclockwise away from anticyclones).

Canadian Geographers in the Field

'*This photo shows* Nothofagus, *near Harberton, Tierra del Fuego, Argentina.* Nothofagus *is the only tree genus present in Tierra del Fuego. The forms of the tree vary greatly with the local climate conditions that they are exposed to, including temperature, snow loading, and prevailing wind speed and direction. This tree was shaped by the prevailing westerly winds in southern Tierra del Fuego, causing it to grow eastward. In the local Spanish vernacular, these are referred to as "flag trees". By sampling the rings of the tree using a small-diameter borer (which doesn't harm it), the changing climate conditions during the lifetime of the tree can be studied.*'

Norm Catto is Professor of Geography, Memorial University of Newfoundland.

contrasting thermal responses to energy input. Land surfaces heat and cool rapidly, whereas water bodies exhibit a more moderate temperature regime.

During the day a land surface heats up quickly, and the air layer in contact with it rises in response to the increased air temperature. This rising air produces a low-pressure cell over the coastal land or island. Since the air over the adjacent water is cooler, it subsides to produce a surface high-pressure cell. A pressure gradient is thereby produced, and air in contact with the surface now moves from high pressure to low pressure. Thus, during the day, shore-zone areas generally experience air moving from water to land—a **sea breeze** (Figure 8.10A). At night, when the temperature above the land surface has dropped sufficiently, the circulation reverses because the warmer air (and lower pressure) is over the water, resulting in air moving from land to water—a **land breeze** (Figure 8.10B).

Note that when generated, sea and land breezes produce a circulation cell composed of the surface breeze, rising and subsiding air associated with the lower- and higher-pressure areas, respectively, and an airflow aloft in the direction opposite to that of the surface (Figure 8.10). Although it modifies the wind and temperature conditions at the coast, the effect of this circulation diminishes rapidly as one moves inland. Note also that we use the word *breeze*. This accurately depicts a rather gentle circulation in response to a fairly weak pressure gradient. The sea breeze/land breeze phenomenon can easily be overpowered if stronger pressure systems are nearby. Figure 8.11 illustrates the distribution of wind speeds in Canada (1971–2000), indicating the influence of the coastal environment on higher winds.

Mountain/Valley Breeze Systems

Mountain slopes, too, are subject to the reversal of day and night local circulation systems. This wind circulation is also thermal, meaning that it is driven by temperature differences between adjacent topographic features. During the day, mountain terrain facing the Sun tends to heat up more rapidly than do shadowed, surrounding slopes. This causes low pressure to develop, spawning an upsloping *valley breeze*. At night, greater radiative loss from the mountain slopes cools them more sharply, high pressure develops, and a downsloping *mountain breeze* results. Figure 8.12 shows the operation of this type of oscillating, diurnal wind system in a highland valley that gently rises away from the front of the diagram.

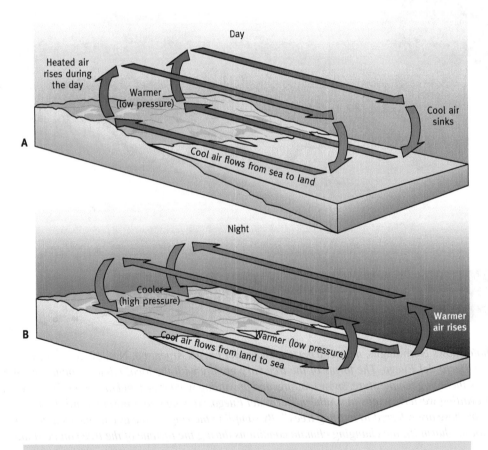

Figure 8.10 Sea breeze/land breeze local air circulation systems. These reversing, cell-like airflows develop in response to pressure differentials associated with day/night temperature variations at the land and water surfaces.

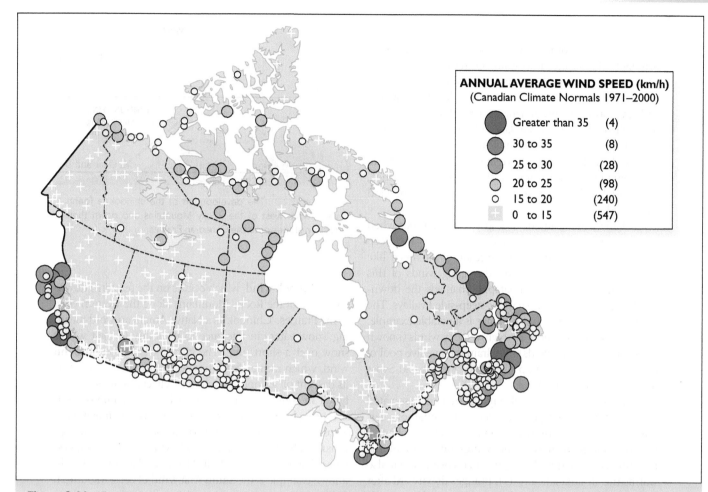

Figure 8.11   The distribution of wind speeds in Canada (1971–2000), indicating the influence of the coastal environment on higher winds.

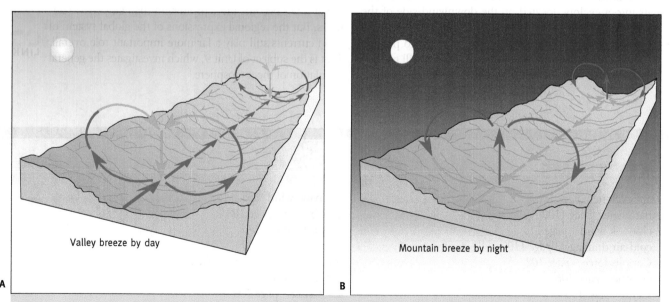

Figure 8.12   Formation of valley (daytime) and mountain (nighttime) breezes. Red arrows represent warm winds; blue arrows indicate colder winds.

Other Local Wind Systems

Another category of local wind systems involves **cold-air drainage**, the steady downward oozing of heavy, dense, cold air along steep slopes under the influence of gravity. The winds that result are known as **katabatic winds** and are especially prominent under calm, clear conditions where the edges of highlands plunge sharply towards lower-lying terrain. These winds are fed by large pools of very cold air that collect above highland zones. They are also common around major ice sheets, such as the huge, continental-scale glaciers that cover most of Antarctica and Greenland.

Katabatic winds can attain destructive intensities when the regional windflow steers the cold air over the steep edges of uplands, producing a cascade of air much like water in a waterfall. The most damaging winds of this type occur where local topography channels the downward surge of cold air into narrow, steep-sided valleys. The Rhône Valley of southeastern France is a notable example: each winter it experiences icy, high-velocity winds (known locally as the *mistral* winds) that drain the massive pool of cold air that develops atop the snowy French and Swiss Alps to the valley's northeast.

Yet another type of local wind system is associated with the forced passage of air across mountainous terrain (which is discussed in detail in Unit 12). Briefly, this transmontane movement wrings out most of the moisture contained in the original mass of air, and it also warms the air adiabatically as it plunges downward after its passage across the upland. Thus, the area that extends away from the base of the mountain's backslope experiences dry and relatively warm winds, which taper off with increasing distance from the highland. Occasionally such winds can exceed hurricane-force intensity (greater than 120 km/h). This happens when they are reinforced by an anticyclone upwind from the mountains that feeds air into a cyclone located on the downwind side of the upland.

Surprisingly, atmospheric scientists have yet to provide a generic name for such wind systems, which still go only by their local names. The best-known Canadian example

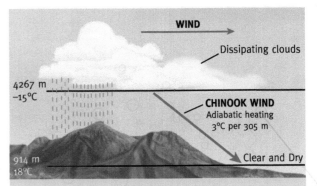

Figure 8.13 The development of the chinook, a foehn wind, from west of the Rocky Mountains and down their eastern slopes onto the Canadian Prairies.

is the **chinook wind**, which occurs on the (eastern) downwind side of the Rocky Mountains along the western edge of the Prairies. 'Chinook' is a Native American word meaning 'snow eater', in reference to its ability to melt winter snow over a short time. The chinook is a type of **foehn** wind, which means that it has been warmed and dried by its descent off a slope. The chinook effects are most strongly felt in southwestern Alberta, where the chinooks funnel through the Crowsnest Pass, subsequently moving out across southern Alberta and Saskatchewan. There are approximately 30 chinook days each winter in the Crowsnest Pass, 25 in Calgary, and 20 in Medicine Hat. Another well-known example is the **Santa Ana wind** of coastal southern California, an occasional hot, dry airflow whose unpleasantness is heightened by the downward funnelling of this wind from the high inland desert (where it is generated by an anticyclone) through narrow passes in the mountains that line the coast. Such winds can also exacerbate wildfires during the dry season.

In many locations, as we have just seen, local winds can at times become more prominent than larger-scale airflows. But the regional expressions of the global system of wind currents still play a far more important role overall. That is the subject of Unit 9, which investigates the general circulation of the atmosphere.

LINK

KEY TERMS

anticyclone   *page 106*
barometer   *page 100*
chinook wind   *page 110*
cold-air drainage   *page 110*
Coriolis force   *page 102*
cyclone   *page 106*
foehn   *page 110*
frictional force   *page 102*
geostrophic wind   *page 106*
isobar   *page 106*

katabatic wind   *page 110*
land breeze   *page 108*
leeward   *page 104*
pressure   *page 100*
pressure-gradient force   *page 101*
Santa Ana wind   *page 110*
sea breeze   *page 108*
wind   *page 100*
wind chill temperature (WCT) index   *page 105*
windward   *page 104*

REVIEW QUESTIONS

1. Define atmospheric pressure, and describe its vertical structuring within the atmospheric column.

2. What are the forces that determine wind speed and direction?

3. Define the Coriolis force and describe its operations in both the Northern and Southern Hemispheres.

4. What is a geostrophic wind? Where does it occur and why?

5. Describe the air circulation patterns associated with cyclones and anticyclones.

6. Describe the operation of the sea breeze/land breeze local wind system.

REFERENCES AND FURTHER READINGS

Atkinson, B.W. 1981. *Meso-Scale Atmospheric Circulations*. New York: Academic Press.

CBC News. 2004. 'Wind Chill', 20 Jan. At: <www.cbc.ca/news/background/forcesofnature/windchill.htm>.

Dutton, J.A. 1976. *The Ceaseless Wind: An Introduction to the Theory of Atmospheric Motion*. New York: McGraw-Hill.

———. 1995. *Dynamics of Atmospheric Motion*. New York: Dover.

Edinger, J.G. 1967. *Watching for the Wind*. Garden City, NY: Doubleday.

Gedzelman, S.D. 1980. *The Science and Wonders of the Atmosphere*. New York: Wiley, ch. 15.

Glanz, J. 2001. 'Wind Chill: Cheer Up, It Used to Be Even Colder', *New York Times*, 25 Nov., WK3.

Gross, J. 1988. 'When the Fog Rolls In, the Bay Area Hears Music', *New York Times*, 22 June, 10.

Hidy, G.M. 1967. *The Winds*. New York: Van Nostrand-Reinhold.

Middleton, W.K. 1964. *The History of the Barometer*. Baltimore: Johns Hopkins Univ. Press.

New York Times. 1993. 'The Santa Ana Winds', 29 Oct., A10.

Palmén, E., and C.W. Newton. *Atmospheric Circulation Systems*. New York: Academic Press.

Scientific American. 1996. 'Where the Wind Blows' (Dec.): 44.

Simpson, J.E. 1994. *Sea Breeze and Local Winds*. New York: Cambridge Univ. Press.

Whiteman, C.D. 2000. *Mountain Meteorology: Fundamentals and Applications*. New York: Oxford Univ. Press.

 ## WEB RESOURCES

www.ace.mmu.ac.uk/eae/ General description of atmospheric pressure measurement, global movement of air masses, and links to other weather-related topics.

www.on.ec.gc.ca/weather/winners/intro-e.html How does your city or town rank among the rainiest, sunniest, windiest, or snowiest?

www.windatlas.ca/en/index.php Environment Canada's Canadian Wind Energy Atlas.

Unit 9

Circulation Patterns of the Atmosphere

Objectives

- To develop a simple model of the global atmospheric circulation.

- To discuss the pressure systems and wind belts that constitute that model circulation and the complications that arise when the model is compared to the actual atmospheric circulation.

- To introduce the basic workings of the upper atmosphere's circulation.

Unit 8 introduced the basic causes of air movements in the atmosphere. In this unit focus is placed on the global air currents that constitute the general atmospheric circulation. In the short run these air currents carry along, and to a certain extent cause, the weather systems that affect us daily. The longer-term operation of this general circulation, in conjunction with atmospheric energy flows, produces the climates of the Earth.

To be sure, the workings of the general atmospheric circulation are very complex, and scientists still do not understand the exact nature of some of these circulation features. Nonetheless, we can deduce many of these features using our knowledge of the basic causes of air movement, which can be used to develop a model to describe and explain the major processes. Let us begin by considering the atmosphere's near-surface circulation, and then make some observations regarding windflow in the upper atmosphere.

Causes of Atmospheric Circulation

Two basic factors explain the circulation of air in the atmosphere: (1) the Earth receives an unequal amount of heat energy at different latitudes, and (2) it rotates on its axis. If we examine the amount of incoming and outgoing radiation by latitude, as shown in Figure 9.1 for the Northern Hemisphere (the Southern Hemisphere's general pattern is identical), we find a marked surplus of net radiation between the Equator and the 35th parallel. At latitudes poleward of 35°N, outgoing radiation exceeds incoming radiation. The main reason for this is that rays of energy from the Sun strike the Earth's surface at higher angles, and therefore at greater intensity, in the lower latitudes than

in the higher latitudes (see Figure 4.12). As a result, the Equator receives about two and one-half times as much annual solar radiation as the poles do.

If this latitudinal imbalance of energy were not somehow balanced, the low-latitude regions would be continually heating up and the polar regions cooling down. Energy, in the form of heat, is transferred towards the poles, and the amount of heat transferred by atmospheric circulation (and to a much lesser extent, oceanic circulation) is also indicated in Figure 9.1. We can see from the heat-transfer curve that the maximum transfer occurs in the middle latitudes. Consequently, the weather at these latitudes is characterized by frequent north–south movements of air masses.

Imagine for a moment that the Earth is stationary and that there are no thermal differences between landmasses and oceans. Under these circumstances, heat transfer could occur by a simple cellular movement: warm air would rise at low latitudes, travel toward the poles at a high altitude, descend as it cools, and then return to the low latitudes as a surface wind. This type of circulation, however, is prohibited by the rotation of the Earth and the differing energy-absorbing characteristics of land and water.

A Model of the Surface Circulation

Unit 8 illustrated the probable arrangement of the global atmospheric circulation on a uniform, non-rotating Earth: a single, girdling cell of low pressure around the Equator, where air would rise, and a cell of high pressure at each pole, where air would subside. The surface winds on such a planet would be northerly in the Northern Hemisphere and southerly in the Southern Hemisphere, moving directly

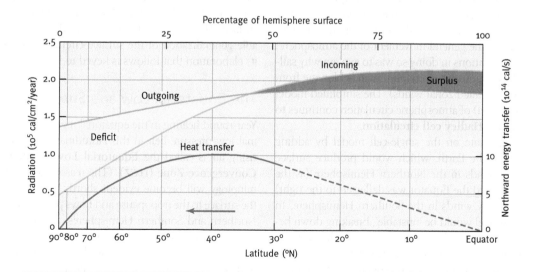

Figure 9.1 Latitudinal radiation balance averaged over all Northern Hemisphere longitudes and the consequent poleward transfer of heat.

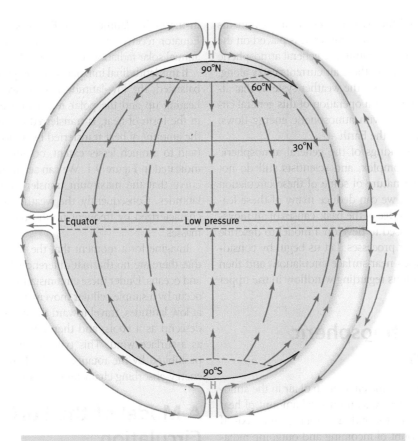

90°N

60°N

30°N

Equator — — — — — — Low pressure — — — — — —

90°S

Figure 9.2 Hypothetical atmospheric circulation on a featureless, non-rotating Earth. Polar high pressure and equatorial low pressure would result in northerly surface winds in the Northern Hemisphere and southerly surface winds in the Southern Hemisphere. The rotation of the Earth, the variation in the latitude of the vertical Sun position, and land/water heating contrasts at the surface prevent this simple general circulation from developing.

from high pressure to low pressure across the pressure gradient, as shown in Figure 9.2. This simplified model of atmospheric circulation is attributed to George Hadley (1685–1768), who proposed the simple circulation pattern to describe the general movement of the atmosphere. One of his motivations in doing so was to explain why sailors in the lower latitudes often found winds blowing from east to west (so-called zonal winds). The simplified model (single-cell model) of atmospheric circulation continues to be referred to as **Hadley cell circulation**.

We can elaborate on the single-cell model by adding the rotation of the Earth, which would produce surface northeasterly winds in the Northern Hemisphere (as the air moving toward the Equator was deflected to the right) and southeasterly winds in the Southern Hemisphere. In fact, such a model would be 'unstable', breaking down because of one simple problem: achievement of this scenario would require slowing down the Earth's rate of spin, since everywhere on the planet the atmosphere would be moving *against* the direction of Earth rotation. As it turns out, there are areas of low pressure at the Equator and high pressure at the poles, but the situation in the mid-latitudes is more complex.

We will introduce the actual effects of rotation on our hypothetical planet but, for the present, will ignore seasonal heating differences and the land/water contrast at the surface. The model that results is an idealized but reasonable generalization of the surface circulation pattern, and its elaboration that follows is keyed to Figure 9.3.

The Equatorial Low and Subtropical High

Year-round heating in the equatorial region produces a thermal low-pressure belt in this latitudinal zone. That belt of rising air is called the **Equatorial Low** or **Inter-Tropical Convergence Zone** (**ITCZ**). (The reason for this latter terminology will become evident shortly.) The air rises from the surface to the tropopause and flows poleward in both the Northern and Southern Hemispheres. Air cools as it rises, causing clouds to develop and favouring regions throughout these equatorial and lower latitudes with heavy precipitation. The ITCZ is the rainiest latitudinal region in the world.

Much of this cooled, poleward-moving air descends at approximately latitudes 30°N and 30°S. (Subsidence here is most likely associated with the 'piling up' of air aloft because of its increased westerly flow, a directional curvature

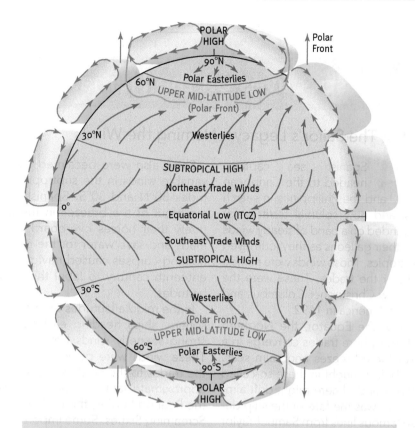

Figure 9.3 Idealized version of the global atmospheric circulation pattern showing the major pressure belts, the cell-like airflows that develop between them, and the Coriolis deflection of surface winds.

caused by the strengthening Coriolis force; see Figure 8.5.) The descending air produces a belt of high pressure at the surface near both these latitudes; the two high-pressure belts, therefore, are termed the **Subtropical Highs**. Because air is descending in these regions, cloud formation is suppressed, and desert conditions are common in the subtropical latitudes.

The Trade Winds and the Westerlies

Remembering that surface airflows diverge out of areas of high pressure, we can easily deduce the nature of the wind movement, both equatorward and poleward, of this high-pressure belt. Air returning towards the Equator in the Northern Hemisphere is deflected to the right and forms a belt of northeasterly winds, called the **Northeast Trades** (see 'Perspectives' box). Air returning towards the Equator from the Subtropical High in the Southern Hemisphere is deflected to its left to form the **Southeast Trades**. As you can see in Figure 9.3, these two wind belts converge—hence the rationale for calling this low-latitude area the *Inter-Tropical Convergence Zone*.

Air moving poleward from the two Subtropical Highs acquires the appropriate Coriolis deflection and forms two belts of generally west-to-east–flowing winds (one in the Northern Hemisphere, one in the Southern Hemisphere) known as the **Westerlies**. These prevailing winds form broad mid-latitude belts from about 30 to 60°N and 30 to 60°S.

The Polar High, Polar Easterlies, and Polar Front

Windflows emanate from the **Polar Highs**, large cells of high pressure centred over each pole. Here, air moving towards the Equator is sharply deflected to become the **Polar Easterlies**. You can see in Figure 9.3 that the Polar Easterlies flowing out of the Polar Highs will meet the **Westerlies** flowing out of the Subtropical Highs.

The atmospheric boundary along which these wind systems converge is called the **Polar Front**. Along the Polar Front in each hemisphere (located equatorward of 60°N and 60°S, respectively), the warmer air from the Subtropical High is forced to rise over the colder, denser polar air. This rising air produces a belt of low pressure at the surface called the **Upper Mid-latitude Low**.

Overall, the now completed model of the surface circulation for a uniform, rotating planet has seven pressure features (an Equatorial Low, two Subtropical Highs, two Upper Mid-latitude Lows, and two Polar Highs) and six intervening wind belts (the Northeast and Southeast Trades plus the Westerlies and Polar Easterlies of each hemisphere). Note that the circulation patterns of the Northern and Southern Hemispheres are identical except for the opposite Coriolis deflection (Figure 9.3).

Perspectives on the Human Environment

The Sailor's Legacy—Naming the Winds

Spanish sea captains headed to the Caribbean and the Philippines in search of gold, spices, and new colonial territory for Spain. They depended on a band of steady winds to fill the sails of their galleons as they journeyed westward in the tropics. Those winds were named the trade winds, or the trades. These were the winds that first blew Christopher Columbus and his flotilla to North America in 1492.

In the vicinity of the Equator, the Northern and Southern Hemisphere trades converge in a zone of unpredictable breezes and calm seas. Sailors dreaded being caught in these so-called **doldrums**. A ship stranded here might drift aimlessly for days. That was the fate of the ship described in these famous lines from Samuel Taylor Coleridge's 'The Rime of the Ancient Mariner':

Day after day, day after day,
We stuck, nor breath nor motion;
As idle as a painted ship
Upon a painted ocean.

Ships also were becalmed by the light and variable winds in the subtropics at about latitudes 30°N and 30°S. Spanish explorers who ran afoul of the breezes in these hot regions threw their horses overboard to lighten their loads and save water for the crew. The trail of floating corpses caused navigators of the seventeenth century to label this zone the horse latitudes.

In the middle latitudes of the Southern Hemisphere, ships heading eastward followed the strong westerly winds between 40 and 60°S. These winds were powerful but stormier than the trades to the north; so, depending on their approximate latitude, they became known as the Roaring Forties, the Furious Fifties, and the Screaming Sixties. Some important terminology that is applied to wind belts dates from the early days of transoceanic sailing.

The Actual Surface Circulation Pattern

In contrast to the idealized pattern of the surface circulation model, the actual pattern (Figure 9.4) is considerably more complex because it incorporates two influences ignored in the model. Remember that the location of maximum solar heating shifts throughout the year as the latitude of the (noonday) vertical Sun changes from 23½°N at the Northern Hemisphere's summer solstice to 23½°S at its winter solstice. Of great significance is that the continents respond more dramatically to this latitudinal variation in heating than do the oceans (as we note in Unit 7). This has the effect of producing individual pressure cells (which we can call *semi-permanent highs and lows*) rather than uniform, globe-girdling belts of low and high pressure. Moreover, because the Northern Hemisphere contains two large landmasses whereas the Southern Hemisphere is mostly water, the two hemispheres exhibit somewhat different atmospheric circulations. Nonetheless, they are similar enough to be considered together.

Climates are governed by complex interactions between atmospheric circulations and the movement and properties of oceanic waters. The Southern Oscillation, a variable pressure gradient in the equatorial zone of the Pacific Ocean, influences the formation and intensity of *El Niños* (both are discussed in Unit 10). Other pressure systems elsewhere also affect climate and weather. To understand these links, one must examine the prevailing global pressure patterns and then look more closely at embedded systems that govern climate as well as weather across the planet.

The Equatorial Low (ITCZ)

Careful inspection of Figure 9.4 reveals the following modifications to the simplified picture seen in Figure 9.3. The Equatorial Low, or ITCZ, migrates into the 'summer' hemisphere (the Northern Hemisphere during July, the Southern Hemisphere during January), a shift most prominent over landmasses. Note that in July (Figure 9.4B), the Equatorial Low is located nearly 25 degrees north of the Equator in the vicinity of southern Asia. But

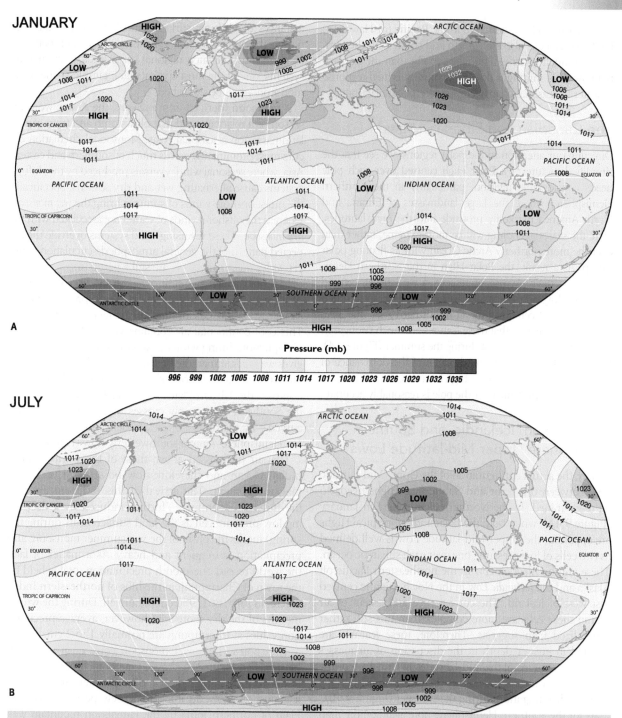

Figure 9.4 Global mean surface pressure patterns in January (A) and July (B). Maps adapted from *Goode's World Atlas*, 19th edition. © 1995 by Rand McNally R.L.

ITCZ migration is subdued over oceanic areas because bodies of water are much slower to respond to seasonal changes in solar energy input received at the surface. Note, too, that the migration of the Equatorial Low into the Southern Hemisphere in January (Figure 9.4A) is far less pronounced. This makes sense because there are fewer large landmasses in the tropics south of the Equator; the Equatorial Low is, however, considerably displaced poleward over Africa and Australia, and to a lesser extent above South America.

The Bermuda and Pacific Highs

In contrast to our model's Subtropical High pressure belts (straddling 30°N and 30°S), the actual semi-permanent highs at these latitudes are more cellular. There are five such cells of semi-permanent high pressure on the map, one above each subtropical ocean (Figure 9.4). These cells are most evident in the 'summer' hemisphere. In the Northern Hemisphere, the North Atlantic's high-pressure cell is called the **Bermuda** (or Azores [Azoric]) **High**, and the

North Pacific cell is referred to as the **Pacific** (or Hawaiian) **High**. These cells also shift north and south with the Sun, but to a much lesser extent, latitudinally, than the Equatorial Low. This shifting is due to the more subdued response of water to seasonal changes in the receipt of solar energy.

The Canadian and Siberian Highs

Directing our attention to the polar regions, we see that the simplified picture of a Polar High centred over each pole needs considerable revision, particularly in the Northern Hemisphere, where the large landmasses of Eurasia and North America markedly protrude into the high latitudes. Here the seasonal cooling will be most extreme, rather than over the more northerly Arctic Ocean with its floating polar icecap. As a result, the Polar High in the Northern Hemisphere is actually two separate cells, a weaker cell centred above northwestern Canada (the *Canadian High*) and a much more powerful cell covering all of northern Asia (the *Siberian High*). Note, too, that these features are much stronger in winter and at their weakest during the summer (Figure 9.4). In the Southern Hemisphere, because of the dominance of the Antarctic landmass in the high latitudes, the model's single cell of high pressure over the pole is reasonably accurate.

The Aleutian, Icelandic, and Southern Hemisphere Upper Mid-latitude Lows

Finally, the actual configuration of the Upper Mid-latitude Low between the Polar and Subtropical Highs needs to be re-examined. In the Northern Hemisphere in January (Figure 9.4A), when both the Polar and Subtropical Highs are apparent, the Upper Mid-latitude Low is well defined as two cells of low pressure, one over each subarctic ocean. These are the *Aleutian Low* in the northeastern Pacific off Alaska and the *Icelandic Low* in the North Atlantic centred just west of Iceland. The convergence and ascent of air within these cells are more complex than this still rather generalized map suggests. Therefore, these features are covered in greater depth in the discussion of air masses and storm systems of the mid-latitudes in Unit 13. For the time being we also note that these cells, too, weaken to the point of disintegration during the summer (Figure 9.4B).

LINK

As for the Southern Hemisphere, note again on the map that the Upper Mid-latitude Low is evident in both winter and summer. The persistence of the Polar High over Antarctica makes this possible. Moreover, the absence of landmasses in this subpolar latitudinal zone causes the Upper Mid-latitude Low to remain beltlike rather than forming distinct cells over each ocean.

Secondary Surface Circulation: Monsoonal Windflows

The global scheme of wind belts and semi-permanent pressure cells we have just described constitutes the **general circulation** (or *primary circulation*) system of the atmosphere. At a more localized scale, there are countless instances of 'shifting' surface wind belts that create pronounced winter/summer contrasts in weather patterns. Here, to illustrate such regional (or *secondary*) circulation systems, one of the most spectacular examples—the Asian monsoon—will be described.

A **monsoon** (derived from *mawsim*, the Arabic word for season) is a regional wind that blows onto and from certain landmasses on a seasonal basis. Monsoonal circulation occurs most prominently across much of southern and eastern Asia, where seasonal wind reversals produced by the shifting systems cause alternating wet and dry seasons. Specifically, the moist onshore winds of summer bring the *wet monsoon*, whereas the offshore winds of winter are associated with the *dry monsoon*. These reversing wind systems override the expected pattern of the general atmospheric circulation—and yet, as we are about to see, are still a part of it.

In January, high pressure over the interior of southern Asia (particularly the Indian subcontinent) produces northeasterly surface winds for much of the region (Figure 9.5A). This cool continental air contains very little moisture, so precipitation during winter is at a minimum. But as spring gives way to summer, the high-pressure cell dissipates, and the ITCZ (Equatorial Low) shifts far northward to a position over the Tibetan Plateau. As a result, the airflow from the Southeast Trades now crosses the Equator and is re-curved—by the opposite Coriolis deflection of the Northern Hemisphere—into a southwesterly flow (Figure 9.5B).

This air has passed above most of the warm tropical Indian Ocean and therefore now possesses a very high moisture content. The arrival of this saturated air over the Indian subcontinent (further induced by a deepening low-pressure cell as the land surface heats during the spring) marks the onset of the wet summer monsoon, and precipitation is frequent and heavy. As a matter of fact, the world record one-month precipitation total is held by the town of Cherrapunji in the hills of northeastern India, where, in July 1861, 930 cm of rain fell. During the winter months of the dry monsoon, however, average precipitation values at Cherrapunji are normally 1 to 2 cm.

The southwestern wet monsoon consists of two main branches, as Figure 9.6 shows. One branch penetrates the Bay of Bengal to Bangladesh and northeastern India, where it is pushed westward into the densely populated Ganges Plain of northern India by the Himalayan mountain wall (Figure 9.7). A second branch to the west of the subcontinent, with a tendency to split into two airflows, arrives from the Arabian Sea arm of the Indian Ocean. The rains from both branches gradually spread across much of the subcontinent, soak the farm fields, and replenish the wells.

These wet-monsoon rains, however, are not continuous, even during the wettest of years. Once the onshore wind movement is established, they depend on the recurrence of smaller-scale low-pressure cells within the prevailing southwesterly airflow. These depressions reinforce the lifting of the moist air, and enhance the formation and continuation of rain throughout the summer months. When they fail to materialize, disastrous drought can result. Their dramatic failure in the summer of 1987 triggered one of India's worst dry spells of the past century and great crop losses.

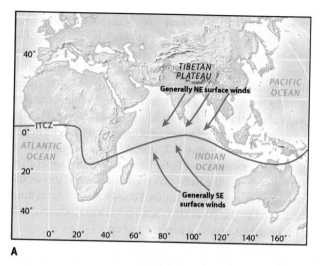
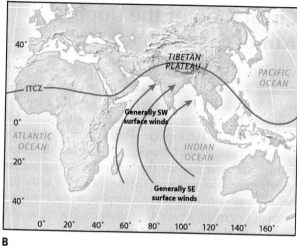

A

B

Figure 9.5 Wind reversals associated with the dry winter monsoon (A) and wet summer monsoon (B) in southern Asia. This phenomenon is usually most pronounced on the Indian subcontinent, one of the world's greatest concentrations of human settlement.

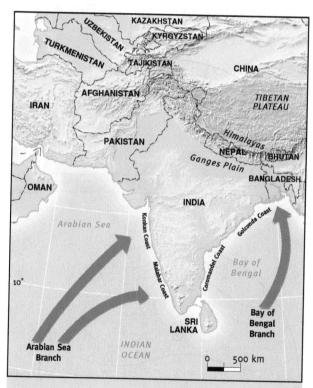

Figure 9.6 The main branches of the southwestern wet-monsoon windflow over South Asia.

Figure 9.7 One of the Earth's steepest topographic gradients links the ice-capped Himalayas (top) to the plain of the Ganges River (bottom). This gigantic mountain barrier blocks the onshore windflow of the summer monsoon, steering it westward onto the Gangetic lowland, where its torrential rains nourish one of humanity's largest and most heavily populated agricultural regions.

This peculiar South Asian monsoonal circulation also owes its identity to subtle seasonal variations in the windflows of the upper atmosphere, especially the behaviour of the tropical, subtropical, and Polar Front jet streams (which are introduced in the following section). In fact, the same is true everywhere: airflow patterns in the upper atmospheric circulation exert a decisive influence on what happens at the surface.

Circulation of the Upper Atmosphere

Windflow in the upper atmosphere is geostrophic (perpendicular to the pressure gradient, as shown in Figure 8.8), with the higher pressure on the right looking downwind in the Northern Hemisphere and on the left in the Southern Hemisphere. Furthermore, the general circulation aloft is much simpler, since we lose the effects of the land/water contrast that made the surface pattern decidedly cellular. However, the specific nature of the upper atmospheric circulation is complex, and we will not attempt to explain how it is maintained, but rather will note some relevant generalizations.

First and foremost, the upper atmospheric circulation is dominated by **zonal flow**, meaning *westerly* in its configuration. Thus the winds of the upper atmosphere generally blow from west to east throughout a broad latitudinal band in both hemispheres; essentially, windflow is westerly poleward of 15°N and 15°S. But the pressure gradient in the upper atmosphere is not uniform, and two zones of concentrated westerly flow occur in each hemisphere: one in the subtropics and one along the Polar Front. These concentrated, high-altitude, tubelike 'rivers' of air are called **jet streams**.

A cross-sectional profile of the atmosphere between the Equator and the North Pole (Figure 9.8) reveals that these two jet streams—appropriately called the *subtropical jet stream* and the *Polar Front jet stream*—are located near the altitude of the tropopause (12 to 17 km). The diagram also shows the existence of a third jet stream, the *tropical easterly jet stream*, which is a major feature of the opposite, east-to-west flow in the upper atmosphere of the equatorial zone south of 15°N. Interestingly, the tropical easterly jet stream occurs

in the Northern Hemisphere only, whereas the subtropical and Polar Front jet streams exist in both hemispheres. The two latter jet streams are instrumental in moving large quantities of heated air from the equatorial to higher latitudes. They usually flow at extremely high rates of speed (occasionally reaching 350 km/h), and can thus achieve the heat and volume transfers that could not be accomplished at the far more moderate velocities associated with the cell circulations depicted in Figure 9.3. It should also be pointed out that the subtropical and Polar Front jet streams are at their strongest during the half-year centred on winter. You would be correct in presuming that the Polar Front jet stream must be related to the Polar High semi-permanent pressure cell, but the details need not concern us here.

Another important generalization concerns the frequency of deviations from zonal windflow in the mid-latitudes, particularly above the heart of North America. For a variety of rather complicated reasons, waves develop in the upper atmospheric pressure pattern. These alternating sequences of *troughs* (areas of low pressure) and *ridges* (areas of high pressure) cause the geostrophic wind to flow northwesterly and southwesterly around them (Figure 9.9). Those deviations

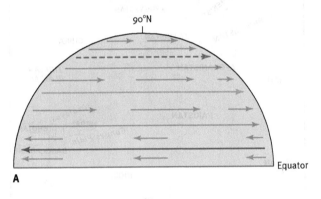

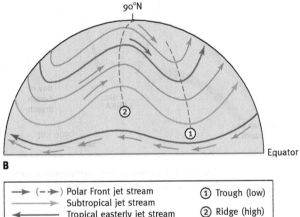

Figure 9.9 Zonal (westerly) flow dominates in the upper atmosphere of the Northern Hemisphere (A). Azonal (meridional) flow (B) is characterized by pronounced troughs and ridges, and a generally stronger Polar Front jet stream. Azonal flow promotes warm-air movement to the north beneath the ridges and cold-air movement to the south beneath the troughs.

Figure 9.8 Atmosphere of the Northern Hemisphere in cross-section, with its three jet streams highlighted.

from westerly airflow are important because they reflect substantial *meridional* (north–south) air exchange. As you are aware, the fundamental cause of atmospheric circulation is a heat imbalance between the polar and tropical regions. These periods of **azonal** (meridional) **flow** help correct that heat imbalance (Figure 9.9). It is also worth noting that episodes of pronounced azonal flow produce unusual weather for the surface areas they affect. The next time you notice an unseasonable weather event, it is likely to be a result of waves developing in the upper atmospheric pressure pattern. Together, ridges and troughs create wave-like flows of air in the upper atmosphere of mid-latitude regions. The largest of these is referred to as a long wave or **Rossby wave**. There are typically three to seven Rossby waves circulating the globe, and although they remain in relatively fixed positions, they do migrate from west to east and occasionally from east to west. They fluctuate according to the seasons as well, with higher frequencies and

strongest winds associated with their presence in winter. The features of Rossby waves can have a significant impact on our weather conditions at the surface of the Earth. They can transport warm air from the subtropics to higher latitudes and cold polar air from the high latitudes to the low latitudes, operating to modify our weather by altering the temperature based on the source region of the particular air mass that is being drawn towards a region.

In a sense, it is misleading to treat the surface and upper atmospheric pressure patterns and their resultant windflows separately because they must always be interrelated. Indeed, strong surface pressure gradients are invariably reinforced by strong upper atmospheric pressure gradients. In truth, they are both the cause and effect of each other. But keep in mind that there is another component of this cause–effect relationship: the circulation of the world ocean, which will be described in Unit 10.

KEY TERMS

azonal flow   *page 121*
Bermuda High   *page 117*
doldrums   *page 116*
Equatorial Low   *page 114*
general circulation   *page 118*
Hadley cell circulation   *page 114*
Inter-Tropical Convergence Zone (ITCZ)   *page 114*
jet stream   *page 120*
monsoon   *page 118*
Northeast Trades   *page 115*

Pacific High   *page 118*
Polar Easterlies   *page 115*
Polar Front   *page 115*
Polar High   *page 115*
Rossby waves   *page 121*
Southeast Trades   *page 115*
Subtropical High   *page 115*
Upper Mid-latitude Low   *page 115*
Westerlies   *page 115*
zonal flow   *page 120*

REVIEW QUESTIONS

1. List the seven semi-permanent pressure belts of the surface atmospheric circulation and give their approximate locations.
2. List the six wind belts that connect these semi-permanent highs and lows.
3. Discuss the shifting of these wind and pressure systems with the seasons of the year.
4. What are some of the main differences between the ideal model and the actual pattern of surface atmospheric circulation?
5. Describe the mechanisms of the monsoonal circulation of South Asia.
6. Describe the zonal circulation pattern of the upper atmosphere, its relation to the jet streams, and why azonal flow occurs.

REFERENCES AND FURTHER READINGS

Atkinson, B.W. 1981. *Meso-Scale Atmospheric Circulations*. Orlando, Fla: Academic Press.

Chang, J. 1972. *Atmospheric Circulation Systems and Climates*. Honolulu: Oriental Pub. Co.

Fein, J.S., and P.L. Stephens, eds. 1987. *Monsoons*. New York: Wiley.

James, I.N. 1994. *Introduction to Circulating Atmospheres*. New York: Cambridge Univ. Press.

Lorenz, E. 1967. *The Nature and Theory of the General Circulation of the Atmosphere*. Geneva: World Meteorological Organization.

Palmén, E., and C.W. Newton. 1969. *Atmospheric Circulation Systems: Their Structure and Physical Interpretation*. New York: Academic Press.

Perry, A.H., and J.M. Walker. 1977. *The Ocean–Atmosphere System*. London/New York: Longman.

Reiter, E.R. 1967. *Jet Streams*. Garden City, NY: Anchor/Doubleday.

Schneider, S.H., ed. 1996. *Encyclopedia of Climate and Weather*, 2 vols. New York: Oxford Univ. Press.

Webster, P.J. 1981. 'Monsoons', *Scientific American* (Aug.): 109–18.

Weisman, S.R. 1987. 'Worst Drought in Decades Hits Vast Area of India', *New York Times*, 16 Aug., 8.

Wells, N. 1997. *The Atmosphere and Ocean: A Physical Introduction*, 2nd edn. New York: Wiley.

 # WEB RESOURCES

csc.gallaudet.edu/monsoon/definition/1987-and-198802.html An animation of the 1987–8 Asian monsoon.

pubs.usgs.gov/gip/deserts/atmosphere Article relating the effects of the atmosphere on aridity, including a discussion of the major global wind belts.

www.ucar.edu/communications/quarterly/winter99/TIME.html A discussion of the general model of upper air circulation and of new models being developed by researchers.

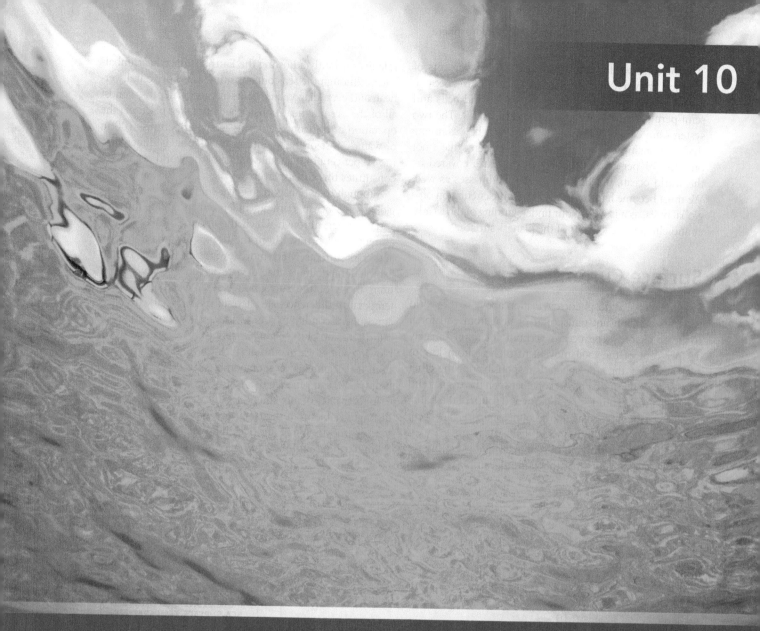

Unit 10

Hydrosphere: Circulation of the World Ocean

Objectives

- To relate the surface oceanic circulation to the general circulation of the atmosphere.

- To describe the major currents of oceanic circulation.

- To demonstrate the role of oceanic circulation in the transport of heat at the Earth's surface.

LINK

In this unit we focus on the large-scale movements of water, known as **ocean currents**, that form the oceanic counterpart to the atmospheric system of wind belts and semi-permanent pressure cells treated in Unit 9. The two systems are closely integrated, and we will be examining that relationship in some detail. Ocean currents affect not only the 71 per cent of the face of the Earth covered by the world ocean, but the continental landmasses as well. We must become familiar with the oceanic circulation on a global basis, as it is vital to our understanding of the weather and climate of each part of the planet's surface.

Surface Currents

LINK

Like the global atmospheric circulation above it, the world ocean is a significant transporter of heat from equatorial to polar regions. The oceans account for approximately 13 per cent of the total movement of heat from low to high latitudes; the atmosphere is responsible for the other 87 per cent. But in the broad zone between the tropics and the upper mid-latitudes, both north and south of the Equator, the oceans are estimated to account for up to 25 per cent of the poleward heat movement (Figure 10.1).

LINK

Specifically, it is through the circulation of water masses in large-scale currents that the world ocean plays its vital role in constantly adjusting the Earth's surface heat imbalance. Although the sea contains numerous horizontal, vertical, and even diagonal currents at various depths, almost all of the oceanic heat-transfer activity takes place via the operation of horizontal currents in the uppermost 100 m of water. Most of the attention in this unit is directed to the 10 per cent of the total volume of the world ocean that constitutes this surface layer.

Although they transport massive volumes of water, most global-scale ocean currents differ only slightly from the surface waters through which they flow. So-called 'warm' currents, which travel from the tropics towards the poles, and 'cold' currents, which move towards the Equator, usually exhibit temperatures that deviate by only a few degrees from those of the surrounding sea. Nevertheless, these temperature differences are often sufficient to markedly affect atmospheric conditions over a wide area. As demonstrated in our discussion of the *maritime effect* (p. 91), onshore winds blowing across warm currents pick up substantial moisture from the heightened evaporation of seawater, whose latent heat (p. 83) can generate rising currents of air.

In their rates of movement, too, most currents are barely distinguishable from their marine surroundings. Currents tend to move slowly and steadily, averaging only about 8 km per hour and they are called **drifts** because they lag far behind the average speeds of surface winds blowing

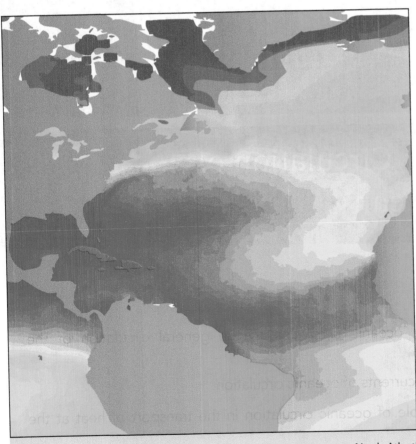
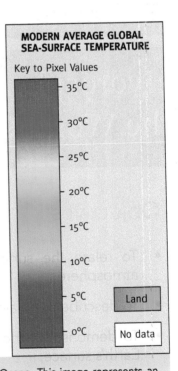

MODERN AVERAGE GLOBAL SEA-SURFACE TEMPERATURE

Key to Pixel Values

- 35°C
- 30°C
- 25°C
- 20°C
- 15°C
- 10°C
- 5°C — Land
- 0°C — No data

Figure 10.1 Average sea-surface temperature for August, western North Atlantic Ocean. This image represents an averaging of weekly and monthly sea-surface temperatures for August over a 10-year period, October 1981 to December 1990. The warmer water temperature in hues of green spreading to the northeast is the effect of the Gulf Stream.

in the same general direction. Faster-moving currents are usually found only where straits squeeze the flow of water, such as between Florida and Cuba or in the Bering Sea between Alaska and northeastern Russia. Slower-moving currents exist as well but are mainly confined to the deeper oceanic layers below 100 m, where the friction caused by the high pressure of overlying water is much greater.

Generation of Ocean Currents

Ocean currents can be generated in several ways. Sometimes water piles up along a coastline, yielding a slightly higher sea level than in the surrounding ocean. A good example is the tropical South Atlantic Ocean just south of the Equator, where the landmass of northeastern Brazil protrudes well out to sea. When westward-flowing water piles up against this shore, gravity forces it back, forming an eastward-moving current along the Equator (Figure 10.2). The eastward rotation of the Earth reinforces this piling-up phenomenon, which occurs to some degree along the western edge of every ocean basin. Alternatively, surface waters do not experience such squeezing along the eastern margins of an ocean, and water movement there is more diffuse.

Another source of oceanic circulation, which largely affects deeper zones below the surface layer, is variation in the density of seawater. Density differences can arise from temperature differences, as when the chilled surface water of the high latitudes sinks and spreads towards the Equator, or from salinity differences. The part of the ocean beneath a dry subtropical high-pressure zone is more saline than the part under an equatorial rain belt. The saltier water, being denser than the less saline water, tends to sink and to give way to a surface current of lower salinity.

These influences notwithstanding, the leading generator of ocean currents is the frictional drag on the water surface set up by prevailing winds. Frictional drag transfers kinetic energy, the energy of movement, from the air to the water. Once set in motion, as is the case with moving air, the water is subjected to the deflective Coriolis force. As a rule, when the prevailing wind blows over the ocean surface of the rotating Earth, the Coriolis force steers the surface current to flow at an angle of about 45 degrees to the right of the wind in the Northern Hemisphere (and at approximately 45 degrees to the left in the Southern Hemisphere). This surface motion also influences the waters below to a depth of around 100 m. Within this column, the motion in each underlying water layer is increasingly to the right (or left in the Southern Hemisphere) as depth increases, and exhibits a decreasing speed of flow.

Flow Behaviour of Ocean Currents

In our discussion of oceanic circulation so far, we have for the most part been dealing with models that describe ideal situations. Of course, we are aware that nature is more complex; the currents of the world ocean are no exception. A large-scale ocean current is not an unswerving river of water that follows exactly the same path and exhibits constant movement characteristics. Deviations from the 'norm' occur all the time. With the rapid expansion over the past

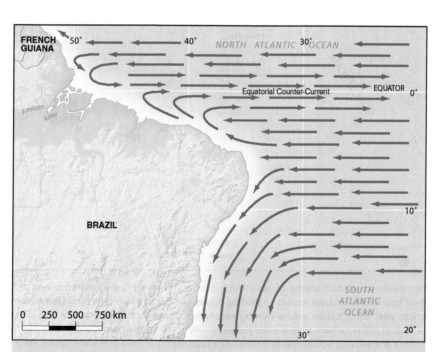

Figure 10.2 The pile-up of ocean water against the northeastern coast of Brazil forces a return flow, generating the Equatorial Counter-Current, which moves eastward against the surrounding dominant westward current.

three decades of oceanographic research based on satellite data, much has been learned about the detailed dynamics of surface currents. In many ways, their flow patterns (if not their speeds) resemble those of the Polar Front jet stream discussed in Unit 9.

Most ocean currents develop river-like *meanders*, or curving bends, which can become so pronounced (especially after the passage of storms) that many detach and form localized *eddies*, or loops, that move along with the general flow of water. These phenomena are most common along the boundaries of currents, where opposing water movements heighten the opportunities for developing whorl-like local circulation cells. Figure 10.3 diagrams such a situation, involving the western edge of the warm Gulf Stream current off the Middle Atlantic coast of North America.

Gyre Circulations

Prevailing winds, the Coriolis force, and sometimes the configuration of bordering landmasses frequently combine to channel ocean currents into cell-like circulations that resemble large cyclones and anticyclones. In the ocean basins these continuously moving loops are called **gyres**, a term used for both clockwise and counterclockwise circulations. Gyres, in fact, may be so large as to encompass an entire ocean. Since ocean basins are usually more extensive in width than in length, most gyres assume the shape of elliptical cells elongated in an east–west direction.

The model of gyre circulation in the world ocean, shown in Figure 10.4, displays a general uniformity in both the Northern and Southern Hemispheres. As with

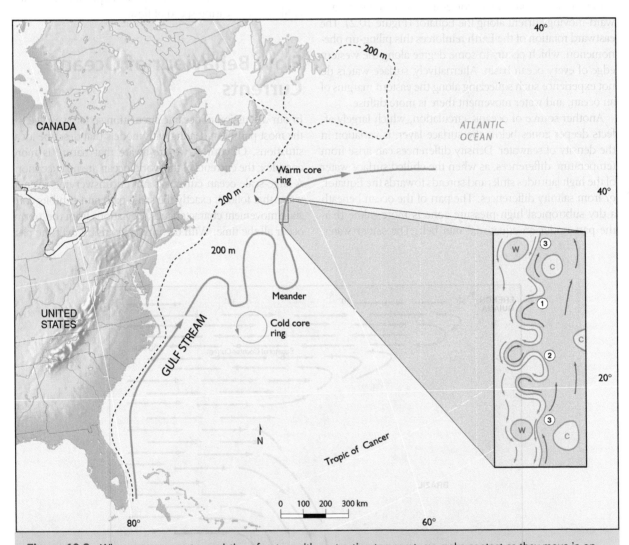

Figure 10.3 When ocean currents consisting of waters with contrasting temperatures make contact as they move in opposite directions, their boundaries become masses of swirling eddies. As the northward-moving Gulf Stream begins to move off the North American east coast, colder waters moving southward create such a situation. In this sketch of the Middle Atlantic coastline, a section of the contact zone is enlarged (inset). At ① the contact surface between the contrasting waters becomes indented. At ② the swirling eddies create balloon-like protrusions of cold and warm water. At ③ these warm and cold masses are separated from the main bodies on the opposite sides of the boundary. The broken line on the map is the 200 m bathymetric line, indicating that the areas of water within these lines are 200 m or shallower.

the model of the general circulation of the atmosphere, these hemispheric flow patterns essentially mirror one another. Each hemisphere contains tropical and subtropical gyres. Differences in high-latitude land/water configurations give rise to a fifth (subpolar) gyre in the Northern Hemisphere that is not matched in the Southern.

Subtropical Gyres   The **subtropical gyre** dominates the oceanic circulation of both hemispheres. In each case, the subtropical gyre circulates around the Subtropical High that is stationed above the centre of the ocean basin (see Figure 9.4). The two clockwise-circulating gyres of the Northern Hemisphere are found beneath two such high-pressure cells: the Pacific (Hawaiian) High over the North Pacific Ocean and the Bermuda (Azores) High centred above the North Atlantic Ocean. In the Southern Hemisphere, there are three subtropical gyres that each exhibit a counterclockwise flow trajectory; these are located beneath the three semi-permanent zones of subtropical high pressure, respectively centred over the South Pacific Ocean, the South Atlantic Ocean, and the southern portion of the Indian Ocean.

The broad centres of each of these five gyres are associated with subsiding air and generally calm wind conditions, and are therefore devoid of large-scale ocean currents. The currents are decidedly concentrated along the peripheries of the major ocean basins, where they constitute the various segments, or *limbs*, of the subtropical gyre. Along their equatorward margins, the subtropical gyres in each hemisphere carry warm water westward. These currents diverge as they approach land. Some of the water is reversed and transported eastward along the Equator as the Equatorial Counter-Current, but most of the flow splits and is propelled poleward as warm currents along the western edges of each ocean basin (Figure 10.2).

As Figure 10.4 indicates, when polar waters are encountered in the upper mid-latitudes, the currents swing eastward across the ocean. In the Northern Hemisphere, these eastward drifts remain relatively warm currents because the colder waters of the subpolar gyre to their north are largely blocked by landmasses from mixing with this flow. When they reach the eastern edge of the ocean, the now somewhat cooled waters of the subtropical gyre turn towards the Equator and move southward along the continental coasts. These cool currents parallel the eastern margins of the ocean basins and finally converge with the equatorial currents to complete the circuit and once again form the westward-moving (and now rapidly warming) equatorial stream.

Gyres and Windflow   The side panels in Figure 10.4 remind us that a subtropical gyre circulation is continuously

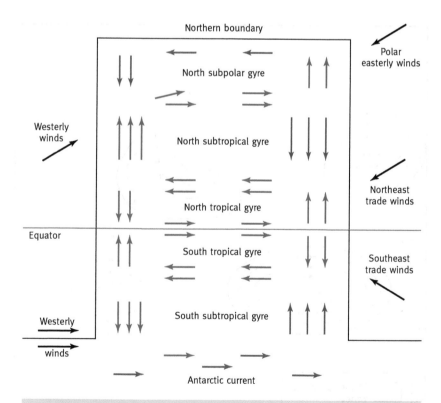

Figure 10.4 Generalized pattern of currents in a typical ocean basin, showing the major circulation cells (gyres) and their influencing wind systems. Relatively warm currents are shown in red; relatively cool currents in blue. Note that the Northern Hemisphere differs from the Southern Hemisphere because of the variation in continental landmass configurations.

maintained by the operation of the wind belts above it. The trade winds in the tropical segments of the eastern margin of an ocean work together with the Westerlies in the mid-latitude segments of the western periphery to propel the circular flow. If you blow lightly across the edge of a cup of coffee, you will notice that the liquid begins to rotate; with two such reinforcing wind sources to maintain circular flow, it is no wonder that these gyres never cease. The circulations of the narrow **tropical gyres**, composed of the equatorial currents and returning countercurrents, are also reinforced by winds—the converging Northeast and Southeast Trades.

The circulatory interaction between the sea and the overlying windflows is more complicated in the case of the Northern Hemisphere **subpolar gyres**, where landmasses and sea ice interrupt surface ocean flows. Along the southern limbs of these gyres, westerly winds drive a warm current across the entire ocean basin. This flow remains relatively warm because, as indicated before, the southward penetration of cold Arctic waters is largely blocked by continents, squeezing through only via the narrow Bering Strait in the northernmost Pacific and the slender channel separating Canada and Greenland in the northwestern North Atlantic. In the more open northeastern Atlantic between Greenland and Europe, a branch of the warm eastward-moving drift enters the subpolar gyre (Figure 10.4), frequently driven across the Arctic Circle by a reinforcing southwesterly tail wind associated with storm activity along the Polar Front. The subpolar gyres are non-existent in the Southern Hemisphere. Instead, an eastward-moving cold current is propelled by the upper mid-latitude Westerlies, which, in the absence of continental landmasses, girdle the globe.

Upwelling   Another feature of the subtropical gyre circulation is represented in Figure 10.4 by the wider spacing of arrows representing currents along the eastern sides of ocean basins. This wide spacing indicates that surface waters are not squeezed against the eastern edge of the basins, as they are against the west. It also suggests the presence of an additional influence that reinforces the actions of prevailing winds: upwelling. **Upwelling** involves the rising of cold water from the ocean depths to the surface where the Coriolis force prompts ocean currents to diverge from continental coastlines. As warmer surface waters are transported out to sea, they are replaced by this cold water, which lowers the surface air temperatures and the local rate of evaporation. Not surprisingly, some of the driest coastal areas on Earth are associated with upwelling, particularly in latitudes under the influence of the semi-permanent subtropical high-pressure cells.

Figure 10.5 maps four such upwelling zones in the Pacific and Atlantic Oceans. Each subtropical west coast on the continent adjacent to the shaded upwelling zone

LINK

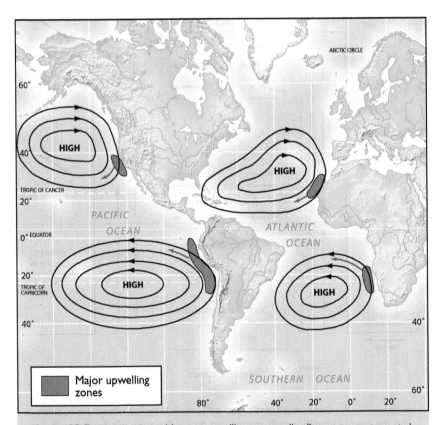

Figure 10.5 Four major cold-water upwelling zones, all adjacent to west coasts in the subtropical latitudes of the eastern Atlantic and Pacific ocean basins. The Coriolis force and high-pressure atmospheric systems drive waters offshore (red arrows), to be replaced by nutrient-rich, upwelling waters near the coast (indicated in dark blue). In each such location coastlines are arid, but offshore fishing industries are very productive.

experiences aridity. Much of coastal northwestern Mexico, as well as northern Chile and Peru bordering the Pacific, exhibits desert conditions. Moreover, in the areas of northwestern and southwestern Africa bordering the Atlantic upwelling zones, we find two of the driest deserts in the world—the Sahara and the Namib, respectively. Although it can result in desiccation on nearby coasts, upwelling does produce one important benefit for humans: it carries to the surface nutrients that support some of the most productive fishing grounds in the world ocean.

The Geography of Ocean Currents

The basic principles of oceanic circulation are now familiar to us, and they can be applied at this point to the actual distribution of global-scale surface currents mapped in Figure 10.6. As we know, these currents do respond to seasonal shifts in the wind belts and semi-permanent highs and lows. However, those responses are minimal because seawater motion changes quite slowly and usually lags weeks or even months behind shifts in the atmospheric circulation above. The geographic pattern of ocean currents shown in Figure 10.6, therefore, is based on the average annual position of these flows. But most currents deviate only slightly from these positions. On the world map, the only noteworthy departures involve the reversal of smaller-scale currents under the influence of monsoonal air circulations near the coasts of southern and southeastern Asia (see Figure 9.5). Now let us briefly survey the currents of each major ocean basin.

Pacific Ocean Currents   The Pacific Ocean's currents closely match the model of gyre circulations displayed in Figure 10.4. In both the Northern and Southern Hemisphere components of this immense ocean basin, surface flows are dominated by the subtropical gyres. In the North Pacific, the limbs of this gyre are constituted by the clockwise flow of the North Equatorial, Japan (Kuroshio), North Pacific, and California Currents. Because the Bering Strait to the north admits only a tiny flow of Arctic seawater to the circulation, all of this gyre's currents are warm except for the California Current. That current is relatively cold as a result of upwelling and its distance from the tropical source of warm water. The lesser circulations of the tropical and subpolar gyres are also evident in the North Pacific. The tropical gyre encompasses the low-latitude Equatorial Counter-Current and the North Equatorial Current. The subpolar gyre consists of the upper mid-latitude loop of the North Pacific, Alaska, and Kamchatka (Oyashio) Currents.

The South Pacific Ocean is a mirror image of the Northern Hemisphere flow pattern, except for the fully expected replacement of the subpolar gyre by the globe-encircling movement of the West Wind Drift (Antarctic Circumpolar Current), where the Pacific gives way to the Southern Ocean at approximately 45°S. The strong subtropical gyre that dominates the circulation of the South Pacific includes the South Equatorial, East Australian, West Wind Drift, and Peru Currents. The South Pacific's tropical gyre is comprised of the Equatorial Counter-Current and the South Equatorial Current.

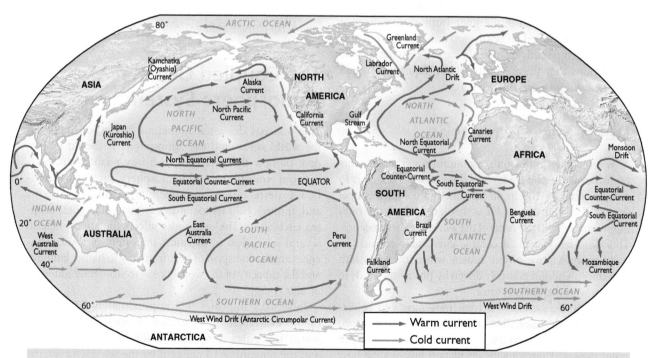

Figure 10.6   World distribution of ocean currents, showing average positions and relative temperatures in each of the ocean basins.

Atlantic Ocean Currents   The Atlantic really consists of two ocean basins because of the hourglass-like narrowing between South America and Africa in the vicinity of the Equator. Nevertheless, the overall pattern of Atlantic currents is quite similar to that of the Pacific. The subtropical gyre—composed of the North Equatorial Current, Gulf Stream, North Atlantic Drift, and Canaries Current—dominates circulation in the North Atlantic Ocean. The subpolar gyre, as noted before, is modified by sea ice and high-latitude land bodies, but the rudiments of circular flow are apparent on the map. In the equatorial latitudes, despite the east–west proximity of continents, both tropical gyres have enough space to develop their expected circulations.

Proceeding into the South Atlantic Ocean, the subtropical gyre is again dominant, with the warm waters of the Brazil Current bathing the eastern shore of South America and the cold waters of the Benguela Current, reinforced by upwelling that parallels the dry southwestern African coast. South of 35°S the transition to the Southern Ocean and its West Wind Drift is identical to the pattern of the South Pacific.

Indian Ocean Currents   The Indian Ocean's circulatory system is complicated by the configuration of the surrounding continents, with an eastward opening to the Pacific in the southerly low latitudes and the closure of the northern part of the ocean by the South Asian coast. Still, we can observe some definite signs of subtropical gyre circulation in the Indian Ocean's Southern Hemisphere component. Moreover, a fully developed pair of tropical gyres in the latitudinal zone straddling the Equator operates for a good part of the year. During the remaining months, as is explained in the discussion of the wet monsoon in Unit 9, the Inter-Tropical Convergence Zone (ITCZ) is pulled far northward onto the Asian mainland. This temporarily disrupts the air and even the oceanic circulations that prevail north of the Equator between October and June (see Figure 9.5).

Deep-Sea Currents

As noted earlier in this unit, significant water movements occur below the surface layer of the sea, which extends to a depth of about 100 m. In fact, another complete global system of currents exists *below* that level, where the bulk (approximately 90 per cent) of the world ocean's water lies. This deep-sea system of oceanic circulation operates in sharp contrast to the surface system, which interfaces with the atmosphere and is largely driven by prevailing winds in tandem with the Coriolis force.

The deep-sea system of oceanic movement can be categorized as a **thermohaline circulation**, because it is controlled by differences in the temperature and/or salinity of water masses. Thermohaline circulation involves the flow of currents driven by differences in water density. Because of the greater pressure of overlying water below 100 m,

increased frictional resistance acts to slow the speed of currents substantially. Another factor that makes deep-sea currents much slower than their surface-layer counterparts is that the latter are strictly horizontal whereas the former are much more likely to exhibit vertical motion.

The temperature and salinity differences that trigger thermohaline circulation are generated at the ocean surface in the high-latitude wind belts. Water density gradients high enough to spawn deep-sea currents are developed by the actions of two related processes. One process entails the sinking of surface water, which gets colder, and therefore denser, when it is in contact with polar-area air temperatures. The other is the freezing of surface seawater, which increases the salinity—and density—of the water just under the ice (which consists mainly of non-saline freshwater).

Recent research has established that thermohaline circulation is part of a *global conveyor belt* that moves masses of cold, deep-sea water from high to lower latitudes (Figure 10.7). Note that each ocean basin has its own deep-water circulation, with the only inter-oceanic exchanges occurring in the depths of the Southern Ocean. Note, too, that cold bottom water from each polar oceanic zone flows into different oceans: the deep-sea currents of the North and South Atlantic emanate from the Arctic Ocean, whereas those of the Pacific and Indian Oceans are generated in the waters surrounding Antarctica. Figure 10.7 also shows that the deep-sea limb of the global conveyor belt is connected to a surface-layer limb of warm water that transports vast amounts of heat energy among the same ocean basins. A growing number of researchers believe that the total conveyor system varies its rate of flow over time, and they are studying the implications of these oscillations for both short- and long-term climate change.

LINK

The Coupled Ocean–Atmosphere System

This unit has discussed numerous interactions between the world ocean and the atmosphere. It should be evident by now that a *coupled*, two-way relationship exists between atmospheric and hydrospheric processes. Wind-flow patterns in the atmosphere create surface currents and, through cold temperatures at higher latitudes, deep-sea circulation. The ocean also affects the atmosphere in several ways. Two of the most important of those influences are the transport of heat from low to higher latitudes and the capacity of the world ocean to store huge amounts of heat energy.

Table 10.1 indicates that approximately 87 per cent of the movement of heat away from the Equator towards the poles is accounted for by the atmosphere and the remaining 13 per cent by the sea. However, the breakdown shown in the table reveals that the oceans transport considerably more heat at certain latitudes,

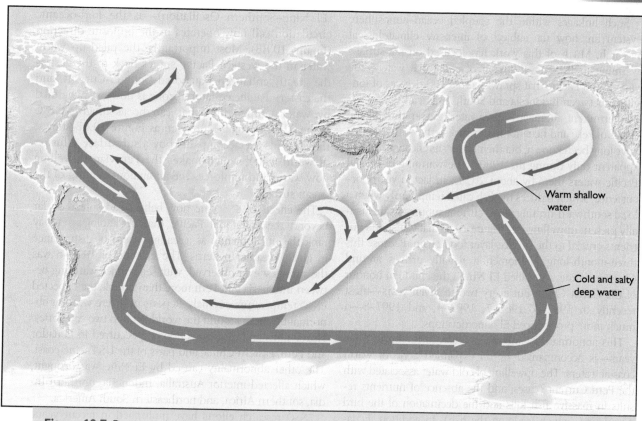

Figure 10.7 Deep-sea circulation system of the world ocean, which is part of the larger global conveyor belt that links thermohaline currents to a warm surface-layer flow among the same ocean basins.

Table 10.1 Average Annual Heat Flow at the Earth's Surface in Units of 10^{14} Calories per Second

Latitude	Total	Ocean (%)		Atmosphere (%)	
60°	7.6	0.7	(9.2)	6.9	(90.8)
50°	8.2	1.3	(15.9)	6.9	(84.1)
40°	12.0	1.8	(15.0)	10.2	(85.0)
30°	11.0	2.1	(19.1)	8.9	(80.9)
20°	8.4	1.3	(15.5)	7.1	(84.5)
10°	4.6	−0.3	—	4.9	(106.5)
Totals	51.8	6.9	(13.3)	44.9	(86.7)

Source: Information from M.I. Budyko (1958).

and it has been estimated that the sea is responsible for as much as 25 per cent of the global heat movement in the low and middle latitudes. With the excess heat of the tropical oceans systematically dissipated by its poleward transport, the world ocean exhibits a general pattern of temperature decline as the latitude increases (see Figure 7.10).

Many climatologists assert that the single most important influence of the world ocean on the atmosphere is its heat storage capacity. Unlike the atmosphere, which is far less capable of storing heat for any length of time, the sea is known to act as a vast heat reservoir. Scientists are now closely investigating this component of the ocean–atmosphere system, and some are concerned that if this excess heat were to be released rapidly, it could have a significant warming effect on the global climate. A related concern is the warming of the world ocean itself, which produces an increase in water volume that can lead to a eustatic (global) rise in sea level. (Researchers now estimate that about one-third of the 10-cm rise in global sea level during the twentieth century was caused by warming in the upper layers of the oceans.)

LINK

El Niño and Southern Oscillation

A vital component in the general circulation of the atmosphere is the rising motion of air in the warm tropics near the Equator. Since nearly 80 per cent of the surface that the Equator traverses is ocean, significant fluctuations in the temperature of that sea surface could temporarily modify the pattern of semi-permanent low-pressure cells that mark the ITCZ in these latitudes. This, in turn, could produce short-term, global-scale changes in weather patterns capable of disrupting human activities.

Such linkages within the coupled ocean–atmosphere system are now the subject of intensive climatological research. Much of this work has focused on sea-surface warming in the largest stretch of equatorial water—the vast central Pacific that sprawls across 160 degrees of longitude between Indonesia and South America.

Intermittent anomalies in seawater temperature off the coasts of Peru and Ecuador in northwestern South America have long been known, but their larger significance became apparent only during the 1980s. The warming of coastal Pacific waters there by about 2°C is, in fact, a yearly occurrence, which reduces the fish catch temporarily when a local southward-drifting warm current suppresses the usually present upwelling (see Figure 10.5) that transports nutrients crucial to the surface-layer food chain. Because this three-month-long phenomenon usually arrives around Christmas time, it is called **El Niño** ('the child') in honour of the Christ Child. But every two to seven years—most recently in 1982–3, 1986–7, 1992–4, and 1997–8—a much more pronounced El Niño develops.

This abnormal El Niño—which can linger up to three years—is accompanied by an expanded zone of warm coastal waters. The upwelling of cold water associated with the Peru Current ceases, and the absence of nutrients results in massive fish kills and the decimation of the bird population (which feeds on the fish). In addition, Ecuador and Peru experience increases in rainfall that can result in crop losses as well as in severe flooding in the heavily populated valleys of the nearby Andes Mountains. These localized El Niño effects, in fact, are but one symptom of a geographically much wider anomaly in the relationship between the equatorial ocean and the atmosphere. The cause of this abnormal El Niño is rooted in the temporary reversal of surface sea currents and airflows throughout the Pacific's equatorial zone.

The eastern portion of that oceanic zone is normally an area of high atmospheric pressure, because the upwelling Peru and California Currents converge (Figures 10.5 and 10.6), and the cool surface water creates a condition of stability that inhibits the air from rising to form the equatorial low-pressure trough. These cool waters then move westward into the Pacific as the Equatorial Current, propelled not only by the converging trade winds but also by a strong surface airflow from the eastern Pacific High towards the semi-permanent low in the western equatorial Pacific, which is positioned over Indonesia and northern Australia. As Figure 10.8A shows, a cell of air circulation forms above the Equator, with air rising above the western low, flowing eastward at high altitude, and subsiding over the eastern Pacific.

For reasons that still are not fully understood, during pronounced El Niño episodes there is a collapsing both of this pressure difference (between the eastern Pacific High and the western Pacific Low) and the resultant westward surface windflow. (These corresponding atmospheric events are called the **Southern Oscillation**.) What then occurs is a swift reversal in the flow of equatorial water and wind—known in combination as **ENSO**

(El Niño–Southern Oscillation)—as the mid-oceanic circulation cell now operates in the opposite direction (Figure 10.8B). Most importantly, the piled-up warm water in the western Pacific surges back to the east as the greatly enhanced Equatorial Counter-Current, and the eastern Pacific equatorial zone is now overwhelmed by water temperatures that can be as much as 8°C higher than normal. Moreover, as Figure 10.8B shows, these events are accompanied by a subsurface infusion of warm water, which makes the Peruvian upwelling flow warm and reinforces the anomalous heating of the ocean surface.

The effects of ENSO are now believed to spread so far beyond the equatorial Pacific that climatologists today rank the phenomenon as a leading cause of disturbance in global weather patterns. The El Niño of 1997–8 was the strongest ever observed, with sea-surface warming between Indonesia and Peru more than double the expected ENSO temperature anomaly. Reports of severe weather abnormalities from around the world fell into two categories. Heavy rains and disastrous flooding occurred in Ecuador and Peru, eastern China, and parts of the US Pacific coast. The other abnormality caused by El Niño was drought, which affected interior Australia, Indonesia, northern India, southern Africa, and northeastern South America.

ENSO research efforts have multiplied in recent years, and much has been learned. Among the more important findings is that extratropical Pacific sea-surface temperatures can remain elevated long after an El Niño event has ended. Satellite imagery has demonstrated that the 1982–3 El Niño produced so much eastward-moving warm water that a sizable mass of it in the northern tropics ricocheted off the North American landmass. Subsequently, this huge pool of water migrated slowly northwestward and was still evident a decade later, thousands of miles away in the mid-latitudes east of Japan. Since that part of the northern Pacific is a spawning ground for North American weather systems, there may be a linkage between this pool and some of the extreme weather events that have plagued the United States over the past decade.

Today many ENSO-related studies are focusing on **La Niña** (feminine 'child' in Spanish). This term was coined to indicate the lull between ENSO episodes—the counterpart of El Niño—but further investigation has revealed that these interims of supposedly 'normal' conditions can be marked by sea-surface *cold events*, which represent an opposite extreme to a fully developed El Niño. Researchers are now examining the atmospheric implications of this discovery, particularly the impact of La Niña on distant weather patterns. They are also beginning to redesign their models to reflect what may well be three distinctly different states of air–sea interaction in the Pacific's tropical latitudes (an effort discussed in several chapters in Glantz, 2002).

Intensive studies of ENSO have prompted scientists to search for other large-scale anomalies of this type that may affect global weather patterns. They are particularly interested in such influences on the climate of heavily populated regions in the middle latitudes (see 'Perspectives'

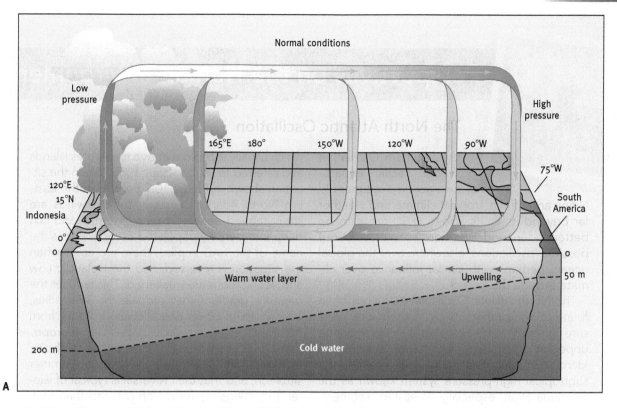

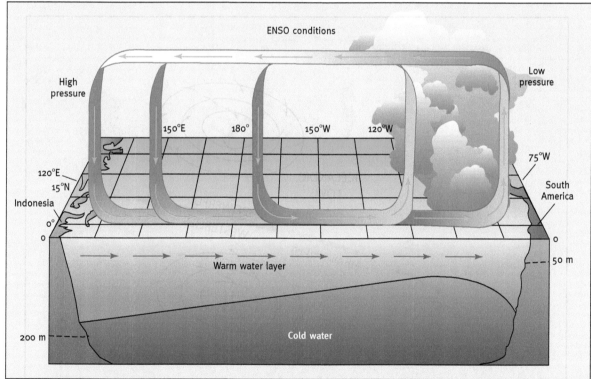

Figure 10.8 Equatorial Pacific waters and overlying airflows during normal (A) and El Niño–Southern Oscillation (B) conditions. Adapted from Ramage, 'El Niño'. Copyright 1986 by Scientific American, Inc. All rights reserved.

box). This work continues today on a number of fronts, and is forging a new subfield of climatology known as *teleconnections*—the study of long-distance linkages between weather patterns.

On a normal day-to-day basis, the latent heat released in the evaporation of seawater helps to power the general circulation of the atmosphere. That evaporative process simultaneously adds vital moisture to the air, a topic explored in Unit 11.

Perspectives on the Human Environment

The North Atlantic Oscillation

The Southern Oscillation of the Pacific equatorial zone governs recurrent El Niños and affects tropical climate and weather far beyond its limits. When ENSO came to be better understood, questions soon arose about possible 'oscillations' elsewhere over the global ocean, perhaps with similar influence over climate outside the tropics.

The **North Atlantic Oscillation** (NAO) has been found to do just that. This is an alternating pressure gradient between that semi-permanent, upper mid-latitude low-pressure system we identified in Unit 9 as the Icelandic Low and the subtropical high-pressure system known as the Bermuda High, especially its eastern segment, which usually is centred above the Azores Islands and referred to as the Azoric High. When the situation shown in Figure 10.9 prevails in the eastern North Atlantic, westerly surface winds are strengthened, sending oceanic warmth and rain deep into densely populated Europe. But as the name of the NAO implies, there are times when the situation is reversed, and the Icelandic Low and Azoric Highs are weakened. This reduces the pressure gradient that propels the Westerlies, slowing them down and allowing cold air from Arctic and Siberian sources to push into Europe.

We might conclude that the conditions shown in Figure 10.9 represent the normal summer situation, and that their reversal is typical of winter. But things are more complicated than that.

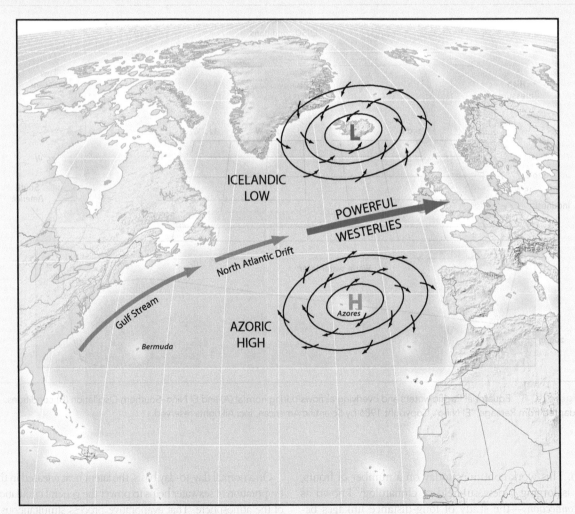

Figure 10.9   The North Atlantic Oscillation at high-pressure gradient.

Such seasonal see-sawing does occur, but there are also times when the Icelandic Low develops late, or not at all, so that the Westerlies are all but stopped and cold air has free reign over Europe, even in summer. Conversely, the Icelandic Low may persist for several years, right through the winters, giving Europe warm, moist winters and stormy summers. Ongoing research is showing that these oscillations can last as long as 20 years or more. Several centuries ago, long-term failure of the Icelandic Low led to frigid conditions in Europe (see Unit 18).

The NAO involves more than pressure gradients and windflows. It is a complex, dynamic system that incorporates (1) the Gulf Stream and its out- flow, the North Atlantic Drift current; (2) the sinking of warm water southwest of Greenland and north of Iceland, starting these salt-laden waters on an ocean-floor path to the Southern Hemisphere (Figure 10.7) and creating a heat-pump effect that draws more warm water northward; (3) the upwell- ing of cold water off northwest Africa (Figure 10.5); and (4) several additional components. As more becomes known about the NAO and its intricate mechanisms, one wonders what would happen if some crucial component (such as the heat pump) were to fail. The consequences for Europe would be far worse than the known devastations El Niños can cause.

Pacific Decadal Oscillation

In addition to the North Atlantic Oscillation, the North Pacific and Pacific Ocean in general experience alternat- ing warm, dry and cold, wet conditions (linked in part to the ENSO cycle). The so-called **Pacific Decadal Oscillation** (PDO) specifically refers to the patterns of climatic variability that occur approximately every 20–30 years in the Pacific (Figure 10.10). It is distinct from the El Niño pattern of cli- mate variability in that PDO events have been documented to have a longer duration than ENSO events (the former per- sisting for decades while the latter persists only for months), and the presence of the PDO is primarily in the North Pacific, while ENSO occurs in the Southern Hemisphere.

The PDO is a relatively recently observed phenomenon, having been first documented by Steven Hare, a fisheries scientist who had been studying the connections between Alaskan salmon production cycles and the Pacific climate. Precise causes for the PDO remain unknown.

The Arctic Oscillation

The **Arctic Oscillation** (AO) is closely related to the North Atlantic Oscillation and occurs as a result of variations in air mass conditions at mid- and high latitudes in the Northern Hemisphere. The AO fluctuates between positive (warm) and negative (cold) phases. The positive phase of the AO is characterized by low pressure in the upper atmo- sphere over the polar region and high pressure over south- ern Canada and the United States. The impacts of the posi- tive phase include temperatures warmer than average over southern Canada and colder than usual across Greenland and much of northern Canada, including Newfoundland.

The negative phase of the AO is characterized by high pressure in the upper atmosphere over the Arctic and low pressure in the upper atmosphere at lower latitudes. This can result in colder than usual tempera- tures across the Canadian Prairies, southern Ontario, and the Maritimes.

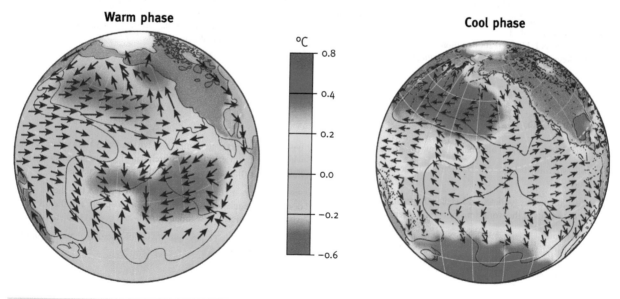

Figure 10.10   Typical wintertime sea-surface temperature (colours), sea-level pressure (contours), and surface windstress (arrows) anomaly (departure from average) patterns during warm and cool phases of the Pacific Decadal Oscillation.

KEY TERMS

Arctic Oscillation   *page 135*
drift   *page 124*
El Niño   *page 132*
ENSO   *page 132*
gyre   *page 126*
La Niña   *page 132*
North Atlantic Oscillation (NAO)   *page 134*
ocean current   *page 124*

Pacific Decadal Oscillation (PDO)   *page 135*
Southern Oscillation   *page 132*
subpolar gyre   *page 128*
subtropical gyre   *page 127*
thermohaline circulation   *page 130*
tropical gyre   *page 128*
upwelling   *page 128*

REVIEW QUESTIONS

1. Describe the ways in which ocean currents develop.
2. What is the relationship between the subtropical gyres and the overlying atmospheric circulation?
3. Name the major currents of the Pacific Ocean and their general flow patterns.
4. Name the major currents of the North and South Atlantic Oceans and their general flow patterns.

5. Describe the general pattern of deep-sea currents. What factors influence those currents?
6. Briefly describe what is meant by El Niño–Southern Oscillation and discuss this phenomenon's major mechanisms.

REFERENCES AND FURTHER READINGS

Bigg, G.R. 1996. *The Oceans and Climate.* New York: Cambridge Univ. Press.

Broad, W.J. 1997. *The Universe Below: Discovering the Secrets of the Deep Sea.* New York: Simon & Schuster.

Budyko, M.I. 1958. 'The Heat Balance of the Earth's Surface', trans. N.A. Stepanova, from *Teplovi balans zemnoi poverkhnost.* Washington: US Department of Defense.

Changnon, S., ed. 2000. *El Niño, 1997–1998: The Climate Event of the Century.* New York: Oxford Univ. Press.

Couper, A.D., ed. 1989. *Atlas and Encyclopedia of the Sea.* New York: Harper & Row.

Glantz, M.H. 1996. *Currents of Change: El Niño's Impact on Climate and Society.* New York: Cambridge Univ. Press.

———, ed. 2002. *La Niña and Its Impacts: Facts and Speculation.* Tokyo: United Nations Univ. Press.

Hare, S.R., and N.J. Mantua. 2000. 'Empirical Evidence for Northeast Pacific Regime Shifts in 1977 and 1989', *Progress in Oceanography* 47, 2–4: 99–102.

Kraus, E.B., and J.A. Businger. 1994. *Atmosphere–Ocean Interaction,* 2nd edn. New York: Oxford Univ. Press.

Pedlosky, J. 1996. *Ocean Circulation Theory.* New York: Springer-Verlag.

Philander, G. 1989. *El Niño, La Niña and the Southern Oscillation.* Orlando, Fla: Academic Press.

Prager, E.J., and S. Earle. 2000. *The Oceans.* New York: McGraw-Hill.

Ramage, C.S. 1986. 'El Niño', *Scientific American* (June): 76–85.

Scientific American Presents. 1998. 'The Oceans' (Fall).

Steinberg, P.E., guest ed. 1999. 'Focus: Geography of Ocean-Space', *Professional Geographer* 51: 366–450.

Stevens, W.K. 1999. 'Scientists Studying Deep Ocean Currents for Clues to Climates', *New York Times,* 9 Nov., D5.

Wells, N. 1997. *The Atmosphere and Ocean: A Physical Introduction,* 2nd edn. New York: Wiley.

 ## WEB RESOURCES

jisao.washington.edu/ao/ Information about the Arctic Oscillation.

jisao.washington.edu/pdo/ Information about the Pacific Decadal Oscillation.

oceancurrents.rsmas.miami.edu/ Detailed information, including graphic depictions of the world's major ocean currents

seawifs.gsfc.nasa.gov/OCEAN_PLANET/HTML/oceanography_currents_1.html Discussion of movement of ocean currents, including Dynamic Ocean Topography data from the TOPEX/POSEIDON mission.

www.elnino.noaa.gov Comprehensive site for El Niño information with forecasts, observations, research data, La Niña information, and links to animations, graphics, and other educational sites.

www.factmonster.com/ce6/sci/A0860100.html A fact sheet describing the relationship between the atmosphere and the ocean, with links to information about currents and ocean circulation.

www.ldeo.columbia.edu/res/pi/NAO Information about the North Atlantic Oscillation.

Atmospheric Moisture and the Water Balance

Objectives

- To discuss the various forms of water and to understand the important heat transfers that accompany changes of these physical states.

- To explain the various measures of atmospheric humidity, how they are related, and the processes responsible for condensation.

- To explain the adiabatic process whereby vertically moving air heats and cools.

- To outline the hydrologic cycle and the relative amounts of water that flow within this cycle.

- To introduce the concept of precipitation.

- To describe the Earth's surface water balance and its variations.

Our physical world is characterized by energy flows and mass transfers. Energy and matter are never destroyed; they continually pass from one place to another. One of the best examples of such cyclical motion is the flow of water on the Earth. The *hydrosphere* encompasses the global water system, whose flows occur in the world ocean, on and within the land surface, and in the atmosphere. In Unit 10 we examined the oceans, and in Part Four water movements on and beneath the ground are explored.

In this unit we focus on water in the atmosphere and its relationships with the Earth's surface. Our survey considers the continual movement of water among various Earth spheres that leads to a balance of water at the planetary surface. This circulation of water is powered by radiant energy from the Sun, a form of heat whose inflows and outflows also balance at the Earth's surface.

The Physical Properties of Water

Human bodies are 70 per cent water. Each of us requires 1.4 litres of water a day in order to survive, and our food could not grow without it. Water is everywhere. It covers 71 per cent of our planet's surface. We breathe it, drink it, bathe in it, travel on it, and enjoy the beauty of it. We use it as a raw material, as a source of electric power, as a coolant in industrial processes, and as medium for waste disposal.

The single greatest factor underlying water's widespread importance is its ability to exist in three physical states (shown in Figure 11.1) within the temperature ranges encountered near the Earth's surface. The solid form of water, ice, is composed of molecules linked together in a uniform manner. The bonds that link molecules of ice can be broken by heat energy. When enough heat is applied, ice changes its state and becomes the liquid form we know as water. The molecules in the liquid are not arranged in

an evenly spaced pattern but exist together in a random form. In the liquid state, the individual molecules are freer to move around. The introduction of additional heat completely frees individual molecules from their liquid state, and they move into the air. These airborne molecules constitute a gas known as **water vapour**.

Water is so common and consistent in its physical behaviour that we use it as a reliable measure of heat. We say that 1 *calorie* (cal) is the amount of heat energy required to raise the temperature of 1 gram (g) of water by 1°C. It takes about 80 cal to change 1 g of water from the solid state to the liquid state, a process we call *melting*. When it was first discovered that 80 cal of heat was needed to break the molecular bonds in solid water, the required heat appeared to be hidden, or *latent*. Thus the heat involved in melting is called the **latent heat of fusion**. Similarly, it takes 597 cal to change the state of 1 g of water at 0°C from a liquid to a gas. This change is called **evaporation** or *vaporization*, and the heat associated with it is known as the **latent heat of vaporization**. Sometimes ice can change directly into water vapour. In this process, called **sublimation**, the heat required (677 cal) is the sum of the latent heats of fusion and vaporization.

One of the beauties of these physical processes is that they are completely reversible. Water vapour can change back into water in the **condensation** process; water can change into ice through **freezing**; and water vapour can change directly into ice as well, a process that is also called sublimation (or *deposition*). In reversing these processes, the identical quantities of latent heat are given off.

Measuring Water Vapour

Lord Kelvin, the inventor of the absolute temperature scale, once said that we do not know anything about anything until we can measure it. How, then, do we measure water in its three physical states? The measurement of solid ice and liquid water is quite straightforward—we simply weigh them. We also employ this method indirectly when we measure the vapour pressure of water vapour in a column of air. (*Vapour pressure* is the pressure exerted by the molecules of water vapour.) Other atmospheric measurements of water vapour are also of value, the most useful ones being relative humidity, specific humidity, and the mixing ratio.

To use any of these methods of measurement, water vapour must first be condensed into liquid water. One way of condensing water vapour is to cool it together with the surrounding air. **Saturated air** is air that is holding all the water vapour molecules it can possibly contain at a given temperature. Condensation takes place when a parcel of saturated air is cooled further, or when more water vapour is transferred from the surface to the atmosphere.

Condensation occurs when warmer air contacts the surface of a cold soft-drink bottle or can. As the air in contact with the container is cooled, its saturation

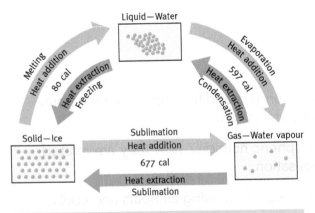

Figure 11.1 Schematic view of the molecular structure of water in its three physical states and heat-energy exchange among those states. The latent heat-exchange numbers between the arrows are explained in the text.

level is reached and the excess vapour in the cooled air condenses into liquid water droplets on the container. The same process occurs when the Earth cools at night, subsequently cooling and saturating the air next to it. The excess water vapour beyond the saturation level contained in such a layer of air condenses into fine water droplets that we call **dew** on surfaces at and near the ground. Accordingly, the temperature at which air becomes saturated, and below which condensation occurs, is called the **dew point**.

Relative Humidity

Relative humidity tells us how close a given parcel of air is to its dew-point temperature, or saturation level. Consequently, we can define **relative humidity** as the proportion of water vapour present in a parcel of air relative to the maximum amount of water vapour that air could hold at the same temperature. Relative humidity is expressed as a percentage, so that air of 100 per cent relative humidity is saturated and air of 0 per cent relative humidity is completely dry. Relative humidity, which is dependent on the air temperature, often varies in opposition to that temperature. Relative humidity is usually lower in early and mid-afternoon when the diurnal temperature reaches its high, because the warmer the air, the more water vapour it can hold. At night, when the temperature falls, the colder air holds less water vapour, and so the air approaches its dew point and the relative humidity is higher.

Specific Humidity and the Mixing Ratio

The other measurements used to assess the amount of water vapour in the air need less explanation. *Specific humidity* is the ratio of the weight (mass) of water vapour in the air to the combined weight (mass) of the water vapour plus the air itself. The *mixing ratio* is the ratio of the mass of water vapour to the total mass of the dry air containing the water vapour.

The relative humidity, the mixing ratio, and the specific humidity may be found by using a **psychrometer**, an instrument with two thermometers. The bulb of one thermometer is surrounded by a wet cloth; water from the cloth evaporates into the air until the air surrounding the bulb is saturated. The evaporation process results in cooling, and that thermometer reaches a temperature called the *wet-bulb temperature*. The other thermometer, not swaddled in cloth, indicates the *dry-bulb temperature*. The difference in temperature between the wet-bulb and dry-bulb thermometers is computed, and the relative humidity and/or the mixing ratio is then determined by referring to the appropriate set of published humidity tables.

Now that we are armed with some basic terminology and an understanding of the ways in which water changes from one physical state to another, we can proceed to find out how water circulates through the Earth System. The natural cycle describing this circulation is called the hydrologic cycle.

The Vertical Distribution of Temperature

Tropospheric Temperature and Air Stability

The troposphere is the layer of the atmosphere we live in, and it is here that the weather events and climates affecting humans occur. As shown in Figure 5.5, its temperature typically decreases with increasing altitude until the tropopause is reached. Another distinctive feature of the troposphere is the possibility and frequency of vertical, as well as horizontal, movement of air. Any long continuation of vertical movement depends on the rate of change of temperature with height—the *lapse rate*. As we note in Unit 5, the average tropospheric lapse rate is 0.65°C/100 m of elevation.

The lapse rate determines the **stability** of the air, a concept illustrated in Figure 11.2 by a wedge of wood. When it is resting on its side (A), a small push at the top may move it horizontally, but its vertical position remains the same. It is therefore *stable*. When the wood rests on its curved base (B), a similar push might rock it, but it will still return to its original position; it is still stable. But if we balance the wedge of wood on its pointed edge (C), a small push at the top knocks it over. It does not return to its original position; hence it is *unstable*.

We use the same terminology to refer to the vertical movement of a small parcel of air. If it returns to its original position after receiving some upward force, we say it is stable. But if it keeps moving upward after receiving the force, then we say it is unstable. In order to understand air stability, we must first consider that air is a poor conductor of heat. Without any air movement, it takes a long time for heat to pass from one air molecule to the next. Therefore a parcel of air of one temperature that is surrounded by a mass of air at another temperature will neither gain nor lose heat energy in a short period of time. When heat is neither gained from nor lost to the surrounding air, the process is called **adiabatic**.

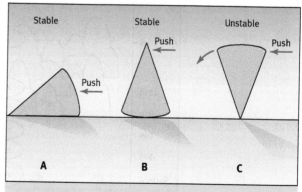

Figure 11.2   Concept of stability. The block of wood, like parcels of air, is considered stable as long as it returns to its original position after a small push.

Adiabatic Lapse Rates

LINK

If you have ever used a bicycle pump, you know that when the air is compressed at the bottom of the pump the air's temperature rises and the bottom of the pump becomes hot. The opposite occurs when the volume of a given mass of air is forced to expand: the temperature of the air decreases. A similar thing happens in the atmosphere. If a parcel of air rises to a higher altitude, it expands and cools (as if it were contained inside an expanding balloon). This is an adiabatic process because that air parcel neither gains heat from nor loses heat to its surroundings. Hence such air-parcel lapse rates in the troposphere are called adiabatic lapse rates (see Figure 11.3).

Dry Adiabatic Lapse Rate (DALR)   When an air parcel is not saturated with water vapour, it cools with an increase in altitude at a constant rate of 1°C/100 m. This is the **dry adiabatic lapse rate (DALR)**. But because air sometimes is saturated, and because mechanisms (especially radiant energy exchange) are involved in heating and cooling the atmosphere, any particular atmospheric lapse rate may not be the same as the DALR. The lapse rate at any particular time or location is called the **environmental lapse rate (ELR)**, which may be thought of as the vertical temperature profile of the atmosphere (as would be measured from an ascending balloon), which changes from day to day and from place to place. In the context of our example, the ELR is the temperature decline with height in the stationary mass of air in the atmosphere that surrounds our cooling parcel of air. The troposphere's ELR is highly variable, changing from day to day and place to place, as well as from one altitude to another within the atmospheric column.

What happens to a parcel of air in two different environments with two different ELRs. In Figure 11.4A, the parcel of air rises from the ground (because it is either warmed by the surface or forced upward mechanically). Because it neither gains heat from nor loses it to the surrounding air mass, it cools at the DALR, decreasing its temperature 1°C for each 100 m of ascent. But in this case the ELR is 0.5°C/100 m, so after rising 100 m, the air parcel has a temperature 0.5°C lower than its surroundings. The colder the air, the denser it is. Therefore the air parcel is now denser and heavier than the surrounding air and tends to fall back to Earth. This would happen even if the parcel rose to 300 m, where it would be 1.5°C colder than its surroundings. The cooled parcel thus returns to its original position on the surface. We would say the whole of the air in that environment is stable, meaning *it resists vertical displacement*. In contrast, Figure 11.4B shows the ELR to be 1.5°C/100 m. Under these conditions, an air parcel rising and cooling at the DALR would be warmer than its surroundings. The warmer the air, the less dense it is, so the air parcel that is lighter and less dense than the surrounding air continues to rise. We would call the air in this environment unstable, because it does not return to its original position.

One can often tell whether or not a portion of the atmosphere is stable by looking at it. A stable atmosphere is marked by clear skies or by flat, layerlike clouds. An unstable atmosphere is typified by puffy, vertical clouds, which sometimes develop to great heights. A photograph of Florida taken from a spacecraft, shown

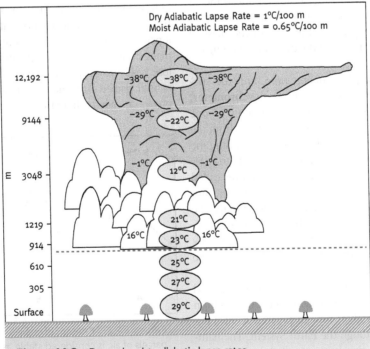

Figure 11.3   Dry and moist adiabatic lapse rates.

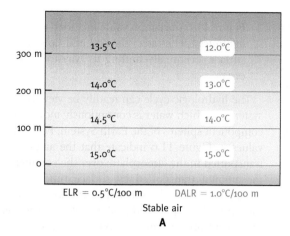
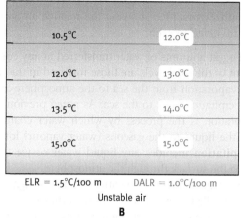

ELR = 0.5°C/100 m   DALR = 1.0°C/100 m
Stable air
A

ELR = 1.5°C/100 m   DALR = 1.0°C/100 m
Unstable air
B

Figure 11.4 Environmental lapse rate conditions for a mass of stationary air (shown in blue) that surrounds an individual parcel of air (shown in white) rising through it. When the ELR is less than the DALR, an air parcel is stable (A). When the ELR is greater than the DALR, an air parcel is unstable (B).

in Figure 11.5, illustrates the two conditions. Over the Atlantic Ocean to the east and the Gulf of Mexico to the west, the ELR is less than the DALR, so parcels of air

Figure 11.5 Looking southward at the Florida peninsula and surrounding waters from the NASA's ill-fated space shuttle Columbia passing over the Jacksonville area. In this classic summertime view, the land area of southern Florida is almost perfectly defined by its cloak of puffy clouds, the signature of atmospheric instability associated with rising hot air.

remain near the sea surface. But the higher temperatures of the land surface in daytime make the ELR higher than the DALR. The resulting instability allows parcels of hot air to rise in the atmosphere, forming those puffy clouds as they cool.

Saturated Adiabatic Lapse Rate (SALR) The situation is somewhat different when the air contains water vapour that is changing to water droplets as it cools. Latent heat (a concept introduced in Unit 6) is given off when the state of water changes from a gas to a liquid, a process called *condensation*. The resultant lapse rate when condensation is occurring is less than the DALR. This lapse rate is called the **saturated** (or *wet*) **adiabatic lapse rate (SALR)**.

Unlike the DALR, the value of the SALR is variable, depending on the amount of water condensed and latent heat released. A typical value for the SALR at 20°C is 0.44°C/100 m, compared with 1°C/100 m for the DALR. As a rule, we may assume that the atmosphere will be stable if the ELR is less than the SALR, and unstable if the ELR is greater than the DALR. If the ELR lies between the SALR and DALR, the atmosphere is said to be *conditionally unstable*. The conditions depend on whether the gaseous water vapour in the air changes into liquid water and thereby adds heat to the air.

The Hydrologic Cycle

Early scientists believed that the wind blew water from the sea through underground channels and caverns and into the atmosphere, removing the salt from the water in the process. Today's scientists talk in terms of the **hydrologic cycle**, whereby water continuously moves from the atmosphere to the land, plants, oceans, and freshwater bodies and then back into the atmosphere. The hydrologic cycle model consists of a number of stages, with Figure 11.6 showing the relative amounts of water involved in each:

1. The largest amounts of water transferred in any component of the total cycle are those involved in the direct evaporation from the sea to the atmosphere and in precipitation back to the sea. As noted previously, evaporation is the process by which water changes from the liquid to the gaseous (water vapour) form. **Precipitation** includes any liquid water or ice that falls to the surface through the atmosphere.
2. The passage of water to the atmosphere through leaf pores is called *transpiration*, and the term *evapotranspiration* encompasses the joint processes by which water evaporates from the land surface and transpires from plants. Evapotranspiration combines with the precipitation of water onto the land surface to play a quantitatively smaller, but possibly more important, part in the hydrologic cycle.
3. If surplus precipitation at the land surface does not evaporate, it is removed via the surface network of streams and rivers, a phenomenon called **runoff**. In

Figure 11.6 the runoff value includes some water that *infiltrates* (penetrates) the soil and flows beneath the surface, eventually finding its way to rivers and the ocean.

The hydrologic cycle can readily be viewed as a closed system, in which water is continuously moved among the component spheres of the Earth System. For example, the values in Figure 11.6 indicate that the amount of water transported in the atmosphere over the continents equals the amount transported by surface runoff back to the ocean. Water circulates between the lower atmosphere, the upper lithosphere, the plants of the biosphere, and the oceans and freshwater bodies of the hydrosphere—or is sequestered in the ice, snow, and permafrost of the cryosphere for varying lengths of time. The system can also be split into two subsystems, one consisting of the precipitation and evaporation over the oceans and the other involving evapotranspiration and precipitation over land areas. The two subsystems are linked by horizontal movement in the atmosphere (known as *advection*) and by surface runoff flows.

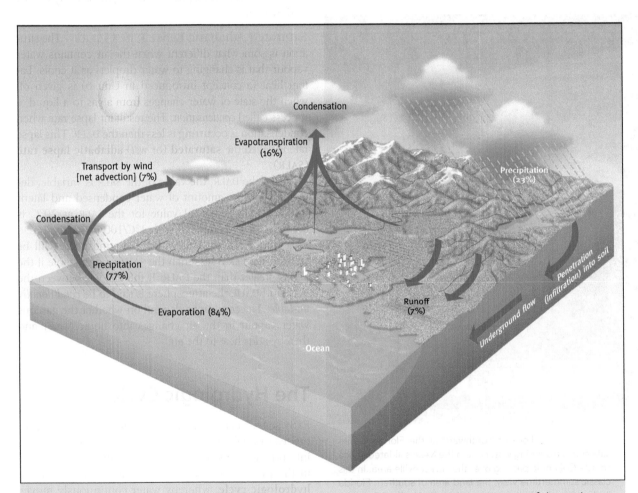

Figure 11.6   Hydrologic cycle. The numbers attached to each stage of the cycle show the percentage of the total water annually circulating in the system that is involved in any single stage. Surface flow and underground flow are considered as land runoff.

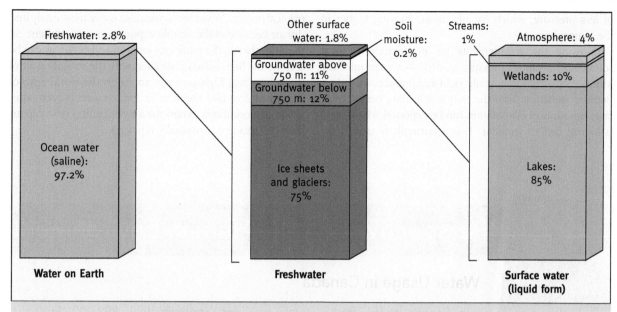

Figure 11.7 Distribution of water in the hydrosphere. Of the 2.8 per cent of total hydrospheric water that is fresh, only about one-tenth is easily available to humans.

LINK

The time required for water to traverse the full hydrologic cycle can be quite brief. A molecule of water can pass from the ocean to the atmosphere and back again within a matter of days. Over land, the cycle is less rapid. Groundwater goes into the soil or subsurface and can remain there for weeks, months, or years. The circulation is even slower where water in the form of ice in the cryosphere is concerned. Significant water has been locked up in the major ice sheets and glaciers of the world for many thousands and, in some cases, millions of years.

Water is quite unequally distributed within the hydrosphere, as Figure 11.7 reminds us. The world ocean contains 97.2 per cent of all terrestrial water, but the high salt content makes it of little direct use to people. Of the remaining 2.8 per cent, which constitutes the world's freshwater supply, three-quarters is locked up in ice sheets and glaciers. The next largest proportion of freshwater, about one-seventh, is accessible only with difficulty because it is groundwater located below 750 m.

Therefore the freshwater needed most urgently for our domestic, agricultural, and industrial uses must be taken from the relatively small quantities found at or near the surface—in the rivers, lakes, soil layer, and atmosphere. These storage areas contain less than two-hundredths of the freshwater in the hydrosphere, and that finite supply is increasingly taxed by growing human consumption and abuse (see 'Perspectives' box). Moreover, this very modest amount of freshwater must keep circulating within the hydrologic cycle through evaporation, condensation, and precipitation.

Evaporation

We cannot see the evaporation of water, but its results are sometimes visible. When you see mist rising from a lake that is warm in comparison to the cold air above it, you are seeing liquid water droplets that have already condensed. You can imagine molecules of invisible water vapour rising upward in the same way.

Conditions of Evaporation

Evaporation occurs when two conditions are met. First, heat energy must be available at the water surface to change the liquid water to a vapour. This heat is sometimes provided by the moving water molecules, but most often the radiant heat of the Sun, or both sources together, provides the necessary heat energy.

The second condition is that the air must not be saturated—it must be able to absorb the evaporated water molecules. Air near a water surface normally contains a large number of vapour molecules. Thus the *vapour pressure*, caused by the density and movement of the vapour molecules, is high. But air at some distance from the water surface has fewer molecules of vapour and, consequently, a lower vapour pressure. In this case we say there is a *vapour-pressure gradient* between the two locations. A vapour-pressure gradient exists above a water surface as long as the air has not reached its saturation level (dew point). Just as people tend to move from a very crowded room to a less crowded one, molecules of water vapour tend to move along the vapour-pressure gradient to areas of less pressure, which usually means moving higher in the atmosphere.

Knowing the requirements for evaporation—a heat source and a vapour-pressure gradient—we can infer the kinds of situations that would yield maximum evaporation. Because radiation from the Sun is a leading heat source, large amounts of evaporation can be expected where there is a great deal of sunlight. This is particularly true of the tropical oceans. Water molecules also move most easily into dry air because of the sizable vapour-pressure gradient. So the drier the air, the more evaporation will occur, as can be seen by the high values associated with the subsiding air of the subtropical high-pressure zones on the world map of latent heat loss (see Figure 6.7). Evaporation is even faster in windy conditions, when the air containing new vapour molecules can be continually replaced.

Perspectives on the Human Environment

Water Usage in Canada

In Canada today, freshwater—drawn from lakes, rivers, and subsurface deposits—is consumed in prodigious quantities at a daily rate of more than 340 litres per person, or more than 1500 m³ of water per household per year. And, according to Statistics Canada reports, Canadians are the world's second largest consumers of water, second only to the United States (Figure 11.8). This may not seem like a particularly worrying statistic, given the fact that about 9 per cent of Canada's total area (or approximately 892,000 km²) is covered by freshwater lakes, ponds, and rivers. Canada is therefore a water-rich country, compared to most other nations. So why should there be any concerns regarding the quantities of water consumption in Canada? The answer is that our vast water use may, in fact, be threatening the country's freshwater resources. Lower levels on rivers and lakes can affect navigation; water quality is affected by lowered water levels; and on the economic side, high levels of water consumption require expensive investments in water-system infrastructure to maintain high extraction levels. Even though efforts have been made to conserve water usage in Canada, our consumption is still several times higher than that of many Western European nations and hundreds of times higher than that of most developing nations. Given this massive rate of consumption, there is the potential for further environmental and economic consequences. A geographic and sectoral breakdown of the problem sheds light on where further changes will be necessary.

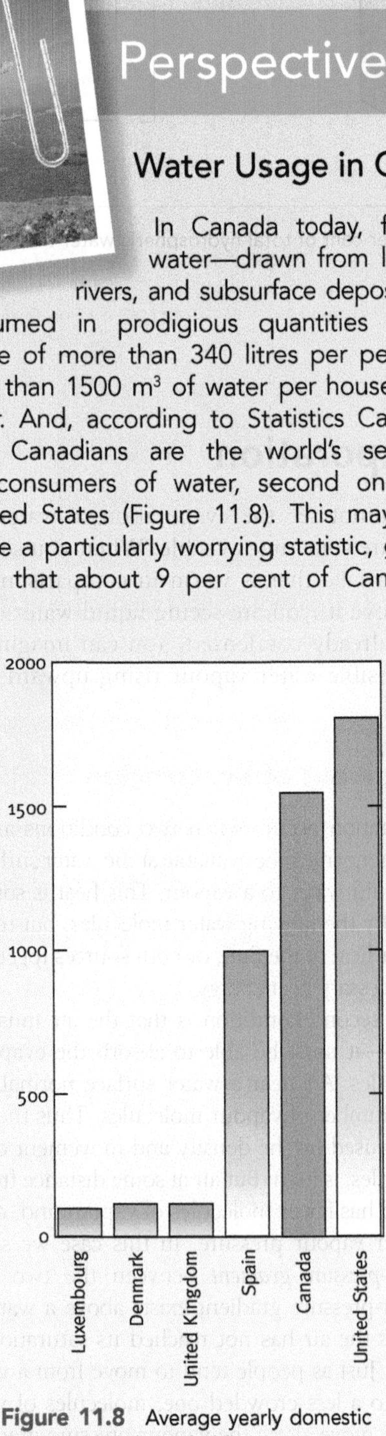

Even though Canada is a relatively water-wealthy country, most of our water flows north, while the majority of our population lives closer to the southern border. The spatial distribution of the proportion of the population that relies heavily on the use of groundwater as a source of freshwater illustrates that at least one-fifth of the population in every province and territory is dependent on groundwater. The provinces with higher rural populations (Saskatchewan, the Atlantic provinces) have a higher reliance on groundwater resources. The main use of water in Canada by sector is hydroelectric power generation. Although this is a non-consumptive use, to generate hydroelectric power, Canada has diverted more water by damming rivers than any

Figure 11.8 Average yearly domestic water use (per household).

other country. Of the users that withdraw water, the primary sectors by consumption are (1) thermal power generation (64 per cent), (2) manufacturing (14 per cent), (3) municipalities (10 per cent), (4) agriculture (9 per cent), and (5) mining (1 per cent) (see Figure 11.9). When factoring in the efficiency of these uses as a function of the percentage of water returned to the system, we find that agriculture is worst, with only a 30 per cent return, which makes it the largest consumer of water. Alberta accounts for most of the water withdrawn for agricultural uses in Canada. The highest domestic consumers are in southern Alberta and British Columbia.

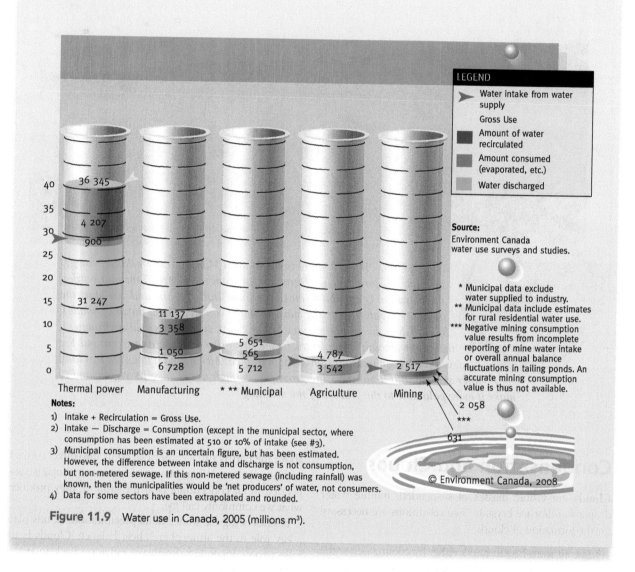

Figure 11.9 Water use in Canada, 2005 (millions m³).

Evapotranspiration

Most of the evaporation into the atmosphere occurs over the ocean. Over land, water evaporates from lakes, rivers, damp soil, and other moist surfaces. The water that plants lose to the air during photosynthesis (transpiration) is another major source. As we know, **evapotranspiration** is the passage of moisture from the land surface to the atmosphere through the combined processes of evaporation and transpiration.

Physical geographers draw a distinction between potential evapotranspiration and actual evapotranspiration. *Potential evapotranspiration* (PE) is the maximum amount of water that can be lost to the atmosphere from a land surface with abundant available water. *Actual evapotranspiration* (AE) is the amount of water that can be lost to the atmosphere from a land surface with any particular soil-moisture conditions. AE can equal PE when the land surface is saturated, but when the soil moisture is less than its maximum value, AE is usually less than PE.

Now that water has entered the atmosphere, let us see how it makes its way through this component of the hydrologic cycle and moves back to the surface. We begin with the formation of clouds and then trace the development of precipitation.

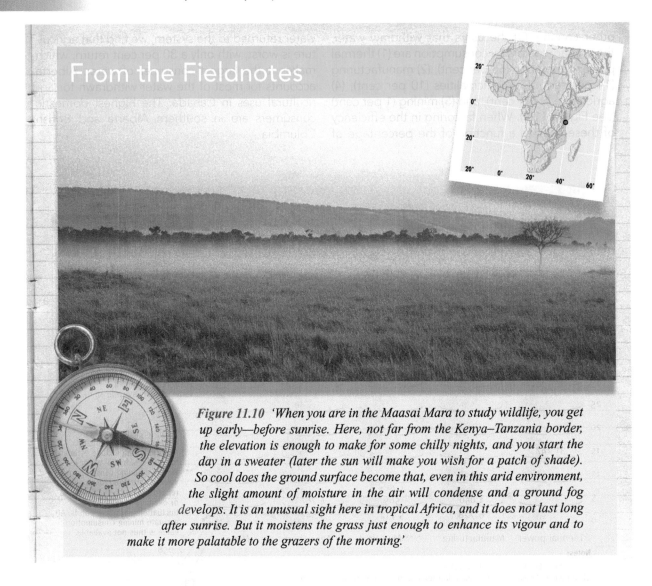

From the Fieldnotes

Figure 11.10 '*When you are in the Maasai Mara to study wildlife, you get up early—before sunrise. Here, not far from the Kenya–Tanzania border, the elevation is enough to make for some chilly nights, and you start the day in a sweater (later the sun will make you wish for a patch of shade). So cool does the ground surface become that, even in this arid environment, the slight amount of moisture in the air will condense and a ground fog develops. It is an unusual sight here in tropical Africa, and it does not last long after sunrise. But it moistens the grass just enough to enhance its vigour and to make it more palatable to the grazers of the morning.*'

Condensation and Clouds

Clouds are visible masses of suspended, minute water droplets and/or ice crystals. Two conditions are necessary for the formation of clouds:

1. The air must be saturated, either by cooling below the dew point (causing water vapour to condense) or by evaporating enough water to fill the air to its maximum water-holding capacity. Parcels of air may cool enough to produce condensation when they rise to the higher, cooler parts of the atmosphere, or when they come into contact with colder air or a colder surface.

2. There must exist a substantial quantity of small airborne particles called **condensation nuclei**, around which liquid droplets can form when water vapour condenses. Condensation nuclei are almost always present in the atmosphere in the form of dust or salt particles.

The greater the moisture content of cooling air, the greater the condensation and the development of the cloud mass. Although most clouds form and remain at some elevation above the Earth's surface, they can come into direct contact with the surface. When masses of fine water droplets suspended in air concentrate near the ground, they produce what we commonly call *fog*.

Besides being the source of all precipitation, clouds play a key role in the atmosphere's heat balance. Clouds both reflect some incoming shortwave radiation back to space at their tops and scatter another part of this incoming solar radiation before it can strike the surface directly (see Figure 6.2). At the same time, clouds absorb part of the Earth's longwave radiation and re-radiate it back towards the land and the sea.

Cloud Classification

Cloud-type classification, a common practice in meteorology and climatology, is based on the criteria of general structure, appearance, and altitude.

One major cloud-type grouping encompasses **stratus clouds**. As this term implies, stratus clouds are layer-like in appearance. They also are fairly thin and normally cover a

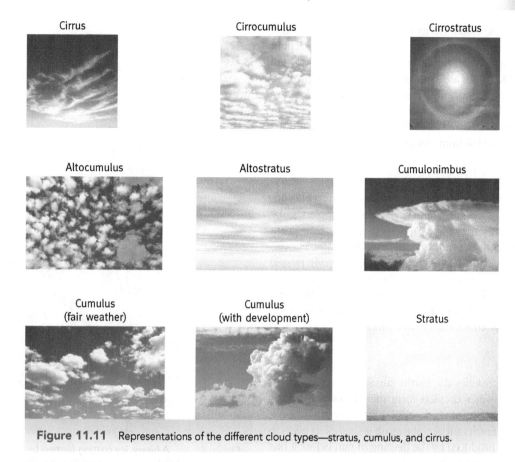

Figure 11.11 Representations of the different cloud types—stratus, cumulus, and cirrus.

wide geographic area. Stratus clouds are classified according to their altitude. Below 3 km, they are simply called *stratus* clouds—or *nimbostratus* if precipitation is occurring. Between 3 and 6 km, they are designated *altostratus* clouds, and above 6 km, *cirrostratus* clouds.

A second major cloud-type category involves **cumulus clouds**, which are thick, puffy, billowing masses that often develop to great heights (Figure 11.11). These clouds are also subclassified into the same lower, middle, and upper altitudinal levels, proceeding in ascending order through *cumulus* or *stratocumulus, altocumulus,* and *cirrocumulus*. Very tall cumulus clouds, extending from 500 m at the base to about 12 km at their anvil-shaped heads, are called *cumulonimbus*. These are often associated with violent weather, including heavy rain, high winds, lightning, and thunder.

A third cloud-type category consists of **cirrus clouds**. These are thin, wispy, streak-like clouds that consist of ice particles rather than water droplets. They invariably occur at altitudes higher than 6 km and are signalled by the prefix *cirro*, as in cirrocumulus and cirrostratus.

Precipitation

Clouds are prerequisite for precipitation to fall to Earth. However, not all clouds produce precipitation because water droplets and ice crystals first must undergo some intermediate transformations before they are ready to fall to the surface. When water droplets within clouds first form, they are so small that the slightest upward air current keeps them airborne for long periods. We now examine the processes by which these droplets grow large enough to fall out of a cloud as precipitation.

The Ice-Crystal Process

Probably the most common process, the *ice-crystal process* was first identified in the 1930s by meteorologists Tor Bergeron and Von Findeisen. This process requires the presence of both liquid droplets and ice particles in a cloud. Ice particles are normally present if the temperature is below 0°C and if there are small particles called *freezing nuclei*. Freezing nuclei perform the same function for ice particles that condensation nuclei perform for water droplets.

When a cloud contains both ice particles and water droplets, the water droplets tend to evaporate, and the resultant water vapour sublimates (changes from a vapour to a solid) directly onto the ice crystals. The ice crystal attracts more of the water vapour because the vapour pressure over the ice crystal is lower than that over the water droplet. Thus, the ice crystal grows at the expense of the liquid droplet.

The ice crystals become larger and often join together to form a snowflake. When the snowflake is heavy enough, it drops out of the cloud. On its way down it usually encounters higher temperatures and melts, eventually reaching the surface as a liquid raindrop. Most rainfall and snowfall in the mid-latitudes are formed by the ice-crystal process, but in the tropics the temperature of many clouds does not necessarily drop below the freezing point. Therefore, a second process—coalescence—is thought to make raindrops large enough to fall from clouds.

The Coalescence Process

The *coalescence process* (sometimes called the collision-coalescence process) requires some liquid droplets to be larger than others, which happens when there are giant condensation nuclei. As they fall, the larger droplets collide and join with the smaller ones. But narrowly missed smaller droplets may still be caught up in the wake of the larger ones and drawn to them. In either case, the larger droplets grow at the expense of the smaller ones and soon become heavy enough to fall to Earth.

Forms of Precipitation

Precipitation reaches the Earth's surface in several forms. Large liquid water droplets form *rain*. If the ice crystals in the ice-crystal process do not have time to melt before reaching the Earth's surface, the result is *snow*. *Sleet* refers to pellets of ice produced by the freezing of rain before it hits the surface. If the rain freezes after reaching the ground, it is called *freezing rain* or *glaze* (Figure 11.12). Soft *hail* pellets (sometimes called snow pellets) can form in a cloud that has more ice crystals than water droplets, and eventually fall to the surface. True *hailstones* result when falling ice crystals are blown upward from the lower, warmer part of a cloud, where they gain a water surface, to the higher, freezing part, where the outer water turns to ice. This process, which often occurs in the vertical air circulation of thunderstorms, may be repeated over and over to form ever larger hailstones.

LINK

The Surface Water Balance

As far as humans are concerned, the most crucial segment of the hydrologic cycle occurs at the planetary surface. Here, at the interface between Earth and atmosphere, evaporation and transpiration help plants grow, and precipitation provides the water needed for that evapotranspiration. Here at the surface we may measure the **water balance**. An accountant keeps a record of financial income and expenditures and ends up with a bottom-line balance. The balance is positive when profits have been earned and negative when excess debts have been incurred. The balance of water at the Earth's surface can be described in similar terms, using methods devised by climatologist C. Warren Thornthwaite and his colleagues.

Water can be gained at the surface by precipitation or, more rarely, by horizontal transport in rivers, soil, or groundwater. Water may be lost by evapotranspiration or

Figure 11.12   A heavy, icy coating formed by freezing rain on tree branches frames the Peace Tower on Parliament Hill in Ottawa. Although freezing rain can produce spectacular landscapes in much of Canada, it also can cause spectacular damage to infrastructure and agriculture, as the ice storm of January 1998 in eastern Ontario, southern Quebec, and New Brunswick demonstrated, and freezing rain creates danger for those driving or on foot.

through runoff along or beneath the ground. The water balance at a location is calculated by matching the gains from precipitation with the losses through runoff and evapotranspiration. When actual evapotranspiration is used for the computation, the balance (in the absence of such human intervention as importing irrigation water) is always zero because no more water can run off or evaporate than is gained from precipitation. However, when potential evapotranspiration is taken into account, the balance may range from a constant surplus of water at the Earth's surface to a continual deficit. Figure 11.13 illustrates this range.

A water balance equation can be used to describe and account for the flows of water in and out of the system (a system being a hydrological domain such as a column of soil or a watershed). A general water balance equation incorporates:

$$P = Q + E + \Delta S$$

where P is precipitation, Q is runoff, E is evapotranspiration, and ΔS is the change in storage (in the soil or the bedrock).

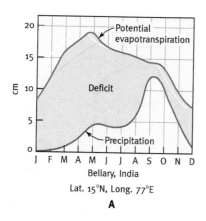

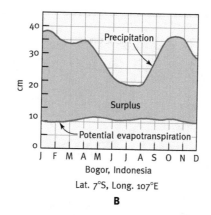

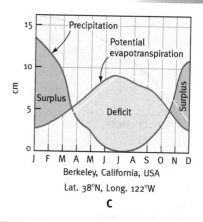

Figure 11.13 Range of water balance conditions. (A) Bellary, India, experiences a constant deficit because potential evapotranspiration always exceeds precipitation. (B) At Bogor, Indonesia, the situation is reversed, and a constant water surplus is recorded. (C) At Berkeley, California, across the bay from San Francisco, the intermediate situation occurs, with a combination of surplus and deficit at different times of the year.

The water balance can be used to assist in the management of water supplies and to predict potential shortages, as well as in irrigation planning and flood control.

The Range of Water Balance Conditions

Bellary, located in the centre of southern India, exemplifies the water balance at a deficit (Figure 11.13A). Throughout the year, the potential evapotranspiration exceeds the water gained in precipitation. On average, even during the time of the late-summer rains, the soil contains less water than it could hold. Because plants depend on water, the vegetation in this region is sparse, except where irrigation is possible.

At Bogor, on the most heavily populated Indonesian island of Java, the situation is reversed (Figure 11.13B). During every month of the year, rainfall, sometimes as much as 45 cm in a single month, exceeds the amount of water that can be lost through evapotranspiration. The surplus water provides all that is needed for luxuriant vegetation, and still leaves copious quantities to run off the land surface.

An intermediate situation exists in Berkeley, California, adjacent to San Francisco (Figure 11.13C). From November to March precipitation exceeds the potential evapotranspiration, but from April through October there is a water deficit. Starting in April, when potential evapotranspiration surpasses precipitation, soil moisture from below the ground is used in evaporation. Most of it is drawn up through the roots of plants and evaporates from their leaves. This process continues until the end of October, when rainfall once more exceeds potential evapotranspiration and the stock of available soil water is recharged. During this time runoff is more plentiful from California's winter storms.

The amount of runoff in any location cannot exceed the amount of precipitation, and usually there is much less runoff than precipitation. This is because some water almost always evaporates and/or infiltrates the soil. In 2004 the Canadian government (through Natural Resources

Canada, Statistics Canada, and Environment Canada) established 'The Canada Water Accounts' as the first-ever attempt to produce a 'budget' of Canada's water resources. These 'accounts' reconcile supply from stream flow and precipitation with natural losses owing to evaporation, runoff, and water use. The water balance accounts can

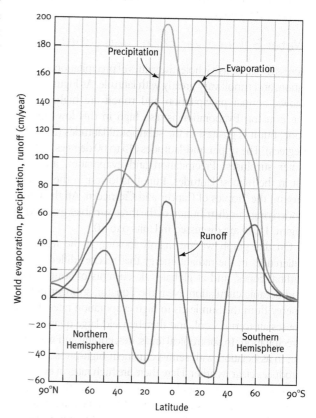

Figure 11.14 Average annual latitudinal distribution of precipitation, evaporation, and runoff for the entire surface of the Earth.

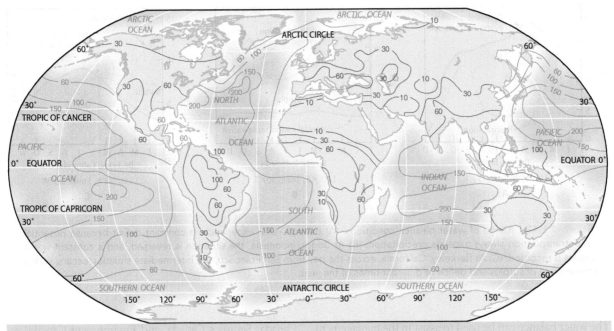

Figure 11.15   Global distribution of annual evaporation and evapotranspiration in centimetres, with land elevations adjusted to sea level. Red isolines show the pattern over land; blue isolines over the oceans.

then be used to identify which areas are near water limitation, and therefore help us develop adaptation strategies to reduce vulnerability.

Water Balance Variations and Latitude

Across the globe as a whole, the values of precipitation, evaporation, and runoff vary greatly with latitude. As Figure 11.14 shows, annual precipitation and runoff are highest near the Equator. Evaporation is also high in this low-latitude zone, but it is greatest in the subtropical latitudes (20 to 35 degrees). The upper mid-latitudes (45 to 60 degrees) exhibit water surpluses. Precipitation and evaporation are lowest in the highest latitudes. Runoff is lowest in the regions around the Tropics of Cancer and Capricorn. All the forces underlying this distribution of the three variables graphed in Figure 11.14 are discussed in Units 6 to 10.

On this graph we are mainly looking at the results of differences in the radiant energy that reaches different latitudinal zones, and at global-scale currents of atmospheric and oceanic circulation. Near the Equator, stronger radiant energy from the Sun leads to high evaporation rates. It also causes air to rise, cool, and thereby yield large quantities of precipitation. In subtropical areas, descending and warming air, in association with semi-permanent high-pressure cells, produces clear weather. Here there are high rates of evaporation over the oceans, but little evaporation over the land surfaces because of the scarcity of moisture to be evaporated.

In the higher mid-latitudes, eastward-moving storms (driven by the Westerlies and the Polar Front jet stream) provide moderate amounts of precipitation in most areas, but smaller quantities of radiant energy evaporate less of that water than would be the case in the low latitudes. In

the high latitudes, the cold air can hold little water vapour. Consequently there is little precipitation, and given the low amounts of radiant energy received here, rates of evaporation are minimal. These relationships should be kept in mind as we now consider and compare the world distributions of evapotranspiration and precipitation.

LINK

Population and the Water Balance

As a final exercise in this unit, let us reconsider the distribution of the Earth's population (see Figure 2.5) in the context of the global patterns of evapotranspiration (Figure 11.15) and precipitation (Figure 11.16). This comparison will reveal that most people live in areas where there are neither great surpluses nor great deficits in the water balance.

For example, the great fertile zones of North America, Europe, and much of China are concentrated in mid-latitude areas, which, year in and year out, do not usually experience excessive conditions of precipitation or evapotranspiration. Thus 75 cm of annual rainfall in the US Corn Belt or the North China Plain may be far more effective for raising crops than the 200 cm received at a tropical location, where much of the moisture is removed by evapotranspiration.

The variability of precipitation is a phenomenon that concerns farmers around the world. In general, variability increases as the yearly precipitation total decreases. We pursue this matter in our survey of the dry climates in Unit 17, which features a map of the global distribution of annual precipitation variability (see Figure 17.10).

Weather systems play a major role in shaping the temperature and moisture regimes of many climate types. Unit 12 relates the atmospheric moisture flows we have just learned about to the formation of weather systems.

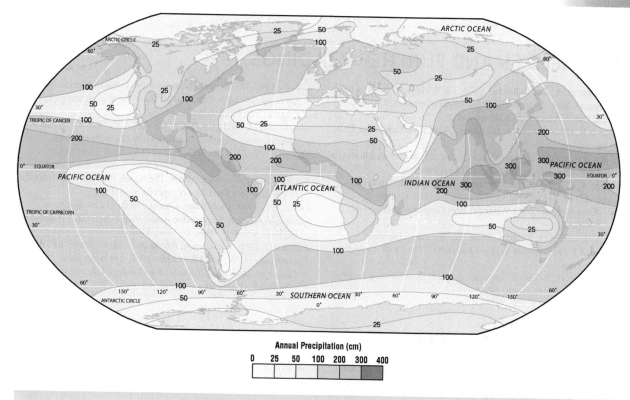

Figure 11.16   Global distribution of annual precipitation in centimetres.

KEY TERMS

adiabatic   *page 139*
cirrus clouds   *page 147*
cloud   *page 146*
condensation   *page 138*
condensation nuclei   *page 146*
cumulus clouds   *page 147*
dew   *page 139*
dew point   *page 139*
dry adiabatic lapse rate (DALR)   *page 140*
environmental lapse rate (ELR)   *page 140*
evaporation   *page 138*
evapotranspiration   *page 145*
freezing   *page 138*
hydrologic cycle   *page 141*

latent heat of fusion   *page 138*
latent heat of vaporization   *page 138*
precipitation   *page 142*
psychrometer   *page 139*
relative humidity   *page 139*
runoff   *page 142*
saturated air   *page 138*
saturated (wet) adiabatic lapse rate (SALR)   *page 141*
stability   *page 139*
stratus clouds   *page 146*
sublimation   *page 138*
water balance   *page 148*
water vapour   *page 138*

REVIEW QUESTIONS

1. Describe the energy requirements for the melting of ice and the evaporation of water.
2. Describe the various measures of atmospheric humidity and their relation to one another.
3. How does evaporation differ from evapotranspiration?
4. How does potential evapotranspiration differ from actual evapotranspiration?

5. Describe the two processes of raindrop formation.
6. Describe the necessary conditions for surface runoff within the context of the water balance.
7. What is the difference between stable and unstable air?
8. What is the adiabatic process? Define DALR and SALR.

REFERENCES AND FURTHER READINGS

Baumgartner, A., and E. Reichel. 1975. *The World Water Balance: Mean Annual Global, Continental, and Maritime Precipitation, Evaporation, and Runoff*. Amsterdam: Elsevier.

Bigg, G.R. 1996. *The Oceans and Climate*. New York: Cambridge Univ. Press.

Gleick, P.H. 2000. *The World's Water 2000–2001: The Biennial Report on Freshwater Resources*. Washington: Island Press.

Houze, R.A., Jr. 1993. *Cloud Dynamics*. San Diego: Academic Press.

Legates, D.R., and J.R. Mather. 1992. 'An Evaluation of the Average Annual Global Water Balance', *Geographical Review* 82: 253–67.

Leopold, L.B. 1974. *Water: A Primer*. San Francisco: Freeman.

Mason, B.J. 1975. *Clouds, Rain and Rainmaking*. New York: Cambridge Univ. Press.

Mather, J.R. 1978. *The Climate Water Budget in Environmental Analysis*. Lexington, Mass.: Heath, 1978.

———. 1997. 'Water Budget Climatology', in Susan Hanson, ed., *Ten Geographic Ideas That Changed the World*. New Brunswick, NJ: Rutgers Univ. Press, 108–24.

———, and M. Sanderson, 1996. *The Genius of C. Warren Thornthwaite, Climatologist-Geographer*. Norman: Univ. of Oklahoma Press.

Miller, D.H. 1977. *Water at the Surface of the Earth*. New York: Academic Press.

National Geographic. 1993. 'Water: The Power, Promise, and Turmoil of North America's Fresh Water', special issue (Nov.).

Pielou, E.C. 1998. *Fresh Water*. Chicago: Univ. of Chicago Press.

Stevens, W.K. 1998. 'Expectation Aside, Water Use in U.S. Is Showing Decline', *New York Times*, 10 Nov., A1, A16.

Sumner, G. 1988. *Precipitation: Process and Analysis*. New York: Wiley.

Thornthwaite, C.W., and J.R. Mather. 1955. *The Water Balance*. Centerton, NJ: Drexel Institute of Technology, Laboratory of Climatology, Publications in Climatology, vol. 8.

 # WEB RESOURCES

atlas.gc.ca/site/english/maps/freshwater/consumption/ This Natural Resources Canada site provides maps of water consumption in Canada as well as a discussion of sectoral water uses.

ga.water.usgs.gov/edu/waterproperties.html A discussion of the physical and chemical properties of water, with links to information about capillary action and a self-quiz.

physics.edu/~mrc/astro/NASA_Space_Science/observe.arc.nasa.gov/nasa/earth/hydrocycle/hydro1.html Overview of the components of the hydrologic cycle with graphics and animations.

www.ec.gc.ca/water/e_main.html Environment Canada's freshwater website.

www.ec.gc.ca/Water/en/manage/use/e_use.htm Environment Canada's water use website.

Precipitation, Air Masses, and Fronts

Objectives

- To explain the formation and growth of cloud droplets.

- To discuss the four basic mechanisms for producing precipitation.

- To develop the concept of air masses—their character, origin, movement patterns, and influence on precipitation.

- To distinguish between cold fronts and warm fronts, and to describe their structure and behaviour as they advance.

On a day-to-day basis, the atmosphere is organized into numerous weather systems that blanket the Earth. In this unit the connection is made between the atmospheric moisture flows covered in Unit 11 and the formation of those weather systems. Much of our attention is directed at the forces that cause the atmospheric lifting of moist air, thereby producing precipitation. This unit also introduces the concept of air masses—large uniform bodies of air that move across the surface as an organized whole—and the weather contrasts that occur along their advancing edges.

The Formation and Growth of Cloud Droplets

How do cloud droplets grow and develop into precipitation? Why do some clouds generate rain and others do not? To explain this, we need to start with the average size of a cloud droplet, which has a radius of 10 μm (micrometres). A typical raindrop, on the other hand, has a radius of 1000 μm (Figure 12.1). Most cloud droplets are so small that they remain suspended in the sky, falling only a short distance before being vaporized in the unsaturated air beneath the cloud base. The speed of a falling cloud droplet is regulated by the force of gravity, which accelerates the particle downward, and the opposing force caused by resistance of the air as the particle descends. As the particle accelerates, it is met with increased resistance (whereas the gravitational force remains the same). Once the resisting force equals the force of gravity, the so-called *terminal* velocity is reached and the particle will move at a constant speed, with the terminal velocity generally increasing with the size of the particle. Cloud particles have such low terminal velocities that they remain suspended or vaporize before reaching the surface. So in order for cloud droplets

to fall from the sky, they need to grow in size. There are several processes which can lead to the growth of a cloud droplet into potential precipitation. The formation of precipitation can generally be attributed to one of the following processes: (1) condensation, (2) collision-coalescence, or (3) ice-crystal processes.

Condensation

As air rises and cools adiabatically, condensation develops around particles in the atmosphere (condensation nuclei). Condensation can lead to the rapid growth of small water droplets, but only until they reach a radii of about 20 μm, which is far too small for these droplets to fall as precipitation. The explanation for this is that there is relatively little water vapour available for the condensation process, meaning that water droplets do not grow very large as a result of the condensation process alone. If condensation were the only process that increased the size of cloud droplets in our atmosphere, we would not experience much precipitation (if any at all!) on Earth. To reach the particle sizes required to generate such precipitation, we need to look to processes that are responsible for the further growth of droplets.

Collision-Coalescence

Within so-called *warm clouds* (clouds at temperatures above the freezing point of water), droplets can grow by colliding and subsequently coalescing (merging) with one another. The **collision-coalescence** process requires that there are droplets of differing diameters in the cloud mass. If the particle sizes were all similar or the same, collision would be unlikely, since they would be dropping at the same speed (terminal velocity). With droplets of differing sizes, some will drop faster than others (the larger droplets) and will collide with the slower-moving droplets. The droplets that collide will coalesce and increase in size (Figure 12.2). This will increase the collector droplet's terminal velocity and further collisions will increase. Eventually, the droplets will be large enough to fall to Earth's surface as precipitation.

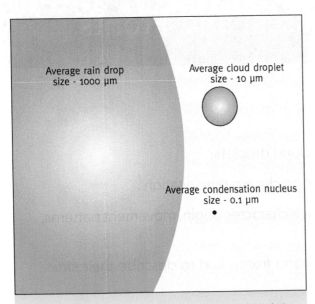

Figure 12.1 The formation of precipitation: the relative sizes of cloud droplet nucleus, droplet, and raindrop.

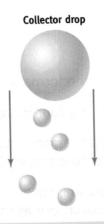

Figure 12.2 The collector drop collides with droplets as it descends.

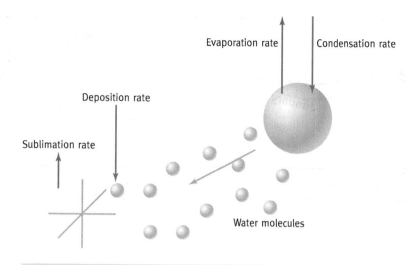

Figure 12.3 A comparison of the rates of movement between liquid and frozen forms of water within clouds.

Ice-Crystal Process

The collision-coalescence process does not account for all precipitation that reaches Earth's surface. It is the dominant process in warmer latitudes, but the ice-crystal (*Bergeron*) process explains much of the precipitation that reaches Earth's surface at higher latitudes. The process was named after a Scandinavian meteorologist (Tor Bergeron) who, in 1933, described how the process operates in so-called *cold clouds* (those which are at temperatures below 0°C). For this process to occur, the presence of water vapour, ice crystals, and super-cooled water droplets is required. A super-cooled water droplet is one that is below the freezing point but remains in liquid form as a result of not having a solid nucleus around which to crystallize. Ice crystals are found coexisting with the super-cooled water in cold clouds. When this occurs, the ice crystals will grow at the expense of the water droplets. Water can evaporate off the droplet and deposit on the ice in response to the water vapour gradient. The droplet will dissipate in size while the ice crystal grows into a snowflake (Figure 12.3). Once the snowflake is large enough, it will fall to the surface. Thus, precipitation that falls in the middle and high latitudes starts out as snow. Whether it hits the surface as snow or rain depends on the temperature conditions through which the snowflake falls.

Lifting Mechanisms That Produce Precipitation

All precipitation originates from parcels of moist air that have been adiabatically cooled below their condensation level (dew-point temperature). This is accomplished through the lifting of air from the vicinity of the surface to higher levels in the atmosphere. The occurrence of at least one of four processes is necessary to induce the rising of

moist air that will result in significant precipitation. On many occasions more than one process occurs, which may enhance the production of precipitation. These four precipitation-producing mechanisms involve (1) the forced lifting of air where low-level windflows converge; (2) the spontaneous rise of air, or convection; (3) the forced uplift of moving air that encounters mountains; and (4) the forced uplift of air at the edges of colliding air masses associated with cyclonic storms.

Convergent-Lifting Precipitation

Where warm, moist airflows converge at or very near the surface, particularly in the tropical latitudes, their molecules are forced to crowd together. This increases molecular kinetic energy, warms the combining windstreams, and induces the air to rise. Because the equatorial zone of convergence is already an area of relatively low atmospheric pressure (having pulled those winds towards it in the first place), the lifting of air here becomes more pronounced. The cooling of large quantities of water vapour in the uplifted air causes the rainfall that is so common in the wet tropics. As we would expect, the most prominent and durable tropical weather systems marked by this process of **convergent-lifting precipitation** lie where the trade winds from the Northern and Southern Hemispheres come together at the ITCZ.

The Inter-Tropical Convergence Zone

In the discussion of global wind belts and semi-permanent pressure zones in Unit 9, it was noted that the Northeast and Southeast Trade Winds converge in the equatorial trough of low pressure. The rising air that results is responsible for the cloudiness and precipitation that mark the Inter-Tropical Convergence Zone (ITCZ). The ITCZ occurs at low latitudes all around the Earth, most notably

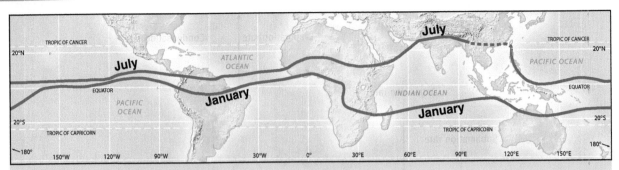

Figure 12.4 Average positions of the ITCZ in January and July. The wide annual swing over the northern Indian Ocean is associated with the regional-scale atmospheric circulations that produce the dry and wet monsoons in southern Asia.

above the oceans, particularly the equatorial Pacific. But the rainfall that its clouds deliver over the intervening continents and islands is vital to millions of inhabitants of tropical lowlands and hillsides, especially in the Indonesian archipelago of Southeast Asia and the Congo Basin in western equatorial Africa.

The ITCZ changes its location throughout the year, generally following the latitudinal corridor of maximum solar heating. Accordingly, as Figure 12.4 demonstrates, the average July position of the ITCZ lies at about 10°N, whereas in January, at the opposite seasonal extreme, it is found hundreds of kilometres to the south. Although the ITCZ owes its origin to the position of the overhead Sun, this is not the only factor that determines its location. The distribution of land and sea and the flows of the tropical atmosphere also are important. Therefore, at any given moment the ITCZ may not be where generalized theory tells us it ought to be.

Closer inspection of Figure 12.4 shows that in July the ITCZ is entirely absent in the Southern Hemisphere, when it is drawn northward to a latitudinal position beyond 20°N over southern Asia—as was pointed out in the discussion of the wet monsoon in Unit 9. Yet in January the ITCZ ranges from a southernmost extreme of 20°S, above northern Australia, to a northernmost position within the Northern Hemisphere tropics in the oceans adjoining South America. Not unexpectedly, the moisture regimes of areas lying inside the broad latitudinal band mapped in Figure 12.4 are decidedly boosted as the ITCZ continually shifts across this region.

Convectional Precipitation

Convection denotes spontaneous vertical air movement in the atmosphere, and **convectional precipitation** occurs after condensation of the upward-moving air. The process of convection is generally localized, usually covering only a few square kilometres of the surface. Convection begins when this relatively small area is heated steadily and intensely by insolation and the parcel of overlying air is rapidly warmed through its contact with the warmed surface.

A rising column of air, known as a *convection cell*, develops quickly. The temperature of this upward-flowing air cools at the dry adiabatic lapse rate (DALR) of 1°C per 100 m. (As noted in Unit 11, the DALR is the cooling rate of rising unsaturated air.) This cooling rate continues as long as the relative humidity of the rising air remains below 100 per cent. When the dew point is reached, condensation commences and a small cumulus cloud forms. That cloud soon mushrooms as the added energy of the latent heat released by the condensing water vapour converts the original convection cell into an ever more powerful updraft.

Very large cumulus clouds of the towering cumulonimbus type can develop if three conditions are met. First, there must be sufficient water vapour in the updraft to sustain the formation of the cloud. Second, the immediate atmosphere must be unstable, so that the upward airflow originally triggered in the surface-layer convection cell is able to persist to a very high altitude. And third, there must be relatively weak winds aloft. With these conditions satisfied, we are likely to encounter the type of weather associated with *thunderstorms*.*

Thunderstorms

LINK

Thunderstorms are common in the low and middle latitudes, especially during afternoon hours in the warmest months of the year. Like the larger-scale storm systems discussed in Unit 13, thunderstorms have a distinct life cycle. Although that cycle rarely lasts longer than a few hours, these smaller-scale weather systems can attain sizeable dimensions. For example, the massive thunderclouds shown in Figure 12.5 were easily discerned by astronauts as they

---

*Although thunderstorms are discussed here in conjunction with convectional precipitation, it should be noted that this type of severe weather can also be produced by other lifting mechanisms. All thunderstorms are triggered by the uplifting of moist, unstable air and the release of enough latent heat to fuel continuing uplift. Some of the most severe are squall-line thunderstorms generated by particularly abrupt uplifting in advance of a rapidly moving cold front, which we discuss below in the section on frontal precipitation.

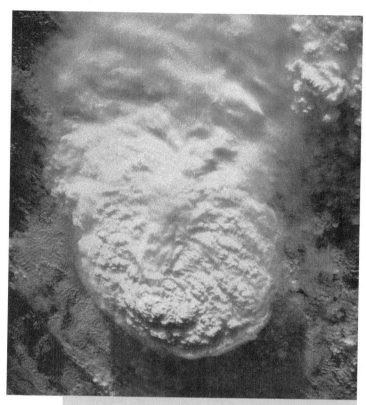

Figure 12.5 Massive thunderstorm photographed from an orbiting space vehicle over the Indian Ocean east of Madagascar. With a diameter of nearly 100 km and an anvil cloud reaching 16 km in height, a storm of this type generates powerful windflow at the surface and strong vertical currents resulting in heavy rains.

orbited above the tropical Indian Ocean to the east of the African continent.

The life cycle of a **thunderstorm** begins with the onset of the convection process in an unstable atmosphere as moist heated air rises, undergoes condensation, and releases large quantities of latent heat. This heat energy makes the air much warmer than its surroundings, and the resulting updrafts of warm air attain speeds of about 10 m per second. They can sometimes move as fast as 30 m per second in this *developing stage*. Raindrops and ice crystals may form at this stage, but they do not reach the ground because of the updrafts.

When the middle, *mature stage* is reached, the updrafts continue, producing towering cumulonimbus clouds. More significantly, however, enough raindrops fall to also cause downdrafts of cold air. Evaporation from the falling drops accentuates the cooling. Heavy rain begins to fall from the bottom of the cloud (Figure 12.6B), and cold air at that level spreads out in a wedge formation. At the same time, the top of the cloud is often drawn out by upper-air winds to form an *anvil top* (the shape of a blacksmith's anvil).

Within a few hours, the moisture in the storm is used up. The final, *dissipating stage* occurs when the latent heat source starts to fail. Downdrafts gradually predominate over updrafts, and this situation continues until the storm dies away (Figure 12.6C).

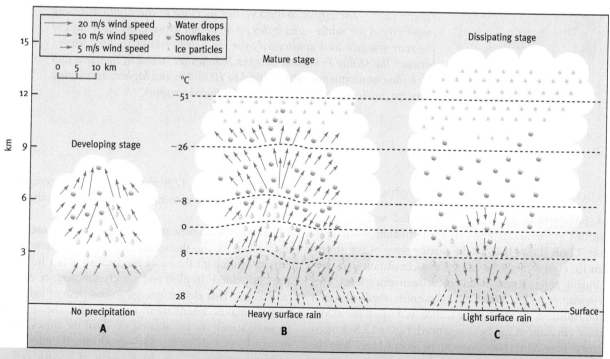

Figure 12.6 Life cycle of a thunderstorm. The developing stage (A) involves increasingly rapid updrafts, the mature stage (B) is associated with both updrafts and downdrafts, and the dissipating stage (C) is largely one of cool downdrafts. The arrows indicate the direction and speed of the vertical air currents.

From the Fieldnotes

Figure 12.7 *'The city of Singapore lies as close to the Equator as any major city in the world—and it lies on an island as well. On most days of the year you can look southward over the warm, island-studded waters between the Malay Peninsula and the Indonesian island of Sumatra and watch the cumulonimbus clouds build to 10,000 m and higher, developing windswept anvils and generating powerful thunderstorms.'*

Thunderstorm-Related Phenomena

A precipitation phenomenon associated with thunderstorms in the mid-latitudes is the formation of *hail*. Figure 12.6B shows that, in the mature stage of the storm, an ice crystal might be caught in a circulation that continually moves it above and below the freezing level. This circulation pattern can create concentric shells of ice in the hailstone. In some storms, such as a *squall-line storm*, these circulations can be exaggerated. Figure 12.8 demonstrates how falling hailstones can be scooped back into the main cloud by the intense circulation around such a storm system. Thus, hailstones may experience several journeys through the freezing level before falling to Earth. Many a farmer's crop has been destroyed because of these conditions, when hailstones as large as softballs can bombard the ground. Figure 12.8 also indicates that squall-line storms can generate even more severe weather in the form of *tornadoes*.

Lightning and *thunder* are related phenomena, and both are a result of the thunderstorm's powerful vertical air currents. Although the exact mechanism is not fully understood, cloud droplets and ice crystals acquire electrical charges. This electric energy, in the form of lightning strokes, makes intermittent contact with the ground. These lightning strokes also rapidly heat the surrounding air, which expands explosively—producing thunder.

Thunderstorms do not usually exist as a single cell as illustrated in Figure 12.6. Radar studies have shown that thunderstorms actually consist of several cells organized into clusters, ranging from 2 to 8 km in diameter. Occasionally these clusters expand over a much wider area and

LINK

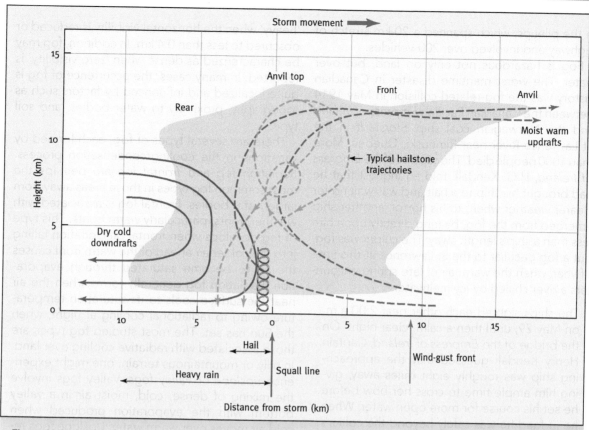

Figure 12.8 Model of a thunderstorm producing sizable hailstones. This squall-line storm is advancing from left to right.

Perspectives on the Human Environment

Fog

On Canada's highways, more than 50 fatal collisions occur each year in dense fog/smog/mist conditions (Transport Canada, 2001). From a global perspective, Canada is home to some of the foggiest places on Earth. On 3 September 1999, a dense early-morning fog enveloped sections of Highway 401 near Windsor, contributing to one of the worst road disasters in Canadian history. Eight people died, and a total of 82 vehicles were destroyed in the pileup, many having fused together in the intense heat. Moments before the crash, visibility had been reduced to about a metre by the sudden occurrence of dense fog just after sunrise. Because of the small scale of the fog event and lack of *in situ* measurements in the area of the accident, it was difficult to analyze the fog and no definitive answers on its formation could be provided. On 17 March 2003, a series of accidents on Highway 400 near Barrie, Ontario, was blamed on another occurrence of thick morning fog, the result of warm temperatures and rapidly melting snow. Two dozen people were injured in the pileups, which spanned a 20-km stretch of highway and involved over 200 vehicles.

Fog is hazardous not only on land, but over water. The worst maritime disaster in Canadian history was the fog-related collision in May 1914 between the Canadian Pacific's *Empress of Ireland* and the Norwegian coal ship *Storstadt* in the St Lawrence River near Rimouski, Quebec. More than 1000 people died. The captain of the *Empress of Ireland*, H.G. Kendall, told an inquest that he had brought his ship to a halt and was waiting for clearer weather when, to his horror, another ship emerged from the fog, bearing directly upon him less than a ship's length away. The culprit was fog, but a fog peculiar to the St Lawrence at this time of year, when the warm air of late spring encounters a river chilled by icy meltwater.

> The ships sighted each other near 2:00 a.m. on May 29, until then a calm, clear night. On the bridge of the *Empress of Ireland*, Captain Henry Kendall guessed that the approaching ship was roughly eight miles away, giving him ample time to cross her bow before he set his course for more open water. When he judged he was safely beyond the collier's path, he did so. If he held his new course, the two ships should pass starboard side to starboard side, comfortably apart. Moments after he had executed this maneuver, a creeping bank of fog swallowed the Norwegian ship, then the *Empress*. (www.pbs.org/lostliners/empress.html)

Within Canada, meteorologists and the aviation community define *fog* as a suspension of very small water droplets that reduces the horizontal visibility to less than 1 km. The fog is defined as

'heavy' when the horizontal visibility is reduced or obscured to less than 0.4 km. In addition, fog may be characterized as dense when 'zero visibility' is reported. In many cases, the occurrence of fog is quite localized and influenced by factors such as topography, proximity to water bodies, and soil type.

There are several types of **fog**, each formed by variations in the cooling/condensation process. *Radiation fog* and *frontal fog* are perhaps the most common fog types in those areas away from large water bodies. Frontal fog is associated with weather fronts, particularly warm fronts. This type of fog develops when frontal precipitation falling into the colder air ahead of the warm front causes the air to become saturated through evaporation. Radiation fog generally forms when the air near the surface cools to its saturation temperature owing to radiational cooling at night, when the Sun has set. The most studied fog types are those associated with radiative cooling over land. In hilly or mountainous terrain, one might experience *upslope* or *valley fogs*. Valley fogs involve the mixing of dense, cold, moist air in a valley bottom with the evaporation produced when cold air moves over warm water. Upslope fogs result from air that is forced to rise upslope along a topographic barrier, cooling as it rises. During that cooling, if the air temperature falls below the dew point, the resulting condensation will form a cloud. If that cloud hugs the ground, it becomes fog at that surface.

Advection fog, another relatively well-studied fog type, is associated with the advection of a moist air mass that has contrasting temperature properties with respect to the underlying surface. Advection fog is produced when air that is warmer and more moist than the ground surface moves over the ground surface. The term *advection* means a horizontal movement of air. Unlike radiation fog, advection fog can occur in windy conditions. Also unlike radiation fog, advection fog can occur when the skies aloft are initially cloudy. The set-up for advection fog often includes an advection pattern that brings in warmer and moister air from the south. The primary form of fog in the Maritimes region is due to advection of high dewpoint air relative to cool sea surface temperatures (SSTs). The SSTs in the Northumberland Strait between Prince Edward Island and Nova Scotia and New Brunswick become warmer faster (20°C to 21°C by late July) than along the Atlantic coast of mainland Nova Scotia. Also, there are frequent cool water upwelling events along Nova Scotia's Atlantic coast.

LINK

Figure 12.9   The *Empress of Ireland*, which went down in May 1914 after a collision with a coal freighter in the St Lawrence River in thick springtime fog.

Many coastal regions of Canada also suffer from *coastal fog* that forms when moist air is cooled to saturation point by travelling over a cooler sea. The wind may then take the fog into coastal regions. This type of fog tends to occur in spring and summer, and particularly affects parts of Newfoundland and Nova Scotia, as well as Prince Edward Island (Figure 12.10). So-called *sea fog* is an example of advection fog that is well known in coastal regions of Canada. Because sea fog typically occurs as a result of warm marine air advection over a region affected by a cold ocean current, it is common at sea in locations where boundaries with cold ocean currents can be found, such as the Grand Banks of Newfoundland (Gultepe et al., 2007).

One of the foggiest parts of the country is Newfoundland, where the total number of hours of bright sunshine is usually less than 1600 hours a year, which is well below Summerside's (PEI) average of 1959 hours, Calgary's 2314 hours, and the Canadian average of 1925 hours. The waters off the Avalon Peninsula and over the Grand Banks are among the foggiest in the world. The fogs, sometimes known as 'sea smoke', develop when warm, humid air from the south strikes the cold, sometimes ice-infested waters of the Labrador Current. These fogs may occur in all seasons, but on average they are most frequent in the spring and early summer when the contrast between sea and air temperatures is greatest (anywhere between 5°C and 15°C). Surprisingly, the fogs are often accompanied by strong winds. Normally, winds can be expected to disperse fog, but here the fog is frequently so dense and widespread that the winds have little clearing effect. The resulting conditions can be hazardous for shipping and for drilling rigs, especially when icebergs are present.

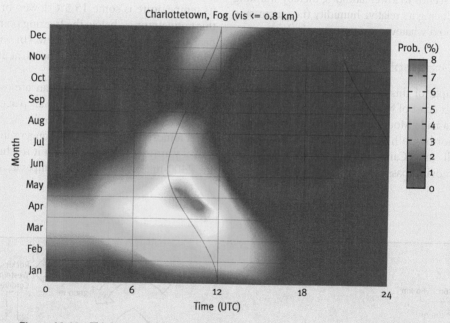

Figure 12.10   This image shows that the likelihood of fog at Charlottetown, PEI, is greatest in the morning hours during spring and summer.

assume their own rotation, thereby forming *supercells* and even larger *mesoscale convective complexes*. As the storms advance, new cells develop to replace old ones that dissipate. If the downdrafts of two cells meet at the surface, a new updraft and a new cell can form.

Convectional thunderstorms are the dominant type of precipitation in the equatorial zone and are especially active in the vicinity of the ITCZ (where the convergence of the trade winds accentuates the uplifting of air). Heat is a constant feature of the surface environment in the low latitudes. That heat, coupled with the generally high water-vapour content of tropical equatorial air, produces impressive convectional storms of the type seen in Figure 12.5.

Orographic Precipitation

Mountains, and highlands in general, strongly influence air and moisture flows in the atmosphere. During *orographic uplift* (*oros* is the Greek word for mountain), a moving mass of air encounters a mountain range or other upland zone over which it is forced to rise, propelled by surface winds and the push of air piling up behind it. When a mountain range is close to and parallels the coast, and when prevailing onshore winds carry maritime air laden with moisture, not much cooling is needed to trigger condensation during the forced ascent of this airflow. The rain (and often snow) that results from this lifting process is called **orographic precipitation**.

This precipitation on the range's windward slopes, however, is not matched on the inland-facing leeward slopes. Quite to the contrary, the lee side of the range is marked by dryness because much of the water vapour gained over the ocean has been precipitated out during the windward-slope ascent. Once the mass of air crests the range in a stable atmosphere that does not force it to continue to rise, the air immediately descends to lower altitudes, thereby warming rapidly and reducing its relative humidity (i.e., increasing its capacity to hold whatever moisture remains).

Stages of Orographic Uplift

A classic example of this orographic effect exists along most of the west coast of North America, where the Sierra Nevada, the Cascade Mountains, and the coastal mountains form a north–south wall extending from southern California well into Canada. Figure 12.11 illustrates the eastward-moving passage of moist Pacific air across the Coastal and Cascade Mountains of southwestern British Columbia, specifically between Vancouver at the edge of the southern Strait of Georgia and Kamloops in the Thompson Valley, located in south-central British Columbia. Between these two cities lies Stein Valley Provincial Park, with peaks rising to 2925 m at the summit of Skihist Mountain.

Let us assume that a parcel of air with a temperature of 21°C arrives at the near-sea-level western base of the coastal mountains in Vancouver. This parcel of air begins its forced ascent of the mountain range and starts to cool at the DALR (1°C/100 m). At this rate, the air parcel cools to 15°C by the time it reaches 600 m. Now assume that the air reaches its dew point at this temperature and condensation begins. Clouds quickly form, and continued cooling soon leads to heavy rainfall as the air parcel continues to make its way up the windward slope.

Because saturation has occurred and condensation has begun, however, the air above 600 m cools more slowly at the saturated adiabatic lapse rate (SALR)—here assumed to average 0.65°C/100 m. By the time the uplifted air reaches the mountaintop at an altitude of 3000 m, its temperature is some 15.5°C lower, or −0.5°C. Since this temperature is below the freezing point, precipitation near the summit will fall as snow. (In winter, of course, freezing and snowfall will commence at a lower elevation on the mountainside.)

Having crested the range in an atmospheric environment presumed to be stable, the air parcel seeks its original level and swiftly descends to the warmer layer of the lower atmosphere. The air is no longer saturated, so the air parcel warms at the DALR. When it reaches the bottom of the 2400-m leeward slope, its temperature will have risen

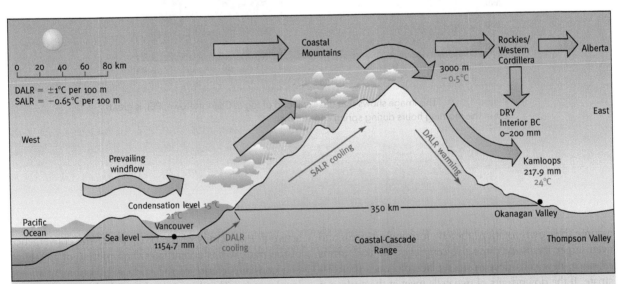

Figure 12.11 Orographic precipitation on the upper windward slope of the Coastal-Cascade Mountains in western British Columbia. Note the significant temperature and moisture differences between the windward and leeward sides of this major mountain barrier. (Horizontal scale is not exact.)

by 24.5°C to 24°C. The air parcel has become noticeably warmer on the lee side of the range, even though the elevation around Kamloops is 300 m higher than at Vancouver. It is also much drier, as explained before, and the generally dry condition caused by this orographic process is termed the **rain shadow effect**.

In the absence of new moisture sources, rain shadows can extend for hundreds of kilometres. This is the case throughout most of far western North America, because once Pacific moisture is removed from the atmosphere, it cannot be replenished locally. Figure 12.12 vividly illustrates the rain shadow covering the central region of British Columbia. Secondary orographic precipitation occurs as air rises over the Rocky Mountains in the province's eastern border with Alberta. Leeward areas also frequently experience the rapid movement of warm, dry air known as a *foehn* ('fern' with the 'r' silent) wind. Above the western plateaus of Canada and the United States, these airflows

are called *chinook* winds and can sometimes reach sustained speeds approaching 50 m per second.

Frontal (Cyclonic) Precipitation

A fourth process that generates precipitation is associated with the collision of air masses of significantly different temperatures. Such activity is a common occurrence in the middle and upper-middle latitudes, where the general atmospheric circulation causes poleward-flowing tropical air to collide with polar air moving towards the Equator. Because converging warm and cold air masses possess different densities, they do not readily mix. Rather, the denser cold air will inject itself beneath and push the lighter warm air upward. And if the warmer air approaches a stationary mass of cooler air, it will ride up over the cooler air. In both

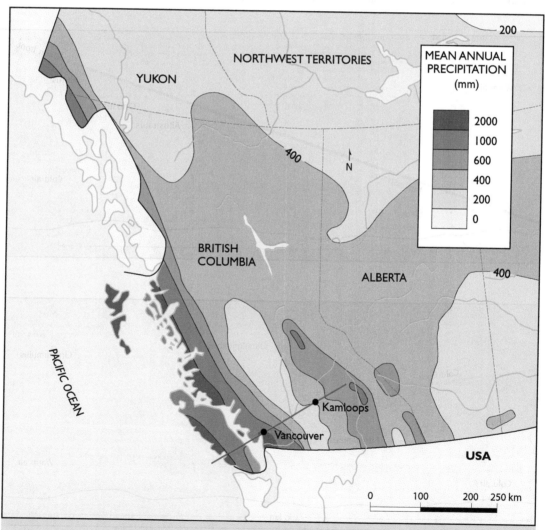

Figure 12.12 British Columbia's precipitation pattern, with the distribution of isohyets exhibiting the results of the orographic effect as westerly winds off the Pacific are forced across the north–south-trending Coastal-Cascade Mountains. The transect across the Coastal-Cascades between Vancouver and Kamloops, diagrammed in Figure 12.11, is marked by a red line.

situations we have the lifting of warm, often moist air, the cooling of which soon produces condensation, clouds, and precipitation.

Air masses are bounded by surfaces along which contact occurs with neighbouring air masses possessing different characteristics. Therefore such narrow boundary zones mark sharp transitions in density, humidity, and especially temperature. Whenever warm and cool air contact like this, the boundary zone is called a **front**. Although fronts can be stationary, they usually advance; a moving front is the leading edge of the air mass built up behind it. When warm air is lifted, cooled, and its water vapour condensed as a result of frontal movement, **frontal (cyclonic) precipitation** is produced.

When a warm air mass infringes upon a cooler one, the lighter warmer air overrides the cooler air. This produces a boundary called a **warm front** (Figure 12.13A). Warm fronts, because of their gentle upward slope, are associated with wide areas of light to moderate precipitation that extend out well ahead of the actual surface passage of the front. As indicated in the diagram, warm fronts involve the entire sequence of stratus clouds, ranging from upper-level cirrostratus down through altostratus and nimbostratus layers (see Figure 11.11).

The behaviour of a cold front is far more dramatic. A **cold front** is produced when the cold air, acting like a bulldozer, hugs the surface and pushes all other air upward as it wedges itself beneath the warmer air (Figure 12.13B). A cold front also assumes a steeper slope than a warm front, causing more abrupt cooling and condensation in the warm air that is lifted just ahead of it. This produces a smaller but much more intense zone of precipitation, which usually exhibits the kind of stormy weather associated with the convectional precipitation process discussed earlier. Not surprisingly, cold fronts exhibit a variety of cumulus-type clouds, particularly the clusters of cumulonimbus clouds that are the signature of squall-line thunderstorms. But once the swiftly passing violent weather ends, the cool air mass behind the front produces generally fair and dry weather.

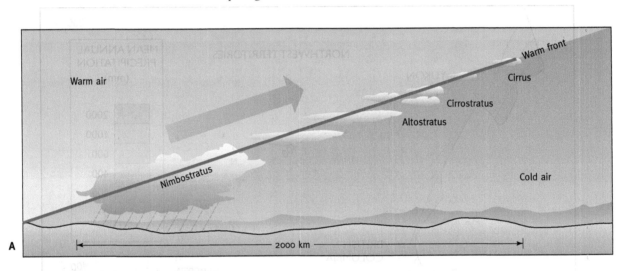

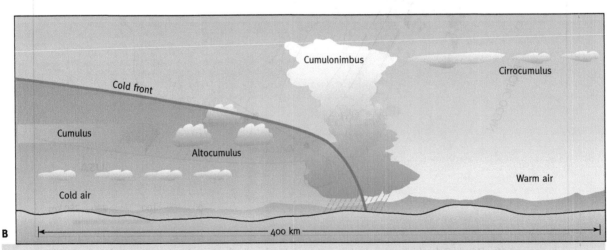

Figure 12.13 Warm front (A) and cold front (B) in cross-sectional profile, showing their associated cloud types. Note that the spatial extent of a cold front (up to 2000 km) is much broader than the spatial extent of a warm front (up to 400 km).

Frontal precipitation is frequently called *cyclonic precipitation* because it is closely identified with the passage of the warm and cold fronts that are essential components of the cyclones that shape the weather patterns of the mid-latitudes. In Unit 13, on weather systems, we examine the life cycle of these storm cells and their fronts, extending the discussion developed here. The rest of this unit takes a closer look at air masses (whose movement triggers these weather systems) and introduces a geographic classification based on the source regions of air masses.

Air Masses in the Atmosphere

In large, relatively uniform expanses of the world, such as the snow-covered Arctic wastes or the warm tropical oceans, masses of air in contact with the surface may remain stationary for several days. As the air hovers over these areas, it takes on the properties of the underlying surface, such as the icy coldness of the polar zones or the warmth and high humidity of the maritime tropics. Extensive geographic areas with relatively uniform characteristics of temperature and moisture form the **source regions** where air masses can be produced.

The air above a source region will reach an equilibrium with the temperature and moisture conditions of the surface. An **air mass** can thus be defined as a very large parcel of air in the boundary layer of the troposphere that possesses relatively uniform qualities of temperature, density, and humidity in the horizontal dimension. In addition to its large size, which is regarded by meteorologists to be at least 1600 km across, an air mass must be bound together as a cohesive unit. This is necessary because air masses travel as distinct entities, covering hundreds of kilometres as they are steered away from their source regions by the airflows of the general atmospheric circulation.

Classifying Air Masses

To keep track of their identities as they migrate, air masses are given the following letter codes that reflect the type of surface and the general location of their source region: maritime (*m*) or continental (*c*); tropical (*T*) or polar (*P*). In a warm source region, such as the Caribbean Sea, the equilibrium of temperature and moisture in an overlying air mass is established in two or three days. Unstable air in either a maritime tropical (*mT*) air mass or a continental tropical (*cT*) air mass is warmed to a height of about 3000 m.

In contrast, within cold source regions air masses can take a week or more to achieve equilibrium with their underlying surfaces. Only a relatively shallow layer of air, up to about 900 m, cools in continental polar (*cP*) or maritime polar (*mP*) air masses. Of course, the air above that level is cold as well, but for reasons other than contact with the surface. It takes a relatively long time for a cold air mass to become established because cooling at its base stabilizes lapse rates, thereby preventing vertical mixing and prohibiting efficient heat exchange.

In addition to the four leading types of air masses (*mT*, *cT*, *mP*, and *cP*), three more can be recognized. The first is found in the highest latitudes and is called continental Arctic (*cA*) (or continental Antarctic [*cAA*] in the Southern Hemisphere); paradoxically, these form at higher latitudes than the polar air masses do. The final two are found in the lowest latitudes astride the Equator and are continental equatorial (*cE*) and maritime equatorial (*mE*). The letter pairs used to label air masses are sometimes supplemented by letters that indicate whether the mass is colder (*k*) or warmer (*w*) than the underlying surface, and whether the air is stable (*s*) or unstable (*u*). Thus a maritime tropical air mass that is warmer than the ocean below it and unstable is designated as *mTwu*.

Movements of Air Masses

If you live in the US Midwest, you can testify to the bitterness of the polar air that streams southward from Canada in the winter and the oppressiveness of the warm humid air that flows northward from the Gulf of Mexico in the summer. Air masses affect not only their source areas, but also the regions across which they migrate. As an air mass moves, it may become somewhat modified by contact with the surface or by changes within the air, but many of its original characteristics remain identifiable far from its source region. This is a boon to weather forecasters, because they can predict weather conditions more accurately if they know the persisting characteristics of a moving air mass as well as its rate and direction of movement.

The principal air masses affecting North America are shown in Figure 12.14. Once the jet stream picks them up, the frontal systems (the meeting points between opposing air masses) move from the west to the east. The arrows represent the most common paths of movement away from the various source regions indicated on the map. If the contents of this map look like a military battle plan, that may be because opposing air masses fight for supremacy throughout the year. Losses and gains of territory in this battle are controlled by one important factor: the Polar Front and its associated jet stream. The main current of a river does not let eddies pass from one bank to another, and so it is with the Polar Front jet stream, which provides an unseen barrier to advancing air masses. This is a key to understanding weather in most of Canada, and our discussion of the Polar Front jet stream, begun in Unit 9, is developed further in Unit 13.

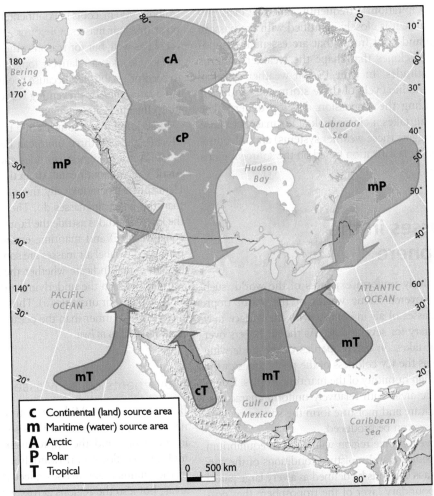

Figure 12.14 Source regions and the most likely paths of the principal air masses that affect North America.

KEY TERMS

air mass   *page 165*
cold front   *page 164*
collision-coalescence   *page 154*
convection   *page 156*
convectional precipitation   *page 156*
convergent-lifting precipitation   *page 155*
fog (types of)   *page 160*

front   *page 164*
frontal (cyclonic) precipitation   *page 164*
orographic precipitation   *page 164*
rain shadow effect   *page 163*
source region   *page 165*
thunderstorm   *page 157*
warm front   *page 164*

REVIEW QUESTIONS

1. What are the processes that lead to the development of precipitation in warm and cold clouds?

2. What are the necessary conditions for convectional precipitation? What are some of the more severe types of weather associated with this type of precipitation?

3. Describe the geographic pattern of precipitation on the windward and leeward flanks of a mountain range.

4. Describe the general precipitation characteristics associated with a warm front.

5. Describe the general precipitation characteristics associated with a cold front.

6. Describe the characteristics of the four major air mass types: *mT, cT, mP,* and *cP*.

7. Describe the different kinds of fog and the processes that cause them to form.

REFERENCES AND FURTHER READINGS

Battan, L.J. 1984. *Fundamentals of Meteorology*, 2nd edn. Englewood Cliffs, NJ: Prentice-Hall, chs 6 and 7.

Few, A.A. 1975. 'Thunder', *Scientific American* (July): 80–90.

Gultepe, I., R. Tardif, S.C. Michaelides, J. Cermak, A. Bott, J. Bendix, M.D. Müller, M. Pagowski, B. Hansen, G. Ellrod, W. Jacobs, G. Toth, and S.G. Cober. 2007. 'Fog Research: A Review of Past Achievements and Future Perspectives', *Pure and Applied Geophysics* 164: 1121–59.

Hanson, B. 2006. 'Study of Fog Climatology of Canada'. At: <collaboration.cmc.ec.gc.ca/science/arma/climatology/regions.html>.

Heidorn, K. 2002. 'The Fog Rolls In'. At: <www.islandnet.com/~see/weather/almanac/arc2002/alm02sep.htm>.

Kessler, E., ed. 1986. *Thunderstorm Morphology and Dynamics*, 2nd edn. Norman, Okla: Univ. of Oklahoma Press.

Middleton, W. 1968. *History of Theories of Rain and Other Forms of Precipitation*. Chicago: Univ. of Chicago Press.

Paul, A. 1982. 'The Thunderstorm Hazard on the Canadian Prairies', *Geoforum* 13: 275–88.

Transport Canada. 2001. 'Trends in Motor Vehicle Traffic Collision Statistics, 1988–1997', Prepared by the Road Safety and Motor Vehicle Regulation Directorate, Feb.

Whiteman, C.D. 2000. *Mountain Meteorology: Fundamentals and Applications*. New York: Oxford Univ. Press.

Williams, E.R. 1988. 'The Electrification of Thunderstorms', *Scientific American* (Nov.): 88–99.

 ## WEB RESOURCES

archive.greenpeace.org/climate/flood_report/1-3.html An explanation of the geographic distribution of precipitation, as well as descriptions of the different types of precipitation.

www.ps-sp.gc.ca/res/em/nh/isif/index-eng.aspx Public Safety Canada site that includes information on icebergs, sea ice, and fog.

www.tpub.com/weather1/4c.htm A description of cloud and precipitation features of warm and cold fronts, with satellite imagery of frontal systems.

Unit 13

Weather Systems

Objectives

- To demonstrate the importance of migrating weather systems in the global weather picture.

- To discuss the significant tropical weather systems.

- To explain how mid-latitude cyclones are formed, and to describe the weather patterns associated with them.

LINK

LINK

LINK

LINK

Weather systems are organized phenomena of the atmosphere—with inputs and outputs and changes of energy and moisture. Unlike the semi-permanent pressure cells and windflows of the general circulation, these transient weather systems are secondary features of the atmosphere that are far more limited in their magnitude and duration. Such recurring weather systems, together with the constant flows of moisture, radiation, and heat energy, make up our daily weather. This unit focuses on the migrating atmospheric disturbances we call **storms**. We begin by looking at the storm systems of the tropics, which are typically associated with heavy precipitation. We then shift our focus from the low latitudes to the storm systems that punctuate the weather patterns of the middle and higher latitudes.

Low-Latitude Weather Systems

The equatorial and tropical latitudes are marked by a surplus of heat, which provides the energy to propel winds and to evaporate the large quantities of seawater that are often carried by them. The abundance of water vapour, convergence of the trade winds, and frequent convection produce the heavy rains that are observed in the tropics. Two of the major low-latitude weather systems are covered in other units. In Unit 12 we discussed the largest system, the Inter-Tropical Convergence Zone (ITCZ), and in Unit 9 we examined the related monsoonal circulation of coastal Asia. Here we investigate the smaller-scale, moving weather systems that recur in tropical regions—easterly waves and hurricanes.

Easterly Waves

For centuries, people have known about the trade winds, the constant easterly surface flow of tropical air between 30°N and 30°S latitude. But only within the past four decades has it been discovered that this flow is frequently modified by wavelike phenomena that give rise to distinctive weather systems. Unit 8 explains that geostrophic winds parallel isobars. If we apply this relationship to Figure 13.1, we see that the isobars indicate the easterly trade winds blowing across the tropical North Atlantic Ocean. The **easterly wave** depicted represents a vertical perturbation within the general flow of these winds.

Through fairly complex mechanisms, this easterly wave produces both uplift and descent of air. Westward-moving air is forced to rise on the upwind side of the wave and descend on the downwind side. Therefore, on the eastern side of such a wave, we can expect to find towering cumulus clouds and frequent heavy rainfall. But clear weather occurs on the leading western side of the low-pressure wave trough because the air column decreases in depth, and atmospheric subsidence prevails.

Weather systems associated with easterly waves (which also go by their more popular name, *tropical waves*) are most frequently observed in the Caribbean Basin. Similar phenomena are also common in the west-central Pacific and in the seas off China's central east coast. These systems travel westward at about 18 to 26 km/h and are relatively predictable in their movement. But for reasons that are not well understood, each year certain easterly waves increase their intensity. As these weak low-pressure troughs deepen, they begin to assume a rotating, cyclonic organization.

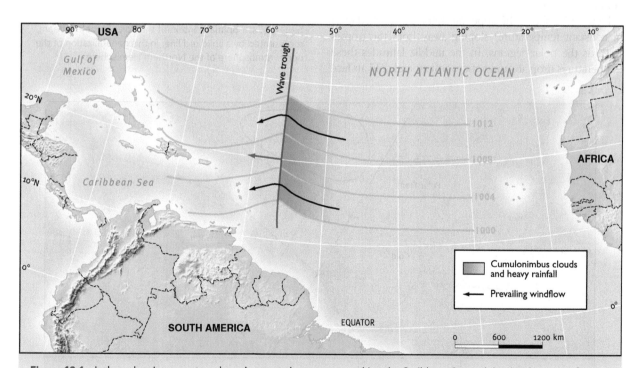

Figure 13.1 Isobars showing a westward-moving easterly wave approaching the Caribbean Sea and the development of towering rain clouds along its trailing limb.

Such a disturbance is called a **tropical depression**. If the low intensifies and sustained wind speeds surpass 63 km/h, the weather system becomes a **tropical storm**. If the fully formed tropical cyclone exhibits sustained winds in excess of 119 km/h, a hurricane is born. Hurricanes, as well as other forms of severe weather, are discussed in detail in Unit 14.

Weather Systems of the Middle and Higher Latitudes

LINK

The general atmospheric circulation of the middle and higher latitudes exhibits some basic differences from that of the tropical latitudes. The principal difference is the frequent interaction of dissimilar air masses. In the higher latitudes, high-pressure and low-pressure systems moving eastward are carried along by the westerly winds of the upper air. In the middle latitudes, air of different origins—cold, warm, moist, dry—constantly comes together, and fast-flowing jet streams are associated with sharp differences in temperature. Therefore, the weather is much more changeable in the higher latitudes than in the tropics.

The Polar Front Jet Stream

Unit 10 explains how the fast-flowing upper air currents of the jet streams are related to the process of moving warm air from the tropics and cold air from the high latitudes. Unit 12 points out that jet streams may also be thought of as boundaries between large areas of cold and warm air. One of them, the Polar Front jet stream, although not in itself a weather system, controls the most important mid-latitude weather systems.

Figure 13.2 shows the upper-air isotherms (dashed lines of constant temperature) sloping away from the tropics towards the polar regions. In the middle latitudes these temperatures drop abruptly, and warm air and cold air face

each other horizontally. As we know, such a narrow zone of contact constitutes a front. The *Polar Front*, therefore, separates relatively cold polar air from relatively warm tropical air, and the jet stream associated with this temperature divide is called the **Polar Front jet stream** (Figure 13.2). As noted in Unit 9, at the core of the wavelike westerly winds of the upper troposphere, the Polar Front jet stream snakes its way around the globe in large meanders (Figure 13.3).

These meanders develop in response to fairly complex physical laws that govern the movement of high-velocity air currents in the upper atmosphere. The important thing to remember is that they cause airflows to converge and diverge strongly in the vicinity of the meander bends. The upper atmospheric convergence and divergence cause the air to subside (under the area of convergence) or ascend (under the area of divergence). As a result, these zones have important implications for the surface pressure pattern and attendant weather. The significance of the Polar Front jet stream can be demonstrated by considering the process of **cyclogenesis**—the formation, evolution, and movement of mid-latitude cyclones.

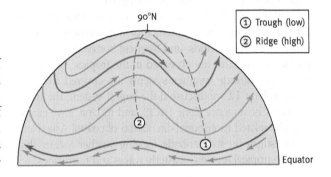

Figure 13.3 Spatial context of the Polar Front jet stream, represented by a solid red line, in this generalization of the upper atmosphere of the Northern Hemisphere.

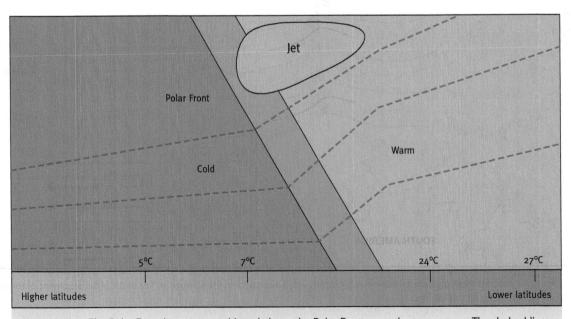

Figure 13.2 The Polar Front jet stream positioned above the Polar Front, near the tropopause. The dashed lines represent upper-air isotherms (lines of constant temperature).

Perspectives on the Human Environment

LINK

Mount Everest and the Jet Stream

Winds blow at hurricane strengths at the summit of Mount Everest nearly all year long. Why is it so windy at the so-called 'top of the world'? The explanation can be found in the jet stream, which is a constant wind force at 6.4–9.6 km above Earth's surface. Observers can tell when the jet stream is blowing on the summit of Everest from the long white stream of ice crystals extending out from the tip of the mountain. Mountain climbers have to plan their ascent itinerary very carefully: the mountain is most inviting in early May, when the jet stream is pushed northward over Tibet by the arrival of the monsoon. There is also a window of opportunity in the fall when the Jet Stream is again pushed northward. In the spring of 2002

a National Geographic 50th Anniversary Everest Expedition set out to commemorate the first ascent of the world's highest mountain, by Edmund Hillary and Tenzing Norgay in May 1953. During the ascent, jet-stream winds of up to 120 km/hr trapped several climbing expeditions on the slopes of Mount Everest, including the group sponsored by the National Geographic Society. At the summit the winds were estimated to have reached in excess of 200 km/hr! The climbers were fortunate to have remained at lower elevations where the winds remained a relatively 'calm' 70–120 km/hr. The summit of Everest is the windiest place on Earth. The highest forecasted wind speed during 2002–4 was 280 km/hr, above the threshold for a Category 5 hurricane.

Figure 13.4   A plume of ice crystals blown by the jet stream from the top of Mount Everest.

LINK

In addition to extreme winds, the air is very thin on Everest. As the altitude *increases*, the oxygen content of the air *decreases* dramatically. At 3000 m, for example, the air contains about two-thirds of the oxygen present in air at sea level. At 6000 m, the proportion of oxygen drops to about half. The air at 8844 m, the summit of Everest, includes only a third of the oxygen contained in air at sea level.

Mount Everest is situated at the edge of the Tibetan Plateau, on the border between Nepal and Tibet. The climate of Mount Everest is naturally extreme. In January, the coldest month, the summit temperature averages about −36° C and can drop as low as −60° C. In July, the warmest month, the average summit temperature is −19° C. At no time of the year does the temperature on the summit rise above freezing. In winter and spring the prevailing westerly wind blows around the summit.

Moisture-laden air rises from the south slopes of the Himalayas and condenses into a white, pennant-shaped cloud pointing east; this 'flag cloud' sometimes enables climbers to predict storms. When the wind reaches about 80 km/hr, the flag cloud is at a right angle to the peak. When the wind is weaker, the cloud tilts up; when it is stronger, the flag tilts down—a sign to climbers to avoid a run for the summit.

From June through September, Everest is in the grip of the Indian monsoon, a period when wind and precipitation blow in from the Indian Ocean. Masses of clouds and violent snowstorms are common during this time. In winter, from November to February, the global southwest-flowing jet stream moves in from the north, beating the summit with winds of hurricane force that may reach more than 285 km/hr.

Mid-latitude Cyclones

The weather at the Earth's surface in the mid-latitudes is largely determined by the position of the Polar Front jet stream. In Figure 13.5A, the jet stream passes across North America 9000 m above the ground. The air in the jet stream converges at point **X**, as shown in cross-section (Figure 13.5B). The converging air undergoes an increase in density, and so it descends. The descending air causes high pressure at the surface, as shown in Figure 13.5C, and spreads out or diverges from the surface anticyclone. At point **X**, therefore, we could expect fair weather because of the descending air.

Meanwhile, farther downwind in the eastward-flowing jet stream, at point **Y**, the air in the jet stream diverges. The diverging air aloft must be replaced, and air is drawn up from below. As air is drawn up the column, a converging cyclonic circulation develops at the surface, exhibiting its characteristic low pressure. The rising air cools, forming clouds that soon produce precipitation. In this manner, the jet stream becomes the primary cause of fair weather when it generates upper atmospheric convergence, and of stormy weather when it produces divergence.

Life Cycle of a Mid-latitude Cyclone On most days, spiral cloud bands can be observed in the mid-latitude atmosphere. The unit-opening satellite image shows a huge, spiralling mid-latitude cyclone over the North Atlantic Ocean northwest of the British Isles. These are the most common large-scale weather systems found outside the tropics. The mid-latitude cyclone, like its low-latitude counterpart, goes by several names. It is often called a *depression* or an *extratropical* (meaning outside the tropics) *cyclone*. A mid-latitude cyclone is characterized by its circular windflow and low-pressure field as well as by the interaction of air of different properties. As with many atmospheric weather systems, it possesses a definite life cycle.

LINK

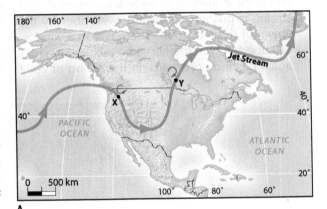

A

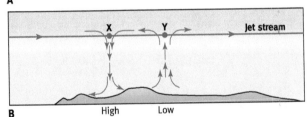

B

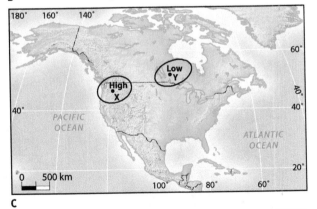

C

Figure 13.5 Relationship between the Polar Front jet stream and surface pressure patterns. (A) Position of the jet stream 9000 m above North America. (B) Associated air movement around points **X** and **Y** in vertical cross section. (C) Resulting surface pressure conditions.

Figure 13.6A shows the early stage in the development of a mid-latitude cyclone. A mass of cold air and a mass of warm air lie side by side, with the boundary between them called a **stationary front**. Divergent upper airflow causes a slight cyclonic motion at the surface, and a small kink

North

Cold air

Warm air

Early stage

A

Cold air

Warm air

Open-wave stage

B

Warm

Cold air

Cold

Warm air

Occluded stage

C

Warm

Cold air

Warm air

Dissipating stage

D

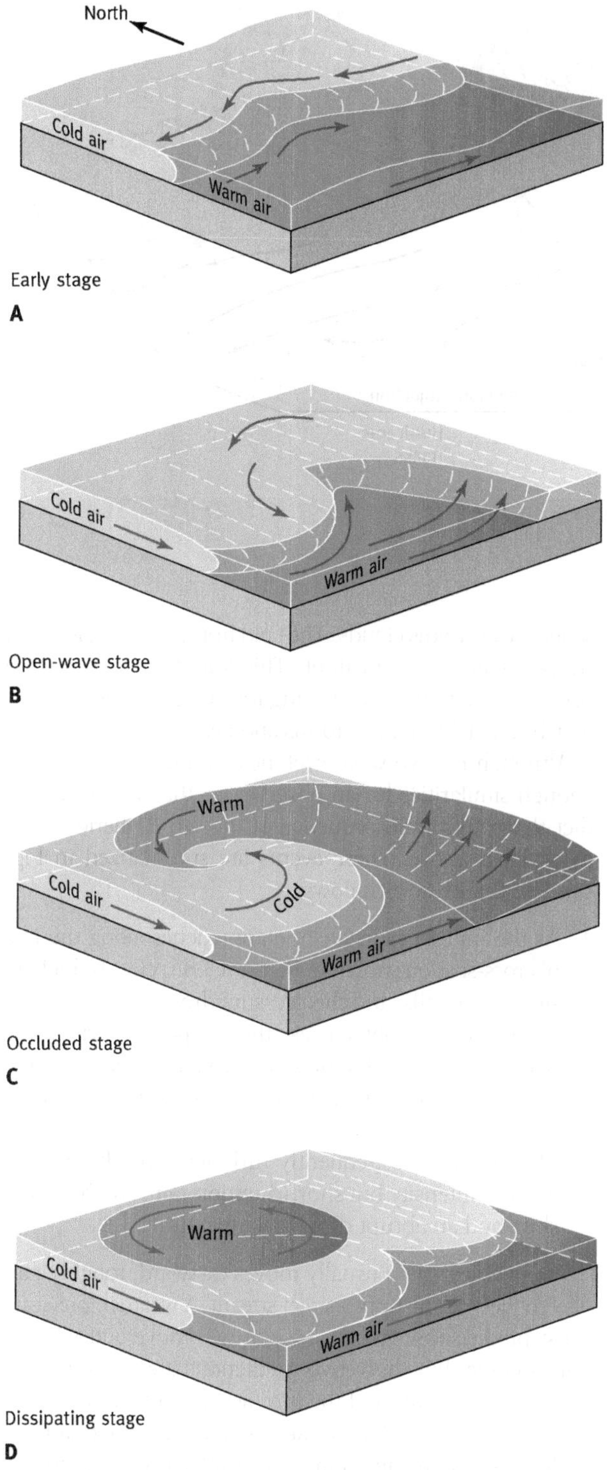

Figure 13.6 Four stages in the life cycle of a mid-latitude cyclone: (A) early, (B) open wave, (C) occlusion, and (D) dissipation. After Arthur N. Strahler, copyright Arthur N. Strahler.

appears in the stationary front. As the surface cyclonic motion develops, the kink grows larger and becomes an **open wave**, as indicated in Figure 13.6B. In this open-wave stage, the warm air and cold air interact in distinct ways. On the eastern side of the cyclone, warm air now glides up over the colder air mass along a surface that has become a warm front. To the west, the advancing cold air—now a cold front—injects itself beneath the warm air in an action resembling that of a snowplow.

The open-wave stage represents maturity in the life cycle of a mid-latitude cyclone, but generally the energy of the circulation is spent within a few days. Figure 13.6C shows how the better-defined cold front travels faster than the warm front, overtaking it first at the centre of the cyclone. When this happens, the snub-nosed cold front lifts the warm air entirely off the ground, causing an **occluded front**—the surface boundary between the cold and cool air—to form. In time the entire wedge of surface warm air is lifted to the colder altitudes aloft, and the cyclone dissipates (Figure 13.6D). This weather system, however, does not die where it was born: the Polar Front jet stream has continually steered the cyclone eastward during its lifespan.

This wave model of the mid-latitude cyclone was first proposed by Norwegian weather forecasters more than 75 years ago. It has turned out to be a good forecasting tool, and we can see why if we look more closely at the open-wave stage.

Mid-latitude cyclones are distinct from tropical cyclones or hurricanes in that they generally occur at different altitudes and have different impacts. Hurricanes involve much greater amounts of atmospheric energy exchange. With increasing distance from the equator, the energy available to fuel a weather system decreases as the amount of solar radiation and heat declines. Mid-latitude cyclones can have winds as strong as those associated with a weak hurricane, however. For example, in March 1993, a mid-latitude cyclone migrated up the east coast of the United States and Canada, producing a severe blizzard and killing more than 240 people. The highest winds ever recorded in Atlantic Canada (233 km/h) occurred in this storm. At one point during the storm, over 3 million people were left without electricity because of high wind and falling trees, a reminder of society's vulnerability to the features of severe weather systems.

Frontal cyclones tend to be most disruptive to human activity during winter months, when storms can produce heavy snowfalls or freezing rain. In January 1998, a storm in eastern North America resulted in more than 20 human deaths, billions of dollars of damage, the loss of electrical power in some areas for up to two weeks, and the destruction of extensive tracts of deciduous trees because of the weight of ice.

Some winter storms in Canada are topographically affected. The passage of an **extratropical cyclone** through topographically varying terrain can lead to the development of strong surface winds. Atlantic Canada and the west coast are particularly prone to this effect. Mountain ranges along

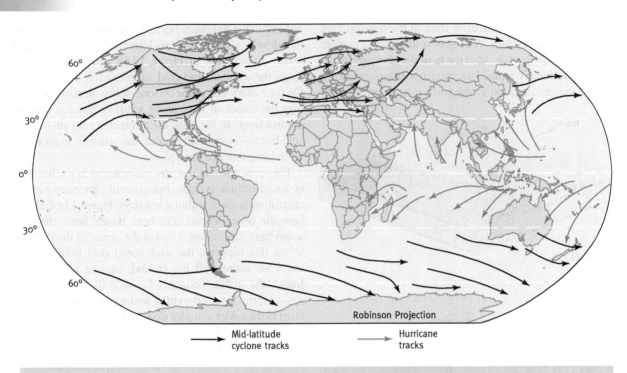

Figure 13.7   Mid-latitude cyclone tracks and hurricane tracks.

the west coasts of Cape Breton Island and Newfoundland are aligned southwest to northeast. When cyclones move relatively close to the coast, a strong southeasterly gradient wind is set up perpendicular to these mountain ranges. The southeasterly wind creates a mountain wave effect, which often brings severe downslope windstorms to the lee of the mountains (90–200 km/h). These winds occur several times a year and are well-known in local lore. In the Wreckhouse region of southwest Newfoundland, 20 km west of Port Aux Basques, they are called 'Wreckhouse winds', while the Acadians in Cape Breton refer to them as 'Les Suêtes'.

Weather Forecasting and the Open-Wave Stage   The most obvious features of Figure 13.8A, which shows a series of mid-latitude cyclones forming along the Polar Front, are the roughly circular configuration of the isobars and the positions of the fronts. Although the isobars are generally circular, they tend to be straight within the area enclosed by the cold and warm fronts. This wedge of warm air is called the *warm sector*. Also noteworthy is the *kinking*, or sharp angle, the isobars form at the fronts themselves.

Prevailing winds tend to cross the isobars at a slight angle—just as they should when friction at the Earth's surface partially upsets the geostrophic balance. Air gradually accumulates at the centre of the low-pressure cell. This converging air rises and cools, especially when it lifts at the fronts, and its water vapour condenses to produce a significant amount of precipitation. Maritime tropical air (**mTw**), warmer than the surface below it, forms the warm sector, and cold continental polar air (**cPk**) advances from the northwest.

In the cross-sectional view in Figure 13.8B, the warm front has the expected gentle slope. As the warm air moves up this slope, it cools and condenses to produce the characteristic

sequence of stratus clouds. The cold front, however, is much steeper than the warm front. This forces the warm air to rise much more rapidly, creating towering cumulus clouds, which can yield thunderstorms and heavy rains.

Although no two wave cyclones are identical, there are enough similarities for an observer on the ground to predict the pattern and sequence of the atmospheric events as outlined above. These events are summarized in Figure 13.8C and are as follows:

1. As the mid-latitude cyclone approaches along the line of cross-section shown in Figure 13.8A, clouds thicken, steady rain falls, and the pressure drops.
2. As the warm front passes, the temperature rises, the wind direction shifts, pressure remains steady, and the rain lets up or turns to occasional showers with the arrival of the warm sector.
3. Then comes the frequently turbulent cold front, with its high-intensity but short-duration rain, another wind shift, and an abrupt drop in temperature.

The whole system usually moves eastward, roughly parallel to the steering upper-air jet stream. A weather forecaster must predict how fast the system will move and when it will occlude. But those two predictions are often difficult and account for most of the forecasts that go awry.

Because it is so influential and prevalent, the mid-latitude cyclone is a dominant climatic control outside the tropics. These weather systems follow paths that move towards the poles in summer and towards the Equator in winter, always under the influence of the Polar Front and its jet stream. Their general eastward movement varies in speed from 0 to 60 km/h in winter, and from 0 to 40 km/h in summer. These wave cyclones may be from 300 to 3000 km in diameter

LINK

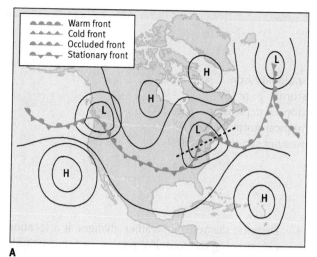

A

B

C

Post Cold Front	Warm Sector	Pre Warm Front	Sector / Weather Condition
Heavy rain, then clearing	Showers	Rain and fog	Precipitation
↘ ↘	↗ ↗	↗ ↗	Surface Wind Direction
Rising	Low steady	Falling	Pressure
Lower	Higher	Lower	Temperature

Figure 13.8 Mid-latitude cyclones over North America. (A) Pressure fields, windflows, and fronts. (B) Cross-sectional view along the dashed line mapped in (A). (C) Summary of surface weather conditions along the cross-sectional transect.

and range from 8 to 11 km in height. They provide the greatest source of rain in the mid-latitudes and they generate kinetic energy that helps power the primary circulation of the atmosphere.

Energy and Moisture within Weather Systems

As can be seen in satellite images and as your own experiences probably confirm, every day a multitude of weather systems parade across the planetary surface.

These systems entail the large-scale atmospheric disturbances of the tropical, middle, and higher latitudes discussed in this unit, which are fundamental to an understanding of the climates of those zones. They also involve the meso- (medium-) and small-scale systems that make up the daily texture of the atmosphere, such as monsoonal circulations (covered in Unit 9) and thunderstorms (Unit 12). Each weather system, though distinctive in detail, has a characteristic internal organization. In each, warm air is transformed into faster-moving air, and moisture becomes precipitation.

The processes of such transformations form a unique system, which is diagrammed in Figure 13.9. There are two inputs into this system: (1) warm air carrying the energy of heat, and (2) moisture in the form of water vapour. The heat energy of the rising warm air adds potential energy to the system, and the system's centre of gravity lifts higher off the ground. At the same time, the moisture condenses, which has two effects. First, the latent heat that is released helps to swell the store of potential energy; and second, the condensed moisture appears as clouds. There are outputs from the system as well. The growing store of potential energy changes to kinetic energy, and air movement increases. This kinetic energy leaves the system in the form of winds. Meanwhile, the droplets in the clouds grow to precipitable size. They, too, are exported from the system, via the various forms of precipitation that fall to Earth.

These events occur in clouds of the ITCZ, in tropical easterly waves, and in the wet monsoons. You may be able to envision them best in the more dramatic weather produced by tropical cyclones and thunderstorms. Yet, whether in a tornado or in a mid-latitude cyclone, these events take place in a similar way. Because of the inputs and outputs of energy and moisture to many of these phenomena, we have considerable justification for calling them weather *systems*. Unit 15 looks at how we track and forecast weather systems such as these, and Units 16 and 17 demonstrate how these systems combine with the general atmospheric circulation to form the climates of the Earth.

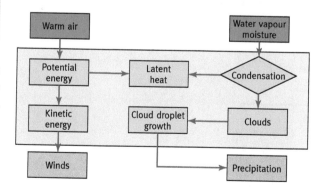

Figure 13.9 Schematic representation of the energy and moisture transformations within a weather system.

KEY TERMS

cyclogenesis   *page 170*
easterly wave   *page 169*
extratropical cyclone   *page 173*
occluded front   *page 173*
open wave   *page 173*
Polar Front jet stream   *page 170*

stationary front   *page 173*
storm   *page 169*
tropical depression   *page 170*
tropical storm   *page 170*
weather system   *page 169*

REVIEW QUESTIONS

1. How does the Polar Front jet stream contribute to the formation of a mid-latitude cyclone?

2. Describe the internal structure of a mid-latitude cyclone.

3. What is an occluded front, and what sort of weather is associated with it?

4. Describe the general weather changes at a location experiencing the complete passage of a mid-latitude cyclone.

REFERENCES AND FURTHER READINGS

Aguado, E., and J.E. Burt. 2004. *Understanding Weather and Climate*, 3rd edn. Upper Saddle River, NJ: Prentice-Hall.

Barry, R.G., R.J. Chorley, and N.J. Yokoi. 2004. *Atmosphere, Weather, and Climate*, 8th edn. London: Routledge.

Carlson, T. 1991. *Mid-Latitude Weather Systems*. London/New York: Routledge.

de Blij, H.J., ed. 1994. *Nature on the Rampage*. Washington: Smithsonian Institution Press.

Harman, J.R. 1971. *Tropospheric Waves, Jet Streams, and United States Weather Patterns*. Washington: Association of American Geographers, Commission on College Geography, Resource Paper No. 11.

Hastenrath, S. 1991. *Climate Dynamics of the Tropics*. Dordrecht, Netherlands: Kluwer.

McGregor, G.R., and S. Nieuwolt. 1998. *Tropical Climatology*, 2nd edn. Chichester, UK: Wiley.

Musk, L.F., and S. Baker. 1988. *Weather Systems*. New York: Cambridge Univ. Press.

Reiter, E.R. 1966. *Jet Streams*. Garden City, NY: Anchor/Doubleday.

Schneider, S.H., ed. 1996. *Encyclopedia of Climate and Weather*, 2 vols. New York: Oxford Univ. Press.

Whitlow, J.B. 2001. *The Penguin Dictionary of Physical Geography*, 2nd edn. Harmondsworth: Penguin.

WEB RESOURCES

henry.pha.jhu.edu/ssip/asat_int/cyclogen.html This site provides some background information about the development and morphology of the mid-latitude cyclone and provides some examples of notable storm systems for your observations.

www.eoearth.org/article/Mid-latitude_cyclone An explanation of mid-latitude cyclones from 'The Encyclopedia of Earth'.

www.islandnet.com/~see/weather/elements/jetstream1.htm A description of the various jet streams including the polar jet stream.

www.usatoday.com/weather/wstorm0.htm A page of links covering the topics of air pressure and weather, storm formation, fronts, and types of weather systems.

Severe Weather

Objectives

- To differentiate between natural hazards and natural disasters.

- To provide an overview of the variety of severe winter and summer weather conditions.

Natural disasters occur when a hazard triggers vulnerability and the damage is so extensive that the affected community cannot recover through the use of its own resources. **Natural hazards** can affect anyone, anywhere. People are threatened by hazards because of their social, economic, and environmental vulnerability. Approximately half of all Canadian disasters—whether natural or not—have been weather-related, and this percentage has increased dramatically in recent years. Over the past decade, Canada has experienced many of its largest natural disasters, and experts believe that even bigger and more devastating ones are inevitable. While geophysical disasters, such as earthquakes, have remained relatively constant in this country over the past 50 years, weather-related disasters have escalated. Climate change is projected to exacerbate this situation in the future, as it is expected to increase the frequency and severity of some extreme weather events.

Weather events can be classified as severe or extreme according to various factors, such as the economic impact (insurance costs), social effects (loss of life), or environmental changes (destruction of habitat). Extreme weather is a relative phenomenon; what may be considered extreme in one locale might be the norm in another. Weather events that are infrequent or rare are the ones that tend to be considered extreme or severe. The classification of an event often depends on what a region is used to experiencing and what it is prepared for. A 20-cm snowfall is an extreme event for Washington, DC, for example, but not for Montreal. In Washington such an event would come close to an emergency situation. In Montreal it is merely an inconvenience. Today's definition of severe weather is extremely broad. Given the concept of vulnerability, extreme weather can mean anything that causes hardship or has an economic impact.

Natural Disasters versus Natural Hazards

Researchers differentiate between the terms *natural disaster* and *natural hazard*. The term *disaster* is often reserved for those cases where humans and their infrastructure are impacted. In many cases, the extreme events that humans suffer from can be rejuvenating for the natural environment. Forest fires replenish soil fertility, and hurricanes bring nutrients to coastal wetlands. However, natural phenomena like hurricanes, floods, earthquakes, and tornadoes can be hazards that have the potential to harm people and damage property. These hazards only become disasters when they interact with vulnerable communities in a way that overwhelms the communities' ability to cope.

Natural disasters were believed to be 'acts of God' in centuries past. It is now understood that human decisions play a significant role in determining our vulnerability and capacity to cope with the consequences of extreme events. *Vulnerability* refers to the likelihood that a community will suffer injuries, deaths, or property damage from a hazardous event. It is a measure of how well prepared and equipped the community is to avoid or cope with such events. There is little doubt that society as a whole has become more vulnerable to extreme weather. Population and infrastructure continue to increase in areas that are vulnerable to such extremes as flooding, storm damage, and severe heat or cold. Populations are too often being concentrated in risky areas such as flood plains, for example, and the destruction of forests and wetlands is harming the capacity of the environment to withstand hazards. Looming above all this is the threat of global climate change and rising sea levels as a result of increased greenhouse gas concentrations in the atmosphere caused by human activity.

Weather Warnings and Watches

For the safety of people and property, Environment Canada issues severe weather warnings, watches, and advisories to the public via the media, weather outlets, and Weatheradio Canada. A **weather advisory** means that actual or expected weather conditions may cause general inconvenience or concern but are not serious enough to warrant a warning. An advisory may be issued in advance of a warning. A **weather watch** alerts the public to conditions favourable for the development of severe weather. A **weather warning** informs the public that severe weather is occurring or that hazardous weather is highly probable. Severe thunderstorm or tornado warnings can only be issued less than an hour in advance, while other weather warnings can be issued up to 48 hours in advance (in the case of marine wind warnings, for example). Table 14.1 provides the variety of weather warnings and watches that are issued in Canada.

An example of one day's watches and warnings from Environment Canada demonstrates the variety of active weather that Canadians have come to expect. On 8 June 2008, tornado watches and warnings were in effect in parts of southern Saskatchewan, southwestern Ontario, and central New Brunswick, winter storm warnings and freezing rain warnings were in effect for parts of Nunavut, heavy rainfall and wind warnings were in effect for western British Columbia, and dozens of communities were under a severe thunderstorm watch.

Table 14.1 Environment Canada's Weather Warnings and Watches

Severe thunderstorm watch	Conditions are favourable for the development of severe thunderstorms with large hail, heavy rain, intense lightning, or damaging winds within the areas and times specified in the watch. You should secure or put away loose objects such as outdoor furniture, put your car in the garage, bring livestock to shelter, and listen carefully for an updated weather report.
Severe thunderstorm warning	A severe thunderstorm has developed, producing one or more of the following conditions: heavy rain, damaging winds, hail of at least 20 mm in diameter, and intense lightning. Severe thunderstorms may also produce tornadoes. The storm's expected motion and developments will be given in the warning. If you are in the area specified, take shelter indoors.
Tornado watch	Conditions are favourable for the development of tornadoes within the areas and times specified in the watch. Be prepared to take shelter, preferably in the lower level of a sturdy building.
Tornado warning	One or more tornadoes are occurring in the area specified. The expected motion, development, and duration will be given in the warning. If you are in the path of a tornado, take emergency precautions immediately. If you are near the area specified in the warning, be alert for the development of additional tornadoes or severe thunderstorms.
Freezing rain warning	Expect slippery walking and driving conditions and possible damage to trees and overhead wires due to rain freezing on contact with objects to form a coating of ice. Avoid travel.
Heavy rain warning	Issued when heavy or prolonged rainfall is sufficient to cause local/widespread flooding. Expect 50 mm of rain over 12 hours or less or 80 mm of rain in less than 24 hours.
Frost warning	Issued when air temperatures are expected to fall to near freezing or below during the growing season, approximately 15 May to 15 October. Protect your plants!
Wind warning	Expect winds blowing steadily at 60 km/hr or more, or winds gusting to 90 km/hr or more, for at least one hour. Secure or put away loose objects such as outdoor furniture, put your car in the garage, and bring livestock to shelter.
Marine wind warnings	Small craft warning: issued if winds of 20–33 knots are forecast Gale warning: issued if winds of 34–47 knots are forecast Storm warning: issued if winds of 48–63 knots are forecast Hurricane force wind warning: issued for winds of 64 knots or more
Dust storm advisory	Issued in prairie provinces when blowing dust caused by high winds has reduced visibility to 1 km or less. Under extreme conditions of widespread zero visibility, this bulletin may be issued as a warning. Dust can impair breathing for people and animals and make travel hazardous.
Blizzard warning	Expect snow or blowing snow, with severe wind chill and visibility reduced to less than 1 km, for 4 hours or more. Stock up on heating fuel and food. Stay indoors and wait out the storm.
Heavy snowfall warning	Expect a snowfall of 10 cm or more (15 cm or more in Ontario) in 12 hours or less. Travel can become hazardous.
Winter storm warning	Issued in Ontario when two or more winter conditions reach warning proportions (e.g., wind and snow or freezing rain followed by heavy snowfall). Be prepared to cancel travel plans and stay indoors.
Wind chill warning	Expect combination of very cold temperatures and wind to create outdoor conditions hazardous to human activity. Be prepared to stay indoors.
Cold wave advisory	Temperatures are expected to drop by 20°C or more within 18 hours. Dress warmly and check weather forecast before travelling or venturing outdoors.

LINK

Winter Season Severe Weather

LINK

As discussed in the previous unit, the most common cause of severe winter weather in Canada is the mid-latitude cyclone, which can produce the following:

- Heavy snowfall and blowing snow (i.e., blizzards)
- Freezing rain
- Severe cold snaps
- Severe Atlantic and Pacific coastal storms.

A nor'easter (Figure 14.1) is an intense mid-latitude cyclone that tracks up the east coast of North America. Nor'easters aren't as powerful as hurricanes, but they can be very destructive. They can occur at any time of year, although they are most common between October and April. These systems tend to strike land only along the North American Atlantic coast, from Cape Hatteras

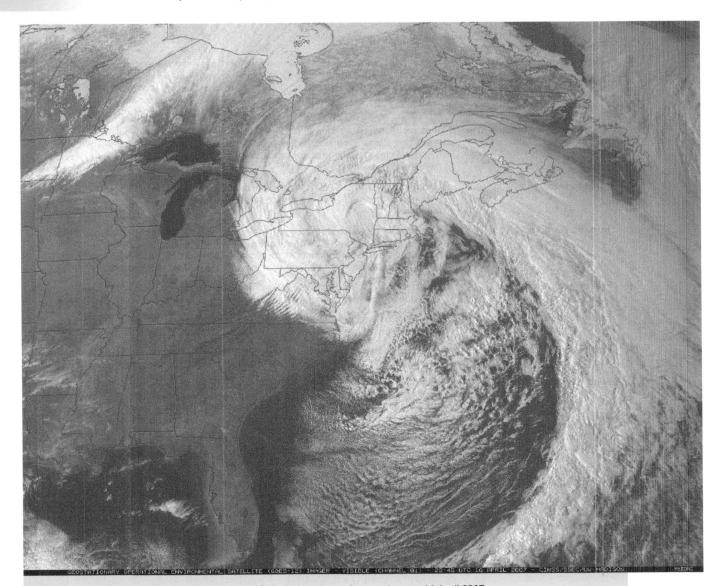

Figure 14.1 Satellite image of the east coast of North America under a nor'easter, 16 April 2007.

north to the Canadian Maritimes and Newfoundland, bringing gale-force winds (63–87 km/hr), heavy precipitation, and heavy surf along the coast. Nor'easters move towards the northeast and, if centred offshore, can produce strong onshore winds that can cause considerable coastal erosion, flooding, and property damage. They have become infamous along the Atlantic coast of Canada, notable examples being the Blizzard of '88, the 'Perfect Storm' of 1991, and the snowstorm of February 2004, dubbed 'White Juan'.

Snow and Blizzards

There doesn't need to be a lot of snow on the ground for drifting and blowing snow conditions to occur. So-called whiteout conditions contributed to a 50-vehicle pileup north of Toronto on 20 January 2008, although there was only a minimal amount of snow on the ground. As wind speeds increase, snow can be entrained by the wind and lifted above the land surface, progressing from drifting conditions (snow particles raised to a height of less than 2 m) to blowing snow (restricted horizontal visibility and snow particles raised more than 2 m). **Blizzards** can be differentiated from snowstorms or blowing snow by their wind speeds of 40 km/hr or more, by snow or drifting snow and wind chill factors of up to –25°C, and by their duration for at least four consecutive hours. According to Environment Canada, blizzards pose the greatest threat of any Canadian weather phenomenon. They are most common in northern Yukon, the southern Prairies, Atlantic Canada, and Nunavut, although no region of Canada is completely immune. The feature that makes blizzards so hazardous is limited visibility (less than 1 km in blowing or drifting snow). There doesn't even have to be a snowfall for there to be a blizzard. In fact, some of our worst blizzards have occurred with very little new snow—just old snow being pushed around. At least one or two people and much livestock perish from exposure to blizzards each year.

Outside of Canada, some of the snowiest places on Earth include the Japanese Alps of Honshu Island, where the greatest snow depth ever recorded on Earth was an astonishing 11.8 metres in 1927. The nearby city of Takada averages about 665 cm of snowfall in a season. The homes in this region of Japan have been modified to withstand such large accumulations of snowfall. The homes have long eaves that overhang the sidewalks to keep them clear of snow. Some roadways are equipped with underground sprinklers that spray warm water to melt the snow.

Freezing Rain and Ice Storms

Freezing rain is defined as consisting of super-cooled liquid water drops larger than 0.5 mm in diameter that freeze on impact with the ground or other objects. Freezing drizzle also freezes on impact with the ground, but it is composed exclusively of droplets less than 0.5 mm in diameter. Freezing rain occurs when warm, moist air that is above the freezing point overlies cold air at ground level that is below the freezing point. As rain falling from the warmer air passes through the colder layer, it freezes instantly on contact with the ground. The precipitation occurs as sleet when partially melted snow drops refreeze upon meeting the colder layer of air near the ground (Figure 14.2). This process commonly occurs along fronts where warm and cold air masses on opposite sides of the freezing point meet, but the fronts generally move along quickly and thus the freezing rain conditions are short-lived. The severity of ice storms depends largely on the accumulation of ice, the duration of the event, and the location and extent of the area affected. There are always unique exceptions to the norm, as was the case with the January 1998 ice storm, which was the product of moist air out of the American South, a steady flow out of the northeast that maintained a shallow layer of cold air in the lowlands of the Ottawa and St Lawrence River Valleys, and a stagnant ridge of high pressure over the Atlantic that kept the whole system centred over eastern Ontario, southern Quebec, and parts of New Brunswick, upstate New York, and New England. Damage to trees,

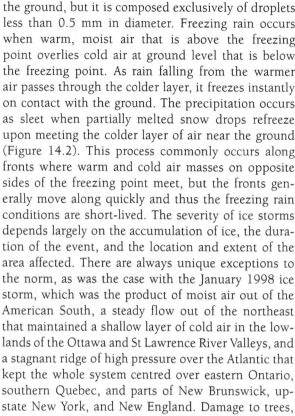

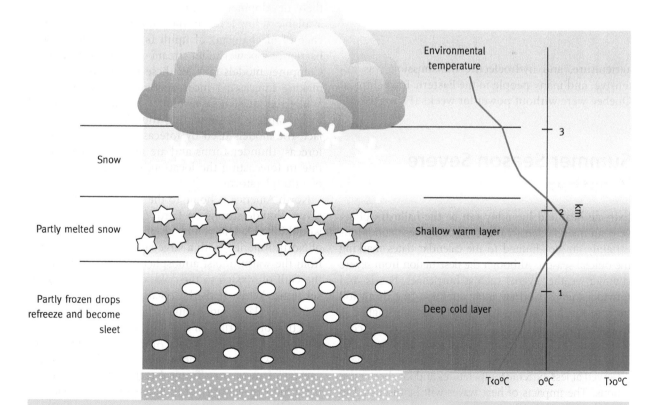

Figure 14.2 The production of sleet.

LINK

Figure 14.3 High voltage towers near Montreal, Quebec, collapsed under the pressure of the January 1998 ice storm. The storm left more than a million households without electricity.

agriculture, and hydroelectric transmission was extensive, and many people in the Eastern Townships of Quebec were without power for weeks (Figure 14.3).

Summer Season Severe Weather

Extreme heat and humidity can be the hallmark of severe summer season weather, although these conditions certainly are not limited to the calendar dates marking the official season. Although the destruction from severe summer weather events such as hurricanes, floods, and tornadoes tends to draw more attention, the death toll from severe heat waves can be substantially higher. A **heat wave** is defined as a period of more than three consecutive days of maximum temperature at or above 32°C, although the adverse effects of heat on humans have been observed at less extreme temperatures and for shorter durations. The impacts of heat waves will be discussed in more detail in Unit 19.

Thunderstorms

Thunderstorm activity increases in the warm season months. Severe thunderstorms are most likely to occur when the atmosphere is unstable and there is abundant low-level moisture, when there is strong wind shear, and when a trigger mechanism exists that can release instability. These conditions are strongly influenced by topography and air mass climatology. Thunderstorms fall into three main categories: air mass (single-cell) thunderstorms, multi-cell thunderstorms (or squall-line storms), and super-cell thunderstorms. The air mass thunderstorm is a common and usually non-severe system that forms away from frontal systems. Multi-cell storms can form in a line known as a squall line, where continuous updrafts are fed by low-level convergence. Super-cell storms, which include most of the severe thunderstorms, are characterized by massive cumulonimbus clouds that grow rapidly into individual thunderstorms. These super-cells are sometimes embedded in a larger cluster of thunderstorms, particularly in eastern Canada (see Figures 14.4 and 14.5). West of the Great Lakes, where there is less low-level moisture, super-cell thunderstorms tend to form in isolation.

A critical factor in the development of a thunderstorm is the *lapse rate*, or the change in temperature of the ambient atmosphere with a rise in elevation. The greater the temperature difference, the more likely a thunderhead will expand upwards. Other factors in their development include the amount of moisture available at low levels in the atmosphere and the presence of mechanisms of uplift (such as a topographic barrier or a powerful jet stream drawing air upwards). Computer models take all these factors into account, making forecasting more accurate than ever before. While the latest high-resolution models have proved to be capable of simulating thunderstorms after the fact, the models used by forecasters do not explicitly forecast thunderstorms and are not particularly accurate in forecasting the location, character, or severity of a thunderstorm.

North America is home to the highest frequencies of severe thunderstorms on Earth (India and Bangladesh would follow). This is a result of the unique geography of North America, with a large land mass that stretches from the warm, moist atmosphere of the subtropics of the Gulf of Mexico to the cold, dry atmosphere of the subarctic. While both the Asian and European continents have large mountain barriers that block the interaction of differing air masses, there are no west–east mountain barriers in North America. As a result, the clash between warm, moist air and cool, dry air can cause violent storms. Tropical regions of the world receive the vast majority of thunderstorms not related to air mass.

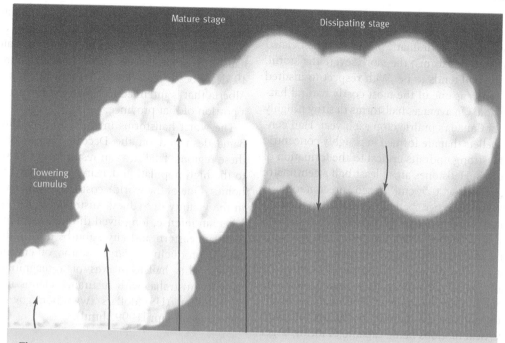

Figure 14.4 Profile of a summer thunderstorm.

Figure 14.5 The anvil head of a cumulonimbus cloud.

Hail

Hail is one of the most dramatic phenomena associated with severe thunderstorms; the more severe the storm, the larger the hail tends to be. With respect to insured costs, hail ranks as one of the most costly natural hazards in Canada. On average, hailstorms destroy roughly 3 per cent of Canada's prairie crop each year. Hail consists of ice pellets that are formed in roughly concentric layers in the strong updrafts critical to the formation of thunderstorms. Hailstones are at least half a centimetre in diameter; below 0.5 cm, frozen precipitation is defined as snow or ice pellets. Initially, an updraft carries water droplets above the freezing level to form the core of a hailstone. When the pellet falls from the updraft and collides with liquid droplets, the core is coated with a film of water. If the pellet is lifted by the updraft again, the process is repeated, enabling the hailstone to grow in diameter. The final size of the hailstone depends on the intensity of the updraft, with stronger vertical motions being capable of lifting larger hailstones. With very strong updrafts, hailstones can grow larger than 10 cm in diameter (about the size of a grapefruit; Figure 14.6). Hail can hit the ground at 130 km per hour, causing severe damage to crops, houses, and vehicles, as well as injuries to people and animals. For many Canadians, a hailstorm is an intriguing rarity, but for farmers whose crops are crushed—or for those whose homes and cars are damaged—a hailstorm can translate into a financial burden. Unit 19 describes a so-called hail suppression initiative in Alberta that is intended to lessen the impacts of hail in a portion of that province.

The worst hailstorms in the world tend to occur in Bangladesh and on the Deccan Plateau of India. In these regions, fatalities can result from hail strikes due to the high population density and poorly constructed homes. One of the world's costliest hailstorms occurred in the vicinity of Sydney, Australia, on 14 April 1999, when an intense, long-lived thunderstorm moved over Sydney's eastern and city suburbs during the evening hours, producing a large swathe of enormous hailstones. This hailstorm was of a magnitude seldom seen in Australia, with insurance claims in excess of $1.5 billion (US) dollars (www.bom.gov.au/weather/nsw/sevwx/14april1999.shtml).

Hurricanes

An intensely developed tropical cyclone is one of the most fascinating and potentially destructive features of the

Figure 14.6   Hailstones as large as grapefruit are an infrequent occurrence, but they can cause significant damage to property and to people. In Canada, hailstorms cause significant crop damage.

Figure 14.7 In this image the eye of Hurricane Mitch was still over water, but the 1998 storm was poised to strike Central America. It was the costliest natural disaster in the modern history of the Western Hemisphere. Honduras, the country hit the hardest, had nearly 10,000 deaths and lost over 150,000 homes, 34,000 km of roads, and 335 bridges. When it was over, nearly one-quarter of the country's 6.4 million people were homeless, and most of the agricultural economy was ruined. Honduras and adjacent areas of Nicaragua will carry Mitch's scars for generations to come.

atmosphere. These severe storms go by different names in different regions of the world. In the western Atlantic and eastern Pacific Oceans they are called **hurricanes**, the term we employ here. Elsewhere they are known as *typhoons* (western North Pacific) or *tropical cyclones* (Indian Ocean).

The tropical cyclone is a tightly organized, moving low-pressure system, normally originating at sea in the warm, moist air of the low-latitude atmosphere. As with all cyclonic storms, it has distinctly circular wind and pressure fields (see Figure 8.9A). In Figure 14.7, a satellite image of Hurricane Mitch, which ravaged parts of Central America in 1998, the circular windflow extends vertically, and the pinwheel-like cloud pattern associated with the centre of the system reminds us of its cyclonic origin.

The World Meteorological Organization describes a hurricane as having wind speeds greater than 119 km/h and a central surface pressure below 900 mb. However, in the most severe storms, such as Hurricane Gilbert (which in 1988 exhibited the lowest pressure ever recorded in the Western Hemisphere as it smashed its way westward across the Caribbean Sea),

wind speeds can exceed 320 km/h and cause massive destruction.

The hurricane's structure is diagrammed in Figure 14.8. A striking feature is the open **eye** that dominates the middle of the cyclonic system, the 'hole in the doughnut' from which spiral bands of cloud extend outward, often reaching an altitude of 16 km. The strongest winds and heaviest rainfall (up to 50 cm per day) are found in the **eye wall**, the towering cloud tube that marks the rim of the eye. Within the eye itself, which extends vertically through the full height of the storm, winds are light and there is little rain as dry cool air descends down the entire length of the central column. Temperatures vary little throughout the area of a tropical cyclone, which has an average diameter of about 500 km—but the diameter can vary from 80 km to about 2500 km. In general, the greater the amounts of energy and moisture involved in the system, the more extensive and powerful the hurricane will be.

Hurricane Development Hurricanes are efficient machines for drawing large quantities of excess heat away from the ocean surface and transporting them into

LINK

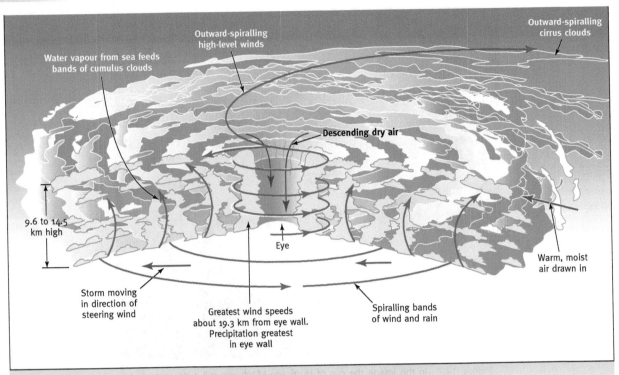

Figure 14.8   Cross-sectional view of a hurricane showing its mechanics and component parts.

the upper atmosphere. Accordingly, they are most likely to form in late summer and autumn when tropical sea surfaces reach their peak annual temperatures (i.e., greater than 27°C). The origin of these tropical storms appears to be related to easterly waves and the equatorial trough of low pressure. However, many aspects of hurricane formation are only partially understood, particularly the exact triggering mechanism that transforms fewer than 1 of every 10 easterly waves into a tropical cyclone. Nonetheless, meteorologists are making progress in their efforts to forecast these storms, and the development of new predictive tools has improved the accuracy of hurricane-track forecasting by more than 25 per cent since 1990.

From studies of past storms it is known that hurricanes form when latent heat warms the centre of a pre-existing storm and helps to intensify an anticyclone present in the upper troposphere. Once the tropical cyclone has developed, it becomes self-sustaining. Vast quantities of heat energy are siphoned from the warm ocean below and transported aloft as latent heat. This energy is released as sensible heat when clouds form. The sensible heat provides the system with potential energy, which is partially converted into kinetic energy, thereby causing the hurricane's violent winds.

Hurricanes originate between 5 and 25 degrees latitude in all tropical oceans except the South Atlantic and the southeastern Pacific, where the ITCZ seldom occurs.

These latitudinal limits are determined by the general conditions necessary for hurricane formation: equatorward of 5 degrees the Coriolis force is too weak to generate rotary air motion, whereas poleward of 25 degrees sea-surface temperatures are too cool. Once hurricanes are formed, their movement is controlled by the steering effects of larger-scale air currents in the surrounding atmosphere; these can be erratic, and a hurricane is often likened to a block of wood floating in a river with complicated currents.

In the Northern Hemisphere, hurricanes usually travel first westward and then to the northwest before curving around to the north and east, where they come under the influence of the westerly winds of the middle latitudes. The paths of typical Atlantic hurricanes are mapped in Figure 14.9, and they underscore the vulnerability of the US southeastern coast, the entire rim of the Gulf of Mexico, and eastern Canada. Hurricanes usually advance with forward speeds of 16 to 24 km/h. If they pass over a large body of land or cooler waters, their energy source—the warm ocean—is cut off, and they gradually weaken and die.

Hurricane Destruction   Before these tropical cyclones die, normally within a week of their formation, they can cause considerable damage on land. The Saffir–Simpson scale, which ranks hurricane intensity from 1 to 5 (Table 14.2), is used to estimate the potential property

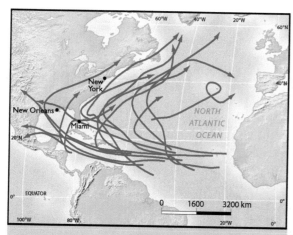

Figure 14.9 Typical hurricane tracks in the North Atlantic Ocean. The path of every storm in this part of the world since 1871 is mapped in the National Hurricane Center's 'track book', which is updated annually.

Table 14.2 Saffir–Simpson Scale of Hurricane Intensity

Intensity Category	Wind Speed (km/h)	Description of Effects
1	119–53	Damage primarily to unanchored mobile homes, shrubbery, tree branches; power lines blown down
2	154–77	Damage to roofing material, doors and windows; small trees blown down; unprotected marine craft break moorings
3	178–209	Damage to small buildings; large trees blown down; mobile homes destroyed; flooding near coast destroys many structures
4	210–49	Extensive roof failures on houses and smaller commercial buildings; major damage to doors and windows, and lower floors of near-shore structures; flooding up to 9 km inland from coast
5	>249	Widespread roof failures and destruction of many smaller-sized buildings; major damage to all structures less than 4.5 m above sea level; flooding up to 16 km inland from coast

Source: Information from NOAA, National Hurricane Center.

damage and flooding expected from a hurricane landfall. Much of this damage is done by high winds and torrential rains. However, near coastlines, waves and tides rise to destructive levels, particularly when wind-driven water known as the **storm surge** (which can surpass normal high-tide levels by more than 5 m) is hurled ashore. The destructive potential can be imagined when you consider that the amount of energy unleashed by a hurricane in one hour equals the total electric power generated in the United States in an entire year. With the exception of tornadoes—which sometimes are spawned in the inner spiral rain bands of the strongest hurricanes—tropical cyclones are the most dangerous of all atmospheric weather systems.

Not surprisingly, the most powerful hurricanes to strike the United States and Canada have ranked among the landmark weather events of the past century. Before World War II (and the development of sophisticated weather tracking), hurricanes in 1900 and 1935 caused enormous destruction on the coasts of Texas and the Florida Keys, respectively; in 1938, much of southern New England was devastated. In eastern Canada in 1891, two Category 1 hurricanes and one Category 2 hurricane hit Nova Scotia within a two-month period, one of which resulted in the collapse of the first bridge that spanned the Halifax harbour. After 1945, hurricanes were named in alphabetical order of their occurrences each year. Among the most destructive of these have been Hazel (1954), Camille (1969), Agnes (1972), and Hugo (1989). Overall, since 1900, hurricanes have cost more than 1500 lives and untold billions of dollars in damage.

Hurricane Katrina was one of the strongest storms to impact the coast of the United States during the last 100 years. Katrina struck southern Louisiana on 29 August 2005 and caused devastation along much of the north-central Gulf Coast of the US. The most severe effects of Katrina occurred in New Orleans, parts of which were built in areas below sea level that were protected by the series of levees. The levee system failed catastrophically, hours after the storm had moved inland, as waters from adjacent Lake Pontchartrain washed into the city through a breach in the 17th Street Canal levee and then the Industrial Street Canal levee was breached. Katrina's sustained winds during landfall were over 200 km/h (a strong Category 3 hurricane on the Saffir–Simpson scale) and its minimum central pressure was the third lowest on record at landfall (920 mb). At least 1836 people lost their lives in Hurricane Katrina and in the subsequent floods, most of whom lived in the poorer, low-lying areas of the city and outlying districts. The storm (Figure 14.10) is estimated to have been responsible for US$81.2 billion in damage, making it the costliest natural disaster in US history. There was widespread criticism of federal, state, and local government reaction to the storm; on the other hand, the National Hurricane Center and National Weather Service in the US were widely commended for accurate forecasts and abundant lead time.

Figure 14.10   Relief efforts for people stranded by floodwaters after Hurricane Katrina.

The costliest hurricane to strike eastern Canada in recent history was Hurricane Juan, which struck on 28–9 September 2003 (Figure 14.11). In its path across Nova Scotia and Prince Edward Island, this Category 2 hurricane was the first to hit one of the nation's larger metropolitan areas—Halifax—with its full force (wind speeds up to 158 km/h). The hurricane's impact took many by surprise: eight lives were lost, hundreds of thousands were without power (lasting up to two weeks in some locations), physical damage was done to homes and property, and trees blown down were widespread. Estimates of the final economic losses exceeded $100 million with insurable losses at over $80 million.

However, as is clear from the massive devastation caused by Katrina, many comparatively worse hurricanes have hit metropolitan areas in the United States. Prior to Katrina, the costliest hurricane to strike the United States (and the third most expensive natural disaster in American history to that time) was Hurricane Andrew in 1992. In its path across southern Florida, this relatively small but ferocious hurricane was the first to directly hit one of the United States' largest metropolitan areas—Miami—with average winds of 267 km/h. The final accounting was truly staggering:

95,400 private homes completely destroyed; a total of $16.04 billion paid to settle 795,912 property insurance claims; more than 125,000 people left homeless and 86,000 jobless; and a cleanup effort involving the removal of 35 million tons of debris at a cost of $600 million.

It is not unusual for the death toll in a single storm of high hurricane strength to be in the thousands. In fact, the second greatest natural disaster of the twentieth century was the tropical cyclone that smashed into Bangladesh in 1970, killing upward of 300,000 people (and perhaps as many as half that number perished when another cyclone struck the country in 1991). On 2 May 2008, Cyclone Nargis, a strong tropical cyclone, caused the deadliest natural disaster in the recorded history of Burma (Myanmar). The cyclone caused catastrophic destruction and at least 90,000 fatalities, with a further 56,000 people still missing. It is believed that the Myanmar government's official death toll is grossly under-reported, as the dead were not officially counted to minimize political fallout. It is believed that many more could have died as a result of disease, since the country's military dictatorship stalled in accepting international relief efforts, and once some relief workers were allowed

Figure 14.11 Some of the worst damage caused by Hurricane Juan (28–9 September 2003) was to trees. On some streets, such as this one in Dartmouth, Nova Scotia, every tree lining the street was blown over, giving an immediate impression of the direction the wind had been blowing.

into the country they were severely restricted in their movements and ability to provide relief. According to the United Nations, outside agencies have made estimates of up 1.5 million being 'severely affected' by the cyclone and its aftermath. Damage was estimated at over US$10 billion, which made it the most damaging cyclone ever recorded in this tropical cyclone basin (Figure 14.12). Beyond the toll in human lives, hurricanes can also cause catastrophic disruptions in the social and economic life of a nation.

Although the tropics are generally marked by monotonous daily weather, violence and drama accompany the occasional storms that are spawned in the energy-laden air of the low latitudes. Weather systems in the middle and higher latitudes are often less dramatic, but are usually more frequent, involve wider areas, and affect much larger populations.

Lightning

Lightning is 'an atmospheric discharge of electricity', which typically occurs during thunderstorms and sometimes during volcanic eruptions or dust storms. When charges reach sufficient strength to overcome the insulating threshold of the local atmosphere, lightning may occur. In thunderstorms, this process results in the accumulation of positive charges towards the top of clouds and an accumulation of negative charges in the base of clouds. The accumulated electrical potential is then neutralized by the electrical discharge either from one cloud to another or from a cloud to the ground. A flash of lightning occurs when a 'leader' from the cloud base meets an upward 'streamer' coming from the surface. A lightning bolt can reach up to 60,000 m/s in speed and 30,000°C! Since February 1998, the Canadian Lightning Detection Network (CLDN) has provided continuous lightning detection in space and time, its range being to about 65°N in the west, 55°N in the east, and offshore to about 300 km. The CLDN consists of approximately 82 sensors that detect lightning over most of Canada, providing Canadians with the basic systems to detect and monitor this deadly facet of severe weather.

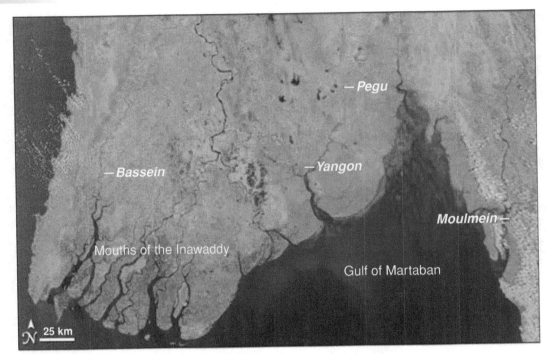

—Pegu

—Bassein   —Yangon

Moulmein—

Mouths of the Inawaddy

Gulf of Martaban

25 km

15 April 2008

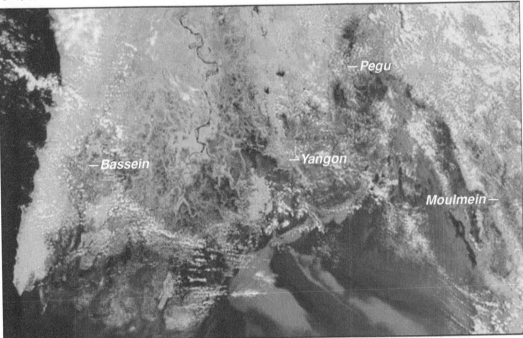

—Pegu

—Bassein   —Yangon

Moulmein—

5 May 2008

Figure 14.12   NASA images of the Irawaddy Delta in Burma (Myanmar) before and immediately after Cyclone Nargis, showing the extent of land flooded by this cyclone.

Perspectives on the Human Environment

Tornadoes and Their Consequences

The interiors of large continents, especially in the spring and early summer, experience severe thunderstorms, which can produce tornadoes, nature's most vicious weather. A **tornado** is a small vortex of air, averaging 100 to 500 m in diameter, that descends to the ground from rotating clouds at the base of a violent thunderstorm. If the twister forms over a water surface, it is called a **waterspout**.

The pressure in the centre of such a spinning funnel cloud may be 100 to 200 mb below the pressure of the surrounding air. This triggers highly destructive winds, whose speeds can range from 50 to 130 m per second. Tornadoes tend to follow rather straight paths that can leave swaths of destruction up to 160 km long and 900 m wide. Their awesome, often dark colour is accentuated by the vegetation, loose soil, and other objects sucked into the centre tube of this gigantic vacuum cleaner (Figure 14.13).

Most people are aware of the havoc that tornadoes wreak in parts of the United States, but few are aware of how frequently and severely Canada is struck by tornadoes. In an average year, approximately 80 tornadoes strike Canada, resulting in an average for each of two deaths in addition to tens of millions of dollars in property damage. Numerous others may go undetected in more remote or rural areas. This still contrasts sharply with the United States, which experiences more severe thunderstorms than any other landmass on Earth. Each year these 10,000-plus storms spawn more than 1000 tornadoes, resulting in an average of 90 deaths per year. About 20 per cent of these tornadoes are classified as 'strong', and even those categorized as 'weak' can exhibit winds in excess of 45 m per second. These tornadoes typically develop over the Great Plains and the Midwest, particularly in the north–south corridor known as 'Tornado Alley', which extends

Figure 14.13 Nature's most violent weather is associated with tornadoes. At least 80 of these twisters strike Canada in any given year, most commonly during the spring and summer months of May to September.

through central Texas, Oklahoma, Kansas, and eastern Nebraska. In this region, dry air from the high western plateaus moves eastward into the Plains, where it meets warm, moist, low-level air swept northward from the Gulf of Mexico. When this maritime tropical Gulf air collides with the drier air, the different temperature and humidity characteristics of these air masses create a volatile mixture that can unleash especially violent thunderstorms. Canada's 'tornado alleys' are located in southern Ontario, Alberta, and southeastern Quebec, as well as in a band that stretches from southern Saskatchewan and Manitoba through to Thunder Bay. The interior of British Columbia and western New Brunswick also have tornado zones.

The deadliest twister on record in the United States was the so-called Tri-State Tornado which, on 18 March 1925, barrelled across parts of Missouri, Illinois, and Indiana, killing 689 people and injuring another 1980 in less than 45 minutes. The deadliest tornado to strike Canada occurred on 30 June 1912, slashing through six city blocks in Regina. The twister killed 28 people, injured hundreds, and destroyed 500 buildings in only three minutes. The largest outbreak of tornadoes in a 24-hour period occurred on 3 April 1974, when 148 twisters killed 315 people in the American Midwest and Southeast. One of the worst disasters in recent Canadian history occurred when a tornado ripped through the Green Acres campground at Pine Lake, Alberta, on 14 July 2000 (Figure 14.14). The popular vacation site was crowded with over 1000 campers, resulting in 11 people being killed and 136 injured.

The conditions that triggered the Green Acres tornado were detected by Environment Canada and reported as a severe thunderstorm watch. The warning also included a reminder that some severe thunderstorms can produce tornadoes. In Canada and the United States, tornado warnings are usually issued on visual confirmation of funnel clouds having touched down or with Doppler radar evidence. At 7:05 p.m. MDT the RCMP notified Environment Canada's Prairie Storm Prediction Centre that a tornado had just been reported at Pine Lake. The severe thunderstorm warning was immediately upgraded to a tornado warning. Warnings and watches were continued through the evening hours of 14 July. More than 40 watches and warnings were issued for Alberta and Saskatchewan.

Figure 14.14   Tornado damage at Pine Lake, 2000.

Although the alert came too late for those at Pine Lake, forecasters continue to improve their predictions with Doppler radar and more-advanced weather-tracking equipment. Meteorologists today are integrating radar, satellite, and computer technology to make tornado detection and warning more precise than ever, and the occurrence of unpredicted tornadoes is becoming a rare event.

Tornado warnings do not always require high technology, however. Across Canada, volunteer 'weather watchers' have achieved what technology may have failed to do. When weather watchers spot tornadoes, thunderstorms, or other severe weather, they report it to Environment Canada. On 31 July 1987, a deadly tornado heading towards Edmonton was spotted by a volunteer observer, Tom Taylor, a pharmacist in Leduc, Alberta, 24 km away. He immediately called Environment Canada, which promptly issued a life-saving warning to thousands of Canadians.

KEY TERMS

blizzard   *page 181*
eye (hurricane)   *page 185*
eye wall   *page 185*
freezing rain   *page 181*
hail   *page 184*
heat wave   *page 182*
hurricane   *page 185*
lightning   *page 189*

natural disaster   *page 178*
natural hazard   *page 178*
storm surge   *page 187*
tornado   *page 191*
waterspout   *page 191*
weather advisory   *page 178*
weather warning   *page 178*
weather watch   *page 178*

REVIEW QUESTIONS

1. What is the difference between a natural hazard and a natural disaster?
2. What is the difference between a snowstorm and a blizzard?
3. How does freezing rain develop?
4. Describe the formation of a severe thunderstorm.
5. Describe the formation of hail.
6. What are the processes involved in the development of a hurricane? Describe some of the more severe impacts that can result.
7. Describe the internal structure of a tornado and explain why these twisters are capable of so much destruction.

REFERENCES AND FURTHER READINGS

Applebome, P. 1987. 'After a Twister [in Saragosa, Texas]: Coping in a Town That Isn't There', *New York Times*, 24 May, 1, 18.

Birkmann, J., ed. 2006. *Measuring Vulnerability to Natural Hazards*. Tokyo: United Nations University Press.

Bluestein, H.B. 1999. *Tornado Alley: Monster Storms of the Great Plains*. New York: Oxford Univ. Press.

Burt, C. 2004. *Extreme Weather: A Guide and Record Book*. New York: Norton.

Canadian Broadcasting Corporation. 2000. 'Tornado Terror', CBC News Report, 14 July. At: <www.cbc.ca/news/indepth/facts/tornado.html>.

Conrad, C. 2008. *Severe and Hazardous Weather in Canada: The Geography of Extreme Events*. Toronto: Oxford Univ. Press.

de Blij, H.J., ed. 1994. *Nature on the Rampage*. Washington: Smithsonian Institution Press.

Diaz, H.F., and R.S. Pulwarty, eds. 1997. *Hurricanes: Climate and Socioeconomic Impacts*. New York: Springer-Verlag.

Drye, W. 2002. *Storm of the Century: The Labor Day Hurricane of 1935*. Washington: National Geographic Society.

Eagleman, J.R. 1990. *Severe and Unusual Weather*, 2nd edn. Lenexa, Kan.: Trimedia.

Elsner, J.B., and A.B. Kara. 1999. *Hurricanes of the North Atlantic: Climate and Society*. New York: Oxford Univ. Press.

Environment Canada. 2003. 'Natural Disasters on the Rise', *Science and the Environment Bulletin* (Mar.–Apr.).

Grazulis, T.P. 2001. *The Tornado: Nature's Ultimate Windstorm*. Norman: Univ. of Oklahoma Press.

Haque, C.E. 2005. *Mitigation of Natural Hazards and Disasters*. Dordrecht: Springer.

International Panel on Climate Change. 2007. 'Climate Change 2007: The Physical Science Basis', Contribution of Working Group I to the Fourth Assessment Report of the IPCC.

McLeod, D. 2003. *Hurricane Juan: The Unforgettable Storm*. Halifax: Formac.

Robinson, A. 1993. *Earth Shock: Hurricanes, Volcanoes, Earthquakes, Tornadoes and Other Forces of Nature*. New York: Thames and Hudson.

Simpson, R.H., and H. Riehl. 1981. *The Hurricane and Its Impact*. Baton Rouge: Louisiana State Univ. Press.

Tompkins, H. 2002. 'Climate Change and Extreme Weather Events: Is There a Connection?', *Cicerone* 3: 1–5.

Tornado Project. 1993. *Significant Tornadoes: 1871–1991*. St Johnsbury, Vt: Tornado Project.

United Nations. 2004. *Living with Risk: A Global Review of Disaster Reduction Initiatives*. At: <www.e11th-hour.org/public/natural/living.with.risk.html>.

 ## WEB RESOURCES

severewx.atmos.uiuc.edu/index.html This University of Illinois website, based on the text *Severe and Hazardous Weather: An Introduction to High Impact Meteorology*, includes case studies, photos and images, and explanation of various types of stormy weather, from lake-effect snowstorms and extratropical cyclones to tornadoes and hurricanes.

www.atl.ec.gc.ca/weather/hurricane/index_e.html The Canadian Hurricane Centre provides information to Canadians on storms of tropical origin that affect Canada or its territorial waters. This site includes forecasts, storm summaries, and a range of information related to the science of hurricanes.

www.mcwar.org/articles/noreasters/NorEasters.html Information about Nor'easters and winter storm preparedness.

www.nhc.noaa.gov/index.shtml The US National Weather Service's Tropical Prediction Center, which tracks all hurricane activity in the Atlantic-Caribbean and Eastern Pacific zones that border the US.

www.pnr-rpn.ec.gc.ca/air/summersevere/ae00s02.en.html Environment Canada's tornado website.

www.spc.noaa.gov/faq/tornado Guide to general tornado information, including real-time monitoring.

Unit 15

Weather Tracking and Forecasting

Objectives

- To discuss the general network of weather stations and the types of data collected from each.

- To illustrate typical weather maps compiled from weather data and to provide some elementary interpretations of them.

- To outline weather forecasting methods and comment on their formulation and reliability.

On New Year's Eve, 2001, in Rio de Janeiro, citizens were looking forward to a night of celebration after a period of particularly deadly floods in Brazil. Heavy rains had triggered mudslides in the greater Rio area, in southeastern Brazil, killing more than 60 people. The public had perhaps been disappointed to hear the forecast for this particular New Year's Eve. A local meteorologist, a veteran with over 35 years of experience, predicted rain, and as a result only 2 million people came to the city to celebrate (much less than in previous years). The cold front that was anticipated to bring the rain broke up earlier than expected, however, and the rain did not come. In this case, however, the mayor of Rio decided that the forecaster should be held accountable for the inaccurate forecast, which could have caused panic in a city that had very recently been hammered by devastating rains. The charge was punishable by up to six months in prison. One might argue that the meteorologist had determined it was better to be safe than sorry. Can a case be made against the meteorologist for making a bad weather forecast?

This instance is a reminder that, even with today's sophisticated knowledge of the atmosphere and high-technology equipment to monitor its every murmur, weather forecasting very much remains an art as well as a science. In this unit we explore the forecasting process by discussing the collection of weather data, the manipulation and mapping of these data, and the critical interpretations made by analysts that lead to weather predictions.

The Canadian public today is probably more aware of weather conditions than ever before; they stampede to supermarkets and hardware stores when a snowstorm is forecast. This is due, in no small part, to the improvement in the news media's weather coverage in recent years. Today we are likely to see weather reporters with **meteorology** degrees who use animated maps, satellite imagery, and colour radar (Figure 15.1). Moreover, with millions of Canadian households now wired to receive the Weather Network on cable TV and such websites as wunderground. com and weather.com, viewers and Internet surfers are better informed than ever.

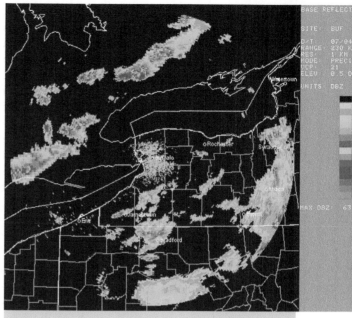

Figure 15.1 Radar reveals a squall line of thunderstorms in southwestern Ontario (4 July 2001). Thunderstorms (shown in red and orange) may produce damaging winds and hail, conditions that may favour the development of tornadoes. This squall line spawned four confirmed tornadoes and several floods throughout the region.

Weather Data Acquisition

The World Meteorological Organization, an agency of the United Nations, supervises the World Weather Watch, a global network of about 20,000 weather stations and moving vehicles. More than 130 nations participate in this monitoring system, which co-ordinates and distributes weather information from its processing centres in Washington, Moscow, and Melbourne. Every six hours, beginning at midnight GMT, or Greenwich Mean Time (also known as Universal Coordinated Time [UTC]), a set of standard observations on the local state of the atmosphere are taken around the globe and reported to those centres from about 10,000 land-based stations, more than 1000 upper-air observation stations, and at least

LINK

9000 ships, buoys, aircraft, and satellites in transit. High-powered computers rapidly record, manipulate, and assemble these data to produce **synoptic weather charts**, which map meteorological conditions at that moment in time across wide geographic areas.

Although reliable weather instruments have been available since about 1700, comprehensive simultaneous observation could not begin before the invention of long-distance communications. The arrival of the telegraph in the 1840s provided the initial breakthrough. The Meteorological Service of Canada was established in 1871 as a national program for the official recording and observation of climate in Canada. Forecasting services have been consistently provided to Canadians since that time, with a brief interruption of services during World War II, when the Canadian and American governments banned publishing and broadcasting weather information for fear that it might aid the enemy. The program was renamed the Atmospheric Environment Service in 1970.

LINK

Today, Environment Canada oversees a number of divisions that relate to weather and climate, including the Canadian Meteorological Centre (CMC) and the present-day Meteorological Service of Canada (MSC), Canada's source for meteorological information. Environment Canada's weather forecasting services include a weather-warning service and five-day forecasts that are available 24 hours a day, 365 days a year. The Canadian weather forecasting service oversees 14 regional weather centres across the country; these centres provide

Canadians with toll-free and pay-telephone services that cover their own and surrounding communities. A series of Weatheradio transmitters across southern Canada reaches 85 per cent of Canadians, and forecasts are also made for inland and coastal waters as well as the Arctic. In addition, forecasts of ice conditions are prepared on a seasonal basis for Arctic and coastal waters, the Great Lakes, and the St Lawrence Seaway. This information utilizes data from Canada's surface weather stations, marine buoys (Canada's Marine Network overseas 45 moored and six drifting buoys in addition to vessel-based monitoring on approximately 300 vessels), and a network of upper-air stations, together with satellite technology.

Weather Stations

Within Canada, more than 2000 observation stations report surface weather conditions. Each station deploys a number of instruments and obtains their readings. These include thermometers, barometers, rain gauges, hygrometers (to measure the moisture of the air), weather vanes (to indicate wind direction), and anemometers (to measure wind speed). The following data are then reported to the synoptic network: air temperature, dew-point temperature, air pressure and its direction of change, precipitation (if any), wind speed and direction, visibility, relative amount of cloudiness, cloud types present, estimated height of cloud base, and any significant weather that might be occurring. This data cluster for each station is then processed by the central facility for placement in shorthand, symbolic form on the synoptic weather chart, as shown in Figure 15.2. Figure 15.3 identifies the various symbols used in this method of reporting weather. Of the several hundred surface **weather stations** in Canada, 290 have been designated as reference climate stations, which are weather stations that have more than 30 years of continuous record, with no significant gaps, and are of high quality. This network of surface stations may provide invaluable data regarding the trends in surface weather conditions in Canada, as well as an insight into climate trends.

Surface conditions, however, represent only a single dimension of the overall weather picture. To gain a fuller understanding, meteorologists must go beyond this bottom slice of the atmosphere to acquire a more complete profile of its current vertical structuring. One way this is accomplished is through **radiosondes**, radio-equipped instrument packages carried aloft by balloon. Canada has 37 radiosonde stations, part of a worldwide network that transmits readings to receiving facilities on the ground every 12 hours (noon and midnight GMT). Whereas most of these upper-air observations of temperature, humidity, and pressure are obtained for altitudes up to 32 km above the surface, a number of radiosonde stations now release more powerful balloons that can reach heights well beyond 32 km. High-altitude radar also is a useful tool for acquiring information about the upper atmosphere, and equipped stations regularly make **rawinsonde**

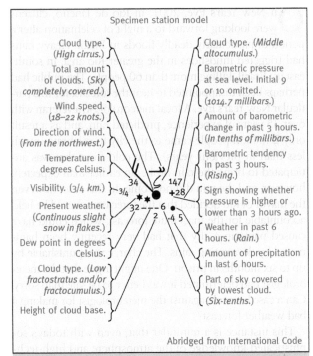

Figure 15.2 Data cluster for each weather station, which is entered in this shorthand form on the synoptic weather chart. This diagram, which represents a specimen station, is the key to interpreting the weather data for the cities shown in the daily surface weather map produced by the Meteorological Service of Canada (see Figure 15.5).

observations (radar trackings of radiosonde balloons) that provide information about wind speed and directions at various vertical levels.

Weather Satellites

Perhaps the most important sources of three-dimensional atmospheric data today are the dozens of orbiting weather satellites that constantly monitor the Earth. Many of these satellites operate within longitudinal, **polar orbits** about 1100 km high, which pass close to the poles, so that they survey a different meridional segment of the surface during each revolution. In this manner a complete picture of the globe can be assembled every few hours. More satellites are being placed much higher (around 35,000 km) above the Equator in orbits called **geosynchronous orbits**—that is, they revolve at the same speed as the planet, making them stationary above a given surface location. A 'fixed' satellite at this altitude can monitor continually the same one-third or so of the Earth, and with infrared (IR) capability it can perform that task in darkness as well as in daylight.

Particularly important are the US geostationary orbiters of the GOES (Geostationary Orbiting Environmental Satellite) series. GOES-10 and GOES-12 are especially important for Canadian forecasting. They transmit images to ground facilities twice an hour, and many of these images appear in daily television and newspaper weather

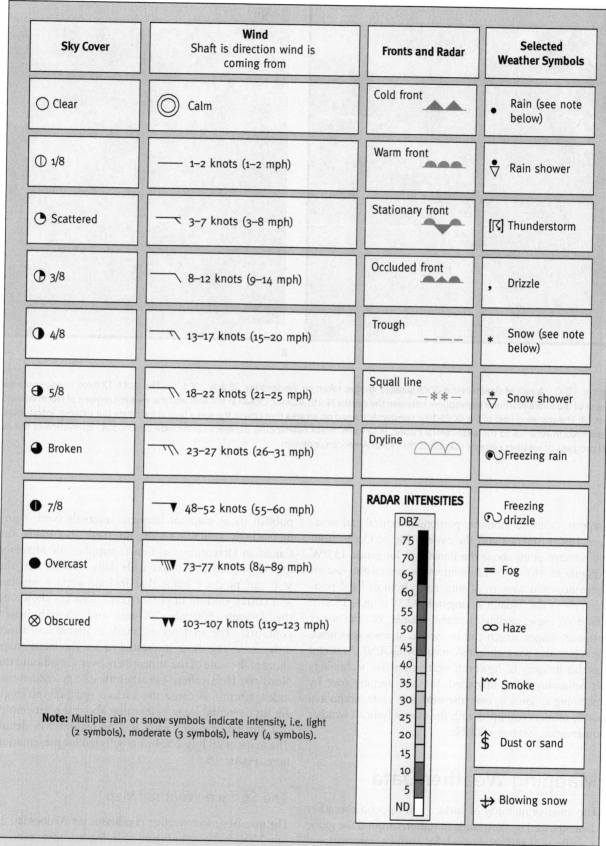

Figure 15.3 Map symbols used by the American Meteorological Society and the Meteorological Service of Canada for synoptic weather charts.

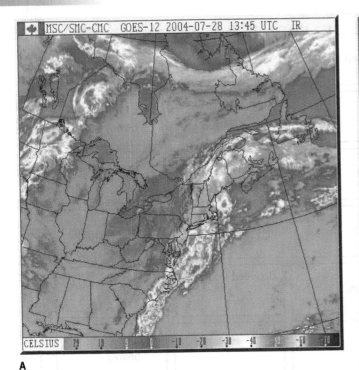

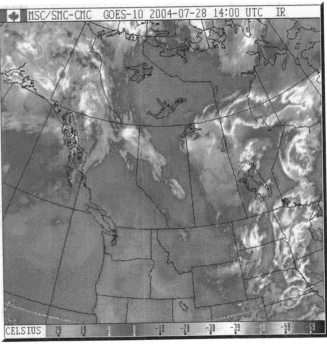

Figure 15.4   A pair of simultaneous GOES satellite images taken on Wednesday, 28 July 2004. (A) The GOES-12 fixed image scans the atmosphere of the entire Northern Hemisphere between the central North Atlantic Ocean in the east and the western regions of North America in the west. (B) The scanning field of the GOES-10 is constantly trained on an area that covers the same latitudinal range but extends longitudinally from eastern North America to the west-central Pacific. In tandem, these overlapping perspectives provide continuous observation of the evolution and progress of weather systems that affect the North American continent.

reports. GOES-10 monitors portions of central and western North America and the eastern Pacific Ocean from its vantage point above the Equator at longitude 135°W (Figure 15.4B). GOES-12 monitors the central and eastern provinces and western Atlantic Basin from its fixed position above the Equator at longitude 90°W (Figure 15.4A). Both of these satellites transmit visible, IR, and water vapour images, which can be viewed at www.goes.noaa.gov (see also www.ghcc.msfc.nasa.gov/GOES/). As useful as this imagery is, however, weather-satellite technology is constantly being upgraded. NOAA is keeping pace by planning to launch, over the next few years, additional GOES orbiters equipped with the most advanced weather observation systems available.

Mapping Weather Data

The massive quantity of surface and upper-air weather data reported by thousands of stations around the globe is collected and organized by various international and national processing centres so that forecasters may begin their never-ending work. Synoptic weather charts are crucial to this task, and the meteorological services of most of the world's countries prepare and

publish these maps at frequent intervals (with many increasingly available on the Internet). In Canada, the Canadian Meteorological Centre supplies the Meteorological Service of Canada with daily data so that the MSC can produce maps that include surface weather and corresponding upper-air conditions (as shown by the 250-mb, 500-mb, 700-mb, and 850-mb height contours). The analyses are made available four times a day, enabling those interested to see the latest snapshots of the state of the atmosphere over Canada and the Northern Hemisphere (weatheroffice.ec.gc.ca/analysis/index_e.html). Because the surface and 500-mb maps are fundamental tools in learning about the geography of Canadian weather, each will be reviewed in detail. The maps of 28 July 2004 were selected for presentation here (Figure 15.5).

The Surface Weather Map

The map of surface weather conditions for Wednesday, 28 July 2004, is shown in Figure 15.5. But before we proceed to interpret its contents, it is necessary to become familiar with the map's point, line, and area symbols.

Each weather station is represented by a point symbol that shows up on the map as a data cluster arranged

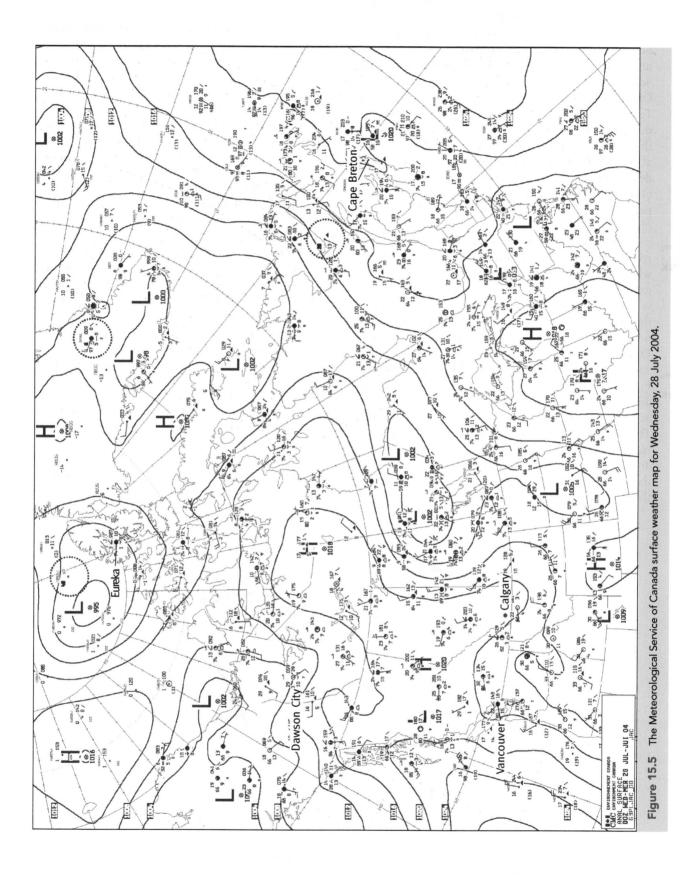

Figure 15.5 The Meteorological Service of Canada surface weather map for Wednesday, 28 July 2004.

around a central circle—an application of the specimen station model displayed in Figure 15.2. In the central circle, the percentage of blackening indicates the proportion of the sky covered by clouds; on the 28 July map, for instance, the skies above Cape Breton, Nova Scotia, are completely covered, while the area around Dawson City (towards the western border of the Yukon Territory) is completely cloudless. Among the numbers distributed around the central circle, the most noteworthy are current temperature in degrees Celsius (shown at the 10 o'clock position with respect to the circle), dew-point temperature (8 o'clock), and air pressure (1 o'clock). Thus, on the map, Vancouver reports a temperature of 22°C, a dew point of 15°C, and a pressure of 1014.9 mb.

LINK

Among these symbols, most important are wind direction and speed. Wind direction (always indicated by where the wind comes *from*) is represented as the line extending outward from the central circle; wind speed is indicated by the number of hash marks attached to the end of that line. Calgary's wind is from the north-northwest at about 14 to 19 km/hr, whereas the wind in Eureka, Nunavut, on Ellesmere Island, is from the south-southeast at about 33 to 40 km/hr. The line symbols in Figure 15.6 represent the jet stream and the fronts, and are calculated on the basis of the surface station weather and upper-air analysis chart information in Figure 15.5. Thunderstorms are expected across the low-pressure regions of central North America, the western Atlantic and northern portions of Alberta, British Columbia, and the Yukon Territory, with generally clear conditions for the remaining portions of the continent.

The Upper-Air Weather Map

The significance of vertical atmospheric data for weather forecasting has already been established. Accordingly, the Meteorological Service of Canada's Canadian Meteorological Centre, based on radiosonde and raw-insonde observations, issues a 500-mb height contours map as part of its daily synoptic chart package. In addition, it produces 250-mb, 700-mb, and 850-mb height contours maps. The 500-mb chart is particularly useful in the analysis of the upper atmosphere. In reading a 500-mb chart, one should remember that the higher the altitude of the 500-mb level, the warmer the surface temperature of the air beneath it; therefore, the gradient of the 500-mb surface should always dip in the general direction of the higher latitudes. Winds on the 500-mb chart are geostrophic, flowing parallel to the isobars (or, in this case, height contour lines), with high pressure on the right looking downwind. Extreme curvature signifies upper-air cyclonic and anticyclonic circulations.

The 500-mb chart for 28 July 2004, compiled at the same moment as the surface weather map (Figure 15.5), is shown in Figure 15.7. Symbolization here should be quite easy to interpret. The height contours on this map are calibrated in 10-m units, called decametres. Wind speeds and directions are represented by the same symbols used for surface weather stations. A departure in wind-speed depiction is the triangular pennant (which equals five hash marks in the style of Figure 15.2), indicating velocities in excess of 88 km/h.

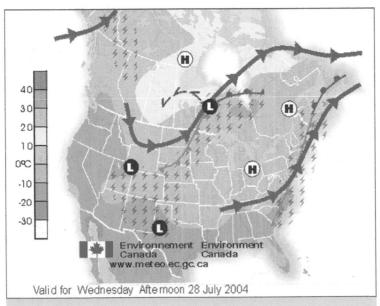

Figure 15.6 North American weather systems (jet stream, fronts, low- and high-pressure systems) for Wednesday, 28 July 2004.

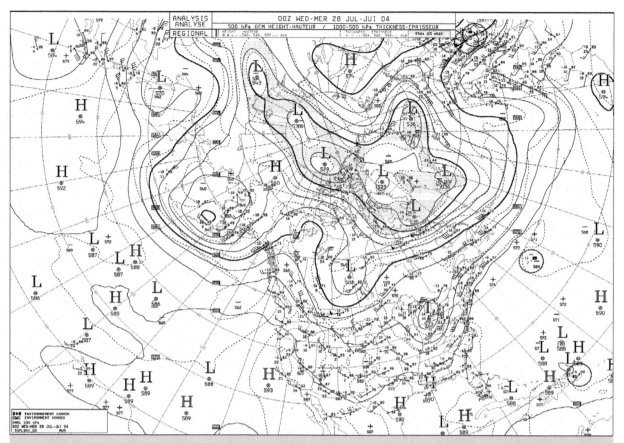

Figure 15.7 A 500-mb chart for 28 July 2004, compiled at the same moment as the surface weather map in Figure 15.5. Heights are given in 10-m units, known as decametres.

The configuration of the 500-mb surface resembles the ground-level pressure pattern (Figure 15.5) in a number of ways. Most prominent is the upper-air trough that dips out of north-central Canada to cover much of interior Canada. Around this trough is the fast-flowing jet stream, which can be seen by the presence of the number of hash marks on the wind line symbol. A second stream can be picked out around the low centred on southwestern Ontario and extending up the eastern seaboard of North America. Bad weather in the form of frontal precipitation and patches of thunderstorms occur in areas where the jet stream flows towards the North Pole (compare with Figure 15.6). Conversely, fair weather is observed along the western interior of British Columbia, where the jet stream moves towards the Equator.

Weather Forecasting

Unlike weather forecasters, who must make projections into an unknown future, we have the luxury of being able to check the outcome of our prediction by simply consulting the next daily weather map, for 29 July 2004. That surface map is shown in Figure 15.8. Note that the frontal system along the eastern seaboard of North America has moved off the map (having moved offshore). The low-pressure system that was centred on western Ontario has since moved further north and east towards north-central Ontario and the western boundary of Quebec and Ontario. Showers are now moving into areas that were to the immediate east of the system on 28 July 2004.

Although it is safe to say that those who issued the actual forecast on 28 July 2004 had more data and experience on which to base their predictions, much of the salient information they needed was summarized in the surface and 500-mb synoptic charts we have discussed. Whereas the 7:00 a.m. EST maps represent 'freeze frames', forecasters had access to the 'motion picture' of the dynamic atmosphere, as satellites, radar, and other instruments constantly monitored its every change. Yet even these data, when run through highly sophisticated computers, could provide only small additional clues as to what was about to happen. Weather prediction, especially in North America, remains an art as well as a science, because forecasters oversee a geographic domain that

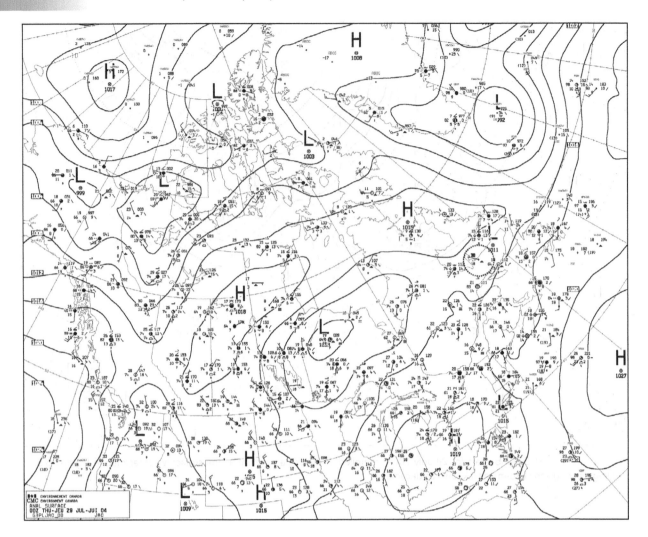

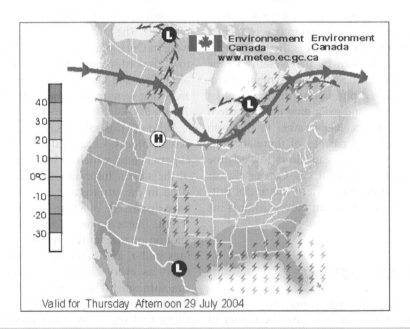

Figure 15.8   The Meteorological Service of Canada surface weather map for Thursday, 29 July 2004.

experiences some of the most variable weather on Earth, which frequently swings from one extreme to another (see 'Perspectives' box).

The Forecasting Industry

Environment Canada's Meteorological Service provides weather forecasts and warnings of extreme weather events and hazardous air quality. The MSC is one of the most highly automated weather services in the world, with infrastructure ranging from traditional (thermometers and rain gauges) to high-tech (radar and satellite technology). Forecasts are issued from 14 regional weather centres distributed across the country, as well as from specialized service offices, such as the Canadian Hurricane Centre, which is part of Halifax's Maritimes Weather Centre. The Canadian Meteorological Centre is located in Montreal and serves as the hub of the national telecommunications, weather modelling, and emergency-preparedness services, with an IBM supercomputer installed in 2005 that is nearly the size of two tennis courts. This computer, which has 936 individual processors, is so large 'it has its own "weather pattern"—in winter, the supercomputer's thermal energy is used to heat the five-storey [Meteorological Centre] building' (Hyndman, 2005).

This computer forecasting method is called **numerical weather prediction** and is based on projections by small increments of time. For example, a forecast is prepared for the weather 15 minutes from now. Once those conditions are determined, the computer repeats the process by using them to make predictions for 15 minutes after that and so forth until the desired future time of the forecast is reached. Obviously, unavoidable errors begin to creep in immediately, and they are magnified as the length of the forecast period increases. The American Meteorological Society has pronounced that the accuracy of forecasts up to 48 hours ahead is now 'considerable'. While that may be true nationally, your local experiences may not always fit that designation!

It has been pointed out that northeastern North America is a region of particularly changeable weather. Inevitably, more forecasts have gone wrong there than in any other part of the nation. Winter storms have proven especially difficult to predict even a few hours ahead, and the need for better snow and ice warnings in this heavily urbanized region has prompted the intensification of research efforts. Meteorologists are most interested in learning more about the sudden genesis of the fierce snowstorms they call 'bombs'.

[A 'bomb' is a] relatively mild winter weather disturbance that drifts northward in the Atlantic from the Cape Hatteras area off North Carolina and then, when it is off New York or Cape Cod, the 'bombing range',

suddenly and inexplicably explodes within six hours or so into a surprising, freezing fury that threatens unsuspecting shipping and paralyzes unprepared coastal cities and towns with heavy sheets of snow and ice. (Ayres, 1988)

Over the past half-century, dozens of these storms have caught the Northeast off guard, and forecasters are still unable to do much more than closely watch the area when conditions are ripe and report a storm as it swiftly materializes. Meteorologists suspect that 'bombs' are the product of a collision of Arctic and moist tropical air. This contrast is heightened along the Mid-Atlantic seaboard by the trapping of large quantities of cold air in the nearby Appalachian Mountains and the infusion of warm-surface seawater by the Gulf Stream (see Figure 10.3). During the 1990s, a data-gathering network of sea buoys and monitoring instruments was put in place offshore, and researchers are hopeful that this technology will enable them to better understand and predict these dangerous storms.

LINK

Because the predictions of Environment Canada are for broad regions and are occasionally unreliable, the needs of businesses whose activities are closely related to weather conditions have given rise to a private forecasting industry. This is particularly prevalent in the United States, where hundreds of companies concentrate on tailoring forecasts to the special needs of their corporate clients. Agricultural concerns comprise the biggest single-user category. Private forecasters can prepare surprisingly specific predictions, particularly with respect to moisture conditions, and the recent growth of their clientele demonstrates that an important need is being met. Many subscribers, such as electrical utilities and fuel oil distributors, require hour-by-hour information in order to be ready to meet customer demands as temperatures rise or fall. A whole host of firms engaged in outdoor activities, from airline companies to motion picture producers to construction contractors, are also frequent customers of private forecasting services. In Canada the general public is probably most familiar with the news media's use of private forecasts. The Weather Network's patented Pelmorex Forecast Engine (PFE) technology, for example, allows their meteorologists to issue weather forecasts for the entire country down to a 10-km² grid.

Long-Range Forecasting

Long-range forecasting constitutes a lively new frontier for weather scientists and poses some of the toughest research challenges they face today. In response to the need and desire for longer-term outlooks, the Canadian Meteorological Centre began producing, through the Meteorological Service of Canada, seasonal temperature and precipitation anomaly forecasts, starting

Perspectives on the Human Environment

Weather Extremes

Since climatologists no longer concentrate their work on average figures, a brief consideration of the extreme weather conditions that increasingly concern them is a worthwhile exercise. In early 1987, Athens, Greece, experienced its first recorded snowfall and then, a few months later, its hottest summer ever—only

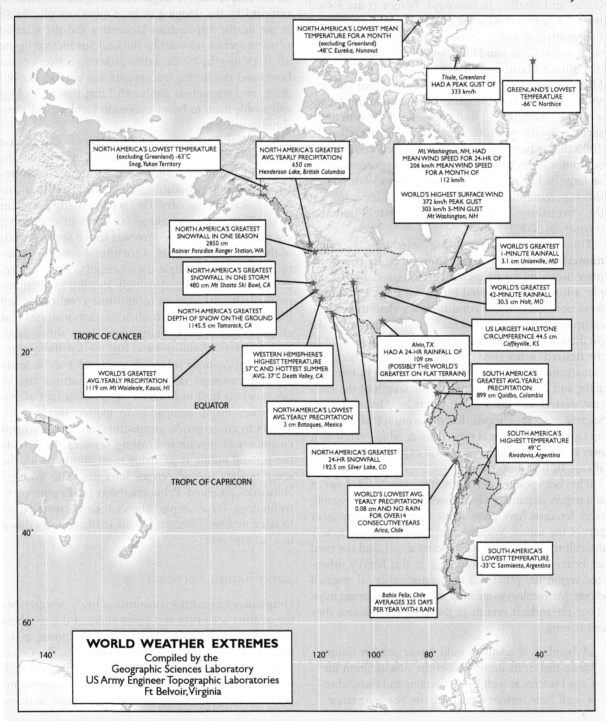

NORTH AMERICA'S LOWEST MEAN
TEMPERATURE FOR A MONTH
(excluding Greenland)
-48°C Eureka, Nunavut

Thule, Greenland
HAD A PEAK GUST OF
333 km/h

GREENLAND'S LOWEST
TEMPERATURE
-66°C Northice

NORTH AMERICA'S LOWEST TEMPERATURE
(excluding Greenland) -63°C
Snag, Yukon Territory

NORTH AMERICA'S GREATEST
AVG. YEARLY PRECIPITATION
650 cm
Henderson Lake, British Columbia

Mt. Washington, NH, HAD
MEAN WIND SPEED FOR 24-HR OF
206 km/h MEAN WIND SPEED
FOR A MONTH OF
112 km/h

WORLD'S HIGHEST SURFACE WIND
372 km/h PEAK GUST
303 km/h 5-MIN GUST
Mt Washington, NH

NORTH AMERICA'S GREATEST
SNOWFALL IN ONE SEASON
2850 cm
Rainier Paradise Ranger Station, WA

WORLD'S GREATEST
1-MINUTE RAINFALL
3.1 cm Unionville, MD

NORTH AMERICA'S GREATEST
SNOWFALL IN ONE STORM
480 cm Mt Shasta Ski Bowl, CA

WORLD'S GREATEST
42-MINUTE RAINFALL
30.5 cm Holt, MO

NORTH AMERICA'S GREATEST
DEPTH OF SNOW ON THE GROUND
1145.5 cm Tamarack, CA

US LARGEST HAILSTONE
CIRCUMFERENCE 44.5 cm
Coffeyville, KS

TROPIC OF CANCER

20°

Alvin, TX
HAD A 24-HR RAINFALL OF
109 cm
(POSSIBLY THE WORLD'S
GREATEST ON FLAT TERRAIN)

WESTERN HEMISPHERE'S
HIGHEST TEMPERATURE
57°C AND HOTTEST SUMMER
AVG. 37°C Death Valley, CA

SOUTH AMERICA'S
GREATEST AVG. YEARLY
PRECIPITATION
899 cm Quidbo, Colombia

WORLD'S GREATEST
AVG. YEARLY PRECIPITATION
1119 cm Mt Waialeale, Kauai, HI

EQUATOR

NORTH AMERICA'S LOWEST
AVG. YEARLY PRECIPITATION
3 cm Bataques, Mexico

SOUTH AMERICA'S
HIGHEST TEMPERATURE
49°C
Rivadavia, Argentina

NORTH AMERICA'S GREATEST
24-HR SNOWFALL
192.5 cm Silver Lake, CO

TROPIC OF CAPRICORN

WORLD'S LOWEST AVG.
YEARLY PRECIPITATION
0.08 cm AND NO RAIN
FOR OVER 14
CONSECUTIVE YEARS
Arica, Chile

40°

SOUTH AMERICA'S
LOWEST TEMPERATURE
-33°C Sarmiento, Argentina

Bahia Felix, Chile
AVERAGES 325 DAYS
PER YEAR WITH RAIN

60°

140°   120°   100°   80°   40°

WORLD WEATHER EXTREMES
Compiled by the
Geographic Sciences Laboratory
US Army Engineer Topographic Laboratories
Ft Belvoir, Virginia

Figure 15.9 Some noteworthy global weather extremes.

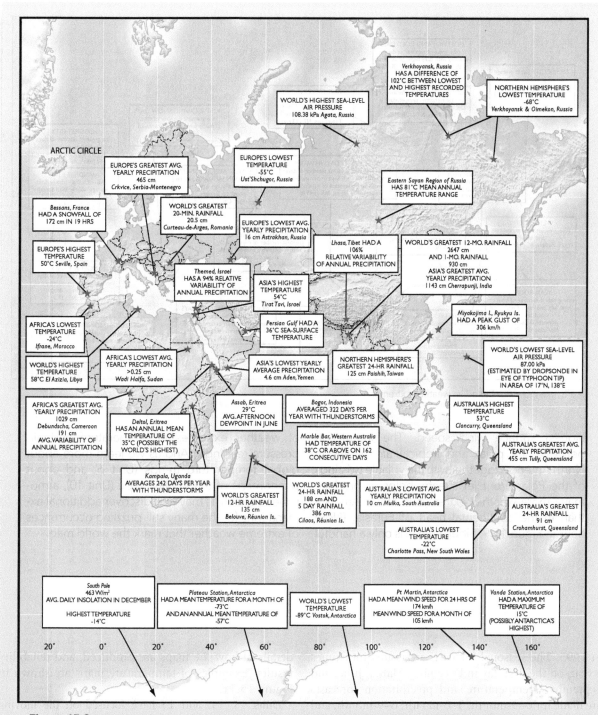

ARCTIC CIRCLE

WORLD'S HIGHEST SEA-LEVEL
AIR PRESSURE
108.38 kPa Agata, Russia

Verkhoyansk, Russia
HAS A DIFFERENCE OF
102°C BETWEEN LOWEST
AND HIGHEST RECORDED
TEMPERATURES

NORTHERN HEMISPHERE'S
LOWEST TEMPERATURE
-68°C
Verkhoyansk & Oimekon, Russia

EUROPE'S GREATEST AVG.
YEARLY PRECIPITATION
465 cm
Crkvice, Serbia-Montenegro

EUROPE'S LOWEST
TEMPERATURE
-55°C
Ust'Shchugor, Russia

Eastern Sayan Region of Russia
HAS 81°C MEAN ANNUAL
TEMPERATURE RANGE

Bessans, France
HAD A SNOWFALL OF
172 cm IN 19 HRS

WORLD'S GREATEST
20-MIN. RAINFALL
20.5 cm
Curteau-de-Arges, Romania

EUROPE'S LOWEST AVG.
YEARLY PRECIPITATION
16 cm Astrakhan, Russia

Lhasa, Tibet HAD A
106%
RELATIVE VARIABILITY
OF ANNUAL PRECIPITATION

WORLD'S GREATEST 12-MO. RAINFALL
2647 cm
AND 1-MO. RAINFALL
930 cm
ASIA'S GREATEST AVG.
YEARLY PRECIPITATION
1143 cm Cherrapunji, India

EUROPE'S HIGHEST
TEMPERATURE
50°C Seville, Spain

Themed, Israel
HAS A 94% RELATIVE
VARIABILITY OF
ANNUAL PRECIPITATION

ASIA'S HIGHEST
TEMPERATURE
54°C
Tirat Tsvi, Israel

Miyakojima I., Ryukyu Is.
HAD A PEAK GUST OF
306 km/h

AFRICA'S LOWEST
TEMPERATURE
-24°C
Ifrane, Morocco

Persian Gulf HAD A
36°C SEA-SURFACE
TEMPERATURE

WORLD'S LOWEST SEA-LEVEL
AIR PRESSURE
87.00 kPa
(ESTIMATED BY DROPSONDE IN
EYE OF TYPHOON TIP)
IN AREA OF 17°N, 138°E

WORLD'S HIGHEST
TEMPERATURE
58°C El Azizia, Libya

AFRICA'S LOWEST AVG.
YEARLY PRECIPITATION
>0.25 cm
Wadi Halfa, Sudan

ASIA'S LOWEST YEARLY
AVERAGE PRECIPITATION
4.6 cm Aden, Yemen

NORTHERN HEMISPHERE'S
GREATEST 24-HR RAINFALL
125 cm Paishih, Taiwan

AFRICA'S GREATEST AVG.
YEARLY PRECIPITATION
1029 cm
Debundscha, Cameroon
191 cm
AVG. VARIABILITY OF
ANNUAL PRECIPITATION

Deltol, Eritrea
HAS AN ANNUAL MEAN
TEMPERATURE OF
35°C (POSSIBLY THE
WORLD'S HIGHEST)

Assab, Eritrea
29°C
AVG. AFTERNOON
DEWPOINT IN JUNE

Bogor, Indonesia
AVERAGED 322 DAYS PER
YEAR WITH THUNDERSTORMS

AUSTRALIA'S HIGHEST
TEMPERATURE
53°C
Cloncurry, Queensland

Marble Bar, Western Australia
HAD TEMPERATURE OF
38°C OR ABOVE ON 162
CONSECUTIVE DAYS

AUSTRALIA'S GREATEST AVG.
YEARLY PRECIPITATION
455 cm Tully, Queensland

Kampala, Uganda
AVERAGES 242 DAYS PER YEAR
WITH THUNDERSTORMS

WORLD'S GREATEST
24-HR RAINFALL
188 cm AND
5 DAY RAINFALL
386 cm
Cilaos, Réunion Is.

AUSTRALIA'S LOWEST AVG.
YEARLY PRECIPITATION
10 cm Mulka, South Australia

AUSTRALIA'S GREATEST
24-HR RAINFALL
91 cm
Crohamhurst, Queensland

WORLD'S GREATEST
12-HR RAINFALL
135 cm
Belouve, Réunion Is.

AUSTRALIA'S LOWEST
TEMPERATURE
-22°C
Charlotte Pass, New South Wales

South Pole
463 W/m²
AVG. DAILY INSOLATION IN DECEMBER

HIGHEST TEMPERATURE
-14°C

Plateau Station, Antarctica
HAD A MEAN TEMPERATURE FOR A MONTH OF
-73°C
AND AN ANNUAL MEAN TEMPERATURE OF
-57°C

WORLD'S LOWEST
TEMPERATURE
-89°C Vostok, Antarctica

Pt Martin, Antarctica
HAD A MEAN WIND SPEED FOR 24 HRS OF
174 km/h
MEAN WIND SPEED FOR A MONTH OF
105 km/h

Vanda Station, Antarctica
HAD A MAXIMUM
TEMPERATURE OF
15°C
(POSSIBLY ANTARCTICA'S
HIGHEST)

20°   0°   20°   40°   60°   80°   100°   120°   140°   160°

Figure 15.9 (Continued)

to learn the following December that the average yearly temperature came out almost exactly 'normal'. On 11 August 1984, residents of Miami, Florida, experienced both the highest (35.5°C) and lowest (21°C) temperatures ever recorded on that day—only to see it noted that the mean temperature for the day came very close to the normal daily average of 28°C. These are only two isolated cases, but they underscore how averages can misrepresent actual weather conditions and the accompanying human adjustments to the physical environment of a particular place.

Figure 15.9 illustrates some of the noteworthy global weather extremes, while Figure 15.10 shows weather extremes in Canada. With some of the most changeable weather occurring in the mid-latitudes, North America has a number of record-breakers. Among the world weather records held in places throughout North America are greatest yearly average precipitation and

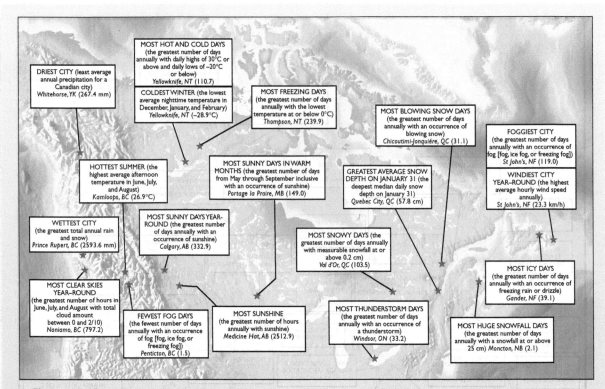

Figure 15.10   Canadian weather extremes.

LINK

highest surface wind speed. The interaction between the polar and tropical air masses in North America, together with the volatile twistings of the Polar Front jet stream, helps to produce many more weather extremes in North America than in the continental heart of Eurasia. (Note how, in Figure 15.9, Siberia records only a handful of weather extremes in temperature and air-pressure readings.) And as we learn more about global temperature trends (Unit 6) and about phenomena of the El Niño type (Unit 10), atmospheric scientists may well discover additional explanations for the many still-puzzling occurrences of extreme weather that mark the world map.

in 1995. The seasonal forecasts are issued four times a year, on the first day in December, March, June, and September. Temperature and precipitation forecasts are made for 0–3-month, 3–6-month, 6–9-month, and 9–12-month periods. The maps represent air temperature and precipitation that is expected to be below normal, near normal, and above normal (deterministic forecasts). In addition, probabilistic forecasts are produced; these indicate the respective probability of the temperature and precipitation being below, near, or above normal. The Canadian Meteorological Service's seasonal forecast web page (weatheroffice. ec.gc.ca/saisons/index_e.html) includes forecast maps,

details of how the maps are produced, and reliability results. Examples of temperature maps are shown in Figure 15.11.

Units 13, 14, and 15 have focused on the moving weather systems that blanket the Earth at any given moment. These recurring systems, together with the constant flows of radiation, heat energy, and moisture, make up our daily weather. Over time, a region's weather conditions exhibit regular rhythms and patterns that are characteristic of a certain type of climate. Unit 16 provides a basis for the classification and regionalization of climate types, which is subsequently applied in Unit 17 to all of the Earth's land areas.

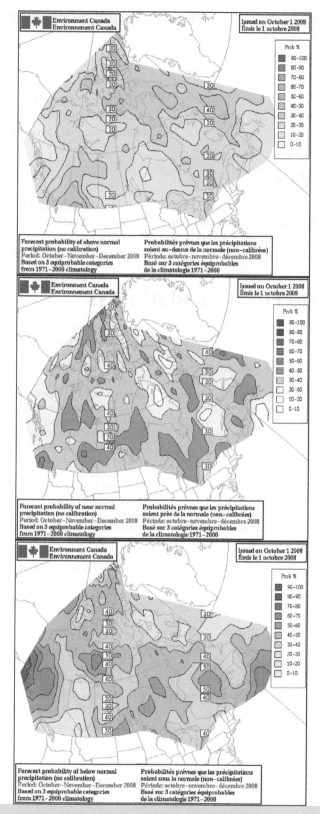

Figure 15.11 State-of-the-art weather forecasting by the Canadian Meteorological Service. These three maps, issued on 1 October 2008, indicate the percentage likelihood of above-normal, near-normal, and below-normal temperatures for October–December 2008. Similar maps also are issued for precipitation and for longer time periods.

KEY TERMS

geosynchronous orbit   *page 196*
meteorology   *page 195*
numerical weather prediction   *page 203*
polar orbit   *page 196*

radiosonde   *page 196*
rawinsonde   *page 196*
synoptic weather chart   *page 195*
weather stations   *page 196*

REVIEW QUESTIONS

1. Describe the basic weather elements whose variations are observed and recorded at weather stations.
2. What is a radiosonde station and what kinds of atmospheric data does it provide?
3. How does the 500-mb chart aid in the forecasting of surface weather?
4. What tools are used by meteorologists in the generation of a short-term weather forecast?

REFERENCES AND FURTHER READINGS

Ahrens, C.D. 2006. *Meteorology Today: An Introduction to Weather, Climate, and the Environment.* 8th edn. Belmont, Calif.: Thomson-Brooks/Cole.

Ayres, B.D., Jr. 1988. 'Volatile Weather "Bomb" Is Tracked', *New York Times*, 14 Mar., 8.

Bader, M.J., et al., eds. 1995. *Images in Weather Forecasting: A Practical Guide for Interpreting Satellite and Radar Imagery.* New York: Cambridge Univ. Press.

Burroughs, W. 1991. *Watching the World's Weather.* New York: Cambridge Univ. Press.

Carleton, A.M. 1991. *Satellite Remote Sensing in Climatology.* London: Belhaven.

Chaston, P.R. 1997. *Weather Maps: How to Read and Interpret All the Basic Weather Charts.* Kearney, Mo.: Chaston Scientific.

Cox, J.D. 2002. *Storm Watchers: The Turbulent History of Weather Prediction from Franklin's Kite to El Niño.* New York: Wiley.

Danielson, E.W., J. Levin, and E. Abrams. 2003. *Meteorology*, 2nd edn. Dubuque, Iowa: McGraw-Hill.

Eagleman, J.R. 1990. *Severe and Unusual Weather*, 2nd edn. Lenexa, Kan.: Trimedia.

Feder, B.J. 1996. 'Highs and Lows Are Their Business: More Companies Are Relying on Private Weather Forecasters', *New York Times*, 22 Oct., C1, C3.

Fishman, J., and R. Kalish. 1994. *The Weather Revolution: Innovations and Imminent Breakthroughs in Accurate Forecasting.* New York: Plenum.

Hodgson, M. 2008. *Basic Essentials Weather Forecasting.* Helena, Mont.: Falcon Publishing.

Hyndman, R. 2005. 'New Canadian Weather Computer Technology', 3 Mar. Available at: <www.robhyndman.com/2005/03/03/new-canadian-weather-computer-technology>.

Monmonier, M. 1999. *Air Apparent: How Meteorologists Learned to Map, Predict, and Dramatize Weather.* Chicago: Univ. of Chicago Press.

Pearce, E.A., and C.G. Smith. 1990. *World Weather Guide.* New York: Random House.

Thomas, M.K. 1991. *Beginnings of Canadian Meteorology.* Chicago: Independent Publishers Group.

Thornes, J.E., and D.B. Stephenson. 2001. 'How to Judge the Quality and Value of Weather Forecast Products', *Meteorological Applications* 8: 307–14.

Wagner, R.L., and B. Adler Jr. 1994. *The Weather Sourcebook: Your One-Stop Resource for Everything You Need to Feed Your Weather Habit.* Guilford, Conn.: Globe Pequot.

 # WEB RESOURCES

wunderground.com Weather Underground is one of the most common Internet sites for obtaining international weather data.

www.msc.ec.gc.ca/education/severe_weather/page02_e.cfm Environment Canada's volunteer weather watchers site, with the 'Severe Weather Watcher Handbook'.

www.msc.ec.gc.ca/msc/brochure_e.html The Meteorological Service of Canada.

www.ncdc.noaa.gov/oa/reports/weather-events.html Worldwide weather and climate events with links to many extreme weather-event sites.

www.theweathernetwork.com Canada's Weather Network.

www.weatheroffice.gc.ca/canada_e.html Environment Canada weather.

ww2010.atmos.uiuc.edu/(Gh)/guides/maps/home.rxml 'Reading Weather Maps' from the University of Illinois.

Climate Classification and Regionalization

Objectives

- To define climate and discuss the general problems of climate classification based on dynamic phenomena.

- To explain the primary factors controlling the geographic distribution of climate.

- To outline a useful climate classification scheme devised by Köppen, based on temperatures and precipitation amounts and timing.

- To apply the modified Köppen classification system to the Earth and briefly describe appropriate climate regions as they appear on a hypothetical continent and the world map.

Climatology is the study of the Earth's regional climates, whereas meteorology is the study of short-term atmospheric phenomena that constitute weather. To understand this distinction, we may use the rule that weather happens now but climate goes on all the time. Climate involves the aggregate weather conditions each of us expects to experience in a particular place. If we live in Florida or Hawaii, we expect to wear light clothes for most of the year; if we live in Nunavut, we expect to wear heavy jackets. Climate, therefore, is a synthesis of the succession of weather events we have learned to expect in any particular location.

Because there is a degree of regularity in the heat and water exchanges at the Earth's surface and in the general circulation of the atmosphere, there is a broad and predictable pattern of climates across the globe. But this pattern is altered in detail by such additional **climatic controls** as the location of land and water bodies, ocean currents, and mountain ranges and other highlands. More specifically, the **climate** of a place may be defined as the average values of weather elements, such as temperature and precipitation, over at least a 30-year period and the important variations from those average values. In Unit 17 we examine how broad patterns and fine details create distinctly different climates across the Earth. This unit provides a framework for that investigation by discussing the classification of climate types and their global spatial distribution.

Classifying Climates

Because of the great variety and complexity of recurring weather patterns across the Earth's surface, it is necessary for atmospheric scientists to reduce countless local climates to a relative few that possess important unifying characteristics. Such classification, of course, is the organizational foundation of all the modern sciences. Where would chemistry be without its periodic table of the elements, geology without its time scale of past eras and epochs, and biology without its Linnaean system of naming plant and animal species?

The ideal climate classification system would achieve five objectives:

1. It should clearly differentiate among all the major types of climates that occur on Earth.
2. It should show the relationships among these climate types.
3. It should apply to the whole world.
4. It should provide a framework for further subdivision to cover specific locales.
5. It should demonstrate the controls that cause any particular climate.

Unfortunately, in the same way that no map projection can simultaneously satisfy all of our requirements (see Unit 3), no climate classification system can simultaneously achieve all five of these objectives. There are two reasons. First, so many factors contribute to climate that

we must compromise between simplicity and complexity. We have values for radiation, temperature, precipitation, evapotranspiration, wind direction, and so forth. We could use one variable—as the Greeks used latitude to differentiate 'torrid', 'temperate', and 'frigid' zones—and have a classification system that would be too simple to be useful. Or, on the other hand, we could use all the values to gain infinite detail—but overwhelming complexity.

The second reason is that the Earth's climates form a spatial continuum. Sharp areal breaks between the major types of climate are rarely found, because both daily and generalized weather patterns change from place to place gradually, not abruptly. Yet any classificatory map forces climatologists to draw lines separating a given climate type from its neighbours, thereby giving the impression that such a boundary is a sharp dividing line rather than the middle of a broad transition zone.

When confronted with these problems, climatologists focus their compromises on a single rule: the development or choice of a climatic classification must be determined by the particular use for which the scheme is intended. With so many potential uses, it is not surprising that many different classification systems have been devised. Whereas qualitative and/or subjective criteria could be used to distinguish climates (see 'Perspectives' box), the practicalities of contemporary physical geography demand an objective, quantitative approach. Moreover, for our purposes, the classification system must be reasonably simple and yet reflect the full diversity of global climatic variation. The **Köppen climate classification system** provides us with that balanced approach, offering a descriptive classification of world climates that brilliantly negotiates the tightrope between simplicity and complexity. To Wladimir P. Köppen (1846–1940), the key to classifying climate was plant life.

The Köppen Climate Classification System

In 1874 the Swiss botanist Alphonse de Candolle produced the first comprehensive classification and regionalization of world vegetation based on the internal functions of plant organs. It is to Wladimir Köppen's everlasting credit that he recognized that a plant, or assemblage of plants, at a particular place represents a synthesis of the many variations of the weather experienced there. He therefore looked to de Candolle's classification of vegetation to solve the puzzle of the global spatial organization of climates.

Köppen (pronounced KER-pin with the 'r' silent) compared the global distribution of vegetation mapped by de Candolle with his own maps of the world distribution of temperature and precipitation. He soon identified several correlations between the atmosphere and biosphere and used them to distinguish one climate from another. For

Perspectives on the Human Environment

Climate in Daily Human Terms

1. 'The butter, when stabbed with a knife, flew like very brittle toffee. The lower skirts of the inner tent are solid with ice. All our [sleeping] bags were so saturated with water that they froze too stiff to bend with safety, so we packed them one on the other full length, like coffins, on the sledge.'

2. 'The rain poured steadily down, turning the little patch of reclaimed ground on which his house stood back into swamp again. The window of this room blew to and fro: at some time during the night, the catch had been broken by a squall of wind. Now the rain had blown in, his dressing table was soaking wet, and there was a pool of water on the floor.'

3. 'It was a breathless wind, with the furnace taste sometimes known in Egypt when a khamsin came, and, as the day went on and the sun rose in the sky it grew stronger, more filled with the dust of Nefudh, the great sand desert of Northern Arabia, close by us over there, but invisible through the haze.'

4. 'The spring came richly, and the hills lay asleep in grass—emerald green, the rank thick grass; the slopes were sleek and fat with it. The stock, sensing a great quantity of food shooting up on the sidehills, increased the bearing of the young. When April came, and warm grass-scented days, the flowers burdened the hills with color, the poppies gold and the lupines blue, in spreads and comforters.'

5. 'The east wind that had blown coldly across the Channel that morning had brought a dusting of snow to Picardy. Snow in April! It lay in a thin covering on hillsides, like long, torn bed sheets, the earth showing through in black streaks. It made the ordinary-looking landscape seem dramatic, the way New Jersey looks in bad weather, made houses and fences emphatic, and brought a sort of cubism to villages that would otherwise have been unmemorable. Each place became a little frozen portrait in black and white.'

These excerpted selections attempt to convey a sense of climate, the impact a particular climate—especially a demanding and harsh climate—has on people who attempt to explore and live in it. Description of climate is one of the cornerstones of the literature of exploration and travel. Perhaps nothing conveys a sense of an environment as efficiently and dramatically as notation of its winds, precipitation, and temperatures. And, as these skillful writers show, climate tells you a great deal about the 'feel' of a place.

Were you able to identify the five locations? Selection 1 is from Robert Falcon Scott's memoirs of his explorations in the Arctic, published posthumously in 1914. Selection 2 is by Graham Greene, who, after being stationed in West Africa during World War II, wrote *The Heart of the Matter*. Selection 3 is by Thomas Edward Lawrence ('Lawrence of Arabia'), the British soldier who organized the Arab nations against the Turks during World War I. Selection 4 is by John Steinbeck, writing in *To a God Unknown* during the 1930s about the Mediterranean climate of central California. Selection 5 is from travel writer Paul Theroux, who, in *Riding the Iron Rooster*, recorded his mid-1980s train-window impression of northern France en route from London to a year of journeying on China's railroads.

example, he observed that in the high latitudes the boundary marking the presence or absence of trees closely coincided with the presence or absence of at least one month in the year with an average temperature of 10°C. He noted many other such correlations, and in 1900 he published the first version of his classification system. This regionalization scheme, subsequently modified by Köppen and other researchers (notably Rudolf Geiger), was to become the most widely used climatic classification system.

Figure 16.1 presents a simplified version of the Köppen system, which will be used in this book. Just as code letters are used to describe air masses, the Köppen classification uses a shorthand notation of letter symbols to distinguish different characteristics of the

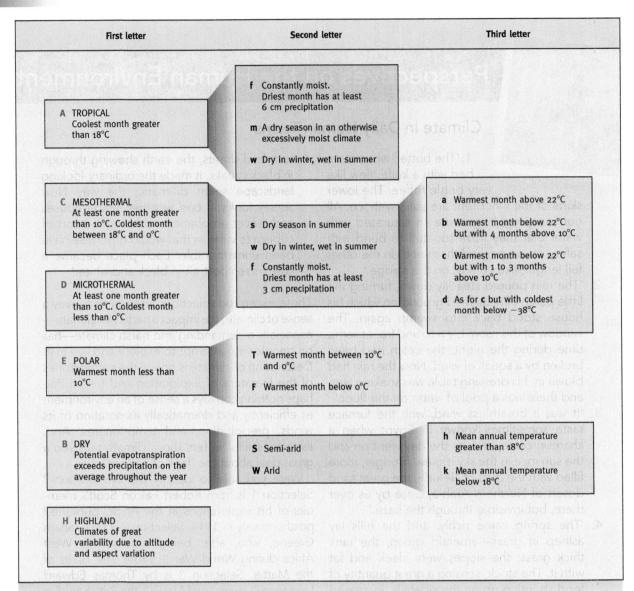

First letter	Second letter	Third letter

A TROPICAL
Coolest month greater than 18°C

f Constantly moist.
Driest month has at least 6 cm precipitation

m A dry season in an otherwise excessively moist climate

w Dry in winter, wet in summer

C MESOTHERMAL
At least one month greater than 10°C. Coldest month between 18°C and 0°C

D MICROTHERMAL
At least one month greater than 10°C. Coldest month less than 0°C

s Dry season in summer

w Dry in winter, wet in summer

f Constantly moist.
Driest month has at least 3 cm precipitation

a Warmest month above 22°C

b Warmest month below 22°C but with 4 months above 10°C

c Warmest month below 22°C but with 1 to 3 months above 10°C

d As for **c** but with coldest month below −38°C

E POLAR
Warmest month less than 10°C

T Warmest month between 10°C and 0°C

F Warmest month below 0°C

B DRY
Potential evapotranspiration exceeds precipitation on the average throughout the year

S Semi-arid

W Arid

h Mean annual temperature greater than 18°C

k Mean annual temperature below 18°C

H HIGHLAND
Climates of great variability due to altitude and aspect variation

Figure 16.1 Simplified version of the modern Köppen climate classification system.

major climates. The six major climate groups (column 1) are labelled **A, B, C, D, E,** and **H**. The major tropical (**A**), mesothermal (**C**), microthermal (**D**), and polar (**E**) climates are differentiated according to temperature. (*Mesothermal* implies a moderate amount of heat, and *microthermal* implies a small amount—as the temperature criteria in their respective boxes in Figure 16.1 indicate.) The major dry (**B**) climates are distinguished by potential evapotranspiration exceeding precipitation. The variable highland climates (**H**) are grouped into a separate major category.

As Figure 16.1 shows, these major climate groups are further subdivided in terms of heat or moisture by the use of a second letter (column 2) and in some cases a third letter (column 3). In the second column, the lower-case letters **f, m, w,** and **s** tell us when precipitation occurs during the year, and are applicable to **A, C,** and **D** climates. Capital

letters **S** and **W** indicate the degree of aridity in dry (**B**) climates, with **S** designating semi-arid conditions and **W** full aridity. Letters referring to moisture conditions are shown in the green-coloured boxes in Figure 16.1; letters referring to heat are shown in the peach-coloured boxes. The heat modifiers of the third column—lower-case letters **a, b, c,** and **d**—provide details on the temperatures of **C** and **D** climates. The third letters **h** and **k** do the same for the **B** climates, and the second letters **T** and **F** subdivide the temperatures in polar (**E**) climates.

Many different climates can be defined with this shorthand code, including all that can be represented and mapped at the world regional scale. As we proceed through each major climate type in the next unit, you will be able to decode any combination of Köppen letter symbols by referring back to Figure 16.1. For instance, an **Af** climate is a tropical climate in which the average temperature of every month exceeds 18°C and total monthly precipitation always exceeds 6 cm. Before considering each of the six major climate groups, we need to establish their spatial dimensions, both in general terms and on the world map.

The Regional Distribution of Climate Types

Figure 16.2 illustrates the spatial distribution of world climate. The climate of a particular place is the function of a number of controlling factors. These factors include:

1. **Latitude and its influence on climate.** Latitude is a fundamental control on every climate. It affects temperature by influencing the seasonal range in solar intensity. It influences precipitation inasmuch as evaporation is temperature dependent.

2. **Location of global high and low pressure zones.** The Earth's average pressure patterns and resulting winds influence climate patterns by advecting temperature and moisture, causing areas of surface convergence and divergence, and influencing mid-latitude storm tracks.

3. **Heat exchange from ocean currents.** Sea-surface temperature influences air temperature as the ocean exchanges heat with the overlying atmosphere. It also influences evaporation rates, which are generally higher where sea-surface temperature is higher.

4. **Altitude.** Temperature generally decreases adiabatically with altitude. Two locations at the same latitude but at different altitudes will have very different climatic characteristics.

5. **Air mass influences and pattern of prevailing winds.** Prevailing winds influence local climate. If the prevailing winds flow across a large body of water, then the climate is more likely to have maritime characteristics as opposed to another location that experiences prevailing winds from a continental source region. Some coastal locations in the eastern US do not have maritime climates (e.g., Norfolk, Virginia) because of this.

6. **Distribution of land and sea.** Because land heats and cools faster and more intensely than water, continental locations have a larger seasonal temperature range than maritime locations. Maritime locations often have more precipitation because of their proximity to a large moisture source.

7. **Topography.** Landforms such as hills or mountains can alter wind flow. Because winds can be forced upward by an elevated landform, the exposed (windward) side can often have a different weather and climate than the sheltered (leeward) side. As air travels up a mountain, moisture is 'squeezed' out of the air as it cools, condenses, and falls as precipitation. Air temperature and the amount of moisture in the air are

usually decreased as the air flows down the sheltered side of the mountain.

So the climate of any particular place is influenced by a host of interacting factors, including latitude, elevation, nearby water, ocean currents, topography, vegetation, and prevailing winds. **Climographs** such as the examples in Figure 16.3 are used to visualize temperature (red line graph) and precipitation (blue bar graph) characteristics in the study of climate.

The Distribution of A Climates

The tropical **A** climates straddle the Equator (Figure 16.2), extending to approximately 25 degrees latitude in both the Northern and Southern Hemispheres. The heart of the **A** climate region is constituted by its wet subtype, the *tropical rainforest* climate (**Af**), named for the vegetation it nurtures. On the poleward margins of the tropical rainforest, forming transitional belts between the **A** and **B** climates, lies the **Aw** climate, which exhibits a distinct winter dry season. This is called the *savanna* climate because of the tall grasses that grow there, dominating the vegetational spaces between clumps of trees and/or thorny bushes. A third **A** climate, the **Am**, or *monsoon*, variety of the rainforest climate, is often found at coastal corners of the **Af** region and is subject to even more pronounced seasonal fluctuations in rainfall.

Closer inspection of the tropical climate zone on a **hypothetical continent** will also reveal that areas of **A** climate are widest on the eastern side of the world island. This occurs because the trade winds blow onshore from the northeast and southeast, and the difference in overall latitudinal extent of the **A** region is about 20 degrees greater on the east coast of a continent than on the west coast.

In the Americas, the **A** climates are centred around the Equator, reaching to about 25°N and S on the eastern coasts and islands, and to about 20°N and S in western Central and South America, respectively. The African pattern is similar south of the Equator, but to the north the **A** climates are compressed because the moist northeast trades are blocked by the landmass of southern Asia. For reasons identified in Unit 9, the Asian tropical climates are dominated by the monsoon effect. The prevalence of oceans and seas between Southeast Asia and northern Australia has sharply reduced the areal extent of tropical climates over land, but many of the islands of the lengthy Indonesian archipelago still exhibit rainforest climates over most of their surfaces.

The Distribution of B Climates

The dry **B** climates are located poleward of the **A** climates on the western sides of continents. These climates are associated with the subsiding air of the subtropical high-pressure

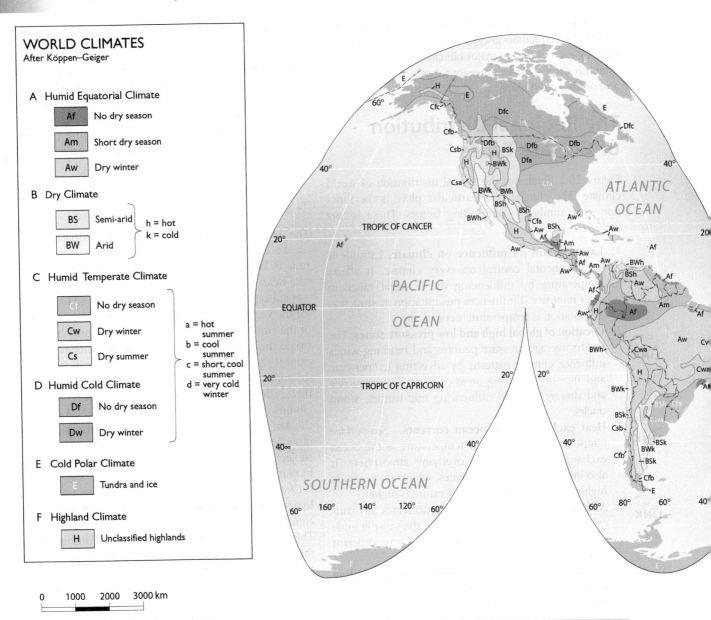

Figure 16.2   Global distribution of climates according to the modified Köppen classification system.

zones, whose influence is greatest on the eastern side of the oceans. This leads to a major intrusion of arid climates onto neighbouring continents in both the Northern and Southern Hemispheres. This occurs at the average latitudes of the Subtropical High between 20° and 30°N and S. Once inland from the west coast of the continent, however, the **B** climate region curves poleward, following the airflows of the Westerlies in each hemisphere and reaching to about 55°N and 45°S, respectively. As shown in Unit 17, continentality also plays a significant role in the occurrence of **B** climates, particularly on the Eurasian landmass.

The heart of the **B** climate region contains the driest climatic variety, true *desert* (**BW**—with **W** standing for *wüste*, the German word for desert). It is surrounded by the semi-arid short-grass prairie, or *steppe* (**BS**), which is a

moister transitional climate that lies between the **BW** core and the more humid **A**, **C**, and **D** climates bordering the dry-climate zone.

The desert climate (**BW**) dominates the subtropical-latitude land that stretches east–west across northern Africa and then curves northeastward through southwestern and central Asia where it forms a more or less continuous belt between northwestern Africa and Mongolia, interrupted only by narrow seas, mountain corridors, and a handful of well-watered river valleys. Included among these vast arid basins are North Africa's Sahara, the deserts of the Arabian Peninsula and nearby Iran, and China's Takla Makan and Gobi Deserts. Note that these **BW** climates become colder north of 35°N (as indicated by the third Köppen letter **k** replacing **h**) and that all the

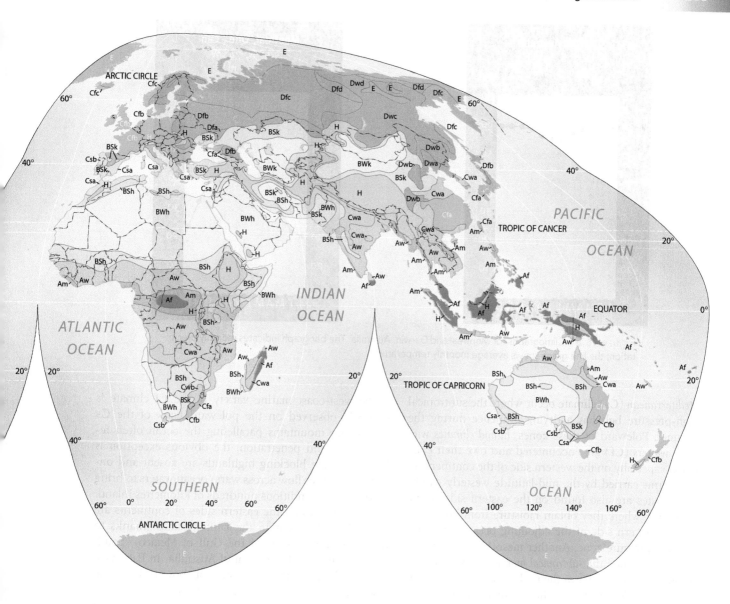

deserts are framed by narrow semi-arid, or steppe, (**BS**) zones that also change from **h** to **k** in the vicinity of the 35th parallel.

In North America the arid climates occur on a smaller scale, but in about the same proportion and relative areal extent vis-à-vis this smaller continental landmass. The rain shadow effect (see Unit 12) plays an important role in the dryness of the western United States and Canada, where high mountains parallel the Pacific coast and block much of the moisture brought onshore by prevailing westerly winds. In the Southern Hemisphere, only Australia is reminiscent of the **B** climate distributions north of the Equator because this island continent comprises the only large body of land within the subtropical latitudes. On the tapering landmasses of South America and southern Africa, the arid climate zones are compressed but still correspond roughly to the regional patterns of the hypothetical continent.

The Distribution of C Climates

The mesothermal (moderate-temperature) **C** climates are situated in the middle latitudes. The land/water differential between the Northern and Southern Hemispheres, however, becomes more pronounced poleward of the subtropics. North of the Equator, as the world island's greatest bulk is approached, the absence of oceanic-derived moisture in the continental interior produces an arid climate zone that interrupts the east–west belt of **C** climates lying approximately between the latitudes of 25° and 45°N. In the Southern Hemisphere **C** climates reach nearly across the remaining landmass south of 40°S.

The subtypes of the **C** climate group reflect the hemispheric differences just discussed, but some noteworthy similarities exist as well. On the western coast, adjacent to the **B** climate region, small but important zones of

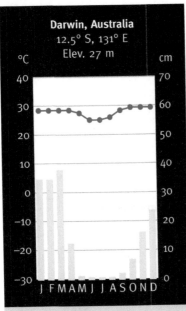

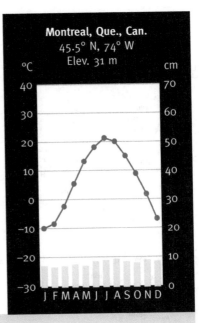

Figure 16.3   Climographs for Montreal and Darwin, Australia. The bar graph indicates monthly precipitation; the line graph shows average monthly temperature.

Mediterranean (**Cs**) climate occur where the subtropical high-pressure belt has a drying influence during the summer. Poleward of these zones, *humid climates with moist winters* (**Cf**) are encountered and owe their existence, especially on the western side of the continent, to the storms carried by the mid-latitude westerly winds. **Cf** climates are also found on the eastern side of the continent, where they obtain moisture from humid air on the western side of the adjoining ocean's subtropical high-pressure zone. Another mesothermal subtype, sometimes called the *subtropical monsoon* (**Cw**) climate, is found in the interior of the **C** climate region and represents a cooler version of the savanna climate, where the **Aw** regime spills across the poleward margin of the tropics.

Both Eurasia and North America exhibit the central **B** climate interruption of the mesothermal climatic belt, with the **C** climates less prominent on the Eurasian landmass where distances from maritime moisture sources are much greater. Southern Hemisphere patterns are also generally consistent with the model, although the **C** climates are often confined to narrow coastal strips that result from rain shadow effects produced by South America's Andes Mountains, South Africa's Great Escarpment, and Australia's east-coast Great Dividing Range.

The individual **C** climates further underscore the linkages between the hypothetical continent and the real world. Mediterranean (**Cs**) climates are located on every west coast in the expected latitudinal position (around 35 degrees), and even penetrate to Asia's 'west coast', where the eastern Mediterranean Sea reaches the Middle East.

The west-coast marine variety of the **Cf** climate is generally observed on the poleward flank of the **Cs** region, but mountains paralleling the ocean often restrict its inland penetration; the obvious exception is Europe, where blocking highlands are absent and onshore Westerlies flow across warm ocean waters to bring mild weather conditions hundreds of kilometres inland. The **Cf** climates on the eastern sides of continents are particularly apparent in the United States (thanks to the moderating effects of the Gulf of Mexico), South America, and the Pacific rim of Australia. In East Asia, this **Cf** subtype is limited by the more powerful regional effects of monsoonal reversals, but where it does occur in eastern China and Japan, it is associated with a massive population concentration that contains over one-eighth of humankind.

The **Cw** climates of the Northern Hemisphere are confined mainly to the subtropical portions of southern and eastern Asia, and, of course, are closely related to the monsoonal weather regime. The Southern Hemisphere **Cw** climate regions function as transitional zones, in both Africa and South America, between the equatorial-area savannas to the north and the subtropical arid and humid climates to the south.

The Distribution of D Climates

The microthermal **D** climates, which receive relatively small amounts of heat, are found exclusively in the Northern Hemisphere. There are no large landmasses in the Southern Hemisphere between 50° and 70°S, so latitude and the effect of continentality do not support the cold winters of the **D** climates.

Two subtypes of the **D** climate group can be observed. The **Df** variety experiences precipitation throughout the year; it can exhibit a fairly warm summer near the **C** climate boundary and certain coastal zones, but in the interior and towards the higher latitudes the summers are shorter and much cooler. The other subtype—**Dw**—is encountered where the effects of continentality are most pronounced. Annual moisture totals there are lower, and the harsh winters are characterized by dryness. The extreme cooling of the ground in midwinter is associated with a large anticyclone that persists throughout the cold season and blocks all surface winds that might bring in moisture from other areas.

The distribution of **D** climates (Figure 16.2) extends east–west across both Eurasia and North America, dominating the latitudes lying between 50° and 65°N. The only exceptions occur along the western coasts, where the warm North Atlantic Drift and Alaskan Current bathe the subpolar coastal zone with moderating temperatures. In the Eurasian interior, extreme continentality pushes the microthermal climates to a higher average latitude, a pattern not matched in eastern Canada, where the colder polar climates to the north penetrate farther south.

North America, wide as it is, does not contain sufficient bulk to support the **Dw** climate or even the coldest variant of the **Df** climate (**Dfd**). Only Eurasia exhibits these extreme microthermal climates, which are concentrated on the eastern side of that enormous landmass. Two reasons underlie the eastward deflection: (1) the overall altitude of the land surface is much higher in the mountainous Russian Far East and northeastern China, and (2) northeastern Asia lies farthest from the warm waters off western Eurasia that pump moisture into the prevailing westerly winds that sweep around the globe within this latitudinal zone.

The Distribution of E Climates

In both hemispheres, land areas poleward of the Arctic and Antarctic Circles (66½°N and S, respectively), with deficits of net radiation, exhibit polar **E** climates. The world Köppen map illustrates the concentration of **E** climates in Antarctica, Greenland, and the poleward fringes of northernmost Eurasia and North America. As for subtypes, the *tundra* climate (**ET**), where the warmest month records an average temperature between 0°C and 10°C, borders the warmer climates on the equatorward margins of each polar region. The highest latitudes in the vicinity of the poles themselves—as well as most of interior Greenland and high-lying Antarctica—experience the *icecap* or *frost* climate (**EF**), in which the average temperature of the warmest month fails to reach 0°C.

The **E** climates are often associated with the high-altitude areas of lower latitudes, particularly in the upper reaches of mountainous zones that are too cold to support vegetation. In these situations, they are labelled **H** (*highland*) climates.

Boundaries of Climate Regions

The classification system developed by Köppen and his associates has been criticized because it does not consider the causes of climate and because some of its climate–vegetation links are not very strong. Yet, it remains the most used classification scheme, and it has obviously proven itself both useful and appropriate for the purpose of introducing students to the complexity of global climatic patterns. Earlier in this unit, we discussed the shortcomings of any geographical classification of climate. We conclude by again reminding you that what look like sharp regional boundaries on the hypothetical continent and world Köppen maps really are zones of transition from one climate type to another.

The Köppen regional scheme, therefore, which was designed for the broad global or regional scale, is less well suited for microclimatological studies. It is not possible to accurately place a climate-region boundary in a local area, because only a few places in any city or county have compiled the necessary weather data for climatic analysis. Think of your local weather report. The 'official' temperature and other weather statistics are obtained at a single site for the whole area, such as at the airport or a downtown park, or for a handful of communities scattered across your immediate area.

Another problem in applying Köppen boundaries at the microscale is that these boundaries change over time. Climates, as we will see, are highly dynamic, and substantial change can occur over long periods. And even over shorter time spans, such change can be seen on the map. A good example is shown in Figure 16.4, which maps the poleward boundary of the **Aw** climate in tropical south Florida. Note that in 1941 the January 18°C isotherm was located between 40 km and 120 km to the northwest of its 1971 position. Over those four decades, the tropical zone contracted, and cities such as Ft Myers, Naples, and Ft Pierce 'shifted' into the mesothermal (**Cfa**) climatic zone. These 'changes', of course, are very subtle, and even a resident of Ft Myers who has lived there since 1940 would almost certainly not be aware of any meaningful change. But this little exercise about boundaries is instructive and should interject healthy skepticism in preparation for the more detailed overview of climate regions covered in Unit 17.

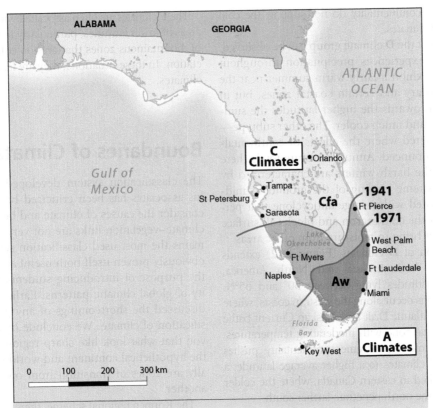

Figure 16.4 Changing location of the January 18°C isotherm in southern Florida, 1941–71.

KEY TERMS

climate   *page 210*
climatic controls   *page 210*
climograph   *page 213*

hypothetical continent   *page 213*
Köppen climate classification system   *page 210*

REVIEW QUESTIONS

1. How is a location's climate determined from weather data?
2. What are the thermal criteria for tropical, mesothermal, microthermal, and polar climates in the Köppen system?
3. What are the factors that control the geographic distribution of climates?
4. Outline the interpretation of the second and third letters of the codes used in the Köppen system. For

example, how does an **Af** climate differ from an **Aw** climate?
5. Describe two advantages of the Köppen climate classification system.
6. Describe two problems or shortcomings of the Köppen climate classification system.
7. Why should Köppen regional-scale boundaries not be used to ascertain climate-zone boundaries at the local scale?

REFERENCES AND FURTHER READINGS

Critchfield, H.J. 1983. *General Climatology*, 4th edn. Englewood Cliffs, NJ: Prentice-Hall.
Eagleman, J.R. 1976. *The Visualization of Climate*. Lexington, Mass.: Heath.
Haurwitz, B., and J.M. Austin. 1944. *Climatology*. New York: McGraw-Hill.

Houghton, J.T., ed. 1984. *The Global Climate*. New York: Cambridge Univ. Press.
Kendrew, W.G. 1961. *The Climates of the Continents*, 5th edn. New York: Oxford Univ. Press.

Linacre, E. 1992. *Climate Data and Resources: A Reference and Guide.* London/New York: Routledge.

Lockwood, J. 1985. *World Climatic Systems.* London: Edward Arnold.

Lydolph, P.E. 1985. *The Climate of the Earth.* Totowa, NJ: Rowman & Allanheld.

Oke, T.R. 1981. *Boundary Layer Climates*, 2nd edn. London/New York: Methuen.

Riley, D., and L. Spalton. 1981. *World Weather and Climate*, 2nd edn. New York: Cambridge Univ. Press.

Trewartha, G.T. 1981. *The Earth's Problem Climates*, 2nd edn. Madison: Univ. of Wisconsin Press.

——— and L.H. Horn. 1980. *An Introduction to Climate*, 5th edn. New York: McGraw-Hill.

Wilcock, A.A. 1968. 'Köppen after Fifty Years', *Annals, Association of American Geographers* 58:12–28.

WEB RESOURCES

geography.about.com/od/physicalgeography/a/koppen.htm An overview of the Köppen climate classification system with links to a Köppen climate chart and other climate websites.

people.cas.sc.edu/carbone/modules/mods4car/ccontrol/index.html An interactive site that explains climate controls in detail.

www-das.uwyo.edu/~geerts/cwx/notes/chap16/clim_class.html Climate classification with a historical perspective.

www.fao.org/WAICENT/FAOINFO/SUSTDEV/EIdirect/climate/EIsp0002.htm Interactive site with global climate maps.

www.uwsp.edu/geo/faculty/ritter/geog101/uwsp_lectures/lecture_climate_class.html A lecture-based website that is easy to follow and which provides a thorough set of examples of climatic regions and their primary controlling factors.

www.worldclimate.com Page that gives average climate data for any city name entered.

Unit 17

Global Climates

Objectives

- To expand our understanding of tropical (**A**), arid (**B**), and mesothermal (**C**) climates using climographs developed for actual weather stations.

- To interpret representative climographs depicting actual conditions in these climate areas.

- To highlight major environmental-climatic problems in many of these areas—tropical deforestation, desertification, and drought.

- To expand the discussion of typical **D**, **E**, and **H** climates and to interpret representative climographs for these zones.

- To highlight a major environmental-climatic problem of many **D** climate regions—acid precipitation.

Unit 16 set the stage for a global survey of the principal climate types based on the Köppen classification and regionalization system. This unit will focus on **A** (tropical), **B** (dry or arid), and **C** (mesothermal) climates in the first part, then microthermal (**D**) climates that dominate the Northern Hemisphere continents, the polar (**E**) climates that blanket the highest latitudes, and finally, the highland (**H**) climates, which are often reminiscent of **E**-type temperature and precipitation regimes because they lie at altitudes high enough to produce Arctic-like conditions regardless of latitude. We will use Figure 16.2 as a guide to the spatial distribution of all the world's major climate types. In addition to providing greater detail about each of the principal subdivisions of these climates, we focus on the leading environmental problem of each major climate group.

The Major Tropical (A) Climates

Contained within a continuous east–west belt astride the Equator, varying latitudinally from 30 to 50 degrees wide, are the warmth and moisture of the **tropical (A) climates**. Warmth is derived from proximity to the Equator (**A** climate temperatures must average higher than 18°C in the coolest month); moisture comes from the rains of the ITCZ (Inter-Tropical Convergence Zone), wet-monsoon systems, easterly waves, and hurricanes. The tropical climates can be subdivided into three major types: the *tropical rainforest*, the *monsoon rainforest*, and the *savanna*.

The Tropical Rainforest (Af) Climate

The **Af**, or tropical rainforest, zone exhibits the greatest effects of heat and moisture. In areas undisturbed by human intervention, tall evergreen trees completely cover the land surface. This dense forest has very little undergrowth, however, because the trees let through only a small amount of sunlight. Any serious discussion of this environment today must begin by considering the appalling rush towards the destruction of rainforests throughout the tropical latitudes.

Only a generation ago, lush rainforests clothed most of the land surfaces of the equatorial tropics and accounted for 10 per cent of the Earth's vegetation cover. Since 1980, however, industries and millions of residents of low-latitude countries have been destroying billions of those trees through rapid **tropical deforestation**—the clearing and destruction of rainforests to make way for expanding settlement frontiers and the exploitation of new economic opportunities. In Brazil's Amazon Basin, an area about the size of Prince Edward Island is burned annually, half of it virgin forest and the other half jungle regrowth, to briefly replenish the infertile soil. If this prodigious removal rate endures, the planet's tropical rainforests—already effectively reduced to two large patches in west-equatorial Africa and the central Amazon Basin—will disappear by the middle of this century.

As rainforests are eradicated, they do not just leave behind the ugly wastelands seen in Figure 17.1. The smoke from their burning releases particles and gases that rise thousands of metres into the atmosphere and are then transported thousands of kilometres around the world. A

Figure 17.1 While the burning of the Amazonian rainforest is the subject of many news stories and of much scientific research, other remaining areas of rainforest and their inhabitants also suffer. The loss in Africa is accelerating, the situation in Borneo is deteriorating, and even in remote Papua New Guinea (shown here) the rainforest recedes. (Authors' photo)

From the Fieldnotes

Figure 17.2 'Traversing the Panama Canal turned out to have several geographic benefits, in addition to learning about the history of the project and understanding better the changing relationship between Panama and the United States. I was unaware that the forests flanking the Canal had been used to train US military forces in advance of their assignment to Vietnam in the Indochina War. Nor did I expect to see pristine rainforest of the kind shown here, on Barro Colorado Island. I was reminded that the Köppen map shows this part of Panama as an **Am** climate, and the vegetation reflects it.'

number of atmospheric scientists believe that the effects of such fires, together with the removal of massive stands of carbon-dioxide-absorbing trees, could have an increasingly harmful effect on global climate.

The climatic characteristics of the tropical rainforest are illustrated in Figure 17.3, which uses three graphic displays for a typical weather station in the **Af** zone. The place chosen for such a presentation is São Gabriel de Cachoeira, a Brazilian village situated almost exactly on the Equator deep within the heart of the Amazon Basin. The climograph in Figure 17.3 reveals that average monthly temperatures in São Gabriel are remarkably constant, hovering consistently around 26°C throughout the year. In fact, the diurnal (daily) temperature may vary as much as 6°C, an amount greater than the annual range of 1.6°C.

Rainfall also tends to occur in a diurnal rather than a seasonal rhythm. A normal daily pattern consists of relatively clear skies in the morning, followed by a steady buildup of convectional clouds from the vertical movement of air with the increasing heat of the day. By early afternoon, thunderstorms burst forth with torrential rains.

In São Gabriel, no month receives less than 130 mm of rain, and in May about 10 mm of rain falls per day. The average total rainfall for the year is 2800 mm. Such large amounts of rain keep the water balance in perpetual surplus, as Figure 17.3B indicates. Evapotranspiration in this area constantly occurs at its potential rate; much of the surplus water runs off into the Rio Negro (on which the village is located) and from this tributary directly into the Amazon itself. As a result, most of the net radiation is used in latent

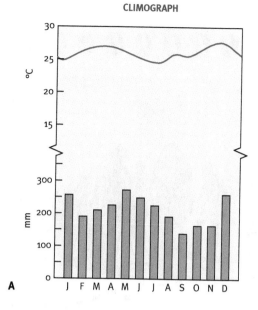

CLIMOGRAPH

Af - Tropical rainforest climate
*São Gabriel da Cachoeira, Brazil
(1°S, 67°W)*

Average annual temperature = 26°C
Average annual precipitation = 2824 mm

A

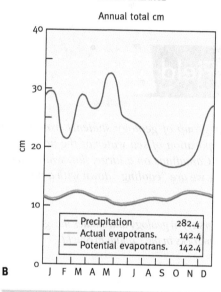

WATER BALANCE

Annual total cm

— Precipitation	282.4
— Actual evapotrans.	142.4
— Potential evapotrans.	142.4

B

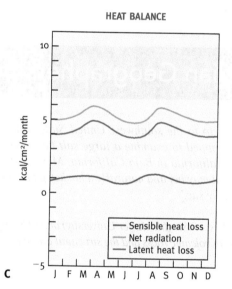

HEAT BALANCE

— Sensible heat loss	
— Net radiation	
— Latent heat loss	

C

Figure 17.3 Climograph and related graphic displays for a representative weather station in the tropical rainforest (**Af**) climate zone.

heat (Figure 17.3C), and so the moisture in the highly humid air is continuously replaced. When the moisture condenses, latent heat adds to the monotonous warmth of the atmosphere. When the Sun passes directly overhead at the equinoxes, the rainfall values are not noticeably affected because they are always high. But the heat balance is markedly affected, as demonstrated by the relatively higher values of net radiation and latent heat loss in the graph.

The Monsoon Rainforest (Am) Climate

The monsoon rainforest (**Am**) climate is restricted to tropical coasts that are often backed by highlands. It has a distinct dry season in the part of the year when the Sun is lower, but almost always a short one; a compensating longer season of heavy rainfall generally prevents any soil-moisture deficits. These characteristics are seen in the representative climograph for this climate type (Figure 17.4), the city of Trivandrum located near India's southern tip on the narrow Malabar Coast at the base of the Cardamom Uplands.

In some places, such as the hills leading up to the Himalayas in northeastern India, the highlands add an orographic effect to the wet-monsoon rains. The station of Cherrapunji (see Figure 17.23) in this hilly region averages an annual total of 11,437 mm of rain—most of it occurring during the three summer months! The vegetation of the monsoon rainforest zone consists mainly of evergreen trees, with occasional grasslands interspersed. The trees,

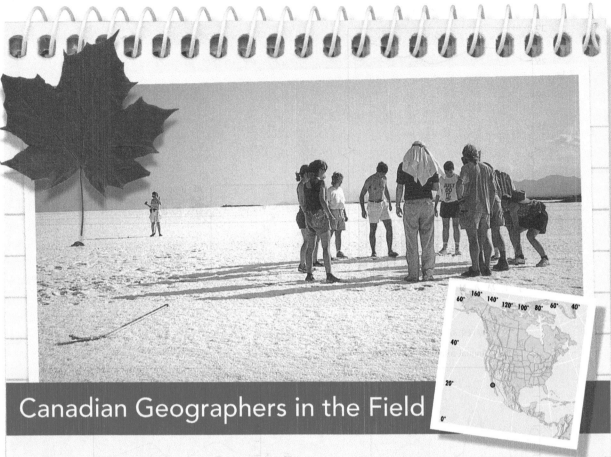

Canadian Geographers in the Field

'On a field trip to the southwest United States and Mexico, our group of geology students from Queen's University stopped to examine a large salt flat formed by the evaporation of sea water at the north end of the Gulf of California in Baja California, Mexico. Put a group of Canadians on a large, flat, white surface, however hot it may be, and naturally a hockey game broke out. Here we are "cooling" down with a post-game round of hacky sac.'

Blair Hrabi has a B.Sc. (McMaster University) and M.Sc. (Queen's University) in geology and studies the geochemical composition of volcanic rocks and the structural evolution of Precambrian rocks in the Canadian Shield.

---

however, are not as dense as those found in the remaining areas of true tropical rainforest.

The Savanna (Aw) Climate

The savanna (**Aw**) climates are found in the transitional, still-tropical latitudes between the subtropical high-pressure and equatorial low-pressure belts. Although these areas often receive between 750 and 1750 mm of rain per year, there is an extended dry season in the months when the angle of the Sun is at its lowest. Moisture deficits in the soil can occur during the dry season, whose length and severity are proportional to a given savanna area's distance from the Equator. The climograph for Nkhata Bay, Malawi, in southeastern Africa (Figure 17.5) shows the typical trend in temperatures and precipitation totals in a normal year. Do not be misled, however, by the decline of both variables in the middle months of the year, because on this occasion we deliberately selected a Southern Hemisphere

station to remind you of the opposite seasonal patterns that exist south of the Equator.

In the region of East Africa to the north of Malawi, the pastoral Maasai people traditionally move their herds of cattle north and south in search of new grass sprouted in the wake of the shifting rains that correspond to the high Sun.* The vegetation of this region, besides its tall, coarse seasonal grasses, also includes clumps of trees or individual trees and thorn bushes (Figure 17.6). Extensive

LINK

---

*The rainy season corresponds to the period of high Sun ('summer') and the dry season corresponds to the period of low Sun ('winter'). High Sun and low Sun refer to the angle of the Sun's rays and, therefore, the amount of incoming solar radiation. The terms 'summer' and 'winter' are not used because there is a lack of seasonality in these latitudes: high and low Sun conditions replace those terms in equatorial and tropical environments. The variation in solar radiation is sufficient, however, to provide for rainy and dry seasons.

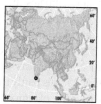

Am - Tropical monsoon climate
Trivandrum, India
(8°N, 77°E)

Annual average
temperature = 27°C

Annual average
precipitation = 1835 mm

CLIMOGRAPH

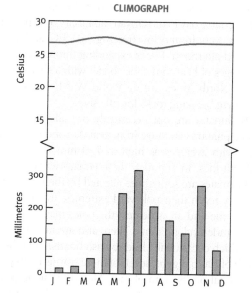

Figure 17.4 Climograph of a monsoon rainforest (**Am**) weather station.

Aw - Tropical savanna climate
Nkhata Bay, Malawi
(15°S, 35°E)

Average annual
temperature = 23°C

Annual average
precipitation = 1676 mm

CLIMOGRAPH

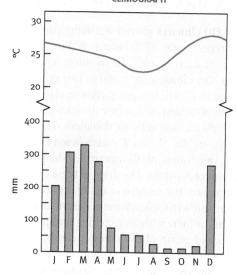

Figure 17.5 Climograph of a tropical savanna (**Aw**) weather station.

Figure 17.6 Tree-dotted savanna of Kenya's Maasai Mara game reserve. (Authors' photo)

areas of savanna climate are found, most prominently, in parts of tropical South America, South Asia, and Africa (see Figure 16.2). Along the poleward margins of this climate zone, however, rainfall is so unreliable that these peripheral areas are considered too risky for agricultural development in the absence of irrigation systems.

The Major Arid (B) Climates

The **arid (B) climates** provide a striking visual contrast to the A climates (Figure 17.7) because in these areas potential evapotranspiration exceeds the moisture supplied by precipitation. Dry climates are found in two general locations (see Figure 16.2). The first group consists of two interrupted bands near 30°N and 30°S, where the semi-permanent subtropical high-pressure cells are dominant. The largest areas of this type are the African–Eurasian desert belt (stretching from the vast Sahara northeastward to Mongolia) and the arid interior of Australia. The driest of these climates are often located near the western coasts of continents. Weather stations in northern Chile's Atacama Desert, for instance, can go 10 years or more without recording precipitation.

The second group of dry climates can be attributed to two different factors. First, a continental interior remote from any moisture source and experiencing cold high-pressure air masses in winter can have an arid climate (the central Asian countries east of the Caspian Sea are a good case in point). And second, rain shadow zones in the lee of coast-paralleling mountain ranges often give rise to cold deserts, as in the interior far west of North America and southern Argentina's Patagonia.

Figure 17.7 One of the world's driest landscapes—a rocky desert in the western Sahara near the border between Morocco and Algeria.

Average annual temperatures in arid climates are usually typical of those that might be expected at any given latitude—high in the low latitudes and low in the higher latitudes. However, the annual *range* of temperature is often greater than might be expected. In North Africa's central Sahara, for example, a range of 17°C at 25°N is partly the result of a continental effect. The diurnal range of temperature can also be quite wide, averaging between 14° and 25°C. On one unforgettable day in the Libyan capital city of Tripoli, the temperature went from below freezing (-0.5°C) at dawn to 37°C in mid-afternoon! Rocks expanding through such extreme changes of heat sometimes break with a sharp crack; soldiers in North Africa during World War II occasionally mistook these breaking rocks for rifle shots.

The **B** climates are not necessarily dry all year round. Their precipitation can range from near 0 to about 625 mm per year, with averages as high as 750 mm in the more tropical latitudes. In summer, these equatorward margins of the **B** climates are sometimes affected by the rains of the ITCZ as they reach their poleward extremes. In winter, the margins of the arid areas nearest the poles may be subject to mid-latitude cyclone rains. There also are rare thunderstorms, which occasionally lead to flash floods. At Hulwan, just south of Cairo, Egypt, seven of these storms in 20 years yielded a total of 780 mm of rain. Moreover, along coasts bathed by cold ocean currents, rather frequent fogs provide some moisture; Swakopmund, in southwestern Africa's Namibia, adjacent to the Benguela Current (see Figure 10.6), experiences about 150 days of such fog each year.

The Desert (BW) Climate

For the most part, however, considerable dryness is the rule in **B** areas. This aridity is exemplified by Yuma, Arizona, where the average annual temperature is 23.5°C, with an annual range of some 23°C. The climate here is **BWh**—a hot, dry desert. The small amount of rainfall shown in Figure 17.8 (89 mm) comes either from occasional winter storms or from the convectional clouds of summer. The water balance diagram below the climograph shows a marked deficit throughout the year: potential evapotranspiration greatly exceeds precipitation. Most water that falls quickly evaporates back into the dry atmosphere. But as the heat balance diagram for Yuma indicates, there is little water for evaporation, so latent heat loss is negligible. Consequently, most of the heat input from net radiation, which is markedly seasonal, is expended as sensible heat—adding even more warmth to the already hot air. (Daily highs between May and October almost always exceed 38°C.)

The Steppe (BS) Climate

As the world climate map (Figure 16.2) shows, the most arid areas—deserts (**BW**)—are always framed by semi-arid zones. This is the domain of the **steppe (BS)** climate (also known in western North America as the *short-grass prairie*), which can be regarded as a transitional type between fully developed desert conditions and the subhumid margins of

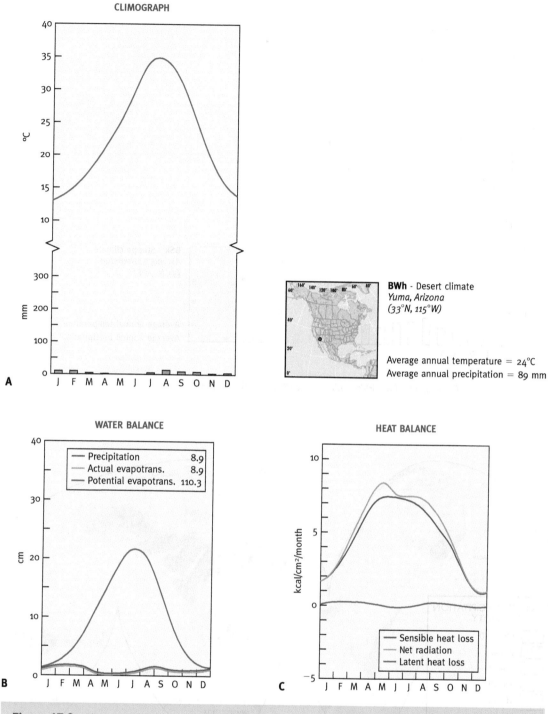

Figure 17.8 Climograph and related graphic displays for a representative weather station in the hot, dry desert (**BWh**) climate zone.

the **A**, **C**, and **D** climates that border **B** climate zones. The maximum and minimum amounts of annual rainfall that characterize semi-arid climates tend to vary somewhat by latitude. In general, lower-latitude **BS** climates range from 375 to 750 mm yearly; in the middle latitudes, a lower range (from 250 to 625 mm) prevails. Astana, the capital of the central Asian republic of Kazakhstan, which lies at the heart of the Eurasian landmass, is a classic example of the cold subtype of the steppe climate (**BSk**). The climograph for this city (Figure 17.9) shows its proximity to the Turkestan

Desert, which lies just to the south: rainfall totals only 279 mm per year. As for the monthly temperature curve, an enormous range of 39°C is recorded, reflecting one of the most pronounced areas of continentality on the Earth's surface.

Drought and Desertification in B Climates

The problem of **drought** (see 'Perspectives' box) is an ever-present environmental hazard in all semi-arid

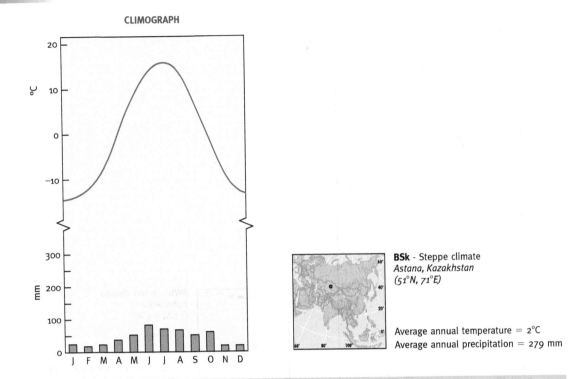

Figure 17.9   Climograph of a mid-latitude steppe (**BSk**) weather station.

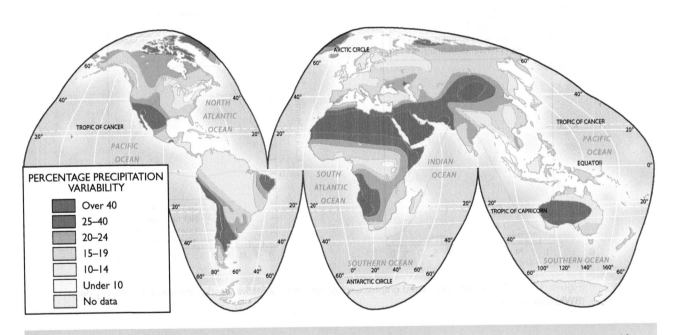

Figure 17.10   Global distribution of annual precipitation variability, shown as percentage departures from normal. Map adapted from *Goode's World Atlas*, 19th edition. ©1995 by Rand McNally R.L. 92-S-82-renewal 95.

areas, and the Great Plains region has suffered many severe dry spells since it was settled by farmers during the late nineteenth and early twentieth centuries. The global distribution of precipitation variability is mapped in Figure 17.10 and underscores this dilemma. Perversely, for human purposes, rain falls most reliably where it is abundant, whereas the arid areas experience the greatest variations from year to year (as even a cursory comparison of Figures 16.2 and 17.10 reveals).

Perspectives on the Human Environment

The Drought of 2001

The drought that plagued so much of Canada in 2001, one of the worst since the dust bowl of the 1930s, was a classic example of this major environmental problem. At its peak in late summer, extreme and severe drought conditions extended across southern and western Canada. As severe as the 2001 drought was, with economic losses estimated at $5 billion, the 1961 drought remains the single most severe growing-season drought to occur on the Canadian Prairies (Figure 17.11). These dry spells have always been part of the gamble of living and farming in the B climate areas of the Canadian Prairies and interior British Columbia. Southern parts of the Prairies usually have a moisture deficit and highly variable precipitation, and western Canada has experienced at least 40 severe droughts in recorded history. The 2001 drought was particularly unusual because it tended to extend almost coast to coast, into D climate areas. In Ontario (a Dfb climate), corn and soybean farmers reported substantially reduced crop yields. Arid conditions extended into other Dfb climates, such as Moncton, New Brunswick, which received 17.3 mm of rain in July 2001, compared to the normal 102 mm it receives during July. Forest fires broke out in extensive parts of British Columbia and in pockets of Newfoundland, and in Nova Scotia, blueberries, the province's biggest farm export, shrivelled in the scorched conditions. In the Prairie provinces, however, conditions were most critical, as farmers had to cope with the extreme drought in addition to swarms of grasshoppers in some locations. The dry weather created perfect egg-laying conditions, and consequently the crops were affected by both dry weather and an infestation of insects.

Unlike desertification, which is largely a process of human degradation that affects many B climate environments, drought is a natural hazard that recurs in seemingly irregular cycles. In general, a drought involves the below-average availability of water in a given area over a period of at least several months. Specifically, there are three types of drought that may occur separately or simultaneously: meteorological (precipitation

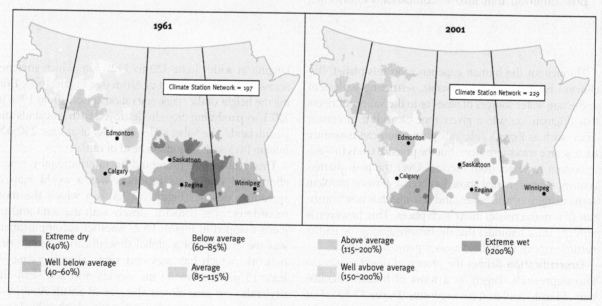

Figure 17.11 Drought conditions on the Canadian Prairies in 1961 and 2001, expressed as a per cent of average precipitation.

is below normal for a prolonged period of time), agricultural (low soil moisture and scarce water supplies stunt crop growth, reduce yields, and threaten livestock), and hydrological (a prolonged meteorological drought that causes reduced levels of the groundwater table, rivers, and lakes). The conditions that constitute a drought are clear enough: a decrease in precipitation accompanied by warmer than normal temperatures (2001 was the third warmest year on record at that time) and the shrinkage of surface- and soil-water supplies. If the drought reaches an extreme stage of development, all of these conditions intensify further and may result in the spreading of grass and/or forest fires as well as in the blowing away of significant quantities of topsoil by hot, dry winds.

However dramatic it may become at its height, a drought has no clear beginning or end. It develops slowly until it becomes recognized as a crisis, and it tends to fade away as more normal moisture patterns return. Because droughts encompass no spectacular meteorological phenomena, they were not intensively studied before the 1970s. But the Sahel disaster of that decade in northern Africa finally aroused the interest of climatologists, whose subsequent research is providing a clearer understanding of droughts and their often far-reaching consequences.

As these studies proceeded, it quickly became evident that a drought was not simply a meteorological/hydrological aberration but a complex phenomenon that also encompassed economic, sociological, and even political dimensions. In 2001 and during the subsequent drought in 2002, the worsening water shortage in vast regions of the Prairies and abnormal weather conditions throughout much of Canada became national news, dominating newscasts and headlines daily from May through September. As the heavily publicized plight of farmers and the disruptions of their lives reached unprecedented levels, the federal government invested $60 million in a prairie water development program and a new farm-aid package to help farmers cope through the hard, dry summers.

The non-governmental 'Say Hay' initiative (from the drought-induced shortage of hay across western Canada) raised over $1.5 million through two benefit concerts in Edmonton and Calgary (with more than 30 Canadian country singers performing), in addition to money raised through silent auctions, radio pledges, and a national telethon. Without hay, farmers were being forced to sell their cattle and livestock for fear that the animals would starve over the winter. The money raised through Say Hay was used to pay for the transportation of hay donated from Ontario and Atlantic Canada, as well as to establish the Say Hay Farm Assistance Program. Any definition of drought, therefore, must be expressed in terms that exceed the physical-geographic aspects of a prolonged water shortage. As the 2001–2 experience demonstrated, drought is no longer strictly an agricultural disaster.

Throughout the human experience on this planet, dry climates have proven inhospitable, restricting settlement to the rare water sources of oases or to the valleys of rivers that originate outside a given zone of aridity. In certain cases, such as Egypt's Nile Valley, irrigation can maximize these scarce water resources, but the practice tends to wash important minerals from the soil. Over the past quarter-century, environmental abuse has been a growing problem at the margins of arid zones, and *desertification* now constitutes a serious crisis in many such places. This, however, is only the latest reminder that the balance among the Earth's natural systems in dryland areas is particularly fragile.

Desertification defines the process of desert expansion into steppelands, largely as a result of human degradation of fragile semi-arid environments (Figure 17.12). This term was added to the physical geographer's lexicon in the 1970s following the disastrous famine, caused by rapid and unforeseen desiccation, which struck the north-central African region known as the Sahel. This name means 'shore' in Arabic—specifically the southern shore of the Sahara, an east–west semi-arid (**BSh**) belt straddling latitude 15°N,

ranging in width from 320 to 1120 km, which stretches across the entire continent of Africa (see Figure 16.2). During the height of the tragic starvation episode from 1968 to 1973, as paralyzing drought destroyed both croplands and pasturelands, the Sahel suffered a loss of at least 250,000 human lives and 3.5 million head of cattle.

This catastrophe prompted an international research effort, and one of its products was a world map of spreading deserts (Figure 17.13), on which the most hazardous zones coincide closely with the semi-arid regions mapped in Figure 16.2. Another accomplishment was the creation of a global desertification monitoring network, which has provided some alarming data. At least 15 million km² of the world's arid and semi-arid drylands—an area almost the size of South America—have now become severely desertified, thereby losing over 50 per cent of their potential productivity. Another 34.8 million km²—an area greater than the size of Africa—has become at least moderately desertified, losing in excess of 25 per cent of its potential productivity. Moreover, an estimated 64,800 km²—an area almost as

LINK

Figure 17.12 The desert encroaches on human settlement near Nouakchott, the capital of Mauritania in West Africa. A dune-stabilization effort in the foreground gives temporary protection to the poorest of the city's inhabitants, who live in the squatter settlement just beyond.

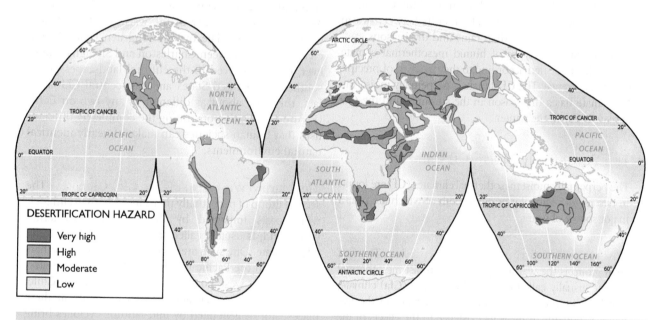

DESERTIFICATION HAZARD

- Very high
- High
- Moderate
- Low

Figure 17.13 Degree of desertification hazard according to the scientists of the United Nations Environmental Programme. The red areas indicate a critical situation; the orange zones experience serious effects; the tan areas represent a significant problem.

large as New Brunswick—are being added to the total of severely desertified land each year. In the process, more than a billion people (over one-sixth of humankind) are already affected by desertification—and the world's arid-land population is growing at a rate 50 per cent faster than in adequately watered areas.

When desertification was first studied, it was believed that climate change played a significant role. Today, however, we have learned enough to know that the process is more heavily controlled by human actions, the consequences of which are accentuated in years of lower than normal precipitation. The British geographer Andrew Goudie has noted that semi-arid areas are particularly susceptible because rainfall there is sufficient to swiftly erode carelessly used soils and because farmers often misinterpret short-term success during years wetter than normal as a sign of long-term crop-raising stability.

The Major Mesothermal (C) Climates

The moderately heated **mesothermal (C) climates** are dominant on the equatorward sides of the middle latitudes, where they are generally aligned as interrupted east–west belts (see Figure 16.2). On a global scale, mesothermal climates may be viewed as transitional between those of the tropics and those of the upper mid-latitude zone, where polar influences begin to produce climates marked by harsh winters. The specific limiting criteria are (1) an average temperature below 18°C but above 0°C in the coolest month, and (2) an average temperature of not less than 10°C for at least one month of the year. Such limits tell us that temperature is now a more important climatic indicator than in the lower latitudes, and that the annual rhythms of the C climates are more likely to involve cyclical shifts between warm and cool seasons rather than rainy and dry seasons.

Three major subtypes of humid mesothermal climate can be distinguished according to their pattern of precipitation occurrence. The **Cf** climate is perpetually moist; the **Cs** climate has a dry season in the summer; and the **Cw** climate is dry in the winter.

The Perpetually Moist (Cf) Climates

The perpetually moist mesothermal climates (**Cf**) are found in two major regional groupings, both of which are near a major source of water.

The Humid Subtropical (Cfa) Climate   The first such group is the warmer, perpetually moist mesothermal climate, usually called the *humid subtropical* (**Cfa**) climate, which is situated in the southeastern portions of the five major continents. It owes its existence to the effects of the warm moist air travelling northwestward (in the Northern Hemisphere) around the western margins of the oceanic subtropical high-pressure zones. Additional moisture comes from the movement of mid-latitude cyclones towards the Equator in winter and from tropical cyclones in summer and autumn.

Miyazaki, located on the east coast of the southern Japanese island of Kyushu, exhibits the strong seasonal effects of the humid subtropical climate (Figure 17.14). Average monthly temperatures there range from 6.8°C in mildly cold January to 26.7°C in hot humid August; the mean annual temperature is 16.7°C. Rainfall for the year almost totals that of the tropical rainforest—2560 mm, peaking in early summer. The water balance at Miyazaki is never at a deficit, not even during the relatively dry winter. Throughout the year, actual evapotranspiration always equals the potential evapotranspiration. The heat balance diagram also demonstrates the humid nature of this climate. Most of the net radiation is used to evaporate water, and a relatively small proportion passes into the air as sensible heat.

The similarities of the humid subtropical climate in diverse parts of the world are underscored in the climographs for Charleston, South Carolina (Figure 17.15), and Shanghai, China (Figure 17.16). Both cities lie on the southeastern seaboard of a large landmass (North America and Asia, respectively) near latitude 32°N. Compared to Miyazaki (Figure 17.14), Charleston and Shanghai exhibit significantly lower annual precipitation totals—undoubtedly a function of stronger windflows off the continent lying to their west—whereas offshore Kyushu is more constantly bathed by the moist southeasterly winds generated by the North Pacific's Subtropical High.

Slight differences can also be detected in a comparison of all three **Cfa** stations. For example, whereas summer temperatures are strikingly alike, Charleston has a noticeably milder winter because of the smaller bulk of North America (which does not develop as cold and durable a winter high-pressure cell as interior Asia) and the proximity of the warm Gulf of Mexico to the southwest. The overall congruence of climatic characteristics between Charleston and Shanghai, however, is not observed in the cultural landscapes of the southeastern United States and east-central China. In fact, these are about as different as any two on Earth (Figure 17.17), demonstrating the completely different uses that human societies can make of nearly identical natural environments.

The Marine West Coast (Cfb, Cfc) Climate   The second group of perpetually moist mesothermal climates, with coasts impacted by the prevailing Westerlies year-round, is usually called the *marine west coast* (**Cfb, Cfc**) climate. One such area is in Western Europe; others are found in the Pacific Northwest of the United States, the adjacent west coast of Canada, southern Chile, southeastern Australia, and New Zealand. In all these places, storms generated by mid-latitude cyclones bring a steady flow of moist, temperate, maritime air from the ocean onto nearby land surfaces. The extent of inland penetration depends on topography. Where few orographic barriers exist, such as in Europe north of the Alps, the **Cfb** climate reaches several hundred kilometres eastward from the North Atlantic; but where mountains block the moist onshore winds, such as in western North America and Chile in southernmost South America,

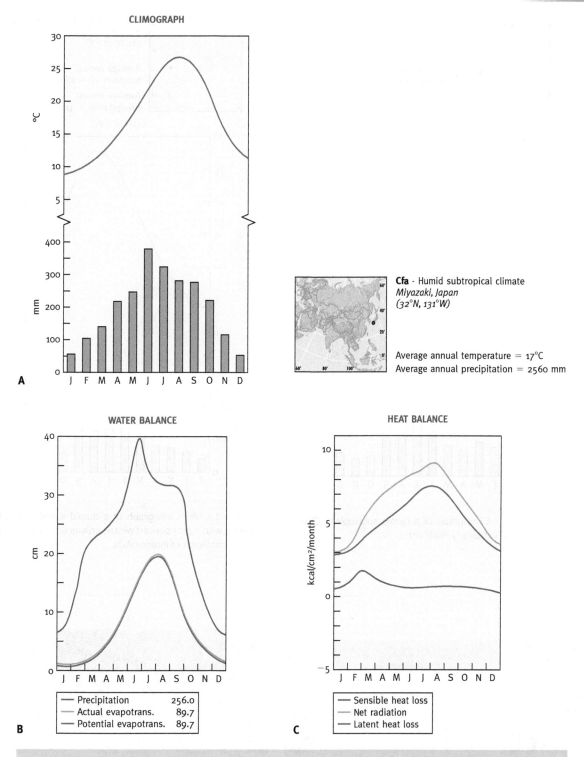

Figure 17.14 Climograph and related graphic displays for a representative weather station in the humid subtropical (**Cfa**) climate zone.

these climates are confined to coastal and near-coastal areas.

There are rarely any extremes of temperature in marine west coast climates. Average monthly temperatures never exceed 22°C, and at least four months record mean temperatures above 10°C in the **Cfb** zones (the cooler **Cfc** subtype experiences less than four months of mean temperatures above 10°C). The **Cfb** patterns are seen in the climographs for Vancouver and London, England (Figures 17.18 and 17.19). In your comparisons you will

Cfa - Humid subtropical climate
Charleston, South Carolina
(33°N, 80°W)

Average annual
temperature = 18°C

Average annual
precipitation = 1247 mm

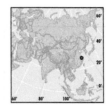

Cfa - Humid subtropical climate
Shanghai, China
(32°N, 122°E)

Average annual
temperature = 16°C

Average annual
precipitation = 1135 mm

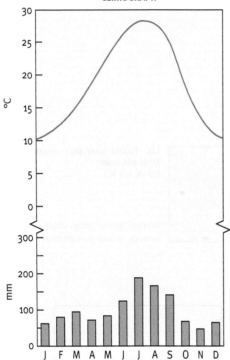

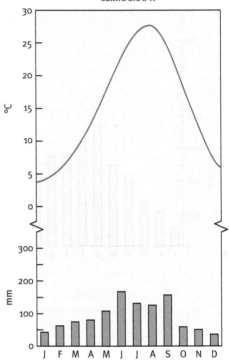

Figure 17.15 Climograph of a humid subtropical (**Cfa**) location with a particularly mild winter.

Figure 17.16 Climograph of a humid subtropical (**Cfa**) location with a pronounced winter, enhanced in this case by the dry monsoon of interior Asia.

A

B

Figure 17.17 A pair of farming areas in similar **Cfa** climatic zones, but these agricultural landscapes could not be more different. (A) In the southeastern United States large fields, independent farmsteads, and highway transport prevail. (B) In east-central China small rectangular plots, clustered villages, and water transport dominate.

note that despite its popular image as a rainy city, London receives on average only 583 mm of precipitation annually, equivalent to the yearly total in the moistest semi-arid climate. But London does indeed experience a great number of cloudy and/or rainy days each year (the hallmark of many a marine west coast climate location), with much of its precipitation occurring as light drizzle. The cooler **Cfc**

pattern is shown in the climograph for Reykjavik, Iceland (Figure 17.20), which records only three months with mean temperatures at or above 10°C.

The **Cfb** climates are situated precisely in the middle of the mid-latitude, prevailing westerly wind belts. The cooler **Cfc** climates are found only in the Northern Hemisphere at higher latitudes, where strong warm

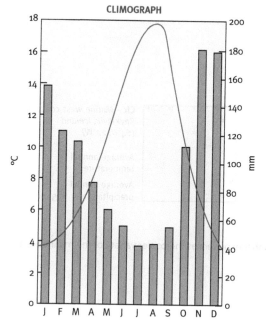

CLIMOGRAPH

Cfb - Marine west coast climate
Vancouver, Canada
(48°N, 122°W)

Average annual
temperature = 12°C

Average annual
precipitation = 1013 mm

Figure 17.18 Climograph of a marine west coast (**Cfb**) weather station in the Canadian Pacific northwest.

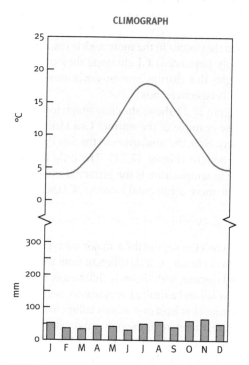

CLIMOGRAPH

Cfb - Marine west coast climate
London, United Kingdom
(52°N, 0°)

Average annual
temperature = 10°C

Average annual
precipitation = 583 mm

Figure 17.19 Climograph of a marine west coast (**Cfb**) location in maritime Europe. Despite its image as a rainy city, note that London annually receives only about half the precipitation of Vancouver.

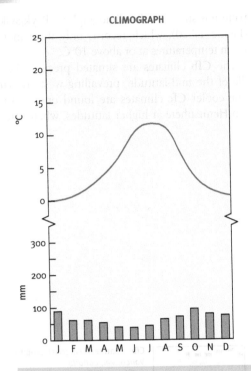

CLIMOGRAPH

Cfc - Marine west coast climate
*Reykjavik, Iceland
(64°N, 22°W)*

Average annual
temperature = 5°C

Average annual
precipitation = 805 mm

Figure 17.20 Climograph of a weather station that experiences the cooler variety of the marine west coast (**Cfc**) climate.

ocean currents sweep poleward along western continental shores (such as off Iceland, Norway, and Alaska). Western civilization moved to the **Cfb** climates of northwestern Europe after leaving its Mediterranean hearth. The adequate year-round precipitation naturally produces a forest of evergreen conifers and broadleaf trees that shed their leaves in winter. Although dry spells are not unknown in these areas, the soil rarely has a moisture deficit for a long period of time.

The Dry-Summer (Cs) Climates

The second major mesothermal subtype is the dry subtropical, or *Mediterranean*, (**Cs**) climate. It is frequently described, particularly by people of European descent, as the most desirable climate on Earth. This is the climate that attracted filmmakers to southern California, so famous for its clear light and dependable sunshine. The warmer variety of Mediterranean climate, **Csa**, is found in the Mediterranean Basin itself as well as in other interior locations. The cooler variety, **Csb**, is found on coasts near cool offshore ocean currents, most notably in coastal areas of California, central Chile, southern and southwestern Australia, South Africa, and Europe's Iberian Peninsula (northern Portugal and northwestern Spain).

In the **Cs** climate, rainfall arrives in the cool season, largely as a result of the winter storms produced by midlatitude cyclones. Annual precipitation totals are moderate, ranging from approximately 400 to 650 mm. The long

dry summers are associated with the temporary poleward shift of the wind belts, specifically the warm-season dominance of subsiding air on the eastern side of the oceanic subtropical high-pressure zone. Thus, extended rainless periods are quite common in Mediterranean climates. But when they occur in the more widely distributed (and more heavily populated) **Cf** climates, they can lead to serious *droughts* that disrupt human–environmental relationships (see 'Perspectives' box).

Figure 17.21 shows the climograph for Athens, Greece, a classic example of the warmer **Csa** Mediterranean climate variety. Note the similarities to the San Francisco precipitation pattern (Figure 17.22). The only noteworthy difference in temperature is the greater annual range produced by the more continental location of Athens.

The Dry-Winter (Cw) Climates

The **Cw** climate, the third major subtype of humid mesothermal climate, is little different from the tropical savanna (**Aw**) climate, with the only differences being the amounts of rainfall and a distinct cool season, with the average temperature of at least one month falling below 18°C. The **Cw** climate, therefore, is the only subdivision of the C climates found extensively in the tropics. For this reason it often shares with the **Aw** climate the designation *tropical wet-and-dry* climate.

In many cases the winter dry season of **Cw** climates is a result of offshore-flowing winds that accompany a winter

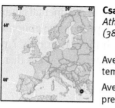

Csa - Mediterranean climate
*Athens, Greece
(38°N, 24°E)*

Average annual
temperature = 18°C

Average annual
precipitation = 402 mm

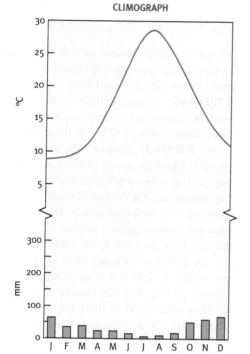

Figure 17.21 Climograph of a weather station that experiences the warmer variety of the Mediterranean (**Csa**) climate.

monsoon. (Indeed, the **Cw** climate is sometimes called the *subtropical monsoon* climate.) In South and Southeast Asia as well as in northeastern Australia, rainfall is provided by the wet summer monsoon. In other cases, such as in south-central Africa, the winter dry season occurs because the rains of the ITCZ migrate into the Northern Hemisphere with the Sun.

The **Cw** climates are also associated with higher elevations in the tropical latitudes, which produce winter temperatures too cool to classify these areas as **A**. Cherrapunji, in the Khasi Hills of northeastern India, is a good example (Figure 17.23). Because of its location near the subtropics at latitude 25°N, combined with its altitude of 1313 m, this highland town exhibits the characteristics of the cooler variety of this climatic subtype (**Cwb**). Cherrapunji's enormous annual rainfall (which averages 11,437 mm), as explained in the discussion of the **Am** climate, is the result of wet-monsoon winds that encounter particularly abrupt orographic lifting on their way inland from the Bay of Bengal to the blocking Himalayan mountain wall not far to the north.

The Major Humid Microthermal (D) Climates

Northern Hemisphere continental landmasses extend in an east–west direction for thousands of kilometres. In northern Eurasia, for instance, the distance along 60°N between Bergen on Norway's Atlantic coast and Okhotsk on Russia's Pacific shore is almost 9000 km. Indeed, Russia alone is so broad that the summer Sun rises above the eastern Pacific shoreline before it has set over the Baltic Sea in the west—10 time zones away! Consequently, vast areas of

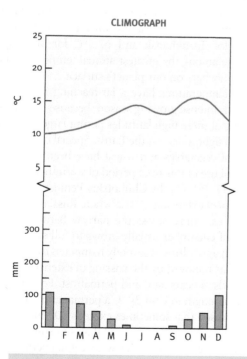

Csb - Mediterranean climate
*San Francisco, California
(38°N, 122°W)*

Average annual temperature = 14°C
Average annual precipitation = 551 mm

Figure 17.22 Climograph for a representative weather station in the Mediterranean (**Csb**) climate zone.

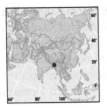

Cwb - Subtropical monsoon climate
Cherrapunji, India
(25°N, 92°E)

Average annual
temperature = 17°C

Average annual
precipitation = 11,437 mm

CLIMOGRAPH

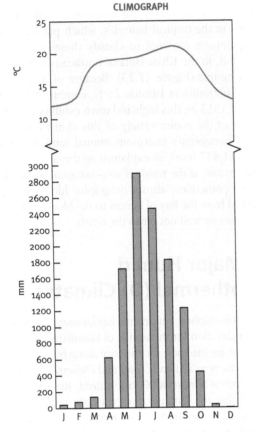

Figure 17.23   Climograph of a weather station in the **Cwb** zone, sometimes called the subtropical monsoon climate.

uplands and on the eastern sides of continental landmasses. These microthermal climates represent the epitome of the continentality effect—although they cover only 7 per cent of the Earth's surface overall, they cover no less than 21 per cent of its land area.

The Humid Continental (Dfa/Dwa, Dfb/Dwb) and Taiga (Dfc/Dwc, Dfd/Dwd) Climates

The humid microthermal climates are usually subdivided into two groups. In the upper middle latitudes, where more heat is available, we observe the *humid continental* (**Dfa/ Dwa** and **Dfb/Dwb**) climates. Farther north towards the Arctic, where the summer net radiation cannot raise average monthly temperatures above −2°C , lie the subarctic *taiga* (**Dfc/Dwc** and **Dfd/Dwd**) climates. (Taiga means 'snow-forest' in Russian.) Both groups of climates usually receive enough precipitation to be classified as moist all year round (**Df**). But in eastern Asia, the cold air of winter cannot hold enough moisture, so a dry winter season (**Dw**) results.

All **D** climates show singular extremes of temperature throughout the year. In Unit 6 we observed the heat balance for the northern Siberian town of Turukhansk (see Figure 6.6D). In July the temperature there averages a pleasant 14.7°C, but the January mean plunges to −31°C. However, brutal as the latter reading might be, Turukhansk is only an example of the **Dfc** climatic subtype, which is not the most extreme category. The harshest subtype, **Dwd**, is exemplified by Verkhoyansk, a remote far northeastern Russian village 2100 km northeast of Turukhansk, whose particularly extreme temperatures are discussed in Unit 7 (see Figure 7.4). As the climograph in Figure 17.24 shows, the *average* January temperature in Verkhoyansk is an astonishing −46.8°C. Also fascinating are the *ranges* of temperature, the difference between the highest and lowest monthly averages: 45.7°C for Turukhansk and 62.5°C for Verkhoyansk. These are among the greatest annual temperature ranges found anywhere on our planet's surface.

Such temperatures have a far-reaching impact. There is a short, intense growing season, because the long summer days at these high latitudes permit large quantities of heat and light to fall on the Earth. Special quick-growing strains of vegetables and wheat have been developed to make full use of this brief period of warmth and moisture (Figure 17.25). On the Chukotskiy Peninsula, the northeasternmost extension of Asia where Russia faces Alaska's western extremity across the narrow Bering Strait, one variety of cucumber usually grows to full size within 40 days. But agriculture is severely hampered by the thin soil (most was removed by the passing of extensive ice sheets thousands of years ago) and permafrost. Permafrost, discussed at length in Unit 39, is a permanently frozen layer of the subsoil that sometimes exceeds 300 m in depth.

Although the top layer of soil thaws in summer, the ice beneath presents a barrier that water cannot permeate. Thus the surface is often poorly drained. Moreover, the yearly

LINK

land in the middle and upper latitudes are far away from the moderating influence of the oceans. The resulting continentality shapes a climate in which the seasonal rhythms of the higher latitudes are carried to extremes, one of distinctly warm summers balanced by harsh frigid winters. These are the **humid microthermal (D) climates**, distinguished by a warm month—or months—when the mean temperature is above 10°C, and a period averaging longer than a month when the mean temperature is below freezing (0°C). The people who live in **D** climates have acquired lifestyles as varied as their wardrobes to cope with such conditions.

The cold-winter **D** climates are found mainly in the middle- and upper-latitude continental expanses of Eurasia and North America (see Figure 16.2). As the world map shows, these areas are sometimes punctuated by regions of the entirely summerless **E** climates, especially in northeastern Asia and the Canadian Arctic. The **D** climates are also found in certain Northern Hemisphere mid-latitude

LINK

LINK

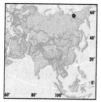

Dwd - Taiga climate
Verkhoyansk, Russia
(68°N, 133°E)

Average annual
temperature = −15°C

Average annual
precipitation = 155 mm

CLIMOGRAPH

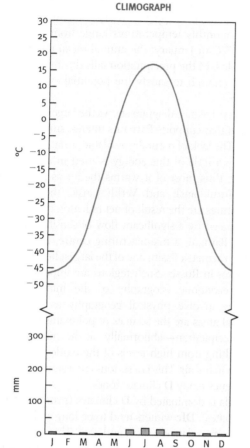

Figure 17.24 Climograph of a weather station in the **Dwd** zone, the harshest extreme of the humid microthermal climate regions.

Figure 17.25 Short growing season, luxuriant growth. These giant cabbages are among many varieties of vegetables grown during the brief summer in a typical **D** climate.

freeze–thaw cycle expands and contracts the soil, making construction of any kind difficult, as Figure 17.26 demonstrates. Because of the soil's instability, the trans-Alaska oil pipeline built during the 1970s must be elevated above ground on pedestals for much of its 1300-km length. This prevents the heated oil in the pipeline from melting the permafrost and causing land instability that might damage the pipe. The consequences of climate change are expected to be felt particularly hard in this sensitive environment, a subject that will be discussed in detail in Unit 18.

Long-lasting snow cover has other effects. It reflects most of the small amount of radiation that reaches it, so that little is absorbed. It cools the air and contributes to the production of areas of high atmospheric pressure. It presents difficulties for human transport and other activities, but, paradoxically, it does keep the soil and dormant plants warm because snow

Figure 17.26 A once straight-standing historic building in Dawson City, Yukon, is now tilted by melting permafrost.

is a poor conductor of heat. Measurements in St Petersburg, Russia's second largest city, have shown that ground temperatures below a layer of snow can be as high as −2.8°C when the air overlying the cover is a bitter −40°C.

In the humid microthermal climates, most of the precipitation comes in the warmer months. This is not just because the warmer air can hold more moisture. In winter, large anticyclones develop in the lower layers of the atmosphere. Within the anticyclones the air is stable, and these high-pressure cells tend to block mid-latitude cyclones. In summer, convection in the unstable warmer air creates storms, so mid-latitude cyclones can pass through **D** climate areas more frequently during that time of year. In some places there is also a summer monsoon season. China's capital city of Beijing (**Dwa**) experiences a pronounced wet monsoon (Figure 17.27), which is typical of upper mid-latitude coastal areas on the East Asian mainland.

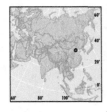

Dwa - Humid continental climate
*Beijing, China
(40°N, 117°E)*

Average annual
temperature = 12°C

Average annual
precipitation = 623 mm

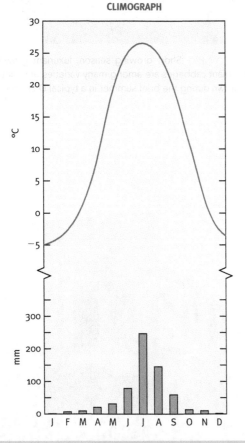

Figure 17.27 Climograph of a weather station in the **Dwa** climate zone, which also experiences a marked summer monsoon.

The more detailed features of the microthermal climate type are seen in the temperature, precipitation, water balance, and heat balance data displayed in Figure 17.28. These graphs are for the southern Siberian city of Barnaul, located in a **Dfb** region within the heart of Eurasia at 53°N near the intersection of Russia and China with the western tip of Mongolia. The extreme seasonal change of Barnaul's climate is apparent everywhere in Figure 17.28. Average monthly temperatures range from 20°C in July to −17.7°C in January; the annual mean temperature is 1.4°C. Most of the precipitation falls during summer, but it is not enough to satisfy the potential evapotranspiration rate.

The heat balance diagram shows the large amount of net radiation that supports Barnaul's intense summer growing season. The lack of naturally available surface water means that only a little of this energy is used in evaporation in summer; thus most of it warms the air as sensible heat. As in Turukhansk and Verkhoyansk, the low winter temperatures are the result of net radiation deficits that are not balanced by a significant flow of sensible heat to the surface. Barnaul, a manufacturing centre, is also located near the Kuznetsk Basin, one of the largest heavy-industrial complexes in Russia. Such regions are important features of the economic geography of the middle latitudes, and they involve physical geography as well because industrial areas are the sources of pollutants that produce acid precipitation—abnormally acidic rain, snow, or fog resulting from high levels of the oxides of sulfur and nitrogen in the air. This is a serious environmental problem that plagues many **D** climate zones.

Canada is dominated by **D** climates (primarily **Dfb** and **Dfc** climates). **Dfc** winters tend to be long and severe, and summers are relatively short and cool. This climate type is the most widespread in Canada, occupying the northern half of the country, with its southern boundary coinciding approximately with the northern limit of cultivation. The humid continental type (**Dfb**), second in spatial extent, corresponds roughly with the aspen parkland and mixed forest regions. Winters are long and cold, but summers are rather warm and pleasant. As discussed in Unit 16, these climate boundaries are not fixed, but rather evolve and fluctuate over time. For example, during the 1930s, a boundary shift towards the north was indicative of a dry and warm decade, while the 1920s showed a shift to the south, a result of wetter and colder conditions. With global warming, it would be expected that climate boundaries could shift significantly.

The Polar (E) Climates

Beyond the Arctic and Antarctic Circles (66 ½°N and S, respectively), summer and winter become synonymous with day and night. Near the poles there are six months of daylight in summer, when the monthly average temperature may 'soar' to −22°C. In winter, six months of darkness and continual outgoing radiation lead to the

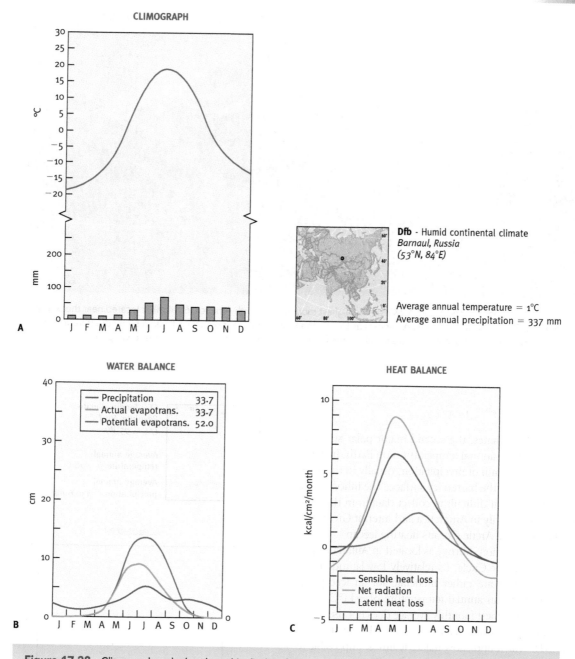

Figure 17.28 Climograph and related graphic displays for a representative weather station in the **Dfb** climate zone.

lowest temperatures and most extensive icefields on the planetary surface. The lowest temperature ever recorded on Earth (−89°C) was on a memorably chilly day at one of the highest-altitude stations in central Antarctica, the Russian research facility Vostok.

The Tundra (ET) Climate

Polar (E) climates are defined as those climates in which the mean temperature of the warmest month is less than 10°C. There are two major subtypes of polar climate. If the warmest average monthly temperature is between 0° and 10°C, the climate is called *tundra* (**ET**), after its

associated vegetation of mosses, lichens, and stunted trees (Figure 17.29). Practically all of the **ET** climates are found in the Northern Hemisphere, where the continentality effect yields particularly long and bitter winters. Furthermore, many of the **ET** areas border the Arctic Ocean, which provides a moisture source for frequent fogs when it is not frozen. In summer, poor drainage leads to stagnant water, the breeding grounds for enormous swarms of flies and mosquitoes. Precipitation, mainly from frontal mid-latitude depressions in the warmer months, seldom exceeds 300 mm for the year. The climograph for Resolute, on Cornwallis Island in the Northwest Territories (Figure 17.30), displays the typical **ET** regimes of temperature and moisture.

Figure 17.29 Snowcapped Mount McKinley, the highest mountain in North America (6194 m), is located near the centre of the Alaska Range. Known to Native Americans as Denali (the High One), the mountain is flanked by tundra (foreground). The boundary between **ET** and **EF** climates lies along the foothills between the snowy peak and the lower plain.

The Icecap (EF) Climate

In *icecap* (**EF**) climates, the second major polar subtype, we find the lowest annual temperatures on Earth. In a given year about 90 mm of precipitation, usually in the form of snow, falls onto the barren icy surface. The inhospitable climate has made it difficult to collect data from these areas, which lie mainly in Antarctica and interior Greenland as well as atop the Arctic Ocean's floating icecap.

The Russian station, Mirnyy, is located in Antarctica just inside the Antarctic Circle. Its relatively low latitude hosts temperatures that are rather moderate for an icecap climate, but the mean annual temperature of −11°C is not high, and the warmest monthly average does not rise above the freezing point—the hallmark of an **EF** climate (Figure 17.31). Year-round snow makes it almost impossible to obtain accurate water balance data, but Russian scientists have measured the heat balance components, which vividly characterize the frigid **EF** climate. There is significant positive net radiation at Mirnyy for only about four months of the year; more radiation leaves the Earth than enters during the other months. Sensible heat flow throughout the year is directed from the air towards the ground, the final result of the general circulation of the atmosphere moving heat towards the poles. Sensible heat and net radiation can provide energy for some evaporation in the warmer months, but in the winter condensation of moisture onto the surface provides only a minor source of heat.

These extreme conditions notwithstanding, a number of scientists now live and work in icecap climates, studying the environment or searching for oil and other secrets of the Earth. But every one of them depends for survival on artificial heating and food supplies flown in from the

ET - Tundra climate
Resolute, NWT
(74°N, 95°W)

Average annual
temperature = −20°C

Average annual
precipitation = 139.6 mm

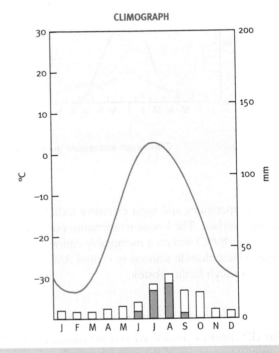

Figure 17.30 Climograph of a high-latitude tundra (**ET**) weather station. On the precipitation graph, white indicates snowfall and green indicates rainfall.

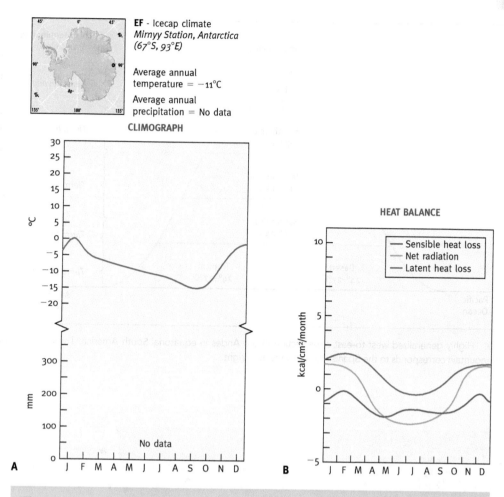

EF - Icecap climate
Mirnyy Station, Antarctica
(67°S, 93°E)

Average annual
temperature = −11°C

Average annual
precipitation = No data

CLIMOGRAPH

HEAT BALANCE

Sensible heat loss
Net radiation
Latent heat loss

No data

Figure 17.31 Climograph and heat balance diagram for a representative weather station in the icecap **(EF)** climate zone. There are no precipitation data available for this remote Antarctic location.

outside world, without which human life could not exist in the coldest climate on the planet.

High-Altitude (H) Climates

Our overview of the mosaic of climates covering the Earth's land surface would not be complete without some mention of the climates of highland regions. The mountains of the highest uplands reach into the lower temperatures and pressures of the troposphere. Thus, as one moves steadily upward into a highland zone, the corresponding changes in climate with increasing elevation mimic those observed in a horizontal passage from equatorial to progressively higher latitudes.

One of the outstanding features of **highland (H) climates** is their distinct **vertical zonation** according to altitude. Nowhere has this been better demonstrated than in the tropical Andes mountain ranges of northwestern South America. Figure 17.32 combines the characteristics of many of these highlands into a single model. The foothills of the Andes lie in a tropical rainforest climate in the Amazon Basin in the east and in arid climates tem-

pered by a cool Pacific Ocean current in the west. Above 1200 m, tropical climates give way to the subtropical zone. At 2400 m the mesothermal climates appear, with vegetation reminiscent of that found in Mediterranean climatic regions. These in turn give way to microthermal climates at 3600 m, and above 4800 m permanent ice and snow create a climate like that of polar areas.

These altitudinal zones mainly reflect the decrease of temperatures with rising elevation. But wind speeds tend to increase with height, as can rainfall (and snowfall), fog, and cloud cover. Moreover, the radiation balance is markedly altered by altitude. Because less shortwave radiation is absorbed by the atmosphere at higher elevations, greater values are recorded at the surface. This is especially true of the ultraviolet radiation responsible for snow blindness as well as the suntans of mountaineers and skiers. Where there are snow-covered surfaces, much of the incoming radiation is reflected and not absorbed, which further acts to keep the temperatures low.

Mountainous areas are often characterized by steep slopes, and these slopes have different orientations or

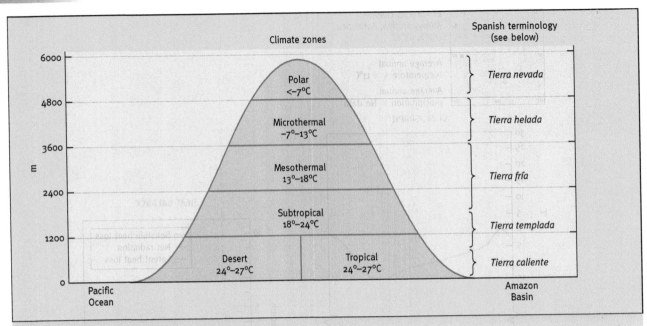

Figure 17.32   Highly generalized west-to-east cross-section of the Andes in equatorial South America. The vertical climatic zonation shown on the mountain corresponds to the Spanish terminology at its right.

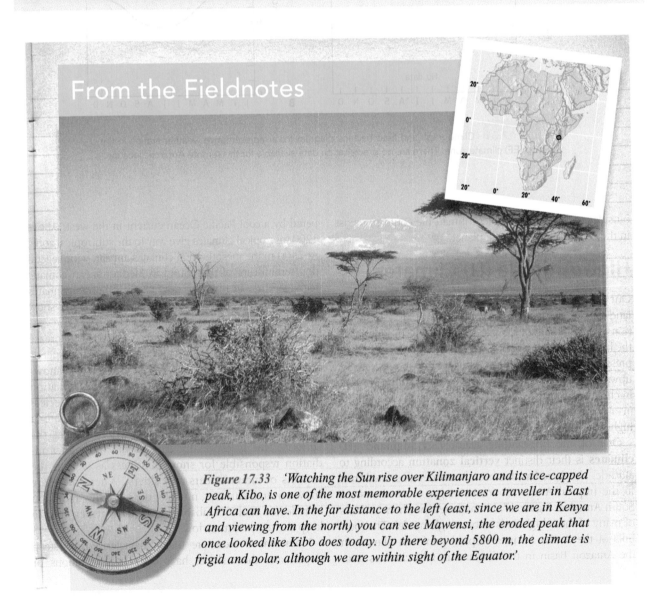

Figure 17.33   'Watching the Sun rise over Kilimanjaro and its ice-capped peak, Kibo, is one of the most memorable experiences a traveller in East Africa can have. In the far distance to the left (east, since we are in Kenya and viewing from the north) you can see Mawensi, the eroded peak that once looked like Kibo does today. Up there beyond 5800 m, the climate is frigid and polar, although we are within sight of the Equator.'

aspects (they may face in any compass direction). In the Northern Hemisphere, southerly aspects receive far more solar radiation than do north-facing slopes, which may receive no direct solar radiation for much of the winter season. These differences in radiation receipt are often manifested as vegetation contrasts on different slope aspects. South-facing slopes are commonly drier and exhibit a sparser vegetation cover. North-facing slopes are typically more lush, since temperatures, and hence evaporation rates, are lower. Rugged terrain also influences local windflow patterns that may have an effect on climatic conditions. Finally, the climate of a particular upland area depends on its location with respect to the global-scale factors of climate, such as the general circulation of the atmosphere.

A broadly simple pattern of climates occurs because of the heat and water exchanges at the Earth's surface and because of the spatial organization of the general circulation of the atmosphere. This pattern is altered in detail by the specific location of land and water bodies, ocean currents, and upland regions. The resulting mosaic of climates may be classified in different ways. We have mainly followed the system first devised by Köppen, who divided the climates of the Earth into six major types and a number of additional subtypes.

In Units 18 and 19, respectively, two additional aspects of the geography of climate are explored: (1) climatic variations over time and what these changes may portend for the future distribution of climate regions, and (2) the interactions between humans and their climatic environment.

KEY TERMS

arid (**B**) climates   *page 226*
desertification   *page 230*
drought   *page 227*
highland (**H**) climates   *page 243*
humid microthermal (**D**) climates   *page 238*
mesothermal (**C**) climates   *page 232*

polar (**E**) climates   *page 241*
steppe   *page 226*
tropical (**A**) climates   *page 221*
tropical deforestation   *page 221*
vertical zonation   *page 243*

REVIEW QUESTIONS

1. Describe the general latitudinal extent of **A** climates.
2. Describe the general latitudinal extent of **B** climates.
3. Why is ongoing tropical deforestation regarded as a catastrophe by so many natural scientists?
4. Describe the circumstances leading to desertification.
5. What are the major precipitation patterns associated with Mediterranean (**Cs**) climates?

6. What is meant by the term *drought*?
7. How do humid continental climates differ from taiga climates?
8. What is permafrost and how does it form?
9. Describe the effects of increasing altitude on temperature, precipitation (types and amounts), and wind speeds.

REFERENCES AND FURTHER READINGS

Allan, T., and A. Warren. 1993. *Deserts: The Encroaching Wilderness.* New York: Oxford Univ. Press.

Arakawa, H., ed. 1969. *Climates of Northern and Eastern Asia.* Amsterdam, Elsevier, World Survey of Climatology, vol. 8.

Barry, R.G. 2008. *Mountain Weather and Climate*, 3rd edn. New York: Cambridge Univ. Press.

Beniston, M., ed. 1994. *Mountain Environments in Changing Climates.* London/New York: Routledge.

Bliss, R.G. 1981. *Tundra Ecosystems: A Comparative Analysis.* New York: Cambridge Univ. Press.

Bryson, R.A., and F.K. Hare, eds. 1974. *Climates of North America.* Amsterdam, Elsevier, World Survey of Climatology, vol. 11.

Cole, M.M. 1986. *The Savannas: Biogeography and Geobotany.* Orlando, Fla: Academic Press.

Coupland, R.T., ed. 1979. *Grassland Ecosystems of the World.* New York: Cambridge Univ. Press.

Di Castri, F., and H.A. Mooney, eds. 1973. *Mediterranean-Type Ecosystems: Origin and Structure.* New York: Springer-Verlag.

French, H.M., and O. Slaymaker, eds. 1993. *Canada's Cold Environments.* Montreal and Kingston: McGill-Queen's Univ. Press.

Gerrard, A.J. 1990. *Mountain Environments: An Examination of the Physical Geography of Mountains.* Cambridge, Mass.: MIT Press.

Goodall, D.W., et al. 1979. *Arid Land Ecosystems.* New York: Cambridge Univ. Press.

Goudie, A.S. 2000. *The Human Impact on the Natural Environment*, 5th edn. Cambridge, Mass.: MIT Press.

Gourou, P. 1980. *The Tropical World: Its Social and Economic Conditions and Its Future Status*, 5th edn, trans. S.H. Beaver. London/New York: Longman.

Hare, F.K. 1983. *Climate and Desertification: A Revised Analysis*. Geneva: World Meteorological Organization/UNEP, World Climate Program, vol. 44.

Harris, S.A. 1986. *The Permafrost Environment*. Totowa, NJ: Rowman & Littlefield.

Heathcote, R.L. 1983. *The Arid Lands: Their Use and Abuse*. London/New York: Longman.

Houston, J.M. 1964. *The Western Mediterranean World: An Introduction to Its Regional Landscapes*. New York: Praeger.

Ives, J.D., and R.G. Barry, eds. 1974. *Arctic and Alpine Environments*. London: Methuen.

Kellman, M., and R. Tackaberry. 1997. *Tropical Environments: The Functioning and Management of Tropical Ecosystems*. London/New York: Routledge.

Lydolph, P.E., ed. 1977. *Climates of the Soviet Union*. Amsterdam: Elsevier, World Survey of Climatology, vol. 7.

McClaran, M.P., and T.R. van Devender, eds. 1995. *The Desert Grassland*. Tucson: Univ. of Arizona Press.

Mather, J.R. 1984. *Water Resources: Distribution, Use, and Management*. New York: Wiley/V.H. Winston, 362–82.

Middleton, N.J., and D.S.G. Thomas. 1997. *World Atlas of Desertification*, 2nd rev. edn. London: Edward Arnold.

Natural History. 1988. 'The Long, Hot Summer of '88', special issue (Jan.).

Palmer, W.C. 1965. *Meteorological Drought: Its Measurement and Classification*. Washington: US Weather Bureau, Research Paper No. 45.

Pielou, E.C. 1995. *A Naturalist's Guide to the Arctic*. Chicago: Univ. of Chicago Press.

Price, L.W. 1981. *Mountains and Man: A Study of Process and Environment*. Berkeley: Univ. of California Press.

Raven, P.H. 1988. 'The Cause and Impact of Deforestation', in H.J. de Blij, ed., *Earth '88: Changing Geographic Perspectives*. Washington: National Geographic Society, 212–29.

Reading, A.J., et al. 1994. *Humid Tropical Environments*. Cambridge, Mass.: Blackwell.

Repetto, R. 1990. 'Deforestation in the Tropics', *Scientific American* (Apr.): 36–42.

Stewart, G.R. 1947. *Storm*. New York: Modern Library.

Thomas, D.S.G., and N.J. Middleton, 1994. *Desertification: Exploding the Myth*. New York: Wiley.

Wallen, C.C., ed. 1970. *Climates of Northern and Western Europe*. Amsterdam: Elsevier, World Survey of Climatology, vol. 5.

———, ed. 1977. *Climates of Central and Southern Europe*. Amsterdam: Elsevier, World Survey of Climatology, vol. 6.

Whiteman, C.D. 2000. *Mountain Meteorology: Fundamentals and Applications*. New York: Oxford Univ. Press.

Williams, M.A.J., and R.C. Balling. 1995. *Interactions of Desertification and Climate*. New York: Wiley.

 # WEB RESOURCES

earthobservatory.nasa.gov/Features/Deforestation The causes of deforestation are explored, as well as deforestation rates and processes.

ecotect.com/archive/index.php?climate/koppenA.html An overview of **A** climates, with photographs of typical dwellings for each climatic subtype.

gsc.nrcan.gc.ca/permafrost/regional_e.php Geological Survey of Canada's permafrost regional studies site.

pubs.usgs.gov/gip/deserts/desertification Review of the causes of desertification, global monitoring techniques, and remediation strategies.

www.agr.gc.ca/pfra/drought/ Agriculture and Agri-Food Canada's 'Drought Watch'.

www.arctic.noaa.gov/ National Oceanographic and Atmospheric Administration's Arctic information site.

www.canadainfolink.ca/climate.htm Canadian climate data and climate graphs. Part of the Teaching and Learning about Canada website.

www.drought.noaa.gov Background information about cause of droughts, US drought outlook, and many links to water resource websites.

www.ec.gc.ca/acidrain Environment Canada's acid rain site, including case studies and information about what's being done about the acid rain problem.

www.epa.gov/acidrain Overview of the chemical components of acid precipitation, its formation, its effects, and how it can be reduced. Glossary of terms is provided.

Dynamics of Past and Present Climate Change

Objectives

- To examine various lines of evidence for climate change.

- To trace the history of climatic change on Planet Earth, focusing on the past 2 million years.

- To discuss mechanisms that can cause climatic variations.

Planet Earth, as was noted in Unit 4, had turbulent origins. For hundreds of millions of years following its birth, geochemical processes generated such surface heat that life as we know could not have existed. The gigantic collision that led to the formation of the Moon was only one incident in a series of impacts that cratered the surface while volcanoes poured out molten rock from below. Slowly the Earth's crust cooled enough for slabs of solid rock to form and endure, and eventually almost all of the planet's outer skin solidified. Next the global ocean began to fill the basins and a primitive atmosphere, loaded with such gases as methane, ammonia, and helium, and later carbon dioxide and nitrogen, formed. Oxygen, the atmospheric gas upon which we depend for life, was but a trace 4 billion years ago, but a few hundred million years later photosynthesis had begun and the abundance of oxygen in the atmosphere started its slow, uninterrupted rise. Not only did the still young Earth have an atmosphere, it also had climates, seasons, and daily weather variations. And global climates have been changing ever since.

It would seem reasonable to assume that the Earth continued to cool throughout its geologic history, eventually experiencing ice ages that pushed glaciers far from the frigid poles into the middle latitudes. But research yields data that suggest something quite different. About 800 million years ago, when the atmosphere's oxygen content was about one-twentieth of its present level, or just 1 per cent of total volume, the first single-celled animals (the protozoa) had emerged, and nothing much changed for millennia. But something happened suddenly. Land and sea were frozen over and, according to the *Snowball Earth hypothesis*, the planet went into a deep freeze. What might have caused this is unknown; perhaps the Sun's radiation output fell sharply for some reason. The Earth was in a full-scale ice age, and the protozoa responded by developing into multi-celled metazoa, many of which acquired protective shells using the plentiful calcium carbonate being precipitated on the ocean floor. When the ice age ended and the planet warmed up again, the stage was set for life's *Cambrian explosion*, the burgeoning of marine organisms in unprecedented diversity.

Whether or not the Snowball Earth hypothesis withstands verification, we know that the Earth's climatic environments change continuously. In the approximately 570 million years since the opening of the Cambrian period (the geological time scale is shown in Figure 28.7), our planet has been repeatedly warmed to tropical levels, only to be cooled to ice-age conditions, although no later ice age has been as frigid as that of Snowball Earth. Throughout this time, however, there were always mild refuges where many life forms could survive.

The two most recent ice ages are quite well known, because the evidence is well preserved. An ice age started during the Pennsylvanian (late Carboniferous) period and lasted tens of millions of years into the Permian. After that ice age ended, tropical warmth replaced Arctic cold, luxuriant vegetation spread poleward, and life took on

Figure 18.1   Information derived from fossils, such as this dinosaur skeleton exposed at Dinosaur National Monument on the Colorado–Utah border, can reveal much about the environment that prevailed during their lifetimes. During the Jurassic, climates over much of the Earth were warmer and more moist than today, creating vast forests and swamps, which supported numerous species of large herbivores (plant eaters) and carnivores.

the exuberance of 'Jurassic Park'. The dinosaurs predominated, and much smaller mammals survived in protected settings (Figure 18.1). But then, as we shall see in Unit 21, the age of the dinosaurs likely ended with an impact from space, and among the survivors were those small mammals whose descendants would inherit the Earth. The Cretaceous/Tertiary (K/T) boundary, some 65 million years ago, marked the beginning of the Cenozoic Era, and in its early period nothing suggested what lay ahead. But by about 35 million years ago, it would have been clear to any weather forecaster that the Earth was headed for another ice age. The Antarctic landmass acquired permanent ice; glaciers formed on the world's highest mountains; tree lines dropped to lower elevations; vegetation shifted equatorward; mammals everywhere, including primates, migrated and evolved in response to the climatic challenge.

Unlike what happened during the Snowball Earth episode, more recent ice ages have been less extreme and less pervasive. Warm periods have interrupted the cooling, allowing for the recovery of plants and animals; glaciers have expanded and then receded again. The Earth today is experiencing such a warm phase, and in recent years we have worried more about global warming than about global cooling.

Evidence of Climate Change

Climate change is the norm, not the exception, on our planet. But how is it possible to reconstruct climates of millions, even hundreds of millions, of years ago? The evidence exists in various forms. When glaciers expand, they scour

Figure 18.2   Core samples drilled from the ocean floor reveal the conditions on that part of the planet many years ago. A 40 m ocean sediment core spans 12,000 years of Earth history.

the surface, breaking off, grinding up, and carrying away part of the bedrock below. Later, when they melt away, they leave behind telltale effects in the form of deposits that leave no doubt as to their former presence (see Units 36 and 37). Particular types of soils form under certain environmental conditions (such as thick tropical soils and thin desert soils). When such soils are buried by subsequent geologic events, they form a durable record of climatic conditions at the time of their formation. Occasionally, entire diagnostic landforms are buried and preserved, for example, fossilized sand dunes, which may tell us more than just the fact that it was dry when and where they formed; from their morphology we may even be able to determine the prevailing winds at the time, millions of years ago.

Animal and plant fossils provide compelling evidence as well. Specific kinds of marine fauna formed under cold or warm conditions, and certain types of plants grew under warm and moist conditions rather than in cool, dry environments. From a combination of fossil data it has been determined that much of the Earth was warm and moist during the heyday of the dinosaurs, with luxuriant tropical vegetation, swamps, and marshes providing an environment that supported a profusion of many forms of life. But before the era of the dinosaurs opened, the cold of an ice age kept animals small, thick-shelled, and relatively sparse, and much of the planet was not only cool but also dry.

Evidence from sediments deposited over long periods on ocean floors and lake bottoms is also crucial in this scientific detective work. Samples (**sediment cores**) of these deposits are tested for accumulations of the fossils of tiny sea creatures, for mineral composition, even for ash

(Figure 18.2). The ash from volcanic eruptions that occurred hundreds of thousands of years ago dropped from the atmosphere and sank to the ocean floor, forming thin layers that can be correlated against other evidence and provide valuable timelines. Most valuable of all is information derived from nuclear particles embedded in the seafloor deposits, because these differ in significant ways. The nucleus of an atom is made up of positively charged protons and uncharged neutrons. Two separate atoms of one element, for example oxygen, may have different numbers of neutrons, but they will always have the same number of protons. These related but different forms of the same element are called *isotopes*, and their differences reveal variations in the environmental conditions prevailing during their formation.

By coring ocean-floor sediments in higher latitudes and thick ice sheets in Greenland and Antarctica, scientists have been able to reconstruct the climatic record for hundreds of thousands of years past. Obviously, the closer we come to the present, the more detailed the information, which is why the Snowball Earth idea is still a hypothesis. However, the Late Cenozoic Ice Age is beyond doubt, although the picture we have is still very general. Climate swings dra-matically, even over the short term, and pieces of the environmental puzzle for the past several thousand years still are being fitted into place.

Evidence of past climates can be retrieved from ice cores (Figures 18.3 and 18.4). **Ice cores** are cylinders of ice about ten centimetres in diameter that are collected by drilling deep into the ice. The cores are brought to the surface in lengths of approximately three metres at a time.

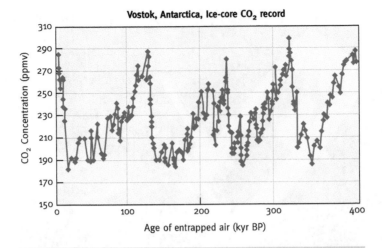

Figure 18.3   Ice core graph based on data from the Russian Vostok station in Antarctica showing changes in atmospheric CO_2 levels over the past epochs.

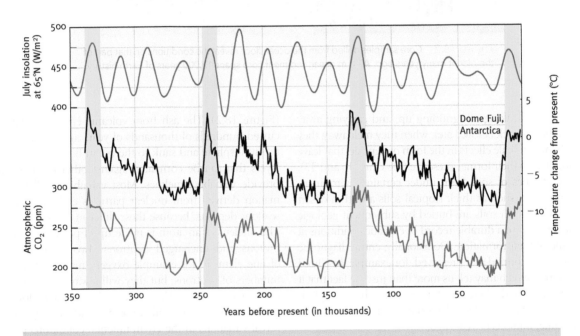

Figure 18.4   Antarctic ice core data on changes in atmospheric CO_2, temperature, and insolation over the past 350,000 years.

The age limit of any core is determined by the thickness of the ice. While portions of Antarctica have been covered in ice for more than 20 million years, scientists don't expect to retrieve cores more than 1 million years old.

When snow falls, it picks up whatever chemicals and particulate matter are in the atmosphere, and fallen snow never melts in the Antarctic. Over time, as new snow falls, older snow turns to ice, trapping tiny pockets of air in the process. These pockets of air act as time-capsules of the atmosphere when they were trapped. By extracting the air from the ice cores, the chronology of the particles, chemicals, and gases in the changing atmosphere of the past can be studied. Studies of these changes show the dramatic increase in greenhouse gases caused by human use of fossil

fuels as well as natural changes that accompany glacial/interglacial climate shifts. Studying this chronological record allows scientists to see how the global climate responded to variations of greenhouse gases in the past. Another type of information that can be obtained from ice cores comes from the frozen water itself. Naturally occurring hydrogen and oxygen both come in rare heavier forms called isotopes. In the oceans, one in about every 500 oxygen atoms is the heavy isotope, and one in about 70 hydrogen atoms is heavy. As water evaporates and is transported to polar regions, the mix of the heavy isotopes changes. These changes are mostly influenced by temperature, thus, by measuring water isotopes in ice cores researchers can infer temperatures when the snow originally fell.

LINK

LINK

In January 1998, a collaborative ice-drilling project between Russia, the United States, and France at the Russian Vostok station in East Antarctica yielded the deepest ice core ever recovered, reaching a depth of 3623 m. The Vostok ice-core record extends through numerous climate cycles, with ice older than 700,000 years. Because of its length, multiple data sets, and precision in dating, the Vostok ice core from Antarctica provides one of the best records of glacial–interglacial cycling. One of the interesting findings from Vostok is the nearly simultaneous changes in temperature, carbon dioxide, and methane through time. The Vostok record also shows the 'sawtooth' character of the glacial–interglacial cycle. Temperature and carbon dioxide decreased in a series of progressively cooler steps towards peak glacial conditions. Each glacial period ended abruptly with a rapid transition to the full interglacial state marked by the warmest temperatures and highest levels of carbon dioxide in the atmosphere.

Evidence for Recent Climatic Variation

The Earth in the twenty-first century is not in an ice age. Glaciers are confined to high latitudes and high-mountain elevations, and in many parts of the world they are melting, showing little sign of advance. The planet has been warm for about 11,000 years, and with some minor variations the world climate map (Figure 16.2) represents the pattern that has prevailed for most (though not all) of the past 6000 years. During that period, humanity has expanded numerically and spatially to fill almost every niche, inhabit virtually every environment, and exploit practically every resource on land and at sea.

But the climate has indeed fluctuated even as humankind expanded, and the fluctuations have sometimes had significant, even disastrous consequences. Compared to the geologic advent of ice ages, these variations have been minor. Yet they reveal how, in our huge numbers, we are now at risk from even modest perturbations.

How do we know what has happened over the past several thousand years? Here the evidence is rather different from that discussed in the preceding section, although ice cores do play a role in the reconstruction. But other data come from tree rings, fossil pollen, paired annual lake sediments known as *varves*, fruit harvests (winegrowers' harvest dockets are especially valuable), historical narratives, farmers' trade records, and even the work of artists. Over the past 150 years, scientific instruments have made their appearance, and today huge quantities of data on every aspect of the planet's environments are being recorded.

Each bit of evidence, corroborated from a second and possibly third source, helps us build a picture of past climates. But each piece of the puzzle usually tells us only about conditions in one area and in one limited span of time. It is risky to generalize about global climate except in the most indefinite terms.

Figure 18.5   Ice-core drilling in Antarctica.

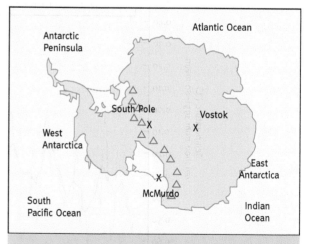

Figure 18.6   The Russian Vostok station, located at the Southern Geomagnetic Pole, is the coldest place on Earth and receives, on average, only 4.5 mm of precipitation per year. By month, the average daily temperatures range from –32.1°C (December and January) to –67.6°C (August). In contrast, the American McMurdo station on the coast has average temperatures ranging from –2.9°C (January) to –26.1°C (August).

The Climatic History of the Earth

Most history books start with the oldest times and work their way forward. In contrast, most descriptions of past climates start with the most recent times and work backward. Much more information is available on recent times, which allows statements to be made with greater certainty. Another advantage of such an approach is that it allows investigators to use certain climatic events as landmarks as they delve farther into the increasingly obscure past. The following account also begins with the more recent time periods, and we use certain events for guides as we shift time scales within our examination of the climatic past.

The Past 150 Years

Although there is much evidence of past climate change and weather variability, accurate record-keeping based on reliable instruments began only during the last 150 years. Weather records spanning a century or more still are rare, and come from weather stations mostly in Western Europe and North America. Many crucial areas of the world have climate records less than a half-century old. Political upheavals have interrupted record-keeping in other areas. In West Africa, for example, good records from weather stations established by the French and the British ended, or were interrupted, during the instabilities of the 1960s. Moreover, satellite observations of global weather

conditions are just a few decades old, and to this day surface verification is inadequate over large parts of the Earth's landmasses and oceans. Undeniably, the absence of dependable long-term data is a major obstacle in our efforts to gauge climate change.

Nevertheless, the available record indicates considerable temperature variations over the past 140 years (Figure 18.7). The most notable features of the average annual temperature of the world's landmasses over the past century and a half are a warming trend beginning in the 1880s, a cooling trend from 1940 into the 1970s, and another warming trend since then.

Different parts of the world have experienced these changes to a greater or lesser degree. For instance, the 1940–75 cooling trend was most strongly felt in the Atlantic sector of the Arctic region, where average winter temperatures in some locations dropped almost 3°C. On the other hand, no cooling at all was detected during that 35-year period in parts of the Southern Hemisphere (such as New Zealand), where the warming trend launched in the 1880s continued.

Recent research indicates that this regional variation in warming and cooling is a hallmark of climate change. Computer models that project **global warming** during the twenty-first century, for example, indicate that any such warming will be felt most strongly in the higher latitudes—not evenly around the world. *Global* warming (or cooling) may, therefore, turn out to be a misnomer—while certain regions experience one trend, others may record the opposite.

LINK

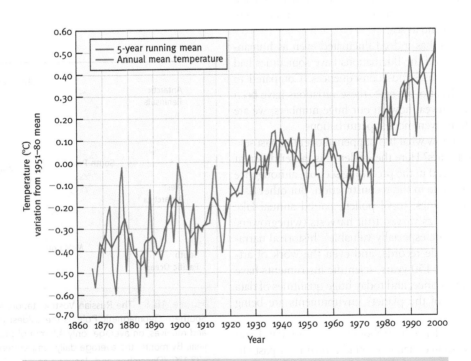

Figure 18.7   Variation of annual mean surface temperatures for the world's land areas, 1866–2000. Because this graph incorporates data from many different places, annual mean temperatures are expressed as a deviation from the average annual mean temperature for the 1951–1980 period.

The Past 1500 Years

To gauge climate and weather over the past 1500 years, we must depend on less exact information. Tree rings, lake sediments, ice cores, cave deposits, harvest records, diaries, and other sources produce a picture of considerable variation and even quite sudden change.

Apparently the Earth was warm and becoming warmer during the centuries prior to 1000 CE—a trend not unlike the one we are experiencing today. Sea level was high, low-lying coastal countries coped with rising water (in Holland the Dutch learned to build dikes and polders during this period), and high-latitude environs, even Greenland and Iceland, proved amenable to permanent settlement. The Romans had planted grapevines in Britain, and the wine industry thrived there under the mild conditions of what climatologists have come to call the **Medieval Optimum**.

In *The Little Ice Age* (1988), Jean Grove describes the conditions:

> For several hundred years climatic conditions in Europe had been kind; there were few poor harvests and famines were infrequent. The pack ice in the Arctic lay to the north and long sea voyages could be made in the small craft then in use . . . Icelanders made their first trip to Greenland about AD 982 and later they reached the Canadian Arctic and may even have penetrated the North West Passage. Grain was grown in Iceland and even in Greenland; the northern fisheries flourished and in mainland Europe vineyards were in production (500 km) north of their present limits. (Grove, 1988: 1–2)

Were these conditions representative only of the higher latitudes of the Northern Hemisphere or of the world as a whole? There are clues from the Southern Hemisphere that the Medieval Optimum may have been a global phenomenon. Even as the Scandinavians traversed the Atlantic and, led by Leif Eriksson (the son of Eric the Red), reached northern North America, Polynesians in the Southern Hemisphere for the first time managed to land in (upper mid-latitude) New Zealand. This group of Polynesians (the Maori) had been sailing the South Pacific for centuries, never having reached the largest islands in their realm. The warmth and tranquility of the Medieval Optimum may have given them the same sort of opportunity the Scandinavians seized in the far north.

The Medieval Optimum seems to bear some resemblance to the current warming trend. Many glaciers were in retreat, winters were generally mild, crops were plentiful. The frontiers of human settlement pushed into higher latitudes. But then, as Grove tells us, things changed quite suddenly:

> The beneficent times came to an end. Sea ice and stormier seas made the passages between Norway, Iceland, and Greenland more difficult after AD 1200; the last report of a voyage to Vinland [North America] was made in 1347. Life in Greenland became harder;

the people were cut off from Iceland and eventually disappeared from history toward the end of the fifteenth century. Grain would no longer ripen in Iceland, first in the north and later in the south and east . . . life became tougher for fishermen as well as for farmers. In mainland Europe, disastrous harvests were experienced in the latter part of the thirteenth and in the early fourteenth century . . . extremes of weather were greater, with severe winters and unusually hot or wet summers. (Grove, 1988: 2)

From the late thirteenth century onward, Europe was in the grip of climatic extremes as the Medieval Optimum gave way to the **Little Ice Age**. Britain's wine industry was extinguished in a few years; the limit of agriculture was driven southward by hundreds of kilometres. Not only Europe was affected. In China, the rulers of the Ming Dynasty found themselves facing drought and famine as the northern wheat fields lay bare. Having just embarked on a series of explorations of the Indian Ocean and beyond by large fleets carrying thousands of men, the emperors called these adventures to a halt, ordered the ships (the most advanced ever built) burned, and directed the ship-building industry to construct only barges that could carry rice from warmer central China to the starving north.

Not until the fifteenth century did the Little Ice Age moderate somewhat (it may be no coincidence that this marked the revival of Atlantic navigation, including Columbus's crossings). But in the mid-sixteenth century the cold returned, not to yield again until the mid-nineteenth—marking the start of the warming trend to which we may now be contributing through our industrial pollution of the atmosphere.

Is the Little Ice Age over? At the moment we have no more evidence to suggest that it is than we have to conclude that it is not. The current warming phase may be just a prelude to the return of the conditions of the thirteenth century, the time of weather extremes that threw Europe into disorder.

The Past 15,000 Years

By going back 15,000 years, we must rely on even less dependable evidence for our reconstruction of climate. There is no written human record of the weather, although archaeologists draw useful conclusions from the seeds, tools, and other artifacts recovered from ancient inhabited sites. And now another line of evidence becomes critical—the geologic record. Just 15,000 years ago, the world was a very different place, and its geology bears witness.

Fifteen thousand years ago, the Earth still was in the grip of a major **glaciation**, which had lasted about 80,000 years. Great ice sheets covered most of northern North America; ice stood as far south as the Ohio River and New York City. Virtually all of what is today Canada was buried under thousands of metres of ice. Much of the United States resembled Siberia. In Europe the ice covered Scandinavia and nearly all of Britain and Ireland. Most of northern Asia

LINK

was under glaciers, and the higher mountains of the Earth (the Rockies, Andes, Alps, and Himalayas among them) lay under icecaps.

Yet there were signs, 15,000 years ago, that this glaciation—known as the Wisconsinan—was coming to an end. The ice had reached its maximum extent just 3000 years earlier, and the margins were melting. Vast amounts of meltwater poured into the US Midwest and flowed into the oceans. Pulverized rock, pebbles, and boulders carried by the ice were deposited by these meltwaters. Landmarks such as the Great Lakes and Cape Cod were in the making.

But the warming phase would not continue without a hiccup. Those melting and thinning ice sheets still covering much of present-day Canada became unstable. Not only had they become less heavy, but they became liquefied at their bases even as they melted around their margins and upper surfaces. About 12,000 years ago, one of those ice sheets slid into the North Atlantic, causing disastrous waves along its coasts and chilling the ocean right back to glaciation-like temperatures. This event, named the *Younger Dryas* after a tundra wildflower, must have been catastrophic for thousands of people living in coastal zones at ever-higher latitudes. Those who survived the flooding were confronted with glacial conditions unlike anything felt for several thousand years. But the Younger Dryas was a short-lived event. Within a thousand years, the post-Wisconsinan warming had resumed and the remaining glaciers had resumed their recession. The end of this Younger Dryas episode, about 11,000 years ago, therefore marks the start of the *Holocene* epoch on most geologic calendars.

By about 10,000 years ago, therefore, it would have been clear to modern scientists that this was no ordinary, brief interlude of the kind experienced so many times during the Wisconsinan glaciation. This would be a new epoch of sustained warmth lasting thousands of years, one truly **interglacial** (the term for a prolonged warm period between glaciations). By about 7000 years ago, the great ice sheets had melted away approximately to their present dimensions, and for about 2000 years the Earth was even warmer than it is today. Since then, the global climate appears to have been not only warm but also relatively stable. Even the fluctuations of the Little Ice Age are mild aberrations against the background of a full-scale glaciation.

One lesson learned from research into the Holocene (the epoch that has witnessed the entire drama of the emergence of human civilization) is that reversals of temperature are sudden and seem to be preceded by opposite trends. For example, the warmest period of the Holocene was preceded by the temporary but severe cooling of the Younger Dryas. As in the case of the Little Ice Age, trends in one direction seem to presage sudden reversals to the other. This is one concern arising from the current 'greenhouse warming' phenomenon—that this global warming, far from foreshadowing an overheated world, portends a precipitous return to full-scale glaciation.

The Past 150,000 Years

One hundred and fifty thousand years ago, the Earth was locked in another great glaciation, which preceded the Wisconsinan. We have the geologic evidence to confirm that this glaciation, too, was experienced worldwide and spread its ice sheets deep into the heart of the present-day US. Of particular interest is the warm spell that separated this glaciation from its successor, because this interglacial is similar to the Holocene epoch of today.

This warm spell, called the Eemian interglacial, began about 130,000 years ago and lasted about 10,000 years. Evidence from ice cores taken from the Greenland Ice Sheet, which has survived the interglacials and carries valuable information, indicates that the Eemian resembled the Holocene in some ways but differed in others. One similarity lies in the timing of maximum warmth: like the Holocene, the Eemian began with nearly 3000 years of high temperatures, but even higher than those of the early Holocene. Then, the Eemian's equable climate was frequently interrupted by cold episodes much more severe than those we have known during the Holocene.

The well-defined length of the Eemian—just 10,000 years—gives rise to concern. The Holocene already has lasted longer, and the question is, how long will our interglacial continue? When the Eemian ended, one last surge of rising temperatures was summarily terminated by a massive onset of severe cold. That cold marked the beginning of 110,000 years of global glaciation, interrupted only by a comparatively slight warming (about halfway through), which was not intense enough to be called a true interglacial.

We should also take note of a cataclysmic event that occurred during the period under discussion. About 73,000 years ago, a huge volcanic eruption took place on the Indonesian island of Sumbawa, where the volcano named Toba exploded and spewed vast quantities of ash and dust high into the atmosphere. The Earth already was in the grip of a glaciation. Now the crucial tropical latitudes were deprived of sunlight as these airborne ejected materials were carried around the globe by high-altitude winds. Anthropologists and archaeologists report that humankind came very close to extinction during this twin assault by nature. When the skies finally cleared, there was little to suggest that the next interglacial would witness the rise of modern civilization.

The Past 1,500,000 Years

The sequence just described—of long-lasting glaciations separated by relatively brief interglacials—has marked the last 1.5 million years and beyond. The past 1.5 million years constitute almost all of an intensified phase of the Late Cenozoic Ice Age, which began about 1.8 million years ago. The word 'intensified' is appropriate, because the cooling that foreshadowed this period began more than 30 million years ago and followed a significant drop in global temperatures during the Pliocene epoch

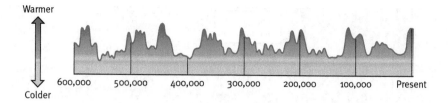

Figure 18.8 Graph of surface temperature changes over the past 600,000 years, based on a composite of seven independent estimates, demonstrating the repeated alternation between cold and warm conditions.

around 6 million years ago. By the time this subsequent *Pleistocene* epoch began, primates and hominids that had survived the Pliocene cooling were those best able to accommodate sudden swings in climate.

The Pleistocene is sometimes misnamed an ice age, but in fact it is only the most recent phase of the Late Cenozoic Ice Age, which has witnessed the rise of mammals and of humanity. It is an epoch marked by repeated glacial advances and recessions—perhaps as many as 20 over its 1.8-million-year span. The last four of these advances are the best known, and the latest, the Wisconsinan, is the one whose end led to the warmth we enjoy today. In turn, the start of the Wisconsinan glaciation marked the end of the previous warm phase, the Eemian.

It has become clear that the Pleistocene epoch marked the depth of the Late Cenozoic Ice Age: for most of its nearly 2 million years the Earth has been frigid, with only brief warm interglacials. Figure 18.8 suggests what conditions may have been like over the past approximately 600,000 years—glaciations last around 100,000 years; warm interglacials average about 10,000 years. It is a datum that should give us pause. Temperatures fluctuate somewhat during interglacials (witness the Little Ice Age and the Medieval Optimum). What would happen if the current warming phase ended as suddenly as the Eemian did, and nearly 7 billion people faced the prospect of a rapidly cooling, drying Earth?

Issues relating to ice ages and glaciations will be examined in Part Four, but the foregoing raises a general question: what is 'normal' for our planet? Ice ages are known to last for tens of millions of years, but the Earth is 4.6 billion years old, and all the known ice ages together span no more than 10 per cent of this lifetime. Indeed, scientists report that most evidence points to an overall warm planetary climate, with temperatures about 5°C higher than those of the Late Cenozoic. Such balmy conditions, familiar to the dinosaurs if not to us, seem to have prevailed ever since the Snowball Earth episode, and possibly longer than that.

The Mechanisms of Climate Change

The picture of past climates and their variations that we have just sketched is still a hazy one. It does become clearer as we focus on more recent times, but there is still a need for more information. One fact, however, will be apparent to you by now—climates certainly do change. But how?

One of the issues related to climate change is that there are many probable causes, all acting at different scales in time and geographic space. A further complicating factor is that many forces shaping climate are linked and interact with one another, so that changes in one trigger changes in others. As if this were not enough, there are still gaps in our knowledge of the exact way the atmosphere and the oceans operate, both separately and in tandem. And there may even be additional major variables that have not yet been considered.

Given these difficulties, a framework for ideas and facts concerning the causes of climatic change can nonetheless be compiled. But first the parameters of the system within which climate changes take place must be specified. This system cannot deal with the atmosphere alone: it must also account for the ice of the cryosphere as well as the oceanic component of the hydrosphere. Such an interlinked atmosphere–ocean–ice–Earth system is shown in Figure 18.9. Within this system, both the heat-energy system and the hydrologic cycle are at work; moreover, the diagram models the interactions of wind, ice, and ocean characteristics (including surface currents). Outside the climatic system, a number of boxes list forces, such as a change in radiation coming from the Sun, that have the power to alter the system externally. The important thing to remember is that a change in any one or more of these processes creates a climatic change.

External Processes

At night any particular Earth location receives far less radiation from the Sun than during the day. In a similar way, solar radiation changing over a longer period of time affects the Earth's climate. There are both short-term and long-term variations in the behaviour of the Sun. Short-term changes take place when storm areas occur on the surface of the Sun; these are called **sunspots** and occur in cycles that peak about every 11 years (Figure 18.10 shows sunspots at their maximum and minimum development). Sunspots may also affect terrestrial weather, but research findings are still inconclusive as to whether they significantly influence the amount of solar radiation received at the Earth's surface.

Longer-term changes also occur because of three cyclical peculiarities in the orientation of the Earth's orbit and axis. One is a periodic variation in the shape of the Earth's orbit around the Sun (Figure 18.11A). During cycles lasting

LINK

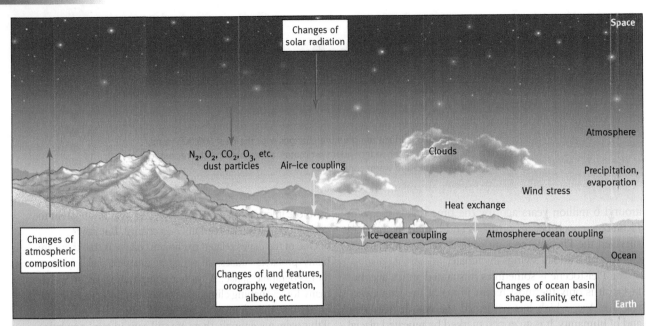

Figure 18.9   Atmosphere–ocean–ice–Earth climatic system. Red arrows denote external processes; yellow arrows indicate internal processes.

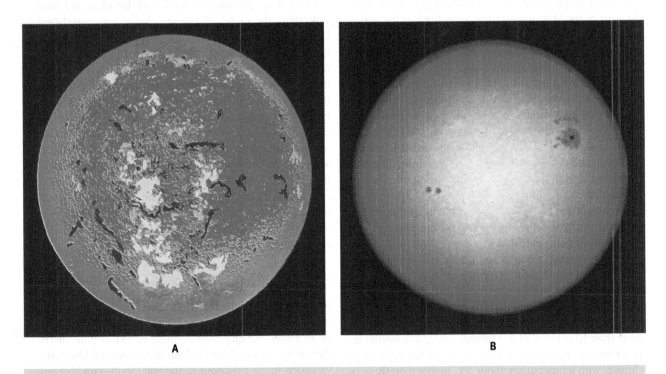

Figure 18.10   Two views of the Sun, showing an occurrence of sunspots (A) and intervening normalcy (B). The dark colour of the sunspots reflects the reduced temperatures in these areas on the Sun's surface. Scientists theorize that intense localized magnetic fields interfere with the convection process that brings hot material to the surface. Sunspots develop in cycles that peak approximately every 11 years, and their occurrence brings an increase in the solar wind, resulting in enhanced auroras (see p. 73) and interference in radio transmissions on and from Earth.

about 100,000 years, the Earth's orbit 'stretches' from nearly circular to markedly elliptical and back to nearly circular. The resulting fluctuation in the distance between the Earth and Sun is as much as 17.5 million km. Another

variation in the Earth–Sun relationship, which follows an approximately 41,000-year cycle, is due to the oblique-ness of the Earth's axis. In other words, the Earth 'rolls' like a ship (Figure 18.11B), so that the angle between

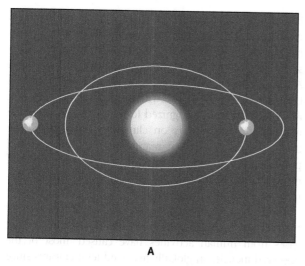
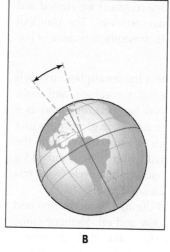
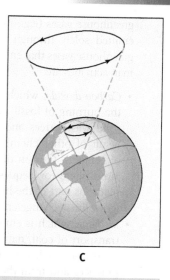

Figure 18.11   Long-term changes in the Earth's orbit and axis: (A) stretch, (B) roll, (C) wobble.

our planet's axis and the plane of the ecliptic (see Unit 4) changes from 65.6 to 68.2 degrees (the present angle of 66.5 degrees is therefore not constant). The major effect of this axial shifting is to alter the annual distribution of solar radiation received at the surface. The third variation might best be described as a 'wobble' because, like a spinning top, the Earth's axis swivels once every 21,000 years or so (Figure 18.11C). This affects the distance between the Earth and the Sun during any given season, which gradually changes as the cycle proceeds.

These variations individually produce episodes of some cooling and warming. But when the cooling periods of all three cycles coincide, the variation in solar radiation estimated to reach the Earth is strikingly parallel to the waxing and waning of the global ice cover over the past 1.5 million years. However, these orbital and axial variations presumably also took place during the 90 per cent of Earth history when ice ages did not occur.

Other external processes that might lead to climatic change are considered elsewhere in this book (start with the 'Perspectives' box in Unit 36). They include volcanism (the subject of Unit 25), the uplifting and wearing away of the land surface (Units 24, 28, and 29), the shifting distribution of landmasses and oceans caused by plate tectonics (Unit 24), and the hypothesized intensification of the greenhouse effect (Unit 6).

Internal Processes

LINK Units 6 through 13 describe the heat and water exchanges within the atmosphere, the way the general circulation distributes heat and moisture across wide areas of the Earth, and the weather systems forming the fine grain of atmospheric movement and operation. All these are internal processes, and many of them function as systems by themselves. Although changes in any one of them could lead to climatic variation, they are linked by feedback mechanisms (see Unit 1).

An increase in unusual variations in ocean temperature provides an example of *positive feedback*. A change in the temperature of the sea surface may modify the amount of sensible heat transferred to the overlying air, thereby altering atmospheric circulation and cloudiness. Variations in radiation, wind-driven mixing of ocean water, and other factors may, in turn, affect the temperature of the original ocean surface. In the tropical Pacific Ocean, the sea-surface temperature has increased for several years at a time because of positive feedback mechanisms such as those just described.

An example of *negative feedback* occurs when a snow-covered surface reduces atmospheric temperatures. The cooler atmosphere holds less water vapour, and thus less snow falls; Antarctica's low precipitation levels are partly a result of such negative feedback. Many other examples of both positive and negative feedback exist. Researchers today are particularly interested in *teleconnections*, newly discovered relationships between weather phenomena that involve distant parts of the globe.

Anthropogenic Forces

Anthropogenic factors are human activities that change the environment and influence climate. Various hypotheses for human-induced climate change have been debated for many years, although the scientific debate has moved on from skepticism, as there is consensus that human activity is the main contributor for the current rapid climate changes. The biggest factor of present concern is the increase in CO_2 levels due to emissions from fossil fuel combustion. Other factors, including aerosol emissions, land use, ozone depletion, animal agriculture, and deforestation, also affect climate.

Gases that trap heat in the atmosphere are often called **greenhouse gases**. Some greenhouse gases such as carbon dioxide occur naturally and are emitted to the atmosphere through natural processes and human activities. Other greenhouse gases (e.g., fluorinated gases) are created and emitted solely through human activities. The principal greenhouse gases that enter the atmosphere because of human activities are:

- *Carbon dioxide*, which enters the atmosphere through the burning of fossil fuels (oil, natural gas, and coal), solid waste, trees and wood products, and also as a result of other chemical reactions (e.g., manufacture of cement). Carbon dioxide is also removed from the atmosphere (or 'sequestered') when it is absorbed by plants as part of the biological carbon cycle (www.epa.gov/climatechange/emissions/co2.html).
- *Methane*, which is emitted during the production and transport of coal, natural gas, and oil. Methane emissions also result from livestock and other agricultural practices and from the decay of organic waste in municipal solid waste landfills (www.epa.gov/methane/sources.html).
- *Nitrous oxide*, which is emitted during agricultural and industrial activities, as well as during combustion of fossil fuels and solid waste (www.epa.gov/nitrousoxide/sources.html).
- *Hydrofluorocarbons, perfluorocarbons,* and *sulphur hexafluoride*, which are synthetic, powerful greenhouse gases that are emitted from a variety of industrial processes. Fluorinated gases are sometimes used as substitutes for ozone (i.e., CFCs, HCFCs, and halons). These gases are typically emitted in smaller quantities, but because they are potent greenhouse gases, they are sometimes referred to as High Global Warming Potential (GWP) gases (www.epa.gov/highgwp/sources.html).

Many, but not all, human sources of greenhouse gas emissions are expected to rise in the future. This growth may be reduced by ongoing efforts to increase the use of newer, cleaner technologies and other measures. In addition, our everyday choices about such things as commuting, housing, electricity use, and recycling can influence the amount of greenhouse gases being emitted (see 'Perspectives' box for ways to reduce your personal emissions).

The Climatic Future

Perhaps one of the greatest agents of climatic change in the coming decades and centuries will be those that are anthropogenically induced. If we understand the mechanisms of climate, is it possible to predict the climatic future of the Earth? Unfortunately, despite the availability of better information than ever before and the advances in knowledge that have recently taken place, forecasting climates remains a difficult challenge. These constraints notwithstanding, it is still possible to conjecture what lies ahead.

The most recent (fourth) report of the Intergovernmental Panel on Climate Change (IPCC) provides a status report as well as future projections of climate change scenarios. The IPCC was established in 1988 by the World Meteorological Organization (WMO) and the United Nations Environment

Programme (UNEP) and is mandated with assessing the most up-to-date scientific, technical, and socio-economic research in climate change. The IPCC produced major assessment reports in 1990, 1995, and 2001, and its *Fourth Assessment Report* was completed in 2007. The IPCC shared the 2007 Nobel Peace Prize with former US Vice-President Al Gore, who were recognized for helping to educate the international community on climate change issues. The IPCC bases its assessment mainly on peer-reviewed and published scientific literature. National and international responses to climate change generally regard the UN climate panel as authoritative.

The 2007 IPCC report finds that it is 'very likely' (greater than 90 per cent likelihood) that emissions of heat-trapping gases from human activities have caused 'most of the observed increase in globally averaged temperatures since the mid-twentieth century'. Evidence that human activities are the major cause of recent climate change is even stronger than in prior assessments. The report concludes that it is 'unequivocal' that Earth's climate is warming, 'as is now evident from observations of increases in global average air and ocean temperatures, widespread melting of snow and ice, and rising global mean sea level'. The report also confirms that the current atmospheric concentration of carbon dioxide and methane 'exceeds by far the natural range over the last 650,000 years'. Since the dawn of the industrial era, concentrations of both gases have increased at a rate that is 'very likely to have been unprecedented in more than 10,000 years'.

Additional IPCC findings on recent climate change include:

Rising Temperatures
- Eleven of the last 12 years rank among the 12 hottest years on record (since 1850, when sufficient worldwide temperature measurements began).
- Over the last 50 years, 'cold days, cold nights, and frost have become less frequent, while hot days, hot nights, and heat waves have become more frequent.'

Increasingly Severe Weather (storms, precipitation, drought)
- The intensity of tropical cyclones (hurricanes) in the North Atlantic has increased over the past 30 years, which correlates with increases in tropical sea surface temperatures.
- Storms with heavy precipitation have increased in frequency over most land areas. Between 1900 and 2005, long-term trends show significantly increased precipitation in eastern parts of North and South America, northern Europe, and northern and central Asia.
- Between 1900 and 2005, the Sahel (the boundary zone between the Sahara desert and more fertile regions of Africa to the south), the Mediterranean, southern Africa, and parts of southern Asia have become drier, adding stress to water resources in these regions.
- Droughts have become longer and more intense, and have affected larger areas since the 1970s, especially in the tropics and subtropics.

LINK

Melting and Thawing

- Since 1900 the Northern Hemisphere has lost 7 per cent of the maximum area covered by seasonally frozen ground.
- Mountain glaciers and snow cover have declined worldwide.
- Satellite data since 1978 show that the extent of Arctic sea ice during the summer has shrunk by more than 20 per cent.

Rising Sea Levels

- Since 1961, the world's oceans have been absorbing more than 80 per cent of the heat added to the climate, causing ocean water to expand and contributing to rising sea levels. Between 1993 and 2003 ocean expansion was the largest contributor to sea-level rise.
- Melting glaciers and losses from the Greenland and Antarctic ice sheets have also contributed to recent sea-level rise.

Projected climate change for the second half of this century depends on the level of future heat-trapping emissions.

The IPCC based its projections on six emission scenarios, running each one through sophisticated climate simulation programs. The lowest temperatures currently projected for the end of this century, representing the lowest scenario the IPCC chose to evaluate, assume a mid-century peak in global population, a rapid change towards a service and information economy, and a shift towards clean and resource-efficient technologies. The highest temperatures projected for the end of this century represent the highest scenario the IPCC chose to evaluate, which assumes a mid-century peak in global population, rapid economic growth, and 'fossil-intensive' energy production and consumption. Even if we act today to reduce our emissions from cars, power plants, land use, and other sources, we will see some degree of continued warming because past emissions will stay in the atmosphere for decades or more. If we take no action to reduce emissions, the IPCC concludes that there will be twice as much warming over the next two decades than if we had stabilized heat-trapping gases and other climate-relevant pollutants in the atmosphere at their year 2000 levels.

Perspectives on the Human Environment

Reducing Our Carbon Footprint

A **carbon footprint** is a measure of the impact human activities have on the environment in terms of the amount of greenhouse gases produced, measured in units of carbon dioxide. This concept is intended to be useful for individuals and organizations to attempt to quantify their personal (or organizational) impact in contributing to global warming. In other words, when you drive a car, the engine burns fuel that creates a certain amount of carbon dioxide (CO_2), depending on its fuel consumption and the driving distance. When you heat your house with oil or gas, you also generate CO_2. Even if you heat your house with electricity, the generation of the electrical power may also have emitted a certain amount of CO_2. When you buy food and products, the production of the food and goods also emitted some quantities of CO_2.

Your carbon footprint is the sum of all emissions of CO_2 that were induced by your activities in a given time frame. Usually a carbon footprint is calculated for the time period of a year. The carbon footprint is a very powerful tool for understanding the impact of personal behaviour on global warming. Most people are shocked when they see the amount of CO_2 their activities create. If you choose to minimize your carbon emissions, the calculation and constant monitoring of your personal carbon footprint is important.

By measuring the carbon footprint through such tools as carbon calculators, we can get a better sense of what the individual impact is and which parts of our lifestyle deserve the greatest attention. There are dozens of carbon calculators available on the Internet; one endorsed by numerous Canadian researchers is the 'zerofootprint' calculator (www.zerofootprint. net/). Zerofootprint provides information, products, and services for the global network of consumers and businesses who wish to reduce their environmental impact. There are carbon calculators tailored specifically for children,

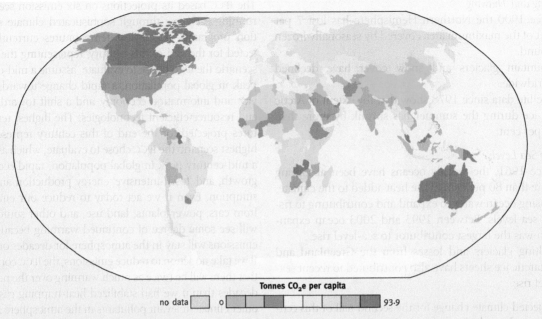

Figure 18.12   Per capita greenhouse gas emissions by country in 2000 (including land-use change).

Tonnes CO$_2$e per capita

no data   0   93.9

adults, and organizations. A number of studies have calculated the carbon footprints of organizations and nations. One such study examined age-related carbon emissions based on expenditure and consumption. The study found that on average people aged 50–65 years have higher individual carbon footprints than those in any other age group. Studies have been conducted on the basis of education and income, and one found that those with the highest education and income levels had the largest carbon footprint (as a result of having greater purchasing power coupled with poor choices).

In many instances, reducing your personal carbon footprint costs nothing and can be implemented immediately:

- Sign up with a green energy supplier that generates electricity from renewable sources (such as wind power). One example is Bullfrog Power in Ontario.
- Turn off and unplug electrical items when not in use (e.g., lights, television, DVD player, stereo equipment, computer).
- Turn down the heat (try just 1–2°C).
- Check the central heating timer setting—remember, there is no point heating the house after you have left for work.
- Fill your dishwasher and washing machine with a full load—this will save you water, electricity, and washing powder.
- Unplug your cellphone as soon as it has finished charging.

- Hang out the washing to dry rather than using a clothes dryer.
- Only drive when you really need to. Walk, bike, carpool, or take transit to get to one of your regular destinations each week.
- Take care of your trash. Compost all organic waste, recycle paper, cardboard, cans, and bottles. This will help reduce the greenhouse gas emissions associated with landfills.
- Eat wisely. Choose foods that are local, organic, and low on the food chain whenever possible. Make the most of seasonal foods.
- Don't buy bottled water if your tap water is safe to drink (especially if the bottled water has been shipped from far away).
- Don't buy overly packaged products.
- Turn off your office computer at the end of the day and turn the lights off when you leave the room.

Things you can gradually implement over the longer term also can result in savings on your energy bills:

- Use energy-saving light bulbs.
- Insulate your hot water tank; add insulation to the loft/attic and walls.
- Replace your old fridge/freezer (if it is over 15 years old) with a new energy-efficient one.
- Choose energy-efficient appliances when others need replacing (stove, washer, etc.).
- Check the Canadian government's Auto Smart ratings for the next car you intend to buy to make sure it's fuel-efficient and low-polluting.

- Learn about the impacts of air travel and consider vacationing close to home.

In addition, when you do have to travel by air, car, train, or bus, you can theoretically 'neutralize' your emissions of carbon dioxide by purchasing a 'carbon offset'. A 'carbon offset' is an emission reduction credit from another organization's project that results in less carbon dioxide or other greenhouse gases in the atmosphere than would otherwise occur. Carbon offsets are typically measured in tons of CO_2 equivalents (or 'CO_2e') and are bought and sold through a number of international brokers, on-line retailers, and trading platforms. Critics of this system, however, say that they allow people to justify their indulgences and simply pay to emit. Buyers need to choose their offsets carefully, particularly as the offset market is largely unregulated. The 'Gold Standard' is widely considered to be the highest standard in the world for carbon offsets. It ensures that key environmental criteria have been met by offset projects that carry its label. Only offsets from energy efficiency and renewable energy projects qualify for the Gold Standard, as these projects encourage a shift away from fossil fuel use (www.cdmgoldstandard.org/).

KEY TERMS

carbon footprint   *page 259*
climate change   *page 248*
glaciation   *page 253*
global warming   *page 252*
greenhouse gases   *page 257*
ice core   *page 249*

interglacial   *page 254*
Little Ice Age   *page 253*
Medieval Optimum   *page 253*
sediment core   *page 249*
sunspots   *page 255*

REVIEW QUESTIONS

1. What are proxy climatic data, and why are they important in the reconstruction of past climates?
2. Describe the general climatic history of the past 1.5 million years.
3. What is the Late Cenozoic Ice Age?
4. Describe the primary external processes that might contribute to climatic fluctuations.
5. What is a carbon footprint? How can it be reduced?

REFERENCES AND FURTHER READINGS

Balling, R.C., Jr. 1992. *The Heated Debate: Greenhouse Predictions versus Climate Reality*. San Francisco: Pacific Research Institute for Public Policy.

Bigg, G.R. 1996. *The Oceans and Climate*. New York: Cambridge Univ. Press.

Bradley, R.S. 2000. 'Past Global Changes and Their Significance for the Future', *Quaternary Science Reviews* 19: 391–402.

———, and P. Jones, eds. 1995. *Climate Since A.D. 1500*, 2nd edn. London/New York: Routledge.

Bryson, R.A. 1988. 'What the Climatic Past Tells Us about the Environmental Future', in H.J. de Blij, ed., *Earth '88: Changing Geographic Perspectives*. Washington: National Geographic Society, 230–46.

Burroughs, W. 1999. *The Climate Revealed*. New York: Cambridge Univ. Press.

Cohen, S., B. Bass, D. Etkin, B. Jones, J. Lacroix, B. Mills, D. Scott, and G.C. van Kooten. 2004. 'Regional Adaptation Strategies', in H. Coward and A. Weaver, eds, *Hard Choices: Climate Change in Canada*. Waterloo, Ont.: Wilfrid Laurier Univ. Press, 151–78.

Cronin, T.M. 1999. *Principles of Paleoclimatology*. New York: Columbia Univ. Press.

Crowley, T.J. 2000. 'Causes of Climate Change over the Past 1000 years', *Science* 289 (14 July): 270–7. At: <www.ncdc.noaa.gov/paleo/pubs/crowley.html>.

Fagan, B. 2000. *The Little Ice Age: How Climate Made History, 1300–1850*. New York: Basic Books.

Glantz, M.H., ed. 2002. *La Niña and Its Impacts: Facts and Speculation*. Tokyo: United Nations Univ. Press.

Grove, J.M. 1988. *The Little Ice Age*. London/New York: Methuen.

Hoyt, D.V., and K.H. Schatten. 1997. *The Role of the Sun in Climate Change*. New York: Oxford Univ. Press.

Intergovernmental Panel on Climate Change (IPCC). 2007. Working Group I: The Physical Basis of Climate Change. Working Group I Contribution to the *Fourth Assessment Report of the IPCC Intergovernmental Panel on Climate Change*. Cambridge: Cambridge Univ. Press.

Kondratyev, K.Y., and A.P. Cracknell. 1998. *Observing Global Climate Change*. Bristol, Penn.: Taylor & Francis.

Kraus, E.B., and J.A. Businger. 1994. *Atmosphere–Ocean Interaction*, 2nd edn. New York: Oxford Univ. Press.

Lamb, H.H. 1995. *Climate, History, and the Modern World*, 2nd edn. London/New York: Routledge.

Monbiot, G. 2007. *Heat: How to Stop the Planet from Burning*. Toronto: Doubleday Canada.

Otberg, R.I., and T.K. Rabb. 1981. *Climate and History*. Princeton, NJ: Princeton Univ. Press.

Ruddimann, W.F. 2000. *Earth's Climate: Past and Future*. New York: Freeman.

Silver, C.S., and R.S. de Fries. 1990. *One Earth, One Future: Our Changing Global Environment*. Washington: National Academy Press.

Stevens, W.K. 2000. *The Change in the Weather: People, Weather, and the Science of Climate*. New York: Delacorte Press.

Wilson, R.C.L., S.A. Drury, and J.A. Chapman, eds. 2000. *The Great Ice Age: Climate Change and Life*. London/New York: Routledge.

Wrogjt, H.E., et al. 1994. *Global Climates Since the Last Glacial Maximum*. Minneapolis: Univ. of Minnesota Press.

 ## WEB RESOURCES

adaptation.nrcan.gc.ca/index_e.php Natural Resources Canada home page for climate change impacts and adaptation.

paoc.mit.edu/paoc/research/abrupt.asp Climate change research at MIT.

www.giss.nasa.gov NASA's Goddard Institute for Space Studies website includes extensive climate change information, as well as videos.

www.ipcc.ch/ Intergovernmental Panel on Climate Change.

www.ncdc.noaa.gov/paleo/abrupt/index.html A paleo perspective on abrupt climate change from the National Climatic Data Center of the National Oceanographic and Atmospheric Administration in the US.

www.realclimate.org/ Climate science blog.

www.ucsusa.org/global_warming/science/ipcc-highlights1.html Union of Concerned Scientists site on Global Warming.

Human–Climate Interactions and Impacts

Objectives

- To relate our understanding of atmospheric processes to the human environment.

- To illustrate the utility of using energy balance concepts to characterize systems of the human environment.

- To focus on several of the impacts humans have had, and may come to have, on our climatic environment.

This closing unit on the physical geography of the atmosphere treats some key relationships between humans and their climatic environment, and highlights the impact of human activities on the functioning of climate at various scales. The unit begins by specifying the interaction of the human body with its immediate surroundings and shows how our comfort depends on access to adequate shelter. Most modern dwellings tend to be clustered in urban areas that exhibit **microclimates** (climate regions on a localized scale) of their own. The cities that anchor this metropolitan landscape usually contain concentrations of the wrong things in the wrong place at the wrong time—a phenomenon known as pollution. We examine those aspects of pollution that occur in the atmosphere and how urban air affects the surrounding countryside. Our inquiry then expands to the macroscale as we briefly discuss humankind as a possible agent of world climatic change. We therefore proceed from the level of the individual to that of the entire globe. A good way to start that progression is to consider the human body as a heating and cooling system.

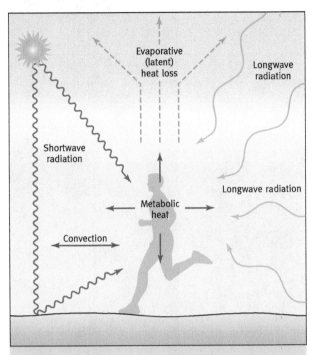

Figure 19.1   Heat-energy flows to and from the human body.

The Heat Balance of the Human Body

Unit 6 describes the concept of heat balance with respect to the surface of the Earth. The idea of examining the flows of heat energy to and from an object can usefully be applied to the human body as well. It is essential that the internal temperature of our bodies remain at about 37°C. Depending on the person, temperature fluctuations exceeding 3–6°C result in death. The body, therefore, has to be kept within a very limited range of temperature by regulating the flows of heat to and from it. Four kinds of heat flows can be altered—radiant, metabolic, evaporative, and convectional—and they are diagrammed in Figure 19.1.

First, humans all live in a radiation environment. We receive shortwave radiation from the Sun and longwave radiation from our surroundings—clothing, walls, the planetary surface, and other objects. Humans also emit longwave radiation. Our radiation balance, the sum of incoming and outgoing radiation, can be positive or negative, depending on our environment. More often than not, the balance is a positive one, so net radiation is usually a heat gain for us, especially during daylight hours.

Another heat gain is the heat that our bodies produce, called **metabolic heat**. The body produces metabolic heat by converting the chemical energy in the food we assimilate into heat energy. The amount of metabolic heat we produce depends on, among other things, our age, activity level, and environmental temperature. An older person at rest produces metabolic heat equal to that used to power a 75-watt lightbulb. A five-year-old child produces the equivalent of 120 watts, and an active adult about 260 watts (this rate could double if the adult were, for example, playing tennis). We produce even more metabolic heat when exposed to colder temperatures. At 33°C an adult creates 3100 calories (cal) per day, whereas at 0°C an adult's metabolism creates 3930 cal per day.

Metabolic heat is always a heat source to the human body. But the evaporation of water from the skin through perspiration is always a heat loss. Perspiring is a vital function, because some of the heat used in evaporating the perspired water is taken from the body and thereby cools it down. One of the factors determining how much evaporation can take place is the amount of water vapour already present in the surrounding air, as measured by relative humidity. As we all know, we can feel fairly comfortable on a hot day if the relative humidity is low, but we feel distinctly uncomfortable, even at a lower temperature, if the humidity is high. You can see in Figure 19.2 that if other heat losses and gains are kept constant, relative humidity acts as an index of how efficient our evaporative cooling system is. It could even become a deciding factor between life and death.

Finally, a flow of sensible heat can act as either a cooling or as a heating mechanism, depending on the relative temperatures of the body and the air, by means of a *convectional* heat flow. Hot air blowing onto our bodies makes us gain heat, whereas a cold wind leads to a rapid heat loss. When we breathe, we pass air into and out of our lungs; this air may be warmer or cooler than our lungs. For convenience, we can regard the loss or gain of heat through breathing as a convective heat flow.

Our bodies consciously and unconsciously regulate these four types of heat flows so that the body temperature stays within the narrow vital range. For example, if our environmental temperature changes over a short period of time from 40°C to 10°C, the metabolic heat production might stay the same, as Figure 19.3 shows. But radiant and convectional heat flows change from being a slight heat

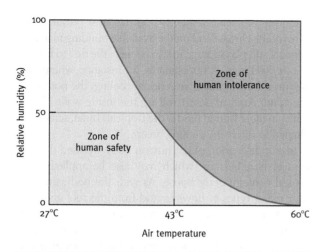

Figure 19.2 Limitation imposed on our evaporative cooling system by relative humidity.

gain to being a marked heat loss. Evaporative cooling of the body moves from a high level to a relatively low level in the cooler environment. Many of our feelings of comfort or discomfort and almost all of our artificial adaptations to the environment, such as shelter and clothing, are related to the balance of these energy flows that maintain our constant internal temperature.

Too Cold or Too Hot?

Extreme cold temperatures are associated with continental arctic air masses, but the actual temperature reached depends specifically on the nature of the cold air mass and where it originated. Although cold temperatures are dangerous in their own right, they become more so in conjunction with strong winds. The combination produces a *wind chill* factor—heat loss measured in watts/m^2 (W/m^2). On a calm day, our bodies insulate us somewhat from the outside temperature

LINK

by warming up a thin layer of air close to our skin, known as the boundary layer. When the wind blows, it takes this protective layer away, exposing our skin to the outside air. It takes energy for our bodies to warm up a new layer, and if each one keeps getting blown away, our skin temperature will drop and we will feel colder. Many groups and organizations use the wind chill system to regulate their outdoor activities. Schools use wind chill information to decide whether it is safe for children to go outdoors at recess. Hockey clubs cancel outdoor practices when the wind chill is too cold. People who work outside for a living, such as construction workers and ski-lift operators, are required to take indoor breaks to warm up if wind chill conditions are severe.

In 2001, a team of scientists and medical experts from Canada and the United States worked together to develop a new wind chill index (see Table 8.1). The research branch of the Canadian Department of National Defence, already familiar with the issue because of its knowledge about how troops are affected by cold weather, contributed to the effort by conducting experiments using human volunteers. In Canada, exposure to extreme cold claims more lives directly than any other atmospheric extreme.

On the other end of the temperature spectrum, a *heat wave* can be thought of as a period of unusually hot weather, but according to Environment Canada's more scientific and absolute definition (1996), it is a period of more than three consecutive days of maximum temperature at or above 32°C. The adverse effects of heat on humans, however, have been observed at less extreme temperatures and for shorter durations. Heat waves have notable effects on human mortality, regional economies, and ecosystems.

Two well-documented international examples are the Paris heat wave of August 2003 and the Chicago heat wave of 1995. Across Central Europe, 2003 was the hottest summer recorded since 1500. The Paris heat wave was considered responsible for the death of an estimated 14,802 individuals, the large majority of whom were elderly

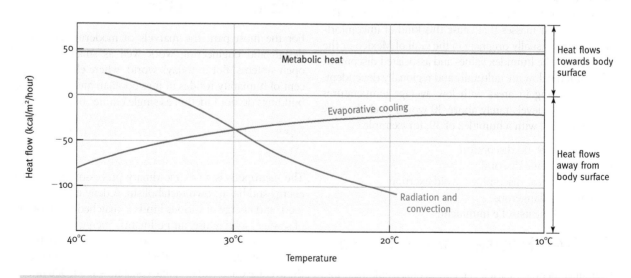

Figure 19.3 Adjustment of heat flows under changing environmental temperatures to maintain a constant internal body temperature.

individuals over the age of 75. Heat waves in the United States in 1980 and 1988 resulted in an estimated 10,000 and 5,000–10,000 deaths, respectively. The public health measures that were implemented in many parts of Europe after the 2003 heat wave have centred almost exclusively on heat health-warning systems that use forecasts of high-risk weather conditions to trigger public warnings. The 1995 Chicago heat wave led to approximately 600 heat-related deaths over a period of five days as temperatures soared to 41°C in mid-July of that year. Impacts from the Chicago heat wave were aggravated by inadequate warnings, power failures, inadequate ambulance service and hospital facilities, and lack of preparedness.

Several characteristics of heat waves, such as their frequency, duration, and intensity, affect their impact. If cooling occurs in the evening to offer relief from daily highs, their effects are not as severe. In areas where hot and humid summer conditions are common, physiological, behavioural, and infrastructural adaptations are likely to have taken place, reducing the harmful effects of heat stress. In areas where extremely hot weather is relatively uncommon, such adaptations are less likely to have been made, leaving populations more vulnerable to harmful effects. No population, however, is completely immune to very hot weather, and studies generally indicate that mortality increases at extreme temperatures.

High *humidity* is often associated with heat waves and is a general term that refers to the concentration of water vapour in the atmosphere (discussed in detail in Unit 11). The **humidex** is a Canadian innovation, first used in 1965, that was devised to describe how hot, humid weather feels to the average person. The humidex combines temperature and humidity into one number to reflect the perceived temperature. Because it takes into account the two most important factors that affect summer comfort, it can more accurately convey how stifling the air actually feels than either factor can do alone. The humidex is widely used in Canada, although extremely high readings are rare except in the southern regions of Ontario, Manitoba, and Quebec. Generally, the humidex decreases as latitude increases. The hot, humid air masses that cause this kind of uncomfortable weather usually originate in the Gulf of Mexico or the Caribbean. The humidex values and associated discomfort levels listed below are culturally and regionally dependent. People residing in areas with low average temperatures and humidity levels rarely above 30 would likely be very uncomfortable with a humidex of 39, for example.

- Less than 29: no discomfort
- 30 to 39: some discomfort
- 40 to 45: great discomfort; avoid exertion
- Above 45: dangerous
- Above 54: heatstroke imminent.

Shelter, Houses, and Climate

Ever since people first felt the effects of sensible heat loss by winds or an increased evaporative cooling when they were rained upon, they have sought some form of shelter.

The form of shelter depended on the most prevalent features of the climate and on the available building materials. Climate still plays a large role in some of the design features of our dwellings. In hot climates, for instance, where there is a need to promote convectional cooling, the nomads of the Saudi Arabian desert roll up the inside walls of their tents; in more humid (and more tropical) India, screens are aligned to catch any cooling breeze.

In our discussion of the human body we used the concept of heat balance, which may also be applied to the typical contemporary house. As with the body, there are four major types of flows to and from the roof and walls of a house. Instead of—but analogous to—metabolism, the house contains an artificial heating (and/or cooling) system. An artificial heating system usually channels heat from the central interior towards the walls and roof of the building. The evaporative cooling part of the house is normally designed with a sloping roof that removes surface water or snow as rapidly as possible. However, most houses have the important function of reducing the amount of convectional cooling by wind; they provide shelter from the wind and facilitate control of the inside climate via the heating system.

Radiant heating and cooling applies to the outside of a house much as it applies to the body, and architects take it into consideration in several ways. If they want to use radiation for heating the house by means of the greenhouse effect, they can ensure that the windows of the building are open to the direct rays of the Sun. Sometimes they use a partial shade to cut out direct rays coming from high Sun angles in the summer, when heating is not required; but rays from low Sun angles bypass the shade and supply winter heating. Thus, by adapting their designs to the operation of the four factors of the heat balance system, architects can provide our houses with a small environment capable of adjustment to the changing seasonal needs of our bodies.

Urban Microclimates

For the most part, the marvels of modern architectural design and engineering work well as small, individual open systems. But in today's world, where close to 50 per cent of humanity resides in metropolitan areas, individual buildings do not function as single entities but as a group.

Mass, Energy, and Heat in Metropolitan Areas

The metropolis is an extraordinary processor of mass and energy and has its own metabolism. A daily input of water, food, and energy of various kinds is matched by an output of sewage, solid refuse, air pollutants, energy, and materials that have been transformed in some way. The quantities involved can be enormous. Each day, directly or indirectly, the average Canadian urbanite consumes about 500 litres of water, 2 kg of food, and 8 kg of fossil fuel. This is converted into roughly 400 litres of sewage, 2 kg of refuse, and more than 1 kg of air pollution. Multiply these figures by the population of your metropolitan area, and you will get some idea of what a large processor it is, even without including its industrial activities and motor vehicle emissions. Many aspects of this energy use affect the atmosphere of the city, particularly in the production of heat.

In winter, the values of heat produced by a central city and its suburban ring can equal or surpass the amount of heat available from the Sun. All the heat that warms a building eventually transfers to the surrounding air, a process that is quickest where houses are poorly insulated. But an automobile produces enough heat to warm an average house in winter; and if a house were perfectly insulated, one adult could also produce more than enough heat to warm it. Therefore, even without any industrial production of heat, an urban area tends to be warmer than the adjacent countryside.

The burning of fuel, such as by cars, is not the only source of this increased heat. Two other factors contribute to the higher overall temperatures in cities. The first is the heat capacity of the materials that constitute the cityscape, which is dominated by concrete and asphalt. During the day, heat from the Sun can be conducted into these materials and stored—to be released at night. But in the countryside, materials have a significantly lower heat capacity because a vegetative blanket prevents heat from easily flowing into and out of the ground. The second factor is that radiant heat coming into the metropolis from the Sun is trapped in two ways: (1) by a continuing series of reflections among the numerous vertical surfaces that buildings present, and (2) by the **dust dome** (dome-shaped layer of polluted air) that most urban areas spawn. Just as in the greenhouse effect, shortwave radiation from the Sun passes through the pollution dome more easily than outgoing longwave radiation does; the latter is absorbed by the gaseous pollutants of the dome and re-radiated back to the urban surface (Figure 19.4).

LINK

Urban Heat Islands

The above are the reasons why the metropolis will be warmer than its surrounding rural areas, and together they produce the phenomenon known as the **urban heat island**. If we regard isotherms (lines of constant temperature) as analogous to contour lines of elevation on a map, then the distribution of temperatures within a metropolis gives the general impression of an area of higher land—or an island of higher temperatures—set above a more uniform plain. This effect is clearly seen in Figure 19.5, which maps the distribution of average late-winter low (nighttime) temperatures in the heart of metropolitan Montreal.

Note that the mildest temperatures on this surface are recorded above the city centre. From central Montreal, temperatures drop with either elevation (as indicated by adjacent Mont Royal) or with increasing distance from the city centre. At the urban/rural boundary (located at Site 2

Figure 19.4 View of Montreal's urban pollution dome.

at the time this map was originally created in 1978), surface temperatures are 2°C cooler than in the downtown regions of Montreal.

Heat islands develop best under the light wind conditions associated with anticyclones, but in large cities they can form at almost any time. The precise configuration of a heat island depends on several factors. The island can be elongated away from the prevailing wind; pools of cold air can be found over unbuilt parkland and other open space within the metropolis; and sometimes tongues of warmer air follow the courses of rivers. When the heat island is well developed, microscale variations can be extreme. In winter, busy streets in cities can be 1.7°C warmer than the side streets; the areas near traffic lights can be similarly warmer than the areas between them because of the effect of idling cars.

The maximum difference in temperature between neighbouring urban and rural environments is called the **heat-island intensity** for that region. In general, the larger the metropolitan complex is, the greater its heat-island intensity. The actual level of intensity depends on such factors as physical layout, population density, and the productive activities of a metropolis.

Recent studies have shown that some of the greatest heat-island intensities are found in rapidly urbanizing desert environments. For example, Phoenix, Arizona, which is located in the American Southwest, has had a dramatic rise in its summer nighttime temperatures. Average temperatures in the central city have soared by 5.5°C since 1960.

The consequences of higher temperatures in urban areas should not be overlooked. During the 2003 heat wave that extended across much of Europe, the city of Paris, France, was hit particularly hard. Within the urban core, the higher-than-average temperatures rose to 40°C. It has been estimated that in Paris up to 180 people died in one day alone—all linked directly or indirectly to the abnormally high temperatures. A contributing cause of the deaths was believed to be the lack of air conditioning in most European homes, simply because it was not needed before

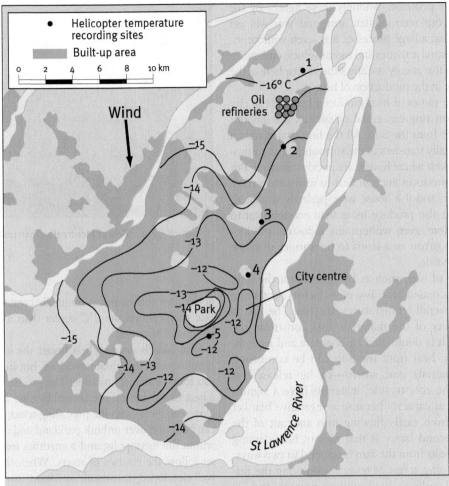

Figure 19.5 Urban heat island of Montreal, as represented by isotherms of mean late-winter low temperatures.

the summer of 2003. That the nation's health system could allow such a death toll became a matter of controversy in France. The European heat wave of 2003 has been linked to unprecedented weather extremes in other parts of the world in the same general period (e.g., the worst drought in recorded history in Australia and massive floods in the United States) and attributed to global warming.

Recent work on so-called **green roofs** (roofs with a vegetated surface and substrate) has proved that they are a promising mechanism to reduce the urban heat-island effect. During warm weather, green roofs reduce the amount of heat transferred through the roof, lowering the energy demands of air-conditioning systems in the buildings. In addition, the vegetated surfaces that replace dark and impervious surfaces act to increase the surface albedo (amount of solar radiation reflected back into the atmosphere). A study of Toronto indicated that if 50 per cent of the city's buildings had green roofs, the temperature reductions could be as great as 2°C in some areas.

Peculiarities of Metropolitan Climates

The surface–atmosphere relationships inside metropolitan areas understandably produce a number of climatic pecu-

liarities. For one thing, the presence or absence of moisture is affected by the special qualities of the urban surface. With much of the built-up landscape impenetrable by water, even gentle rain runs off almost immediately from rooftops, streets, and parking lots. Thus city surfaces, as well as the air above them, tend to be drier between precipitation episodes. With little water available for the cooling process of evaporation, relative humidities are usually lower.

Wind movements are also modified by the cityscape because buildings increase the friction on air flowing over and around them. This tends to slow the speed of winds (by as much as 80 per cent at a height of 30 m), making them far less efficient at dispersing **pollutants** when they travel above large cities. At certain locations within the metropolis, on the other hand, air turbulence increases in association with high-velocity, skyscraper-channelled airflows and wind eddies on street corners. Other unique aspects of city climates originate in the artificially modified air over the urban landscape. As we know, a dust dome forms, which often gives rise to the wind circulation cells shown in Figure 19.6. In the 'Perspectives' box in Unit 7, we discuss the impact of dust domes on the urban radiation balance; here we examine the dome's effects on the atmospheric moisture of cities.

LINK

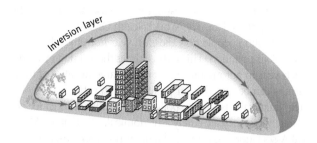

Figure 19.6 Wind circulation in an urban dust dome.

Within the dust dome there are far more airborne particles that can act as condensation nuclei than in corresponding rural areas, and this significantly modifies the moisture content of the urban atmosphere. Although little water vapour rises from the city surface, horizontal flow in the atmosphere brings just as much moisture to the city as to the nearby countryside. Because of the greater number of particles in the air above a city, there is a greater propensity for condensation and the formation of small droplets of liquid mist, fog, and cloud. As a result, fog is more frequent in cities than in surrounding areas, an effect heightened when there are local moisture sources such as lakes and rivers within the metropolitan area.

Not surprisingly, the presence of a metropolis also increases the amount of rainfall. Most cities seem to have about 10 per cent more precipitation than the surrounding area. But some, such as the urban areas of Champaign–Urbana, Illinois (Figure 19.7), and St Louis, Missouri, exhibit larger increases. The cause appears in part to be greater turbulence in the urban atmosphere, the result of hot air rising from the built-up surface. However, as we will see in the following section, artificially produced pollution can also play a major role.

Air Pollution

The most important climate modifications of urban areas are summarized in Table 19.1, and many of them can be attributed to the pollutants that cities discharge into the air. We say that air is polluted when its composition departs significantly from its natural composition of such gases as nitrogen and oxygen. However, we might call cigarette smoke pollution but not the aroma of a charbroiled steak. We are therefore concerned with factors that are in some way detrimental to, or uncomfortable for, human life.

The Nature of Air Pollution

We can group airborne pollutants into two categories: primary and secondary. **Primary pollutants**, which may be gaseous or solid, come directly from industrial and

Table 19.1 The Effect of Cities on Climatic Elements

Element	Comparison with Rural Environment
Radiation	
Global	15–20% less
Ultraviolet, winter	30% less
Ultraviolet, summer	5% less
Sunshine duration	5–15% less
Temperature	
Annual average	0.5°–1.0°C more
Winter low (average)	1°–2°C more
Contaminants	
Condensation nuclei and particles	10 times more
Gaseous mixtures	5–25 times more
Wind speed	
Annual average	20–30% less
Extreme gusts	10–20% less
Calms	15–20% more
Precipitation	
Totals	5–10% more
Days < 5 mm	10% more
Snowfall	5% less
Cloudiness	
Cover	5–10% more
Fog, winter	100% more
Fog, summer	30% more
Relative humidity	
Winter	2% less
Summer	8% less

Source: Information from H.E. Landsberg (1970), copyright World Meteorological Organization.

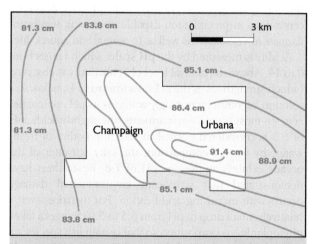

Figure 19.7 Average yearly precipitation in Champaign–Urbana, Illinois.

domestic sources and the internal combustion engines of motor vehicles. The principal gaseous primary pollutants are carbon dioxide, water vapour, hydrocarbons, carbon monoxide, and oxides of sulphur and nitrogen—in particular sulphur dioxide and nitrogen dioxide. The effluents toward the end of this list are sometimes called 'status-symbol' pollutants because they are especially associated with the industrially developed countries. The leading solid primary pollutants are iron, manganese, titanium, lead, benzene, nickel, copper, and suspended coal or smoke particles. Except where coal or wood is burned in homes, these pollutants also emanate mainly from industrial sources.

Secondary pollutants are produced in the air by the interaction of two or more primary pollutants or from reactions with normal atmospheric constituents. There also are two varieties of secondary pollution. The first is the *reducing type*. An example occurs when sulphur dioxide changes to sulphur trioxide during combustion or in the atmosphere. The sulphur trioxide then combines with atmospheric water to form droplets of sulphuric acid. This acid is corrosive, irritating, and attracts water, thereby enhancing the development of rain droplets—and acid precipitation. The other kind of secondary pollution is called the *oxidation type*. Here the effects of sunlight—known as photochemical effects—play a role. An example is nitrogen dioxide, the source of the brown colour of urban dust domes (see Figure 19.4) when it reacts with sunlight to form nitrogen monoxide and one odd oxygen atom. The freed oxygen atom can then combine with normal oxygen (O_2) to form ozone (O_3), which acts as an irritant.

LINK

Air pollution is an old, persistent, and costly problem. Indeed, a treatise on London's polluted air was published as long ago as the late seventeenth century. An oft-quoted death toll of 4000 during the infamous London smog episode of December 1952 (Figure 19.8) is evidence enough of the dangerous effects of air pollution. More recent data, published in conjunction with every major smog outbreak, indicate that substantial increases in respiratory disease accompany the severely polluted air. The World Health Organization reports that 3 million people now die each year from the adverse effects of air pollution. This is three times the 1 million who die each year in automobile accidents. A large number of these deaths can be traced to air pollution from vehicle emissions. The financial costs of air pollution are difficult to gauge accurately, but they are surely astronomical. The Ontario Medical Association has estimated that air pollution costs Ontario citizens more than $1 billion a year in hospital admissions, emergency room visits, and absenteeism.

In Unit 7 we considered the conditions that lead to the formation of smog and pollution domes over cities, particularly the influence of local *temperature inversions*. These inversions can prevent urban air from rising more than a few hundred metres, thereby acting as an atmospheric 'lid', which traps airborne pollutants and greatly increases their concentration in the city's surface layer. Horizontal flushing by winds can play a significant role in relieving air pollution in an urban area. But this means that using the skies above a metropolis as a dumping ground quickly becomes someone else's problem as the effluents are transported downwind, often for considerable distances when pollutants are discharged via smokestacks taller than 300 m. We now turn to examine such impacts by considering the macroscale effects of airborne pollution, including acid precipitation.

Acid Precipitation

Acid precipitation has been a major environmental problem since the mid-twentieth century. Acid rain is the most common form of this phenomenon, but the effects of acid precipitation are also associated with snow, fog, clouds, and even dust particles contained in the boundary layer of the atmosphere.

When fossil fuels (oil, coal, and natural gas) are burned, they release sizable quantities of sulphur dioxide (SO_2) and nitrogen oxides (NOx) into the surrounding air. These effluent gases then react chemically with water vapour in the atmosphere and are transformed into precipitable solutions of both sulphuric and nitric acid. In sufficient quantity, these gaseous pollutants can produce acid concentrations in precipitation capable of causing significant damage to vegetation as well as to animal and aquatic life.

Acidity is measured by the **pH scale**, which ranges from 0 to 14. Above the neutral level of 7, alkalinity is observed (which strengthens as the pH rises towards 14); below 7, a solution becomes increasingly acidic as its pH approaches zero. In most humid environments, the slightly acidic pH of 6.5 is considered normal in standing bodies of freshwater; by way of comparison, the salty seawater of the oceans exhibits an average pH of 7.8. Researchers have demonstrated that significant environmental damage occurs with increasing acidification. For instance, even a relatively small drop in pH from 6.5 to 5.9 changes a lake's phytoplankton composition so that certain fish species are eliminated from the food chain and disappear. When a pH of 5.6 is reached, large patches of slimy algae appear on the surface, begin to choke off the lake's oxygen supply, and block sunlight from filtering down into lower water

Figure 19.8 In the infamous London fog of December 1952, a blanket of dense smog hid most of the city from view. Traffic slowed to crawl, hospitals were filled with people suffering from respiratory problems, and the British capital was virtually paralyzed. The Scots Guards, however, maintained their traditional sentry duty at the Buckingham Palace gates, barely visible in the background.

layers. These effects would climax should the pH drop to 5.0 (about 30 times the normal acidity level), a point at which no fish species would be able to survive.

Besides freshwater lakes, there is considerable evidence that acid precipitation can also devastate marine life near heavily industrialized coastal zones. Forests are another major casualty of waterborne acid pollution, and vast areas of the upper middle latitudes have experienced damage to formerly healthy woodlands over the past three decades. Even human endeavours are being increasingly affected: in rural areas acid-sensitive crops are threatened constantly, whereas in the cities the deterioration of older buildings and concrete is noticeably hastened.

The geography of acid rain in North America corresponds decreasingly to the spatial distribution of sulphur dioxide and nitrogen oxide sources because of measures taken since the 1960s to reduce atmospheric pollution at the local level. In an effort to improve the air quality of industrial areas, much higher smokestacks (often in excess of 300 m) were constructed to disperse the effluents released by fossil-fuel burning. These measures did achieve their local goals, but instead of dispersing, the pollutants entered higher-level, longer-distance windflows, which tended to channel and transport them in still-high concentrations. Thus, in effect, certain distant areas became the new dumping grounds for these emissions. The 380-m 'Superstack' built in 1972 at Inco's smelting operations in Sudbury, Ontario, is a case in point: by the end of the 1980s the local environment had begun to recover and look less like a 'moonscape', but the pollutants from the Sudbury operations moved eastward on the prevailing winds. In the case of the US Midwest,

the largest North American regional source of sulphur and nitrogen oxides, prevailing winds steered these acid-precipitation-producing wastes hundreds of kilometres to the northeast (and eventually south as well). Over half of the acid rain received in eastern Canada originates in emissions in the United States. Areas of Ontario, such as the Muskoka–Haliburton region, and Quebec receive three-quarters of their acid deposition from the US.

A strong relationship exists between pollutant-laden winds and the spatial distribution of acid rain. The crisis is particularly acute in the heavily wooded **Dfb** zone of south-eastern Canada, where fish kills and other serious environmental damage have been widespread. North America, however, is not alone. Similar effects of acid precipitation are now spreading across Eurasia, most notably in Northern and Eastern Europe as well as in many of the vast wilderness areas that blanket Siberia and the Russian Far East.

Larger-Scale Air Pollution

The problem of **air pollution** is no longer a local one, and its effects are increasingly felt over wide areas. Just as individual houses tend to interact within a metropolis, urban regions have significant effects beyond their immediate vicinities, thereby contributing to pollution on a broader scale. We are already familiar with the concept of the urban dust dome (see Figure 19.6). When the prevailing wind is greater than 13 km/h the dome begins to detach itself from the metropolis, and the airborne pollutants stream out above the surrounding countryside as a **pollution plume**. As Figure 19.9 shows, the plume emanating from

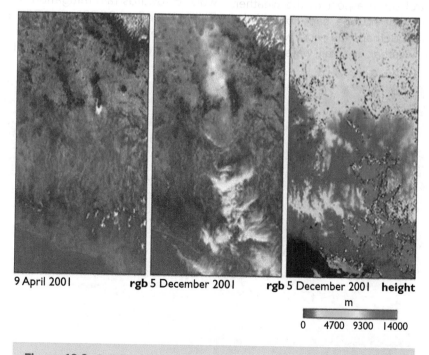

9 April 2001   rgb 5 December 2001   rgb 5 December 2001   height

m

0   4700 9300 14000

Figure 19.9 Pollution plume of Mexico City and the surrounding regions. The images at the far left and centre are natural colour views acquired by NASA's Terra satellite on 9 April and 5 December 2001. Mexico City can be identified in the centre panel by the large area of haze accumulation. The right image is an elevation field corresponding to the 5 December view.

Perspectives on the Human Environment

Weather Modification

'Everybody talks about the weather, but nobody does anything about it.'

–Mark Twain

Local and regional weather patterns have the potential to be significantly altered by human activities. Sometimes **weather modification** is intentional, sometimes inadvertent. It has been well documented that human activities such as biomass burning, agriculture, and industry can modify local and regional weather conditions. Recent studies of urban areas in tropical regions, for example, have confirmed that significant modification of weather conditions can occur in this climatic zone leading to cloud and precipitation increases of 10 to 20 per cent. Can we intentionally change the weather to create more favourable conditions?

Many nations have undertaken weather modification initiatives, beginning in the latter half of the twentieth century. Weather modification is the general term that refers to any human attempt to control some aspect of the weather. Scientists know that no one can 'control' the weather and that perhaps the most we can do is change the weather in small ways, such as

by squeezing a little more precipitation out of clouds than would have otherwise fallen. Today, dozens of nations are undertaking more than 100 weather modification projects. Nations that are particularly arid and semi-arid, with scarce water resources, are at the forefront in undertaking such projects, even though direct evidence that weather (such as precipitation, hail, lightning, or winds) can be significantly modified artificially is limited. Nevertheless, weather modification remains a big business both in North America and abroad. Commercial companies now attempt to enhance rainfall by 'seeding' clouds and assist farmers by firing 'hail cannons' to shock summertime storms into reducing hail.

Weather modification is an established service in places like China, where the Chinese Meteorological Administration has a Weather Modification Office. The Chinese have frequently been engaged in enhancing rainfall to improve agricultural production in otherwise parched locations (Figure 19.10). For the 2008 Summer Olympics, however, they actively worked towards rain mitigation to ensure that Beijing's roofless 91,000-seat Olympic stadium would have fine weather. Any rain-heavy clouds near the stadium were seeded with chemicals

LINK

Figure 19.10 Chinese attempts at weather modification, like many other recent technologies developed for tracking, forecasting, and learning about weather and climate, are led by the military.

to shrink droplets so that rain wouldn't fall until those clouds had passed over. A coolant made from liquid nitrogen is used to increase the number of droplets while decreasing their average size. As a result, the smaller droplets are less likely to fall, and precipitation can be reduced. August is part of Northeast Asia's rainy season; chances of precipitation over Beijing on any day that month approached 50 per cent. Still, while tests with clouds bearing heavy rain loads haven't always been successful, the results with light rain have supposedly been satisfactory.

In Canada, the federal and provincial governments have determined to closely monitor and limit the use of weather modification until it is shown conclusively that such modifications do not in any way affect or alter weather patterns and precipitation levels in non-target areas. Nonetheless, in 1996 a Hail Suppression Project was initiated and funded by insurers in Alberta. When a developing storm approaches, aircraft seed the clouds with silver iodide particles, a tactic intended to greatly reduce the size of hailstones and subsequently reduce the damage. In 1999 hail suppression aircraft flew more missions than ever before, and as a result, according to the insurance industry, no hailstorm cost more than $200,000. From 1988 through 1998 insurance losses attributed to hail in the province of Alberta exceeded $1 billion. During the 2001 and 2002 droughts (see 'Perspectives' box, Unit 17), farmers contended that hail suppression operations might be contributing to the reduced rainfall. The weather modification industry quickly set out to counter those contentions (see Krauss and Santos, 2003). Figure 19.11 illustrates the location of the Alberta Hail Suppression Project.

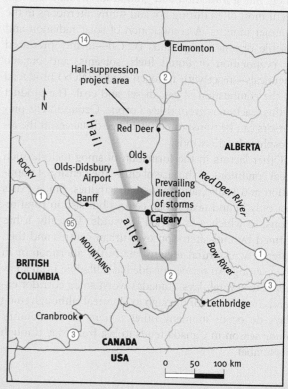

Figure 19.11 The Alberta Hail Suppression Project area.

Mexico City extends great distances vertically as well as horizontally into the atmosphere. Similarly, population clusters around the world are affected by pollution plumes that originate in industrial cities.

As it advances, the heat- and dust-bearing plume brings with it many of the climatic characteristics associated with cities. For instance, the amount of shortwave solar radiation received on a clear day in the countryside beyond the urban perimeter depends markedly on which way the wind is blowing out of the central city. Pollution plumes affect more than the particulate content and heat levels of the atmosphere. New research suggests that air pollution may have the tendency to mitigate rain and snow (see 'Perspectives' box). The abnormally small pollution particles allow cloud moisture to condense into smaller than usual droplet size. This, in turn, affects the collision and coalescence processes responsible for the production of rain droplets large enough to fall to the Earth.

Another factor reinforcing the problem of macro-scale air pollution is that many industrial centres are concentrated in certain regions. For example, the metropolitan areas of the US northeastern seaboard—as well as many in Western Europe and Japan—are geographically so close to one another that their pollution plumes merge and act together rather than individually. These coalesced, multi-metropolitan regions (called *conurbations* by urban geographers) are now so large that they function as pollution sources on a continental scale. Thus, the release of sulphur dioxide above western Germany's Rhine Valley can lead to an increase in the acidity of precipitation in Norway and Sweden.

The latest evidence reveals that certain plumes can extend for thousands of kilometres, thereby facilitating the intercontinental transfer of pollutants. Quite prominent among these is the pollution plume that carries industrial effluents, pesticides, and desert dust from northeastern China clear across the Pacific Ocean to western North America. The connecting windflows are strongest during the springtime months, and require less than a week to transport their load of airborne particles. Studies in the mountains of the US Pacific Northwest have shown that these pollutants include measurable quantities of potentially harmful heavy metals and are very likely contributing to the increasing acidity of the region's streams.

Smog

The word **smog** is a combination of 'smoke' and 'fog' and refers to the brownish haze that can hang over cities. Ground-level ozone (as opposed to the ozone layer found in the high atmosphere) is the main constituent of urban smog. Smog formation and ground-level ozone buildup occur most often during hot and sunny afternoons in the summer months. A combination of solar radiation and volatile organic compounds (VOCs)—mainly produced by evaporation of liquid fuels, solvents, and organic chemicals—react with nitrogen oxides (NOx) produced by the combustion of gas, diesel, and coal. The product of this reaction is ground-level ozone. Ozone and its precursors can be transported over large distances in the atmosphere by the winds.

Other factors in the formation of smog include such local conditions as the size of cities, the density of population and traffic, and industrial activities. Smog exists not only in and near urban centres but also in rural regions, to which it is carried by winds. Typically, it has formed by mid-afternoon over urban centres and then spreads across rural regions late in the afternoon or in the evening. An ozone episode has a lifetime from a few hours to several days. Canada's worst smog corridor extends from Windsor through to Montreal, although smog days do occur in many other regions of the country. Smog season in Canada tends to last from May through September.

Human Activities and the Global Climate Machine

At the global scale, human climatic impacts may be reaching a level capable of interfering with certain natural processes of the atmosphere, as we have seen in regard to ozone depletion (Unit 5), deforestation (Unit 17), and desertification (Unit 17). Because little is being done worldwide to counteract these human-induced environmental problems, they are likely to persist well into the future.

Despite the advances of contemporary environmental science, we have only begun to develop an understanding of the longer-term consequences of atmospheric pollution and their possible linkage to the forces of climatic change. Recent experience has shown that monitoring and forecasting methods need to be improved, because instead of slow, incremental change, certain pollutants may build up silently for years. Then, only after they surpass a critical mass, do they produce rapid and potentially far-reaching environmental change.

With scenarios such as these to contend with, soon it may no longer be possible to regard the Earth's climate as a finely tuned natural machine in long-term equilibrium, constantly correcting itself to maintain exactly the right balance of warmth and moisture required to sustain the range of life on this planet. Today, many scientists assert that humans have begun to disturb the delicate workings of that machine, and what that portends is becoming one of the leading pursuits of the atmospheric, life, and Earth sciences.

KEY TERMS

acid precipitation   *page 270*
dust dome   *page 267*
green roof   *page 268*
heat-island intensity   *page 267*
humidex   *page 266*
metabolic heat   *page 264*
microclimate   *page 264*
pH scale   *page 270*

pollutant   *page 268*
pollution (air)   *page 271*
pollution plume   *page 271*
primary pollutants   *page 269*
secondary pollutants   *page 270*
urban heat island   *page 267*
weather modification   *page 272*

REVIEW QUESTIONS

1. Describe the various sources of energy and heat received by and lost from the human body.
2. Describe how an urban heat island develops and the meteorological consequences of this climatic modification.

3. What are primary pollutants? What are secondary pollutants? Give examples of both.
4. What is a pollution plume and how does it develop?

REFERENCES AND FURTHER READINGS

Bailey, W.G., T.R. Oke, and W.R. Rouse. 1997. *The Surface Climates of Canada*. Montreal and Kingston: McGill-Queen's Univ. Press.

Bonsal, B., X. Zhang, L. Vincent, and W. Hogg. 2001. 'Characteristics of Daily and Extreme Temperatures over Canada', *Journal of Climate* 14: 1959–76.

Burnett, R.T., S. Cakmak, and J.R. Brook. 1998. 'The Effect of the Urban Ambient Air Pollution Mix on Daily Mortality Rates in 11 Canadian Cities', *Canadian Journal of Public Health* 89: 152–6.

Chang, K. 2000. 'Scientists Watch Cities Make Their Own Weather', *New York Times*, 15 Aug., D1, D2.

Changnon, S.A. 1992. 'Inadvertent Weather Modification in Urban Areas: Lessons for Global Climate Change', *Bulletin of the American Meteorological Association* 73: 6619–27.

Condella, V. 1998. 'Climate Islands: Sprawling Cities Affect Air Patterns Overhead and Change the Weather around Them', *Earth Magazine* (Feb.): 54–6.

Cotton, W.R., and R.A. Pielke. 1995. *Human Impacts on Weather and Climate*. New York: Cambridge Univ. Press.

Dolney, T., and S. Sheridan. 2006. 'The Relationship between Extreme Heat and Ambulance Response Calls for the City of Toronto, Ontario, Canada', *Environmental Research* 101: 94–103.

Elsom, D. 1992. *Atmospheric Pollution: A Global Problem*, 2nd edn. Cambridge, Mass.: Blackwell.

Environment Canada. 2002. *Annual Progress Report on the Canada-Wide Acid Rain Strategy for Post-2000*. Ottawa: Environment Canada. At: <www.ec.gc.ca/acidrain/res-pub.html>.

Goudie, A.S. 2000. *The Human Impact on the Natural Environment*, 5th edn. Cambridge, Mass.: MIT Press.

———, ed. 1997. *The Human Impact Reader: Readings and Case Studies*. Malden, Mass.: Blackwell.

——— and H. Viles. 1997. *The Earth Transformed: An Introduction to Human Impacts on the Environment*. Malden, Mass.: Blackwell.

Government of Canada. 2002. 'Introduction: Smog and Health', Parliamentary Research Branch.

Heidorn, K. 2005. '*And Now . . . the Weather*', Calgary: Fifth House.

Jacobson, M.Z. 2002. *Atmospheric Pollution: History, Science, and Regulation*. New York: Cambridge Univ. Press.

Kasperson, J.X., R.E. Kasperson, and B.L. Turner, eds. 1996. *Regions at Risk: Comparisons of Threatened Environments*. New York/Tokyo: United Nations Univ. Press.

Klinenberg, Eric. 2002. *Heat Wave: A Social Autopsy of Disaster in Chicago*. Chicago: Univ. of Chicago Press. Also see: <www.press.uchicago.edu/Misc/Chicago/443213in.html>.

Krauss, T., and J.R. Santos. 2003. 'The Effect of Hail Suppression Operations on Precipitation in Alberta, Canada', *Proceedings, 8th WMO Scientific Conference on Weather Modification*, Casablanca, Morocco.

Landsberg, H.E. 1981. *The Urban Climate*. New York: Academic Press.

Luoma, J.R. 1988. 'Bold Experiment in Lakes Tracks the Relentless Toll of Acid Rain', *New York Times*, 13 Sept., 21, 24.

Meyer, W.B. 1996. *Human Impact on the Earth*. New York: Cambridge Univ. Press.

Oke, T.R. 1978. *Boundary Layer Climates*. London: Methuen.

Schwartz, S.E. 1989. 'Acid Deposition: Unraveling a Regional Phenomenon', *Science* 243 (10 Feb.): 753–63.

Smoyer, K.E., D.G. Rainham, and J.N. Hewko. 2000. 'Heat-Stress-Related Mortality in Five Cities in Southern Ontario: 1980–1996', *International Journal of Biometeorology* 44: 190–7.

Smoyer-Tomic, K., R. Kuhn, and A. Hudson. 2003. 'Heat Wave Hazards: An Overview of Heat Wave Impacts in Canada', *Natural Hazards* 28: 463–85.

Turner, B.L., ed. 1990. *The Earth as Transformed by Human Action: Global and Regional Changes in the Biosphere over the Past 300 Years*. New York: Cambridge Univ. Press.

Winters, H.A., et al. 1998. *Battling the Elements: Weather and Terrain in the Conduct of War*. Baltimore: Johns Hopkins Univ. Press.

 # WEB RESOURCES

eetd.lbl.gov/HeatIsland Abstracts from the Canadian Heat Island Summit, as well as background information about strategies to prevent formation of urban heat islands.

lavoieverte.qc.ec.gc.ca/atmos/smog/fiche_info_e.html An Environment Canada fact sheet on ground-level ozone.

www.greenontario.org/strategy/smog.html Green Ontario information on smog.

www.gsfc.nasa.gov/gsfc/earth/terra/co.htm Data from the NASA/CSA global air pollution monitor are interpreted and presented in full colour as well as in three-dimensional animations.

www.msc-smc.ec.gc.ca/cd/brochures/humidity_e.cfm Environment Canada information on humidity.

www.msc-smc.ec.gc.ca/education/windchill/index_e.cfm Wind chill information from Environment Canada.

PART THREE
The Restless Crust

Units

PART THREE The Restless Crust

Restless Crust

The lithosphere, the oldest of the Earth's spheres, began to form as soon as superheated molten rock first solidified in patches on the planet's turbulent surface more than 4 billion years ago. Ever since, the Earth's crust has thickened and matured, but it has not stabilized. Great slabs of solid crust move, driven by heat from geochemical processes that keep subsurface rock in a molten and mobile condition. When these slabs collide, the lighter continental one overrides the heavier oceanic one, starting a process called subduction in which parts of both continental and oceanic crust are forced downward. At the surface, subduction creates spectacular scenery, causes earthquakes, and generates volcanic activity. Below, the crustal slabs are subjected to such high temperatures and pressures that their rocks remelt and become part of the molten, moving mass beneath the crust. Millions of years later, molten rock may rise along a volcanic fissure, and the cycle continues. Embedded within this giant lithospheric system, which moves continents and threatens people, is the rock cycle, a never-ending system that brings molten rock to the surface, where forces of weathering and erosion attack it. Loose material accumulates and becomes compressed into sedimentary rock, which may be heated and transformed (metamorphosed) into harder rock types; some of it gets caught up in subduction and melts in the asthenosphere. Other metamorphic rocks remain in upper layers of the crust and are exposed by uplift and erosion, and as with volcanic lava, the cycle of weathering and sedimentary accumulation begins all over again.

The Earth seems to be the only planet in the solar system to have been affected by plate tectonics for most of its history. There is some evidence to suggest that Venus may have had incipient plate tectonic activity. There is also some indication that the Jovian moon Ganymede may have some form of crustal tectonics. All of the other Earth-like, or *terran*, planets, e.g., Mars, Mercury, and Venus, have single-plate crusts formed from primary basaltic rocks solidified as the planets cooled down. Earth, on the other hand, has a multiple-plate crust—a granitic continental crust and a basaltic oceanic crust—tectonics, and volcanism. Tectonics and volcanism appear to be mechanisms for controlling the internal temperature of the Earth, e.g., volcanism has been estimated to decrease the internal temperature by 0.2–0.4°C/yr. These processes are also linked to the biosphere and to the atmosphere. Volcanic degassing releases water, carbon dioxide, methane, and other gases.

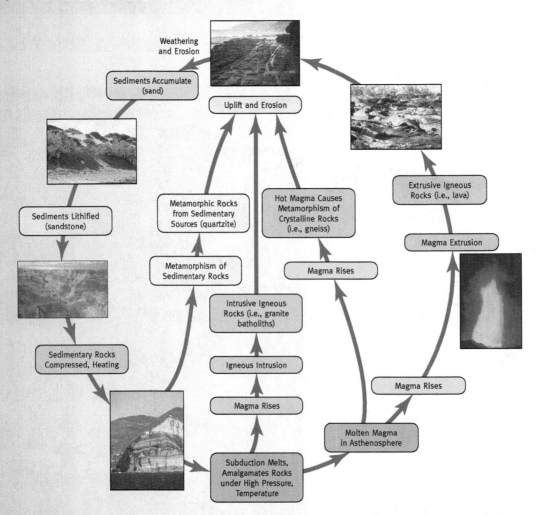

Planet Earth in Profile: The Layered Interior

Objectives

- To outline the relevant properties of the Earth's five internal layers and to discuss some of the evidence leading to their discovery.

- To introduce the salient properties of the Earth's lithosphere, the nature of the crust, and the underlying mantle.

- To investigate the gradational processes that continually build as well as remove rock material at the Earth's surface, creating physical landscapes of great diversity.

In other parts of this book various aspects of the Earth's environments are examined. Several of the *spheres* of our planet are introduced in these parts, including the atmosphere and the hydrosphere (Part Two) and certain properties of the biosphere (Part Five). The atmosphere, hydrosphere, cryosphere, biosphere, and lithosphere are the major visible layers of our planet. Above the effective atmosphere are additional layers of thinner air and different chemical composition; their physical and chemical properties are well known because detailed data about them have been collected by balloons, high-flying aircraft, and space vehicles.

Much less is known, however, about the layers that make up the internal structure of the Earth. Even the directly observable crust of the planet, which we will examine later in this unit, is not well known. No instruments have been sent down very far into the crust. More than a third of a century after people first set foot on the Moon, the deepest boreholes have penetrated barely 12 km into the lithosphere. Since the radius of the planet is 6370 km, we have penetrated less than one five-hundredth of the distance to the centre of the Earth.

Nonetheless, scientists have established the fact that the interior of the Earth is layered like the atmosphere, and they have deduced the chemical composition and physical properties of the chief layers below the crust. This research is of importance in physical geography because the crust is affected by processes that take place in the layer below it, and this layer in turn may be influenced by conditions deeper down. So it is important to understand what is known about the Earth's internal structure and how this information has been acquired.

Evidence of the Earth's Internal Structure

Evidence that supports the concept of an internally layered Earth comes from several sources. The crust affords a glimpse of the nature of rocks normally hidden from scientists because rocks that formed very deep below the surface have occasionally been elevated to levels in the crust where they can be reached by boreholes or are exposed at the surface. From these samples, as well as from analyses of more common rocks, it is possible to deduce the overall composition of the crust and its average density.

By studying the wavelengths of light emanating from the Sun, it is possible to determine the elements the Sun contains and their proportions, because certain specific wavelengths correspond to particular elements. Geophysicists have concluded that these proportions will be the same for the Earth. However, such abundant elements as iron, nickel, and magnesium are relatively depleted in the crust. This suggests that those heavy elements are concentrated in deeper layers of the planet.

This conclusion is strengthened by two pieces of evidence. First, rock samples taken from great depths contain higher concentrations of iron and magnesium than 'average' crustal rocks. Second, when the mass and size of the Earth are measured, the resulting figure is 5.5 grams per cubic centimetre (g/cm³). This is about double the density of rocks found in the continental crust. Again, the heavier, denser part of the Earth should be in the deep interior.

Earthquakes

Further evidence for the internal structure of the Earth comes from the planet's magnetic field and from the high temperatures and pressures known to prevail at deeper levels. Not only does molten rock sometimes flow onto the surface through volcanic vents, but it is also possible to determine the temperatures at which rocks now solid were once liquefied. But the most convincing body of evidence is derived from the analysis of **earthquakes**—the shaking and trembling of the Earth's surface caused by sudden releases of stress within the crust.

Earthquakes occur in many areas of the crust, and their causes are discussed in Unit 26. For the present it should be noted that earthquakes generate pulses of energy called **seismic waves** that can pass through the entire Earth. A strong earthquake in the Northern Hemisphere will be recorded by *seismographs* in the Southern Hemisphere. Today thousands of seismographs continuously record the shocks and tremors in the crust (Figure 20.1), and computers help interpret these earthquake data. This source has given us an important picture of the interior structure of our planet.

Seismic waves take time to travel through the Earth. In general terms, the speed of an earthquake wave is proportional to the density of the material through which it travels. The denser the material, the faster the speed. Seismic waves, like light waves and sound waves, also change direction under certain circumstances. When a seismic

Figure 20.1 The Canadian National Seismograph Network (CNSN) station at the Geological Survey of Canada headquarters in Ottawa uses seismographs like the one above. The pen plotters continuously record the Earth's shocks and tremors as a series of wiggly lines on the slowly rotating paper-covered drum whose motion is precisely regulated by a clock. The printout is called a seismogram.

wave travelling through a less dense material reaches a layer where the density becomes much greater, it may be bounced back; this is known as *seismic reflection* (Figure 20.2A). If the contrast in densities between the adjacent layers is less severe, the wave may be bent rather than reflected; here *seismic refraction* changes the course of the seismic wave (Figure 20.2B).

Types of Seismic Waves

Seismic waves behave differently as they propagate through the Earth. Two types of waves travel across the surface of the crust and are termed *surface (or Long period) waves* (or **L** waves). There are two types: Rayleigh waves and Love waves. Rayleigh waves cause disruption of the surface, creating a wave-like motion radiating out from the epicentre. Love waves move across the surface and cause ground motion zig-zagging from side to side. Two other types of

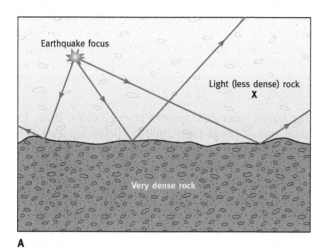

A

B

Figure 20.2 When seismic waves travel through the interior of the Earth, several things happen. When they reach a plane where the rock material becomes much denser, they may be *reflected* back (A). If the contrast in rock density is less, they may be *refracted* (B). Their velocities are also affected. Speeds would be less in the layers marked **X** and greater in layer **Y**.

waves travel through the interior of the Earth and are referred to as **body waves**. The body waves are known as **P** (primary) waves and **S** (secondary) waves. The **P** waves are compressional waves, sometimes called push waves. As they propagate, they move material in their path parallel to the direction of movement. They even travel through material in the liquid state, although their impact is then much reduced. The **S** waves (shear or shake waves) move objects at right angles to their direction of motion. They do not propagate through liquid material. This is of great importance, because if **S** waves fail to reach a seismograph in an opposite hemisphere, it may be concluded that liquid material inside the Earth halted their progress.

When an earthquake occurs, seismographs nearest its point of origin begin to record the passing of a sequence of waves. The seismogram (see Figure 20.1) will reveal the passage of the **P**, **S**, and **L** waves in a nearly continuous sequence, which may reflect great destruction of structures in the area. Farther away, the different speeds of propagation begin to show on the seismogram, and reflected **P** and **S** waves from interior Earth layers make their appearance. Eventually seismographs around the world will record the earthquake. But some stations will not register any **P** or **S** waves, and others will record only **P** waves. From these data significant conclusions about the interior of the Earth can be drawn, as shown below.

The Earth's Internal Layers

The paths of seismic waves, illustrated in Figure 20.3, reveal the existence of a layer beneath the crust that ends at a boundary where **S** waves (shown by grey arrows) are not propagated. If an earthquake occurs at zero degrees, **P** as well as **S** waves are recorded by seismographs everywhere to 103 degrees from its source (a distance of 11,270 km). Then, from 103 to 142 degrees, the next 4150 km, neither **P** nor **S** waves are recorded (except for **P** waves propagated along the crust). But from 142 to 180 degrees (15,420 to 19,470 km distant from the quake), **P** waves—always shown by black arrows—reappear. From this evidence it is concluded that the Earth possesses a liquid or viscous layer that begins about 2900 km below the surface. At the contact between this liquid layer and the layer above it, **S** waves cease to be propagated and **P** waves are refracted.

But some **P** waves that arrive on the far side of the Earth, between 142 and 180 degrees, have not been refracted just once or twice, but four times! Moreover, their speed has increased. This means that the **P** waves that reach the seismographs located antipodally to the earthquake source (i.e., on the exact opposite point of the spherical Earth) must have travelled through a very dense mass inside the liquid layer. Confirmation of the existence of such a dense mass at the core of the Earth comes from the fact that many **P** waves are reflected back at its outer edge (Figure 20.4). From the travel times of these reflected **P** waves and the seismograms inside 142 degrees (Figure 20.3), it is concluded that the Earth has a solid inner

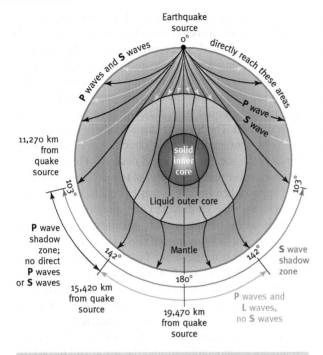

Figure 20.3 Imagine that a strong earthquake occurs at the North Pole (0 degrees on the drawing). This diagram shows the paths of the radiating **P**, **S**, and **L** waves as they travel through the planet. Note that no **P** waves are received over a large shadow zone in the Southern Hemisphere, between 103 and approximately 142 degrees from the quake's source at 0 degrees. This allows us to identify the depth at which the solid mantle yields to the liquid outer core. From the refraction of the **P** waves we can deduce the contrast in density between mantle and outer core materials.

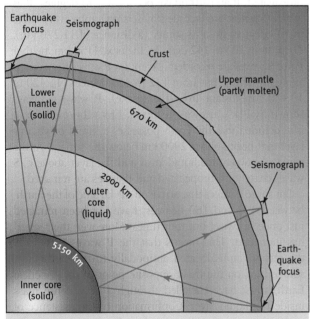

Figure 20.4 Certain **P** waves are reflected back toward the crust when they reach the outer edge of the solid inner core. From their travel times, the position of the contact between solid inner core and liquid outer core can be deduced. *Note:* The refraction of these waves, as they traverse the interior of the Earth, is not shown.

core—a ball of very heavy, dense material. This may well be where the iron and nickel, depleted from the upper layers, is concentrated.

On the basis of seismic and other evidence, therefore, the interior of the Earth is believed to have four layers: a solid inner core, a liquid outer core, a solid lower mantle, and a partially molten upper mantle (Figure 20.5). On top of all this lies the crust, still very thin, and in places it is active and unstable.

Solid Inner Core

The solid **inner core** has a radius of just 1220 km. Its surface lies 5150 km below sea level. Iron and nickel exist here in a solid state, scientists believe, because pressures are enormous—so great that the melting-point temperature is even higher than the heat prevailing in the inner core. There is some evidence from computer models that the inner core acts like a dynamo. It rotates much faster than the Earth, creating waves or currents in the liquid outer core that 'drag' the outer parts of the Earth around.

Liquid Outer Core

The liquid **outer core** forms a layer 2250 km thick. Its outer surface lies at some 2900 km below sea level, just slightly less than halfway to the centre of the planet. The liquid outer core may consist of essentially the same materials as the solid inner core, but because pressures here are less, the melting-point temperature is lower and a molten state prevails. The density of the inner and outer cores combined has been calculated as 12.5 g/cm^3, which compensates for the lightness of the crust (2.8 g/cm^3) and accounts for the density of the planet as a whole (5.5 g/cm^3).

Solid Lower Mantle

Above the liquid outer core lies the solid **lower mantle**. Although the scale of the diagram cannot properly convey it, the contact between mantle and core is not smooth and even, but has relief—rather like the uneven upper surface of the crust. The lower mantle has a thickness of about 2230 km. Seismic data show that the lower mantle is in a solid state. Geologists believe that this layer is composed of oxides of iron, magnesium, and silicon.

Upper Mantle

The partially molten **upper mantle** is of great interest to geologists as well as to physical geographers because it interacts with the overlying crust in many ways. The upper mantle, however, still is not well understood, although it extends from the base of the crust to a depth of just 670 km. The upper mantle is differentiated from the lower mantle on the basis of mineral composition and the

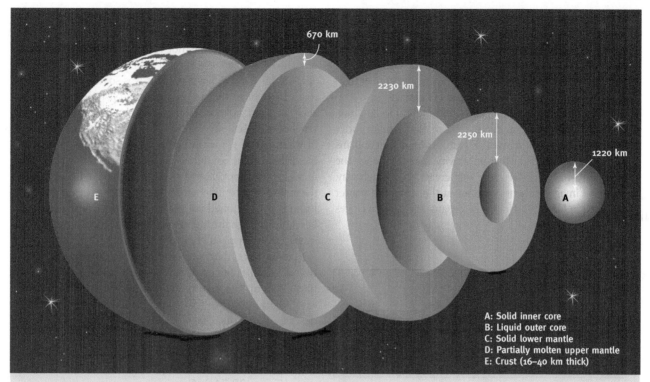

Figure 20.5 Principal layers of the inner Earth.

A: Solid inner core
B: Liquid outer core
C: Solid lower mantle
D: Partially molten upper mantle
E: Crust (16–40 km thick)

state of the rock material. The lower mantle is solid, but the upper mantle above it seems to be viscous (like thick syrup, capable of flowing slowly). However, the zone of the upper mantle just beneath the crust is solid. This portion of the upper mantle contains pockets of molten rock, some of which feed chambers from which lava pours onto the surface of the crust.

The interior of the Earth still retains many of its secrets, but our comprehension increases steadily. New knowledge about the upper mantle continues to emerge, and it may well be that this subcrustal layer can itself be subdivided into a number of additional layers. In any case, our interpretation of what we observe at the surface must begin with an understanding of what lies below. This unit continues with an examination of the lithosphere, and focuses on further aspects of this uppermost layer of the interior of the Earth.

The Earth's Outer Layer

Now that we are familiar with the Earth's interior, we can turn to the surface layer itself, the lithosphere upon which all else—air, water, soil, life—rests. The crust, as just noted, lies directly above the upper mantle (see Figure 20.5). The uppermost parts of the crust are the only portions of the solid Earth about which scientists have direct first-hand knowledge. The rocks that make up the outer shell of our planet have been analyzed from the surface, from mine shafts, and from boreholes. Even

the deepest boreholes, however, only begin to shed light on what lies below.

For many years it was believed that temperatures and pressures below the crust would be so great that the Earth material there would be in a completely molten state. Another subsequent theory, based on the study of earthquake waves, suggested that the mantle beneath the crust was solid. Quite recently more detailed, computer-assisted analyses of the paths and speeds of earthquake waves through the Earth's interior have revealed the existence of a broad viscous layer within the upper mantle (the asthenosphere). Undoubtedly there will be more revelations in the future.

Structural Properties of the Crust

One of the most significant discoveries relating to the Earth's crust occurred in 1909. In that year the Croatian scientist Andrija Mohorovičić concluded from his study of earthquake waves that the density of the Earth materials changes markedly at the contact between crust and mantle. This contact plane has been named the **Mohorovičić discontinuity**, or **Moho**, an abbreviation of his name. Despite a century of far more sophisticated analyses and interpretations, Mohorovičić's conclusion has proven correct—a density discontinuity does indeed mark the base of the Earth's crust.

This information made it possible to calculate the thickness of the crust. Earthquake waves speed up at the Moho discontinuity, indicating that the crust is less dense than the mantle below. In some places this happens a mere 5 km down from the surface; elsewhere the change in earthquake-wave velocity does not come until a depth of 40 km or even more has been reached. This proved that the crust is not of even thickness. It also showed that the crust is thinner than the shell of an egg relative to the planet's diameter.

When the Moho was mapped, it was found to lie much closer to the surface under the ocean floors than under the continental landmasses (Figure 20.6). This confirms a conclusion also drawn from gravity measurements: the continents have crustal 'roots' that create, in a rough way, a reverse image of the topography at the surface (a matter explored in Unit 24). Under the oceans, the crust averages

LINK

only 8 km in thickness; under the exposed continental surfaces, the average depth is about 40 km.

For many years it was not realized that a fundamental difference between continental and oceanic crust might account for these differences. This was so, in part, because rocks brought to the surface from the offshore continental shelves resembled those found on the continents themselves; boreholes in shallow water off the coast produced no hint of what was to come. But then technology made possible the drilling of the continental slope farther out to sea. Those rocks, it turned out, were darker and somewhat heavier than the rocks of the continental landmasses. Advances in drilling technology also raised the possibility of directly punching a borehole through the Moho into the mantle itself—a project earth scientists can still only dream about.

In any case, there are fundamental differences between continental crust and oceanic crust. The rocks that make up the continental landmasses have the lowest density of all, so that the continents are sometimes described as 'rafts' that float on denser material below. These low-density rocks have come to be known as *sialic rocks*, or just **SIAL** (from the chemical symbols of their dominant mineral components—silica and *alumi-num* [Figure 20.7A]). Granite is a common sialic rock, and its density is about the same as the density of the continental landmasses as a whole (2.8 g/cm³). As a result you will see continental crust referred to as 'granitic' or 'granitoid' crust—although the landmasses are made

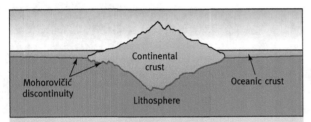

Figure 20.6 The Mohorovičić discontinuity (Moho) marks the base of continental as well as oceanic crust. As the sketch shows, it lies much closer to the crust's surface under the oceans than beneath the land.

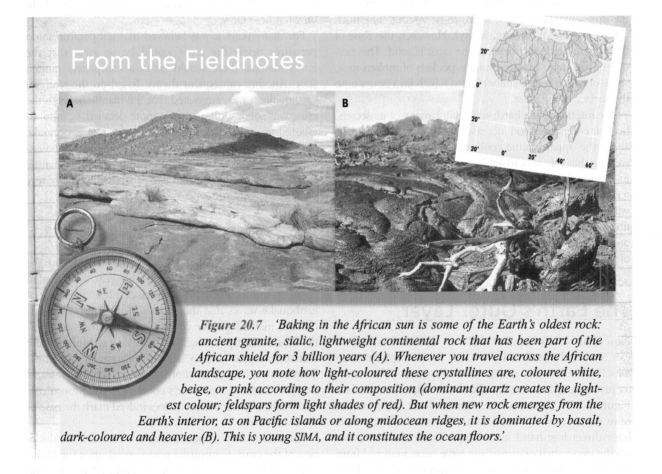

From the Fieldnotes

Figure 20.7 'Baking in the African sun is some of the Earth's oldest rock: ancient granite, sialic, lightweight continental rock that has been part of the African shield for 3 billion years (A). Whenever you travel across the African landscape, you note how light-coloured these crystallines are, coloured white, beige, or pink according to their composition (dominant quartz creates the lightest colour; feldspars form light shades of red). But when new rock emerges from the Earth's interior, as on Pacific islands or along midocean ridges, it is dominated by basalt, dark-coloured and heavier (B). This is young SIMA, and it constitutes the ocean floors.'

LINK

up of many other rocks as well, such as sandstone, limestone, shale, and marble. These are the rocks that, because of their different capacities to withstand weathering and erosion, create the diversity of landscapes we will study later.

Oceanic crust—and the lower crust under the continents, below what is termed the *Conrad discontinuity*, which separates the upper and lower crusts under the continents—consists of higher-density rocks collectively called the *simatic rocks*, or **SIMA** (for *silica*, of which they contain much less than continental rocks, and *magnesium*, a heavy, dark-coloured component [Figure 20.7B]). Here the dominant rock is the heavy, dark-coloured basalt. Oceanic crust, therefore, is often referred to as basaltic crust, although many other rocks also form part of the oceanic crust. In combination, rocks of the oceanic crust have a density of about 3.0 g/cm³. Geologists define continents as having granitic crust over basaltic crust. Because of this definition a number of micro-continents have been found, e.g., Rockall and the Faeroes in the North Atlantic.

Despite these overall differences between low-density granitic continental crust and higher-density basaltic oceanic crust, there are places *on* the continents where oceanic-type basalt can be found. How did this supposedly oceanic rock get there? The answer is that the continental crust sometimes cracks open, allowing molten rock from deep below to penetrate to the surface. (Also, ocean-floor rocks sometimes thrust over continental rocks by a process called *obduction*, as is the case in the Gros Morne area of Newfoundland.) In addition, the basalt that has come to the surface through many fissures proves that heavier, denser rocks exist below the continents—so the notion of the landmasses as rafts on a simatic 'sea' is not so far-fetched!

The Lithosphere

The crust terminates at the Moho, but rocks in the solid state do not. The uppermost segment of the mantle, on which the crust rests, also is rigid. Together the crust and this solid uppermost mantle are called the **lithosphere**, the sphere of rocks. Below the lithosphere, the upper mantle becomes so hot that it resembles hot plastic—it can be made to change shape, it can be moulded.

This soft plastic layer in the upper mantle is called the **asthenosphere** (Figure 20.8). Like the Mohorovičić discontinuity, the asthenosphere begins at a much deeper level below the continental landmasses than it does below the ocean floor. Beneath the landmasses it begins at a depth averaging 80 km below the surface. Beneath the ocean floors, it lies only about 40 km below the surface (i.e., of the seafloor).

The discovery of the existence of the asthenosphere was important to our understanding of what happens in and on the crust. Because the asthenosphere is in a hot plastic state, the lithosphere can move over it. This movement of

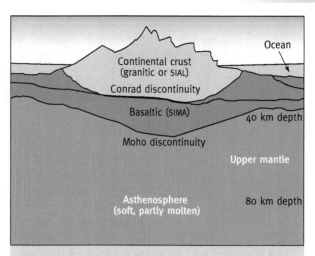

Figure 20.8 Position of the asthenosphere in the Earth's mantle. The boundary between the asthenosphere and the lithosphere is a transition zone rather than a sharp divide. Its depth beneath the surface is about twice as great under the continents as under the oceans.

the crust, which is related to the formation of mountains and even the movement of whole continents, takes place because heat sources deep inside the core and mantle keep the asthenosphere in motion. Unlike the Moho, the contact zone between the rigid lithosphere and the soft asthenosphere is not abrupt. Rather, it is gradual, so that material can pass from one state to the other as it moves vertically as well as horizontally. For many years, geologists wondered what forced molten rock material into the crust, and even through it as magma. Recent research has determined that the buoyancy of such molten material is positive, neutral, or negative with respect to surrounding rock; but only if the buoyancy remains positive will it rise through the crust via diapirism, the vertical movement of magma through the crustal rocks, and onto the surface as lava. Thus, as more became known about the asthenosphere, the mechanisms of such processes came to be better understood.

Much more remains to be learned about the lithosphere and its uppermost layer, the crust. Geophysicists today can create small Earth tremors where earthquakes normally do not originate, and they can study the behaviour of the resulting waves. For example, scientists began to realize that the so-called bright spots revealed by these artificial waves were more common than they had believed since the first one was noticed in 1975. These bright spots are zones in the crust, usually 15 to 20 km below the surface, where the seismic waves are being reflected more than elsewhere in the lithosphere. One theory suggests that there is a transition zone of rock from a brittle state to a soft state within the crust, a kind of mini-Moho. The proof may not come for decades, and the discovery of the bright spots is a reminder of the limited state of our knowledge—even of the crust on which life exists.

Perspectives on the Human Environment

Lithoprobe

The idea for the Lithoprobe project originated in a meeting attended by university and government geologists in Toronto in 1981. The aim of the project was to investigate how North America had been structurally put together and to study a series of geological transects and areas in various regions of the country. When the project began in 1984, it became fully funded by the Natural Sciences and Engineering Research Council, the Geological Survey of Canada, and other sources to the sum of more than $100 million.

Lithoprobe involved many thousands of scientists divided into groups that studied the various areas of Canada (Figure 20.9). The project addressed the following fundamental questions about the evolution of the continent of North America: (1) the origin of the North American continent; (2) how the continent was built up over time; (3) the geological history of North America; and (4) the depth of the lithosphere under various parts of North America.

The Lithoprobe project continues to this day, and has been the world's first national multi-disciplinary investigation of the origin and growth of a continental area. The project has led to the publication of many papers and reports, as well as many workshop sessions, about the geological structure and history of North America.

Figure 20.9 A vibroseis crew at work in Ontario. Four vibroseis (sound source) trucks (called 'dancing elephants') work in unison to send seismic signals into the ground. Nearby recording trucks record the collected signals and feed the data into computers for storage.

Lithospheric Plates

The crust varies in thickness and is also a discontinuous layer. To humans, living on the landmasses, the idea that the crust is not a continuous, unbroken shell is difficult to grasp because there seems to be no evidence of cracks or fractures in it. In fact, the crust and the rest of the lithosphere are fragmented into a number of segments called **lithospheric plates** (or *tectonic plates*). These plates move in response to the plastic flow in the hot asthenosphere. Earth is the only planet in our solar system to show continued plate movement. Many of the Earth's mountain ranges, including the mightiest Himalayas, are zones where the moving plates have come together in gigantic collisions. This aspect of the lithosphere, examined in Unit 24, is of special importance to our understanding of landscapes and landforms.

LINK

LINK

The Crustal Surface

The Earth's crust is subject to tectonic forces from below. The rocks that form the crust are pushed together, stretched, fractured, and bent by the movement of the lithospheric plates. These forces tend to create great contrasts at the crustal surface—jagged peaks and sharp crests, steep slopes and escarpments, huge domes and vast depressions. Before we begin an in-depth examination of those forces in the remaining units of Part Three, it is useful to take another look at the surface of the continents and their varied relief.

Topographic Relief

The term **relief** refers to the vertical difference between the highest and lowest elevations in a given area. Thus, a range of tall mountains and deep valleys, such as the

From the Fieldnotes

Figure 20.10 'Not one square metre of flat land in this dissected, high-relief area on the North Island of New Zealand. High relief prevails throughout most of New Zealand, which is positioned in the boundary zone between the Australian and Pacific Plates and is subject to volcanism and earthquakes. Glaciation, as well as stream erosion, further modifies its topography, so that this is one of the most scenic locales on the planet. But this vista is not the result of nature's work alone. Before human settlers arrived less than one thousand years ago, dense forests covered this area (like much of the rest of the islands). The Maori burned significant portions of it, but it was the Europeans and their livestock who had the greater impact. They converted forest into pasture for millions of sheep, in some areas sparing not a single tree for as far as the eye can see. In this area, the pastures are seeded annually from airplanes, producing a verdant countryside—but one that is a cultural, not a natural, landscape.'

LINK

Rocky Mountains, is an area of *high relief* (Figure 20.10). A coastal plain is an area of *low relief* (Figure 20.11). An area of low relief can lie at a high elevation: a nearly flat plateau with an elevation of 3000 m has lower relief than a mountainous area with peaks no higher than 2000 m and valleys at 500 m. Attempts by physical geographers to classify land surfaces notwithstanding, great liberties are often taken with such features on the map (see 'Perspectives' box below on the naming of topographical features).

When continental landmasses are viewed even at a small scale (see Figure 2.3), it is evident that they have areas of high relief and other areas of low relief. North America, for example, has large areas of low relief, especially in central and eastern Canada, the interior United States, and the coastal plain bordering the Atlantic Ocean and the Gulf of Mexico. High relief prevails in the western third of the continent, from the Rocky Mountains westward. In the east lies an area of moderate relief in the Appalachian Mountains.

The two types of relief just identified represent three kinds of continental geology. The Earth's landmasses consist of two basic geologic components: *continental shields* and their associated platform borderlands and *orogenic belts*. In North America, the region centred on Hudson Bay is a continental shield; expressed topographically as a plain of low relief (the Canadian Shield); around this on three sides are the platform borderlands. The Rocky Mountains represent the topographic results of a period of mountain building and constitute an orogenic belt.

Continental Shields

All the continental landmasses contain shields and platform borderlands as well as orogenic belts. The **continental shields** (with their platform borderlands, called *cratons*) are large, stable, relatively flat expanses of very old rocks, and they may constitute the earliest 'slabs' of solidification of the molten crust into hard rocks (or solidification related to a phase of meteoric impacts). This happened more than 4 billion years ago, and ever since these shields have formed the nuclei of the landmasses (Figure 20.12)

The shield in northern North America is called the *Canadian (Laurentian) Shield* (Figure 20.13). It is larger than the area of ancient rocks presently exposed because it is covered by water in the north and by sedimentary rocks along its southern flank (the platform borderlands). In fact, the Canadian Shield rocks are also exposed in Texas and some other southern states, proof that it underlies most

From the Fieldnotes

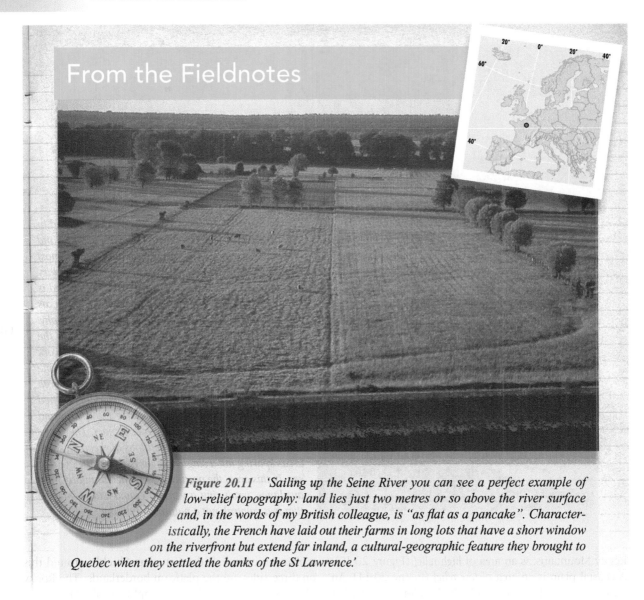

Figure 20.11 *'Sailing up the Seine River you can see a perfect example of low-relief topography: land lies just two metres or so above the river surface and, in the words of my British colleague, is "as flat as a pancake". Characteristically, the French have laid out their farms in long lots that have a short window on the riverfront but extend far inland, a cultural-geographic feature they brought to Quebec when they settled the banks of the St Lawrence.'*

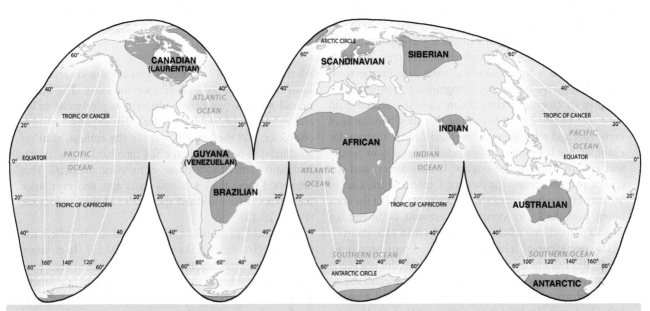

Figure 20.12 Continental shields of the world, representing materials that cooled from the earliest molten surface or after the impact of meteorites early in the geological history of the Earth.

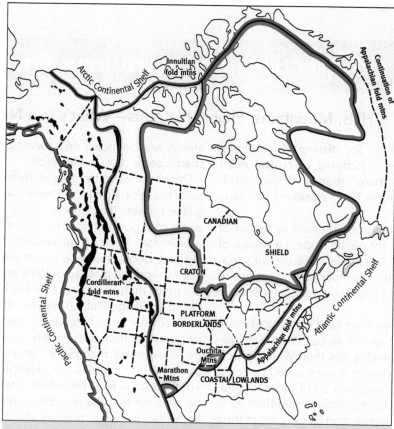

Figure 20.13   The Canadian Shield and other North American crustal landforms.

of the eastern part of North America. In South America there are two major shield zones: the *Guyana (Venezuelan) Shield* and the *Brazilian Shield*. These shield areas, unlike the Canadian Shield, are uplands today and present the aspect of low-relief plateaus rather than plains.

Eurasia has three major shields: the *Scandinavian (Fenno-Scandin) Shield* in the northwest, the *Siberian Shield* in the north, and the *Indian Shield* in the south. The world's largest shield presently exposed is the *African Shield*, a vast region of ancient rocks that extends into the Arabian Peninsula at its northeastern extremity. Some of the oldest known rocks deposited on top of the shield have been found in the *Australian Shield*, which occupies the western two-thirds of that continent. And under the ice in eastern Antarctica lies the *Antarctic Shield*. Wherever these shield zones form the exposed landscape, they exhibit expanses of low relief (Figure 20.14).

Platform borderlands occur around the margins of the shields. They are characterized by a relatively thin cover of fossiliferous sedimentary rocks deposited on top of the shield that are horizontal or nearly horizontal, indicating stability.

Orogenic Belts

In contrast, the **orogenic belts**—series of linear mountain chains—are zones of high relief. The term *orogenic* derives from the ancient Greek word *oros*, meaning

mountain. As we note later, the Earth during its 4.6-billion-year lifetime has experienced many periods of mountain building. These episodes are marked on the topographic map by linear mountain chains, such as the Appalachians and the Rockies in North America. The Andes Mountains in South America, the Alps and Himalayas in Eurasia, and the Great Dividing Range in

Figure 20.14   Stream flowing slowly across the vast tundra east of Yellowknife in Canada's Northwest Territories. This is the Canadian Shield, its crystalline rocks scoured by ice but now ice-free, its depressions and valleys filled with wetlands, lakes, and rivers.

Perspectives on the Human Environment

Hills, Mountains, Plains, Plateaus—What's in a Name?

To distinguish regional patterns of crustal relief more sharply, these land-surface features have been classified by many geographers.

Hills and mountains are defined as terrain of less than 50 per cent gentle slope, i.e., slope of <10°. In terms of local relief, hills exhibit variations of 0 to 300 m, low mountains variations of 300 to 900 m, and high mountains variations in excess of 900 m.

Plains and plateaus are land surfaces of more than 50 per cent gentle slope. Plains are low-lying areas that exhibit less than 90 m of local relief; flat plains exhibit more than 80 per cent gentle slope and less than 30 m of local relief. Plateaus, or tablelands, display more than 90 m of local relief, and more than 50 per cent of their gentle slope occurs in the lower half of their elevational ranges. In addition, plateaus almost always are bounded on at least one side by a sharp rise or drop in elevation.

Despite these attempts at definitional precision, the global map is littered with toponyms (place names) that disregard the geographer's sense of topographic order. Plains and plateaus usually fare better than upland areas. A glaring exception would be South America's large central Andean plateau of Peru and Bolivia that lies more than 3600 m above sea level, which is called the 'High Plain' (Altiplano in Spanish).

When studying hills and mountains on the landscape, therefore, map readers should be forewarned that place namers have taken some blatant liberties. An example from southern Ontario is Blue Mountain, site of a popular ski area on the Niagara Escarpment near Collingwood. Its height reaches about 220 m above sea level. Hamilton Mountain is another part of the same escarpment.

Figure 20.15 Inca-built structures of Machu Picchu, high in the Andes of Peru. This is high relief in the extreme, but the Inca managed to construct large stone buildings and terrace even very steep slopes. The purposes of Machu Picchu still are uncertain. It may have served as a fortress and/or as a ceremonial centre. Anthropologist Jack Weatherford has suggested that the terraces seen here were farm plots to raise high-altitude-adapted crops.

Australia all represent orogenic activity, when rocks were thrust, bent, and crushed into folds like a giant accordion (Fig. 20.15). Ever since, processes in the atmosphere and the other spheres of the Earth System have been eroding those structures; but they persist to the present day, bearing witness to past orogenic activity.

Coastal Lowlands

These are a discontinuous series of low-lying areas between the orogenic belts and the coastline. In some places these are quite extensive, for example, the eastern seaboard and Gulf of Mexico coastal lowlands of North America. The areas of these regions have grown and diminished over geological history. During the maximum extent of the ice in the last (Wisconsinan) glaciation, sea level was about 100 m lower than present and exposed more continental shelf (a continuation of the coastal lowlands) as coastal lowland. As sea level rises because of global warming the sea will encroach onto the coastal lowlands and cause a reduction in size. The landscapes of the coastal lowlands are generally characterized by quite subdued topography with wide river valleys and low intervening hills. In some areas there are large estuaries. The continental shelves (*con-shelves*), at present under water, are a continuation of the coastal lowlands and the continents. *Epicontinental seas*, such as the Caribbean and the Mediterranean Seas, also occur on continents. The continental shelves have the same kind of relief as the coastal lowlands but the outer parts of the shelves are generally smoother because they are covered by a thin veneer of sediment (the seaward gradient is less than 0.25°). At the seaward edge of the continental shelves (at 200 m below sea level) are the continental slopes (*conslopes*). These form the actual ends of the continental blocks. They generally slope at 2–5° (very low in contrast to the continents) but can have have quite steep slopes (over 25°). These gradients are maintained over great distances (over 50 km) and so can represent changes of several thousands of metres. The conslopes are sometimes terraced or stepped, and are associated with submarine canyons, cut by large rivers that extended out onto the continental shelves when sea level was lower (e.g., the St Lawrence Submarine Canyon). The transition from the continental slope to the deep ocean basin is called the *continental rise*. The continental shelves and continental slopes form the *continental margins*.

LINK

Gradational Processes

If the Earth had no atmosphere and no moisture, those shields, platform borderlands, and orogenic belts would stand unchallenged, destroyed only by new tectonic forces. But the Earth does have an atmosphere, and as a result the geological buildup is attacked by a set of processes that work to erode it. These are called **gradational processes** and are the focus of several units in Part Four.

The rocks of which the crust is composed are subject to various forms of *weathering*—the physical, chemical, and even biological processes that operate to distintegrate rocks, break them apart, and make them ready for removal (erosion). The force of gravity plays an important role as the motivating force for *slope movement* of soil and rock, which also takes several forms (an avalanche, for instance, is a form of mass movement). But this mass movement does not carry loosened rock material very far. That requires the longer-distance removal of weathered materials. Great rivers transport rock grains thousands of kilometres from mountain slopes in the deep interiors of continents to their deltas on the coasts. There, and in their valleys upstream, the process of deposition fills the lowlands with the very material removed from the highlands. Glaciers, wind, and ocean waves participate in this erosion of the land thrust up by tectonic forces.

It is a continuous contest that affects some areas of the crust more strongly than others at different times in Earth history. This conclusion is based on the geological record: where great mountains once rose, only their roots now remain. Areas once tectonically active are today quiescent. But other zones now appear to be on the verge of great tectonic activity and will subsequently be attacked by gradational forces. It is all part of the continued recycling of Earth materials within the dynamic lithosphere.

The Structure of the Ocean Floor

Over the last 60 years research has given us an understanding of the character of the ocean basins. It used to be thought that the deepest parts of the oceans were in the centre, but we now know that the deepest parts of the oceans are, in fact, often close to the continents. The depths are far less close to the centre of the basins. The landscape of the continents is incredibly complex, with a very chaotic distribution compared to the relief of the ocean basins. There is a striking similarity of rock types, structures, and morphology associated with the ocean basins compared with the continental areas. It is possible to distinguish three very distinct structural and topographical areas in the ocean basins (Figure 20.16):

1. Mid-oceanic ridges
2. Deep ocean basins
3. Deep marginal trenches (these are absent in some areas, e.g., the North Atlantic Basin, but very common around the Pacific and Indian Ocean basins)

Mid-Oceanic Ridges

The mid-oceanic ridge system is in reality an immense mountain range that forms a global network between 50,000 and 60,000 km long. It is composed of a pile of basaltic lavas. It varies from 1000 to 4000 km wide. Its crest rises 1–2 km above the deep ocean floors on either side of it and is about 2 km below sea level, but it is exposed above sea level in places, e.g., Iceland in the North Atlantic and St Helena in the South Atlantic. The mid-oceanic ridge in the Atlantic Ocean occupies about 33 per cent of the total width of the ocean basin. The ridge system is often asymmetrically positioned in most ocean basins, e.g., the Pacific Ocean.

The ridge is bisected by a rift valley. This feature is well marked in the Atlantic but has very subdued topography in the Pacific. The ridge and the rift system are exposed in some places, e.g., Iceland and the East African Great Rift Valley. The mid-oceanic ridges and rifts are associated with seismic (low-magnitude shallow tensional earthquakes) and effusive basaltic volcanic activity. The volcanoes erupt basaltic lavas and form either shield or row volcanoes. There are also fissures, dykes, and geothermal hot springs (on land) or 'white' or 'black' smokers (under water), which are found in and around the rift valleys.

Deep Ocean Basins

The deep ocean basins (or abyssal plains) lay between 4.5 and 6 km below sea level. They are very flat and have gradients of less than 1:1000. The terrain is subdued and occasionally is broken by isolated volcanic mountains or mountain groups, and sometimes by sills (or small fault escarpments). Most of the area is covered by very fine sediment and globigerina and other oozes. All of the oceans have deep basins, which often are associated

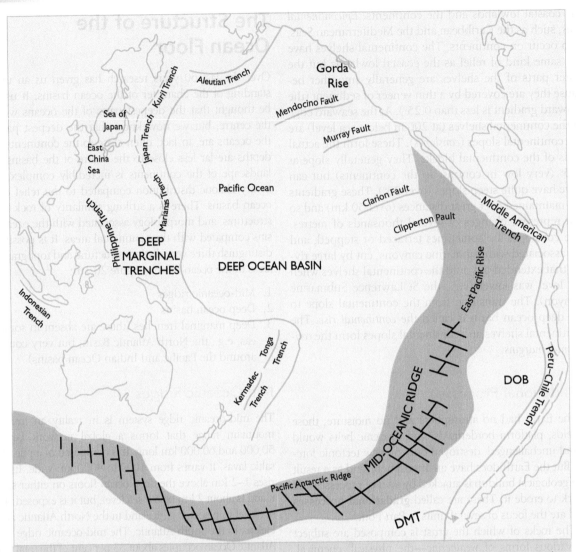

Figure 20.16 Topographical areas of ocean basins. The mid-oceanic ridge system, in reality an immense mountain range, is bounded on both sides by deep ocean basins DOB. Deep marginal trenches DMT occur in some of the world's oceans near the continental shelves, as in this depiction of the Pacific.

with large-scale troughs or submarine canyons. The best example of one of the troughs is the 2000-km-long Mid-Oceanic Canyon in the Labrador Basin situated at the foot of the continental slope (and the lower part of the slope—*the continental rise*) off eastern Canada.

Deep Marginal Trenches

Deep marginal trenches occur close to the continental margins. They form narrow, elongated, often arcuate basins. Some trenches are exceptionally deep, e.g. Challenger Deep in the Marianas Trench (located 306 km southwest of Guam) extends to a depth of 10.9 km below sea level. It is well over 1 km lower than the deep ocean basin. If a 0.5 kg metal ball was dropped into the sea from a ship above this point, it would take nearly 63 minutes to reach the bottom of the trench. This part of the Marianas Trench is deeper than Sagarmatha/Chomalunga/Everest is high (8.9 km), and even deeper than the height of Mauna Kea

(10.2 km), the Hawaiian shield volcano that is the highest mountain on Earth (measured from its base).

The majority of trenches occur around the Pacific Ocean basin. Some trenches have been partially or entirely infilled with sediment. They are associated with seismic and volcanic activity and with fold mountain ranges on neighbouring continents. These trenches display a number of common features:

1. They have an asymmetrical cross section, with a steep slope on the continent side and a less steep slope on the ocean side.
2. The steep continental-side slope often culminates in a volcanically active major fold mountain belt or volcanic island arc.
3. Most trenches are arcuate (bow-shaped).
4. The wall gradients increase with depth, e.g., the Aleutian Trench off Alaska, the Marianas-Japan-Kuril Trench system off East Asia.

KEY TERMS

asthenosphere   *page 285*
body waves   *page 281*
continental shield   *page 287*
earthquake   *page 280*
gradational processes   *page 291*
inner core   *page 282*
lithosphere   *page 285*
lithospheric plate   *page 286*
lower mantle   *page 282*

Mohorovičić discontinuity (Moho)   *page 283*
orogenic belt   *page 289*
outer core   *page 282*
relief   *page 286*
seismic wave   *page 280*
SIAL   *page 284*
SIMA   *page 285*
upper mantle   *page 282*

REVIEW QUESTIONS

1. How do earthquakes and their seismic waves suggest a layering of the Earth's interior?
2. What are the approximate thicknesses of the inner core, outer core, mantle, and crust?
3. What is the Mohorovičić discontinuity, and what is its significance?
4. What are the differences between oceanic and continental crust?
5. What is the significance of the asthenosphere? How does it relate to the concept of lithospheric plates?
6. Which gradational processes contribute to the recycling of the Earth's materials?

REFERENCES AND FURTHER READINGS

Adams, J.J., et al. 2001. 'Seismicity and Seismic Hazards', in G.R. Brooks et al., *A Synthesis of Geological Hazards in Canada 2001*. Ottawa: Geological Survey of Canada Bulletin 548, 7–26.

Bloom, A.L. 1969. *The Surface of the Earth*. Englewood Cliffs, NJ: Prentice-Hall.

Bolt, B.A. 1982. *Inside the Earth: Evidence from Earthquakes*. New York: Freeman.

Bott, M.H.P. 1982. *The Interior of the Earth: Its Structure, Constitution, and Evolution*. London: Edward Arnold.

Davis, G.H. 1976. *Structural Geology of Rocks and Regions*. New York: Wiley.

Ernst, W.G. 1969. *Earth Materials*. Englewood Cliffs, NJ: Prentice-Hall.

Garland, G.D. 1979. *Introduction to Geophysics: Mantle, Core, and Crust*. Toronto: Holt, Rinehart, & Winston.

Gass, I., et al., eds. 1971. *Understanding the Earth*. Cambridge, Mass.: MIT Press.

Hancock, P.L., and B.J. Skinner, eds. 2001. *Oxford Companion to the Earth*. New York: Oxford Univ. Press.

King, P.B. 1977. *The Evolution of North America*. Princeton, NJ: Princeton Univ. Press.

Percival, J.A., et al. 2004. 'PanLITHOPROBE Workshop IV: Intra-Orogen Correlations and Comparative Orogenic Anatomy' (workshop review), *Geoscience Canada* 31, 1: 23–40.

Powell, C.S. 1991. 'Peering Inward', *Scientific American* (June): 100–11.

Press, F., and R. Siever. 1978. *Earth*, 2nd edn. San Francisco: Freeman.

Raymo, C. 1983. *The Crust of Our Earth: An Armchair Traveler's Guide to the New Geology*. Englewood Cliffs, NJ: Prentice-Hall.

Scientific American. 1983. 'The Dynamic Earth'. Special issue (Sept.).

Trewartha, G.T., et al. 1967. *Elements of Geography*, 5th edn. New York: McGraw-Hill. Classification discussed on pp. 262–6.

Weiner, J. 1986. *Planet Earth*. New York: Bantam Books.

 ## WEB RESOURCES

earthquakescanada.nrcan.gc.ca/ The Earthquakes Canada website contains a wealth of information about all aspects of earthquakes.

earthquakescanada.nrcan.gc.ca/stnsdata/cnsn/index_e.php The Canadian National Seismograph Network website shows the location of various seismograph stations and contains data about earthquakes, links, etc.

www.iodp.org This site for the International Ocean Drilling Program explains the basics of this type of research, and provides tutorial information about the internal layers of Earth. Photos are available of operations, as well as a multimedia introductory tour.

www.lithoprobe.ca The website of the Lithoprobe project has a lot of information, maps, images, and links to many government agencies, universities, etc., involved in the study.

Unit 21

Impact Cratering

Objectives

- To introduce the idea of impact cratering as a major Earth surface process and the importance of impacts to Earth history.

- To show the differences between asteroids, comets, and meteorites.

- To discuss the different kinds of impact craters, using Canadian examples.

- To describe the **Torino Impact Hazard Scale**.

All terran, or Earth-like, planets and many satellites (moons) in our solar system show scars of impact cratering caused by *asteroids*, *comets*, or *meteorites* (bolides). Until fairly recently this was not appreciated as a major process on Earth. Studies of **impact craters** have been going on since the early twentieth century and many impact features have been mapped and catalogued. Early workers considered these features to have a volcanic origin (possibly *maars*), but some others, notably Grove Karl Gilbert, suggested extraterrestrial impacts formed impact craters because of the lack of lavas and other volcanic deposits and features. In the last 40 years interest has intensified in the process and its importance on Earth has been recognized. An Impact Hazard Scale has now been devised for near-Earth objects (asteroids, comets) that come close to and may impact the Earth.

During the 1950s, Carlyle S. Beals of the Dominion Observatory in Ottawa studied many meteor impact craters (astroblemes) in Canada and throughout the world. He established the Earth Impact Database (1955), which is now maintained by the Planetary and Space Science Centre at the University of New Brunswick. Beals's pioneering work has been maintained and more detailed analysis has been done by such Canadian scientists as Michael R. Dence and Richard A.F. Grieve.

It was not until the 1980s that the importance of this process was really discussed. At this time, Luis Alvarez and his co-workers suggested that a meteoric impact was responsible for causing a major global climatic and evolutionary change that involved the extinction of 50 per cent of all genera of land and sea creatures—including the dinosaurs—and plants. The basis of this idea came from the finding of a fairly exotic element called iridium (a member of the platinum family) in large amounts in layers of rock that had been laid down during some kind of global event at the end of the Cretaceous era about 60–5 million years ago. Iridium, although somewhat rare on Earth, is found in large amounts in some meteorites. This led to the suggestion that the impact of a very large meteorite and its fragmentation had jettisoned iridium-rich material into the atmosphere and that this had been spread around the globe by the atmosphere and had rained out in deposits.

In 1978 Glen Penfield, a geologist working for PEMEX (the state-run Mexican oil company), made aerial magnetic surveys of the Yucatan Peninsula and found evidence of a large (180 km diameter) buried impact crater straddling its north coast and centred on the town of Chicxulub. He was told by PEMEX not to discuss his findings or publish anything, as there were oil reserves nearby. Around the same time Alan Hildebrand (a Canadian Ph.D. student at the University of Arizona, now a professor at the University of Calgary) was studying possible iridum-rich impact deposits around the Caribbean. His findings suggested that a large impact had occurred in the Yucatan area (Figure 21.1). These studies intensified interest in the importance of meteorites and their impacts on Earth.

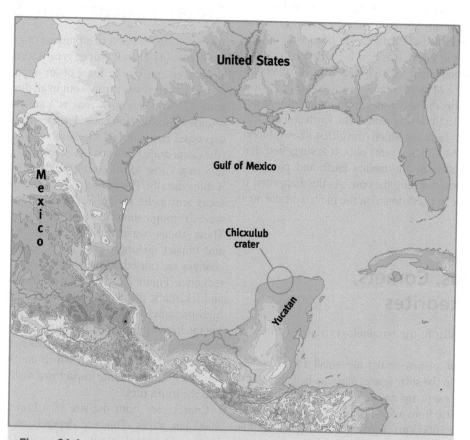

Figure 21.1 The Chicxulub Crater on Mexico's Yucatan Peninsula is a possible explanation for the extinction of the dinosaurs and was caused by the impact of a huge meteorite 180 km in diameter.

Some scientists have argued that the Chicxulub crater does not date to the time of extinction of the dinosaurs and suggest that other unknown impact sites might have been responsible (at least three or four others that are known were formed around the same time) or perhaps large-scale volcanism (such as the eruption of the Deccan Traps and Columbia Plateau basalts) was responsible for the iridium-rich layer and the extinction ('volcanic winter').

In July 1994 the comet Shoemaker-Levy 9 (David Levy is a Canadian) was observed breaking up and crashing into the atmosphere of Jupiter. This was observed on Earth and by the Hubble Space Telescope. Over 20 comet fragments (some as large as 3 to 4 km across) entered the Jovian atmosphere at a speed of 60 km/s, producing violent explosions and leaving giant holes in the atmosphere (some were initially larger than the Earth's diameter). This event started a renewed interest in the significance of impact cratering on Earth. It also made scientists consider that the same kind of multiple impact could have occurred on Earth. It is now thought that all the terran planets and some satellites were affected by a great bombardment of asteroids, comets, and meteorites early on in the history of the solar system. This period on Earth has been dated to about 3.6 to 4.5 billion years ago.

As early as 1878 the famous British astronomer George Howard Darwin (a son of Charles Darwin) suggested that Earth's Moon had been formed by the Sun's gravitational pull wrenching out a mass of material from a much-faster-revolving early Earth. Soon after, the Reverend Osmond Fisher suggested that the Pacific Ocean basin was, in fact, the scar left by this event. It is now hypothesized that the Moon was formed when the still-molten Earth suffered a giant impact by a Mars-sized mass (variously called Theia or Orpheus). This threw out an enormous amount of debris that formed a thick ring around the Earth and eventually coalesced to form the Moon (the oldest known Moon rocks are about 4.4 billion years old). It is suggested that Theia was engulfed by the molten Earth and ploughed through it, almost reaching the core. As this happened it took most of the minerals found in the molten crustal area with it.

Asteroids, Comets, and Meteorites

It is useful to clarify the terminology related to impact cratering.

Asteroids (or planetesimals) are small rocky bodies that have been in the solar system since its beginning and have not been swept up and incorporated into planets. They range in size from a few km to a few tens of km in diameter (up to 1000 km). The largest known asteroid is dwarf planet Ceres (diameter about 950 km and mass of $9.43 \pm 0.07 \times 10^{20}$ kg). Several thousand bodies of nearly this size are known. Most are located in the asteroid belt between Mars and Jupiter.

Comets are generally tens of kilometres in diameter. They are composed of rock and a considerable amount of volatile ices. As they move closer to the Sun these ices evaporate to form their characteristic tails. They are found in two places: the Oort cloud at the edge of the solar system, which is about 50,000 astronomical units (AUs) from Earth (one AU is equal to the mean distance from the Sun to the Earth, or 1.49598×10^{11} m, or 149,598,000 km), is an immense, roughly spherical cloud formed by billions of icy comet-like bodies about 1000 times farther away than Pluto; and, beyond Neptune, the Kuiper Belt is a huge, flat ring of approximately 100,000 icy comet-like bodies, all greater than 100 km in diameter.

Meteorites are solid bodies that have fallen to the Earth's surface (or the surface of any celestial body). They vary in size from a grain of dust to a mass weighing several tonnes. Three types are recognized: stones or stony meteorites (aerolites); stony-iron meteorites (siderolites); and irons or irony meteorites (siderites).

Bolides (a term used by geologists rather than astronomers) are very large impactors of unknown type (an asteroid, comet, or a large meteorite).

Crater Structure and Size

Two areas are common to all impact craters on Earth and elsewhere. (1) The *excavation zone* is a concave area (crater) carved out by the force of an impact. Much of the surface material was thrown out in all directions from this zone. (2) The *deposition zone* is a convex area that surrounds the excavation zone. The ejected material that was deposited here created the familiar crater walls. Debris (the *ejecta drape*) radiates out across the planet surface in this area. Close to the crater the drape is quite deep but it thins distally. The impact causes faulting of underlying rocks and melts surface rocks. An impact sends shock waves through the crust and the interior of the Earth. These shock waves can cause shock metamorphism and impact melting of the target rocks. Other, smaller changes are caused by the shock waves, including: shatter cones (Figure 21.2) in silicate minerals such as quartz and feldspars; diaplectic glass, for example, stishovite (a high-pressure form of quartz), spherules, tektites, and microtektites (tear-shaped glass fragments ejected from the crater at impact and as the rocks melted); and microdiamonds, the largest of which are the size of a pinhead, resulting from the impact and melting of the bolide and the impactites.

Craters vary from the size of a human hand to over 1000 km across. This size depends on the mass of the bolide, its terminal velocity, and gravity. The kinetic energy

LINK

0 1 2 3 4 5 6 7 8 9 10

cm

Figure 21.2 Small, finely sculptured shatter cones in fine-grained limestone, from the Haughton Crater on Devon Island in Nunavut. The cone surfaces show the typical divergence of striae away from the cone apex ('horsetailing').

released by a meteorite impact is related to its mass and terminal velocity:

$$KE = 0.5\,(MV^2)$$

where KE is kinetic energy (joules), M is mass (kg), and V (km/s) is the terminal velocity. So a 30-metre diameter meteorite travelling at 15 km/s would release 1.7×10^6 joules of energy, or the equivalent of about 4 megatons (million tonnes) of TNT. The peak pressure produced by an impact of a *chondritic* or stony meteorite in continental crust (e.g., granite) at a reasonable impact velocity (about 25 km/s) is 900 GPa, or 9 million times atmospheric pressure. This kind of pressure would melt or vaporize the bolide and throw out millions of tonnes of surface rock. An impact of a 30 m diameter meteor at 15 km/s was responsible for the excavation of Meteor (or Barringer) Crater (formerly known as Coon Butte or Coon Crater) in northern Arizona. The crater is over 1 km in diameter; its rim rises about 50 m above the height of the surrounding plain; it is about 200 m deep. It is estimated that over 175 million tonnes of rock were excavated by this impact. The impactor is now called the Diablo Canyon Meteorite.

The Chicxulub crater has a diameter of 180 km. The estimated size of the meteorite responsible for it is 10^{16} kg. The power released by this impact has been estimated as being equivalent to a magnitude 10 or 11 earthquake (or the simultaneous explosion of 100 million hydrogen bombs). An impact of this size would have caused a massive tsunami (as it landed partly in the sea), continental-scale wildfires, darkness (because of all the debris hurled into the atmosphere), and subsequent 'impact winter', which killed off many genera. This was followed by substantial greenhouse

warming. About 25 other very large craters have been found in similar contexts on most of the continents.

A huge ancient crater-like structure or *astron* has been found underlying the Canadian Shield rocks in northwestern Ontario between Hudson Bay and the south shore of Lake Superior. It is believed to have been formed by the impact of a 100–140 km diameter bolide.

Moon Craters

The diameter of most craters on the Moon varies from 25 to 130 km. Moon craters usually have a central peak or ring. The excavation zone is much smaller in proportion to the diameter. The central peak or ring was thrust up by the impact as part of the force reacting in an opposite direction to the impact, much like what is seen when a marble or rock is dropped into water.

Larger craters (over 130 km diameter) also occur on the Moon's surface. These show concentric rings and/or terraces in association with their rims. Their floors are very shallow and because of their size have a convex shape reflecting the curvature of the Moon's surface.

Terrestrial Crater Size and Impact Frequency

Like many other processes discussed, there is a relation between size and frequency of event. As crater size increases the frequency of the impact event decreases.

Table 21.1 The Relation between Crater Size and Impact Frequency

Diameter (km)	Impact Frequency (per 60 million Earth years)
>1	384,000
>1.8	138,000
>3.1	49,800
>5	21,000
>7.2	10,800
>10	6,000
>12.2	4,260
>20	1,740
>31	840
>50	130
>100	24

Source: After Grieve et al. (2006).

Crater Types

It is possible to distinguish three types of craters on Earth: simple craters, complex craters, and complex craters with central uplift, peak, or ring.

Simple craters have diameters up to 4 km, with up-lifted or overturned rim rocks surrounding a smooth bowl-shaped depression partially filled by impact breccias. The depth/diameter ratio ranges from 1:5 to 1:7. Examples of this kind of crater are Meteor Crater in northern Arizona; the Holleford Crater just north of Kingston, Ontario (Figure 21.3); Brent Crater in Algonquin Provincial Park, Ontario (Figure 21.4); West Hawk Lake, Manitoba; and Cratere Pingualuit, Quebec.

Complex craters are generally over 4 km in diameter. They exhibit slumped or terraced rims. Their interiors are partially filled with impact breccia and impact melt rocks (impactites). The depth/diameter ratio varies between 1:10 and 1:20. A good example is Clearwater Lake East, Quebec.

Complex craters with a distinct central uplift, peak, or ring share the same characteristics as complex craters except they exhibit a distinct central uplift and an

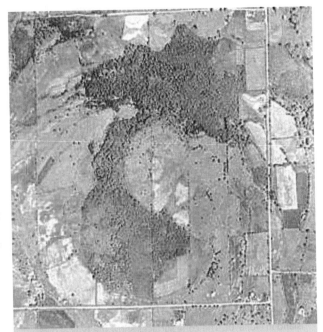

Figure 21.3   Holleford Crater, north of Kingston, Ontario, is an example of a simple crater. Discovered in the 1950s in the course of aerial surveying, it is 2.35 km in diameter and estimated to be 550 million years old.

Height

High   Low

Figure 21.4   Brent Crater (round green-blue area, centre), in Algonquin Provincial Park, Ontario, is an estimated 450 million years old and was discovered in 1951 from aerial photographs.

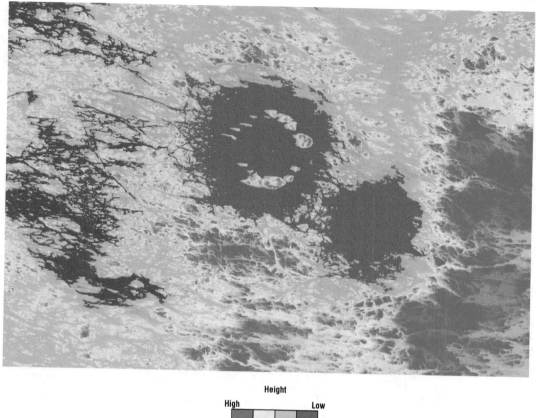

Height

High   Low

Figure 21.5   The Clearwater Lakes in the Canadian Shield region of Quebec near Hudson Bay were formed by a pair of (or paired) meteorites at the same time, approximately 290 million years ago. This view, taken from a space shuttle, shows the central uplift of Clearwater Lake West, which is 36 km in diameter. Both this and Clearwater Lake East (26 km diameter) are complex craters.

annular (ring-shaped) trough. Examples are Clearwater Lake West, Quebec (Figure 21.5); Manicouagan, Quebec (Figure 21.6); and Sudbury, Ontario. Sudbury, in fact, is a very deformed 200–250-km ring basin dated to 1.85 billion years.

Atmospheric Explosions

The best-documented example of an atmospheric explosion of a bolide is the Tunguska Event of 1908. This occurred over a then inaccessible part of Siberia northwest of Lake Baikal. A team was not sent into the area to investigate until the later 1920s because of lack of interest, poor access, World War I, and the Russian Revolution and resulting civil war. It is thought by most scientists to have involved a 30–50 m bolide that exploded several kilometres above the ground surface. It was responsible for flattening, defoliating, and burning about 2000 km² of boreal forest. The air blast from this event was felt around the world. The energy released in the explosion is estimated to have been equivalent to about 15 million tonnes of TNT. Recently, some scientists have suggested a smaller event of the same kind

as Tunguska may have occurred over the Great Lakes and northeastern North America towards the end of the Pleistocene Ice Age (Clovis Comet). It is hypothesized that this event was responsible for 'resetting the radiocarbon clocks' so that the C¹⁴ dates obtained from bones and other organic materials in paleo-Indian sites in this area have been dated as much as 10,000 years younger than materials from similar western sites of the same period. This event also may have killed off some of the larger mammals, such as mammoths, and contributed to cooling that caused the Younger Dryas ice advance in Europe and elsewhere. Smaller such events have occurred over Cando, Spain (1994); near Whitehorse, Yukon (2000); between Crete and Libya (2002); and near Lake Titicaca, Peru (2007).

The Torino Impact Hazard Scale

A scale was devised (and later modified) by MIT researcher Richard Binzel and others to rank the possibility of near-Earth object impact using a 10-point scale. The scale is named after the site of an International Astronomical

Figure 21.6 The Manicouagan Crater, as photographed from a space shuttle in winter. From space the crater has been called 'the Eye of Quebec', and it is the fifth largest impact crater known on Earth. A complex crater with central uplift, it was created 214 million years ago by an asteroid that would have been 5 km in diameter. The crater (Lake Manicouagan), believed to be about 100 km in diameter after impact, now has a visible diameter of 72 km as a result of erosion and sedimentation. The large 'island' in the middle of the circular lake is the central uplift of the crater.

LINK

Union conference in Turin, Italy, which adopted it in 1999. Zero on the scale means there is little or no likelihood of a collision with an asteroid or comet. Small meteors burn up in the atmosphere. Infrequent meteorite falls occur but rarely cause any damage. Ten on the scale means a certain collision will occur that is capable of causing a global climatic catastrophe that may threaten the future of civilization as we know it, whether the impact is on land or in the ocean. Such events occur on average once per 100,000 years or less often (see Figure 21.7), but the possibility has drawn the interest of some moviemakers (see 'Perspectives' box).

Assessing Asteroid and Comet Impact Hazard Predictions in the Twenty-First Century		
No Hazard (White Zone)	0	The likelihood of a collision is zero, or is so low as to be effectively zero. Also applies to small objects such as meteors and bodies that burn up in the atmosphere as well as infrequent meteorite falls that rarely cause damage.
Normal (Green Zone)	1	A routine discovery in which a pass near the Earth is predicted that poses no unusual level of danger. Current calculations show the chance of collision is extremely unlikely, with no cause for public attention or public concern. New telescopic observations very likely will lead to re-assignment to Level 0.
Meriting Attention by Astronomers (Yellow Zone)	2	A discovery, which may become routine with expanded searches, of an object making a somewhat close but not highly unusual pass near the Earth. While meriting attention by astronomers, there is no cause for public attention or public concern, as an actual collision is very unlikely. New telescopic observations very likely will lead to re-assignment to Level 0.
	3	A close encounter, meriting attention by astronomers. Current calculations give a 1% or greater chance of collision capable of localized destruction. Most likely, new telescopic observations will lead to re-assignment to Level 0. Attention by public and by public officials is merited if the encounter is less than a decade away.
	4	A close encounter, meriting attention by astronomers. Current calculations give a 1% or greater chance of collision capable of regional devastation. Most likely, new telescopic observations will lead to re-assignment to Level 0. Attention by public and by public officials is merited if the encounter is less than a decade away.
Threatening (Orange Zone)	5	A close encounter posing a serious, but still uncertain, threat of regional devastation. Critical attention by astronomers is needed to determine conclusively whether or not a collision will occur. If the encounter is less than a decade away, governmental contingency planning may be warranted.
	6	A close encounter by a large object posing a serious but still uncertain threat of a global catastrophe. Critical attention by astronomers is needed to determine conclusively whether or not a collision will occur. If the encounter is less than three decades away, governmental contingency planning may be warranted.
	7	A very close encounter by a large object which, if occurring this century, poses an unprecedented but still uncertain threat of a global catastrophe. For such a threat in this century, international contingency planning is warranted, especially to determine urgently and conclusively whether or not a collision will occur.
Certain Collisions (Red Zone)	8	A collision is certain, capable of causing localized destruction for an impact over land or possibly a tsunami if close offshore. Such events occur on average between once per 50 years and once per several 1000 years.
	9	A collision is certain, capable of causing unprecedented regional devastation for a land impact or the threat of a major tsunami for an ocean impact. Such events occur on average between once per 10,000 years and once per 100,000 years.
	10	A collision is certain, capable of causing global climatic catastrophe that may threaten the future of civilization as we know it, whether impacting land or ocean. Such events occur on average once per 100,000 years, or less often.

Figure 21.7 The Torino Impact Hazard Scale.

Perspectives on the Human Environment

The Impact of Near-Earth Objects on the Film Industry

Over the years, only a smattering of movies have been made about comets, asteroids, or meteorites that have either come close to Earth or actually impacted it with devastating results. Most of these, as might be expected, have taken great liberties with our understanding of such past and potential events.

The technicolour feature film *When Planets Collide* was the first release to deal with impact, and it won the 1951 Academy Award for Special Effects. In this movie a rogue star and its planet have entered the solar system and are on a course that will impact Earth. A few days before the star hits the Earth its planet passes close by and causes earthquakes and tsunamis. A rocket is hurriedly assembled and a few selected individuals are chosen to escape Earth before the collision and the end of the world. In 1958 *The Blob* (also called *The Meteorite Monster* or *The Molten Meteorite*) was in the movie houses. The film's main 'claim to fame' is that it is one of the first movies featuring Steve McQueen.

After *The Blob* there was a hiatus of about 20 years before the next doomsday impact movie was released. *Meteor* (1979) starred Sean Connery (as an American scientist) and Natalie Wood (as his Soviet counterpart). A comet ('Orpheus') is on a collision course with the Earth. Both the US and the USSR have secret orbiting nuclear weapons platforms aimed at each other. Connery's character and the US President (played by Henry Fonda) decide to tell the world that the two superpowers have the capability to use these weapons to blow up or divert the comet. The Soviets, however, do not want their space weapons to become known. Fragments of the comet break off and hit Siberia, burn up over Italy, take out a ski resort in Switzerland, land in the ocean off Hong Kong—causing a tsunami that destroys the settlement—and finally start to rain down on New York City. The Soviets at last agree to use their space weapons in conjunction with those of the US to obliterate or shift the comet off course. The movie was the last of a plethora of 1970s disaster movies because it received universally bad reviews.

The next decade saw the release of two movies that involved near-Earth objects. Released in 1984, *Night of the Comet* was a science-fiction horror-zombie film notable only because it starred Robert Beltran (who later played Commander Chakotay, the first officer in the *Star Trek: Voyager* TV series (1995–2001). In 1986, the satirical horror movie *Maximum Overdrive*, starring Emilio Estevez, was notable for being both written and directed by Stephen King. The plot of the movie is that radiation from a comet (Rhea-M) closely passing by the Earth (in 1987) causes all kinds of electronic appliances and other machines (including hair dryers, pinball machines, ATMs, construction vehicles, and semi-trailer rigs) to become self-aware and commit genocide.

The multiple impacts of fragments of Comet P/Shoemaker-Levy 9 on Jupiter (July 1994), seen on news programs around the world, had a great impact on moviemakers and led to the release of two blockbuster movies in 1998. *Deep Impact* was released a few months before *Armageddon*. The plot of *Deep Impact* revolves around a teenaged astronomer (Elijah Wood) and his teacher who discover a comet on a collision course with Earth. This fact gets to the US government. The President (Morgan Freeman) goes on TV and announces that the comet will hit the Earth. NASA assures him and the US people that they have the technology and protocol—'Messiah'—to destroy the comet before it strikes. Needless to say, the mission is unsuccessful and panic ensues, with millions of people trying to escape the impact area and head for higher ground. The government decides to select a million people to survive the impact in specially designed underground refuges. This select group consists of 200,000 scientists, soldiers, and government officials plus 800,000 ordinary US citizens, who will save mankind from extinction and repopulate the US (or world, depending on the size of the impact).

Armageddon starred Bruce Willis (as Harry Stamper, oil driller extraordinaire), Billy Bob

Thornton (as the head of NASA), Ben Affleck, Steve Buscemi (as 'Rockhound'), and Owen Wilson (as Oscar Choi, a geologist). In this film an asteroid 'the size of Texas' is heading for the Earth. Small fragments of the asteroid destroy a space shuttle in Earth's orbit and go on to decimate New York City. The world's best core-drilling team (headed by Willis) is sent into space to drill a 26–7 m hole into the asteroid and ignite a nuclear device inside it. They have 18 days to train the drilling team for space and accomplish the mission. The idea is to split the asteroid in two and divert the two parts so that they go either side of the Earth. Although *Deep Impact* was hailed as being more scientifically accurate than *Armageddon*, the latter was more successful at the box office.

In the last few years, asteroids and meteorites have been the focus of a number of television documentaries and documentary series, and a dramatic TV series titled *Meteor: Path of Destruction* (starring Christopher Lloyd and Stacy Keach) is now in post-production and is expected to air sometime in 2009. The most recent big-screen 'impact' movie was produced by a Canadian company in 2005. The plot of *Purple Glow* follows a similar course to most of the other movies discussed above, but is much less scientifically rigorous than either *Deep Impact* or even *Armageddon*. In *Purple Glow*, astronomers throughout the world are watching the skies for a meteor on a collision course with the Earth. When it crashes to Earth in Canada, nearby campers go into the forest to find it (of course, no one asks the question 'how did they survive the impact?'). One woman touches the meteorite and is instantly transformed into a flesh-eating monster and goes on a rampage.

KEY TERMS

asteriods   *page 296*
bolides   *page 296*
comets   *page 296*

impact craters   *page 295*
meteorites   *page 296*
Torino Impact Hazard Scale   *page 299*

REVIEW QUESTIONS

1. What is the difference between an asteroid, a comet, and a meteorite?
2. How is the kinetic energy released by a meteorite impact calculated?
3. How are the three types of impact craters differentiated?
4. What is the evidence for a major impact being responsible for the extinction of the dinosaurs at the end of the Cretaceous period?
5. What are tektites and where are they found?

REFERENCES AND FURTHER READINGS

Alvarez, W. 1998. *T. Rex and the Crater of Doom*. Princeton, NJ: Princeton Univ. Press and New York: Vintage/Random House.
——— et al. 1980. 'Extraterrestrial Cause of the Cretaceous-Tertiary Extinction', *Science* 208: 1095–1108.
Dence, M.R. 2002. 'Re-examining Structural Data from Impact Craters on the Canadian Shield in the Light of Theoretical Models', in J. Plado and L.J. Personen, eds, *Impacts in Precambrian Shields*. Berlin: Springer-Verlag.
———. 2003. 'WIRGO in TICS [What (on Earth) Is *Really* Going on in Terrestrial Impact Craters?] or the Structural Evidence of Shock Metamorphism', *Lunar and Planetary Institute Meeting Proceedings*, 1–4.
Deutch, A., et al. 1995. 'The Sudbury Structure (Ontario, Canada): A Tectonically Deformed Multi-ring Impact Basin', *Geol. Rundshau* 84: 697–709.

Dressler, B.O., R.A.F. Grieve, and V.L. Sharpton, eds. 1994. *Large Meteorite Impacts and Planetary Evolution*. Boulder, Colo.: Geological Society of America Special Paper 293.
Firestone, R.B., and W. Topping. 2001. 'Terrestrial Evidence of a Nuclear Catastrophe in Palaeoindian Times', *Mammoth Trumpet* 16, 2; and *Proceedings of the International Nuclear Physics Conference*, 30 July–3 August, Berkeley, Calif.
——— et al. 2007. 'Extraterrestrial Airburst over North America 12.9K Ago', Paper PP41A-01, Joint Assembly, American Geophysics Union, Acapulco, 22–5 May.
——— et al. 2007. 'Evidence for an Extraterrestrial Impact Event 12,900 Years Ago That Contributed to Megafaunal Extinctions and the Younger Dryas Cooling', Paper PP43-01, Joint Assembly, American Geophysics Union, Acapulco 22–5 May.

French, B.M. 1998. *Traces of Catastrophe: A Handbook of Shock-Metamorphic Effects in Terrestrial Meteorite Impact Structures.* Houston: Lunar and Planetary Institute.

Grieve, R.A.F. 1987. 'Terrestrial Impact Structures', *Annual Review of Earth and Planetary Science* 15: 245–70.

———. 2007. 'Impact Structures in Canada', *GeoText* 5 (St John's: Geological Association of Canada).

———, M.J. Cintala, and A.M. Therriault. 2006. 'Large-Scale Impacts and the Evolution of the Earth's Crust: The Early years', in W.U. Reimold and R.L. Gibson, eds, *Processes on the Early Earth*. Boulder, Colo.: Geological Society of America.

——— and E.M. Shoemaker. 1994. 'The Record of Past Impacts on Earth', in T. Gehrels, ed., *Hazards due to Comets and Asteroids.* Tucson: Univ. of Arizona Press, 417–62.

Hildebrand, A.R., et al. 1991. 'Chicxulub Crater: A Possible Cretaceous/Tertiary Boundary Impact Crater on the Yucatan Peninsula, Mexico', *Geology* 19, 9: 867–71.

Mazur, M.J., R.R. Stewart, and A.R. Hildebrand. 2000. 'The Seismic Signature of Meteorite Impact Craters', *Canadian Society of Engineering Geologists Recorder* (June): 12–16.

Morrison, D., et al. 2004. 'Impacts and the Public: Communicating the Nature of the Impact Hazard', in M.J.S. Belton et al., eds, *Mitigation of Hazardous Comets and Asteroids*. Cambridge: Cambridge Univ. Press.

Pilkington, M., and R.A.F. Grieve. 1992. 'The Geophysical Signature of Terrestrial Impact Craters', *Reviews of Geophysics* 30, 2: 161–81.

Sharpton, V.L., and P.D. Ward, eds. 1990. *Global Catastrophes in Earth History: An Interdisciplinary Conference on Impacts, Volcanism and Mass Mortality.* Boulder, Colo.: Geological Society of America Special Paper 247.

Shoemaker, C.S., and E.M. Shoemaker. 1995. 'Introduction', in J.R. Spencer and J. Mitton, eds, *The Great Comet Crash: The Impact of Comet Shoemaker/Levy 9 on Jupiter.* Cambridge: Cambridge Univ. Press.

Shoemaker, E.M. 1999. 'Impact Cratering through Geologic Time', Ruth Northcott Lecture, *Journal of the Royal Astronomical Society of Canada* 92: 297–309.

Stone, R. 2008. 'Target Earth: A Killer Asteroid May Be Headed Our Way', *National Geographic* 214, 2: 134–49.

Thomas, M.D. 1998. 'Gravity Domains and the Assembly of the North American Continent by Collision Tectonics', *Nature* 331: 333–4.

 ## WEB RESOURCES

neo.jpl.nasa.gov/torino_scale.html Web page of NASA's jet propulsion lab on the Torino Scale for Near Earth Objects.

www.mines.edu/academic/geology/faculty/klee/TunguskaImpact.Pdf Website of an emeritus professor of geology at the Colorado School of Mines about the Tunguska Event of 1908.

www.sandia.gov/LabNews/080104.html Website of the US government's Sandia lab (part of the Lawrence Livermore complex). Information about the new computer estimate of the force of the Tunguska Event of 1908.

www.unb.ca/passc/ImpactDatabase Website of the Earth Impact Database. Has lots of information on meteorite craters, a gazetteer of all known impact sites, maps, bibliographies, etc.

Unit 22

Minerals and Igneous Rocks

Objectives

- To understand the relationship between rocks and their constituent minerals.

- To briefly investigate the important properties of minerals and to provide an elementary scheme for their classification.

- To discuss some important aspects of igneous rocks and their influence on landscape forms.

The Earth's outermost solid sphere is the crust, and the crust is the upper layer of the lithosphere. The crust consists of many different types of rocks, which range from concrete-like hardness to soap-like softness. When subjected to pressure, some fracture; others bend and warp. When heated to high temperatures, some melt and flow whereas others remain solid. When exposed to the forces of weathering and erosion, some withstand these conditions better than others. To understand what we see in the physical landscape, it is essential to comprehend the properties of the underlying building materials—the rocks.

Minerals and Rocks

Matter is made up of 92 naturally occurring elements arranged in a periodic table according to their atomic numbers. Elements exist independently or in combination with other elements; each element consists of atoms (which contain protons, neutrons, and electrons) organized into a characteristic matrix. An element cannot be broken down further, either by heating or by chemical reaction. Minerals can consist of a single element, such as diamond (which is pure carbon) and gold (a metallic element), or they can be combinations of elements, such as quartz, a compound of silicon and oxygen. Minerals are **crystalline**; that is, their atoms are arranged in regular, repeating crystallographic patterns. It is often impossible to see these patterns in hand samples, but microscopes and X-ray diffraction instruments reveal them. Sometimes, however, nature displays these crystal structures in spectacular fashion (Figure 22.1). Thus minerals have distinct properties, given to them by the strength and stability of the atomic bonds in their crystal lattices. To summarize all its characteristics, we would say that a **mineral** is a naturally occurring inorganic element or compound having a definite chemical composition, physical properties, and, usually, a crystal structure.

Many minerals can be quickly recognized by the shape of their crystals as well as by their colour and hardness. For crystals of a given mineral to form, there must be time for their atoms to arrange themselves into the proper pattern. As the formation time increases, so does the size of the mineral structure. Imagine a reservoir of molten rock contained somewhere deep inside the crust. This mass of molten rock cools slowly, and its various component crystals have time to develop their lattice structures quite fully. The atoms, therefore, have the opportunity to arrange themselves in the regular patterns of various minerals. When the mass finally hardens, its various component minerals will be large, well formed, and easily recognizable.

But what happens if that mass of molten rock does not cool slowly deep inside the crust, but is instead poured out through a fissure or vent onto the surface of the crust? Now cooling takes place very rapidly, and there is little time for the atoms to arrange themselves

Figure 22.1 Grossuter (garnet) from Jeffrey Quarry, Asbestos, Quebec, on the Canadian Shield.

into orderly patterns. What results is a solid rock in which the atoms are arranged randomly and the mineral structure is hardly discernible. A glass-like form of lava, called obsidian, is an example of such rapid hardening (Figure 22.2). **Rocks**, therefore, are composed of mineral assemblages. A few rocks consist of only one mineral, such as quartzite, which is mainly quartz. But most rocks contain several minerals, and these minerals have much to do with the way rocks break or bend, weather, and erode.

Mineral Properties

As stated above, all minerals exhibit specific properties that enable them to be identified and differentiated. These properties include chemical composition, hardness, cleavage or fracture, colour and streak, and lustre.

Figure 22.2 Obsidian, the shiny volcanic glass, and rhyolite form when lava cools very rapidly under certain circumstances. Dark bands of obsidian can be seen in this extrusion in Inyo National Forest, California.

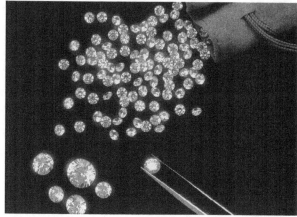

A

B

Figure 22.3 Diamonds reflect this valuable mineral's hardness, clarity, and transparency (A). By contrast, the graphite form of the same carbon exhibits opposite characteristics (B) and is so inexpensive that it is commonly used as pencil 'lead'.

Chemical Composition   Every chemical element is identified by a one- or two-letter symbol. Aluminum, for example, is Al; iron is Fe. This does not mean, however, that all minerals made from each element are the same. Take, for example, the element identified as C, carbon. The mineral *diamond*, one of the hardest substances known, is pure carbon. But so is *graphite*, the soft 'lead' in a pencil. Chemically they are the same, but their crystalline structures differ. In a diamond, all atoms are bonded strongly to each other. In graphite, certain bonds are weaker, creating sheets that are easily split apart. Note, too, that while diamond is clear, transparent, and very hard, graphite is opaque, grey-black, and soft—the very opposite qualities (Figure 22.3). Other minerals are even softer than graphite, and rocks containing such soft minerals are more quickly broken down by weathering and eroded than rocks containing only harder minerals.

LINK

Hardness   Hardness, therefore, is an important property of minerals. This quality can be useful in identifying minerals in the field, and it can suggest much about the overall hardness of the rock in which they occur. As long ago as

1822, Friedrich Mohs noticed that certain minerals could make a scratch mark on other minerals, but not vice versa. Diamond, the hardest mineral of all, will scratch all other natural mineral surfaces, but cannot be scratched by any of the others. So Mohs established a hardness scale ranging from 1 to 10, with diamond (10) the hardest. Mohs determined that talc (the base mineral of talcum powder) was the softest naturally occurring mineral, and this he numbered 1. The **Mohs Hardness Scale** (Table 22.1) continues to be used to this day. Notice that quartz, a commonly appearing mineral, ranks 7 and is quite hard.

Cleavage/Fracture   The crystal form of minerals quickly identifies them in some cases, but not many crystals can grow unimpeded to the full form shown in Figure 22.1. More useful is the property of **cleavage**, the tendency of minerals to break in certain directions along bright plane surfaces, revealing the zones of weakness in the crystalline structure. When you break a rock sample across a large

Table 22.1 The Mohs Hardness Scale

Mineral	Hardness
Diamond	10
Corundum	9
Topaz	8
Quartz	7
Potassium feldspar	6
Apatite	5
Fluorite	4
Calcite	3
Gypsum	2
Talc	1

By way of comparison, here are some everyday items ranked according to their approximate hardness: pocketknife blade, 5–6; glass, 5; copper penny, 3.5; fingernail, 2.5.

Table 22.2 Composition of the Earth's Crust

Element	Percentage (by Weight)
Oxygen (O)	46.6
Silicon (Si)	27.7
Aluminum (Al)	8.1
Iron (Fe)	5.0
Calcium (Ca)	3.6
Sodium (Na)	2.8
Potassium (K)	2.6
Magnesium (Mg)	2.1
TOTAL	98.5

crystal of a certain mineral, the way that crystal breaks may help to identify it. Sometimes minerals do not break as cleanly as this, however. Instead, they **fracture** in a characteristic way. That glass-like obsidian mentioned earlier (Figure 22.2) has a way of fracturing in a concoidal (shell-like) fashion when broken.

Colour/Streak   A mineral's colour is its most easily observable property. Some minerals have very distinct colours, such as the yellow of sulphur and the deep blue of azurite. Other minerals have identical colours or occur in numerous colours, and therefore cannot be differentiated according to this property. However, the colour of a mineral's *streak* (the mineral in powdered form when rubbed against a porcelain plate) can sometimes help identify it. For example, although both galena and graphite are metallic grey in colour, their streaks are grey and black, respectively. Like colour, streak is often unhelpful in that most minerals have white or colourless streaks.

Lustre   A mineral also displays a surface sheen or *lustre*, which, along with colour, can be a useful identifying quality. Lustre can be classified as shiny, vitreous (glassy), metallic (mirror-like), dull, waxy, pearly, etc. For instance, the difference between real gold (dull lustre) and a similar-looking but much less valuable mineral, pyrite (FeS_2) (metallic lustre), can be detected by their comparative lustres. Not surprisingly, pyrite is called fool's gold for good reason!

Mineral Types

Although nearly 100 chemical elements are known in nature, only eight make up more than 98 per cent of the Earth's crust by weight (see Table 22.2). Moreover, the two most common elements in the crust, silicon and

oxygen, constitute almost 75 per cent of it. Geologists divide the minerals into two major groups, the *silicates* and the *non-silicates*. Each group is in turn subdivided. This classification is a central concern of the field of mineralogy.

The silicates, as their name suggests, are the compounds containing silicon (Si) and oxygen (O) and, mostly, other elements as well. The non-silicates include the carbonates, sulphates, sulphides, and halides. Among these, the *carbonates* are of greatest interest in physical geography. All carbonates contain carbon and oxygen (CO_3). With calcium they form calcite, the mineral of which limestone is made. Limestone is fairly widely distributed, and it creates unusual landforms under both humid and arid conditions (see Unit 35). Add magnesium (Mg) to the formula, and the mineral dolomite (or dolostone) is formed. Dolomite, too, creates distinctive landforms.

The *sulphates* (SO_4) all contain sulphur and oxygen. The calcium sulphate, gypsum, in some places lies exposed over sufficiently large areas to be of geomorphological interest. The *sulphides* (SO_3), on the other hand, occur in veins and ores, and do not build or sustain landforms themselves. Pyrite (FeS_2) is such a mineral. The *halides* consist of metals combined with such elements as chlorine, fluorine, and iodine. The most common is halite, a compound of sodium (Na) and chloride (Cl), the substance that makes ocean water salty; but halite rock salt also can create landforms.

Finally, there are the oxides and natural elements. The *oxides* are formed by a combination of metal and oxygen, nothing more. This kind of crystallization takes place in veins and ore chambers, and the result may be an economically important deposit of, for example, hematite (Fe_2O_3) or magnetite (Fe_3O_4). Oxidation also can take place as a result of the intrusion of liquid water or water vapour into concentrations of iron or aluminum. The *natural elements* are those rare and prized commodities that are among the most valuable on Earth: gold (Au), silver (Ag), platinum (Pt), and sometimes copper (Cu), tin (Sn), and antimony (Sb).

Perspectives on the Human Environment

The World's Oldest Rocks

Geologists have known for decades that the Earth was formed about 4.6 billion years ago, condensing from a rotating, gaseous mass along with the other terrestrial planets of the inner solar system. At first our planet consisted entirely of molten rock, but one hypothesis suggests that eventually its heavier constituent elements (iron and nickel) settled to form a solid core. Another idea is that early on in the Earth's history there was a major collision with a large asteroid. The asteroid was incorporated into the Earth, eventually reaching the Earth's core. On its way to the interior it took most of the heavier minerals in the crust with it. Above that inner core, as Figure 20.5 indicates, three concentric layers emerged as the Earth continued to cool: the outer core, the lower mantle, and the upper mantle. Until a few years ago, scientists had little information as to when the upper mantle began to develop a crust, a process they liken to the formation of the crust atop boiling pea soup. But recent discoveries of very old rock formations in the continental shields of Canada, Australia, and Greenland have now begun to shed light on the events associated with the birth of the crust—and have produced field specimens that may rank among the first rocks ever formed.

Since 1990 the age of the oldest known rocks has been pushed back by at least several hundred million years. The Acasta gneisses found about 350 km north of Yellowknife, NWT, have now been dated at 3.96 billion years, and neighbouring rocks may be as old as 4.27 billion years. That is also the age of individual mineral crystals (zircons) found in sedimentary rocks discovered in the Jack Hills about 690 km north of Perth, Western Australia, during the 1980s. The oldest rocks dated from the mantle were found in two outcrops along the rugged coast of Labrador. They have been dated to 4 billion years ago. The older rock into which this rock was intruded is a komatite formed when some of the hot mantle erupted onto the Earth's surface (geologists are now searching for the even older rocks on which this lava was deposited). Clearly, the ancient gneiss specimens prove the existence of continental crust almost 4 billion years ago, whereas the sedimentary grains strongly suggest that the cycle of transformation that affects all rocks (see discussion of the rock cycle in Unit 23) was operating even earlier than that.

These monumental findings have not only filled major gaps in our knowledge of the earliest stage of Earth history, they are also alerting scientists to field research opportunities that, prior to the 1990s, few could even imagine existed. Indeed, in September 2008 the age of the oldest known rocks was pushed back even further when geologists announced the discovery, in 2001, of 4.28 billion-year-old amphibolites found on the eastern side of Hudson Bay in northern Quebec in an area known as the Nuvvuagittuq greenstone belt.

Classification of Rock Types

From what has been said about the minerals that make up the crustal rocks, it is evident that the diversity of rock types is almost unlimited. Still, when rocks are classified according to their mode of origin, they all fall into one of three families. One class—**igneous rocks**—forms as a result of the cooling and solidification of **magma** (molten rock). Because they solidified first from the Earth's primeval molten crust (see 'Perspectives' box), igneous rocks are known as *primary* rocks. The weathering, erosion, transport, deposition, and compression of rock and mineral fragments produces **sedimentary rocks**, and when existing rocks are modified by heat or pressure or both, they are transformed into **metamorphic rocks**. Because they are derivatives of pre-existing rocks, sedimentary and metamorphic rocks are called *secondary* rocks. Igneous rocks are treated in the remainder of this unit; secondary rocks are the subject of Unit 23.

LINK

Igneous Rocks

The term *igneous* means 'born by fire', from the Latin word *ignis*, meaning fire. The ancient Romans, upon seeing the flaming lava erupt from Italy's Mounts Vesuvius and Etna, undoubtedly concluded that fire stoked the rock-forming ovens inside the Earth. But igneous rocks actually form from cooling—the lowering of the temperature of molten magma or **lava** (magma that reaches the Earth's surface). This can happen deep inside the crust or on the surface. Magma is not only a complex melt of many minerals; it also contains gases, including water vapour. It is a surging, swelling mass that pushes outward and upward, sometimes forcing itself into and through existing layers of rocks in the crust, incorporating them as it goes (diapirism). If the upward thrust ceases before the magma reaches the surface, the resulting rocks formed from the cooled magma are called **intrusive igneous rocks**. If it penetrates all the way to the surface and spills out as lava or is erupted as ash or tephra, the rocks formed from these materials are called **extrusive igneous rocks**.

As noted previously, intrusive igneous rocks tend to have larger mineral crystals than faster-cooling extrusive ones. Intrusives such as granite and gabbro are coarse-grained, with mineral crystals as much as 1 cm or more in diameter. For intrusive rocks with exceptionally large crystals, some ranging from 2 to 3 cm long, the cooling process obviously was unusually slow. It is concluded that this occurred at unusual depth and that the magmatic mass must have been very large. Such coarse-grained intrusive rocks are called *plutonic* igneous rocks, another term of Latin origin (Pluto was the Roman god of the underworld).

The colour of igneous rocks can tell us much about their origins. When the original magma is rich in silica (*felsic, acidic,* or *silicic*), it yields rocks rich in feldspar and quartz. Such rocks are light-coloured, with pink or beige-coloured feldspar and glassy quartz dominating. Magma that was poorer in silica (*basic* or *mafic*) yields darker rocks, both intrusives and extrusives. For example, a light-coloured, coarse-grained granite formed as an intrusive rock; had the same magma spilled out onto the surface, it would have yielded a light-coloured but much finer grained rhyolite. But a dark-coloured, coarse-grained gabbro came from a basic magma; had it penetrated to the surface as an extrusive rock, it would have become a fine-grained black basalt.

Intrusive Forms

In the analysis of landscapes, the form an intrusion (a mass of intrusive rock) takes becomes an important factor. Magmas vary not only in composition, but also in viscosity (fluidness). Thick, viscous masses will remain compact; if the magma is very fluid, it can penetrate narrow cracks in existing rock strata and inject itself between layers. Sometimes the pent-up gases in magma will help force it through its chamber walls. Other magmas, containing less gas, are calmer.

In general terms, intrusions may be **concordant** if they do not disrupt or destroy existing structures or **discordant** if they cut across previously formed strata. For instance, a **batholith** is a massive *pluton* (a body of plutonic rock) that has melted and assimilated most of the existing rock structures it has invaded; a *stock* also is discordant but smaller. Sometimes magma inserts itself as a thin layer between strata of existing rocks without disturbing these older layers to any great extent; such an intrusion is called a **sill**. But magma can also cut vertically across existing layers, forming a kind of barrier wall called a *dyke*. The sill is a concordant intrusion; the dyke obviously is discordant. An especially interesting concordant intrusive form is the **laccolith**. In this case a magma pipe led to a chamber that grew, dome-like, pushing the overlying strata into a gentle bulge without destroying them. These variations are shown in Figure 22.4.

Jointing and Exfoliation

Igneous rocks such as granite and basalt display a property that is of great importance in their breakdown under weathering and erosion. **Jointing** is the tendency of rocks to develop parallel sets of fractures without any obvious movement along the plane of separation (such as faulting). Granite often exhibits a rectangular joint pattern so that it breaks naturally into blocks (Figure 22.5). Basalt, on the other hand, usually possesses a columnar joint system that produces hexagonal forms. Jointing in igneous rocks appears to be related to the cooling process of the magma. The contraction of the material produces planes of weakness and separation—*the joint planes*—but jointing is not confined to igneous rocks. Sedimentary and metamorphic rocks also display forms of jointing.

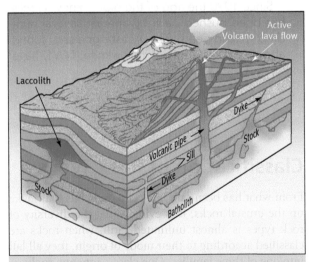

Figure 22.4 Diagrammatic cross-section through the uppermost crust showing the various forms assumed by plutons.

From the Fieldnotes

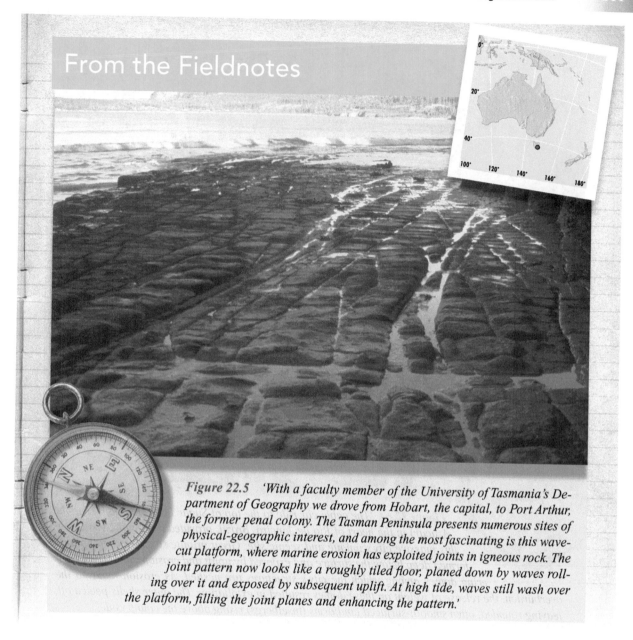

Figure 22.5 *'With a faculty member of the University of Tasmania's Department of Geography we drove from Hobart, the capital, to Port Arthur, the former penal colony. The Tasman Peninsula presents numerous sites of physical-geographic interest, and among the most fascinating is this wave-cut platform, where marine erosion has exploited joints in igneous rock. The joint pattern now looks like a roughly tiled floor, planed down by waves rolling over it and exposed by subsequent uplift. At high tide, waves still wash over the platform, filling the joint planes and enhancing the pattern.'*

A special kind of jointing, found in certain kinds of granite, produces a joint pattern resembling a series of concentric shells—not unlike the layers of an onion. The outer layers, or shells, peel away progressively, leaving the lower layers exposed (Figure 22.6). This phenomenon, called **exfoliation** or spalling, is caused by the release of confining pressure. These granite domes were at one time buried deep inside the crust under enormous pressure. As erosion removed the overlying rocks, the pressure was reduced and these rock masses expanded. The outer shells, unable to resist this expansion force, cracked and peeled along hidden (concentric) joint planes.

Igneous Rocks in the Landscape

Igneous rocks tend to be strongly resistant to weathering and erosion. Intrusive igneous structures often form characteristic landforms when their overburdens are removed

LINK

through weathering and erosion (**etchplanation**). For example, when the strata overlying a laccolith (Figure 22.4) are eroded away, the granitic core stands as a mound above the landscape, encircled by low ridges representing remnants of the softer sedimentary cover. The intrusive sill, which long ago squeezed between sedimentary layers (Figure 22.4), resists erosion longer than the softer sedimentary rocks. Eventually such a remnant of a sill is likely to cap a table-like landform, called a *mesa* (see Figure 33.7). A dyke (Figure 22.4), which is also more resistant than its surroundings, will stand out above the countryside as a serpentine ridge (see photo of New Mexico's Ship Rock, Figure 33.6). Exfoliation also can be seen in progress in many places (some spectacular examples are the domes in California's Yosemite National Park).

The most spectacular landforms associated with igneous rocks undoubtedly are shaped by extrusive structures,

From the Fieldnotes

Figure 22.6 'The cable-car ride to the top of Sugar Loaf Mountain (Pao de Azucar) in the heart of Rio de Janeiro, Brazil, provided a dramatic vista over this massive city's unique and scenic site. Great granite stocks and batholiths, formed deep below the surface and exposed by uplift and erosion, now create towering domes among which the city's structures are nestled. As erosion removed the overburden, the release of weight on these domes resulted in exfoliation. The outer shells peeled off, leaving rounded, often smooth-surfaced landforms (inselbergs) rising above the countryside.'

especially the world's great volcanoes. A famous one is Devil's Tower (it had a starring role in the movie *Close Encounters of the Third Kind*) in Wyoming (Figure 22.7), a columnar structure of basaltic rock formed from an ancient eruption. The violent eruption of Mount St Helens in the US Pacific Northwest in 1980 provided scientists with an opportunity to witness volcanic processes and their consequences. Vesuvius, the great volcano that looms over the Italian city of Naples, is the most legendary of all such mountains. The processes and landforms of volcanism are investigated in Unit 25. But now the survey of the two remaining major rock types continues in Unit 23.

Figure 22.7 Devil's Tower, a columnar basalt structure 263 m high, was the first physical feature to be declared a US National Monument. Located in northeastern Wyoming, it is the remnant of a volcanic intrusion in which conditions favoured the development of basalt's hexagonal jointing.

KEY TERMS

batholith *page 310*
cleavage *page 307*
concordant intrusion *page 310*
crystalline rocks *page 306*
discordant intrusion *page 310*
etchplanation *page 311*
exfoliation *page 311*
extrusive igneous rock *page 310*
fracture *page 308*
igneous rocks *page 309*
intrusive igneous rock *page 310*

jointing *page 310*
laccolith *page 310*
lava *page 310*
magma *page 309*
metamorphic rocks *page 309*
mineral *page 306*
Mohs Hardness Scale *page 307*
rock *page 306*
sedimentary rocks *page 309*
sill *page 310*

REVIEW QUESTIONS

1. What are minerals?
2. How are minerals related to elements and rocks?
3. How are intrusive and extrusive igneous rocks different, and how can they generally be distinguished?

4. How is a *sill* different from a *dyke*?
5. How is a *batholith* different from a *laccolith*?

REFERENCES AND FURTHER READINGS

Barker, D.S. 1983. *Igneous Rocks*. Englewood Cliffs, NJ: Prentice-Hall.

Cox, K.G., et al. 1979. *The Interpretation of Igneous Rocks*. Boston: Allen & Unwin.

Deer, W.A., R.A. Howie, and J. Zussman. 1992. *An Introduction to Rock Forming Minerals*, 2nd edn. New York: Wiley.

Dietrich, R.V., and B.J. Skinner. 1990. *Gems, Granites, and Gravels: Knowing and Using Rocks and Minerals*. New York: Cambridge Univ. Press.

Ehlers, E.G., and H. Blatt. 1982. *Petrology: Igneous, Sedimentary, and Metamorphic*. New York: Freeman.

Hess, P.C. 1989. *Origins of Igneous Rocks*. Cambridge, Mass.: Harvard Univ. Press.

Hilts, P.J. 1989. 'Canadian Rock, at 4 Billion Years, Is Called Oldest', *New York Times*, 5 Oct., 8.

Hurlbut, C.S., Jr. 1969. *Minerals and Man*. New York: Random House.

Klein, C., and C.S. Hurlbut Jr. 1993. *Manual of Mineralogy*, 21st edn. New York: Wiley.

McIlroy, A. 2008. 'Classic Rock: Record-Setting 4-Billion-Year-Old Rocks Uncovered in Northern Quebec', *Globe and Mail*, 26 Sept.

MacKenzie, W.S., et al. 1982. *Atlas of Igneous Rocks and Their Textures*. New York: Wiley/Halsted.

O'Neill, J., et al. 2008. 'Neodymium-142 Evidence of Hadean Mafic Crust', *Science* 321, 5897: 1828–31.

Pough, F. 1960. *A Field Guide to Rocks and Minerals*, 3rd edn. Cambridge, Mass.: Riverside Press.

Prinz, M., et al. 1978. *Simon and Schuster's Guide to Rocks and Minerals*. New York: Simon & Schuster.

Ryan, M.P., ed. 1994. *Magmatic Systems*. Orlando, Fla: Academic Press.

WEB RESOURCES

csmres.jmu.edu/geollab/Fichter/IgnRx/Ighome.html Lynn Fichter's site at James Madison University provides a comprehensive guide to igneous rocks and their classification. Extrusive and intrusive igneous rocks are covered, and there are many links to photos and descriptions. A self-test on classification is provided.

earthsci.org/mineral/mineral.html This Australian Earth science site presents background information on rock formation and structure. The rock cycle is explained, and both minerals and igneous rocks are covered in detail.

nature.ca/collections/earthsci_e.cfm Web pages about Earth science, rocks, and minerals from the Canadian Museum of Nature, Ottawa.

www.mineralogicalassociation.ca Information about minerals, links to relevant sites, etc.

www.rom.on.ca/news/releases/public.php?mediakey=m7zppqh8yu Web page about the Royal Ontario Museum acquiring the Charles Key Mineral Collection.

Unit 23

Sedimentary and Metamorphic Rocks

Objectives

- To discuss the circumstances under which sedimentary and metamorphic rocks form.

- To identify common sedimentary and metamorphic rock types.

- To discuss some observable structures within sedimentary and metamorphic rock masses.

The igneous rocks have been called the Earth's primary rocks—the first solidified material derived from the molten mass that once was the primeval crust. The other two great classes of rocks could therefore be called secondary, because they are derived from pre-existing rocks. These are the sedimentary and metamorphic rocks.

Sedimentary Rocks

Sedimentary rocks result from the erosion, transportation, deposition, and compaction (**lithification**) of rock fragments and mineral grains derived from other rocks. These grains are weathered and broken away from existing rocks by the action of water, wind, and ice, processes explored in Part Four. Again, the ancient Roman scholars understood what they saw: *sedimentum* is the Latin word for settling. Many sedimentary rocks begin their existence as loose deposits of sand or gravel at the bottom of a river, sea, or lake, on a beach, or in a desert (Figure 23.1). Later the sediment is lithified—compressed into rock.

As successive layers of sediment accumulate, the weight of the sediments expels most of the water between the grains. Pressure caused by the weight of the overlying materials will compact and consolidate the lower strata. The rock fragments and grains are squeezed tightly together, especially in fine-grained sediments such as clays and silts. This is the process of **compaction** (Figure 23.2A). Compaction rarely takes place alone. Most sedimentary material has some water in the pore spaces between the grains, and this fluid contains dissolved minerals. This mineral matter, such as silica or calcite, is deposited in thin films on the grain surfaces,

which has the effect of gluing them together. This is the process of **cementation** (Figure 23.2B). Together, compaction and cementation can transform a bed of loose sand into a layer of cohesive sedimentary rock called sandstone.

Clastic and Nonclastic Sedimentary Rocks

The range of agents and materials that combine to produce sedimentary rocks is wide, and as a result the structure and texture of these rocks also vary greatly. Even the finest wind-blown dust can become lithified. The same is true for a mixture of boulders, cobbles, pebbles, and sand swept down by a stream and subsequently compacted and cemented. Sedimentary rocks made from particles of other rocks are referred to as **clastic**, from the ancient Greek *klastos*, meaning broken. The vast majority of sedimentary rocks are clastic. **Nonclastic sedimentary rocks** form from chemical solution by deposition and evaporation, or from organic deposition.

Clastic sediments are most conveniently classified according to the size of their fragments, which can range from boulders to fine clay particles. The coarsest-grained sedimentary rock is the **conglomerate**, a composite rock made of gravels, pebbles, and sometimes even boulders. An important property of conglomerates is that the pebbles or boulders tend to be quite well rounded. This characteristic is evidence that they were transported by water for some distance, perhaps rolled down a stream or washed back and forth across a beach. A large pebble may reveal the area from which it was removed, perhaps telling us something about ancient drainage courses. Sometimes pebbles are elliptical in shape, and in the conglomerate a

Figure 23.1 'You can almost feel the power of the process that transported and deposited this accumulation of poorly sorted sediment in its present location. Boulders lie closer to the surface than smaller pebbles; many fragments are angular, suggesting short-distance transportation and no time for rounding or sorting. It must have happened very suddenly, a burst of force, perhaps during a major flood in this desert environment (we are in a valley near the Gila River in eastern Arizona). This mass of material would become a conglomerate if compaction and cementation followed. More likely, future rainstorms and floods will carry most of it further downslope.'

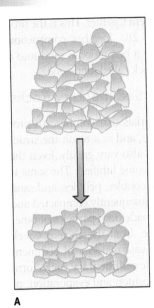
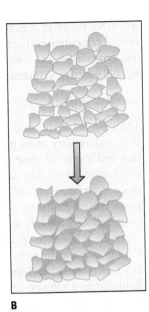

A   **B**

Figure 23.2 Compaction and cementation in sedimentary rocks. (A) In *compaction*, the grains are packed tightly together by weight from above. (B) In *cementation*, the spaces between the grains are filled through the deposition of a cement, such as silica or calcium carbonate.

significant number of them lie cemented with their long axes in the same direction. Such information helps reveal

the orientation of the coastline where the sediment accumulated.

When pebble-sized fragments in a conglomerate are not rounded but angular and jagged, it is called a **breccia** (Figure 23.3). The rough shape of the pebbles indicates that little transport took place prior to lithification. When compaction and cementation occur after a rock avalanche, for instance, the result is a breccia. Again, the properties of the fragments can constitute a key to the past.

Another common and important sedimentary rock is **sandstone**. In a sandstone the grains, as the name implies, are sand-sized, and they usually are quartz grains. Some sandstones are very hard and resist erosion even in humid climates. This is because the cementing material in such sandstones is silica. But other sandstones are less compacted and are cemented by calcite or even iron oxide. Such sandstones are 'softer' and more susceptible to weathering and erosion. Thus sandstones are also a key to the past. They may have rounded or angular grains, depending on the distance travelled and the process of movement.

As with conglomerates, the size of sandstone grains may vary. Rounded, even-sized grains indicate long-distance travel. Variations in particle size and irregular shapes mean poor sorting and rapid deposition. Sandstones also have economic importance: because they are porous, they can contain substantial amounts of water and even oil. Under certain structural circumstances, such water or oil can form a reservoir suitable for exploitation (see 'Perspectives' box).

From the Fieldnotes

Figure 23.3 '*Although it is reasonable to assume that the poorly sorted material in Figure. 23.1 will be eroded away, there are times when another process intervenes. When a fault cuts across an area underlain by such sediment, the rock material caught in the fault plane may be partially melted and welded into a highly resistant rock called breccia. We were travelling through an area of southern Spain when we saw this superb example. Note that a ridge of resistant rock stands in a natural wall between rocks dipping at different angles to the right (under the vegetation) and to the left (exposed in a scarp). The natural wall is made of breccia, formed when the fault occurred. It stands out because it is more resistant than the sediments on either side of the fault; you can judge the height by the shadow it casts.*'

A sedimentary rock even softer than most sandstones is **shale**, the finest-grained clastic sedimentary rock. Shale is compacted mud. Whereas sandstone contains quartz grains that are often visible to the naked eye, shale is made from clay minerals, and the individual mineral grains cannot be seen. Shale has a tendency to split into thin layers, making this already 'soft' rock even more susceptible to weathering and erosion (Figure 23.5). In many places (such as the Appalachian Mountains in eastern North America), the low valleys are often underlain by soft shale and the higher ridges by other rocks, including hard sandstone.

One of the most interesting sedimentary rocks, because of both the way it forms and its response to weathering and erosion, is **limestone**. Limestone can form from the accumulation of marine shell fragments on a beach or on the ocean floor, which qualifies it as a special kind of clastic sedimentary rock. Most limestone, however, results from the respiration and photosynthesis of marine organisms, such as foraminifera or rotifers, in which calcium carbonate is distilled from sea water. The shells of these tiny creatures settle on the ocean floor after they die, and accumulations may reach hundreds of metres in thickness. Limestone can vary in composition and texture, but much of it is fine textured and, when exposed on the continental landscape, hard and resistant to weathering. Limestone, however, is susceptible to solution, and under certain environmental conditions it creates a unique landscape both above and below the ground (see Unit 35).

None of the nonclastic sedimentary rocks play a significant role in the formation of landscape, other than limestone in its chemical form. **Evaporites** form from the deposits left behind as water evaporates. Such evaporites as halite (salt), gypsum, and anhydrite have some economic importance, but their areal extent is small. Biological sediments include the carbonate rocks formed by coral reefs, cherts formed from silica skeletons of diatoms and radiolarians (marine micro-organisms), and, technically, the various forms of coal.

Sedimentary Rocks in the Landscape

A sequence of sedimentary rocks in the landscape is unmistakable because it displays variations in texture, colour, and thickness of the various layers. This layering,

Perspectives on the Human Environment

Oilfield Formation

The first commercial oil well in North America was dug by James Miller Williams at Black Creek (soon renamed Oil Springs), Lambton County, Canada West (now Ontario), in 1858. By 1861 oil production from 400 wells in the Oil Springs area was up to 800 barrels/day. At that time, a barrel of oil sold for $10. Williams alone shipped 1.5 million litres of oil out of Lambton County in two years.

By 1862 Oil Springs had become a boom town with 1000 operating wells and a population of between 3000 and 4000 (see Figure 46.11). It had 12 general stores, nine hotels, and horse-drawn buses that plied the first paved main street in Canada. Oil Springs had gas lighting installed along its Main Street before any of the major cities in North America or Europe. In fact, the first oil company in the world (International Mining and Manufacturing Company) was formed in Oil Springs in 1854 by two brothers, Charles and Henry Tripp, who discovered and utilized oil gum, or tar beds as the basis for small-scale petroleum production for oil lamp fuel. Their company failed, and Williams (a major creditor) took over the property licences. Seven years after the oil rush at Oil Springs, another oil bonanza started up at Petrolea (now Petrolia), about 10 km to the south. The community marked the 150th anniversary of the first commercial oil well in 2008. Producers in Oil Springs average 35,000 barrels a year. In 1861 John Henry was the biggest producer in the area with 24,000 barrels/year; his great-grandson produces the same output and is one of the smallest producers in Canada, according to a recent article in the *Toronto Star* (11 May 2008).

The Earth's proven oil reserves are now estimated to exceed 1 trillion barrels (one barrel equals approximately 159 L, or 0.159 m³). Saudi Arabia possesses the largest petroleum reserves (261 billion barrels), while Iraq has 115 billion barrels, Iran 100 billion barrels, Kuwait 99 billion barrels, and the United Arab Emirates 63 billion barrels (all figures are as of 2003).

In January 2006 Canadian oil reserves were estimated to be 4.7 billion barrels of conventional oil; if oil derived from the Alberta tar sands is included, reserves are estimated to be 178.8 billion barrels, second only to Saudi Arabia. Canadian oil production averaged 3.23 million barrels/day during 2006. Sixty-seven per cent of this oil production came from Alberta (42 per cent of the province's production was from the oil sands), 18 per cent from Saskatchewan, and 13 per cent from the offshore of Newfoundland and Labrador. The large reserves on the continental shelf have not been fully utilized and more exploration is going on.

Canada is the fifth largest energy producer, behind the United States, Russia, China, and Saudi Arabia. It is the largest supplier of US crude oil imports. The latest estimates are that Canada supplies 17 per cent of US crude imports (1.78 million barrels per day in 2006), Mexico 11 per cent, and Saudi Arabia 9 per cent. Canada is also responsible for 87 per cent of US natural gas imports (see Table 23.1). Although Canada is a major oil producer, its oil and refined oil products imports, most of it destined for eastern and central Canada, totalled approximately 18 billion barrels in 2005. In 2006 Canadian imports came from the following sources: the US (23.5 per cent), Norway (22.4 per cent), the UK (16.2 per cent), and OPEC countries including Algeria (20.7 per cent), Saudi Arabia (8.7 per cent), and Iraq (7.4 per cent).

Petroleum occurs in the sedimentary rocks of non-shield zones (Figure 20.12), where

conditions have favoured the development of geological structures capable of containing oil reservoirs. The formation of petroleum itself involved large, shallow bodies of water where, scientists believe, microscopic plant forms (such as diatoms) contained minute amounts of an oily substance. At death, these tiny plants released this substance, so that it became part of the sediments accumulating on the seabed.

Millions of years later, a thick accumulation of sediments—now transformed into sedimentary rock layers—might contain a large quantity of oil. Then, when these rock layers were subsequently compressed and bent into arching structures called folds (see Unit 27), the accumulated oil would be squeezed into a reservoir, as shown in Figure 23.4. Such a reservoir might be an upfold in the rock layers or a dome capped by an impermeable stratum. (Note that natural gas often forms above such an oil pool—the two energy resources frequently occur together—and that the oil also floats above any groundwater that may lie below the upfold in the porous, reservoir rock layer.) There the petroleum deposit remains under pressure until its existence is discovered by exploration. Then a well is drilled, the black liquid is pumped to the surface, and the world's oil production capacity is recorded as having increased.

Table 23.1 Destination of Canadian Oil Exports, 2005

Location	Percentage
US	98.14 (1.78 million barrels/day)
European Union	1.15
Japan	0.14
Mexico	0.01
Other	0.56
Total: 1.8 million barrels/day	

Source: Canadian Minerals Yearbook Online 2005.

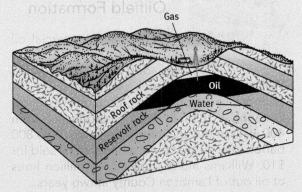

Figure 23.4 *Oil pool* (a body of rock in which oil occupies all the pore spaces) trapped in an upward-arching layer of reservoir rock. These curving rock structures are known as folds; they constitute the most important of all oil traps.

or **stratification**, reminds us that conditions changed as a succession of rock beds or *strata* was being deposited. Often distinct surfaces between strata, or **bedding planes**, are evident. Sometimes it is apparent that the sequence was interrupted and that a period of deposition was broken by a period of erosion before the deposition resumed. Where such an interruption is evident in the **stratigraphy** (order and arrangement of strata) of sedimentary rocks, the

contact between the eroded strata and the strata of resumed deposition is called an **unconformity** (Figure 23.6).

The texture and colour of the sedimentary layers allow us to deduce the kinds of environments under which they were deposited. Sedimentary rocks, therefore, are crucial in the reconstruction of past environments. Even more importantly, sedimentary rocks contain fossils (Figure 23.7). Much of what is known about Earth history

Figure 23.5 Steeply angled limestone and shale jutting out into the water at Broom Pond, Newfoundland. This soft, thin-layered sedimentary rock is easily weathered and eroded.

is based on the fossil record. Interpretations from the fossil record, as well as conclusions drawn from the stratigraphy of sedimentary rock sequences far removed from one another, make correlations possible that provide further evidence for reconstructions of the past.

Sedimentary rocks can be observed as they accumulate today, providing further insight into similar conditions in the distant geological past. You may have seen ripples in the sands of a beach or in a desert area. These ripples can be created by the wash of waves or by the persistent blowing of wind. Most of the time they are erased again, only to reform later. But sometimes they are cemented and preserved in lithifying rock as *ripple marks*. Ripple marks formed millions of years ago have become exposed by erosion—providing evidence of wind or wave directions in the distant past.

Features of Sedimentary Strata

When originally formed, most sedimentary strata are layered horizontally. Another form of layering, **cross-bedding**, consists of successive strata deposited at varying inclines. Like ripple marks, this forms on beaches and in dunes. The sand layers do not lie flat, but at angles caused by wind and water-current action over an irregular bed. We

From the Fieldnotes

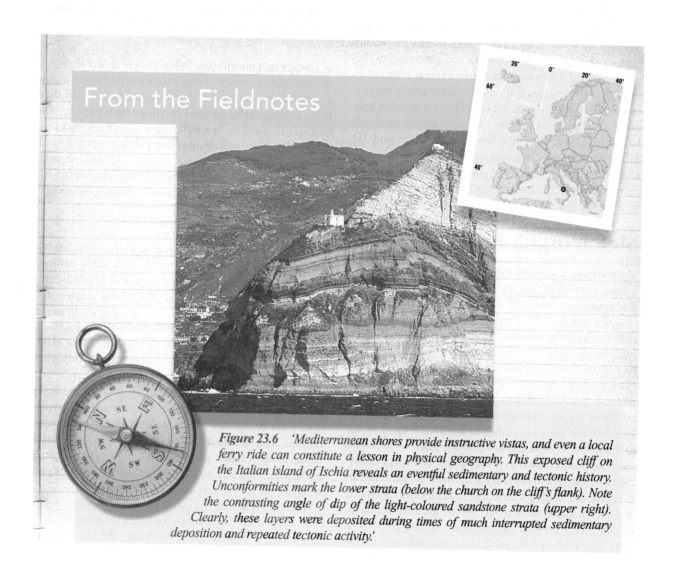

Figure 23.6 'Mediterranean shores provide instructive vistas, and even a local ferry ride can constitute a lesson in physical geography. This exposed cliff on the Italian island of Ischia reveals an eventful sedimentary and tectonic history. Unconformities mark the lower strata (below the church on the cliff's flank). Note the contrasting angle of dip of the light-coloured sandstone strata (upper right). Clearly, these layers were deposited during times of much interrupted sedimentary deposition and repeated tectonic activity.'

Figure 23.7 Fossilized fish contained in Eocene sedimentary rocks provide valuable clues to the geological past. This easily recognized school of fish was found in the Green River Formation in Wyoming and was preserved for about 40 million years. Similar samples have also been found near Cache Creek in the interior of British Columbia.

Figure 23.8 The Colorado River has cut a canyon in the Colorado Plateau that exposes hundreds of millions of years of rock accumulation. Here, at the Marble Canyon segment of the Grand Canyon, sedimentary strata display diverse colours reflecting the environmental circumstances of their deposition. Some are weakly cemented and erode quickly, forming relatively gentle inclines on the canyon wall. Others, like the uppermost layers, are more resistant and form scarps that retain their vertical configuration for a very long time. The exposure seen here is about 900 m high, the last phase of a geologic sequence that began here shortly after the planet's formation and continued intermittently for about 4 billion years.

can see this happening today, and we can compare angles of repose and other aspects of the process to cross-bedded layers in old sedimentary rocks.

As noted previously, all rocks have jointing properties. Not only are sedimentary rocks layered—with their bedding planes often a factor in weathering and erosion—but they also are jointed. Joints are produced by a variety of processes, ranging from desiccation (drying) in sedimentary rocks to unloading caused by erosion of overlaying material in igneous rocks. Furthermore, over time sedimentary rocks may be folded, faulted, and otherwise deformed (see Unit 27). All these circumstances contribute to the rate of erosion in areas where sedimentary rocks dominate the landscape, and they create the sometimes spectacular, multi-coloured, and varied scenery of such places (Figure 23.8).

Metamorphic Rocks

Metamorphic rocks are rocks that have been altered by varying degrees of heat and pressure. The term *metamorphic* comes from a Greek word meaning change, but the complex processes involved in rock metamorphism have only begun to be understood in modern times. All rock types may be subject to metamorphism. Igneous rocks can be remelted and recrystallized. Sedimentary rocks can be fused by heat and pressure into much harder rocks. And metamorphic rocks themselves can be transformed again.

All this happens through tectonic action in the crust (see Unit 24), the impact of comets or asteroids (impact melts), or through volcanic action (see Unit 25). Zones of the Earth's crust are pushed down to deeper levels; other segments of the crust rise. The rocks making up these crustal zones are subjected to changing temperature and pressure conditions, and are modified as a result. When intrusive action by magma occurs, rocks in the zone near a forming batholith or dyke will be affected (Figure 23.9A); this process is known

as **contact metamorphism**. When a sheet of lava flows out over the surface, its heat changes the rocks it covers. Imagine a sedimentary sequence of limestone, sandstone, and shale being interrupted by repeated lava flows from a fissure. The heat and weight of the lava will create metamorphic rocks out of the sedimentary rocks immediately below it (Figure 23.9B). This also happens when a sill forms, with contact metamorphism occurring in the overlying and underlying rocks. Impact melt rocks are a form of metamorphic strata.

Metamorphic Rock Types

LINK

Some metamorphic rocks have quite familiar names. Sandstone, made of quartz grains and silica cement, becomes **quartzite**, a very hard rock that resists weathering. Limestone is converted into much denser and harder **marble**, used by sculptors for statues that can sometimes withstand exposure to the elements for thousands of years. Shale may be metamorphosed into **slate**, a popular building material; slate retains shale's quality of breaking along parallel planes.

Sometimes metamorphism alters the pre-existing rocks so totally that it is not possible to determine what the previous form of the rock may have been. A common metamorphic rock is **schist**. This rock is fine-grained, and it breaks along roughly parallel planes (but very unevenly, unlike slate). If schist was, at least in part, shale in its pre-metamorphic form, there is little resemblance left.

When schist is seen cropping out in the landscape, it displays wavy bands. These bands show that the minerals in the pre-existing rock were realigned during the metamorphic

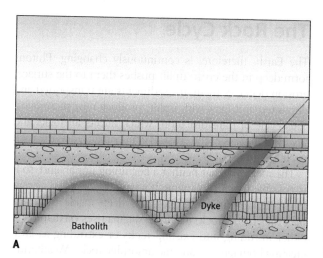

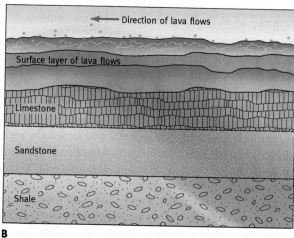

Figure 23.9 Two examples of contact metamorphism, illustrating the effects of two kinds of magmatic intrusions on the existing sedimentary rock strata. (A) Metamorphism radiates deeply into these layers from both the batholith and the dyke. (B) Effects of extrusion, in this case repeated lava flows, on underlying sedimentary layers.

From the Fieldnotes

Figure 23.10 *We were looking for a place to cross the rain-swollen Tana River in eastern Kenya. The nor-mally placid stream was a raging torrent inplaces, and this site, usually a series of rapids, showed nopromise. But the physical geography here was notable because ofthe rocks that cause the rapids. Folia-tion inmetamorphic rocks lines up the minerals inparallel bands so that the recrystallized rocksappearto be streaked with alternating light- and dark-coloured stripes. Metamorphic rockstend to be quite re-sistant to erosion, as thisgneiss outcrop, under constant attack by the river, illustrates.*

process. This realignment indicates that metamorphism did not completely melt the older rocks, but made them viscous enough for the minerals to orient themselves in parallel strips. This process gives certain metamorphic rocks their unmistakable banded appearance, or **foliation**. One of the best and most frequently seen examples is in **gneiss**, the metamorphic rock derived from granite (Figure 23.10). Gneisses show a marked orientation of their mineral crystals and a segregation of mafic (dark-coloured) and felsic (light-coloured) minerals, known as gneissic banding.

Metamorphic Rocks in the Landscape

Because metamorphic rocks have been subjected to heat and pressure, it might be concluded that they would be the most resistant of all rocks to weathering and erosion. But even metamorphic rocks have their weak points and planes (see Figure 23.10). Slate, for example, is weak at the surfaces along which it breaks (cleavage) because water can penetrate along these planes and loosen the rock slabs. Schist often occurs in huge masses and therefore seems to resist weathering and erosion quite effectively. But schist is weak along its foliation bands and breaks down quite rapidly. Even gneiss is weakest along those foliation planes, especially where dark minerals such as biotite micas have collected. In some areas where gneiss is extensive, the dark minerals have been weathered so effectively that soil has formed and vegetation has taken hold in these bands. From the air one can follow the foliation bands by noting the vegetation growing in the weakest ones.

The Earth's first rocks were igneous—solidified from the still molten outer sphere some 4 billion years ago. Ever since, existing rocks have been modified and re-modified, and there are few remains of these original, ancient-shield rocks. What we see in the landscape today are only the most recent forms in which rocks are cast by the processes acting upon them. This explains why it is so difficult to piece together the planet's history from the geological record—subsequent metamorphism has erased much of it.

The Rock Cycle

The Earth, therefore, is continuously changing. Plutons form deep in the crust; uplift pushes them to the surface; erosion degrades them; the sediments are transported and deposited and may, with uplift, produce new mountains. This cycle of transformation, which affects all rocks and involves all parts of the crust, is conceptualized as the **rock cycle** (Figure 23.11).

The rock cycle has neither a beginning nor an end, so it is possible to start following it anywhere on the diagram. High temperatures and pressures deep inside the crust melt the crustal (rock) material. Magma rises via diapirism, either intruding into existing rocks or extruding as lava, creating both igneous and metamorphic rocks. Weathering and erosion attack the exposed rocks; deposition creates sedimentary rocks from the fragments. Crustal forces push sedimentary, igneous, and metamorphic rocks downward, and if they reach the lower levels of the crust, they will be melted and the cycle will start anew—or, rather, continue. In our lifetimes we are witnesses to just a brief instant in a cycle that affects the entire planet in space and its whole history in time.

Now that we have become familiar with the characteristics and cycling of Earth materials, we are ready to consider the forces of the restless crust. Our examination of these processes, which contribute importantly to the shaping of surface landscapes, begins in Unit 24 with an overview of the lithospheric plates that fragment the crust.

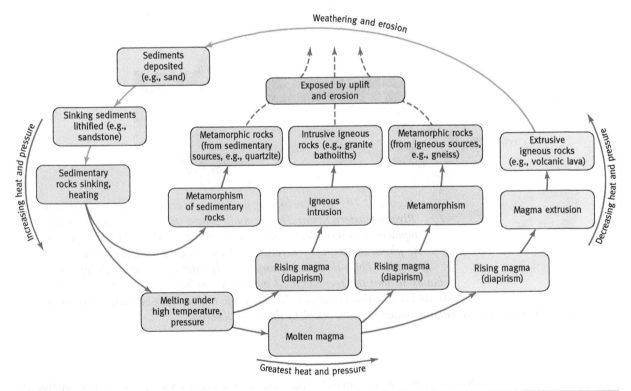

Figure 23.11 The rock cycle. The flow of materials within, above, and below the Earth's crust continually forms and destroys igneous, sedimentary, and metamorphic rocks.

KEY TERMS

bedding planes   *page 318*
breccia   *page 316*
cementation   *page 315*
clastic sedimentary rocks   *page 315*
compaction   *page 315*
conglomerate   *page 315*
contact metamorphism   *page 320*
cross-bedding   *page 319*
evaporites   *page 317*
foliation   *page 321*
gneiss   *page 321*
limestone   *page 317*

lithification   *page 315*
marble   *page 320*
nonclastic sedimentary rocks   *page 315*
quartzite   *page 320*
rock cycle   *page 322*
sandstone   *page 316*
schist   *page 320*
shale   *page 317*
slate   *page 320*
stratification   *page 318*
stratigraphy   *page 318*
unconformity   *page 318*

REVIEW QUESTIONS

1. How are sedimentary rocks formed?
2. How do clastic sedimentary rocks differ?
3. How are metamorphic rocks formed?
4. What are the metamorphic equivalents of sandstone, limestone, and shale?

5. Briefly outline the major components of the rock cycle.

REFERENCES AND FURTHER READINGS

Blatt, H., et al. 1980. *Origin of Sedimentary Rocks*, 2nd edn. Englewood Cliffs, NJ: Prentice-Hall.

Boggs, S. 1987. *Principles of Sedimentology and Stratigraphy*. Columbus, Ohio: Merrill.

Collinson, J.D. 1982. *Sedimentary Structures*. Boston: Allen & Unwin.

Deer, W.A., R.A. Howie, and J. Zussman. 1992. *An Introduction to Rock Forming Minerals*, 2nd edn. New York: Wiley.

Dietrich, R.V., and B.J. Skinner. 1990. *Gems, Granites, and Gravels: Knowing and Using Rocks and Minerals*. New York: Cambridge Univ. Press.

Ehlers, E.G., and H. Blatt. 1982. *Petrology: Igneous, Sedimentary, and Metamorphic*. New York: Freeman.

Hyndman, D.W. 1985. *Petrology of Igneous and Metamorphic Rocks*, 2nd edn. New York: McGraw-Hill.

Mason, R. 1978. *Petrology of the Metamorphic Rocks*. Boston: Allen & Unwin.

Nichols, G. 1998. *Dynamic Sedimentology and Stratigraphy*. Malden, Mass.: Blackwell.

Pettijohn, F.J. 1975. *Sedimentary Rocks*, 3rd edn. New York: Harper & Row.

Reineck, H.E., and I.B. Singh. 1980. *Depositional Sedimentary Environments*, 2nd edn. New York: Springer-Verlag.

Stoneley, R. 1999. *An Introduction to Petroleum Exploration for Non-Geologists*. New York: Oxford Univ. Press.

White, Murray. 2008. 'Oil Industry's Birthplace', *Toronto Star*, 11 May.

WEB RESOURCES

epe.lac-bac.gc.ca/100/205/301/ic/cdc/blackgold/frames.html This website gives information about the Oil Springs–Petrolia oil industry.

plaza.snu.ac.kr/~lee2602/atlas/atlas.html This atlas of sedimentary rocks provides a large number of visual images, including laboratory and textbook photographs.

www.geocities.com/RainForest/Canopy/1080/sedimentary.htm This web page gives basic information about sedimentary rocks, their formation, and their classification.

www.lambtononline.com/oil_museum Site for the Oil Museum of Canada at Oil Springs, Ontario. This National Historic Site is concerned with the Lambton County oil rush of the 1850s–1860s.

www.petroliadiscoveries.com This website features information about the oil industry of Lambton County in the 1860s.

Unit 24

Lithospheric Plates and Plate Movement

Objectives

- To introduce the concepts of continental drift and plate tectonics.

- To identify the major plates of the lithosphere.

- To discuss the important boundary zones between lithospheric plates in which rifting, subduction, and transform faulting occur.

- To outline briefly the mechanisms and processes that move lithospheric plates.

- To discuss the evolution of the Earth's continental landmasses.

- To discuss the concept of isostasy and relate it to the topography of the continents.

When Christopher Columbus reached America in 1492, his discovery was recorded in his ship's log—and on the first map to be based on the Atlantic Ocean's western shores. When Columbus returned on his next three voyages, and as others followed him, the Atlantic coastline of the Americas became better known. During the sixteenth century, Portuguese navigators and cartographers mapped Africa's Atlantic coasts all the way to the Cape of Good Hope at the continent's southern tip.

By the early 1600s, the general configuration of the Atlantic Ocean was fairly well known, even though the maps of the time were often inaccurate in detail. Nonetheless, the great Flemish cartographer Abraham Ortelius, in his *Theatrum Orbis Terrarum*, the first commercially successful atlas, made an observation that contained the kernel of a momentous concept. Looking at the evolving map of the Atlantic Ocean, Ortelius said that the opposite coasts of North and South America and Africa and Europe seemed to fit so well that it looked as though the continents might at one time have been joined, and he suggested that they had been torn apart by floods and earthquakes. It was a notion soon forgotten, however, and not revived until centuries later. And even then the idea that whole continents could move relative to each other was greeted with skepticism and, in some circles, derision.

Nearly a century ago, Alfred Wegener envisioned the continental movement that broke up the supercontinent, Pangaea (see Figure 24.1). Continental drift proved to be one manifestation of plate tectonics, partial evidence for a process of planetary proportions involving immense amounts of energy. Confirmation of the breakup of Laurasia and Gondwanaland, however, raises new questions.

The fragmentation of Pangaea, the collision between India and Asia, the separation of Africa and South America—all this has taken place within the last 160 million years of Earth history. But that period of time is just the last *4 to 5 per cent* of the Earth's total existence as a planet. What happened during previous phases of plate movement? Did earlier movements cause other supercontinents to form through a coalescence of landmasses, only to be pulled apart again? Can remnants of these former supercontinents still be found?

Certainly there are rocks older than 160 million years. As previously noted, the Earth formed more than 4.5 billion years ago. The oldest known rocks are from the geological era known as the Proterozoic or Precambrian Era, and they date from as long as 3.8–4.3 billion years ago (see 'Perspectives' box, Unit 22). These are all igneous and metamorphic rocks, which today form part of the core areas of the landmasses—their shields (see Figure 20.12). Many workers consider that the shields resulted from meteoric or cometary impacts that occurred between 3.5 and 4.5 billion years ago. No rocks resembling the older shield rocks were formed before or after this period. The impacts caused crustal fracturing and melting, and could have initiated plate tectonic movement.

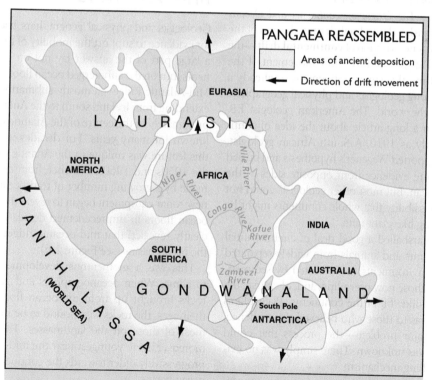

Figure 24.1 The breakup of the supercontinent Pangaea began more than 100 million years ago. Note the radial movement of its remnants away from Africa and how areas of ancient deposition help us understand where today's landmasses were once joined together.

The ancient original shields must have been involved in every phase of crustal movement after their formation. Today the Canadian (Laurentian) Shield forms the geological core of North America; but during the Late Proterozoic period, it probably lay at the heart of a landmass of very different shape and dimensions (see Figure 24.6). This question is of interest in physical geography because the comparatively inactive continental shields carry landscapes that also are very old and have, in some areas, changed very little over many millions of years. These ancient landscapes, found in shield areas of Africa, South America, and Australia, may provide insights into the geomorphology of parts of Pangaea and other earlier supercontinents.

Continental Drift

In 1915 the German Earth scientist Alfred Wegener (1880–1930) published a book that contained a bold new hypothesis. Not just Africa and South America, Wegener suggested, but all the landmasses on Earth once were united in a giant supercontinent. This primeval landmass, which he named **Pangaea** (meaning 'All-Earth'), broke apart, forming the continents and oceans as they are known today. Wegener theorized that Pangaea consisted of two major parts, **Laurasia** in the north and **Gondwanaland** in the south. Today Eurasia and North America are considered to be the remnants of Laurasia; South America, Africa, India, Australia, and Antarctica are considered the principal fragments of Gondwanaland (Figure 24.1).

Wegener's book, *The Origin of Continents and Oceans* (1915), was not translated into English until the end of the 1920s. By then Wegener's notion of **continental drift**—the fragmentation of Pangaea and the slow movement of the continents away from this supercontinent—was already a topic of debate among geologists and physical geographers in many parts of the world. The American geologist F.B. Taylor had written a long article about the idea of continental drift as early as 1910. A South African geologist, L. du Toit, also supported Wegener's hypothesis and busied himself in gathering evidence from opposite sides of the South Atlantic Ocean. But most other geologists could not conceive of the possibility that whole continents might be mobile, functioning like giant rafts.

Wegener had marshalled a good deal of circumstantial evidence: fossil plants and animals from widely separated locales; climatic environments (as indicated by sedimentary rocks) unlike those now prevailing; and, of course, the remarkable jigsaw-like 'fit' of the continents. Plausible as continental drift was to those who believed this evidence, there was one major problem—the process that could move continents was unknown. There simply was no evidence for a propelling mechanism.

As sometimes happens when a new scientific concept emerges, the hypothesis of continental drift lost credibility among many geologists, in part because of the mechanisms proposed by Wegener as well as by others. Wegener suggested that the Earth's gravitational force, which is slightly weaker at the Equator, was over time strong enough to pull the continents apart. Taylor proposed that the Moon was torn from the Earth in what is today the Pacific Basin, and that the continents have been steadily moving into the gap thereby created. Such notions damaged the credibility of the entire continental drift hypothesis, and despite the accumulation of geological and paleontological evidence in favour of it, few geologists (especially in the United States) were willing to accept the possibility.

Some scientists, however, kept working on the problem. One British geologist, Arthur Holmes, proposed as early as 1939 that there might be heat-sustained convection cells in the interior of the Earth and that these gigantic cells could be responsible for dragging the landmasses along. Others argued that the evidence for continental drift had become so overwhelming that notions of a rigid crust would have to be abandoned—there must be a mechanism, and further research would uncover it. The discussion of continental drift was reawakened in the early 1960s by J. Tuzo Wilson (1908–93), a Canadian geophysicist. Wilson studied and named transform faults, theorized about plate movement mechanisms, worked out ways of tracing plate movement using 'hot spots' or mantle plumes, and suggested the supercontinent cycle. He can truly be thought of as the father of modern *plate tectonic theory*.

Continents, Plate Tectonics, and Seafloors

Geologists and physical geographers had been searching for evidence to support the mobility of the landmasses. But a large part of the answer lay not on the exposed continents, but on the submerged ocean floor. The existence of a Mid-Atlantic Ridge—a mostly submarine mountain range extending from Iceland south to the Antarctic latitudes, approximately in the centre of the Atlantic Ocean—had been known for many years. For decades it was believed that this feature was unique to the Atlantic Ocean. But during the 1950s and 1960s, evidence from deep-sea soundings made by a growing number of transoceanic ships carrying new sonar equipment began to reveal the global map of the ocean floors in unprecedented detail. The emerging map clearly revealed that mid-oceanic ridges are present in all the ocean basins (see Figure 2.6).

This was a momentous development, but more was to come. When oceanographers and geologists analyzed rocks brought up from the ocean floor and determined their ages, the rocks were found to be much younger than most of those on the landmasses. These basaltic rocks, moreover, were youngest near the mid-oceanic ridges and progressively older towards the continental margins of the ocean basins.

Further investigations revealed another startling pattern: the mid-oceanic ridges were not just submarine mountain ranges like those on the landmasses, but constituted a global network associated with hot upwelling magma. New basaltic rock was being formed, soon to be pushed away horizontally by still newer rock forcing its way up from below all along the mid-oceanic ridge. The process came to be called **seafloor spreading**. It involved the creation of new crust and its continuous movement away from its source.

Obviously, if the mid-oceanic ridges are zones where new crust forms and diverges, the Earth's crust is divided into segments—large fragments separated along the ridges. These segments of the crust were called *plates* (**lithospheric plates** to denote their rigidity and *tectonic plates* to describe their active mobile character). Now, at last, the scientists were one giant step closer to understanding the mechanism needed to explain continental mobility. The movement of these parts of the crust is called **plate tectonics**.

If ocean floors can move and 'spread', then continents can also be displaced. Moreover, if the ocean floor spreads outward from the mid-oceanic ridges, then the crust must be crushed together elsewhere, and parts of it must be pushed downward to make space for the newly forming crust. Thus the plates of which the crust is made are formed in one zone and destroyed in another. This process of destruction occurs where plates moving in opposite directions collide. Earthquakes, volcanism, and mountain building mark such zones of crustal collision.

Distribution of Plates

When seafloor spreading was first recognized and the map of mid-oceanic ridges took shape, it appeared that the Earth's crust was divided into seven major plates, all but one carrying a major landmass. But as more became known about both ocean floors and landmasses, additional plates were identified. By the 1990s, 18 lithospheric plates had been mapped (Figure 24.2), but there is still uncertainty as to the exact margins and dimensions of several, and others may yet be discovered. The largest plates are as follows:

1. The *Pacific Plate* extends over most of the Pacific Ocean floor from south of Alaska to the Antarctic Plate.
2. The *North American Plate* meets the Pacific Plate along California's San Andreas Fault and related structures. It carries the North American landmass.
3. The *Eurasian Plate* forms the boundary with the North American Plate at the Mid-Atlantic Ridge north of 35°N. It carries the entire Eurasian landmass north of the Himalayas.
4. The *African Plate* extends eastward from the Mid-Atlantic Ridge between 35°N and 55°S. It carries Africa and the island of Madagascar, and it meets the Antarctic Plate under the Southern Ocean and the Australian and Indian Plates beneath the Indian Ocean.
5. The *South American Plate* extends westward from the Mid-Atlantic Ridge south of 15°N. It carries the South American landmass.
6. The *Australian Plate* carries Australia and meets the Pacific Plate in New Zealand.
7. The *Indian Plate* carries the Indian subcontinent and meets the Eurasian Plate at the Himalayas.
8. The margins of the *Antarctic Plate* encircle the Antarctic landmass (which it carries) under the Southern Ocean.

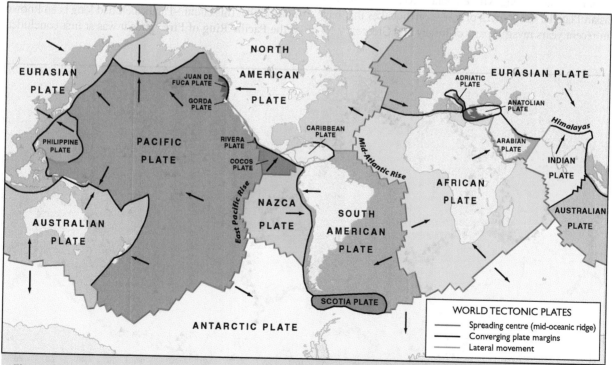

Figure 24.2 Lithospheric plates of the Earth. Each drifts continuously in the direction shown by the arrows. As the legend indicates, plate-margin movement falls into one of three categories: divergence (spreading), convergence, or lateral motion.

Seven of these plates were identified early on. For some years the Australian and Indian Plates were believed to constitute a single plate, but today they appear to be undergoing separation to form two separate plates. Later, a number of smaller plates were detected (Figure 24.2). The largest among these is the *Nazca Plate*, wedged between the South American Plate to the east and the Pacific Plate to the west. Immediately to the north of the Nazca Plate, partly separating the South American Plate from the North American Plate, are two smaller plates. The larger of these, the *Caribbean Plate*, supports most of Central America and the southern Caribbean region. West of it (and thus north of the Nazca Plate) lies the *Cocos Plate*, and its northwestern extension, the *Rivera Plate*, off west-central Mexico. The Cocos and Rivera Plates are all oceanic crust and, unlike the Caribbean Plate, do not support a landmass.

At the southern end of South America lies a plate whose boundary arches eastward around an island chain much like the Caribbean Plate's eastern boundary; this is the *Scotia Plate*. Off the western coast of North America, near the point where the US–Canada boundary reaches the Pacific Ocean, lies the *Juan de Fuca Plate*, and to its south, off southern Oregon and northernmost California, lies the smaller *Gorda Plate*.

Three other smaller but significant plates have also been recognized. One is the *Philippine Plate*, located between the Pacific and the Eurasian Plates, which is involved in the devastating earthquakes that have repeatedly struck the Tokyo area of eastern Japan. Another is the *Arabian Plate*, which supports the landmass known as the Arabian Peninsula. The third is the *Anatolian Plate* (located northwest of the Arabian Plate), along whose contact zone with the Eurasian Plate lie the sources of severe earthquakes that have in recent years ravaged parts of Turkey and Greece.

It is likely that the current map of lithospheric plates will be revised again, because additional smaller plates may not have been identified yet. It is noteworthy, for example, that most of the smaller plates that have been recognized lie in ocean-floor areas of the crust. We also know that the sialic landmasses lie on simatic crust that continues beneath them (see Unit 20). Therefore, it is possible that the crust beneath the landmasses is more fragmented than is now known; later in this unit we examine the map of Africa to explore this possibility.

Location of Plate Margins

Once the notion of seafloor spreading gained acceptance and the segmented character of the crust became known, the search was on for the location of the margins of tectonic plates. Some earlier evidence now acquired new significance: the map showing the global distribution of earthquakes (Figure 24.3) provided an important clue. Note that this map shows that earthquakes often originate in the mid-oceanic ridges, in island arcs, and in mountain belts such as North America's Rocky, Cascade, and Coast Mountains and Asia's Himalayas. It was concluded that these linear earthquake zones represented plate margins, and thus the early idea that there were only seven major lithospheric plates was re-examined.

The map of the world distribution of active volcanoes further supported this theory (Figure 24.3). Of course, continental-surface patterns of volcanic activity were much better known than submarine volcanism. Volcanic activity is so common in western South and North America, in Asia's offshore *archipelagos* (island chains), and in New Zealand that this circum-Pacific belt had long been known as the **Pacific Ring of Fire**. Thus it was at first concluded

LINK

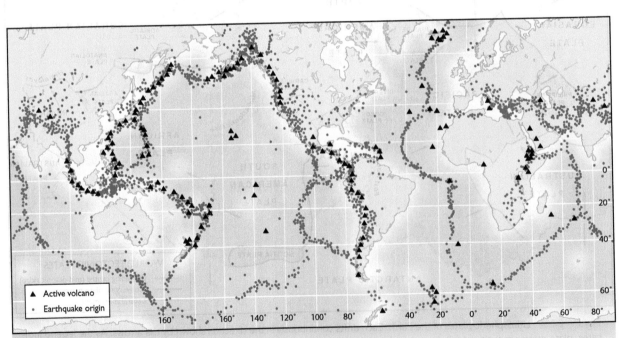

Figure 24.3 Global distribution of recent earthquakes and active volcanoes.

▲ Active volcano
• Earthquake origin

that the entire Pacific Ocean floor constituted a single, giant tectonic plate. Only later, when knowledge of the ocean-floor topography and geology improved, was the existence of smaller plates such as the Juan de Fuca and Cocos recognized.

Figure 24.4 shows the seafloor of most of the Atlantic Ocean. Note that the mid-oceanic ridge is not linear and unbroken, but divided into segments that are offset, giving them an overall zigzag appearance. Right-angle fractures in the crust (*transform faults*) separate the segments. This relates to the conditions that prevail where new crust is created—rock is hot, molten, and viscous. It rises and spreads, beginning to cool as it moves away from the mid-oceanic ridge. But the ridge itself is not rigid and stable enough to sustain continuity. Lateral forces of movement sometimes are stronger in one direction than in the other. Thus, one part of the Mid-Atlantic Ridge (between 20° and 35°N) is dragged to the west; elsewhere, such as just south of the Equator, another part may lag behind or even move slightly to the east. As the rocks harden, a fault develops between the segments, and they are offset. Under the oceans, away from the landmasses, this pattern prevails.

But the map of world lithospheric plates (Figure 24.2) also shows that the plate margins along continental edges take on another form. Along the edge of western South and North America, and off eastern Asia, the plate margins mostly appear on the map as solid black lines. The same is true for the longest plate boundary known to exist across a landmass: the contact zone between the Eurasian Plate and plates to the south of it. No new crust is being created there. Rather, crust is being crushed and may be being pushed downward. From the distribution of these plate-margin types, the movement of the lithospheric plates can be inferred.

Movement of Plates

It is now known that the lithosphere consists of eight major plates and at least ten smaller ones. These plates move relative to one another, apparently maintaining their prevailing directions of movement for millions of years. The term *plate tectonics* refers to this motion. Indeed, plates and landmasses may have been in motion ever since the Earth's crust was formed more than 4 billion years ago; Pangaea existed a mere 200 million years ago. It is quite possible that Pangaea itself resulted from an earlier phase of plate movement during which landmasses coalesced to form a single supercontinent, and is only one phase of a supercontinent cycle.

The movement of lithospheric plates is directly responsible for many of the Earth's major landscapes and landforms. All studies of geomorphological processes and features must take into account the effect of crustal mobility. As plates migrate and carry landmasses along, they push, drag, tilt, bend, warp, and fracture. Lava pours out of fissures and vents. Rocks laid down as horizontal strata are deformed in every conceivable way. The weight of accumulating sediments pushes part of a plate downward. Where weathering and erosion have removed the material turned into sediment, the weight of the upper crust is reduced and the plate will rebound upward—all while movement continues.

Major directions of plate movement can be inferred from the map of the distribution of plates (Figure 24.2). (Recent research has also provided information on the relative velocities of moving plates, the topic of the 'Perspectives' box.) Clearly, the African Plate has moved eastward, and its dominant direction remains eastward today. The South American Plate moves westward. New crust for both these plates is being created along the Mid-Atlantic Ridge. For some other plates, the direction of movement is less clear. What is certain, however, is that plate margins take on three kinds of character: (1) spreading or divergence; (2) collision or convergence; and (3) transform or lateral displacement.

Plate Spreading

Plate spreading or divergence occurs along the mid-oceanic ridges in the process called seafloor spreading. Magma wells up from the asthenosphere, new lithosphere is

Figure 24.4 Central portion of the Atlantic seafloor, between roughly latitudes 55°N and 20°S, highlighting the topography associated with the Mid-Atlantic Ridge.

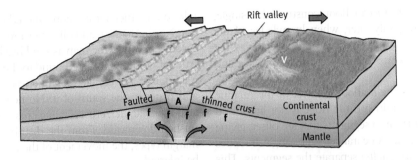

Figure 24.5 Development of a rift valley, which involves tensional movement related to motion in the mantle, faulting (**f**), the collapse of elongated strips of crust (**A**), and crustal thinning. Sometimes lava erupts along the tensional fault planes (**V**). Lakes fill large portions of rift valleys in East Africa (see Figure 27.7).

created, and the lithosphere on opposing sides of the mid-oceanic ridges is pushed apart. Here the tectonic forces are tensional, and the crust is so thin that it **rifts** open. Some geographers have pointed out that this process can also affect continental crust. If tensional forces exist beneath a part of a plate where a landmass occurs, both the simatic crust below and the sialic crust above are pulled apart. At the surface, this results in a sometimes spectacular land-form called a **rift valley** (Figure 24.5).

At present, a major system of rift valleys occurs in eastern Africa (see Figure 27.7), and this system may sig-nal the future fracturing of that continent (and the African Plate) along this zone of apparent crustal thinning. The Red Sea represents a more advanced stage of this process (Figure 27.7): the Arabian Plate has separated from the African Plate, and between them now lies a basalt-floored sea (the Red Sea). As time goes on, this sea is likely to widen and become a new ocean.

Thus the geological term *seafloor spreading* is perhaps better replaced by the geographical one, **crustal spread-ing**. Even today not all spreading is confined to the ocean floor. And when Pangaea was a supercontinent, the first fractures in it occurred as rift valleys. Only when the rifts widened and magma filled the now-collapsed, water-filled trenches did the spreading become 'seafloor'.

The map of Africa, from a physical-geographical stand-point, also cautions against taking the current map of known plates too seriously. The African Plate may well consist of three or four plates, all moving in the same general direction at this moment in geological time, but capable of separating (see Figure 27.9)—as the great East African rifts seem to suggest. An East African Plate may exist east of the easternmost (of Africa's) rift valleys; a small Victoria Plate may exist between the eastern and western rifts (see Figure 27.7). The surface evidence fur-ther suggests that a plate margin may exist, or be form-ing, along a line extending from the Gulf of Guinea to-wards Lake Chad in west-central Africa. Remember that Wegener made effective use of topographic information to develop his hypothesis of continental drift, thereby paving the way for plate tectonics. The landscape is still

a valuable guide, even in this age of satellite remote-sensing, high-technology data analysis, and geographical information systems.

Mechanism of Crustal Spreading

The movement of plates forming the Earth's crust has been established beyond a reasonable doubt (Figure 24.6). Although we can accurately measure plate motion today,

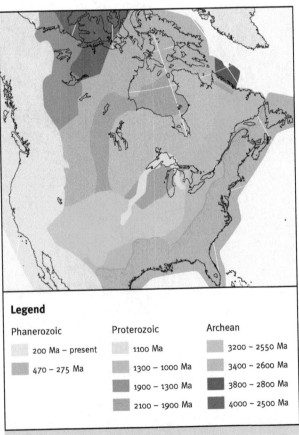

Legend

Phanerozoic	Proterozoic	Archean
200 Ma – present	1100 Ma	3200 – 2550 Ma
470 – 275 Ma	1300 – 1000 Ma	3400 – 2600 Ma
	1900 – 1300 Ma	3800 – 2800 Ma
	2100 – 1900 Ma	4000 – 2500 Ma

Figure 24.6 Simplified tectonic map of North America showing areas accreted (added) to the craton during the Pre-cambrian (Archean and Proterozoic) and Phanerozoic Eons.

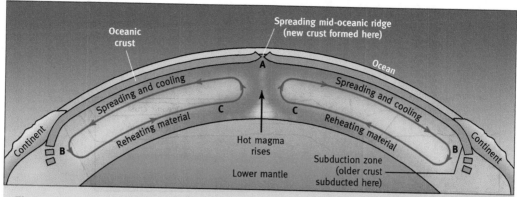

Figure 24.7 Convection cells in the mantle may look like this in cross-section. Hot magma rises at **A**, spreads towards **B**, and in the process drags the existing oceanic crust with it. At the spreading mid-oceanic ridge, new oceanic crust is being created from some of this upwelling magma. As the material below the crust spreads towards **B**, it cools slowly. When it reaches a convergent boundary with a continental landmass, the oceanic crust is subducted. The material in the convection cell now moves towards **C**, reheating at this depth. By the time it has passed **C**, it has enough energy to rise again into the spreading ridge. Speed of movement may be only about 2.5 cm per year.

the mechanism that propels the plates, past as well as present, is still not completely understood. The first model, proposed by Arthur Holmes, involves a set of internal convection cells in the Earth's mantle and has been refined to account for the new knowledge of seafloor spreading. A model proposed by Harry Hess suggests that hot mantle material rises at the spreading mid-oceanic ridges. Some of it emerges to form a new, thin crust; most remains in a hot plastic state, sliding slowly away from the ridges and cooling in the process.

This would explain why the temperature of the ocean-floor crust is highest near the mid-oceanic ridges and drops towards the continental margins. By spreading sideways and dragging the crust along, the sublithospheric magma keeps the spreading ridges open. By the time the new crust and the magma carrying it have spread as far as the continental margin of the ocean basin, they have cooled and thickened sufficiently to become so dense and heavy that they are ready to sink down again. This occurs when, at a collision plate margin, a continental (or other oceanic) plate overrides it. Now subduction takes place, and the material re-enters the asthenosphere and the mantle, where the subducted material is heated up and may make the return journey to the spreading mid-oceanic ridge. All of these relationships are shown in Figure 24.7.

If a set of convection cells such as those shown in Figure 24.7 exists beneath all parts of the Earth's crust, several questions arise, some not yet fully explained. First, how many of these cells exist? Are they all the same size, or do they range in size as the plates themselves do? How deeply do they penetrate the mantle? Evidence suggests that oceanic crust can be subducted to depths of 700 km, which is far below the lower boundary of the asthenosphere. Some geologists suggest that the entire mantle may be in motion, and not just its upper layer. Does the Earth's

internal heat sustain the process, or is a heat-generating process, such as radioactive decay, responsible for the energy to keep convection cells in motion?

Most of the answers to such questions remain as speculative today as Wegener's continental drift hypothesis was many years ago. For example, as the Earth has cooled, the rate of convection in the mantle and asthenosphere may have slowed down. Thus, plate movement before the formation of Pangaea may have been even more rapid than it is today, and convergent margins may have been even more violently active. It follows that continental-margin landscapes had still more relief and variety than those of today's Pacific Ring of Fire.

Plate Collision

If plates form and spread outward in certain areas of the crust, then they must *collide* and converge in other zones. The result of such a gigantic collision depends on the type of lithosphere involved on each side. Continental crust has a relatively lower density, and in these terms, it is 'light' compared to oceanic crust, which is denser, heavier, and more prone to sink or be forced downward where plates collide. When an oceanic plate meets a plate carrying a continental landmass at its leading edge, the lighter continental plate overrides the denser oceanic plate and pushes it downward. This process is termed **subduction**, and the area where it occurs is defined as a *subduction zone* (Figure 24.8).

A subduction zone is a place of intense tectonic activity. The plate being forced down (subducted) is heated by the asthenosphere, and its rocks melt (undergo anatexis). This magma mixes with molten lower-crust material, water seeping down from the ocean floor, and sediment dragged down on the back of the subducting plate. Some of the molten rock forces its way upward through vents and fissures to the surface, so that volcanism is common

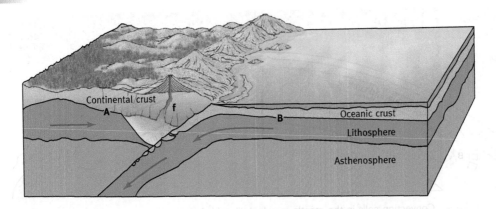

Figure 24.8 When continental plate **A**, moving eastward, meets oceanic plate **B**, moving westward, the process of subduction carries the heavier oceanic plate downward beneath the thicker but lighter continental plate. In this process, high relief develops along the coastline, the continental crust is heavily deformed, and magma can penetrate through vents and fissures (**f**) to erupt as lava at the surface.

along both oceanic and continental subduction zones. The movement of the plates is comparatively slow, averaging 2 to 3 cm per year. But this motion is enough to generate enormous energy, some of which is released through earthquakes. Subduction zones are earthquake prone and rank among the world's most dangerous places to live.

Three types of collision plate margins exist, only two of which result in significant subduction. Subduction occurs where oceanic crust subducts beneath continental crust and where one oceanic plate subducts beneath another. However, where two plates with continental crust converge, a somewhat different sequence of events follows. Let us examine each of the three cases.

Oceanic–Continental Plate Collision   The best example of the kind of oceanic–continental subduction zone just described (Figure 24.8) lies along South America's western margin, where the oceanic Nazca Plate is subducting beneath the continental South American Plate. The crust in the collision zone is dragged downward to form deep oceanic trenches close to shore. A few kilometres to the east, continental rocks are crumpled up into the gigantic mountain ranges of the Andes. Andesitic volcanoes tower over the landscape; earthquakes and tremors are recorded almost continuously. Sediments are caught in the subduction zone and become part of the hot molten magma. Here we can see the rock cycle (see Figure 23.11) in progress: basaltic crust from the ocean floor and granitic and sedimentary rocks from the landmass are melted and forced downward. Their constituent minerals will be absorbed by the lithosphere and may eventually be carried back to the mid-oceanic ridges, where they emerge and solidify, becoming part of the lithosphere once again. The same kind of process occurs in the Cascadia collision zone of British Columbia and Washington/Oregon.

Oceanic–Oceanic Plate Collision   Other convergent plate boundaries involve two oceanic plates. The contrast between lithospheric plate densities is not present, and the crust is thrown into huge contortions. One of the plates will override the other, resulting in subduction; deep trenches form and volcanoes protrude, often above sea level (Figure 24.9). The collision zone between the Pacific, North American, Eurasian, Philippine, and Australian Plates in the northern and western Pacific Ocean creates **island arcs**, such as the Aleutian and Japanese archipelagoes, as well as other segments of the Pacific Ring of Fire.

Continental–Continental Plate Collision   Where collision involves two continental plates, the situation is different. The best example is a segment of the collision between the Eurasian Plate and the Indian Plate. The Eurasian Plate is moving southward, and the Indian subcontinent has moved to the north. (Thus a part of Gondwanaland was carried into collision with Laurasia.) Such continental convergence creates massive deformation and a huge buildup

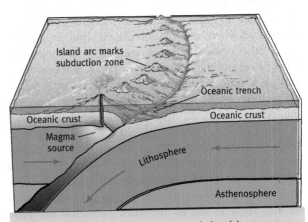

Figure 24.9 Convergent plate margin involving two oceanic plates. Where one oceanic plate is subducted beneath the other, a deep oceanic trench forms. Above the trench, on the margin of the upward-riding plate, a volcanic island arc is created.

Figure 24.10 Two continental landmasses collide at a convergent plate margin. There is much deformation of the crust, and high relief develops (South Asia's Himalayas mark such a convergent continental plate boundary). But while there is considerable thickening of the crust, less actual subduction occurs than when contrasting continental and oceanic plates converge.

of the sialic mass. One continental mass may override the other, but the lower mass is not forced down into the asthenosphere or mantle (Figure 24.10). Rather, the landmass thickens along the contact zone; earthquakes will attend the process, but not the widespread volcanism that accompanies oceanic–continental collisions.

Lateral Plate Contact

For many years California's San Andreas Fault was known to be a place of crustal instability, a source of earthquakes, a line of danger on the map of the Golden State. Not until plate tectonics became understood, however, could the real significance of the San Andreas Fault be recognized. The fault marks a plate margin—not a margin of divergence or convergence, but a margin along which two plates are sliding past each other (Figure 24.11). These

margins are referred to as **transform faults**. Transform (or *lateral*) movement along such plate margins may not have the dramatic topographic consequences displayed by convergent movement, but it, too, is accompanied by earthquakes and crustal deformation.

The area to the west of the San Andreas Fault is part of the Pacific Plate, whereas the area to the east is part of the North American Plate (Figure 24.12). The fault extends southward into the Gulf of California, thereby

Figure 24.11 The San Andreas Fault in action. Rows of trees in a southern California orange grove were offset 4.5 m along a branch of the fault during the May 1940 Imperial Valley earthquake.

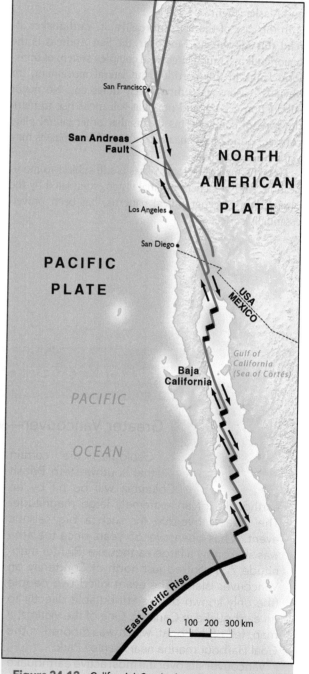

Figure 24.12 California's San Andreas Fault in its regional context. This fault separates the Pacific Plate from the North American Plate, which here are sliding past each other.

also separating Mexico's Baja California from the Mexican mainland, which is part of the North American Plate as well. At its northern end, the San Andreas Fault enters the Pacific Ocean north of San Francisco. Thus Baja California and southern California (including metropolitan Los Angeles) are sliding north-northwestward past the North American Plate (Figure 24.12) because of the northward motion of the Pacific Plate as a whole. This process is going on at a fairly high rate of speed, estimated to average more than 7.5 cm per year. This type of movement can also be seen along the Queen Charlotte–Denali Fault of northwest British Columbia and Alaska (Figure 24.13).

In the case of the San Andreas Fault, earthquakes attend this movement. Moreover, the San Andreas is the major fault in a much larger and complex system of transform faults in this corridor. But lateral movement, for obvious reasons, is comparatively quiescent. No major subduction occurs, and no great volcanoes rise to mark the zone of contact. This means that other lateral plate contact boundaries beneath continental landmasses may yet be undiscovered.

Thus the map of tectonic plates is still subject to modification. And Wegener's original vision, stimulated by the observation of geographical patterns, has been proven essentially correct.

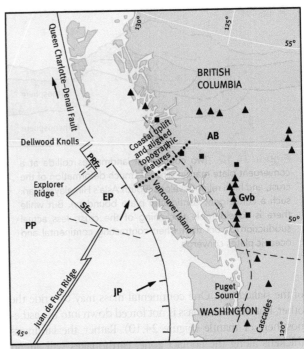

Figure 24.13 Triple junction tectonic setting in the Pacific Northwest showing transform movement (Queen Charlotte–Denali Fault), the Cascadia Collision zone (subduction), and spreading along offshore ridges (e.g., Explorer Ridge). Note the volcanic arcs on the continent. PP–Pacific Plate; EP–Explorer Plate; JP–Juan de Fuca Plate; Sfz–Sovanco fracture zone; PRfz–Paul Revere Fracture zone; AB–Anahim volcanic belt; Gvb–Garibaldi volcanic belt. Triangles are volcanoes; squares are large plutons.

Perspectives on the Human Environment

Greater Vancouver—Waiting for the Big One

Geologists are certain that southwestern British Columbia will be hit by an earthquake of an extremely large magnitude. The area is overdue for such a big seismic event. It has been over 55 years since the area was shaken by a large earthquake (Richter magnitude 7.3) centred just north of Courtenay on Vancouver Island. The event killed two people (the only known deaths attributable directly to an earthquake in Canada). One of the victims, a man, fell off his boat, which was moored in the Coal Harbour marina near Stanley Park.

Vancouver sits over the most active earthquake zone in Canada, and the over 50 years since the occurrence of a large seismic event suggest that pressures are building up along the fault lines between the tectonic plates underlying the region. There are about 300 minor quakes a year in this zone, most of them so small that they are only recorded on seismographs. Once every 20 to 50 years a major earthquake happens. These types of quakes crack walls, cause chimneys to collapse, and cause other such damage (as the Courtenay quake did in 1946). Once every 300 to 600 years the region is affected by a cataclysmic mega-thrust earthquake (Richter magnitude 8.5+) that is accompanied by 10 to 20 m movements along the fault, slope failures, and tsunamis. If such an earthquake should occur under

Greater Vancouver now, it would be catastrophic. Estimates based on an 8.5+ magnitude event suggest that 10 to 30 per cent of all houses would be damaged; 60 to 100 per cent of older masonry buildings, including schools and hospitals, would suffer major damage or collapse. Fifteen per cent of all high-rises would be severely damaged, and many bridges and roads would be rendered unusable. Thousands of people would be killed, many more injured, and hundreds of thousands made homeless. The numbers would depend on the time of day that the quake happened and the amount of water in the sediments of the Fraser Delta. It would be the greatest natural disaster in Canadian history.

The tectonic situation that would cause this event would be the interaction of two major tectonic plates (the North American and Pacific Plates) and a smaller one (the Juan de Fuca Plate), which is wedged between them. Named the Cascadia subduction zone by geologists, this is an example of triple-junction tectonics. The Pacific Plate is moving northwest, and the North American Plate is moving west away from the spreading zone in the middle of the Atlantic Ocean. The North American Plate is also moving to the northwest at the same time. The movement of the Pacific Plate is faster than that of the North American Plate. As the North American Plate moves west, it is overriding the Juan de Fuca Plate. The Juan de Fuca Plate is being subducted; it is being thrust under the North American Plate. Research indicates that the thrust fault is stuck at the present time, but if and when it releases, it will be devastating.

The agency charged with the area's preparedness has put forward two possible quake scenarios. The most likely scenario is based on a moderately strong event, similar in magnitude to the San Francisco and Los Angeles earthquakes of the past 15–20 years (Richter magnitude 6–7). This would cause significant damage, deaths, injuries, homelessness, and so on. Since the San Francisco quake in the late 1980s, a lot of engineering work has been done throughout the Vancouver area to upgrade bridges, dams, and other infrastructure, such as the elevated 'Skytrain' line, to minimize the damage caused by seismic events. However, little has been done to older masonry schools, hospitals, and the older parts of the downtown (e.g., Gastown and Yaletown). Large areas of Greater Vancouver are built on fill or on buried organic material (bogs). Even a moderate quake would lead to the collapse of buildings in these areas. Shaking would mix water and organic materials and fine-grained sediments and cause liquefaction, which would swallow up houses and other buildings. The dykes along the Fraser Valley and Georgia Strait would break, and river and sea water would cause flooding of low-lying areas. Most of Richmond, a major suburb south of Vancouver, sits on Lulu Island in the Fraser Delta. The sediments on which the municipality has been constructed are layers of sand, clay, and bog material. If shaken, these deposits would liquefy and cause collapse and subsidence of all sorts of buildings and infrastructure. The island is surrounded by dykes that would fail and the area would be flooded. A similar scenario could play out on Granville Island in Vancouver (Figure 24.14).

Figure 24.14   Granville Island, in the heart of Vancouver, British Columbia, was converted in 1915 from a sandbar into an industrial core. It is now an important recreational and tourist area with shops, cafés, marinas, and theatres.

The second, less likely scenario is based on an 8.5 mega-thrust quake with its epicentre in the Greater Vancouver area. This would produce severe destruction within a 200-km-wide zone around the epicentre. Many buildings would fail, and liquefaction would probably severely damage the airport, Richmond, and other low-lying areas. Tunnels and bridges would sink into liquefied deposits. Many people would be unable to get out of their immediate area because of damaged bridges and tunnels. The situation would be chaotic. Western parts of the Fraser Valley would flood. Up to 45 per cent of Vancouver's schools would suffer moderate to total collapse. Tsunamis and submarine slumping would damage the shoreline and facilities close to the shore, such as oil refineries and chemical plants. There would be major fires (many houses are wooden).

There would be mass evacuations. The dead and injured would number in the hundreds of thousands. Many more would be left homeless.

Recent news reports indicate that the provincial government's plan to upgrade older masonry schools and other buildings is sadly lagging behind schedule. Only four schools have been modified and it is estimated that to upgrade all the masonry schools in the province would take over 100 years. Also, if a severe earthquake were to occur during a world-class event such as the 2010 Winter Olympic Games, which is planned to be held in Vancouver–Whistler, many hundreds of thousands of people visiting the area from around the world would be affected. While the new sports infrastructure for such an undertaking is built to modern earthquake standards, older hotels, motels, and other older buildings and roads are not.

Evolution of Continents

The evolution and areal growth of continental landmasses is also a largely unsolved riddle. It has been assumed that continental landmasses were created by the solidification of segments of the primitive crustal sphere or by impact fracturing and melting and the eruption of new lava types, perhaps more than 4 billion years ago. This process may have given rise to the igneous and metamorphic shields, which thus have existed ever since as the cores of the **continents**. When methods of dating rocks became more reliable, studies indicated that the oldest shield regions were indeed flanked by successively younger rock regions. Weathering and erosion of the original shield rocks created sedimentary strata around their margins (platform borderland areas). This would imply not only that the rocks of a continent become progressively younger away from the shield core, but also that the continents have grown, continuously or in stages, ever since their cores were first formed (see Figure 24.6).

LINK

Crustal Formation

Other geological evidence, however, suggests that shield areas have not grown by successive consolidation of magma around the original core areas. Rather, it appears that the landmasses were formed from the solidification of the outermost cooling mantle, during a period approximately 2.5 to 3.5 billion years ago. For the last 2.5 billion years the continental landmasses appear to have retained about the same total volume (if not the familiar shapes) as today. The crust has been recycled ever since, material being lost to subduction at convergent plate boundaries and regained by formation at the spreading ridges.

Throughout their existence, the continental shields have lost little, because subduction has affected mostly the sedimentary strata accumulated at their margins. Even when a coalesced landmass became subject to crustal spreading, as happened when Africa and South America separated and the Mid-Atlantic Ridge was formed, the shield thereby fragmented lost no part of its mass. This model of the evolution of continents is still a subject of debate, and it may be modified when more becomes known about the subcrustal convection currents.

But even the continents themselves continue to yield their secrets. Recently, geologists came to realize that certain parts of landmasses do not, geologically speaking, seem to belong where they are located. Their rocks and geological histories are so different from their surroundings that the conclusion is inescapable: these chunks of continent must have been moved from faraway locales to their current, 'foreign' positions.

The Supercontinent Cycle or Wilson Cycle

This idea of a **supercontinent (Wilson) cycle** was suggested by J. Tuzo Wilson as far back as 1966 and was outlined in a paper in *Scientific American* in the early 1990s. The basic concept is that, over time, supercontinents are assembled, exist for up to 100 million years (Ma), and then break up as seafloor spreading occurs. It is possible that supercontinents do not fully form and that while assembly occurred in one area, breakup was occurring elsewhere. Five supercontinents have formed and broken up over the last 3 billion years. The Phanerozoic Eon was dominated by the formation and breakup of Pangaea, which existed from 300 to 200 Ma ago. The biggest mass extinctions occurred during this period of Earth history. Pangaea was huge, covering much of the world, and it was surrounded by the Panthalassa Ocean.

When assembled, a supercontinent acts as an insulator, trapping geothermal heat in the Earth. In consequence the mantle heats up and basalt magmas are formed that may reach the surface. This heralds the breakup of the supercontinent.

The steps in the supercontinent cycle are as follows:

1. Assembly of the supercontinent takes place over some 40 Ma.
2. The development of Atlantic-type ocean basins goes on for about 160 Ma.
3. The development of subduction zones in these oceans forms Pacific-like ocean basins.
4. Assembly of a new supercontinent takes place over 226 to 160 Ma.
5. The supercontinent is stable for approximately 80 Ma, but heat accumulation leads ultimately to its breakup.

There is about a 500 Ma time span for completion of the cycle. The Earth is now either at the end of step 2 or just starting step 3. Six orogenic or mountain-building episodes can, so far, be related to the formation and breakup of the supercontinents. For example:

1. 2.6 Ga (billion years): Archaean–Proterozoic Boundary Orogenic Episode
2. 2.1 Ga: unknown (research continues regarding what happened at this point)
3. 1.7 Ga: Penokean Orogenic Episode associated with the assembly of the North American craton (or shield)
4. 1.1 Ga: Grenville Orogeny associated with the creation of the Supercontinent of Rodinia (Grenville rocks of this stage are found in the Canadian Shield)
5. 650 Ma: Pan-African Orogeny related to Gondwanaland
6. 250–300 Ma: Alleghanian–Hercynian Orogenic Episode, related to closing of an early Atlantic Ocean (Iapetus) and folding that created the Appalachian-Caledonide Mountains and the supercontinent of Pangaea

Terranes and Exotic Terranes

The movement of crustal plates creates complex lithospheric mosaics. Along the margins of a shield-anchored continent it is possible to identify bodies of rock that are unrelated to that landmass, derived from other plates and attached to it in a process called **accretion**. These fragments can be regional in extent; consistent in age, rock type, and structure; and continental or oceanic in origin. Earth scientists refer to them as **terranes**.

But there are times when observed terranes are so mismatched, and their sources so uncertain, that they are called **exotic terranes** (also *suspect terranes*). These rock masses have apparently come from distant locales. They seem to have travelled rapidly to reach their destinations in a process whose mechanics are not clear.

One of the Earth's most complex mosaics involving exotic terranes extends along western North America from Alaska to California, where long-term accretion has expanded the landmass far beyond its Pangaea-stage western margins (Figure 24.15). Many exotic terranes have been mapped here, of which the best

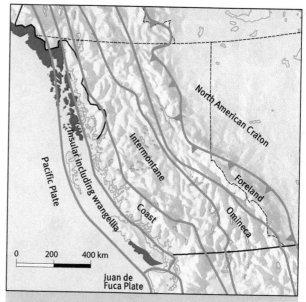

Figure 24.15 Megaterranes in British Columbia, Alberta, and the United States. Megaterranes are groupings of specific types of terranes. A craton is a shield/platform borderland area. The shaded areas are Wrangellia.

known is the Wrangellia terrane, parts of which occur in mainland and peninsular Alaska, in British Columbia, and south of the Canada–US border. Wrangellia is of volcanic, island-arc origin, its exposed fragments standing in sharp contrast to the surrounding regional geology (Figure 24.17).

How these exotic terranes reached their present locations is still a mystery. Similar exotic terranes are known to exist in the mountain belts of other landmasses, but they have not been explained. It is also known that pieces of continental crust are lodged on the ocean floors, often visible on seafloor topographic maps as submerged plateaus. One example of such a continental rock mass rising to the ocean surface lies in the Seychelles Islands off East Africa in the western Indian Ocean. Such comparatively small rock masses of continental origins may be moved along as seafloor spreading proceeds. They may eventually reach a collision plate boundary, and parts of them may become wedged into the mountain belt being formed there. Other exotic terranes may be former island arcs, pushed into continental margins and enveloped by mountain building. Clearly, this is one way a continental landmass may grow in present times, even if the Proterozoic phase of shield formation has long passed. Exotic terranes also occur in the Appalachians of eastern North America.

Isostasy

The upper surfaces of the continents display a high degree of topographic variety. Mountain ranges rise high above surrounding plains; plateaus and hills alternately dominate the landscape elsewhere. Mountain ranges have mass. Because of the law of gravity, they exert a certain attraction on other

Figure 24.16 The Himalayas form an awesome mountain wall when seen from the south. A view such as this undoubtedly greeted George Everest as he took his gravity measurements. This is central Nepal in the vicinity of Annapurna, the world's eleventh tallest peak.

objects. If we were to hang a plumb line somewhere on the flank of a mountain range, we would expect the mountains to attract the plumb line from the vertical towards the range.

More than a century ago, the British scientist George Everest (after whom the world's highest mountain is named) took measurements along the southern flanks of the Himalayas in India (Figure 24.16). He suspended his plumb line and did indeed find that the great Himalaya massif caused some attraction—but far less than his calculations, based on the assumed mass of the mountain range, led him to expect. Everest and his colleagues soon realized the importance of what they had discovered. If the deviation of the plumb line towards the mountains was less than calculated, there must be rocks of lesser density extending far below the Himalayas, displacing the heavier simatic material that would have caused greater attraction. In other words, the lighter sialic rocks appear to extend far down into the simatic rocks, and mountain ranges seem to have 'roots' that penetrate downward farthest where the surface elevations of the mountain ranges are greatest.

This possibility was realized as early as 1855 by George Airy, whose hypothesis of mountain roots is depicted in Figure 24.18. In Figure 24.19 the sialic part of the crust is likened to blocks of copper that, because they are less dense, float in the mercury representing the SIMA. The higher the block stands above the dashed line representing sea level, the deeper the root below pushes into the simulated SIMA. Thus the blocks, or parts of the Earth's crust, reach a kind of balance. Under the Himalayas and

other major mountain ranges, the sialic part of the crust is comparatively thick. Under plateaus it is thinner, and under low-lying plains it is thinner still. Thus the relief of the continental landmasses has a mirror image below. Since the development of plate tectonic theory, described above, we have come to believe that the balance is not a question of sialic 'rafts' floating on a simatic 'sea'. Rather, the balancing movements occur at the base of the lithosphere, far below the Mohorovicic discontinuity (see Unit 20).

The vertical changes in the crust are thought to take place for two reasons: (1) the lithosphere floats on the asthenosphere as the copper blocks float on the mercury; and (2) the lithosphere is subjected to changes of density from time to time. This situation of sustained adjustment, as visualized by Airy and modified by others after him, has come to be known as the principle of isostasy. The source of this term is not difficult to determine: *iso* means equal, and *stasy* comes from the ancient Greek word meaning to stand. Thus, **isostasy** is a condition of equilibrium between floating landmasses and the asthenosphere beneath them, maintained despite the tectonic and erosional forces that tend to change the landmasses all the time.

Isostasy and Erosion

We can use the model shown in Figure 24.19A to envision what would happen if a high mountain range were subjected to a lengthy period of weathering and erosion. If we were to remove the upper 10 per cent of the column marked **A**, we would expect that column to rise slightly—not quite to the height it was before but nearly so. If we were to place the removed portion of **A** on the two columns marked **B**, they would sink slightly, and their upper surface would adjust to a slightly higher elevation than before. Thus column **A** would have a lower height and a shorter root, whereas column **B** would have a greater height and a deeper root.

This tendency explains why erosional forces in the real world have not completely flattened all mountain ranges. Scientific experiments have indicated that, at present rates of erosion, the Earth's mountain ranges would be levelled in a single geologic period, certainly within 50 million years. But mountains hundreds of millions of years old, such as the Appalachians of eastern North America, still stand above their surroundings. What seems to happen is that as erosion removes the load from the ridges, isostatic adjustment raises the rocks to compensate. Rocks formed deep below the surface, tens of thousands of metres down, are thereby exposed to our view and to weathering and erosion.

Some puzzling questions about the deposition of enormous thicknesses of sedimentary rocks can also be answered. One sequence of sedimentary rocks found in Africa involved the accumulation of nearly 6.5 km of various sediments followed by an outpouring of great quantities of lava. Other parts of the world have even

From the Fieldnotes

Figure 24.17 *'Traversing Glacier Bay in southeast Alaska, we were given a seminar by a National Park Service guide who enjoyed asking challenging questions. Knowing some physical geography helped, but here she had me stumped. "Look at that outcrop," she said. "What can you tell me about it?" I said that the rocks looked darker than the regional grey-granite masses rising steeply from the bay, but in the absence of any knowledge of volcanic activity here, I could not do any better. "You're looking at lava," she explained; "this is a fragment of one of those suspect terranes, an old basaltic island arc welded onto the local regional geology. It's called Wrangellia, and pieces of it can be identified from mainland Alaska all the way down the coast to British Columbia and the US Northwest. It's out of place and we don't know how it got here, but it sure stands out in this landscape." That is the kind of field experience you don't forget.'*

thicker deposits. It is possible to deduce the environment under which deposition took place from the character of the deposits themselves. In some areas such deposition took place in shallow water. Although thousands of metres of sediments collected over millions of years, the depth of the water somehow remained about the same. In the accumulating sediments near the Bahamas, for instance, rocks that formed in shallow or intertidal flats are now 5500 m thick.

It can therefore be concluded that some cause, or combination of causes, depresses the region of deposition continuously, keeping the surface at about the same level. Such slowly accumulating sediments might be another place to effectively dispose of waste material produced by human activity, which might slowly sink from sight within the sediments. Slow accumulation is now taking place in the Mississippi Delta. For millions of years, the great river has been pouring sediments into its delta, but these deposits have not formed a great pile, nor have they filled in the Gulf of Mexico (Figure 24.20). The weight of the material and isostatic adjustment constantly lower the material to make room for more.

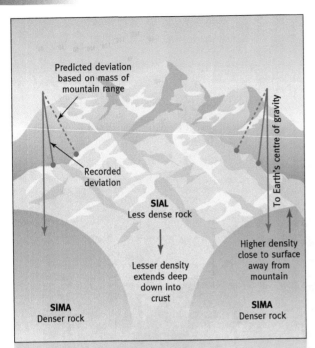

Figure 24.18 The Airy hypothesis: mountain ranges have roots of sialic rock that penetrate the denser simatic rock below.

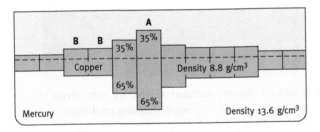

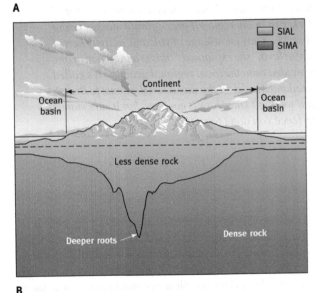

Figure 24.19 Isostasy. The distribution and behaviour of SIAL and SIMA is analogous to blocks of copper floating in mercury. Note that no matter how thick the block, the same percentage (35 per cent/65 per cent) floats above and below the surface. Each block is therefore in balance.

Isostasy and Plate Mobility

If isostasy involves a condition of equilibrium, then the contact and collision of mobile plates must affect that situation greatly. When a continental plate meets an oceanic plate, the oceanic plate plunges below the continental plate, causing the deformation and dislocation shown in Figure 24.8. Along the leading edge of the continental plate, rocks are crushed and folded, sediments are baked into metamorphic rocks, and magma penetrates and erupts along fissures and from volcanoes. In effect, the sialic mass increases in volume and, according to isostatic principles, rises upward. Right next to the high mountains so formed, the downward thrust of the oceanic plate often creates a deep trench, as deep as or deeper than the highest mountains are high. This is the situation along much of the Pacific Ring of Fire, where crustal instability and isostatic maladjustment are greatest. Earthquakes occur continuously along this zone as the plates converge and collide. Shallow tensional earthquakes occur as the oceanic plate bends, and compressional earthquakes increase in magnitude down the subducted plate (**Benioff zone**).

But the process does not go on forever at the same rate. It is not known just why, but the geological record shows that the Earth has gone through various rather distinct periods of mountain building and other quieter periods. Eventually even the Ring of Fire will quiet down, and plate collision and mountain building may start elsewhere. When this happens, erosion becomes dominant and begins to lower the mountains that have been created—but very slowly, because isostatic uplift will occur as mass is removed. The first phase of erosion, however, may be rather rapid.

The sialic mountains along the plate margin may have been pushed beyond the elevations justified by the depth of their roots, and isostatic readjustment will not commence until the overload has been removed. After that, the mountain masses undergo isostatic uplift as mass is eroded, a process that ensures their persistence for a long time. The Appalachians and Southern Africa's Cape Ranges have roots deep enough to ensure their topographic prominence over the past 200 (or more) million years. Some mountain ranges have indeed been flattened by erosion all the way down to their roots, but these are much older still.

Isostasy and Regional Landscapes

In studying the effects of the theory of isostasy, we tend to be preoccupied with mountain ranges, mountain building, plate compression, and associated phenomena. But we should not lose sight of the consequences of isostasy in areas of less prominent, less dramatic relief. Weathering and erosion are active on the continents' plains, too, and millions of tonnes of material are carried away by streams and other erosional agents. Even moving ice and wind denude and reduce land surfaces. Unlike the

LINK

Figure 24.20 Ever since the glaciers melted from the Midwest 12,000 years ago, the Mississippi River and its tributaries have been carrying millions of tonnes of sediment from the interior of North America to its Louisiana delta on the Gulf of Mexico. The weight of this accumulating deposit is in the process of depressing the crust isostatically, but in the interior the disappearance of the ice and the removal of the sediments are causing crustal rebound. This satellite view of the Mississippi Delta shows the lower course of the river, near circular Lake Pontchartrain (in the eastern part of the image), and the 'birdfoot' delta still forming.

LINK

mountainous zones, however, the plains are vast in area and slopes are gentler. Rivers erode less spectacularly on the plains than in the mountains as a consequence of several factors (see Unit 32). All these circumstances mean that eroded material is removed from the plains at a slower rate.

Plains and Uplands   The sialic crust has a certain rigidity. It does not behave, as in Airy's model, as a series of discrete columns. Therefore isostasy affects plains and plateaus in phases. For a certain period, the amount of material removed does not trigger isostatic readjustment because the hardness of the crust prevents continuous uplift. But when the plain has been lowered sufficiently for the push of isostatic uplift to overcome the resistance of the crust, a change takes place. Thus, at any given moment, an area may not be in isostatic equilibrium, awaiting the time when readjustment is forced by the removal of a sufficient mass of landscape.

Scientists suggest that this periodic adjustment may also occur in mountain ranges, especially older ones. In the beginning, when the sialic root is deep, isostatic uplift occurs almost continuously. But as time goes on, the root becomes shorter, erosion continues, and

comparatively more eroded material must be removed for readjustment to occur. In fact, the Appalachians were probably flattened almost completely and then forced up by a recurrence of isostatic uplift. Now the old ridges are being worn down again, and the whole area may be transformed into a plain before another readjustment occurs (Figure 24.21).

Dams and Crustal Equilibrium   Even human works on the surface of the Earth can produce isostatic reaction. When a dam is constructed, the weight of the impounded water behind it may be enough to produce isostatic accommodation in the crust. Measurable readjustment of this kind has taken place in the area of Kariba Lake, formed upstream of the great dam on the Zambezi River in Southern Africa, and around Lake Mead behind Hoover Dam on the Colorado River in Nevada. These changes cannot be seen with the naked eye, but scientific instruments detect them. The pressure on the crust from such large reservoirs can also cause earthquake activity. In our everyday existence, the crust may seem permanent, unchanging, and solid, but even comparatively minuscule human works can disturb its equilibrium.

Figure 24.21   View from Pilot Mountain, North Carolina, overlooking the Piedmont, which yields eastward to the coastal plain. A vista like this suggests that the mountains are being eroded into the lowland topography flanking them, but as the text points out, things are not that simple.

KEY TERMS

accretion   *page 337*

Benioff zone   *page 340*

continent   *page 336*

continental drift   *page 326*

crustal spreading   *page 330*

exotic terrane   *page 337*

Gondwanaland   *page 326*

island arc   *page 332*

isostasy   *page 340*

Laurasia   *page 326*

lithospheric plates   *page 327*

Pacific Ring of Fire   *page 328*

Pangaea   *page 326*

plate tectonics   *page 327*

rift   *page 330*

rift valley   *page 330*

seafloor spreading   *page 327*

subduction   *page 331*

supercontinent (Wilson) cycle   *page 336*

terrane   *page 337*

transform fault   *page 333*

REVIEW QUESTIONS

1. Briefly describe some of the evidence supporting the notion of continental drift.
2. Briefly describe the global map of lithospheric plates.
3. Where are most of the present-day rifting zones located?
4. How are subduction boundaries different from transform-fault boundaries? Give an example of each.
5. Describe the mechanism that is believed to drive lithospheric plate movement.
6. What are mountain 'roots'?
7. What is meant by the term *suspect terrane*?
8. Describe the process of isostatic uplift.

REFERENCES AND FURTHER READINGS

Allegre, C. 1988. *The Behavior of the Earth: Continental and Seafloor Mobility.* Cambridge, Mass.: Harvard Univ. Press.

Anderson, D.L. 1971. 'The San Andreas Fault', *Scientific American* (Nov.): 52–68.

Andrews, J.T. 1970. *A Geomorphological Study of Post-Glacial Uplift with Particular Reference to Arctic Canada.* London: Institute of British Geographers.

Bridges, E.M. 1990. *World Geomorphology.* New York: Cambridge Univ. Press.

Burbank, D., and R. Anderson. 2000. *Tectonic Geomorphology.* Malden, Mass.: Blackwell.

de Blij, H.J., et al. 1997. *Restless Earth.* Washington: National Geographic Society.

du Toit, A.L. 1937. *Our Wandering Continents.* Edinburgh: Oliver & Boyd.

Evolving Earth: Plate Tectonics (CD-ROM). 2001. Halifax: EOA Scientific Systems.

Hallam, A. 1992. *Great Geological Controversies,* 2nd edn. New York: Oxford Univ. Press.

Huggett, R.J. 2002. *Fundamentals of Geomorphology.* London/New York: Routledge.

King, L.C. 1983. *Wandering Continents and Spreading Sea Floors on an Expanding Earth.* Chichester, UK: Wiley.

Kious, W.J., and R.I. Tilling. n.d. *This Dynamic Earth: The Story of Plate Tectonics.* Reston, Va: US Geological Survey.

Miyashiro, A., et al. 1982. *Orogeny.* New York: Wiley.

Murphy, J.B., and R.D. Nance. 1992. 'Mountain Belts and the Supercontinent Cycle', *Scientific American* 226: 84–91.

Nicolas, A. 1994. *The Mid-Oceanic Ridges: Mountains below Sea Level.* New York: Springer-Verlag.

Oreskes, N. 1999. *The Rejection of Continental Drift: Theory and Method in American Earth Science.* New York: Oxford Univ. Press.

Raymo, C. 1983. *The Crust of Our Earth: An Armchair Traveler's Guide to the New Geology.* Englewood Cliffs, NJ: Prentice-Hall.

Schulz, S.S., and R.E. Wallace. 1989. *The San Andreas Fault.* Reston, Va: US Geological Survey.

Seibold, E., and W.H. Berger. 1996. *The Sea Floor: An Introduction to Marine Geology.* New York: Springer-Verlag.

Summerfield, M.A. 1991. *Global Geomorphology: An Introduction to the Study of Landforms.* New York: Wiley/Longman.

Tarling, D.H., and S.K. Runcorn. 1973. *Implications of Continental Drift to the Earth Sciences.* New York: Academic Press.

Taylor, F.B. 1910. 'Bearing of the Tertiary Mountain Belt on the Origin of the Earth's Plan', *Geological Society of America Bulletin* 21: 179–226.

Vita-Finzi, C. 1986. *Recent Earth Movements.* Orlando, Fla: Academic Press.

Wegener, A. 1966. *The Origin of Continents and Oceans.* Trans. J. Biram from 4th edn, 1929. New York: Dover.

Wilson, J.T. 1973. *Continents Adrift.* San Francisco: W.H. Freeman.

———. 1978. *Continents Adrift and Continents Aground.* San Francisco: W.H. Freeman.

Windley, B.F. 1984. *The Evolving Continents,* 2nd edn. New York: Wiley.

Wyllie, P.J. 1976. *The Way the Earth Works.* New York: Wiley.

 # WEB RESOURCES

www.geocities.com/earthhistory/plate3.htm This web page offers a description of the evolution of the continents with coloured graphics from the US Geological Survey server. Plate tectonics are covered, as well as crustal spreading.

pubs.usgs.gov/gip/earthq3/safaultgip.html This US Geological Survey informational page describes the San Andreas Fault in terms of plate tectonics, and also provides background information about earthquake mechanisms, size, and intensity.

pubs.usgs.gov/publications/text/dynamic.html The US Geological Survey presents *This Dynamic Earth: The Story of Plate Tectonics.* Plate motions, hot spots, and the historical perspective are discussed. Colour graphics guide users through this tutorial guide.

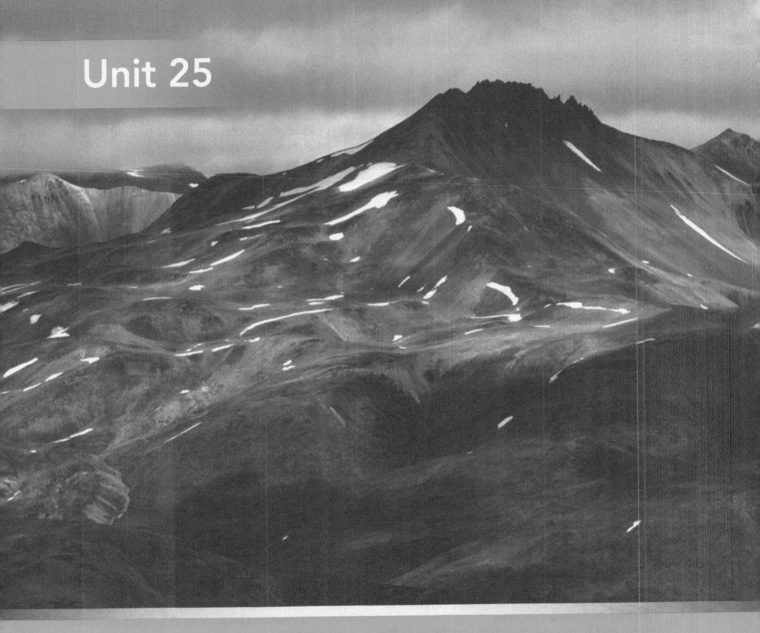

Unit 25

Volcanism and Its Landforms

Objectives

- To relate volcanic activity to plate boundary types.

- To discuss typical landforms produced by volcanic eruptions.

- To cite some dramatic examples of human interaction with volcanic environments.

Volcanism is the eruption of molten rock at the Earth's surface, often accompanied by the ejection of rock fragments and explosive gases. The process takes various forms, one of which is the creation of new lithosphere at the mid-oceanic spreading margins (about 75 per cent of the world's volcanoes are on the seafloor). Along some 50,000 km of ocean-floor fissures, molten rock (magma) penetrates to the surface (where it is called lava) and begins its divergent movement (see Figure 24.7).

This is a dramatic process involving huge quantities of magma, the formation of bizarre submarine topography, the heating and boiling of seawater, and the clustering of unique forms of deep-sea oceanic life along the spreading margins. But it is all hidden by the ocean water above, and what we know of it comes from the reports of scientist-explorers who have approached the turbulent scene in specially constructed submarines capable of withstanding the pressure at great depths and the high temperatures near the emerging magma, as well as by remote-controlled devices with video capability and the ability to retrieve small samples. Volcanism also occurs on the continents in the vicinity of plate margins (see Figures 24.2 and 24.3) and leaves a characteristic signature in the form of volcanic landscapes.

Islands situated on mid-oceanic margins afford a glimpse of a process that is mostly concealed from view. Iceland and smaller neighbouring islands lie on the Mid-Atlantic Ridge between Greenland and Norway in an area where the ridge rises above the ocean surface (see Figure 2.6). Iceland and its smaller neighbours are all of totally volcanic origin, and there is continuing volcanic activity there. In 1973 a small but populated and economically important island off Iceland's southwest coast, Heimaey, experienced a devastating episode of mid-oceanic ridge volcanic activity. First Heimaey was cut by fissures, and all 5300 of its inhabitants were quickly evacuated. In the months that followed, lava poured from these new fissures in the island, and volcanic explosions from the cone of Eldfell rained ash (tephra) and fiery pieces of ejected magma onto homes and commercial buildings in the port town of Vestmannaeyjar (Figure 25.1).

Heimaey actually increased in size, but the lava flows threatened to fill and destroy its important fishing port. This threat led to an amazing confrontation between people and nature. The islanders quickly built a network of plastic pipes at the leading edge of the advancing lava. They pumped seawater over and into the lava, aware that by cooling it more quickly than nature could, the lava would form a solid dam, which might stop the advance and restrain the lava coming behind it. This daring scheme worked: part of the harbour was lost to the lava, but a critical part of it was saved and actually improved. When this volcanic episode ended, life returned to Heimaey. The heat from the lava is used to generate electricity and heat warm water. But Iceland and its neighbours lie on an active mid-oceanic ridge, and volcanism will surely attack them again. What happened above the surface at Heimaey

Figure 25.1 The 1973 eruption on the Icelandic island of Heimaey generated lava flows and ashfalls that forced the evacuation within hours of the town of Vestmannaeyjar and caused considerable destruction—but it also produced a heroic reaction in which local citizens fought back.

is happening at various points along the 50,000 km of submerged spreading margins.

Distribution of Volcanic Activity

Most volcanism not associated with seafloor spreading is related to subduction zones (see Figure 24.8). As the global map (Figure 24.3) shows, volcanic activity is concentrated along spreading and convergent plate margins. Not surprisingly, a majority of the world's active volcanoes lie along the Pacific Ring of Fire. But note that some volcanic activity is associated neither with mid-oceanic ridges nor with subduction zones (it is intraplate). The island of Hawaii, for example, lies in an **archipelago** near the middle of the Pacific Plate. Lava has poured from one of its volcanic mountains, Kilauea, almost continuously since 1983. On the African Plate, where West Africa and Equatorial Africa meet, lies Mount Cameroon, another active volcano far from spreading and subductive margins. The map reveals a number of similar examples, both on ocean-floor crust and on continental crust. This distribution is difficult to explain.

Active, Dormant, and Extinct Volcanoes

Physical geographers differentiate among active, dormant, and extinct volcanoes on the basis, in some measure, of their appearance in the landscape. An **active volcano** is one that has erupted in recorded history (which, geologically speaking, is but an instant in time). A **dormant volcano** has not been seen to erupt, but it shows evidence of recent activity. This evidence lies on its surface: lava tends to erode quickly into gulleys and, on lower, flatter slopes, to weather into soils. If a volcano seems inactive but shows little sign of having been worn down, it may be concluded that its latest eruptions were quite recent, and activity may resume. When a volcano shows no sign of life and exhibits evidence of long-term weathering and erosion, it is tentatively identified as an **extinct volcano**. Such a designation is always risky because some volcanoes have come to life after long periods of dormancy.

As noted earlier, the great majority of continental volcanoes lie in or near spreading and subduction zones. Volcanic activity there is concentrated, and parts of the landscape are dominated by the unmistakable topography of eruptive volcanism. Many of the world's most famous mountains are volcanic peaks standing astride or near plate margins: Mount Fuji (Japan), Mount Vesuvius (Italy), Mount St Helen's and Mount Rainier (US Pacific Northwest), Mount Chimborazo (Ecuador), and many others. Frequently, such mountains stand tall enough to be capped by snow, their craters emitting a plume of smoke. It is one of the natural landscape's most dramatic spectacles.

The Timing of Volcanic Eruptions

There have been some interesting and thought-provoking recent studies concerned with the timing of volcanic eruptions. One study by volcanologists at Cambridge University suggests a seasonality of volcanic eruptions related to the seasonal rise and fall of sea level and changes in atmospheric pressure. For example, these researchers noted that eruptions were more liable to occur in such areas as Central America, the Alaskan peninsula, and Kamchatka during periods of falling regional sea levels and lowering atmospheric pressure. Another study by an American team has looked into the link between volcanic eruptions and the lunar cycle. It found that volcanic activity increased in actively erupting areas during periods of a full moon and also when the Moon was closest to the Earth (perigee). Their study was based on over 20 years of data. Remember that the Moon exerts gravitational pull on the Earth and is very important in terms of tidal motion. Thus, it might influence volcanic activity through variations in the pressure of the water column exerted on the crust (lithospheric plates).

Lava and Landforms

The viscosity (the property of a fluid that resists flowing) of magma and lava varies with its composition. Basaltic lavas, such as those flowing from the mid-oceanic spreading-margin volcanoes, are relatively low in silica and high in iron and magnesium content, and are therefore quite fluid when they erupt. They flow freely and often (on land) quite rapidly—up to 50 km/h on steep slopes. Other lavas are poorer in magnesium and iron but richer in silica—and thus more acidic. These lavas tend to be more viscous, and as a result they flow more slowly. Basaltic lava can flow like motor oil; the less mafic lava moves more like a thick porridge would (e.g., andesite).

Magma also contains steam and other gases under pressure, with variations again a function of its mineral content. The acidic, silica-rich (felsic) magmas tend to contain more gases, and when they erupt as lavas, these gases often escape explosively. Gobs of lava are thrown high into the air, solidifying as they fall back to the mountain's flanks. Such projectiles, not unreasonably, are called volcanic *bombs*. Smaller fragments may fall through the air as volcanic *cinders* or **ash** (also called **tephra**). After the explosive 1980 eruption of Mount St Helens in Washington State, lighter volcanic *dust* fell over a wide area downwind from the mountain. Yakima, not far from the volcano, was covered with up to 600,000 tonnes of ash. Geologists use the term **pyroclastics** for the rock material that formed part of the volcanic edifice that was fragmented and mobilized in an eruption; it usually moves down the sides of a volcano by slope processes known as a **pyroclastic flow** (Figures 25.2 and 25.3). *Pyroclastic* is ancient Greek for 'broken by fire'.

Figure 25.2 Pyroclastic flow down the side of a volcano in Montserrat.

Figure 25.3 Pyroclastic flows can bury villages, as happened here in Plymouth, the former capital of Montserrat.

When lava creates landforms, still other factors come into play. The rate of cooling relates not only to the composition and viscosity of the molten material, but also to the thickness of the flow and the nature of the surface over which the lava spreads. The nature of the **vent**, the opening through the existing crust where the lava has erupted, is an additional factor. Some eruptions do not come from pipe-shaped vents, but from lengthy cracks in the lithosphere. *Fissure eruptions* do not create mountains; rather, they release magma to form lava that extends in sheets across the countryside, creating sometimes extensive plateaus (Figure 25.4), a very common form of eruption along

LINK

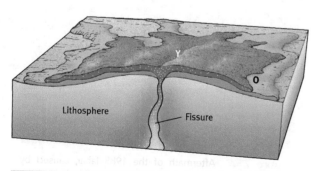

Figure 25.4 During a fissure eruption, lava flows onto the surface and spreads out in a sheet rather than forming a dome. When the fissure opens again, a later, younger flow (Y) will cover all or part of the older lava sheet (O).

spreading margins. In Canada, an excellent example can be found in the interior of British Columbia (Figure 25.5). Just before Gondwanaland broke up, great fissure eruptions (lava floods) produced a vast lava plateau of which parts still exist in India, South Africa, South America, and Antarctica. These were related to 'plumes' or 'hot spots' in the mantle.

Volcanic Mountains

The most characteristic product of volcanic eruption is the towering mountain form or edifice, represented by such peaks as Fuji (Japan), Rainier (US), Popocatépetl (Mexico), Vesuvius (Italy), and Kilimanjaro (Tanzania). But not all volcanic action, even from pipe-shaped vents, produces such impressive landforms. Some volcanoes are even larger in volume but less prominent in shape (e.g., megavolcanoes like Yellowstone or Lake Taupo). Others are smaller and less durable. Four types of volcanic landforms exist—composite volcanoes, lava domes, cinder cones, and shield volcanoes.

Composite Volcanoes

Most of the great volcanoes that formed over subductive margins are **composite volcanoes** (or *stratovolcanoes*)— they disgorge mainly pyroclastic materials including ash as

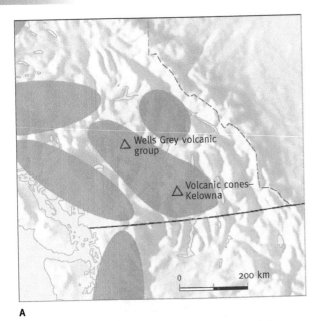

A

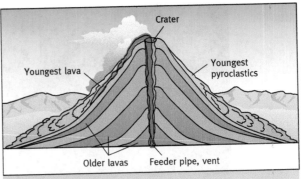

Figure 25.6 Simplified cross-section of a composite volcano, showing a sequence of lavas interspersed with compacted pyroclastics.

B

Figure 25.5 A. The Chilcotin Plateau basalt flows in the interior of British Columbia. B. The Chasm, British Columbia. Erosion has revealed varying tones of red, brown, yellow, and purple, formed by successive lava flows.

well as gases. These edifices are the classic 'volcano' shape. In cross-section such volcanoes look layered, with lavas of various thicknesses and textures interspersed with strata formed by compacted pyroclastics, such as tuff and ignimbrite and ash (Figure 25.6). Neither the heavier pyroclastics nor the rather viscous lava travels very far from the crater. In fact, lavas are fairly minor components in a lot of volcanoes of this type. Thus, the evolving volcano soon takes on its fairly steep-sided, often quite symmetrical appearance. Many composite volcanoes are long-lived and rise to elevations of thousands of metres.

Composite volcanoes, with their acidic, gas-filled lavas, are also notoriously dangerous. They often erupt explosively with little or no warning, and molten lava is not the only threat to life in their surroundings. Pyroclastics can be hurled far from the crater; volcanic ash can go into the stratosphere and affect the climate of a part or the whole of the world. Ash can create health hazards that choke human and animal life away from the volcano.

Lahars On snowcapped volcanoes the hot ash sometimes melts large quantities of the snow and ice, which forms a flood of ash, mud, and water rushing downslope. Such a mudflow can be extremely destructive. In 1985 the Nevado del Ruiz volcano in the Andes of central Colombia erupted, and much of its snowcap melted. In the volcanic mudflow, or **lahar**, that swiftly followed, more than 20,000 people perished. After it was over, the scene at a town in its path at the base of the mountain range was one of utter devastation, a mass of mud containing bodies of people and animals, houses and vehicles, trees and boulders (Figure 25.7). Such a deposit of volcanic origin is called a lahar once it solidifies. Lahars are mainly triggered by eruptions

Figure 25.7 Aftermath of the 1985 lahar, caused by a nearby erupting volcano, which late at night buried the Colombian town of Armero without warning. This 'hot' lahar killed at least 20,000 people in the immediate area, amounting to one of the worst natural disasters of the late twentieth century.

(these are called *hot lahars*), but occasionally they result from intensive, warm-season orographic or cyclonic rainfall. Previously deposited ash can be mobilized, causing a *cold lahar*. The torrential rains related to Hurricane Mitch, for example, caused cold lahars that devastated parts of Central America in 1998, killing approximately 20,000 people in Honduras and Nicaragua.

Nuées Ardentes   Perhaps even more dangerous is the outburst of hot gas and fine ash that may accompany or precede an eruption. Gas is pent up in magma itself, but in some composite volcanoes a large reservoir of gas may accumulate in the magma chamber below the crater. This happens when the crater becomes clogged by solidified lava, which forms a *plug* in the top of the vent. The gas cannot escape, and rising temperatures inside the mountain may well exceed 1000°C. Pressures finally become so great that the side of the volcano may be blown open, allowing the gas to escape, or the plug may be blown out of the top of the volcano's pipe, enabling the gas to rush from the crater along with heavier pyroclastics and lava. Such an event produces a **nuée ardente** (French for *glowing cloud*), which races downslope at speeds exceeding 100 km/h. Everything in its path is incinerated because the force of the descending turbulent, heavier-than-air cloud of gas, plus its searing temperatures, ensures total destruction.

In 1902 a *nuée ardente* burst from Mount Pelée on the eastern Caribbean island of Martinique. It descended on the nearby port town of St Pierre at its base in a matter of minutes, killing an estimated 30,000 persons (the only survivor was a prisoner in a cell in the town's thick-walled prison). The 'Paris of the Caribbean', as St Pierre had been described, never recovered and still carries the scars of its fate more than a century later. Similar glowing cloud activity was associated with the pyroclastic flows that buried Oplontis and Herculaneum when Mount Vesuvius erupted in AD 79. These asphyxiated and burned the people remaining in the towns before they were buried by pyroclastic flows.

Predicting Risk   Among the other dangers posed by volcanoes of the gas-filled, viscous-magma variety are quieter emissions of lethal gases that can reach people and animals at air temperature and kill without warning. Estimating the risk to people living near such volcanoes and predicting dangerous activity have become part of an increasingly exact science, but many volcanoes (especially in developing countries) are not yet subject to such scientific monitoring and hazard mitigation. The 1980 eruption of Mount St Helens had been predicted by volcanologists who had measured the telltale signs of resumed activity, and their warnings probably saved thousands of lives.

Forecasting techniques have been improving since 1980, and a number of volcanoes are now being monitored by scientists in the United States, Japan, Mexico, Italy, Iceland, Papua New Guinea, Montserrat, and elsewhere.

Among their most notable successes were predictions of the eruptions of Alaska's Mount Redoubt in 1989 and of Mount Pinatubo in the Philippines in 1991 (Figure 25.8). But the magnitude of these eruptions went well beyond what had been anticipated, reminding us that volcanic activity still defies exact prediction. Many cities near volcanoes have evacuation plans but these are not necessarily logical or reasonable. For example, the Naples area, with over 3 million people, is among the most densely populated areas close to a volcano (Mount Vesuvius), and the volcano is continuously monitored. The plan of the Italian government emergency agencies is to evacuate the people threatened by any major eruptions to other areas of the country, yet this plan requires two to three weeks while an eruption can take only hours.

Lava Domes

When acidic lava (andesite, dacite) penetrates to the surface, it may ooze out without pyroclastic activity. This process usually produces a small volcanic mound, called a **lava dome**. A lava dome often forms inside a crater following an explosive eruption, as happened at Mount St Helens. But lava domes can also develop as discrete landforms in a volcanic landscape. Although some grow quite large, lava domes, on average, are much smaller than composite volcanoes.

Cinder Cones

Some volcanic landforms consist not of lava, but almost entirely of pyroclastics. Normally such **cinder cones** (which may also include fragments larger as well as smaller than cinders) remain quite small, frequently forming during a brief period of explosive activity. Probably the most extensive areas of cinder-cone development lie in East Africa and Iceland and are associated with the rift-valley system of those regions. They form row volcanoes along fissures (Figure 25.9). In North America, a sporadic row of cinder cones, along with shield volcanoes and tuyas (volcanoes that erupted under an ice sheet), is found running from the BC coast inland to Wells Grey Provincial Park; these form the Anahim Volcanic Belt (Figure 25.10). Also, the Craters of the Moon (Idaho) and Sunset Crater (Arizona) are often cited as examples of older cinder cones. Geologists were able to observe closely the growth of a cinder cone in Mexico from 1943, when it was born in a cornfield in Michoacán state (about 320 km west of Mexico City); growth stopped in 1952. This cinder cone, named Paricutín, grew to a height of 400 m in its first eight months of activity and remained intermittently active for nearly a decade.

Shield Volcanoes

Shield volcanoes are formed from more-fluid basaltic lavas. These lavas contain sufficient or 'certain' gases to create a sometimes dramatic 'fountain' of molten rock (see Figure 25.11) and some cinders, but these are tiny

A

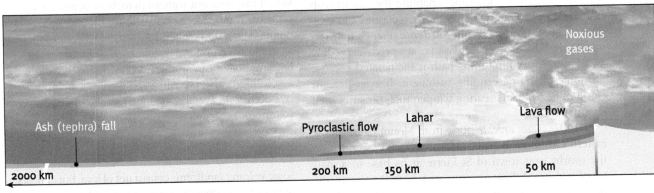

B

Figure 25.8 (A) A huge cloud of volcanic ash and gas rises above Mount Pinatubo in the Philippines on 12 June 1991. Three days later an explosive eruption, one of the largest in the past century, spread a layer of ash over a vast area around the mountain, with environmental as well as political consequences: a dust cloud orbited the Earth and reduced global warming, and a nearby US military base on Pinatubo's island (Luzon) was damaged beyond repair. (B) Diagram showing the various types of hazards associated with a volcanic eruption and the various sizes of areas affected by the hazards.

compared to the explosive eruptions at the craters of composite volcanoes. The basaltic lava is very hot, however, and flows in sheets or floods over a countryside being gradually built up by successive eruptions (Figure 25.12). Compared to their horizontal dimensions, which are very large, the tops of such volcanoes are rather unspectacular and are rounded rather than peaked. This low-profile appearance has given them the name *shield volcanoes*.

The most intensively studied shield volcanoes undoubtedly are those on the main island of Hawaii, where the US Geological Survey operates an observatory. Mauna Loa is the largest active shield volcano there. It stands on the ocean floor, and from there rises 10,000 m, with the uppermost 3500 m protruding above sea level. Mauna Loa is the tallest mountain on Earth. To the north, Mauna Kea's crest is slightly higher. And to the east lies Kilauea, the volcano that has experienced eruptions since the

1970s and also holds a special meaning for native Hawaiians (see 'Perspectives' box). Kilauea has a lava lake at its top that acts as its principal vent—Halema'uma'u (fire pit). The production of lava from this lake has averaged 150–200 tonnes/day over the last 25 years. It peaked in early May 2008, reaching 1320 tonnes/day, but has now decreased again. Some recent eruptive activity has occurred from flank vents located in rifts on the side of the volcano. One vent in particular, Pu'u'O'o, has been the site of important eruptions over the last 25 years. The Pu'u'O'o vent is linked by a lava tube to the sea 16 to 17.5 km away near Pulama Pali. About 120 km² of lava has been erupted over the 25-year period from Pu'u'O'o and has added over 200 hectares to the southern shore of the island. Kilauea's lavas even flowed across a housing subdivision, obliterating homes and streets, and reached the ocean, thereby adding a small amount of land to the island.

From the Fieldnotes

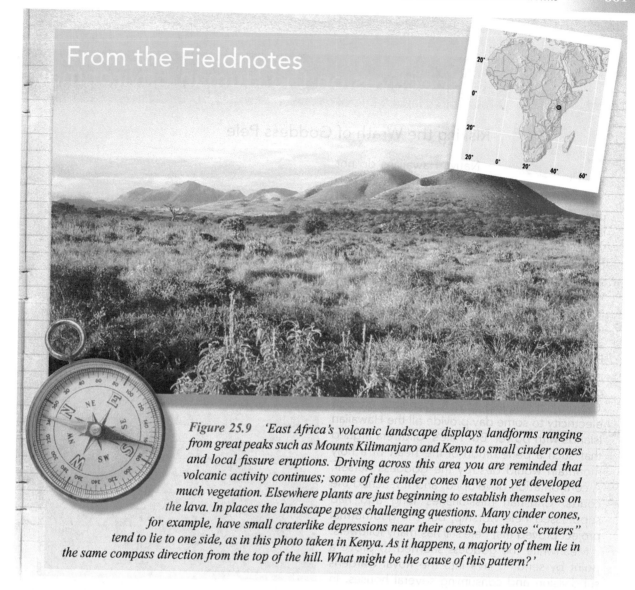

Figure 25.9 *'East Africa's volcanic landscape displays landforms ranging from great peaks such as Mounts Kilimanjaro and Kenya to small cinder cones and local fissure eruptions. Driving across this area you are reminded that volcanic activity continues; some of the cinder cones have not yet developed much vegetation. Elsewhere plants are just beginning to establish themselves on the lava. In places the landscape poses challenging questions. Many cinder cones, for example, have small craterlike depressions near their crests, but those "craters" tend to lie to one side, as in this photo taken in Kenya. As it happens, a majority of them lie in the same compass direction from the top of the hill. What might be the cause of this pattern?'*

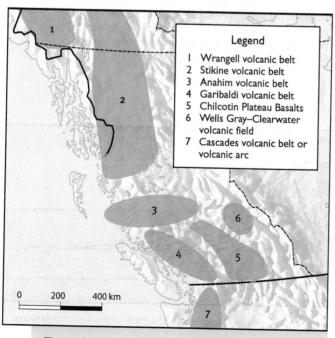

Legend

1 Wrangell volcanic belt
2 Stikine volcanic belt
3 Anahim volcanic belt
4 Garibaldi volcanic belt
5 Chilcotin Plateau Basalts
6 Wells Gray–Clearwater volcanic field
7 Cascades volcanic belt or volcanic arc

0   200   400 km

Figure 25.10 Canadian volcanoes.

Recent studies have shown that the southern side of Kilauea is probably going to give way in a large mass movement. The Hilina Block has an area of 80 km², is 12 km deep, and moves at a rate of 5 cm/yr. If this is subject to a catastrophic failure, it could generate tsunamis along the shores of the Big Island. The same kind of process is going on at another volcano, Cumbre Vieja, on La Palma in the Canary Islands. The prospect of catastrophic failure here is much more threatening. Estimates suggest that if the side of this island fails it could generate a massive tsunami that could affect a lot of major cities along the eastern seaboard of the US and, in Canada, notably Halifax and St John's, and could cause total devastation in low-lying areas like Florida.

The volcanic landscape in Hawaii and other areas displays some interesting shapes and forms. Lava that is especially fluid when it emerges from the crater develops a smooth 'skin' upon hardening. This slightly hardened surface is then wrinkled, as the lava continues to move, into a ropy pattern called **pahoehoe** (Icelandic: *helluhraun*). This kind of lava is associated with the formation of *lava*

Perspectives on the Human Environment

Risking the Wrath of Goddess Pele

Native Hawaiians do not regard their islands' volcanism as simply a geological phenomenon. They have lived with the Hawaiian fountains of fire far longer than the white invaders have been on their islands. The goddess Pele rules here, and she displays her pleasure or wrath through her power over the main island's volcanoes. In accordance with tradition, Hawaiians walk barefoot on the *aa* lava to the very edges of Kilauea (Figure 25.11) and the other steaming craters of the island of Hawaii, pray to Pele, and leave fern garlands for her.

During the 1980s plans were announced to tap geothermal energy from the interior of Kilauea. The project was expected to generate enough electricity to some day provide all the Hawaiian Islands with power. But Pele's followers argued that such a penetration of the heart of a holy mountain would destroy the goddess herself. A confrontation developed, and it reached the courts. Christian missionaries long ago had suppressed Pele worship, but the geothermal project proved that Pele still has many followers.

Meanwhile the goddess seemed to prove a point by sending lava into the Royal Gardens subdivision and consuming several houses. In 1988 the Pele Defense Fund even bought a full-page advertisement in *The New York Times* to state its case. The day it appeared, Kilauea put on a volcanic display described as the most spectacular in more than a year, marking the start of an eruption that is still going on.

Figure 25.11 Unearthly landscape of Kilauea's upper slopes on the island of Hawaii, a classic shield volcano. An eruption is in progress, one of a still continuing series that began more than 20 years ago. Lava emanating here can flow for many kilometres and reach the sea.

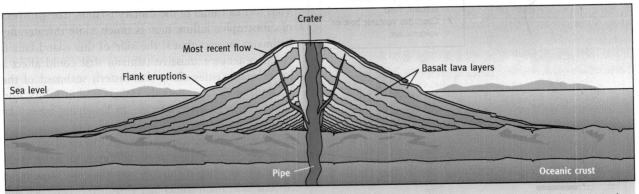

Figure 25.12 Simplified cross-section of a shield volcano. Vertical scale is greatly exaggerated. The base of this volcano extends over 320 km; its height above the ocean floor is around 13 km.

From the Fieldnotes

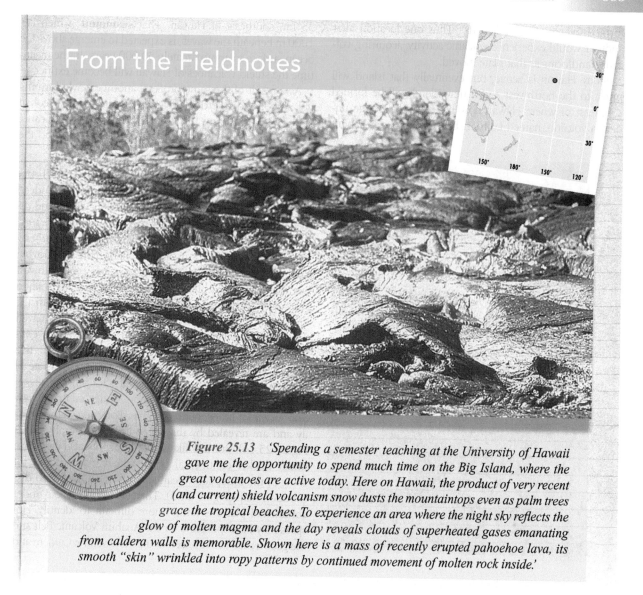

Figure 25.13 *'Spending a semester teaching at the University of Hawaii gave me the opportunity to spend much time on the Big Island, where the great volcanoes are active today. Here on Hawaii, the product of very recent (and current) shield volcanism snow dusts the mountaintops even as palm trees grace the tropical beaches. To experience an area where the night sky reflects the glow of molten magma and the day reveals clouds of superheated gases emanating from caldera walls is memorable. Shown here is a mass of recently erupted pahoehoe lava, its smooth "skin" wrinkled into ropy patterns by continued movement of molten rock inside.'*

tubes where red-hot lava flows under a thin cover of hardened lava. The lava stream can be seen through 'windows' where the surface has collapsed. Molten lavas often flow out of these tubes, leaving them as a long, narrow cave system (Figure 25.13). Less fluid lava hardens into angular, blocky forms called **aa**, so named (according to Hawaiian tradition) because of the shouts of people trying to walk barefoot on this jagged terrain! In Iceland this type of lava is called apalhraun. In the Hawaiian Islands, it is the Big Island—Hawaii—that displays the currently active volcanism. But all the islands in this archipelago originally formed as shield volcanoes. Why should Hawaii contain the only volcanic activity? And why are there volcanoes at all, here in the middle of a lithospheric plate?

These questions are answered in part by the topographic map of the northwestern Pacific Basin (Figure 25.14A). Note that the Hawaiian Islands lie in an arched line from Kauai and its small neighbours in the northwest to Hawaii in the southeast. That line continues northwestward through Midway Island and then bends north-northwestward on

the ocean floor as the Emperor Seamounts. It is remarkable that the only pronounced volcanic activity along this entire corridor is on Hawaii—at the very end of the chain.

Another part of the answer lies on the surface. In general, the rocks of Midway and Kauai (Figure 25.14A) show evidence of much longer erosion than those of Oahu and, of course, Hawaii itself. Midway and Kauai seem to be much older than Oahu and Hawaii, and geological evidence confirms this. When the rocks of these Pacific islands were dated, those of Oahu were found to be around 3 million years old, those of Midway 25 million years old, and those at the northern end of the Emperor Seamounts 75 million years old.

Hot Spots   Geologists theorize that the Pacific Plate has been moving over a **hot spot** in the mantle, a 'plume' of extraordinarily high heat that remains in a fixed location, perhaps stoked by a high concentration of radioactivity. This idea was first suggested by Tuzo Wilson. As the Pacific Plate moved over this hot spot, shield volcanoes formed over it (Figure 25.14B). Thus one location after another would experience volcanic activity, acquiring volcanic landforms as that plate moved.

Today Hawaii is active, but eventually that island will move to the northwest and a new island will be formed southeast of where Hawaii now lies. Already, a large undersea volcano, named Loihi, is being built upward about 35 km southeast of Hawaii. That **seamount**, which lies 1000 m beneath the waves, is expected to emerge above the ocean surface in approximately 50,000 years. In the meantime the shield volcanoes of Hawaii will become extinct.

As a result of the same process, another newly forming volcanic island—Ferdinandea—is forming in the Aeolian Island arc (including the islands of Stromboli, Vulcano, and Lipari) in the Tyrrhenian Sea between Sicily and the Italian mainland.

Hot Spots and Plate Dynamics If the hot-spot theory is correct, and mantle or subcrustal hot spots are indeed stationary, then it is possible to calculate the speed and direction of plate movement. As the map (Figure 25.14A) shows, the Emperor Seamounts extend in a more northerly direction than the Midway–Hawaii chain. Thus the moving Pacific Plate—which today travels towards the northwest (see Figure 24.2)—changed direction about 40 million years ago if the same hot spot is responsible for both the Emperor Seamounts and the Midway–Hawaii chain. Given the age of Midway's lavas (25 million years), we may conclude that the plate travelled some 2700 km over this period. This works out to about 11 cm per year, a rate of movement consistent with average rates for other plates.

The volcanic effects of hot spots under comparatively thin oceanic lithosphere can be discerned rather easily and are revealed by the ocean-floor topography (as in Figure 25.14). But it is likely that hot spots also are active under thicker continental crust, which may account for some of the intraplate volcanism shown on the world distribution map (Figure 24.3). The effect of hot spots under continental plates is rather more difficult to identify. Hot spots may be responsible for the Anahim Volcanic Belt and the geothermal activity seen at the Yellowstone Caldera and

LINK

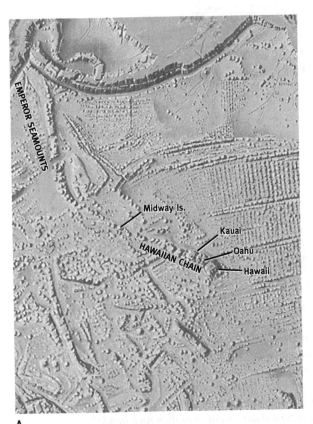

A

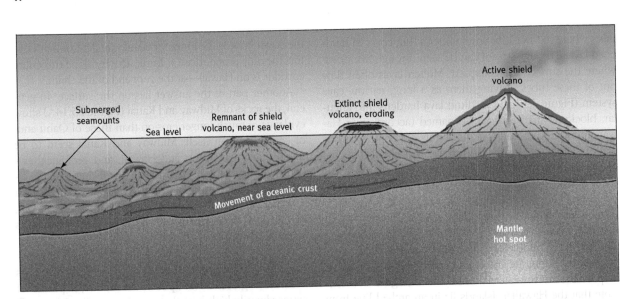

B

Figure 25.14 Ocean floor of the northwestern Pacific, dominated by the Emperor Seamounts and the Hawaiian Chain (A). Volcanic chain formed by the seafloor moving over a geologic hot spot (B). These volcanic landforms become progressively older towards the left.

for some of those giant fissure eruptions like the ones that formed the Columbia Plateau. An isolated zone of volcanic activity (e.g., Mount Cameroon in west-central Africa and the range to the northeast of it) may be associated with hot-spot activity. On the other hand, such linear activity may also represent a yet hidden crustal spreading zone beneath the continental SIAL. The problem is not yet totally solved.

Calderas

A volcano's lavas and pyroclastics come from a subterranean magma chamber, a reservoir of active molten rock material that forces its way upward through the volcanic vent. When that magma reservoir ceases to support the volcano, the chamber may empty out and the interior of the mountain may literally become hollow. Left unsupported by the magma, the walls of the volcano may collapse, creating a **caldera** (Figure 25.15). Such an event can occur quite suddenly, perhaps when the weakened structure of the volcano is shaken by an earthquake. A caldera also can result from a particularly violent eruption, which destroys the peak and crater of the volcano. In such cases, however, the magma chamber below is at the peak of its energy and will soon begin to rebuild the mountain.

Calderas are often large and sometimes filled with water. They also are often misnamed, as, for example, Oregon's Crater Lake, which is a circular caldera 10 km across, with walls more than 1200 m high; a lake 600 m deep fills this caldera. Another misnamed caldera is the Ngorongoro Crater in Tanzania, some 18 km across and 600 m deep. Ngorongoro contains a small lake, but it is best known for the enormous concentration of wildlife that has occupied it and its fertile natural savanna for many thousands of years.

The Volcanic Explosivity Index

The **Volcanic Explosivity Index** is a measure of the size of a volcanic eruption. The index was suggested by volcanologists working for the United States Geological Survey

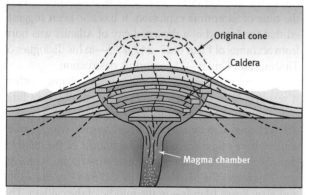

Figure 25.15 When the magma chamber that has long supplied an active volcano is somehow deprived of its conduit to the magma source, it empties out, leaving a hollow chamber beneath the cone. Eventually the structure of the volcano yields and the cone collapses, creating a caldera.

in the early 1980s and has been subsequently revised. It is based on both subjective descriptions and quantitative data—for example, eruptive plume height (height of the ash column), the volume of tephra (ash) erupted, the eruptive style (Vulcanian, Plinian, etc.), eruption frequency, and so on. Each successive class in the index represents about an order of magnitude increase in the size of the events. There are nine classes in the index, starting at VEI 0, i.e., non-explosive eruptions that include the effusive basaltic eruptions common to Hawaiian and Icelandic shield volcanoes, and extending to VEI 8, i.e., mega-colossal eruptions with an eruption frequency of tens of thousands of years, which have not been recorded or seen in historical time. Such events had a long-lasting effect on climate, caused the extinction of animals and plants, and produced large areas of lava and/or ash (Table 25.1).

Some Examples of Volcanic Explosivity Events, Classes 6 and 7 (Colossal and Super-Colossal)

Volcanoes subject to extremely large catastrophic eruptions affect a very large area and may cause changes in terms of atmospheric gases, particulates, aerosols, and temperature. Water, poured on advancing lava, can help cool and consolidate the hot lava and slow down or divert the movement of the flow. But when water penetrates into the magma chamber below a volcano, it has quite a different effect. Just as pouring water on a grease fire only intensifies the blaze, so water entering a super-heated magma chamber results in an explosive reaction—so explosive, in fact, that it can blow the entire top off the volcano above. This may be the reason for the gigantic explosions known to have occurred in recorded history, explosions that involved large composite volcanoes standing in water. Such explosions are called **phreatic** or **magmatophreatic eruptions**, and their effects reach far beyond the volcano's immediate area. Some phreatic eruptions, described in the following subsections, are believed to have changed the course of human history.

Krakatau The most recent major phreatic eruption happened in 1883, when Indonesia's Krakatau volcano blew up with a roar heard in Australia 3000 km away. The blast had a force estimated at 100 million tonnes of dynamite. It rained pyroclastics over an area of 750,000 km^2 and propelled volcanic dust through the troposphere and stratosphere to an altitude of 80 km. For years following Krakatau's eruptive explosion, this dust orbited the Earth, affecting solar radiation and colouring sunsets brilliant red (shown in some Impressionist landscape paintings). Krakatau was an uninhabited, forested island located between Java and Sumatra. Great water waves generated by its explosion dealt death and destruction. First, the explosion itself set in motion a giant *tsunami* (a sea wave set off by crustal disturbance), which radiated to the nearby coasts of Java, Sumatra, and other islands. Next, water rushed into the newly opened caldera, setting off further explosions and successive tsunamis. When these waves reached the more heavily populated coasts of Indonesia,

Table 25.1 Volcanic Explosivity Index: Characteristics and Frequency

VEI	Description	Plume Height	Tephra Volume	Classification	Eruption Frequency	Example	Total Historic Eruptions	Eruptions in Last 10 Years
0	Non-explosive	<100 m	1000 m³	Hawaiian/Icelandic	Daily	Kilauea	487	70
1	Gentle/effusive	100–1000 m	10,000 m³	Hawaiian/Icelandic/Strombolian	Daily	Stromboli	623	124
2	Explosive	1–5 km	1,000,000 m³	Strombolian/Vulcanian	Weekly	Galeras (1992)	3176	125
3	Severe	3–15 km	10,000,000 m³	Vulcanian	Yearly	Nevada Del Ruiz (1985)	733	49
4	Cataclysmic	10–25 km	>0.1 km³	Vulcanian/Plinian	10s of years	Galingongg (1982)	119	7
5	Paroxysmal	>25 km	≥1 km³	Plinian	100s of years	Mount St Helens (1980)	19	1
6	Colossal	>25 km	≥10 km³	Plinian/Ultraplinian	100s of years	Krakatau (1883)	5	0
7	Super-colossal	>>25 km	≥100 km³	Ultraplinian	1000s of years	Tambora (1815)	2	0
8	Mega-colossal	>>>25 km	≥1000 km³	Ultraplinian	10,000s of years	Yellowstone (2 Ma)	0	0

an estimated 40,000 people were killed. These tsunamis were actually recorded as far away as the English Channel, where they affected the height of the tides.

Tambora Explosive eruptions of Krakatauan dimensions occur suddenly but rarely. Nonetheless, Krakatau's actually was the second eruption of the nineteenth century in its corner of the world. In 1815 the phreatic eruption of the Indonesian volcano Tambora was even larger. The volcanic dust it generated interfered so strongly with incoming solar radiation that the weather turned bitterly cold over much of the world, and as a result 1816 was widely described as the 'year without a summer'. Crops failed to ripen in 1816, food and fuel shortages developed, and problems lasted into the ensuing winter and beyond. People in Upper and Lower Canada (Ontario and Quebec) wore their winter clothes during the summer of 1816 because the temperatures were so cold.

Santorini Certainly phreatic eruptions can affect climate for a time. But possibly no such event had a greater impact on human history than the explosion of the Mediterranean volcano of Santorini, or Thera, which took place in the middle of the seventeenth century BCE, more than 3600 years ago. The exact date of this cataclysmic event is still being debated, but its dimensions are clear.

The volcanic island of Santorini stood in the Mediterranean about 110 km north of Crete, where the Minoan civilization thrived. On a fateful day sometime around 1645 BCE, Santorini exploded, possibly as a result of sea water entering its magma chamber. So much volcanic ash was blasted into the air that skies were darkened for days. (It has been suggested that this was the event described in the Bible's Old Testament as the act of God in retribu-

tion against the pharaoh: 'thick darkness in all the land of Egypt for three days'.) The Mediterranean Sea turned into a cauldron of tsunamis that lashed the coasts of other islands and mainland Greece and Turkey.

As for Santorini itself, when daylight reappeared its core was gone, replaced by the protruding margins of a vast caldera now filled with sea water (Figure 25.16). The loss of life cannot be estimated. Fertile, productive, well-located Santorini had towns and villages, ports and farms; fleets of boats carried trade between it, prosperous Crete, and the eastern Mediterranean. Minoan civilization was the Mediterranean's most advanced, and great palaces graced Crete as well as Santorini. Many archaeologists and historical geographers have speculated that the eruption of Santorini spelled the end of the Minoan culture. Whatever the cause, the Minoan civilization went into decline at about the time of Santorini's explosion. It has also been suggested that the legend of a drowned city of Atlantis was born from accounts of Plato (427–347 BCE)—in his dialogues of Timaeus and Critias—of Santorini's destruction.

Santorini's caldera did not form from collapse; rather, it resulted from explosive forces. Geologically, very little time has elapsed since Santorini's explosion, but considerable volcanic activity and associated seismic (earthquake) activity have taken place. Near the middle of the caldera, probably above the original vent, a new lava dome is emerging. This forms the islands of Palea and Nea Kameni—Old and New Burnt Islands—in the middle of the caldera. The lavas forming these islands are all less than 2000 years old. The volcano remains active, and although its caldera rim is quite densely populated today, many inhabitants have fled after each volcanic and seismic event. In the meantime, archaeologists continue to excavate the ruins of a Bronze

From the Fieldnotes

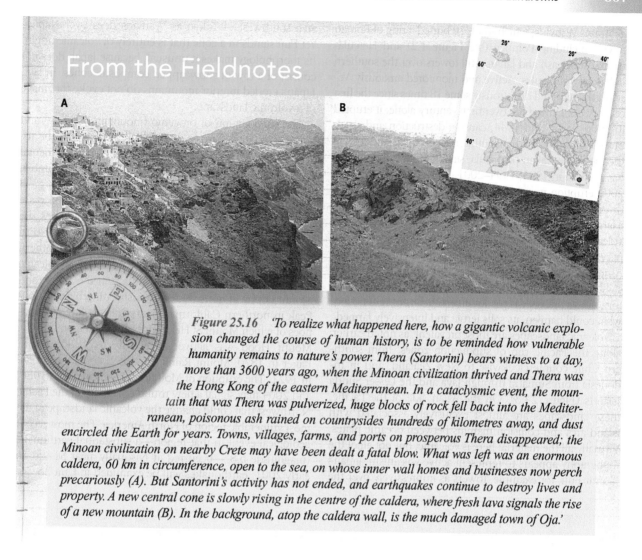

Figure 25.16 *'To realize what happened here, how a gigantic volcanic explosion changed the course of human history, is to be reminded how vulnerable humanity remains to nature's power. Thera (Santorini) bears witness to a day, more than 3600 years ago, when the Minoan civilization thrived and Thera was the Hong Kong of the eastern Mediterranean. In a cataclysmic event, the mountain that was Thera was pulverized, huge blocks of rock fell back into the Mediterranean, poisonous ash rained on countrysides hundreds of kilometres away, and dust encircled the Earth for years. Towns, villages, farms, and ports on prosperous Thera disappeared; the Minoan civilization on nearby Crete may have been dealt a fatal blow. What was left was an enormous caldera, 60 km in circumference, open to the sea, on whose inner wall homes and businesses now perch precariously (A). But Santorini's activity has not ended, and earthquakes continue to destroy lives and property. A new central cone is slowly rising in the centre of the caldera, where fresh lava signals the rise of a new mountain (B). In the background, atop the caldera wall, is the much damaged town of Oja.'*

Age settlement near Akrotiri on the southern edge of the caldera, hoping to learn more about life on Santorini before its catastrophic interruption. We can only speculate on the course history might have taken if the Minoan civilization had spread throughout the archipelago in which Santorini lies, expanded onto the mainland, and given birth to what would have been a very different kind of ancient Greece.

Some Examples of Volcanic Explosivity Index Class 8 Events

These are classified as mega-colossal events (*super-eruptions* or *super-volcanoes*), and are truly large earth-changing events of a scale not seen in historical time. They do not form an edifice. It takes an immense amount of time for the huge magma chambers of these features to fill (>1 million years). Only a few of these are known:

- The eruption of Lake Taupo in New Zealand around 26,500 years before the present (YBP) released approximately 1170 km³ of ash.
- The Lake Toba (Indonesia) event occurred about 75,000 YBP and erupted about 2800 km³ of ash.
- The massive Yellowstone caldera erupted at least three times, releasing an enormous amount of material

preserved in enormous beds of tuff (around 2.2 million YBP—about 2500 km³ of ash; about 640,000 YBP, ~1000 km³; and approximately 1.3 million YBP, ~280 km³).

- The largest known eruption found so far was of the La Garita Caldera in Colorado and occurred around 27 million years ago. The Fish Canyon Tuff erupted by this event contains about 5000 km³ of material.

A documentary (2000) and a subsequent docudrama (2005) based on a possible future eruption of the Yellowstone super-volcano were produced by the British Broadcasting Corporation. These programs showed the environmental, economic, and social worldwide cataclysmic disaster caused by such an immense event.

Landscapes of Volcanism

Volcanic activity, especially the mountainous type, creates unique and distinct landscapes. As Figure 24.3 reminds us, volcanic landscapes are limited in their geographic extent, but they do dominate certain areas. Even a single composite cone, by its sheer size or threat, can dominate physical and mental landscapes over a much wider area.

Mount Vesuvius, which in CE 79 buried a ring of Roman towns, including Pompeii (see Figure 1.2) and Herculaneum, under ash and lahars, still towers over the southern Italian city of Naples. Active and monitored anxiously, Vesuvius has erupted disastrously some 18 times since the first century CE. During the twentieth century alone, it erupted in 1906, 1929, and 1944, causing destruction and death in each instance. Farther south, on Sicily, the island just off the toe of the Italian peninsula, stands Mount Etna, which has erupted in 1992, 1994–2001, 2002–3, and 2004. The 2002 eruption was notable because of the first successful diversion of a lava flow using concrete blocks dropped from a large helicopter. Again 'the mountain', as such dominating volcanic landforms seem to be called wherever they stand, pervades the physical landscape of the entire area. East Africa's Kilimanjaro, 5861 m tall, carries its snowcap within sight of the Equator. It has not erupted in recorded history, but its presence is predominant, its form a reminder of what could happen, its soils fertile and intensively farmed.

Volcanic landscapes are most prevalent, as noted earlier, along the Pacific rim of subduction zones, from southern Chile counterclockwise to New Zealand, and in Indonesia from Sumatra through Java and the Lesser Sunda Islands (Figure 24.3). On the Asian side of the Pacific, these landscapes are almost exclusively associated with island arcs and collision margins between oceanic plates. Virtually all the material here is volcanic, but not all of the topography appears to represent active volcanism. Japan's Mount Fuji, for example, towers as impressively over the area southwest of Tokyo as Vesuvius does over Naples. Yet Fuji stands in a zone that is entirely of volcanic origin. Its morphology makes it unusual, because Japan does not consist of a row of snowcapped composite cones. In fact, Japan's eroded interior mountains do not evoke the image of a volcanic landscape.

The combination of orogenic (mountain-building) and volcanic activity is more dramatically reflected in the topography of the Americas, where oceanic and continental plates are colliding. In Chile, Peru, Ecuador, and Colombia, South America's Andes Mountains are studded with great volcanic cones. Central America and southern Mexico are similarly dominated, in their mountain backbones, by volcanic peaks, craters, and recent lava flows. In North America, the Aleutian Islands and areas of southern Alaska have volcanic landscapes. The Cascade volcanic arc, stretching from Volcano Mountain in the Yukon and Mount Edziza in northwestern British Columbia to Lassen Peak in northern California, incorporates a line of volcanoes of which Mount St Helens is only one (Figure 25.17). Mount Hood was active as recently as 1865, Mount Baker in 1870, Mount Rainier in 1882, and Lassen Peak in 1921. The eruption of Mount St Helens in 1980, 1986, and 2004 may signal a new round of activity in the Pacific Northwest that could change the volcanic landscape of the most vulnerable region of North America. The most recent geological event in that region—a substantial earthquake (magnitude 6.8)—occurred at Nisqually, near Seattle, in early 2001. Earthquakes will be examined in Unit 26.

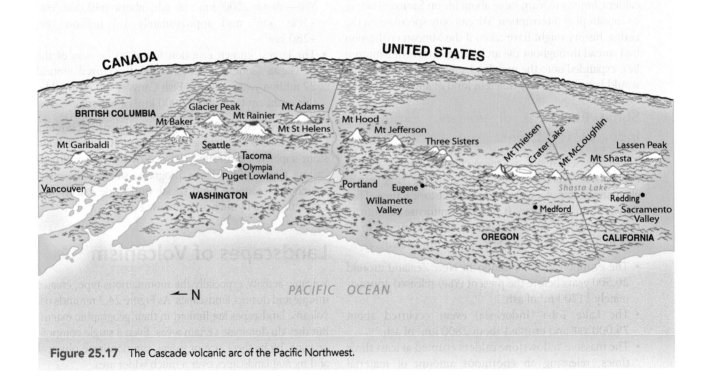

Figure 25.17   The Cascade volcanic arc of the Pacific Northwest.

KEY TERMS

aa *page 353*
active volcano *page 346*
archipelago *page 345*
ash *page 346*
caldera *page 355*
cinder cone *page 349*
composite volcano *page 347*
dormant volcano *page 346*

extinct volcano *page 346*
hot spot *page 353*
lahar *page 348*
lava dome *page 349*
nuée ardente *page 349*
pahoehoe *page 351*
phreatic (magmatophreatic)
  eruption *page 355*

pyroclastics *page 346*
seamount *page 354*
shield volcano *page 349*
tephra *page 346*
vent *page 347*
Volcanic Explosivity Index *page 355*
volcanism *page 345*
volcano *page 349*

REVIEW QUESTIONS

1. In what three geological settings do volcanoes occur?

2. How do shield volcanoes differ from composite volcanoes?

3. What are *hot spots*, and how do they help explain current volcanic activity in the Hawaiian Islands or the Anahim Volcanic Belt?

4. What causes a phreatic eruption?

5. Describe Santorini's monumental volcanic explosion and its impact on regional human activity.

6. What are the characteristics of basaltic versus andesitic volcanic eruptions?

REFERENCES AND FURTHER READINGS

Bevier, M.L. 1989. 'A Lead-Strontium Isotopic Study of the Anahim Volcanic Belt, British Columbia: Additional Evidence for Widespread Suboceanic Mantle beneath Western North America', *Geological Society of America Bulletin* 101: 973–81.

——— et al. 1979. 'Miocene Peralkaline Volcanism in West Central British Columbia–US Temporal and Plate-Tectonics Setting', *Geology* 7: 389–92.

Blong, R.J. 1984. *Volcanic Hazards: A Sourcebook on the Effects of Eruptions*. Orlando, Fla: Academic Press.

Boaz, N.T. 1998. *The Earth in Turmoil: Earthquakes, Volcanoes, and Their Impact on Humankind*. New York: Freeman.

Chester, D. 1993. *Volcanoes and Society*. Sevenoaks, UK: Arnold.

de Blij, H.J., ed. 1994. *Nature on the Rampage*. Washington: Smithsonian Institution Press.

Decker, R.W., and B.B. Decker. 1991. *Mountains of Fire: The Nature of Volcanoes*. New York: Cambridge Univ. Press.

Druitt, T.H., et al. 1999. *Santorini Volcano*. London: Geological Society Memoir No. 19.

Fisher, R.V. 1999. *Out of the Crater: Chronicles of a Volcanologist*. Princeton, NJ: Princeton Univ. Press.

———, G. Heiken, and J.B. Hulen. 1997. *Volcanoes: Crucibles of Change*. Princeton, NJ: Princeton Univ. Press.

Fouque, F.A. 1999. *Santorini and Its Eruptions*. Trans. A.R. McBirney. Baltimore: Johns Hopkins Univ. Press.

Francis, P. 2000. *Volcanoes: A Planetary Perspective*. New York: Oxford Univ. Press.

Green, J., and N.M. Short, eds. 1971. *Volcanic Landforms and Surface Features: A Photographic Atlas and Glossary*. New York: Springer-Verlag.

Hardwerk, B. 2002. 'Volcanic Eruptions and the Lunar Cycle', *National Geographic*, website article, Feb.

Harris, S.L. 1991. *Fire Mountains of the West: The Cascade and Mono Lake Volcanoes*. Missoula, Mont.: Mountain Press.

Levy, M., and M. Salvadori. 1995. *Why the Earth Quakes: The Story of Earthquakes and Volcanoes*. New York: Norton.

Lipman, P.W., and D.R. Mullineaux, eds. 1981. *The 1980 Eruptions of Mt. St. Helens, Washington*. Washington: US Geological Survey, Professional Paper 1250.

MacDonald, G.A., et al. 1983. *Volcanoes in the Sea: The Geology of Hawai'i*, 2nd edn. Honolulu: Univ. of Hawaii Press.

Mason, B.G., et al. 2004. 'Seasonality of Volcanic Eruptions', *Journal of Geophysical Research* 109 (B04206).

——— et al. 2004. 'The Size and Frequency of the Largest Explosive Eruptions on Earth', *Bulletin of Volcanology* 66, 8: 735–48.

Newhall, C.G., and S. Self. 1982. 'The Volcanic Explosivity Index (VEI): An Estimate for Historical Volcanism', *Journal of Geophysical Research* 87 (C2): 1231–8.

Ollier, C.D. 1988. *Volcanoes*. Cambridge, Mass.: Blackwell.

Ritchie, D., and A.E. Gates. 2001. *The Encyclopedia of Earthquakes and Volcanoes*, 2nd edn. New York: Facts on File.

Rogers, G.C. 1981. 'McNaughton Lake Seismicity—More Evidence for an Anahim Hotspot?', *Canadian Journal of Earth Science* 18, 4: 826–8.

Ryan, M.P., ed. 1994. *Magmatic Systems*. Orlando, Fla: Academic Press.

Scarth, A. 1999. *Vulcan's Fury: Man against the Volcano*. New Haven, Conn.: Yale Univ. Press.

Sigurdsson, H. 1999. *Melting the Earth: The History of Ideas on Volcanic Eruptions*. New York: Oxford Univ. Press.

——— et al. 1985. 'The Eruption of Vesuvius AD 79', *National Geographic Research* 1, 3: 332–87.

——— et al. 1999. *Encyclopedia of Volcanoes*. San Diego: Academic Press.

Simkin, T., and L. Siebert. 1994. *Volcanoes of the World: A Regional Directory, Gazetteer, and Chronology of Volcanism during the Last 10,000 years*, 2nd edn. Tucson, Ariz.: Geoscience Press.

Souther, J.G., et al. 1987. 'Nazco Cone: A Quarternary Volcano in the Eastern Anahim Belt', *Canadian Journal of Earth Science* 24, 12: 2477–85.

Supervolcano. 2005. BBC docudrama, DVD, 120 mins. Extras: The truth about Yellowstone.

Supervolcanoes. 2000. BBC *Horizon* Documentary, VHS, 50 mins.

Thornton, I. 1996. *Krakatau: The Destruction and Reassembly of an Island Ecosystem*. Cambridge, Mass.: Harvard Univ. Press.

Winchester, S. 2003. *Krakatoa: The Day the World Exploded, August 27, 1883*. New York: HarperCollins.

Wright, T., et al. 1992. *Hawai'i Volcano Watch: A Pictorial History, 1779–1991*. Honolulu: Univ. of Hawaii Press.

 WEB RESOURCES

gsc.nrcan.gc.ca/volcanoes This Geological Survey of Canada site gives basic and in-depth information about plate tectonics and volcanism. It has a complete catalogue of Canadian volcanoes, as well as links to the US Geological Survey and other websites.

volcanoes.usgs.gov This US Geological Survey page provides basic and historical information about volcanoes, and has links to worldwide volcano monitoring programs. Video, graphics, and satellite information can be accessed.

www.volcano.si.edu/gvp/links The Global Volcanism Program presented by the Smithsonian provides web links to regional volcano research centres worldwide. Links to both tutorial and research pages are available.

Earthquakes and Landscapes

Objectives

- To describe and quantify the magnitude and intensity of earthquakes.

- To relate the spatial pattern of earthquakes to plate tectonics.

- To discuss landscapes and landforms that bear the signature of earthquake activity.

Unit 20 discussed how earthquakes in the crust and upper mantle generate seismic waves that travel through the lithosphere as well as the interior of the Earth (see Figure 20.3). These waves yield key evidence to assist our understanding of the internal structure of the planet. As the seismic database expands and methods of analysis improve, the inferred properties of the Earth's internal structure and composition become better known.

Earthquakes also have an impact at the surface of the crust of the Earth, and they affect physical as well as cultural landscapes. Following a major earthquake, physical evidence of its occurrence can be seen on the ground in the form of dislocated strata, open fractures, new scarps, and lines of crushed rock. Earthquakes also trigger slope failures such as rock avalanches and mudflows. Moreover, the shocks and aftershocks of an earthquake can do major damage to buildings and other infrastructural elements. Add to this the fact that certain areas of the world are much more susceptible to earthquake damage than others, and it is obvious that this environmental hazard should be studied in a geographical context.

Earthquake Terminology

Lithospheric plates collide at collision margins, producing fractures in rocks called faults. A **fault** is a fracture in crustal rock involving the displacement of rock on one side of the fracture with respect to rock on the other side. Some faults, such as the San Andreas Fault, are giant breaks that continue for hundreds of kilometres (see Figure 24.12); others are shorter. Along the contact zone between the North American and Pacific Plates, the upper crust is riddled with faults, all resulting from the stresses imposed on hard rocks by the movement of plates. Like volcanoes, certain faults are active whereas others are no longer subject to stress. In the great continental shields that form the cores of continents lie many faults, fractures that bear witness to an earlier age of crustal instability. Today those faults appear on geological maps, but they do not pose a major earthquake hazard.

When rock strata are subjected to stress, they begin to deform or bend (Figure 26.1). All rocks have a certain rupture strength, which means that they will continue to bend, rather than break, as long as the stress imposed on them does not exceed this rupture strength. When the stress finally becomes too great, the rocks fracture suddenly and move along a plane (the fault) that may or may not have existed before the deformation began. That sudden movement snaps the rocks on each side of the fault back into their original shape and produces an earthquake. Interplate earthquakes associated with plate margins account for 90 per cent of earthquakes; the other 10 per cent are interplate events related to fault movement and/or isostatic readjustment and/or volcanic activity (harmonic tremors).

A recent study has suggested that earthquakes of large magnitude can trigger an increase in small-magnitude events. The study looked at 15 major earthquakes with magnitudes >7 on the Richter scale that have occurred since 1990, including the 9.3 magnitude earthquake off Sumatra in 2004.

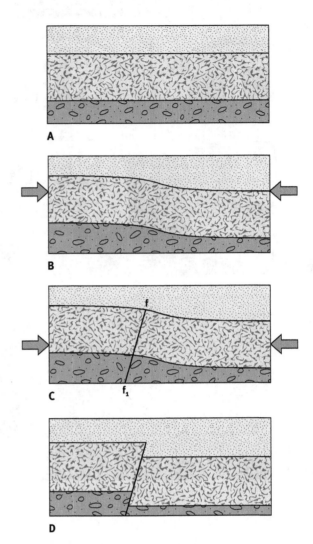

Figure 26.1 When stress (in this case compression) affects horizontal rock layers (A), the strata begin to bend, and they continue to do so as long as their rupture strength is not exceeded (B). When this level is exceeded, a fault plane (f–f₁) develops (C). Often more than one such fault plane will be formed. Sudden movement along this fault plane, accompanied by one or more earthquakes, relieves the now exceeded rupture strength, and the rock strata resume their original (horizontal) positions (D).

The researchers used records from 500 seismic stations for five hours previous to and five hours after the earthquakes. They found that 12 of these were associated with an increase of small-magnitude quakes remote from the epicentre in the five hours immediately after the major earthquake. Globally, the average number of small events is about 600 per five minutes, but after surface waves (Love and Rayleigh waves) from a major quake passed through an area, the number of small events increased dramatically: a 37 per cent increase after the arrival of the Love waves and a 60 per cent increase after the passage of Rayleigh waves. (Love waves radiate out from the epicentre like waves caused by a rock being thrown into a pond and cause disruption of the surface and infrastructure. They travel at rates of 2–6 km/s. Rayleigh waves are surface waves that radiate out from the epicentre in a snaking motion. They have rates of 1–5 km/s.) This led the authors to suggest that the dynamic triggering of small earthquakes by a large quake is ubiquitous and is caused by the arrival of such surface waves. The exact mechanism leading to the small events is not understood at present.

An **earthquake**, therefore, is the release of energy that has slowly built up during the stress of increasing deformation of rocks. This energy release takes the form of seismic waves that radiate in all directions from the place of movement (Figure 26.2). Earthquakes can originate at or near the surface of the Earth, deep inside the crust, or even in the upper mantle. The place of origin is the **focus** (or centre), and the point directly above the focus on the Earth's surface is the **epicentre** (or hypocentre) (Figure 26.2). Earthquakes range from tremors so small that they are barely detectable to great shocks that can destroy entire cities. This reflects their **magnitude**, the amount of shaking of the ground as the quake passes, as measured by a **seismograph** (see Figure 20.1).

Magnitude used to be assessed on the **Richter scale**, which assigned a number to an earthquake based on the measurement of the physical force of that ground motion. This open-ended scale, developed in 1935 by the geophysicist Charles Richter, ranges from 0 to 8+ (Table 26.1). It is logarithmic, so that an earthquake of magnitude 4 causes 10 times as much ground motion as one of magnitude 3 and 100 times as much as a quake of magnitude 2. It should be

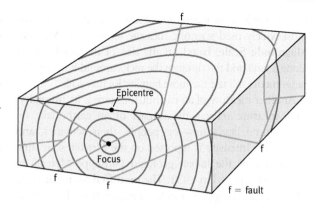

Figure 26.2 In an area honeycombed by faults (f), movement on a particular fault plane (perhaps at intersecting faults) becomes the focus for energy release. The epicentre is the point at the Earth's surface vertically above the point of focus. The energy released at the earthquake's focus radiates outward to other parts of the Earth in the form of seismic waves, represented by the rings spreading from the focus and the epicentre.

noted, however, that the original Richter scale has undergone some recent changes, because more sophisticated equipment and more precise measurements of magnitude have been developed. Thus, when the US Geological Survey now announces a 'Richter magnitude' following an earthquake, it is

Table 26.1 Richter Scale of Earthquake Magnitudes, Compared with Mercalli Intensities

Typology	Magnitude	Approximate Maximum Intensity	Number per Year	Approximate Energy Released in Explosive Equivalents
	0			
	1		} 700,000	0.45 kg TNT
	2			
Weak	2–2.9	II	300,000	
	3			
	3–3.9		49,000	
	4	III		
	4–4.9	Minor	6,200	
	5	VI		Small atom bomb, 84 TJ (terajoule) = the bomb dropped in Nagasaki in 1945 (TNT 20 kilotons)
Moderate				
	5–5.9	Damaging	800	
Strong	6	VII		Hydrogen bomb, 4.2 petajoule (4.2 × 10¹⁵ J) (1 megaton)
	6–6.9	Destructive	120	
Major	7	X		
	7–7.9	Major	18	
	8	XII		
Great	8–8.6	Great	1 every few years	60,000 4.2 petajoule (1-megaton) bombs

Source: After Wyllie (1976), 47.

referring only to the magnitude of surface seismic waves. The most widely used scientific measure today is the **Moment Magnitude Scale**, based on the size of the displacement along a fault and the distance the rocks around it move. The news media still use the more familiar Richter scale.

Another measure of an earthquake's size is its **intensity**. This measure reflects the impact of an earthquake on the cultural landscape—on people, their activities, and structures. Intensity is reported on the *Mercalli scale*, first developed by the Italian geologist Giuseppe Mercalli in 1905 and updated in 1931. The **modified Mercalli scale** (Table 26.2) assigns a number ranging from I to XII to an earthquake (Roman numerals are always used). For instance, an earthquake of intensity IV is felt indoors, and hanging objects swing. Intensity V produces broken windows and dishes, awakens many sleepers, and cracks plaster. Intensity IX damages building foundations and breaks in-ground pipes. At intensity XII, damage is total, and even heavy objects are thrown into the air.

As Table 26.1 indicates, the severest of earthquakes occur on average perhaps once every few years. Tens of thousands of smaller quakes occur annually, many felt only by sensitive seismographs. Great earthquakes that cause death and destruction are long remembered; several of the more recent ones are listed in Table 26.3. Probably the most infamous earthquake in North

Table 26.2 Modified Mercalli Scale of Earthquake Intensities

Intensity	Qualitative Title	Description of Effects
I	Negligible	Detected by instruments only.
II	Feeble	Felt by sensitive people. Suspended objects swing.
III	Slight	Vibration like passing truck. Standing cars may rock.
IV	Moderate	Felt indoors. Some sleepers awakened. Hanging objects swing. Sensation like a heavy truck striking building. Windows and dishes rattle. Standing cars rock.
V	Rather strong	Felt by most people; many awakened. Some plaster falls. Dishes and windows broken. Pendulum clocks may stop.
VI	Strong	Felt by all; many are frightened. Chimneys topple. Furniture moves.
VII	Very strong	Alarm; most people run outdoors. Weak structures damaged moderately. Felt in moving cars.
VIII	Destructive	General alarm; everyone runs outdoors. Weak structures severely damaged; slight damage to strong structures. Monuments toppled. Heavy furniture overturned.
IX	Ruinous	Panic. Total destruction of weak structures; considerable damage to specially designed structures. Foundations damaged. Underground pipes broken. Ground fissured.
X	Disastrous	Panic. Only the best buildings survive. Foundations ruined. Rails bent. Ground badly cracked. Large landslides.
XI	Very disastrous	Panic. Few masonry structures remain standing. Broad fissures in ground.
XII	Catastrophic	Superpanic. Total destruction. Waves are seen on the ground. Objects are thrown into the air.

Source: After Wyllie (1976), 45.

Table 26.3 Noteworthy Earthquakes of the Twentieth and Twenty-First Centuries

Year	Place	Richter Magnitude	Estimated Death Toll
1906	San Francisco, California	8.3	700
1908	Messina, Italy	7.5	120,000
1920	Kansu, China	8.5	180,000
1923	Tokyo–Yokohama, Japan	8.2	143,000
1935	Quetta, Pakistan (then India)	7.5	60,000
1939	Chillan, Chile	7.8	30,000
1962	Northwestern Iran	7.3	14,000
1964	Southern Alaska	8.6	131
1970	Chimbote, Peru	7.8	66,800
1976	Tangshan, China	7.6	242,000*
1985	West-central Mexico	7.9, 7.5	9,500
1988	Armenia	7.0	55,000+
1989	Loma Prieta, California	7.0	63
1990	Northwestern Iran	7.7	40,000+
1992	Landers, California	7.5	1
1994	Northridge (LA), California	6.8	61
1995	Kobe, Japan	7.2	6,400
1999	Western Turkey	7.4	17,900
1999	Taichung, Taiwan	7.6	2,474
2001	Gujarat, India	7.9	20,000+
2001	Arequipa, Peru	8.1	102
2002	Northern Afghanistan	7.4	166
2003	Colima, Mexico	7.6	29
2003	Northern Algeria	6.8	2,200+
2003	Bam, southeastern Iran	6.6	26,271
2004	West Irian, Indonesia	7.0	37
2004	Near Sumatra, Indonesia	9.3	227,898 (including tsunami)
2005	Islands off Sumatra, Indonesia	8.7	1,000+

Table 26.3 (Continued)

Year	Place	Richter Magnitude	Estimated Death Toll
2005	Kashmir, Pakistan and India	7.6	80,361
2005	Kuril Islands, Pacific Russia	8.3	0
2006	Java, Indonesia	6.3	6,200+
2006	South of Java, Indonesia	7.7	530+
2007	Southern Sumatra	8.5	25
2007	Near coast of central Peru	8.0	519
2007	Martinique, French West Indies	7.4	1
2007	Near Antofagasta, Chile	7.7	3
2008	Sichuan, China	7.9	69,000+
2008	Near Selfoss, Iceland	6.1	0
2008 (29 October)	Near Quetta, Baluchistan, Pakistan	6.4	500–600 (early figures)

*This is the official figure; reliable reports (e.g., from the US Geological Survey) persist that as many as 655,000 to 750,000 died and that 799,000 were injured in this deadliest natural disaster of the twentieth century.

Figure 26.4 Earthquakes affecting major urban areas often start fires from broken gas mains, kitchen stoves, and other sources. The damage from the 1906 earthquake that struck San Francisco was worsened enormously by such fires, which raged out of control for days afterward.

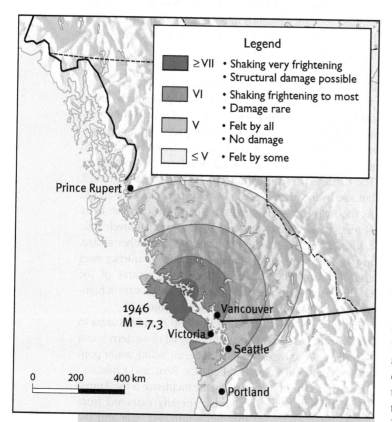

Figure 26.3 In June 1946 an earthquake with a magnitude of 7.3 struck central Vancouver Island just west of Courtenay and Campbell River. It caused considerable damage on the island and was felt as far away as Portland, Oregon, and Prince Rupert, BC.

America during the twentieth century was the 1906 San Francisco quake, which is estimated to have had a moment magnitude of 8.3 and an intensity of XII. A dangerous associated effect of such a severe shock is fire, which rages out of control from many points of origin (especially when natural gas and gasoline lines rupture) and cannot be fought because water supply systems are disrupted or destroyed (Figure 26.4).

Sichuan Earthquake, 2008

The world's most recent serious earthquake had its epicentre in a mountainous area of Wenchuan county about 80 km west-northwest of Chengdu, the capital of Sichuan Province, China. The quake occurred at 2:28 p.m. China Standard Time on 12 May 2008 and registered a moment magnitude of 7.9. It was felt as far away as Beijing and Shanghai and in parts of Bangladesh, Pakistan, India, Taiwan, Thailand, and Vietnam. The focus of the event was 19 km below the surface. It is thought that the quake occurred because of movement along the Longmenshan tectonic fault or a similar fault. Movement was brought about by a buildup of pressure along this feature caused by continued plate movement as the Indian Plate continues to slowly slam into the Eurasian Plate. The official death toll, as of 29 October 2008, stood at 69,197, with about 374,176 injured and 18,222 missing. About 4.8 million people were left homeless by the quake (Western estimates range up to 11 million).

The Chinese government allowed a lot of domestic and foreign press coverage of this event (unlike earlier natural disasters), in large part because of the then-upcoming 2008

Beijing Summer Olympics. The government also sent in lots of troops as part of the recovery effort and to clear rubble. The area is quite remote and most of the infrastructure linking the area with other parts of China has been affected by the collapse of roads, railway lines, and buildings, as well as by landslides and flooding. Many countries sent in specialized crews to search for survivors and help clear the masses of debris. Many quake lakes (over 40) were formed by landslides damming rivers, and Chinese engineers and troops drained some of these before the landslide dams failed because of the water pressure. Concerns also focused on the Zipingpu Hydroelectric Plant and reservoir. The plant was totally destroyed and the reservoir appeared in danger of draining catastrophically. Many buildings erected in the 1960s through to the 1990s collapsed. This has been blamed on the lack of seismic building codes in China and on cheap and shoddy construction techniques used during that period (either by the government, entrepreneurs, or the people themselves). Although many old and new buildings were destroyed or severely damaged, none of the modern high-rise office and other buildings in Chengdu built in the last 10–15 years suffered major damage.

We can compare the extreme devastation caused by this earthquake with others of a similar magnitude that have hit the central California coast, for example, the Loma Prieta earthquake, a 7.0 magnitude earthquake in the fall of 1989, which affected large areas of the San Francisco Bay area but created far less damage. The earthquake, which killed 63 people and resulted in a postponement of baseball's World Series then being played in the Bay area, was a major event and caused considerable damage to buildings, bridges, and roads. But California's building codes saved the region from greater loss of life and property. Buildings and infrastructure have to be constructed to survive earthquakes, and since this event the building codes have been continually upgraded. In the last 10 years some scientists studying faults in the Greater Toronto and western Lake Ontario area think that the building codes of Ontario should be updated to include a greater emphasis on seismic risk.

Earthquake Distribution

The global distribution of earthquake epicentres, whatever the period of record, indicates that a large number of earthquakes fortunately originate in locations less vulnerable than most of the heavily populated places listed in Table 26.3. The greatest concentration is along the **Circum-Pacific belt** of subduction zones associated with the Pacific and Nazca Plates and their neighbouring plates (Figure 26.6). About 80 per cent of all shallow-focus earthquakes (depths of less than 100 km) originate in this belt. As the map indicates, earthquakes with deeper foci in the lower lithosphere are even more heavily concentrated in this zone.

A comparison of Figure 26.6 with a map of the world distribution of population (Figure 2.5) immediately shows

Figure 26.5   This aerial photograph of Bam, Iran, was taken on Tuesday 30 December 2003, three days after the initial quake struck. The earthquake damaged or destroyed 85 per cent of the ancient city and killed more than 26,000 people.

that large numbers of people are at risk from earthquakes. All of Japan's 127 million people live in an area of high earthquake incidence and, therefore, high risk. The Philippines and Indonesia also are earthquake-prone and now home to more than 300 million people. But the earthquake-affected zone then extends into a less populated area of the Pacific Ocean and turns south, lessening in intensity just to the north of New Zealand.

In the north, the Circum-Pacific earthquake zone affects the sparsely populated Aleutian Islands, but also penetrates populated areas of southern Alaska. A particularly severe earthquake struck Anchorage on Good Friday, 1964, causing death and destruction. That earthquake's magnitude was 8.6 (the strongest ever recorded in the United States), and its epicentre was only about 120 km from the coastal city. The damage was caused not only by the shaking ground, but also by the massive ocean waves generated by the shock. As the map shows (Figure 26.6), between the main body of Alaska and Vancouver Island there is comparatively little earthquake risk—but the population is also rather sparse. In the Vancouver–Seattle area, earthquake frequency rises again, endangering the large population centres of the Georgia Strait–Puget Sound areas. This area awaits a high-magnitude mega-thrust event in the near future.

Earthquakes pose a constant threat to populous areas in Mexico and Central America. Virtually all of western South America is an active earthquake zone, including major population centres in Colombia, Ecuador, Peru, and Chile.

Another zone of high earthquake incidence is the **Trans-Eurasian belt**, which extends generally eastward from the Mediterranean Sea through Southwest Asia and the Himalayas into Southeast Asia, where it meets the Circum-Pacific belt. The incidence of major earthquakes in this corridor is not as high as it is in parts of the Circum-Pacific belt, but some important population centres are at risk.

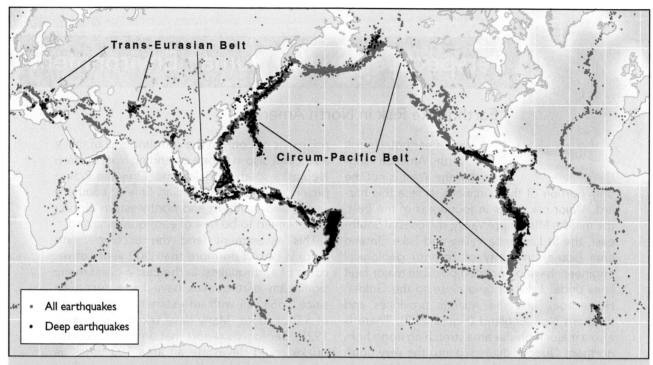

Figure 26.6 Global distribution of recent earthquakes. The deep earthquakes, shown by black dots, originated more than 100 km below the surface.

These include the countries of former Yugoslavia, Greece, Turkey, Iraq, Iran, and the highlands of Afghanistan, northern Pakistan, northernmost India, Nepal, and parts of China.

A third zone of earthquakes is associated with the global system of *mid-oceanic ridges* (compare Figures 26.6 and 2.6). The earthquakes there are generally less frequent and less severe than in the Circum-Pacific belt, and except for population clusters on islands formed by these ridges, this earthquake zone does not endanger large numbers of people.

From Figure 24.2 it is evident that known contact zones between tectonic plates form the Earth's most active earthquake belts. But earthquakes, some of them severe, can and do occur in other areas of the world. Note, in Figure 26.6, the scattered pattern of epicentres in interior Asia, in eastern Africa from Ethiopia to South Africa, and in North America east of the west coast transform/subduction zone. The causes of these **intraplate earthquakes** are still not well understood, but they can produce severe damage because people in the affected areas are less well prepared for earthquakes (India's Bhuj earthquake of 2001 is a classic example). For instance, municipal ordinances governing high-rise construction in the cities of British Columbia, Washington, Oregon, and California take seismic hazards into consideration; in eastern North America, local building codes do not. Yet the most severe earthquake ever experienced in the conterminous United States did not occur in California but in the central Mississippi Valley.

In 1811 and 1812 three great earthquakes, all with epicentres near New Madrid in the 'boot heel' of extreme southeastern Missouri, changed the course of the Mississippi River and created a 7300-hectare lake in the valley. The severity of these quakes has been estimated to have been as high as magnitude 8.5. Had nearby St Louis and Memphis been major cities at that time, the death toll would have been enormous. In 1886 an earthquake of magnitude 7.0 devastated Charleston, South Carolina, and the ground shook as far away as New York City and Chicago. Thus, eastern North America, too, must be considered a potentially hazardous seismic zone (see 'Perspectives' box). Shocks are felt over far larger areas of eastern North America because the rock beds are not 'cut up' by many large faults.

In East Asia the earthquake that cost the largest number of lives in the past century did not originate in the offshore subduction zone but in eastern China. In 1976 the city of Tangshan was destroyed by an earthquake of magnitude 7.6 focused directly beneath the urban area. The exact loss of life will never be known, but estimates persistently range as high as 750,000 (the Chinese government insists the toll was 242,000). Damage occurred over a more-than-80-km-long corridor that reached as far as the major port city of Tianjin and the capital, Beijing.

The global map of earthquake distribution should not lead us to the conclusion that areas outside the plate-contact zones are free from seismic hazard. Even apparently stable shields, such as those of Australia and Africa, can be shaken by significant earthquakes. Beyond the subduction zones, other areas of plate contact, and mid-oceanic ridges, the understanding of the pattern of epicentres is far from complete.

Perspectives on the Human Environment

Earthquake Risk in North America

A map of earthquake risk in North America suggests that the West is not the only portion of the continent to face this hazard. Major risk exists in four areas of the East: the middle Mississippi Valley, the coastal Southeast, the St Lawrence Valley and Lake Ontario area (some University of Toronto geological engineers have pinpointed possible major fault lines under Lake Ontario close to the Golden Horseshoe), and the Atlantic provinces and northern New England (Figure 26.7). There is also a major high-risk area stretching north from northern Quebec (Nunavik) into the very north of the Arctic Archipelago of Canada. Moderate risk exists not only in the surroundings of these areas, but also in a zone extending from eastern Nebraska south to Oklahoma. Only the Prairie provinces and the Canadian Shield, southern Texas, and southern and northwestern Florida are believed to be free of earthquake hazard.

This assessment (and the accompanying map) is based on more than 300 years of records of earthquakes. In the East a great many significant earthquakes have been recorded since 1663, all with an estimated magnitude of 5.0 or more. Many have taken place since 1925. Geologists report that an eastern earthquake could devastate an area 100 times as large as would be affected by an equivalent quake in the West because the shock waves are cushioned much more in the fault-infested crust of the West.

But the map is based on a past that gives little clue to the future. There was no evidence of major earthquake activity in the middle Mississippi Valley or in coastal South Carolina before great earthquakes struck there in 1811–12 and 1886, respectively. Recently it has been suggested that major faults underlie Lake Ontario and may even go close to nuclear power stations. This evidence suggests that inclusion of provisions for seismic hazards in Ontario building codes should be made immediately. The next large quake could strike an area deemed to have only moderate or minor earthquake risk. The science of earthquake prediction is still in its infancy; the available record is short-term and unreliable. In facing earthquake threats, however, western North America is not alone.

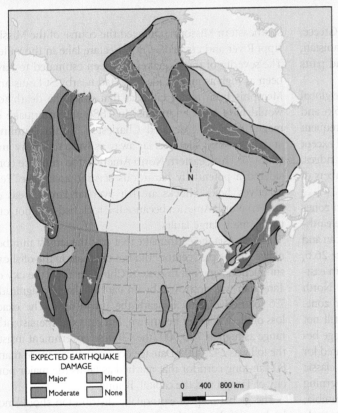

EXPECTED EARTHQUAKE DAMAGE

Major · Minor · Moderate · None

0   400   800 km

Figure 26.7   Earthquake risk in North America.

LINK

Earthquakes, People, and the Land

Earthquakes, as noted earlier, are not comparable to volcanic action as builders of a distinct landscape. But earthquakes do *modify* physical and cultural landscapes, and some landforms actually are created by earthquake movements. When movement along a fault generates an earthquake, or when a fault is newly created following the long-term deformation of rock strata, the result may be visible at the surface in the form of a **fault scarp**. As Figure 26.8 shows, a fault scarp is the exposed cliff-like face of the **fault plane**, the surface of contact along which blocks on either side of a fault move.

Not every earthquake produces a scarp, and in some cases the movement is lateral (sideways) rather than vertical. But if one block is raised with respect to another, a fault scarp is produced. Such a scarp may have a vertical extent (or *face*) of less than 1 m; others may exceed 100 m. Repeated vertical movement along the fault scarp can raise the height of the exposed face in stages. As Figure 26.8 shows, the lower edge of the fault scarp is called the **fault trace**. Imagine that erosion wears down the raised block to the left so that the scarp is no longer visible. The existence of the fault is then only revealed at the surface by the trace. Along the trace may lie a band of crushed, jagged rock fragments called *fault breccia*, evidence of the powerful forces that created the fault.

Earthquakes affect different types of rocks in different ways. When a major earthquake struck Mexico City in 1985, parts of the city were devastated while other areas showed little damage. The reason lay in the underlying geology: where the rocks were solid, there was little impact. But where the buildings stood on the 'soft' ground of an old lake bed on which part of Mexico City is built, the damage was great because the earthquake waves were significantly amplified. Many high-rise structures collapsed or simply fell over as the ground liquefied and wobbled like a bowl of gelatin. In Anchorage the 1964 earthquake had a similar effect: houses and other buildings that stood on solid rock sustained minor damage, but areas of the city underlain by clays or soft and uncemented sedimentary strata sank into liquefied areas or slid downslope. Hundreds of houses were carried away and destroyed, and in places the whole topography of Alaska's leading urban area was changed (Figure 26.9).

The effect of a major earthquake, therefore, is to produce movements of different kinds. In the same affected area, blocks of solid rock will shake but remain stable; loosely compacted sediments, especially on slopes, will slide downhill. When there has been prolonged rain in an area of thick clay, the saturated clay may stay in place—until an earthquake or even a tremor provides the impetus to dislodge or liquefy it (Figure 26.10). In snowy mountain terrain, an avalanche may be started by a slight Earth tremor when otherwise the snowpack would have stayed in place. Avalanches, flows, and other forms of slope movement (discussed in Unit 30) often result from a combination of circumstances among which a quake can be crucial.

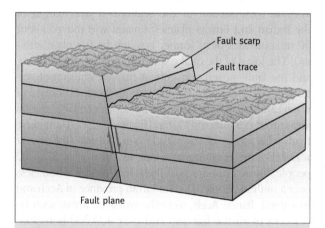

Figure 26.8 Fault scarp resulting from the vertical movement of one block with respect to another. The blocks are in contact along the fault plane, whose exposed face is the fault scarp. If the upper block were eroded down to the level of the lower block, the only surface evidence of the fault plane would be the fault trace.

Figure 26.9 A ferocious earthquake (magnitude 8.6) devastated parts of Anchorage, Alaska, on 27 March 1964. This is Fourth Avenue the day after—only part of the destruction that extended from the harbour to the interior.

Figure 26.10 Landslides are a major hazard arising from earthquakes in high-relief areas. In January 2001 an earthquake (magnitude 7.6) struck near San Salvador, the capital of El Salvador in Central America. The town of Santa Tecla would have been little affected except for this massive landslide, which brought death and destruction.

Undoubtedly, as the photos in this unit demonstrate, the impact of a major earthquake on the cultural landscape is its most dramatic manifestation. Such effects range from the offsetting of linear features such as fences and hedges, roads and pipelines, to the devastation of major structures such as skyscrapers, highways, and bridges. An earthquake's capacity to reduce to rubble a structure built of steel and concrete inspires awe and terror. And the risks involved are not confined to known earthquake zones. A nuclear power plant could be demolished by a quake, resulting in a release of lethal radiation over a wide area.

Tsunamis and Mega-tsunamis

The Japanese word for a great sea wave, **tsunami** (harbour wave), has come into general use to identify a seismic sea wave. When an earthquake's epicentre is located on the ocean floor or near a coastline, its shock will generate one or more waves on the water (these events can also be triggered by volcanic activity). These waves radiate outward from the point of origin. In the open ocean, they look like broad swells on the water surface, and ships and boats can ride them out quite easily. But a tsunami's vertical magnitude, when it reaches the water near shore, may be many times that of an ordinary wind-caused swell. Near the shore it can create huge breakers that smash into coastal towns and villages.

When seismographs in various locales in the Pacific record a severe underwater quake, a tsunami alert is immediately issued. This alert is intended for places along all vulnerable coastlines. But tsunamis travel very fast, reaching 1000 km/h, and warnings do not always arrive in time. Tsunami waves have reached more than 65 m in height, and they have been known to travel all the way across the Pacific Ocean. A major earthquake in Chile in 1960 generated a tsunami that reached Hawaii about 15 hours later, smashing into coastal lowlands with breakers 7 m high. Ten hours later, the still-advancing wave was strong enough to cause damage in Japan. Situated in the Pacific, the Hawaiian Islands are especially vulnerable to tsunamis. In 1946 a tsunami caused by an earthquake near Alaska struck the town of Hilo on the island of Hawaii, killing 156 persons. The tsunami generated by the 1964 Alaska earthquake that devastated Anchorage flooded the port of Kodiak, Alaska, and drowned a dozen people in a California coastal town far to the south (some had gone to the beach to see the wave come in).

The 26 December 2004 Indian Ocean earthquake off Sumatra and its resulting tsunamis ravaged large areas of Indonesia, Malaysia, Thailand, Sri Lanka, India, Myanmar, the Maldives, and other coastal areas of countries in South Asia and East Africa and caused the greatest impact of any tsunami in the last millennium. The earthquake occurred at 6:58 a.m. local time and had a moment magnitude of 9 (the quake was felt as far away as Somalia). It was caused by subductive movement along a 1200–1300-km-long, 100-km-wide section of the seafloor at the margin of the Indian and Burma plates (Sumatra was moved about 30 m southwest of its former position by the plate activity). The focus of the quake was 10 km below the seafloor, and the fault moved vertically. A massive column of water over the area became unstable (billions of tonnes of water) and led to the tsunamis that devastated large coastal areas around the Indian Ocean (Figure 26.11). There were many aftershocks of magnitude 6 and above (the largest was 7.1). The resulting tsunamis killed at least 225,000 people, injured hundreds of thousands, and left homeless over a million people. The Sumatran province of Aceh and its capital, Banda Aceh, were the worst-hit areas, with 66 per cent of all the fatalities and over 400,000 homeless. In Sri Lanka 10,000 people were killed and 150,000 left homeless and in need of food, clothing, and other aid. The tsunamis left over 5 million people needing some form of aid. The search for survivors and the cleanup of vast areas were made difficult by monsoon rains. Aid was rushed in from all over the world to help the survivors. Some experts

LINK

Figure 26.11 A devastated village near the coast of Sumatra after the 26 December 2004 Indian Ocean earthquake and resulting tsunamis. These were the most catastrophic tsunamis of the past millennium.

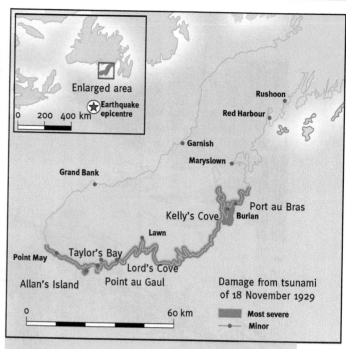

Figure 26.12 The area on the Burin Peninsula, on the south coast of Newfoundland, damaged by the tsunami of 18 November 1929.

have pointed out that the tsunami damage was partly related to the clearance of mangrove forests and sand dune vegetation. Studies have shown that villages in Indonesia, India, Sri Lanka, Thailand, and Somalia that were protected by mangroves and sand dunes were less damaged than villages where these had been cleared.

Kofi Annan, the then-Secretary-General of the United Nations, called the effects of the earthquake and tsunamis 'an unprecedented global tragedy'. Contributing to this tragedy, as noted above, were human impacts on the physical geography of the region. Both mangrove forests and coral reefs provide protective barriers against such natural disasters, but many reefs throughout South Asia have been dynamited to create shipping lanes and shrimp farms, as well as material for low-grade brick-making, and mangrove forests along coastlines have been cleared for firewood, for the grazing of animals, or for tourism and/or aesthetic reasons.

Tsunamis have occurred in Canada. These have been generally small-scale events since European settlement, such as the one triggered by the Courtney, BC, earthquake (7.3 magnitude) on 23 June 1946. A far larger event is recorded in sediments and by the local First Nations peoples on Vancouver Island. This was a mega-thrust earthquake registering magnitude 9 along the Cascadia subduction zone off BC in January 1700, which was accompanied by a tsunami that wiped out some settlements. Another large event happened along the Queen Charlotte Fault in 1949 (8.1 magnitude) but it did not generate a large tsunami. The only significant (in terms of loss of life and damage) historical tsunami occurred along the southern coast of Newfoundland in 1929 (the Burin tsunami).

The Burin tsunami was generated by the Grand Banks earthquake of 18 November 1929 (Figure 26.12). The earthquake struck at 5:02 p.m. Newfoundland time. Its epicentre was located about 250 km south of Newfoundland along the southern edge of the Grand Banks. Its magnitude was 7.2, and it was felt as far away as Montreal and New York. Most of the damage on land from the earthquake itself was restricted to Cape Breton Island, where chimneys were cracked or destroyed and there were minor landslides. A few aftershocks (some over magnitude 6) were felt in Nova Scotia and Newfoundland.

The earthquake caused a very large submarine slump down the continental slope (estimated volume about 200 km³), which broke 12 transatlantic telegraph cables in many places. It also generated a tsunami recorded down the eastern seaboard as far south as South Carolina and as far to the east as Portugal. The tsunami waves travelled at speeds of up to 140 km/hr in the open seas and hit the Burin Peninsula at speeds of 105 km/h. They reached the southern end of the peninsula about two and a half hours (at about 7:30 p.m.) after the earthquake occurred. There were no seismographs in Newfoundland at the time, nor was there any earthquake or tsunami warning system. A few mild tremors had affected the Burin Peninsula but these only lasted about 5 minutes and were very mild. The area had been cut off a day or so earlier when the single telegraph line to St John's had been severed by a storm. Consequently, it took three days for the Newfoundland government to learn about the tsunami and send aid (Figures 26.13 and 26.14).

Figure 26.13   The Grand Banks earthquake off the coast of Newfoundland in November 1929 caused this seismic wave to break on the New England coast. This is probably the only photograph taken of a wave similar to that which swept over the south coast of Newfoundland at the same time.

Figure 26.14   Devastation caused by the November 1929 tsunami at Port au Bras on Newfoundland's Burin Peninsula.

The tsunami occurred in three pulses and lasted about 30 minutes. Local sea level rose by 2 to 7 m along the coast, but the wave was funnelled down some long narrow inlets (such as Port au Bras, St Lawrence, and Taylor's Bay) and reached a height of 13 m. In one or two bays it reached up to 27 m. The first thing people noted was the trough preceding the leading wave. The water receded and parts of the inlet floors and seafloor were visible and boats were left high and dry. The tsunami affected about 40 communities and killed 28 people (25 were killed immediately by the tsunami, including 6 people whose bodies were washed out to sea and never found; 3 died later of shock or injuries). The deaths were confined to six of the worst-hit communities. In Taylor's Bay, for example, only 5 of the 17 houses were left standing. In Point au Gaul the giant waves destroyed close to 100 buildings. Some buildings were floated off their foundations and survived pretty much intact. One was carried 60 m from its base. Numerous homes, businesses, wharves, and ships were destroyed, as were livestock and fishing gear. The tsunami affected about 10,000 people, most of whom were left homeless. Many had to be billeted with friends and relations while the communities were rebuilt. Over 280,000 pounds of salt cod were lost. Rescue efforts were hampered by the isolation of the area and another late autumn storm that engulfed the area the next day. Total damages were estimated at over $1 million 1929 Canadian dollars (about $20 million in 2004 dollars).

Many years after the Burin Peninsula tsunami, the US government announced in 2005 plans for an east coast tsunami warning system and also a global tsunami warning system. Canada announced an east coast system in 2006, but both Canadian and American systems are still in the planning stage. Both countries have well-established warning systems on their Pacific coasts (including Hawaii).

Seismic waves are not tidal waves, as they are sometimes misnamed. Waves with tsunami-like properties are sometimes created by explosive volcanic eruptions, such as those of Santorini and Krakatau (see Unit 25). When these giant waves break onto an exposed shore, they can modify the coastal landscape significantly. Occasionally they can do more to change a coastline in a few moments than normal processes do in centuries of erosion and deposition.

This unit has focused on the sudden, dramatic movements of rocks that produce earthquakes and the accompanying impacts on overlying landscapes. But the surfaces of the Earth's landmasses are also affected by the consequences of less spectacular stresses on their underlying rocks. Unit 27 examines those types of stresses and the rock structures they shape.

KEY TERMS

Circum-Pacific earthquake belt   *page 366*
earthquake   *page 363*
epicentre   *page 363*
fault   *page 362*
fault plane   *page 369*
fault scarp   *page 369*
fault trace   *page 369*
focus   *page 363*
intensity (earthquake)   *page 364*

intraplate earthquake   *page 367*
magnitude (earthquake)   *page 363*
Mercalli scale (modified)   *page 364*
Moment Magnitude Scale   *page 364*
Richter scale   *page 363*
seismograph   *page 363*
Trans-Eurasian earthquake belt   *page 366*
tsunami   *page 370*

REVIEW QUESTIONS

1. Compare the Richter and Mercalli scales for measuring earthquakes.
2. Where on the Earth are earthquakes most frequent? Why?
3. How are fault scarps produced?
4. What is the Circum-Pacific belt of seismic activity?
5. Why are parts of eastern North America considered to constitute a hazardous earthquake region?

REFERENCES AND FURTHER READINGS

Adams, J.J., et al. 2001. 'Seismicity and Seismic Hazards in Canada', in G.R. Brooks et al., *A Synthesis of Geological Hazards in Canada*. Ottawa: Geological Survey of Canada Bulletin 548, 7–26.

Bagnall, N.H., and R.B. Schroeder, eds. 1996. *On Shaky Ground: The New Madrid Earthquakes of 1811–1812*. Columbia: Univ. of Missouri Press.

Boaz, N.T. 1998. *The Earth in Turmoil: Earthquakes, Volcanoes, and Their Impact on Humankind*. New York: Freeman.

Bolt, B.A. 1999. *Earthquakes*, 4th edn. New York: Freeman.

Brumbaugh, D.S. 1998. *Earthquakes: Science and Society*. Upper Saddle River, NJ: Prentice-Hall.

Clague, J.J. 2001. 'Tsunamis', in G.R. Brooks et al., *A Synthesis of Geological Hazards in Canada*. Ottawa: Geological Survey of Canada Bulletin 548, 27–42.

Collier, M. 1999. *A Land in Motion: California's San Andreas Fault*. Berkeley: Univ. of California Press.

Dahdouh-Guebas, F., et al. 2005. 'How Effective Were Mangroves as a Defence against the Recent Tsunami?', *Current Biology* 15, 12: R443–6.

de Blij, H.J., ed. 1994. *Nature on the Rampage*. Washington: Smithsonian Institution Press.

Doyle, H.A. 1996. *Seismology*. New York: Wiley.

Dudley, W.C., and M. Lee. 1998. *Tsunami!*, 2nd edn. Honolulu: Univ. of Hawaii Press.

Fradkin, P.L. 1999. *Magnitude 8: Earthquakes and Life along the San Andreas Fault*. Berkeley: Univ. of California Press.

Gere, J.M., and H.C. Shah. 1984. *Terra Non Firma: Understanding and Preparing for Earthquakes*. New York: Freeman.

Gonzalez, F.I. 1999. 'Tsunami!', *Scientific American* (May): 56–65.

Hough, S.E. 2002. *Earthshaking Science: What We Know (and Don't Know) about Earthquakes*. Princeton, NJ: Princeton Univ. Press.

Levy, M., and M. Salvadori. 1995. *Why the Earth Quakes: The Story of Earthquakes and Volcanoes*. New York: Norton.

Lomnitz, C. 1994. *Fundamentals of Earthquake Prediction*. New York: Wiley.

Mustard, P.S., et al. 1998. 'Geology and Geological Hazards of the Greater Vancouver Area', in P.F. Karrow and O.L. White, *Urban Geology of Canadian Cities*. Geological Association of Canada Special Paper 42, 39–70.

Richter, C.F. 1958. *Elementary Seismology*. New York: Freeman.

Ritchie, D., and A.E. Gates. 2001. *The Encyclopedia of Earthquakes and Volcanoes*, 2nd edn. New York: Facts on File.

Schenk, V., ed. 1996. *Earthquake Hazard and Risk*. Amsterdam: Kluwer.

Velasco, A.A., et al. 2008. 'Global Ubiquity of Dynamic Earthquake Triggering', *Nature Geoscience*. Published on-line, 25 May, at: <d.o.i.10.1038/ngeo204>.

Wallach, J.L., et al. 1998. 'Linear Zones, Seismicity and the Possibility of a Major Earthquake in the Intraplate Western Lake Ontario Area of Eastern North America', *Canadian Journal of Earth Science* 35: 762–86.

Wyllie, P.J. 1976. *The Way the Earth Works*. New York: Wiley.

Yeats, R.S., K.E. Sieh, and C.R. Allen. 1997. *Geology of Earthquakes*. New York: Oxford Univ. Press.

 # WEB RESOURCES

earthquakescanada.nrcan.gc.ca/historic_eq/20th/1929/1929_e.php
Earthquakes Canada site devoted to the Grand Banks earthquake and Burin tsunami of 1929.

earthquakescanada.nrcan.gc.ca/index_e.php Homepage of Earthquakes Canada. This website includes information about earthquakes, earthquake research, and historical earthquakes. It also has maps and links.

gsc.nrcan.gc.ca/index_e.php This Geological Survey of Canada site has a wide range of geological information of all types.

gsc.nrcan.gc.ca/org/sidnex/index_e.php The homepage of the Geological Survey of Canada's Pacific Geosciences Centre has information about the geology of British Columbia, earthquakes, volcanoes, and many other topics.

nctr.pmel.noaa.gov/ The National Oceanic and Atmospheric Administration in the US provides data from its Tsunami Research Program on this website. Information includes tsunami-event data, real-time tsunami information, tsunami modelling graphics, and hazard mitigation program information.

quake.wr.usgs.gov The US Geological Survey earthquake hazards page contains general information and links to research material. A real-time earthquake map is available, as well as strike probability data. Earthquake preparedness information is included, as is a link to an 'ask a geologist' question-and-answer site.

seismescanada.nrcan.gc.ca/hazard/ This Geological Survey of Canada site has information on earthquake risk in Canada.

www.collectionscanada.gc.ca/sos/002028-1100-e.html Canadian Archives collection of Burin tsunami photographs.

www.heritage.nf.ca/law/tsunami29.html Newfoundland and Labrador Heritage site about the Burin tsunami.

Surface Expressions of Subsurface Structures

Objectives

- To introduce basic terminology used in describing rock structure.

- To distinguish between types of fault movements and the landforms they produce.

- To discuss the folding of rocks and relate it to the landforms produced.

The physical landscapes of the continental landmasses are sculpted from rocks with diverse properties. Some of these properties are discussed in other units: the hard, resistant, crystalline batholiths formed deep in the crust and exposed by erosion (Unit 22); the flows of lava (Units 22 and 25); the foliated schists (Unit 23); and the layers of sedimentary strata (Unit 23). Rocks may also be changed after their formation, metamorphosed from one state to another (Unit 23). The geological structure of the rocks reveals the nature of the stress that changed them and reflects the way the rocks reacted to this stress. Brittle rocks fracture under pressure. Rocks exhibiting plastic behaviour can bend or even fold, and when the stress is removed, these structures remain permanent.

LINK

Stresses of many kinds are imposed on rocks. In plate collision margins, rock strata are crushed into tight folds. In continental shield areas and at mid-oceanic ridges, spreading movement driven by processes in the mantle below can pull segments of rock apart, creating parallel faults. Where sediments accumulate, their growing weight pushes the underlying rocks downward. Where erosion removes rock, the crust has a tendency to 'rebound'. Rocks are deformed in so many ways that the resulting forms seem endlessly complicated. But, in fact, certain geological structures occur many times over and can be recognized even on topographic maps that do not contain any stratigraphic information. Our understanding of the surface must begin with what lies below, and in this unit we study the relationships between geological structure and visible landscape.

Terminology of Structure

If we are to describe the nature and orientation of structures below the surface accurately, we must use consistent terminology. Imagine a ridge of quartzite rising above the surface and extending from northeast to southwest (Figure 27.1). This is the **strike** of that ridge—the compass direction of the line of intersection between a rock layer and a horizontal plane. Thus the strike of the ridge is

recorded in field notes as N45°E. The strike of any linear feature is always recorded to range from 0° to 90°E or W.

The ridge of quartzite may consist of a layer of this metamorphic rock that angles downward between less resistant strata (Figure 27.1). This is referred to as the **dip** of that layer, which is the angle at which it tilts from the horizontal. If the quartzite layer tilts 30° from the horizontal, its dip is recorded as 30°. In addition, the direction of the dip must be established. If the quartzite layer tilts downward towards the southeast, its dip is recorded as 30°SE. As the diagram indicates, the direction of dip is always at a right angle to the strike.

A prominent feature such as the quartzite ridge is called an *outcrop*, a locality where exposed rock occurs. Note that it is not correct to say that a certain rock outcrops—it *crops out*. Here the hardness of the rock and its resistance to erosion have combined to create a prominent topographic feature whose length and straightness indicate tilting, but little or no other deformation. Where rock strata are bent or folded, the determination of strike and dip can become difficult, and the field map may have to record many variations in strike and dip along segments of the outcrop.

Fault Structures

LINK

LINK

The rocks of the Earth's crust are divided up by fractures. Some areas, such as the zones near the subductive margins of tectonic plates, are more strongly affected by faulting than other locales. But detailed geological maps of even the 'stable' shields of the continental cores reveal numerous fractures, legacies of earlier periods of stress. Several types of faults related to collision and spreading are expressed at the surface of the crust in the landscape.

A **fault** is a fracture in crustal rock involving the displacement of rock on one side of the fracture with respect to the rock on the other side. A fracture without displacement is called a *joint*, so slippage along the fault plane is key evidence for faulting. Faulting results when brittle rocks come under stress, cannot bend or fold, and therefore break. But even rocks that exhibit plastic behaviour can be subjected to such severe stress that they, too, can fracture (see Figure 26.1).

As explained in Unit 26, sudden slippage along a fault plane generates an earthquake or a tremor, depending on the amount of energy released. Slippage may involve a few millimetres or 100 m or more. At the surface a fault may be completely hidden under more recent rocks (or *blind*; an unknown blind thrust fault was the cause of the Northridge, California, earthquake of 1994), it may be barely visible—or it may be marked by a tall scarp. Sometimes, when a sequence of sedimentary layers is faulted, it is possible to locate the same bed on opposite sides of the fault plane, and the amount of vertical displacement (the *throw*) can be determined. But if the blocks on either side of the fault consist of the same rock (say, a mass of granite), it may not be possible to measure displacement.

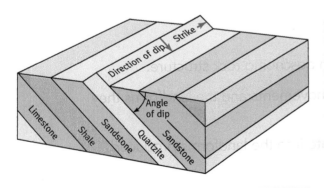

Figure 27.1 Strike, direction of dip, and angle of dip.

LINK Our increased understanding of plate tectonics has contributed to better comprehension of faulting, its causes, and its effects. Where plates converge and collide, **compressional stresses** are strong and rocks are crushed tightly together. The lithosphere is forced to occupy less horizontal space, and rocks respond by breaking, bending, folding, sliding, and squeezing upward and downward. Where plates diverge, and where the crust is subjected to spreading processes elsewhere, the stress is *tensional* and rocks are being pulled apart. Some plastic rocks respond by thinning, but others break and faults result. Where a series of parallel faults develop, blocks of crust between the faults may actually sink down, having been left with less support from below than existed previously. And where plates slide past each other, or where forces below the crust are lateral, the stress is *transverse*. Rock masses that slide past each other also are subject to faulting and associated earthquakes.

Compressional Faults

Where crustal rock is compressed into a smaller horizontal space, shortening of the crust is achieved by one block riding over the other along a steep fault plane between them (Figure 27.2). Such a structure is called a **reverse fault**. When vertical movement occurs during faulting, blocks that move upward (with respect to adjacent blocks) are referred to as *upthrown*, whereas blocks that move downward are termed *downthrown*. In the case of reverse faults, note that the upthrown block creates an initial scarp that overhangs the downthrown block (Figure 27.2A). Such an overhanging scarp soon collapses under the effects of weathering, erosion, and gravity. Rock avalanches and other slope processes (see Unit 30) are associated with such scarps, and these processes soon produce a slope at an angle to the original fault plane (Figure 27.2B). Therefore when we see a fault scarp in the field, we cannot conclude without further investigation that it represents the dip of the fault plane from which it has resulted.

Compressional forces sometimes produce series of nearly parallel (or *en echelon*) faults. A strip of crustal rock positioned between reverse faults may assume the dimensions of a block-like plateau (Figure 27.3). When the angle of a fault plane in a compressional fault is very low, the structure is referred to as a **thrust fault** (sometimes *overthrust fault*) (Figure 27.4). Note that the overriding block slides almost horizontally over the downthrown block, covering much more of it than is the case in a reverse fault. Following erosion, the resulting scarp would be lower and less prominent.

LINK

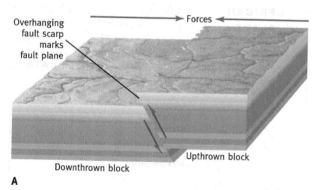

A

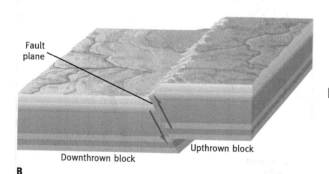

B

Figure 27.2 In a reverse fault, the overhanging scarp of the upthrown block (A) soon collapses, and a new slope, which lies at an angle to the original, is produced by erosional forces (B).

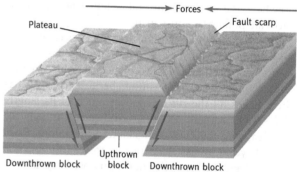

Figure 27.3 Plateau formed by an upthrown block that lies between two reverse faults that run parallel to each other where they intersect the surface.

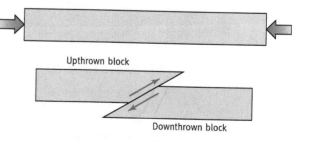

Figure 27.4 Side view of a thrust fault resulting from compression. The low angle of the fault plane produces substantial overriding by the upthrown block.

Tensional Faults

Tensional stresses pull crustal rock apart, so that now the situation is the opposite—there is more horizontal space for crustal material, not less as in compressional faults. The result is one or more **normal faults** (Figure 27.5). The typical normal fault has a moderately inclined fault plane separating a block that has remained stationary, or nearly so, from one that has been significantly down-thrown. As Figure 27.5 shows, the resulting fault scarp initially reflects the dip angle of the fault plane, although erosion may modify it over time. Sometimes the fault scarp has been eroded for so long that it has retreated from its original position. In such instances, the fault trace (see Figure 26.8) reveals the original location of the scarp. The eastern and western sides of the Rocky Mountain Trench in British Columbia are excellent examples of large fault blocks produced by tensional stresses on the crust.

As tensional forces continue to stress the affected area, slippage may continue along a major normal fault. The lower (downthrown) block will continue to sink, and the upper (upthrown) block may rise. But the tensional forces are likely to generate additional normal faults, generally parallel to the original one. This creates conditions favourable to the development of rift-valley topography (Figure 27.6). The mid-oceanic ridge system, as noted elsewhere, is essentially a vast rift system, where tensional forces are pulling the crust apart.

On the continental landmasses, the best example of rift-valley topography lies in eastern Africa (Figure 27.7). You do not need a geological map to see this magnificent example of crustal rifting, because East Africa's Great Lakes fill the rift valley over much of its length. The system actually extends northward, through the Red Sea, into the Gulf of Aqaba and the Jordan River Valley beyond. In eastern Africa it crosses Ethiopia and reaches Lake Turkana, the northernmost large lake in the rifts. South of the latitude of Lake Turkana the system splits into two gigantic arcs, one lying to the east of Lake Victoria and the other to the west. These arcs come

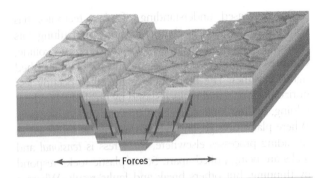

Figure 27.6 Formation of a rift valley as tensional forces generate parallel normal faults between which crustal blocks slide downward.

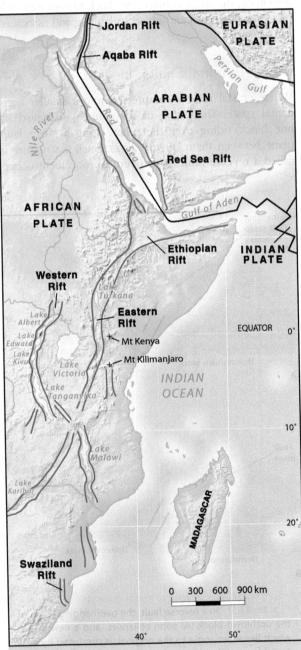

Figure 27.7 The Great Rift Valley extends from the Jordan–Aqaba segment in the north to Swaziland in the south.

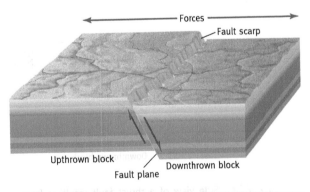

Figure 27.5 Unlike compressional stresses, tensional stresses pull the crust apart. Normal faults result, and the fault scarp often reflects the dip angle of the fault plane.

Figure 27.8 Aerial view of the East African rift valley in southern Ethiopia. The tensional stresses pulling the crust apart here are evident in the fault scarps and the downthrown crustal strips at their base. This scene provides a striking example of the landscape illustrated in Figure 27.6.

together just to the north of Lake Malawi. The system then continues southward through the valley in which that lake lies, and it does not end until it has crossed Swaziland.

As long ago as 1921, the British geomorphologist J.W. Gregory offered an interpretation of the rift valleys of East Africa. He concluded that the floors of the valleys, in places thousands of metres below the adjacent uplands, were **grabens** (sunken blocks) between usually parallel normal faults (Figure 27.8). This theory of a tensional origin of East Africa's rift valleys was later upheld for the arc that lies east of Lake Victoria. But the western arc, in which Lake Tanganyika lies, proved to have compressional origins. The fault scarps looked similar to those of the eastern arc, but they had begun as overhanging scarps (Figure 27.2A). One of Africa's greatest mountain massifs, Ruwenzori, proved to be a **horst**, a block raised between reverse faults (see Figure 27.3).

If the East African rift valleys originated, at least in part, from tensional forces, we should expect volcanism to be associated with them, just as volcanism affects the spreading mid-oceanic ridges. These expectations are confirmed in that composite cones, lava domes, cinder cones, and fissure eruptions all mark the region. Volcanic activity still continues along segments of the East African rifts: as recently as January 2002, a major eruption of Mount Nyiragongo sent lava flows travelling at 65 km/hr into the heart of the Congolese city of Goma—north of Lake Tanganyika and 50 km south of the volcano—destroying half of the abandoned city and killing at least 45 people. Seismic activity, too, is stronger there than in other areas of the great African shield. Some geologists now believe that the African Plate may not be a single tectonic unit, and that an East African Plate (or Somali Plate, as it is also known)

is separating from Africa just as the Arabian Plate did earlier. In that case, millions of years from now a Red Sea–like body of water may invade Africa from near the mouth of the Zambezi River and penetrate northward into Lake Malawi, and a Madagascar-like chunk of the continent will move off the new East African coastline (Figure 27.9).

Transverse Faults

Where blocks of crustal rock move laterally, motion along the fault plane is horizontal, not vertical. Thus, there are no upthrown or downthrown blocks. The fault is **transcurrent**, that is, movement is in the direction of the fault (Figure 27.10). Lateral plate contact is exemplified by the San Andreas Fault, the contact plane between the Pacific and North American Plates (see Figure 24.12). The San Andreas Fault is a special case of transcurrent faulting, being a **transform fault**, which marks the boundary between plates. Because movement at a transcurrent fault takes place along the strike of the fault, transcurrent faults are also known as *strike-slip faults*. To describe the fault completely, we also give the direction of movement. This is determined by looking *across* the fault and stating the direction in which the opposite block is moving. Accordingly, the San Andreas Fault is a right-lateral strike-slip fault. A similar fault is the Queen Charlotte–Denali transform fault off British Columbia and in Yukon and Alaska.

Field Evidence of Faulting

These three types of faults—reverse, normal, and transcurrent—exhibit many variations, and regional fault patterns and structures can become very complicated. Even in the field it is not always easy to distinguish a scarp formed by a fault from one formed by erosion. If the upthrown block contains water-bearing rock, water may pour from the scarp face in springs, probable evidence of faulting. The movement of the rocks along the fault plane may also produce smooth, mirror-like surfaces on the scarp face, and these *slickensides* are further evidence that faulting created the scarp. If the fault trace is marked by a breccia (a shattered rock layer), faulting is indicated as well. Most often, a combination of evidence provides the surest basis for interpretation.

LINK

Fold Structures

When rocks are compressed, they respond to the stress by **folding** as well as by faulting. All rocks—even a sill of granite—have some capacity to bend before fracturing. But the fold structures discussed here are most characteristic of layered sedimentary rocks. Folds, again like faults, come in all dimensions. Some are too small to see; others are

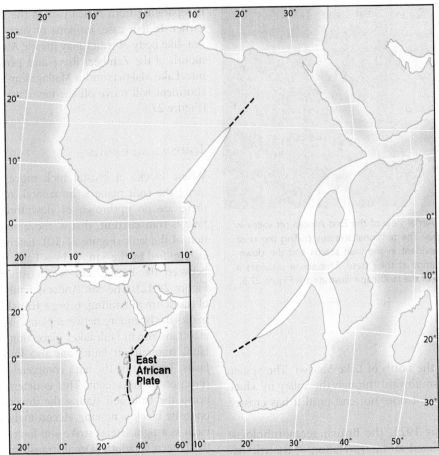

Figure 27.9 Possible configuration of Africa, about 10 million years from now, if the East African Plate (inset map) completes its separation from the rest of the continent.

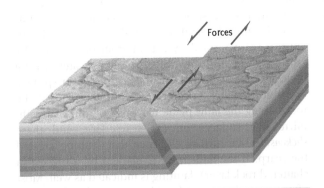

Figure 27.10 Horizontal or transcurrent fault, also known as a strike-slip fault.

road-cut size; still others are the size of entire mountain ridges (Figure 27.11).

Unlike faults, however, folds are primarily compressional features. In areas where crustal rocks are under stress, the crust may bend into basins hundreds of kilometres across in association with normal faulting. But the accordion-like folds in western North America's Rocky Mountains and coastal mountains, the Andes, the Appalachians, and parts of Eurasia's Alpine Mountain system (such as the Zagros Mountains of Iran) are the result of intense compression. Not surprisingly, folding and faulting generally occur together: just as even brittle rocks can bend slightly, so the most plastic rocks have a limited capacity to fold.

Anticlines and Synclines

Folds are rarely simple, symmetrical structures. Often they form a jumble of upfolds and downfolds that make it difficult to discern even a general design in the field. But when we map the distribution of the rock layers and analyze the topography, we discover that recognizable and recurrent structures do exist. The most obvious of these are upfolds, or **anticlines**, and downfolds, or **synclines**. An anticline is an arch-like fold, with the limbs dipping away from the axis (Figure 27.12, left). A syncline, on the other hand, is

LINK

From the Fieldnotes

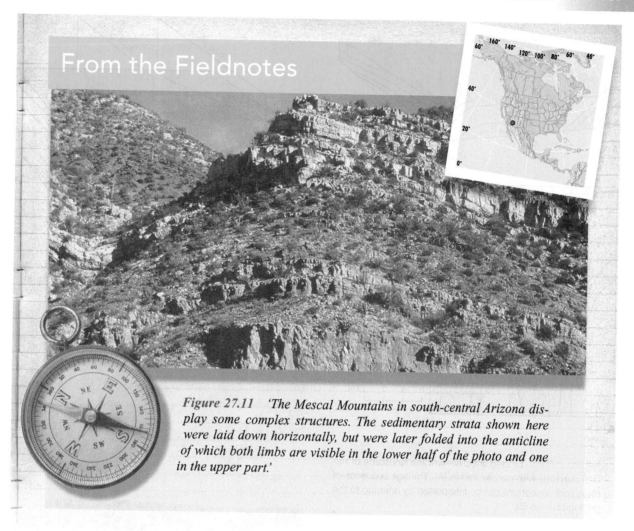

Figure 27.11 *'The Mescal Mountains in south-central Arizona display some complex structures. The sedimentary strata shown here were laid down horizontally, but were later folded into the anticline of which both limbs are visible in the lower half of the photo and one in the upper part.'*

troughlike, and its limbs dip towards its axial plane (Figure 27.12, right).

When flat-lying sedimentary strata are folded into anticlines and synclines, the cores of the synclines are consti-

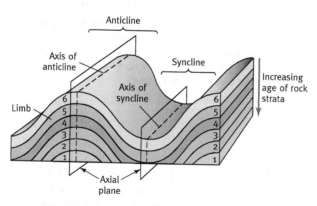

Figure 27.12 Anticlines are arching upfolds while synclines are troughlike downfolds. Note the relative age of rock layers within each type of fold.

tuted by younger rocks. Imagine that erosion removes the upper parts of both anticlines and synclines. What is left are a series of surface outcrops with parallel strikes and a sequence of rocks showing a succession of ages. From these data it is possible to interpret the geological structures here—based on our understanding of anticlines and synclines (Figure 27.13).

Plunging Folds and Associated Landscapes

Folds are rarely as symmetrical as shown in Figure 27.12, however; nor are their axes usually horizontal. Anticlines and synclines often *plunge*, which means that their axes dip. You can easily demonstrate the effect of this by taking a cardboard tube and cutting it lengthwise. Hold it horizontally and you have a symmetrical anticline (and a syncline, if you place the other half adjacent). Now tilt the tube, say, about 30 degrees from the horizontal, by the edge of a table or other flat surface. Draw the horizontal line, and cut the tube along it. The second cut represents the outcrop of the youngest rocks of the

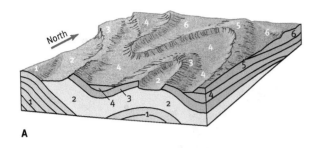

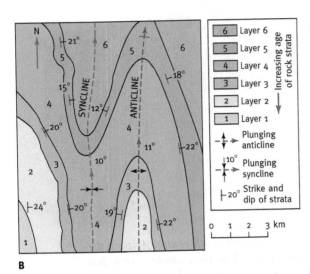

A

B

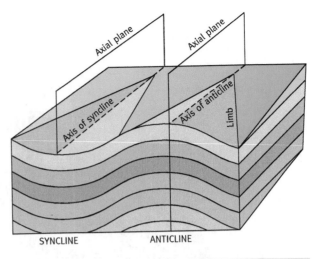

Figure 27.14 Anticline–syncline structure plunging in opposite directions.

Figure 27.15 A striking evenness of the summit levels marks this section of the folded sedimentary rocks in the ridge-and-valley terrain of the Appalachian Mountains in central Pennsylvania, beyond the more mountainous topography of the Blue Ridge to the south.

anticline. Note how they form a 'nose' at one end and open progressively towards the other end. In the field, such an outcrop signals an eroded, plunging anticline; the adjacent syncline would plunge in the other direction (Figure 27.14).

In the intensely folded central Appalachian Mountains, which extend into eastern Canada, plunging anticlines and synclines adjoin each other in wide belts, eroded into attractive scenery by streams over many millions of years. But as the topography of the Appalachians suggests, there is considerable regularity and even symmetry to the pattern (Figures 27.15 and 27.16). That is not always the case in areas of intense compression and folding. Europe's Alps, for instance, are much more severely distorted. Not only are the folds there anticlinal and synclinal, but many of the anticlines have become recumbent (compressed and doubled back, with an axial plane near horizontal) and even overturned (with the axial plane beyond the horizontal). Add to this the presence of intense faulting and erosion by streams and glaciers, and complex spectacular alpine landscapes are produced.

At this point an important distinction must be made between what some geomorphologists call **primary landforms**, the structures created by tectonic activity, and **secondary landforms**, the products of weathering and erosion. Sometimes geologic and topographic maps reveal amazing contradictions. An anticline of less resistant sedimentary rocks may be eroded into a low valley, whereas a nearby synclinal structure, composed of more resistant rocks, stands out as a ridge or upland. Thus the geologic upfold forms a geographical lowland, and vice versa. The

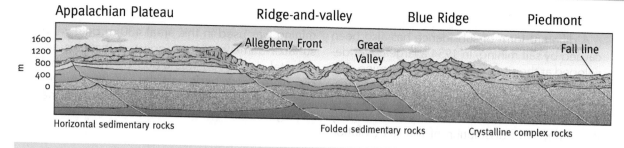

Figure 27.16 Cross-section view of the Appalachian Mountains in the eastern United States, looking north.

relationship between structure, rock resistance, and erosional processes forms a major theme that runs through many units in Part Four.

Regional Deformation

Not all types of crustal deformation are encompassed by the various types of faulting and folding discussed in this unit. Over large areas of stable lithosphere, especially in the major continental shields, the crust undergoes slight deformation *without* being faulted or folded. Geologists in the past gave various terms to these and other crustal movements. *Diastrophism* was one, and *crustal warping* was another. Yet another term, still in occasional use, is *epeirogeny*; it refers to the vertical movement of the crust over very large areas, involving little or no bending or breaking of the rocks.

Such rising or sinking of the upper crust undoubtedly is related to the movement of lithospheric plates over the mantle's convection cells, and in that sense it is subsumed under plate motion. But in physical geography these very slight regional movements are extremely important. Even the slightest change in the slope of a large region can have an enormous impact on an entire drainage basin, rates of erosion and deposition, and other aspects of the regional geomorphology (see 'Perspectives' box). It should be remembered, therefore, that while this unit focuses on the tectonically active zones of the world (present and past), more subtle but still highly significant deformation also affects the more stable sectors of the landmasses.

Perspectives on the Human Environment

Subsidence in the Windsor Area of Southern Ontario

The Salina Formation (upper Silurian age) includes two or three thick beds of halite or salt (NaCl) in the Windsor–Sarnia area of southern Ontario. These beds taken together are approximately 190 m deep and are worked for table and road salt. The Windsor salt mines are some of the most productive on Earth, and the product is shipped all over the world. The salt layers were formed in a shallow tropical sea that invaded the centre of North America in late Silurian times. In some areas the salt was deposited around coral reefs, indicating a shallow tropical environment. Some salt may also have been deposited in shallow seaside lagoons. It is known that salt deposits form close to sea level.

Today the top of the Salina Formation occurs at a depth of about 490 m below the surface, indicating that subsidence has occurred in what is called the Michigan Basin. The downwarping of the Michigan Basin and upwarping of the Canadian Shield has also meant that Paleozoic rocks of southern Ontario, which were deposited close to the horizontal, now dip slightly towards the Michigan Basin at approximately 3 degrees.

A different form of subsidence has also been caused by salt mining. In 1954 a large crater developed at the site of the Windsor salt mine. The subsidence was very rapid. It swallowed a locomotive and a service building. Experts hypothesized that the subsidence had been caused by the undetected dissolution of the salt (solution mining was used in this area) 430 m below the surface. Some experts suggested that this accidental dissolution was aided by the regional dip of the rock beds and the resulting movement of groundwater towards the middle of the Michigan Basin.

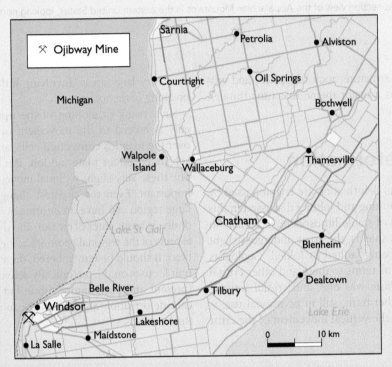

Figure 27.17   Location of the Ojibway Mine of the Canadian Salt Company, Windsor, Ontario.

KEY TERMS

anticline   *page 380*
compressional stresses   *page 377*
dip   *page 376*
fault   *page 376*
folding   *page 379*
graben   *page 379*
horst   *page 379*
normal fault   *page 378*

primary landform   *page 382*
reverse fault   *page 377*
secondary landform   *page 382*
strike   *page 376*
syncline   *page 380*
thrust fault   *page 377*
transcurrent (strike-slip) fault   *page 379*
transform fault   *page 379*

REVIEW QUESTIONS

1. What is the basic difference between normal and reverse faulting?
2. What evidence of faulting might one encounter when looking at an isolated rock outcrop?
3. Differentiate between *anticlines* and *synclines*, and describe how plunging affects their orientation.
4. What is the difference between *primary* and *secondary* landforms?
5. Differentiate between the concepts of strike and dip in describing a ridge on the Earth's surface.
6. What is a rift valley? Why are these formations so widespread in eastern and northeastern Africa?

REFERENCES AND FURTHER READINGS

Bennison, G.M., and K.A. Moseley. 1997. *An Introduction to Geological Structures and Maps*, 6th edn. London/New York: Arnold.

Billings, M.P. 1972. *Structural Geology*, 3rd edn. Englewood Cliffs, NJ: Prentice-Hall.

Bird, J.B. 1980. *The Natural Landscapes of Canada: A Study in Regional Earth Science*, 2nd edn. Toronto: Wiley.

Davis, G.H. 1984. *Structural Geology of Rocks and Regions*. New York: Wiley.

Hills, E.S. 1991. *Elements of Structural Geology*. New York: Wiley/Longman.

Hobbs, B.E., et al. 1976. *An Outline of Structural Geology*. New York: Wiley.

Huder, P.P. 1998. 'Geology and Geotechnical Properties of Glacial Soils in Windsor', in P.F. Karrow and O.L. White, eds, *Urban Geology of Canadian Cities*. Geological Association of Canada Special Publication 42, 225–36.

Miyashiro, A., et al. 1982. *Orogeny*. New York: Wiley.

Ollier, C.D. 1981. *Tectonics and Landforms*. London/New York: Longman.

Powell, D. 1992. *Interpretation of Geological Structure through Maps: An Introductory Practice Manual*. New York: Wiley/Longman.

Ragan, D.M. 1984. *Structural Geology: An Introduction to Geometrical Techniques*, 3rd edn. New York: Wiley.

Sanford, B.V., and W.B. Brady. 1955. *Palaeozoic Geology of the Windsor–Sarnia Area, Ontario*. Ottawa: Department of Mines and Technical Surveys, Geological Survey of Canada Memoir 278.

Trenhaile, A.S. 1998. *Geomorphology: A Canadian Perspective*. Toronto: Oxford Univ. Press.

Weyman, D. 1981. *Tectonic Processes*. Boston: Allen & Unwin.

Windley, B. 1984. *The Evolving Continents*, 2nd edn. New York: Wiley.

 ## WEB RESOURCES

www.platetectonics.com/index.asp This site has information regarding many facets of plate tectonics. Searching the site will reveal articles describing rift valleys, seafloor spreading, and many other subjects. Press releases concerning plate tectonics are also available by hyperlink.

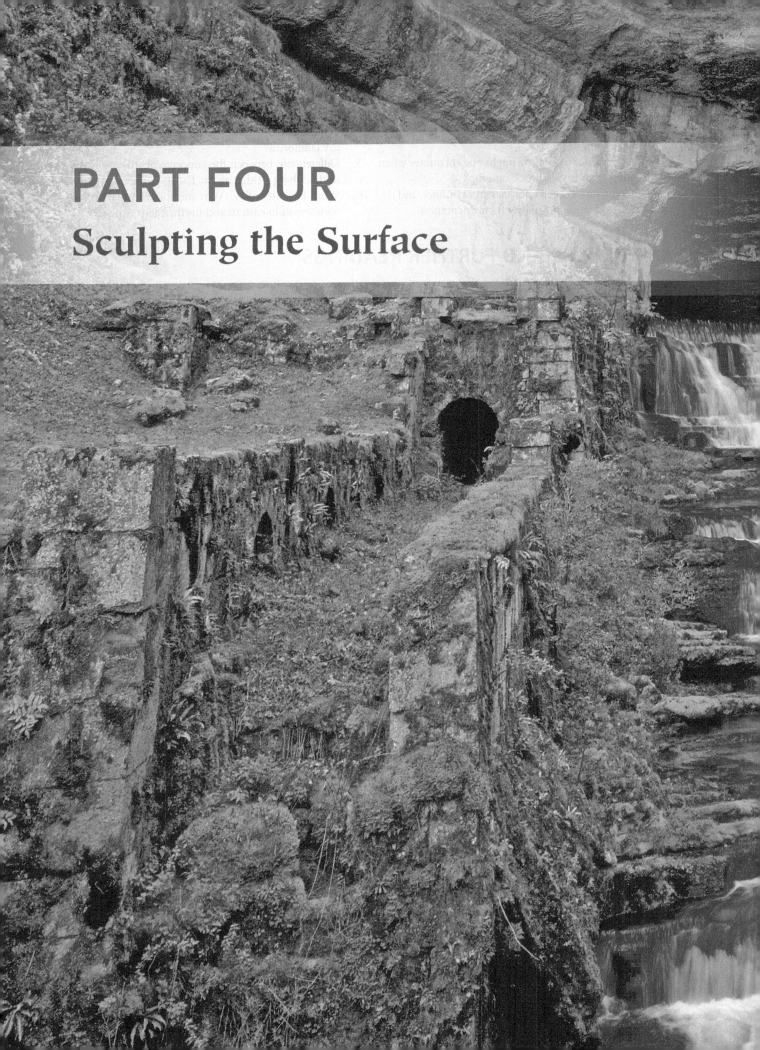

PART FOUR
Sculpting the Surface

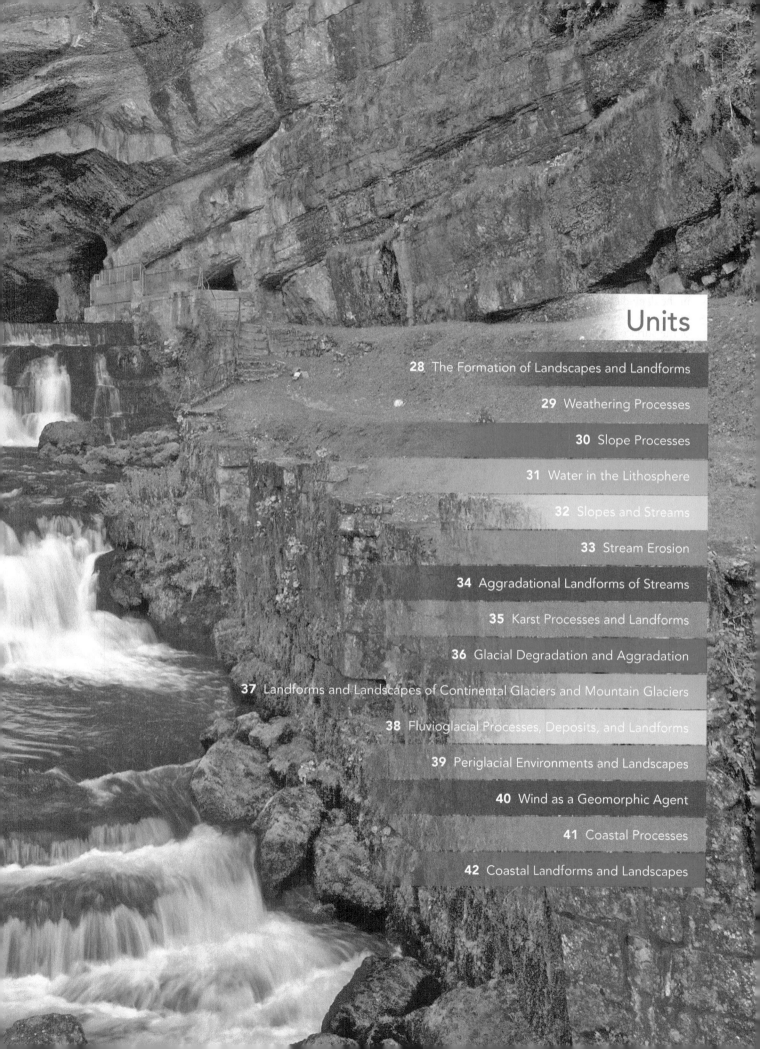

Units

PART FOUR Sculpting the Surface

Degradational and Aggradational Systems

The natural landscapes we observe and study are the products of a set of seven systems of breakdown (degradation) and accumulation (aggradation), whose combined effect is to create the infinite variety that marks the terrestrial surface of our planet. These are open systems, and while it is possible to identify the dominant system at work in a certain region, it is almost never the sole system functioning there. For example, glacial forces have sculpted the general topography of the European Alps and the Rocky Mountains, but stream gradation under milder conditions has modified the landscapes the glaciers forged. Again, wave action fashions coastlines, but the effect of wave power is enhanced where subduction creates deep water immediately offshore. The systems and processes at work range from weathering (decomposition and disintegration) and mass movement (collapse) to stream gradation (valley formation in the degradational form, delta formation in the aggradational form) and from karst processes (the dissolving of rock by slightly acidic water) to wind action, which can erode as well as deposit. All these systems involved in the sculpting of the surface have 'signature' landforms, some of which are shown here. Because they operate over large areas, they tend to produce characteristic landscapes we know by such names as the Rocky Mountains, the Canadian Shield, the Prairies, and the St Lawrence Lowlands.

The Formation of Landscapes and Landforms

Objectives

- To introduce three primary degradational processes: weathering, mass movements, and erosion.

- To focus attention on the aggradational processes that produce secondary landforms.

- To recognize the roles of degradation and aggradation in the formation and evolution of landscapes.

The Earth's landscapes are the temporary result of many processes. As the units in Part Four detail, the continents are affected by the horizontal and vertical movements of tectonic plates. These movements result in the folding, faulting, tilting, and warping of the crust, and are often accompanied by earthquakes and volcanic eruptions. These movements and processes create **primary landforms**. A volcano, for example, can be worn down over a long period of time by various agents of erosion, such as water, wind, and even ice in certain places. But the original mountain is a primary landform created by volcanic activity.

When erosion sculpted the mountain into the form seen today, a **secondary landform** was produced. The same is true, over a larger area, in a subduction zone. Crustal plates move several centimetres per year, and the enormous energy involved is expressed in part by the crushed, folded, and faulted rocks that mark the scenery of these subduction zones (see Figure 20.10). Here it may be more difficult to differentiate between primary and secondary processes because both happen at the same time. Even as the crust buckles and breaks, erosion attacks; in combination, these processes produce characteristic terrain.

All parts of the landmasses, even relatively stable areas unaffected by subduction or other severe deformation, are subject to vertical and horizontal movements that affect the evolution of their landscapes. As the plates carrying the continents move over the mantle, the landmasses are pushed, dragged, pressed, and stretched. Geologists still are not certain about the exact nature of the tectonic activity beneath the landmasses. Hot spots such as those noted for the Pacific Plate (Unit 25) also exist beneath continent-bearing plates; the Anahim Volcanic Belt of British Columbia and the Yellowstone Caldera area are good examples (see Figure 31.16).

As noted in Part Three, at least some of the extensive continental plates may, like the oceanic plates, consist of segments. These segments may exhibit convergent, divergent, and lateral contact. The effect of these movements on the landmasses is not yet completely understood. However, there can be no doubt that they continuously deform the continental crust—and thus its surface, the landscape. Part Four concentrates on the secondary processes that mould the scenery of the continents, but we should keep in mind that the processes sculpting the surface that we observe are the result of forces from below as well as from above.

Landscapes and Landforms

As the title of this unit indicates, the concern here is with the surface configuration of the exposed land, not the submerged seafloor. Thus, reference is made frequently to particular types of *landscapes* and *landforms*. A **landform** is a single and typical unit that forms part of the general topography of the Earth's surface. A solitary mountain (such as a composite volcano), a hill, a single valley, a dune, and a sinkhole are all landforms. A **landscape** is an aggregation of landforms, often the same types of landforms. A volcanic landscape, for example, may consist of a region of composite cones, lava domes, lava flows, and other features resulting from volcanic activity, all modified, to a greater or lesser extent, by weathering and erosion. A dune may be part of a desert landscape or a coastal landscape. So the term *landform* often refers to the discrete product of a set of processes; a *landscape* is the areal (or regional) expression of those processes.

Denudation

Weathering and erosion work to sculpt the surface of landmasses. Landscapes and landforms represent the progress made by the agents of weathering and erosion as they transform the surface of the landmasses rising above sea level. Landscapes reveal the nature of these weathering processes, erosional agents, the hardness and resistance of the rocks, the geological structures below, and the tectonic activity affecting the crust.

The key force is that of the Earth's **gravity**. When soil and loose rock on a hillside become unstable because they are waterlogged or are shaken by an earthquake, the force of gravity pulls them downslope where streams (also responding to gravity) remove them (Figure 28.1). When a mineral grain on a rock face is loosened, gravity causes it to fall to the ground below and the wind may carry it away. Streams flow and glaciers move down their valleys under gravity—steeper slopes mean faster movement. Even winds and waves are subject to the Earth's gravitational pull. Rock avalanches and waterfalls reveal the ever-present force of gravity in the wearing away of the Earth's landmasses.

The result is a carving of relief of the landmasses—the lowering of the mountains, filling of the valleys, and possibly an overall lowering of the continents down towards sea level. Millions of tonnes of sediment are annually carried downstream by the great rivers of the world (Figure 28.2). This material comes from the interior uplands, and it may be deposited in river deltas or on the ocean floor. Some of it is laid down in the valleys of the streams themselves, so that many streams in their lower courses no longer flow in rock-floored channels but over deep wedges of their own sediments.

The wearing away of the landmasses goes on through a combination of processes collectively referred to as **denudation** or **degradation**. This term implies that a landmass is being eroded. When a stream cuts an ever-deeper channel, or a glacier scours its valley, or waves erode a beach, degradation prevails. But the opposite also occurs: a combination of processes removes material from one area and deposits it elsewhere. When a stream builds a delta at its mouth, or when a valley fills with sediment, or when a glacier melts and deposits the material it was carrying, **aggradation** takes place. Aggradation also contributes to landscape development by reducing the height differences (relative relief) between the high points and the low places in an area.

From the Fieldnotes

Figure 28.1 *'Driving westward from Christchurch, New Zealand, across the Canterbury Plain and into the mountains via Arthur's Pass, you encounter diverse landscapes. On the way up, the evidence of recent glaciation is all around, but now subaerial processes (that is, those proceeding under atmospheric conditions) prevail, and the topography is being modified by weathering, mass movement, and stream erosion. Here, in the Craigeburn area, a talus cone, or scree slope, has formed from rock originally loosened under glacial conditions, augmented now by mechanical weathering and moved downslope under the force of gravity. The talus has not moved far from its source; stream erosion is not yet playing a major role here.'*

LINK

Degradational Processes and Landscapes

The processes and agents that work to weather and erode the continental surfaces range from the quiet disintegration of regolith (loose rock material) to the extremely violent cascade of rock in a rock avalanche or torrentially flowing boulder-filled mountain stream. In Part Four we study the multiple processes that combine to destroy and remove the rocks of the continents and the landscapes they create. Denudational or degradational processes can be divided into two general categories: (1) weathering, and (2) slope processes. We devote entire units to weathering and slope processes, and several to the agents and processes of erosion.

A good way to understand how these types of processes differ is to consider the distances travelled by the debris (loosened rock particles). In weathering a rock disintegrates, but the loose grains do not do more than fall to the ground below under the force of gravity (Figure 28.1). Slope processes (such as rock avalanches) move rock material farther downslope over distances that can reach 20 km or more. Erosional processes can carry material hundreds, even thousands, of kilometres.

As the term implies, **weathering** is the breakdown of rocks in situ, that is, their disintegration or decomposition without distant removal. As discussed in Unit 29, rocks can be weakened in many ways: by exposure to temperature extremes, by chemical action, and even by the growth of plant roots. The processes of weathering prepare the rock for later removal by slope processes and other processes of erosion.

LINK

Figure 28.2 The Yangzi (Chang) River in China originates deep in the Asian interior and flows across the heart of the country to the Pacific Ocean. In the process it sculpts numerous dramatic landforms, but perhaps none as scenic as the famous Three Gorges. Now the Chinese government is building a massive dam and flood-control system that will drown the gorges seen here, forever changing the local (and regional) hydrography and altering human–environment relationships that have prevailed here for millennia.

A **slope process** is the spontaneous downslope movement of Earth materials under the force of gravity. Anyone who has witnessed or seen a picture of a rock avalanche or mudflow knows what such slope failure involves. Houses, roads, even entire hillsides tumble downslope, often after the weathered surface material has become destabilized and/or waterlogged (Figure 28.3). Unit 25 makes note of the great volcanic mudflow (or **lahar**) that occurred on Colombia's volcano, Nevado del Ruiz, when it erupted in 1985. Saturated by abruptly melted snow from the volcano's peak, this lahar travelled over 50 km down valleys from

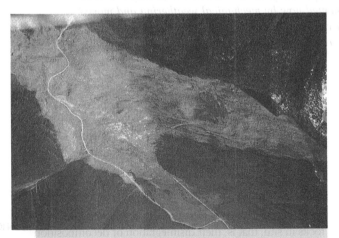

Figure 28.3 On 9 January 1965 the southwestern slope of Johnson Peak, 18 km east of Hope, BC, collapsed, spreading rock, mud, and debris 85 m thick and 3 km wide across the Hope–Princeton Highway, burying four people with their cars. The Hope Slide, by volume, was one of largest landslides in Canadian history.

the base of the mountain and buried at least 20,000 people living in its path (see Figure 25.7). Thus, slope processes (treated in Unit 30) can involve large volumes of material, sometimes with disastrous consequences. But other forms of slope processes are slow and almost imperceptible.

Most of our attention, however, is devoted to the fascinating processes of **erosion**. Here the particles resulting from weathering and mass movement are carried away over long distances. During this process of transportation, additional breakdown occurs, both of the transported particles and of the rocks of the valleys or stream channels through which they travel. For example, a boulder first loosened by mass movement is removed by a stream and bounces along the stream channel as the water transports it. It breaks into smaller pieces, which become rounded into pebbles, and the parts that are broken off during this process form smaller particles. As these and other boulders, pebbles, gravel, and sand move along, they can *abrade* each other and erode pieces of material off the channel bed and banks. In this way, stream erosion involves both transportation and breakdown of rock material.

Running Water Running water is one of the most effective and significant agents of erosion, as noted in Units 31 to 34. Streams are complex gradational systems whose effectiveness relates to many factors, including the gradient (slope) of the valley, the volume of water, and the form of the valley. Few places on Earth are unaffected by the erosional power of water. Even in deserts, water plays a major role in shaping the landscape. Many stream systems consist of a major artery, the **trunk stream**, that is joined by **tributaries**, smaller streams that feed into the main stream (Figure 28.4). The spatial pattern of these systems can reveal much about the rock structures below and the development of the drainage networks. Certain patterns are associated with particular structures and landscapes. Often the configuration of a regional stream system can yield insights about the underlying geology and geomorphological history of an area, as explained in Unit 33.

Glaciers Streams are not the only agents of erosion; ice, in the form of glaciers, is also an important agent of degradation. During the Pleistocene Ice Age, great ice sheets covered much of northern North America and Eurasia.

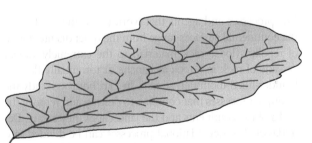

Figure 28.4 Stream system in its drainage basin. The trunk stream is built up by the smaller tributary streams that empty into it.

These ice sheets modified the landscape by eroding regolith and soils, scouring the surface in some areas and depositing the debris elsewhere. At the same time, valleys in high mountain areas (such as the Alps, the Coast Mountains, and the Rockies) were filled by glaciers that snaked slowly downslope. These mountain glaciers widened and deepened their containing valleys, carrying away huge amounts of rock in the process. When the global climate warmed up and the glaciers melted back, the landscape beneath the massive ice sheets had taken on an unmistakable and distinctive character. This is examined in Units 36 to 38.

Wind Wind, too, is a degradational agent. Globally, compared to running water and moving ice, wind is an insignificant factor in landscape genesis. In certain areas of the world such as sandy deserts or along depositional (beach) coasts, however, wind *is* an effective modifier of the surface. Wind can propel sand and dust at high velocities, wearing down exposed rock surfaces in its path. Wind is also capable of moving large volumes of fine material from one place to another, creating characteristic dune landscapes (Figure 28.5). The processes and landscapes of wind action are treated in Unit 40.

Coastal Waves Coastal landscapes are where land and sea make contact, waves attack and rocks resist, and the resulting scenery often is spectacular as well as scientifically intriguing. As in the case of wind action, it is not the waves alone that erode so effectively. When waves contain pieces of loosened rock, these rocks are hurled against the shore, sometimes with enormous impact. The erosional results are represented by wave-cut platforms, cliffs, and other high-relief landforms (Figure 28.6). Coastal landscapes and landforms are the focus of Units 41 and 42.

Chemical Dissolution A special case of degradational action involves the removal of rock not by physical breakdown but by chemical dissolution. As seen in Unit 35, this process produces a landscape of highly distinctive surface and near-surface features called **karst topography**. When soluble rocks, principally limestone, are layered in a suitable way and subjected to certain climatic conditions, the limestone dissolves. Partially carried away in solution, the limestone strata are honeycombed by caves and underground channels. As the roofs of these features are eroded they collapse into these subsurface cavities and the landscape is pocked by sinkholes, evidence of the efficacy of chemical dissolution in sculpting the Earth's surface.

Aggradational Processes and Landforms

Streams, glaciers, wind, and waves are erosional, degradational agents—but they also transport material and have the capacity to build, to deposit, and thus to create aggradational landscapes and landforms. As we study the degradational power of streams, we note that what is removed as boulders and pebbles from interior highlands may be laid down as mud or silt on a floodplain or in a coastal delta.

Figure 28.5 Wind is a frequent (but not the sole) landform sculptor in desert environments. These massive dunes form part of the coastal Namib Desert between Namibia's mountains (seen in the background) and the South Atlantic Ocean behind the photographer.

The Pleistocene ice sheets that scoured the surface of much of the Canadian Shield deposited their processed debris to the south, much of it in the Prairies, the area around the lower Great Lakes, and the US Midwest. Mountain glaciers excavated the upper valleys, but they filled their lower valleys with deposits. Wind action wears rocks down in some places but builds dunes in others. Waves that cut cliffs create beaches in other locales and under different circumstances. So the degradational agents, the agents of erosion, also are aggradational agents, or agents of deposition. The key is transportation: the removal of rocks, their long-distance conveyance, and their processing (pulverization, grinding, abrasion, and sorting) over the course of transport. All of this is part of the rock cycle (see Figure 23.11), which is driven by gravity and sustained by the hydrologic cycle and solar energy (see Figure 11.6), and serves to carve the relief of the landmasses.

Erosion and Tectonics

If the continental landmasses were static (that is, if they were not subject to tectonic forces as parts of lithospheric plates), they could eventually be eroded towards *base level*. Base level is an entropy surface beyond which energy is lacking for further erosion (near the coast the ultimate base level is sea level, while inland it is the height of the stream beds). In the context of the Earth's lifetime, this would not necessarily take very long. To prove this, geomorphologists first calculated the total mass of the continents presently existing above sea level. Next they estimated the quantity of sediment that all the world's streams carried to the oceans in an average year. By dividing the

From the Fieldnotes

Figure 28.6 'Oregon's coastal Route 101 provides some magnificent scenery and many superb field examples of coastal landforms. Drive it southward, so you are on the ocean side! Ample rainfall in this **Csb** environment sustains luxuriant vegetation. Below, the waves do their work even as tectonic forces modify the geology. Here two natural bridges have formed following wave penetration of a fault-weakened section of the coastline, the waters rushing in through one and out through the other.'

total mass by the amount annually removed, and by factoring in the reduced efficiency of streams as the continental areas were reduced, it was possible to estimate the number of years it would take for the continental landmasses to reach an entropy state. The surprising result: 270 million years, just a small fraction (about 6 per cent) of the Earth's total history!

Obviously this calculation is not consistent with the reality that Earth scientists have calculated. Continental landmasses probably have existed for at least 4 billion years, and in approximately their present form (if not shape) for at least 650 million years. The oldest sedimentary rocks are from the **Proterozoic** Eon (see 'Perspectives' box). Thus we know that degradation and aggradation were taking place at least 570 million years ago. It must be concluded that the continents are being tectonically uplifted as they are eroded.

The principle of isostasy (Unit 24) relates to this uplift. According to isostatic principles, the removal of a large volume of rock (or other burden, such as the melting of an ice sheet) from an area of the crust leads to an upward movement of that part of the crust ('rebound'). In other words, erosion is compensated for by the upward movement of the lithosphere. If this is true, then it follows that erosion will go on indefinitely, because the crust will always replace what has been lost through degradation.

This also has implications for the study of landscapes. It may mean that landscapes retain their relief properties much longer than had previously been believed. For instance, topography such as that of the Appalachian highlands may retain its ridge-and-valley scenery (see Figures 27.15 and 27.16) for many millions of years after erosion *should* have drastically eroded them. Compensating isostatic uplift may do more than preserve continental landmasses; it also may preserve landscapes. We return to this theme several times later in Part Four, but as noted elsewhere, it is important to keep in mind the tectonic forces from below when assessing the erosional forces above.

Perspectives on the Human Environment

Using the Geological Time Scale

The **geological time scale**, shown in Figure 28.7, has evolved over many years of research and extrapolation, and it continues to be subject to revision. Its broad outlines, however, are stable and useful in many areas of physical geography. As the figure shows, the broadest division of Earth history is into eons, of which the most recent, the **Phanerozoic**, began about 570 million years ago, when the explosive growth of marine life heralded a new stage of planetary history. Because of the momentous nature of this 'Cambrian Explosion', all that preceded it is often referred to simply as the **Precambrian**.

The Phanerozoic Eon, as the chart shows, comprises only the most recent 12 per cent or so of Earth history. Rocks and fossils from this eon permit a more detailed timetable than is possible for earlier eons such as the Proterozoic and the Archean, although recent research is producing exciting information about these Precambrian times. The Phanerozoic Eon is divided into three eras, of which the **Paleozoic**, beginning with that Cambrian Period of mushrooming marine life, is the longest with more than 300 million years. Next comes the **Mesozoic Era**, when reptilian life as depicted in the movie *Jurassic Park* flourished. The final period of the Mesozoic was the Cretaceous, which came to a cataclysmic end possibly when a comet struck the Earth 65 million years ago, ending the dominance of reptiles and opening the Cenozoic Era, the age of mammals. (The violent transition from the Cretaceous (K) to the following Tertiary Period is referred to as the 'K/T boundary'.)

The Cenozoic Era, for obvious reasons (abundant fossils, 'younger' rocks, more environmental evidence), is the best known and therefore can be further divided into epochs. Around the middle of this era, the Earth's surface temperatures began to cool as the **Late Cenozoic Ice Age** came to dominate global environments. Ice accumulated on high mountains, glaciers filled valleys previously occupied by streams, and permanent ice developed on Antarctic land and on Arctic waters. As global temperatures see-sawed, alternating between long stretches of cold and shorter intervals of warmth, the overall trend was ever colder, making the **Pleistocene** Epoch the most frigid yet (since the Cryogenian glaciation or 'Snowball Earth' phase of the Neoproterozoic Period). Meanwhile, adaptable hominins had made their appearance (such as the Neanderthals— *Homo sapiens neanderthalensis*—and, more than 50,000 years ago, *Homo sapiens sapiens* (anatomically modern humans), the human species that rose to dominate the planet.

Note that the 'geological' time scale displays some anthropocentrism as well. The current epoch, beginning about 10,000 years ago, is designated the **Holocene**—but there is no evidence that this so-called epoch is anything other than another warm phase (interglacial) during the Pleistocene's successive glaciations. What is new about the Holocene is that it marks the rise of human civilization and the explosive growth of humanity's numbers; but to conclude that it also opens a new geological epoch is premature.

It is important to be familiar with the geological calendar in Figure 28.7, because the past in physical as well as human geography often is the key to the present. To better understand the magnitudes of the time periods involved, let us relate the Earth's lifespan to your age. If you are 20 years old and we take as the age of the Earth the time of the formation of the oldest rocks we can find (more than 4 billion years), consider the following:

1. One year of your life equals 230 million years of the Earth's. That puts you in the early Mesozoic just one year ago.
2. One month of your life equals just over 19 million years of the Earth's. The Rocky Mountains started forming just 3½ months ago.
3. One week of your life equals nearly 5 million years of the Earth's. The Pleistocene glaciations began three days ago.
4. One day of your life equals about 630,000 years of the Earth's. Human evolution was still in its early stages just yesterday at this time.

5. One hour of your life equals over 26,000 years of the Earth's. In that single hour, the human population grew from less than 100,000 to over 6 billion, and the major civilizations developed.

Where will we be one hour from now?

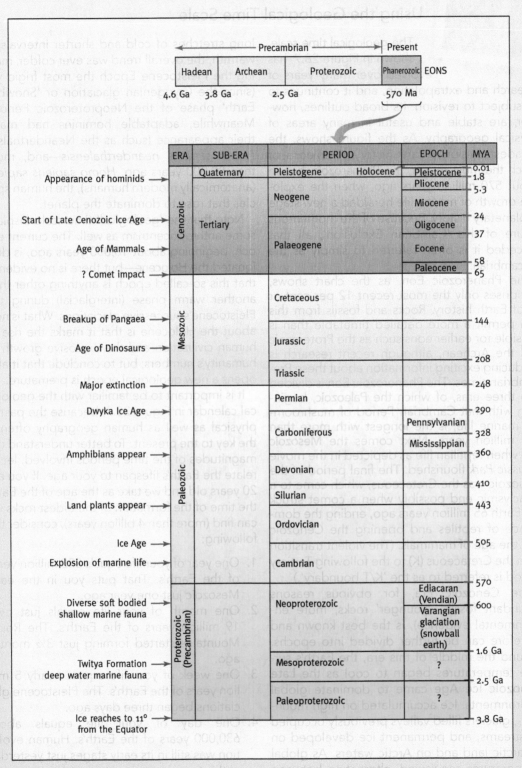

Figure 28.7 Geological time scale, calibrated according to dates established since the late 1990s.

KEY TERMS

aggradation *page 390*
degradation *page 390*
denudation *page 390*
erosion *page 392*
geological time scale *page 395*
gravity *page 390*
Holocene *page 395*
karst topography *page 393*
lahar *page 392*
landform *page 390*
landscape *page 390*
Late Cenozoic Ice Age *page 395*

Mesozoic Era *page 395*
Paleozoic *page 395*
Phanerozoic *page 395*
Pleistocene *page 395*
Precambrian *page 395*
primary landform *page 390*
Proterozoic *page 394*
secondary landform *page 390*
slope process *page 392*
tributaries *page 392*
trunk stream *page 392*
weathering *page 391*

REVIEW QUESTIONS

1. How does a secondary landform differ from a primary landform?
2. Briefly describe the processes of gradation.
3. What is meant by the term *weathering*?
4. What is the difference between *weathering* and *erosion*?
5. Describe the major time divisions of the geological time scale.

REFERENCES AND FURTHER READINGS

Butzer, K.W. 1976. *Geomorphology from the Earth*. New York: Harper & Row.

Curran, H.A., et al. 1984. *Atlas of Landforms*. New York: Wiley.

Goudie, A. 1995. *The Changing Earth: Rates of Geomorphological Processes*. Malden, Mass.: Blackwell.

Hancock, P.L., and B.J. Skinner, eds. 2001. *Oxford Companion to the Earth*. New York: Oxford Univ. Press.

Harland, W.B., et al. 1990. *A Geologic Time Scale 1989*. London/New York: Cambridge Univ. Press.

————. 1990. *A Geologic Time Scale 1989—Wallchart*. New York: Cambridge Univ. Press.

Huggett, R.J. 2002. *Fundamentals of Geomorphology*. London/New York: Routledge.

King, L.C. 1967. *The Morphology of the Earth: The Study and Synthesis of World Scenery*. New York: Hafner.

Ollier, C.D. 1981. *Tectonics and Landforms*. London/New York: Longman.

Phillips, J.D. 1998. *Earth Surface Systems: Order, Complexity and Scale*. Malden, Mass.: Blackwell.

Pitty, A.F. 1989. *Landforms and Time*. New York: Blackwell.

Ritter, D.F. 1986. *Process Geomorphology*, 2nd edn. Dubuque, Iowa: Wm. C. Brown.

Snead, R.E. 1980. *World Atlas of Geomorphic Features*. Huntington, NY: Krieger.

Stoddart, D. 1996. *Process and Form in Geomorphology*. London/New York: Routledge.

Thornbury, W.D. 1969. *Principles of Geomorphology*, 2nd edn. New York: Wiley.

 ## WEB RESOURCES

vulcan.wr.usgs.gov/Glossary/geo_time_scale.html A graphical representation of the geological time scale from the US Geological Survey, with links to the Cascades Volcano Observatory.

Unit 29

Weathering Processes

Objectives

- To differentiate the major categories of weathering—mechanical, chemical, and biological.

- To introduce and briefly discuss common weathering processes.

- To note the general environmental controls over weathering processes.

The fate of old stone and masonry buildings across Canada reminds us of nature's capacity to attack and destroy—not just with swirling streams, howling winds, or thundering waves, but quietly, persistently, and intensively. Nature's own structures are affected just as much as buildings and statues are. As detailed in Unit 44, the first steps in soil formation involve the decay and change of minerals from one type to another and the disintegration of rocks into smaller particles. The same processes that destroy abandoned buildings also contribute to the degradation of landforms. This quiet destruction proceeds in many ways. When the Sun heats an exposed wall, iron particles in that wall expand. At nighttime the minerals will contract because of the cooler temperatures. The bricks may expand more than the mortar that binds them. Day after day, this repeated, differential expansion will destroy the bond between brick and mortar. On vulnerable corners, bricks will fall.

The same process affects rocks, and when various minerals expand at different rates, they will be loosened. Moisture also plays a critical role. Water seeps into rocks along cracks and joints. Once there, the water exploits the weaknesses of the rocks, opening wider cracks and allowing moist air to penetrate. Soon the rocks undergo decay and/or are broken into pieces, and the next rainstorm carries the smaller fragments away. Weathering is thus a precursor to erosion.

Other forces also come into play in the silent, unspectacular breakdown of rocks. In combination, these processes are called *weathering*. Weathering is not merely a response to weather conditions. Weathering goes on continuously, not only at exposed surfaces but also beneath the ground and within rock strata. It is the first stage in that series of processes called denudation or degradation. Several kinds of weathering processes can be recognized. The two principal types are (1) *chemical weathering* and (2) *physical weathering*. Some scientists argue that **biological weathering** should be considered a distinct third type of weathering but it is essentially part of the other two groups of processes with plants and/or animals either releasing organic acids and causing or enhancing chemical weathering, or burrowing or extending roots into rocks and rock joints and causing, or adding to, physical processes. The terms are self-explanatory, and each will be examined in turn. But it must not be assumed that these processes are mutually exclusive or that if one occurs the others do not. In fact, weathering processes usually operate in some combination, and it is often difficult to separate the effects of each process.

The two types of weathering can be defined as follows:

1. **Chemical weathering** causes the decomposition, decay, or rotting of minerals. This takes place because of chemical changes in the minerals caused by *internal disruptive forces* such as water reacting with a mineral.
2. **Physical weathering** causes the disintegration of rocks without chemical changes occurring to the minerals. This is caused by *external disruptive forces* such as the growth of ice or salt crystals in cracks or joints in the rocks.

Emphasis has been placed on the importance of chemical weathering in academic journals and textbooks. Some scientists argue that certain chemical processes merely are manifested as physical consequences, for example, the freezing of water in a crack is essentially a chemical process, but the growth of ice crystals causes a crack in a rock to widen (a physical process).

Chemical Weathering

Rock minerals usually form under extremely different conditions from those at the Earth's surface. Primary minerals form in exceptionally high temperature and in the highly pressurized conditions of a magma chamber. Such minerals in rocks react with water carrying atmospheric and terrestrial chemicals and form secondary minerals, such as clay minerals and oxides. The stability of a mineral (or its tendency to change) is related to the type of crystallization environment in which it formed. The least stable minerals usually form in extremely hot (well over 1000°C) and pressurized magma chambers. An example of such a mineral is olivine, a mafic, green-coloured magnesium or iron silicate—$(Mg, Fe)_2SiO_4$—mineral that crystallizes out of magma at high temperatures and in high-pressure environments. When exposed at the Earth's surface it is rapidly altered to form clay minerals and soluble ions. Quartz (silicon dioxide, SiO_2), on the other hand, crystallizes at much lower temperatures (about 500–600°C) and pressures and is very stable, remaining in the surface environment for millions of years (quartz cycling takes about 10^8 years). It is possible to construct a continuum of mineral stability/weatherability (Figure 29.1).

Seventy five per cent of the continental surface area is composed of sedimentary rocks (52 per cent of the continental surfaces is shale) and only 25 per cent is composed of igneous rocks. Most studies of weathering have been done on igneous rock types. This is because it is easier to see and measure the effect of weathering on primary minerals than on secondary minerals or clastic rocks.

Rock Type

The most important influence on weathering is rock type. This is because it determines:

1. composition, or mineral content;
2. texture, or the size and shape, of the minerals or rock fragments;
3. porosity, or the percentage of voids (pores) per unit volume of the rock;
4. structure (layers, joints, cracks, etc.);
5. bulk properties such as elasticity, strength, and hardness.

Water

The second most important factor in terms of weathering is water. There are three important aspects: availability of water, water temperature, and water chemicals.

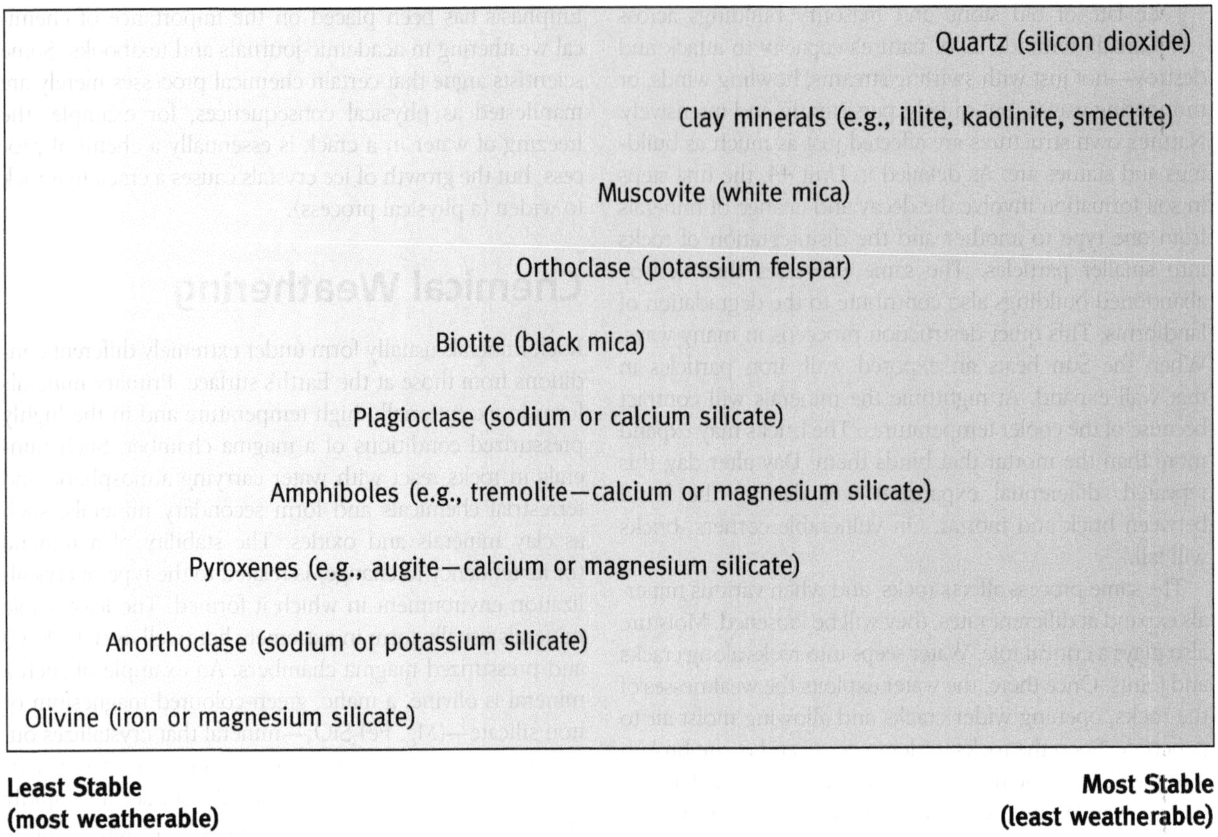

Quartz (silicon dioxide)

Clay minerals (e.g., illite, kaolinite, smectite)

Muscovite (white mica)

Orthoclase (potassium felspar)

Biotite (black mica)

Plagioclase (sodium or calcium silicate)

Amphiboles (e.g., tremolite—calcium or magnesium silicate)

Pyroxenes (e.g., augite—calcium or magnesium silicate)

Anorthoclase (sodium or potassium silicate)

Olivine (iron or magnesium silicate)

Least Stable
(most weatherable)

Most Stable
(least weatherable)

Figure 29.1 Continuum of mineral stability/weatherability.

The Availability of Water In wet or humid environments, granites and other rocks appear rotten or decomposed because of the weathering of feldspars and biotites, which only leaves quartz grains (a process called *granular disintegration*). In very dry conditions rocks appear fresh with no trace of weathering; for example, many ancient buildings and statues in the Egyptian desert that are thousands of years old show no weathering. A good example of the importance of humidity to weathering is Cleopatra's Needle (an ancient syenite obelisk, Figure 29.2), which was erected in Central Park in New York City in 1881. It had stood in Aswan for about 3500 years and was still pristine when taken from Egypt. It lost over 90 kg (200 lbs) of material in the first two years of exposure in New York due to *spallation*, or spalling (the falling off of successive layers of weathered material caused by salt hydration). Its base has also suffered a great deal from the same process. Now it is virtually impossible to read the hieroglyphs because it has been so badly weathered except on its western face, presumably because this side has been sheltered from winds.

Water Temperature The temperature of the water is very important because it influences the rate at which chemical reactions take place. Most reactions double with every 10°C increase in temperature. Thus, chemical weathering should be (and is) more intense and rapid in humid tropical areas than in temperate or polar environments (see Figure 29.12).

Chemicals in the Water Precipitation and groundwater are not pure. Pollution from coal-powered industries such as power generation and iron and steel, plus pollution from traffic in urban areas, has caused the lowering of the pH of various types of precipitation ('acid rain', 'acid snow'). This has been seen in many parts of southern Ontario, which is downwind of US Rust Belt industries and also generates its own pollution. When water vapour condenses in the atmosphere, it assimilates CO_2 from the air. The carbon dioxide content of precipitation can be increased by between 10 and 30 per cent by this process (atmospheric content: 0.03 per cent; precipitation content: 0.3–0.9 per cent). The CO_2 dissolves in water and forms a weak carbonic acid. This process is called **carbonation**. Additional carbon dioxide is added as the water infiltrates through decomposing organic material at and close to the soil surface (peat, mor humus). Bacteria and other microfauna in the topsoil consume organic matter and give off carbon dioxide. In moist aerated soils, bacterial activity can increase the carbon dioxide content of the soil air by over 10 per cent. When carbonic acid comes in contact with carbonate rocks such as limestone (calcite: $CaCO_3$), it reacts and produces calcium bicarbonate ($Ca(HCO_3)_2$), which is water soluble and is

LINK

Figure 29.2A Cleopatra's Needle, a syenite obelisk in Aswan, Egypt, *c.* 1880, prior to its removal to New York City.

Figure 29.2B Salt hydration has caused extensive weather damage to Cleopatra's Needle, now in New York City's Central Park.

removed in solution as water from precipitation or ground-water moves through the rock.

$$\text{Rock (CaCO}_3) + \text{H}_2\text{O} + \text{CO}_2 \leftrightarrows \text{Calcium bicarbonate (Ca(HCO}_3)_2)$$

In this way, exposed and buried limestone surfaces become etched as the joints are widened, producing *karren, lapis,* or *limestone pavements* (Figure 29.3). These are formed of *pinnacles* or *clints* ('paving slabs') separated by the widened joints, called *cutters* or *grykes*. If this process is continued the joints are widened even more and subsurface tunnels and caves form. These may collapse to form *swallow holes, pots,* or *dolines*. This process and these features are very characteristic of *karst topography* (see Unit 35).

LINK

On emergence from the rock on cave walls or at a spring, the reverse process occurs and calcium carbonate is deposited as various types of *speleothems* or *dripstone, flowstone,* or *pool stone*—*stalagmites, stalactites, straws, columns, organ pipes, tufa,* or *travertine*. The water drips or runs off and the carbon dioxide is degassed into the atmosphere.

The rates of limestone solution are related to climate, especially to the amount of precipitation, which, of course, varies considerably from one geographical location to another (Table 29.1).

As can be seen from these rates, **solution weathering** is especially vigorous in humid areas, where carbonate formations such as limestones or dolomites are often deeply pitted and grooved and the evidence of dissolution and decay are prominent. In arid areas, however, these rock types stand up much better, and although they may show some evidence of solution weathering at the surface, they appear in general to be much more resistant strata.

Solution weathering is very important in other rock types, too. Studies of the Karkevagge Valley in northern Sweden, close to the Arctic Circle, indicate that as much as half of the denudation was caused by solution from an area dominated by steep slopes on metamorphic rocks.

Figure 29.3   Karst topography, Yorkshire, UK: an outcrop of limestone weathered by carbonic acid in precipitation to form pinnacles and cutters known as limestone pavement.

Table 29.1   Rates of Limestone Removal by Solution, Selected Locations

Location	Annual Precipitation	Annual Removal by Solution
Los Alamos, New Mexico	25–40 mm	<1 m³/km²
Somerset Island, Nunavut	~130 mm	2 m³/km²
Central France	1500–2000 mm	24 m³/km²
Indonesia	~3000 mm	>83 m³/km²

Other kinds of mineral alteration processes also are important in chemical weathering:

Hydrolysis-Hydration   When minerals are moistened, **hydrolysis** occurs, producing not only a chemical alteration but expansion (hydration) in volume as well; for example, the addition of water to iron produces iron hydroxide. This expansion can contribute to the breakdown of rocks. Hydrolysis, it should be noted, is not simply a matter of moistening, it is a true chemical alteration, and minerals are transformed into other mineral compounds in the process.

For example, feldspar hydrolysis yields clay minerals, and a carbonate or bicarbonate of potassium, sodium, or calcium in solution. The new minerals tend to be less resistant and weaker than their predecessors. In granite boulders, hydrolysis combines with other processes to cause the outer shells to flake off in what looks like a miniature version of exfoliation. This is **spheroidal weathering** (Figure 29.4), and it affects other igneous rocks besides granite.

Oxidation-Reduction   When minerals in rocks react with oxygen in the air, the chemical process is known as **oxidation**. There is plenty of evidence of this process in the reddish colour of soils in many parts of the world and in the reddish-brown hue of layers exposed in such places as the Grand Canyon (see Figure 23.8). The products of oxidation are compounds of iron and aluminum (see Figure 45.13). In tropical areas, oxidation is a very dominant chemical weathering process. *Reduction* is the opposite process. Here oxygen is taken out of the mineral in aerobic conditions to form ferrous iron.

Chelation or Complexing   In chelation, organic acids such as salicylate are supplied by leachate from plants and their bacterial symbionts, lichen (symbionts of fungi

From the Fieldnotes

Figure 29.4 'Walking along the east-facing slope of the Swaziland Lowveld, checking the geological map against rock exposures. Light-coloured granite, rich in silica, suddenly changes to what the map suggests is dolerite (but another map shows it as "dark, large-grained granite"). Whatever the analysis, the exposure of this darker rock is marked by an expanse of boulders, most of them rounded and many undergoing spheroidal weathering. Peeled the shells off the boulder on the right until I reached the yet unaffected core; the one at left is for contrast.'

and algae), or organic matter such as peat. The chelates interact with minerals in the rocks by changing the acidity of the water through the introduction of organic acids and carbon dioxide. These alter the exposed mineral surfaces by the nitrification process and affect water retention. This makes the minerals more soluble and available for solutional removal.

Hydrothermal Alteration *Hydrothermal alteration* involves the movement of super-hot geothermal water laden with minerals in solution through rocks. This action causes a mineral change to occur. The process is often associated with proximity to magma chambers or occurs during metamorphism. One of the best examples of this process is found in granite where the feldspars are sometimes altered to kaolinite (china clay).

Chemical weathering is the more effective agent of rock destruction in humid areas, because moisture promotes chemical processes, and is very important in all environments. Physical or mechanical weathering is important in dry and cold zones. But water plays an important role in the dry as well as the moist environments. The growth of destructive salt crystals in porous rocks in arid areas, for instance, takes place only after some moisture has entered the pores and then evaporated, thereby triggering the crystals' growth. Even in the driest deserts small weathering pits or *tafoni* occur on rock surfaces. These are formed by

dew or a thin ephemeral layer of water deposited by infrequent rainfall. The role of water in all rock-destroying processes is paramount.

Physical Weathering

Physical weathering, also called *mechanical weathering* (Figure 29.5), involves the destruction of rocks through the imposition of certain stresses. This process leads to the disintegration of rocks without any chemical changes taking place. By fragmenting rocks, physical weathering processes increase the total surface area that can be attacked by other (chemical) processes. Physical weathering processes have been considered more important in arid cold or hot environments where water is lacking because of insignificant amounts of precipitation or where it is locked up in snow and ice. Today, many scientists consider most physical weathering processes to be manifestations of chemical changes even where water is scarce.

The type of debris formed by physical weathering processes is determined to a very large extent by two variables: the lithology of the rock (rock type), and the joint structure of the rock. Physical weathering is initiated by the formation of cracks in rock. Crack formation takes place in three ways:

1. differential expansion of the rock minerals (by processes such as *dilitation*, or unloading, and *exfoliation*);

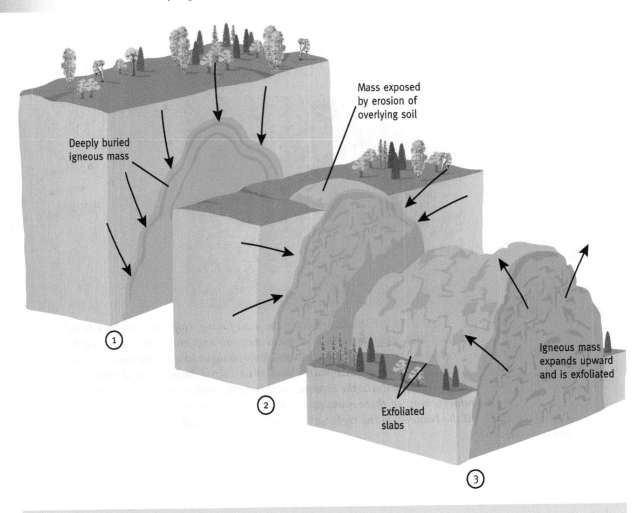

Deeply buried
igneous mass

Mass exposed
by erosion of
overlying soil

Igneous mass
expands upward
and is exfoliated

Exfoliated
slabs

① ② ③

Figure 29.5 Mechanical exfoliation of an igneous mass occurs after the erosion of overlying soil and weathered rock allows the mass to expand upward, fracturing into thin slabs of rock parallel to its exposed surface.

2. chemical decomposition along joints, bedding planes, etc. or at contacts between different rock types;
3. crystal growth processes such as the expansion of freezing water (*congelifraction* or frost weathering) or the expansion of salt crystals in the rock (*haloclasty.*)

Dilitation

LINK

Dilitation is also called *unloading, exfoliation, sheeting,* or *spalling.* This process is caused by stress release or the removal by erosion of rock material or overburden that has pressed down on subjacent rocks. When the stress is released the rocks often suffer unloading and cracks form nearly parallel to the surface. This process can also occur because of the shrinkage (in the dry season) and swelling (in the wet season) of some clay minerals that force the layers of rock apart, causing various types of joint-like fractures in igneous rocks (pseudo-bedding), and is related to the development of *exfoliation domes* such as *inselbergs* (*bornhardts*), *kopjes* (Figure 29.6), *tors* (Figure 29.7), and

other landforms created by this process of unloading and exfoliation, such as the possible development of the classical U-shaped or catenary glaciated valleys seen in mountainous areas.

Congelifraction or Frost Weathering

We are aware of the power of ice to damage roads and sidewalks and to split open water pipes (water increases in volume by about 9 per cent as it freezes). Similarly, the water contained by rocks—in cracks, joints, even pores—can freeze into crystals that shatter even the strongest igneous rock masses. This ice can produce about 1890 metric tonnes of pressure for every 0.1 m².

Of course, **frost action** operates only where winter brings subfreezing temperatures. In high-altitude zones, where extreme cooling and warming alternate, the water that penetrates into the rocks' joint planes or other cracks freezes and thaws repeatedly during a single season, wedging apart large blocks and boulders

Figure 29.6   An exfoliated rock outcrop in southern Africa known as a *kopje*.

Figure 29.7   A *tor*, a ruinous exfoliation dome attacked by glaciation and/or periglaciation, at Haytor, Dartmoor, UK.

Figure 29.8 This massive granite boulder in Joshua Tree National Park, California, has been split in two along a joint plane by temperature fluctuations and the wedging effect of moisture. So far neither part of the boulder has been dislodged from the place where it was wedged apart, but gravity may act differently on the two masses as time goes on.

and separating the fragments completely (Figure 29.8). Then, depending on the local relief, these pieces of rock may either remain more or less where they are, awaiting dislodgement by wind or precipitation, or they may roll or fall downslope and collect at the base of the mountains.

When the fragments of rock accumulate near their original location, they form a **rock sea** (Figure 29.9), also known as *blockfield* or *felsenmeer*. When the rock fragments roll downslope, they create a *scree slope* or **talus cone**. If you have been in the Rocky Mountains or other mountainous areas in western North America, you have probably seen such piles of loose boulders. They often lie at steep angles and seem ready to collapse (Figure 29.10). The same process happens on a very small scale when water freezes in the pores of a rock. As ice crystals form they cause the breakdown of the rocks by granular disintegration and the formation of sands and silts.

Rocky soils can also reflect the action of frost. For a long time physical geographers wondered what pro-

duced the remarkable geometrical structures of stone that mark the soils in Arctic regions (see Figure 39.9). These *stone nets* are created when ice forms on the underside of rocks in the soil, a process that tends to wedge the rock upward and sideways. Eventually, the rocks meet and form lines and patterns that look as though they were laid out by ancient civilizations for some ceremonial purpose.

In arid regions, too, mechanical weathering occurs. There, the development and growth of salt crystals has an effect similar to that of ice. When water in the pores of such rocks as sandstone evaporates, small residual salt crystals form. The growth of those tiny crystals pries the rocks apart (in a process called **salt burst hydration**, salt wedging, or haloclasty) and weakens their internal structure. The salt is supplied by processes such as the chemical weathering of minerals to produce salts in rocks, the passage of saline groundwater through the rocks, and, in coastal areas, by sea spray.

Three mechanisms are involved in salt weathering:

1. the growth of salt crystals from solution in confined spaces in the rocks (pores, cracks, etc.);
2. the expansion of salt crystals in confined spaces as the rock is heated during the warmest part of the day or months of the year;
3. the hydration of salt crystals (the addition of water)—salt burst hydration.

Salt weathering is especially important in arid areas, where evapotranspiration is greater than precipitation, because such areas experience the capillary rise of saline groundwater. As a result, caves and hollows form on the face of scarps, and the water and wind may remove the loosened grains and reinforce the process (see 'Perspectives' box).

The mineral grains that rocks are made of have different rates of expansion and contraction in response to temperature changes. Therefore, the bonds between them may be loosened by continual temperature fluctuations. Although difficult to replicate in the laboratory, this kind of weathering may play a role in the physical disintegration of rocks. Over many thousands of years, daily temperature fluctuations could well have a weakening effect on exposed rocks. But other weathering processes also enter the picture—as the contacts between the grains are loosened, moisture enters and promotes decay of the minerals.

Biological Aspects

As noted above, biological processes can be classed as either chemical or physical types of weathering depending on the process involved. We know that weathering is very important to soil formation (see Unit 44). It is through the breakdown of rocks and the accumulation of a layer of minerals that plants can grow, and

From the Fieldnotes

Figure 29.9 *'Looking up this steep slope formed by loose, angular boulders, I wondered whether there was a risk of sudden collapse. But this felsenmeer (rock sea), developed from mechanical weathering of quartzite, was stable. After having been pried apart, the angular fragments of various sizes have moved very little, creating a distinct element in this Montana landscape.'*

the roots and other parts of these plants, in turn, contribute to the weathering processes. But it is likely that the role of plant roots in forcing open bedding planes and joints is somewhat overestimated. The roots follow paths of least resistance and adapt to every small irregularity in the rock. Roots certainly keep cracks open once they have been formed. More importantly, however, areas of roots tend to collect decaying organic material, which is involved in the chemical weathering processes.

One of the most important aspects of the action of plants and animals is the mixing of soil by burrowing animals and worms (**bioturbation**). Another interesting aspect is the action of lichens, a symbiotic combination of algae and fungi, that live on bare rock surfaces. Lichens draw minerals from the rock by ion exchange (*chelation*; see 'Perspectives' box, Unit 44). The swelling and contraction of lichens as they alternately get wet

and dry may also cause small particles of rock to fall off.

Technically, humans are also agents of biological process. Human activity contributes to various forms of weathering in a number of ways. (1) By polluting the air with various substances, we greatly accelerate some chemical weathering, especially in and around large urban centres (see Unit 19). (2) By quarrying and mining, we accelerate mechanical, chemical, and biological weathering through the exposure of deep strata to these processes (Figure 29.11). (3) By farming and fertilizing, we influence soil-formation processes, sometimes destructively. Through dam construction, excavation of canals, surface mining, deforestation, urban development, road building, and myriad other activities, humans have altered and continue to make significant modifications of the Earth's surface—and may have become one of the planet's most important geomorphological agents.

Canadian Geographers in the Field

'Once in a while geomorphological processes produce intriguing and "grotesque-like" forms within the landscape. This example from Switzerland called "Les Pyramides" is found in the Val d'Herens in Valais. Here, due to differential weathering, a large Late Glacial lateral moraine that contains occasional large boulders has been disaggregated by slope processes due to rainwash resulting in these capped pyramidal cones of glacial debris (till) being left upstanding in the manner of "hoodoos", as can be observed in parts of southern Alberta and Saskatchewan.'

John Menzies, B.Sc., Ph.D., P.Geo., is Professor of Geography and Earth Sciences at Brock University.

Figure 29.11 Human impact on the natural environment. Open-pit mining leaves huge scars on natural landscapes. This was one of the largest pits in Canada, the Iron Ore Corporation of Canada's Schefferville Mine in the Canadian Shield near the Quebec–Labrador border, which was closed in 1983.

Figure 29.10 Talus slope in the southern interior of British Columbia.

Geography of Weathering

As noted, particular weathering processes are more prevalent and effective in certain areas than in others. In very general terms, soils are much thicker in equatorial and tropical areas than in the polar and subpolar latitudes, a contrast that reflects the comparative intensities of weathering in those locales. The heat, high humidity, and often copious rainfall of low-latitude zones are conducive to particularly active weathering. But certain processes occur only under specific conditions. For example, the wedging effect of frost action occurs only in higher latitudes (the **D** climates with their strong seasonal and diurnal temperature contrasts are a good indicator) and at high, frost-affected altitudes. Again, stone nets or patterned grounds of various kinds are formed only where a special set of conditions prevails. This happens in Arctic latitudes, yet not all Arctic areas have patterned ground.

It would be impractical to devise a small-scale global map of weathering incidence because the various processes are not confined to specific regions and different processes are at work in the same areas. But the maps of world temperature (Figure 7.10), world precipitation (Figure 11.16), world climate (Figure 16.2), and world soils (Figure 45.15) provide some indication of what might be expected to happen in particular places. Where moisture (as indicated by the rainfall map) and temperature are high, weathering is intense. Where temperature ranges are high and moisture is low (as in **BW** and **BS** climate regions), mechanical weathering may take a more prominent role, and chemical weathering and biological weathering can be expected to have a somewhat less effective role. In the higher latitudes, the dominant form of mechanical weathering is frost action.

The regional geological map also must be consulted. In regions where precipitation is low, limestone and dolomite are quite resistant to weathering. But where temperatures are moderate to high and where moisture is ample, chemical weathering of limestone and dolomite can be so effective that the whole landscape may be transformed. This special case of chemical weathering forms the basis of Unit 35. In the discussion of the mass removal of loose Earth material in Unit 32, focus is placed on the great rivers that sweep vast amounts of rock fragments and particles downstream. It should not be forgotten that much of that material was first loosened by the quiet, relentless processes of weathering. Gravity acts on weathered materials prior to their removal by streams, and its important influence on slope stability is explored in Unit 30.

The Weathering Zone

The **weathering zone** is the weathered material (*saprolite*) lying above unweathered fresh rock. The junction between the weathering zone and the underlying rock is called the *weathering front* (Figure 29.12). The weathering front is parallel to the surface but usually has more variation in depth/height. The depth of the weathering zone and the shape of the weathering front are determined by the joint pattern of the rock. This is because this pattern causes differential weathering. If the joints are close together, more chemical weathering and decomposition of the rock can occur, so the weathering zone is deeper. If the joints are widely spaced there is not as much decomposition, so the weathering zone will be thinner. In the humid tropics (and in other areas), slope processes and streams have eroded a lot of the saprolite and have exhumed and exposed the higher parts of the weathering front as rock residuals called

LINK

inselbergs (*bornhardts*) or *tors* (*kopjes*). Such landscapes are called *etchplains* and the process is called *etchplanation*. In some parts of the saprolite rock *corestones* remain unweathered where joints are widely spaced so that weathering cannot reach/has not reached the centre of the joint- or crack-bounded block of rock. These are often seen in road cuts.

It is possible to define two types of weathering zones at either end of a continuum:

1. *Shallow weathering zones* (usually only a few mm or cm deep) are characteristic of hot and cold arid environments and formerly glaciated parts of the temperate zone. They are also found on the rock residuals in humid tropical areas. In these areas erosion rates are much higher than weathering rates. The weathering zone is composed of sandy material with large amounts of weatherable minerals.

2. *Deep weathering zones* (usually very deep, e.g., 50 m, 120 m, or 270 m deep) are found in the humid tropical zone and in unglaciated areas of the temperate zone. They are associated with rock residuals and corestones in areas where weathering rates are greater than the rates of erosion. They are characterized by a clayey weathering zone that lacks weatherable minerals. This type of weathering zone may have developed during the warmer, more humid parts of the Cenozoic in the temperate zone and has subsequently been removed by glaciations in many parts. Some scientists believe that it was possibly the source for a lot of the till material deposited by the Pleistocene ice sheets.

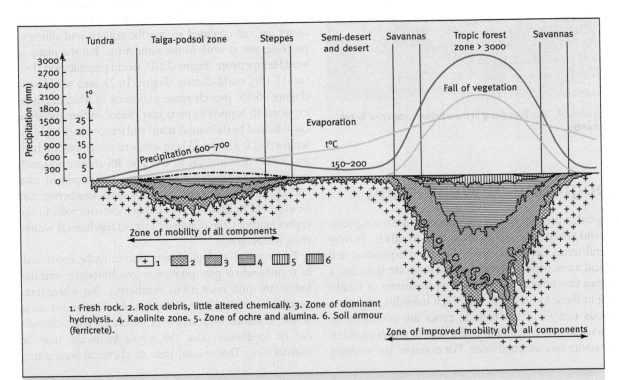

Figure 29.12 Depth of weathering zones in relation to climate and latitude (after Strakhov, 1967).

Perspectives on the Human Environment

The Dust Bowl

In the 1930s the Canadian Prairie provinces and the American Plains states suffered through the Dust Bowl, but today they are very productive grain-growing areas. Kathleen Laird, an ecologist at Queen's University, has reconstructed the past climatic conditions of these areas using diatoms (water-dwelling algae), which indicate salinity and therefore aridity. Her research suggests that the region has had repeated droughts for thousands of years. It has also shown that the last 700 years have been wetter than the average. This work indicates that dust-bowl conditions are not unusual.

Laird took diatoms and water samples from lakes throughout the region and then homed in on Moon Lake, North Dakota. This lake had no streams draining into or out of it, and was therefore reliant on rainfall and evaporation. She took diatom samples from sediments on the lake bottom that had accumulated since the end of the Wisconsinan glaciation (which ended approximately 10,000 years ago). The sediments were radiocarbon-dated, and diatom numbers and species were correlated with the salinity levels of the lake sediments.

Laird's findings indicate that extreme dryness persisted for very long periods and occurred more frequently in the past. The worst periods of drought occurred between 200 and 370 CE, 700 and 850 CE, and 1000 and 1200 CE. The cause of those ancient droughts is unknown, but it is known that poor farming techniques and inadequate land-management practices were definite contributors to the 1930s Dust Bowl.

---

* Much of the information here is from a short article in *Discover* (Apr. 1997).

The Study of Weathering Rates

It is quite difficult to study weathering rates in rocks unless there is some method of accurately dating the time of exposure of the surface of the rock involved. One way of knowing this is to use buildings, statues, or tombstones that have this information on them. This technique was first used by the great Scottish geologist Sir Archibald Geikie in the latter part of the nineteenth century and has been used by many scientists to work out the rate of weathering of different rock types in different environments. There is, however, a controversy over whether the rate of weathering remains constant over time or if it increases, decreases, or reaches an equilibrium state with the environment after a number of years.

A second technique is to collect samples of different rock types and 'weather' them either by exposure to the elements (e.g., on the roof of a university building) or in a laboratory setting. This method requires extrapolation and estimation of rates from a limited time of research.

A third method uses an engineering approach based on the weathering of bricks and stone building materials to predict the severity of weathering in certain areas. This is the case with the Weathering Index of the American Society for Testing and Materials. The Index is based on climatic data (such as the maximum, minimum, and average temperature and precipitation; temperature range; length of the frost-free period) and takes into account three important variables to define and map the severity of weathering (not separated into chemical or physical types) in the US:

1. the average annual number of freeze/thaw cycles;
2. the average annual winter rainfall/precipitation;
3. the dates of the first and last winter frosts.

The Index is dimensionless. Areas below 100 are rated as having negligible weathering, while areas between 100 and 500 are defined as having moderate weathering and those above 500 are considered to have severe weathering (Figure 29.13). The weathering areas and their boundaries can be continued across the border into the southern parts of Canada.

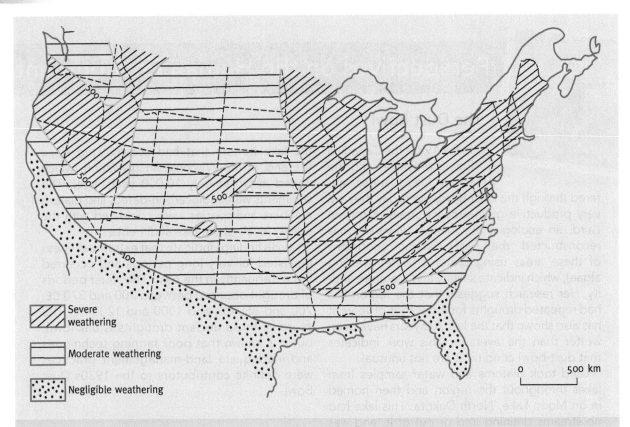

Figure 29.13 Weathering regions in the United States based on the Weathering Index (after the American Society for Testing and Materials: see Web Resources).

Legend:
- Severe weathering
- Moderate weathering
- Negligible weathering

0   500 km

KEY TERMS

biological weathering   *page 399*
bioturbation   *page 407*
carbonation   *page 400*
chemical weathering   *page 399*
frost action   *page 404*
hydrolysis   *page 402*
oxidation   *page 402*

physical weathering   *page 399*
rock sea   *page 406*
salt burst hydration   *page 406*
solution weathering   *page 401*
spheroidal weathering   *page 402*
talus cone   *page 406*
weathering zone   *page 410*

REVIEW QUESTIONS

1. Why is frost action such an aggressive mechanical weathering agent?
2. How does spheroidal weathering occur?
3. Under what environmental conditions could chemical weathering be most aggressive?

4. What is meant by the term *dust bowl*?
5. What is biological weathering?

REFERENCES AND FURTHER READINGS

Birkeland, P.W. 1984. *Pedology, Weathering, and Geomorphological Research*, 2nd edn. London/New York: Oxford Univ. Press.

Bland, W., and D. Rolls. 1998. *Weathering: An Introduction to the Scientific Principles*. New York: Oxford Univ. Press.

Carroll, D. 1970. *Rock Weathering*. New York: Plenum.

Colman, S.M., and D.P. Dethiers, eds. 1986. *Rates of Chemical Weathering of Rocks and Minerals*. Orlando, Fla: Academic Press.

Cooke, R.U., and J.C. Doornkamp. 1990. *Geomorphology in Environmental Management*, 2nd edn. Oxford: Clarendon Press.

Geikie, A. 1880. 'Rock Weathering as Illustrated by Edinburgh Churchyards', *Proceedings, Royal Society of Edinburgh* 10: 518–22.

Keller, W.D. 1962. *The Principles of Chemical Weathering*, 2nd edn. Columbia, Mo.: Lucas Brothers.

Linton, D.L. 1955. 'The Problem of Tors', *Geographical Journal* 121: 470–87.

Meierding, T.C. 1981. 'Marble Tombstone Weathering Rates: A Transect of the United States', *Physical Geography* 2, 1: 1–18.

Ollier, C.D. 1984. *Weathering*, 2nd edn. London/New York: Longman.

Pope, G.A. 2000. 'Weathering of Petroglyphs: Direct Assessment and Implications for Dating Methods', *Antiquity* 74: 833–43.

——— et al. 2002. 'Geomorphology's Role in the Study of Weathering of Cultural Stone', *Geomorphology* 47, 2–4: 211–25.

Rapp, A. 1960. 'Recent Development of Mountain Slopes in Karkevagge and Surroundings, Northern Scandinavia', *Geografiska Annaler* 41: 65–200.

Reiche, P. 1962. *A Survey of Weathering Processes and Products*. Albuquerque: Univ. of New Mexico Publications in Geology, No. 3.

Ritter, D.F. 1986. *Process Geomorphology*, 2nd edn. Dubuque, Iowa: Wm. C. Brown.

Robinson, D.A., and R.B.G. Williams, eds. 1994. *Rock Weathering and Landform Evolution* New York: Wiley.

Selby, M.J. 1982. *Hillslope Materials and Processes*. London/New York: Oxford Univ. Press.

Statham, I. 1977. *Earth Surface Sediment Transport*. London/New York: Oxford Univ. Press.

Whalley, B., and P.J. McCreevy. 1998. *Weathering*. Malden, Mass.: Blackwell.

Winkler, E.M. 1965. 'Weathering Rates as Exemplified by Cleopatra's Needle, New York City', *Journal of Geological Education* 13, 2: 50–2.

———. 1980. 'Historical Implications in the Complexity of Destructive Salt Weathering: Cleopatra's Needle, New York', *Association for Preservation Technology, Bulletin* 12, 2: 94–102.

——— and E.J. Wilhelm. 1970. 'Salt Burst Hydration Processes in Architectural Stone in Urban Atmosphere', *Geological Society of America, Bulletin* 81: 567–72.

Yatsu, E. 1988. *The Nature of Weathering*. Osaka, Japan: Sozosha.

Young, A. 1975. *Slopes*, 2nd edn. London/New York: Longman.

 WEB RESOURCES

soil.gsfc.nasa.gov/soilform/weather.htm This NASA site gives background information on all types of weathering processes, with links to other pages covering soil formation and types, creation of landforms, and mineral classification.

www.astm.org/Standards/C216.htm The American Society for Testing and Materials website gives information on the ASTM Weathering Index.

www.drought.unl.edu The University of Nebraska's National Drought Mitigation Center presents background information on the causes and effects of drought, with historical descriptions of the dust bowl, as well as El Niño data.

Unit 30

Slope Processes

Objectives

- To demonstrate the role of gravity in promoting slope processes in weathered materials.

- To discuss the various types of slope processes and the circumstances under which they usually occur.

In 1998, when thousands of Hondurans were buried by cold lahars as Hurricane Mitch devastated the hills and mountains of this Central American country, the world was again reminded of the dangers posed by unstable slopes. As this ferocious storm slowly made its way across the heart of Honduras for two days, it unleashed almost 2000 mm of wind-driven rain, which mobilized previously deposited blankets of volcanic ash and triggered massive lahars and flooding. Almost 10,000 people died, 1.5 million were left homeless, more than 70 per cent of the country's infrastructure was washed away, and agricultural losses alone resulted in an economic crisis that will continue for the foreseeable future. This disaster was, admittedly, a rather spectacular example of the hazards posed by slope processes. But in all mountain zones, rocks, soil, and other unconsolidated materials can move in quantities ranging from individual boulders to entire hillsides. It happens at different rates of speed. Some rocks actually fall downslope, bounding along and occasionally even landing on highways or railway lines, while other material moves slowly, almost imperceptibly.

There are times when the signs of coming collapse are unmistakable and people at risk can be warned. At other times a collapse occurs in an instant. In 1970 a minor earthquake loosened a small mass of rock material high up on Mount Huascaran in the Peruvian Andes. This material fell about 650 m down the upper part of the slopes. Normally it would have done little damage, but at an elevation of about 6000 m it happened to land on a steep slope of snow and loose rock material on the mountainside. The falling mass, the snow, and the loose material combined and roared down the slope in a rock avalanche. According to later calculations, the combined debris took only two minutes to move 14.5 km, in the process reaching a speed of 270–360 km/h. By the time it stopped, it had travelled 16 km. The loss of life is estimated to have exceeded 25,000 persons. No trace was ever found of entire communities, in particular Yungay (Figure 30.1), which alone accounted for the loss of 17,000 lives. Clearly, slope processes can be devastating.

Slopes are very important elements of the physical landscape. In fact, there are few naturally occurring flat areas other than old lake beds. Slopes have a great influence on the character of an area. Good examples are the steep, debris-mantled slopes of the Rocky and Coast Mountains or the gently undulating till plains of the Prairies and southern Ontario.

Differences in slope form are obviously related to variations of bedrock, climate, glacial history, fluvial erosion, and human-induced changes. In many parts of the Earth—for example, in the mountains of western Canada—slopes have adjusted to ice-age conditions, that is, to the presence of glacial ice that has filled the valleys and eroded and held up the very steep valley sides. However, the ice has melted and many of these slopes, in an attempt to bring their form into equilibrium with the current conditions (i.e., the lack of ice), are undergoing an adjustment (undergoing **relaxation**) by failing.

Figure 30.1 The 1970 debris avalanche that destroyed the Peruvian town of Yungay (left of centre).

LINK

LINK

Slope processes are common all over Canada. Besides in the Rocky and Coast Mountains, they also occur along the sides of the St Lawrence Valley and the valley sides in the Prairies. Unstable slopes occur around the James Bay lowlands, along the shores of the Great Lakes, and on all sea coasts. The permafrost areas of the Canadian North are also affected by slope processes. This area will see more slope failures caused by the melting of the permafrost as global warming continues. Slope deposits associated with volcanic centres indicate past activity similar to that seen during the eruption of Mount St Helens in 1980. Some very large mass movements (e.g., the Frank Slide in Alberta and the Hope Slide in British Columbia) have been associated with earthquake shocks.

The force of gravity plays a major role in the modification of landscape. Gravity pulls all materials down towards *base level*. Solid bedrock can withstand this force because it is strong and tightly bonded. But as weathering or the shock of an earthquake loosens a fragment of bedrock, the first motion of that mass is likely to be caused by gravity. Slopes consist of many different kinds of material. Some are made of solid bedrock; others consist of bedrock as well as loose rock fragments; still others are composed of regolith and

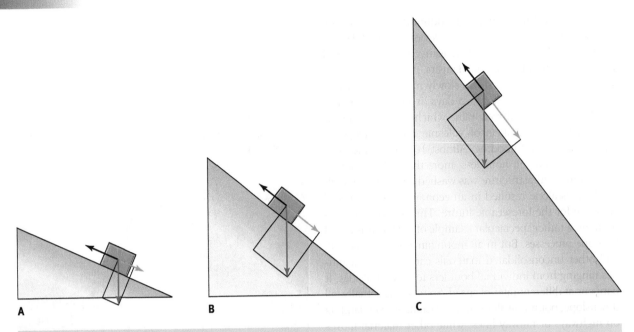

A   **B**   **C**

Figure 30.2   Slope angle and slide potential. In this drawing the length of the green arrow represents the amount of shearing stress on a block of rock placed against a slope. On the low-angle slope (A), the shearing stress is low, and is not enough to dislodge the rock. On the medium-angle slope (B), the shearing stress is greater, and the downslope pull is nearly enough to move the rock. Note how long the green arrow has become on the high-angle slope (C)—it exceeds the friction that held the rock against the other slopes, and the rock will tumble down. Thus the greater the slope angle, the stronger the shearing stress or downward pull on particles large and small. (In these diagrams the black arrows indicate friction; the red arrows, gravity.)

soil. Two key factors are how well these materials are held together and the steepness of the existing slope.

Here is an easy experiment that shows the importance of slope angle. Take a cafeteria tray and cover it with a layer of sand about 2.5 cm thick. Tilt the tray slightly; say at an angle of 5 per cent (note: a 100 per cent slope equals 45°). The material is unlikely to move. Tilt the tray slowly to a steeper angle, and notice that movement will begin at a specific angle. You might see some small particles moving individually at first, but soon the whole mass will move downslope because the **threshold angle** (or angle of repose in granular material) has been exceeded. The threshold angle is the maximum angle at which solid or granular material remains at rest. All slopes have a threshold angle. For solid bedrock the angle may be very steep; for loose sand it is less than 10 per cent. For a slope consisting of **regolith** (weathered and transported material over bedrock) and soil, it may be between 15 and 30 per cent, depending on the composition and if the material is dry or contains a large amount of water.

In our experiment the slope was oversteepened because the tray was tilted to a higher angle. Slopes become oversteepened in nature, too, as, for example, when a stream undercuts its valley sides, exceeding their threshold angle. Then debris from the valley sides falls into the stream and is carried downstream. Oversteepening can also occur because of glacial or coastal erosion. In general, it may be said that the steeper the slope, the stronger the downslope pull or **shear stress**. Counteracting this is the **shear strength** of the slope, which includes the friction and cohesional resistance along the contact between the loose material and the bedrock on

the slope (Figure 30.2). This is easy to imagine. When there is little friction or cohesion between particles, they cannot remain stable on a high-angle slope; for example, had ball bearings or marbles been used in the experiment instead of sand, they would have rolled off the tray at the slightest angle of slope because there would be no friction or cohesional resistance between the hard balls. Another factor in the downslope movement of material is water, or, more technically, fluid. Material below its threshold angle may become unstable when saturated by water from heavy or long-duration rainfall, snowmelt, or groundwater sources. The water has the effect of adding significant weight and of reducing friction because it acts as a lubricant.

The threshold angle of a specific slope can be determined by using the formula for the **factor of safety**:

$$f = \frac{\text{Shear strength (forces resisting movement—e.g., friction and cohesion)}}{\text{Shear stress (forces driving instability—e.g., weight, gravity, slope angle)}}$$

When f equals 1, the shear stress is the same as the shear strength. This is the **critical threshold** (Table 30.1). If f is greater than 1.0, the slope is stable, but when f is less than 1.0, the slope is unstable and liable to fail. Most natural slopes subject to mass movements have a factor of safety ranging between 1.0 and 1.3. Something like an earthquake, stream undercutting, human interference, or increased moisture content can therefore easily trigger movement.

The threshold angle for any material varies with:

a. The type of material(s) involved (e.g., bedrock versus regolith, sand versus clay)

b. Climate

From the Fieldnotes

Figure 30.3 *'From Carmel along G-16 toward the Soledad loop. Vineyards along the river, deeply incised. Mediterranean vegetation on the steeper hillslopes. Noted a small tributary that had oversteepened a slope and caused a landslide not even the dense natural vegetation could prevent.'*

c. Vegetation cover (type and density)
d. Soil moisture and drainage
e. Land use
f. Slope foot processes (e.g., undercutting by a stream or coastal wave action or various types of construction, such as road or rail cuts)

A change in any of the variables can upset the balance and lead to slope processes changing the slope. A well-drained clay slope in Toronto will have a different threshold angle than a slope formed from the same kind of material in other areas because many of the other variables will differ, sometimes drastically from place to place.

Table 30.1 Examples of Threshold Angles in the Greater Toronto Area

Material	Threshold Angle
Consolidated undrained clay	14–20°
Consolidated drained clay	20–24°
Sandy gravel	35–50°
Medium gravel	40–55°
Unconsolidated silt or silty sand	20–22°
Saturated sensitive (quick) clay	flows on slopes of 0°
Bedrock subject to mass movement	>42°

Slope Movement

It is possible to distinguish two distinct groups of slope movement on the basis of how the debris is transported.

1. **Mass movements** (mass wasting, slope failures) are caused by gravity overcoming the strength of the slope materials. The debris is not carried by water, snow, ice, or wind, but merely tumbles, rolls, or generally moves downslope. Processes in this group include:

   a. Snow, rock, and debris avalanches ('landslides')
   b. Rock or debris falls or topples
   c. Rainsplash erosion
   d. Apparent 'flows'/slides
   e. Creep and solifluction

2. **Hillslope processes** involve running water or another agent transporting debris downslope. They include:

   a. Wash (slopewash, sheetwash)
   b. Rilling and gullying
   c. True flows, including debris torrents and lahars
   d. Subsurface processes such as solution, leaching, and lessivation

In reality, two or more mass movement or hillslope processes can act on the same slope at the same time or in sequence.

The characteristics of regolith or sediments associated with stability are important. The more significant aspects to consider are (1) the texture of the material, especially the amount and type of clay minerals; (2) the packing or loading of the material (whether weighted down by ice, etc.); and (3) its moisture content.

The effect of these factors is shown by the **Atterberg limits** of the material. All Atterberg limit tests are carried out on remoulded (i.e., disturbed, mixed up) soil in which all the fabric has been deliberately destroyed. The two most commonly used limits are the **plastic limit** and the **liquid limit**. Together these define the range of moisture contents through which the material behaves as a solid, a plastic, or a liquid. At moisture levels below the plastic limit the material behaves like a brittle solid; at moisture levels above the liquid limit it acts like a liquid if disturbed. The difference between the plastic limit and the liquid limit of any material is called the **plasticity index**. For any material there is a close linear relationship between its plasticity index and moisture content. Quick clays (which are found in some areas along the St Lawrence Valley in eastern Ontario and Quebec) with a high moisture content, for example, can lead to a loss of strength; the soil will behave like a suspension of fine spherical grains because of the post-depositional removal of salt. In this case the two limits are extremely close together.

It is possible to distinguish between two types of slopes—*weathering-limited slopes* and *transport-limited slopes*—and their processes. **Weathering-limited slopes** are characterized by very little regolith, and the effects of erosional processes are restricted because of the lack of debris. The slope form will be strongly influenced by the threshold angle(s) of the rock(s). These slopes are characteristic of arid and semi-arid areas where the dominant slope form is a cliff-pediment assemblage. **Transport-limited slopes**, in contrast, have a deep regolith cover. The slope form and processes are limited by the type and intensity of the processes. All surface processes would be transport-limited, but some subsurface processes may be weathering-limited. The slope form will be strongly influenced by the threshold angle (angle of repose) of the regolith. The deep regolith mantles the cliff-pediment form in these areas.

The Threshold Angle Model of Slope Development

Mass movement processes appear to be important in establishing the initial form of slopes after stream downcutting. They can be considered **slope-creating processes**. If there was a change in any one of the fundamental controlling factors—climate, geology, or base level—fluvial action would have generated new slopes. The mass movement processes reduce these newly formed slopes from their initial instability to their threshold angle, where sliding stops. After this angle is reached, the hillslope processes take over to maintain the slope at that angle or modify it if conditions change. These are considered **slope-modifying processes**.

Mass Movement Processes

Evidence of huge mass movements (mega-landslides) affecting the unstable margins of volcanic oceanic islands has been found in Hawaii, the Canary Islands, and many other places. These immense mass movements have been caused by volcanic and seismic activity and have moved many millions of tonnes of material off the islands into the adjacent oceans. Such movement has sparked large tsunamis, and the possible failure of the western side of Cumbre Vieja volcano in the Canary Islands and the resulting mega-tsunami, which could be big enough to inundate and wipe out Florida, has received lots of coverage both in academic journals and in the press.

Debris or rock **avalanches** form part of a continuum with snow avalanches at one end. Snow avalanches occur in alpine areas, in snow on slopes usually of 30–45° (Figure 30.4). They are generally triggered by the wind (85–90 per cent), by melting, or by overloading of snow. They may occur as a slab failure, affecting a large area of the slope, or they may be channelized. The same kind of process can take place in pure snow or mixtures of snow and other materials. The result of the failure is a turbulent density flow of snow, rock material, and other debris that moves downslope at very high speeds on a cushion of compressed air, dust, and vaporized water. The flow is

LINK

buried features, and detours (e.g., streams and roads). We can calculate the velocity of the event if we know the height of the top of the failure and the distance of travel of the transported debris. A good example of a rock avalanche is the Frank Slide in the mountains of Alberta (see 'Perspectives' box).

Another large rock avalanche, the Hope Slide, occurred in the Nicolum Creek valley in the Cascade Mountains, on the southwest slope of Johnson Peak, about 18 km east of Hope, BC, early on a Saturday morning in January 1965 (Figure 28.3). Forty-seven million m³ of rock material were as involved in the failure. This avalanche covered the valley bottom in 85 m of rubble and buried a 3-km stretch of highway and four people travelling in cars along it.

Rock or Debris Falls or Topples

Falls involve the rapidly falling, leaping, bouncing, and rolling descent of material (Figure 30.7). Topples result from the tilting or rotating of well-jointed rocks. Small falls are common on north-facing slopes in the Rockies between November and March and are related to fluctuations of temperature, freeze–thaw activity, and saturation. This kind of failure can also be triggered by earthquakes. Rock or debris falls or topples can initiate avalanches. The diagnostic landforms and deposits include a scar where the material originated, unsorted angular rock debris (scree, talus), and tree debris—scarred and broken trees. A good example of this kind of activity was the Hell's Gate Rock Fall in the Fraser River Canyon (February 1914). This occurred when Canadian National Railways work crews were blasting rock to construct a rail line through the canyon. It is estimated that 100,000 tonnes of rock fell into the Fraser River at its narrowest point, constricting its width to 25 m. Some blocks were over 100 m³. During the spring flood the rock debris caused the river to rise 25 m above its normal level. This caused back-ponding of the Fraser River for about 100 km, to near Ashcroft, BC. Long bolts were installed in the rock walls above the rail line to stop further large falls. The blockage of the Fraser decreased the cross-sectional area of the river and caused stream velocity to increase to a point where migrating salmon (sockeye, chum, and pink) could not get up the river to spawn; the fish were massed in the 16-km stretch downstream of the blockage and died without mating. Finally, some of the debris in the river was dynamited and the flooding went down. Fish ladders were later installed to get the salmon over the blocked area, but the salmon run on the Fraser never recovered from this event. The number of salmon migrating upriver after the rockfall was 66 per cent less than the pre-fall number.

Recently, a rockfall in 2008 along the Sea-to-Sky Highway connecting Vancouver and Whistler, BC (Figure 30.5), brought into question the readiness and reliability of the transportation infrastructure for the 2010 Winter Olympics to be held in these two locations.

Figure 30.4 Start of a snow avalanche on Mount Dickey, Alaska. As the snow thunders downslope, its volume increases and the area it affects widens.

LINK

preceded by an air blast or shock wave that can knock down trees, houses, and so forth.

Debris and rock avalanches are very important in high mountainous terrain with glacially steepened slopes, especially where the rock beds or structures dip at 35–40° towards the valley floor. The failure usually occurs parallel to the slope face along joints or bedding planes. Movement can be initiated by a rockslide or rockfall, or it can be triggered by earthquakes or a buildup of water pressure along joints, bedding planes, and so on. Many avalanches change their character as they move downslope and mix with water (from surface—stream, wetlands, ice—and subsurface sources) and debris from lower down on the slope and/or in the valley bottom (rock debris, soil, organic material, trees). The debris consists of large angular blocks, rounded blocks (in either case up to 500 tonnes), slabs, boulders, smaller material, tree trunks, and so on. The diagnostic landforms left by this process include a scar on the slope where the material came from and a drape of debris on the valley floor that contains very large-calibre material. In the marginal areas, one sees boulders, flattened trees, defoliated trees,

Figure 30.5   A rockslide in the spring of 2008 cut off land transportation for several days to Whistler, British Columbia, site of the alpine skiing for the 2010 Winter Olympics.

Perspectives on the Human Environment

LINK

The Frank Slide

The Frank Slide near Braemore, Alberta, is the most famous rock avalanche in Canada (Figure 30.6). At 4:10 a.m. on 29 April 1903, about 33 million m³ of rock and debris (3.6 million tonnes) slid down the eastern slope of Turtle Mountain on the south side of the Crowsnest Pass. In less than 100 seconds the leading edge of the debris had crossed the Crowsnest River and valley and climbed up the slopes on the other side of the valley to about the 120 m mark. Above this the trees were defoliated. It is estimated that the material travelled at speeds of between 350 and 400 km/hr and was preceded by a very strong air blast. The debris buried between one-third and one-half of

the coal-mining town of Frank, covered 2.5 km of the Canadian Pacific Railway track, and killed at least 76 people (only 12 bodies were found) —mostly women, children, and older individuals. The men were at work in the mine under Turtle Mountain.

The Frank Slide was the worst disaster in Canada up to that point. The federal government launched a Royal Commission to look into what had happened, but the state of scientific knowledge about any slope processes was poor at that time. It is now known that the avalanche took place down the bedding planes of the limestone rocks. The failure was probably triggered by a heavy frost that followed rather warm weather. There were other triggers, too.

LINK

Coal mining, especially blasting, may have been an added stress. The slope was being undercut by the Crowsnest River, and there may have been a number of small-magnitude earthquakes (there were no seismographs in the area at the time). All of these events added up to disaster. It has been estimated that 100 dump trucks carrying 3-tonne loads and making 10 trips a day would take 66 years to remove all of the debris from the rock avalanche.

To mark the centenary of the Frank Slide the Alberta government announced that it would moni-tor the same face of Turtle Mountain that collapsed in 1903 using an integrated network of seismographs, GPS, laser ranging, satellite technology, and crackometers to ensure the safety of the area (the system has been operational since 2005). Recently, geologists have become concerned about a system of cracks that have appeared and widened near the top of the avalanche scar and that another layer of limestone rock appears to be very slowly breaking way from the mountain and gradually slipping down the same area that saw the deadly 1903 event.

Figure 30.6   View of the Frank Slide.

Apparent 'Flows' (Mantle Slides)

Apparent 'flows' occur as shallow failures where the regolith slides over the bedrock, or as blocks of bedrock break away and shear over subjacent bedrock, or as deep-seated failures occur in deeper uniform materials. The shallow movements are caused by the weight of the regolith or rock concerned and the pull of gravity. This process is typical of slopes in temperate environments. The slide is sometimes masked by a cover of material that gives the impression of a flow, but a lack of deformation in stakes placed in the material involved in the slide shows that movement is taking place en masse. This is indicative of a slide rather than a flow.

This type of movement has been seen affecting a part of the Fitzsimmons Creek drainage basin between Whistler and Blackcomb Mountains in BC. The problem area is about 2 km upstream from part of Whistler Village, where about 0.7 to 1 million m³ of glacial gravel is slowly slipping down the side of the valley into the creek. This is not, by itself, a risk to the ski resort at Whistler, but if the sliding

Figure 30.7   Rockfall—free falling of detached bodies of bedrock from a cliff or steep slope. The loosened boulders usually come to rest at the base of the slope from which they fell.

continues and the creek is blocked by the gravel during a period of peak discharge (snow melt and/or rainfall) or because of an increased rate of slope movement it could dam up the creek, build up a great amount of water (and debris) behind the gravel dam, and cause the dam to collapse and a catastrophic release of water down the creek and into the ski resort. Because of this instability some of the Winter Olympic events have been moved away from this area so as not to cause more instability or put competitors and spectators at risk.

Deep-seated failures are called **slumps**, rotational slides, or slips (Figures 30.8 and 30.9). They occur in uniform incoherent materials like lake or glacial deposits. A shear plane develops in these types of deposits in the form of a segment of a circle, and failure occurs. This is because of the initial angle and the form of the slope. The major stress that results is curved towards the lower ground. The angle between this direction and the failure plane remains the same as in an ordinary block/angled surface situation. This type of mass movement is very common in deep Pleistocene deposits in the Temperate zone, such as along the sides of Prairie river valleys, or in deeply weathered regoliths in the Tropics. The diagnostic landforms include a deep-walled scar where the material originated, a staircase of slumped blocks, and a tongue-shaped lobe of debris on the valley floor.

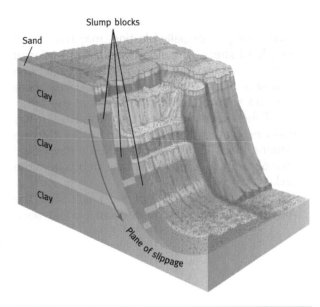

Figure 30.9 Example of slumping in which three slump blocks have moved downslope. Note the backward rotation of each slump block, the scarp at the head of the slump cavity, and the forward flow at the toe of the mass.

Creep

Creep can affect the regolith or the entire slope (slope sagging, mass creep), the soil (soil or seasonal creep), or talus (talus creep). An invigorated form of creep occurs in periglacial areas (solifluction-gelifluction and frost creep). Creep involves the downslope movement of material. It is driven by the weight of the regolith, or soil material, and gravity. It is important in areas where there may be a loss of coherence of slope material because of an increase in moisture content or because of weathering. Slope sagging is effective to a depth of over 100 m in deeply weathered materials. Movement is in the order of 1 mm/yr. The Downie Slide near Revelstoke, BC, is a very large example of this process. It has an estimated volume of between 1 and 2 billion m³ and a surface area of approximately 9 km². Movement began at least 6600 years ago and continues at a rate of a few centimetres a year.

The evidence for creep includes the pulling out of rock beds downslope (outcrop curvature), stone lines, tree deformation (trunk curvature), the tilting of structures (walls, telegraph poles, gravestones—Figure 30.10), and the accumulation of soil on the upslope sides of walls. Talus creep involves the same type of movement of the surface layers of stones or boulder material downslope over talus cones. This may be caused by frost heave.

The same kind of creep process, though much intensified, can be seen in periglacial environments where the *talik*, or active layer, on slopes is subject to shearing over permafrost or lenses of ice during the melt season. This is especially true on south-facing slopes. This process is called *solifluction* or *gelifluction*. **Solifluction** is the downslope flow of supersaturated soil that has reached its liquid limit. **Gelifluction** is solifluction associated with frozen ground.

Figure 30.8 One of the most dramatic photographs ever taken of a slumping event. This hillside flow halted traffic on a major road in the San Francisco Bay Area in 1952.

LINK

Figure 30.10 Effects of soil creep in the cultural and physical landscape—objects tilting downslope.

Frost creep is associated with gelifluction. It involves the expansion of slope material during freezing and its settling on thawing. Stones can be heaved through the talik in this way as it freezes and then settle when thawing takes place. The landforms associated with this process are sheets, lobate (tongue-shaped) features, terraces, benches, or streams of soil material on slopes. The features have crude bedding and tend to thicken downslope. Downslope from these features there is often evidence of wash, as water escaped out of the supersaturated soliflual material and flowed downslope. In areas with bare surfaces, such as the High Arctic, solifluction sheets form smooth terrain with 1–3° gradients. This occurs because the lack of vegetation allows uniform movement to take place. Farther south in the tundra–boreal forest transition zone, lobes and streams of material are more common because of the effect of the presence of patches of vegetation. The lobes may be turf- or stone-banked (turf or stone garlands). This type of process is common in the southern Canadian Rockies. Solifluction lobes have average rates of surface movement of approximately 60 cm/yr on steep slopes and between 0.5 and 4 cm/yr on less-angled slopes. There is very little movement below 50 cm depth and zero movement at 1 m.

The material moved by this kind of movement may become oriented with its long axes parallel to the direction of movement. Delicate weathered minerals, such as feldspars, may be crushed by movement. The soliflucted material thickens in a downslope direction, and there may be evidence of wash on the lower slopes. The soliflucted material may be found with cryoturbation features, such as **involutions**, **ice wedges** or **ice-wedge casts**, and **drag structures**.

Rock glaciers or *block streams* are linear forms of solifluction-gelifluction form. These are composed of slowly moving masses of rock particles, some of which are ice-cored.

Rainsplash Erosion

This process is closely linked to the wash process (see below). It is not as immediately impressive as the catastrophic mass movements discussed so far, although it can be very significant in areas with bare sandy soils—for example, in sandy areas of the Prairies. **Rainsplash erosion** is caused by the impact of raindrops on bare soil surfaces. The disruptive nature of the raindrops' impact is like a greatly scaled-down version of a meteorite impact. Much of the energy of the impact of raindrops is dissipated by vegetation, stones, coarse soil material, plant residues, and water covering the surface. Nevertheless, the impact can break down large **peds**, or clumps of soil, and small soil particles can be thrown up to 2 m horizontally and as much as 70 cm vertically. The process causes finer material to move downslope in a ballistic trajectory, while leaving coarser material in place. The larger material is transported downslope by gravity as it is undermined (*pipkrake effect*). No rounding or wearing of the transported material occurs. The effectiveness of the process depends on a number of factors, including slope angle, the intensity of the rainfall, the extent of vegetation, and the soil texture (fine particles).

As well as causing disruption of small particles, the impact of raindrops can cause compaction of the soil surface (puddling or sealing) to occur. This leads to a decrease in infiltration rates and an increase in runoff and consequently an increase in erosion by wash.

Hillslope Processes

When water falls onto, or snow and ice melt on, a slope, the water can do one of three things: (1) it can sit on the slope surface in puddles and evaporate over time (hence it is not important to slope processes); (2) it can infiltrate into the soil, regolith, or rock and thereby add weight, and thus stress, to the slope, which may lead to mass movements or some kinds of hillslope processes (e.g., true flows); or (3) it can become overland flow when (a) all the voids or pores in the material are full and then runoff (*saturation overland flow*) occurs, or (b) the rainfall intensity is greater than the infiltration rate (**Ri>Ir**) and the water thus builds up in puddles, resulting in runoff (*Hortonian overland flow*). Both types of overland flow are rare.

The Human Factor

Slope processes most frequently are caused by natural forces and conditions, but human activities also contribute. Sometimes people fail to heed nature's warnings, as in the case of the disastrous Langarone landslide in northern Italy in 1963. The materials on the slopes of the Langarone Valley were known to have low shear strengths. Nevertheless, a dam was constructed across the valley, and a large artificial reservoir (Lake Vaiont) was impounded behind it. The water rose and lubricated the inundated valley sides, adding to the risk of failures. When heavy rains pounded the upper slopes in the summer and early autumn of 1963, major instability seemed to be inevitable.

In early October, the severity of the hazard was finally realized, and it was decided to drain the reservoir. But it was too late, and on 9 October a mass of rock debris with a surface area of 3 km² slid into Lake Vaiont, causing a huge splash wave in the reservoir. The wave spilled over the top of the dam and swept without warning down the lower Langarone Valley, killing more than 2600 persons.

Despite this tragic lesson, the building of houses and even larger structures on failure-prone slopes continues in many areas. This includes North America, which contains numerous areas that are susceptible to slope instability risks (Figure 30.11).

True Flows

The movement of material in a true flow is similar to that of a viscous fluid. The velocity decreases with depth because of friction with the underlying material. The flows usually terminate in gently sloping areas like valley floors or at obstructions such as valley walls or stream channels.

True flows can be subdivided on the basis of a number of characteristics: (1) the material involved in the flows (whether they are earth or **mudflows** [earth/mudflows have less than 50 per cent sand; see Figure 30.12] or debris flows [debris flows have coarser material]); (2) their rate of

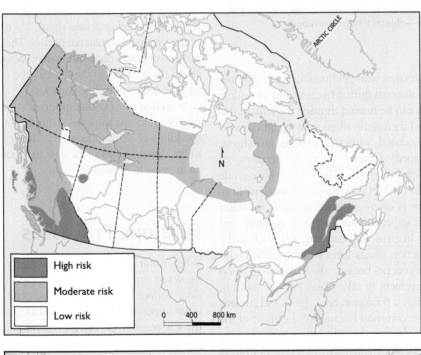

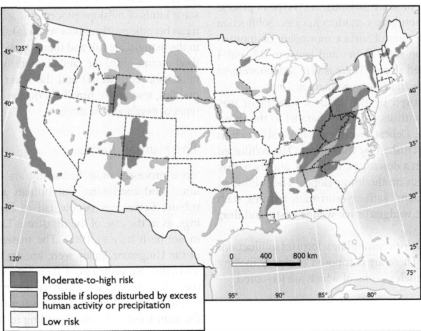

Figure 30.11 Susceptibility to future slope failures in North America.

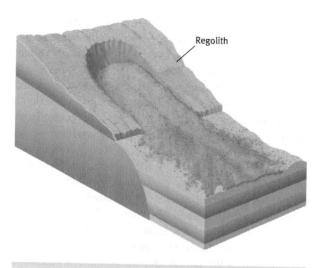

Regolith

Figure 30.12 Earth flow. This lobe-shaped mass leaves a small scarp at its upper end and pushes a tongue of debris onto the valley floor in the foreground.

flow (rapid flows—more than 1 km/hr; slow flows—less than 1 km/yr); and (3) the extent of the flow into slope flows or channel flows.

Slope Flows

These are flat or slab failures affecting large areas of a slope. This type of failure is typically confined to sensitive or quick clays that are subject to liquefaction and structural collapse when moist and shaken by earthquakes or undercut by streams. There are instances in Quebec where heavy vehicles are said to have started this kind of movement. These flows are very rapid, the velocity ranging from 26 km/h to about 330 km/h. There are many examples of this type of failure in the Champlain Sea sediments along the St Lawrence Valley in Quebec and eastern Ontario (over 750 flows are known in an area of more than 4000 km²). These deposits are covered by fluvial or deltaic sands. The infiltration of rainwater into the overlying sands causes saturation of the underlying Leda clay. If shaken or undercut by a stream, the clays liquefy and flow, carrying blocks of the overlying sands along. The flows leave semicircular scars (depletion zones) with steep head scarps in the source areas and tongues of debris leading onto flatter terrain. A good example of this process is the Nicolet Earthflow, which occurred in 1955. It left a crater approximately 215 m long and 122 m wide (22,000 m²). This earthflow killed three people, destroyed several buildings (including a bishop's palace), and damaged part of a large church. The flow also blocked about half of the Nicolet River. Another flow occurred at St Jean Vianney near Chicoutimi, Quebec, in May 1971 (Figure 30.13). It left a crater about 1 km across and 25 m deep. It moved at about 26 km/hr along the valley, causing 31 deaths and carrying 34 houses (a total of 40 were destroyed), a bus, and an unknown number of cars. It also took out a bridge. This failure, which occurred within a much larger relic flow dating from the seventeenth century, was set off by an earthquake.

Figure 30.13 Devastation caused by the slope flow at St Jean Vianney, Quebec, May 1971.

Channel Flows

Channel flows are essentially super-concentrated or excessively loaded stream flows. These flows include debris torrents and lahars. Slow flows are less rapid because they lack moisture and move only a few centimetres to a metre a year. An example is the Drynoch Flow, an approximately 5-km-long (17 million m³ of material) rock glacier that flows into the Thompson Valley in the central interior of British Columbia.

Debris torrents (debris flows) are composed of coarser material flowing in water in a channel. These events deposit sediments on large alluvial fans at the foot of a mountain slope. They have killed approximately 160 people and have caused more than $100 million damage to houses and infrastructure in British Columbia, especially along the Sea-to-Sky Highway. Many of the deaths were caused by bridge washouts in the early 1980s. The number of fatalities increased with the development of the ski areas and an increase in urbanization and the construction of houses on the alluvial fans. Debris torrents usually result from heavy rainfall or snowmelt, which mobilizes debris that has built up in mountain drainage basins (rock and tree debris from avalanches and rockfalls). Logging and construction can cause a greater buildup of material. The velocity of the torrents is between 3 and 12 m/s (10.8–43 km/h), and they usually carry up to 50,000 m³ of debris. Deposition on the fans is mainly coarse, poorly sorted, unstratified material with large boulders, rock fragments, gravel and clays, and trees and tree mulch. Some fans have well-defined levees and terminal lobes. The deposits wrap around trees and structures at the margins of the flows.

Another special type of channel flow is the *lahar*. These are channelled volcanic mud or debris flows composed of mixtures of avalanche debris, pyroclastics, ash, snow, ice, and water from surface and groundwater sources. They can be triggered by volcanic eruptions (hot lahars) or by intense rainfall on previously deposited fine volcanic ash blankets (cold lahars). The lahars triggered by eruptions are often hot and are very large (>10⁷m³). The Toutle Valley Lahar caused by the eruption of Mount St Helens in 1980 travelled 43.2 km in 100 minutes (430 m/min or 26 km/h). This was comparatively slow compared to the Huascaran Lahar in the Peruvian Andes discussed earlier, which travelled at between 270 and 360 km/h. Lahars caused by rainfall on previously deposited ash mantles are cold and generally smaller (10⁵–10⁷m³) and travel at much lower velocities.

Wash

Wash (slopewash, sheetwash) involves the flow of water across the soil surface in a sheet (overland flow). It is closely linked to rainsplash erosion (a mass movement—see above) and usually occurs *pari passu* (at the same time). The sheet of water is usually shallow and lacks any morphological boundaries. The process is variable in form, especially in terms of width. There are great differences in the scale of this process depending on whether it occurs in temperate or tropical areas or with or without a vegetation cover. The water moves in a pulsing motion, as it is dammed by undulations, vegetation debris, and so on, and then breaches these obstacles. In temperate areas the depth of wash tends to be less than 1 mm over bare rock surfaces, but in semi-arid environments it can be several centimetres deep and therefore much wider. In such environments it is associated with the erosion of flat-bottomed valleys called gulches, washes, canyons, or wadis. The volume of water influences the size of material transported, but generally clays, silts, and fine sands are moved. The process sorts debris, and the material it carries is abraded and reduced in size in transport. The rates of wash vary depending on the intensity of the rainfall and the amount of vegetation cover, ranging from less than 60 cm/s to more than 1 m/s. Bare surfaces are essential for this process to be significant, so it is important in semi-arid areas, on glacial debris near the snout of glaciers, and on spoil heaps.

The amount of soil loss by wash and rilling can be calculated using the Universal Soil Loss Equation (USLE) and its refinements (Revised USLE 1 and 2):

$$A = R \times K \times LS \times C \times P$$

where

A is the average annual soil loss (tonnes/ha);

R is the rainfall erosivity index (based on rainfall and runoff; *R* is the meteorological or active factor; all other elements are passive local factors—i.e., erosion cannot occur without rainfall and runoff);

K is the soil erodability factor (cohesiveness, resistance to dislodging and transport);

LS is the topographical index (based on slope length [*L*] and slope angle [*S*]);

C is the cropping and management index (based on plant canopy, surface mulch cover, and root density); and

P is the conservation practice factor (contouring, strip cropping, terracing, etc.)

LS, *C*, and *P* are dimensionless ratios.

In southern Ontario the median loss of material eroded on 5–30° slopes is 0.09 cm³/cm²/yr, but in areas with torrential rainfalls and mainly bare surfaces (e.g., the Black Hills of South Dakota), the loss on pediment surfaces is between 200 and 500 cm³/cm²/yr. In more temperate areas the increased vegetation cover intercepts the raindrops and the roots bind the soil together and cut down the efficacy of the process.

Rilling and Gullying

An arbitrary division is used to distinguish rilling and gullying. These processes arise because of the concentration of wash resulting from the undulations on a slope. They form part of a continuum, with wash at one end and fluvial processes at the other.

Rilling (sapping) refers to the formation of micro-channels on usually bare surfaces such as badlands, unsodded roadsides, and spoil heaps. The micro-channels are limited by self-generated boundaries. The rills are re-occupied several to many times a year or over a period of years. The rill dimensions are usually up to 1 m deep and 2 m across and can be up to 10 m in length. The United States Department of Agriculture defines rills on the basis of their elimination by ploughing or bulldozing. Gullies cannot be eliminated by these means. The process-es associated with rilling are small-scale fluvial and slope processes. The same type of features can be seen in micro-scale (e.g., meandering, sediment bars, slope failures) that can be seen in a stream channel and its valley. A fan or delta develops at the rill mouth.

Rilling rates are lacking in the literature, but there is a rate for soil erosion by wash and rilling for a site in Ot-tawa during a flash rainstorm (74 mm). The slope angle was 9° on clay, and the erosion amounted to 27.3 tonnes/ hectare.

Gullying is distinguished from rilling by the greater size and permanence of the features. Gullies can be taken as the uppermost branches of the fluvial system. They are occupied during periods of peak runoff (during and just after rainfall or snowmelt). The processes occurring in gul-lies are identical to fluvial and slope processes seen in full-sized streams and valleys.

Rills and gullies are generated by a differential increase in the velocity of wash (overland flow) at various points on a slope. The differential increase is in turn initiated by pre-existing irregularities on the slope that concentrate the flow of water and increase the discharge and there-fore the sediment transport. Good examples of rilling and gullying can be seen in the Alberta Badlands, along the sides of valleys in the Prairies, in the central interior of British Columbia, and in areas of lower relief that have been subjected to severe soil erosion, such as the shale badlands in various locations near the Niagara Escarp-ment in southern Ontario (northwest of Milton, at Ingle-wood [the Caledon Badlands], and in the Aldershot area of Burlington).

The rill pattern is subject to changes in position, so that the whole slope is affected over time. Lateral movement occurs on coarse material as debris is deposited in the rill, very much like in a braided stream. Channels persist through flows until they encounter another higher-magnitude event. Weathering tends to obliterate channels cut into finer materials between flow events. The cross-section of a rill or gully can be either V-shaped or trough-shaped. The V-shaped rills and gullies tend to develop in more competent materials, while trough-shaped cross-sections occur in more easily eroded material. The shape is related to the ease with which the sides and bed of the channels are excavated. The prerequisites for rilling and gullying are similar to those for wash but differ in intensity. The concentration of overland flow is especially important.

Once a channel has been established by a large discharge, a smaller discharge will occupy the feature because less en-ergy is needed for the transportation of debris than for the erosion of the channel.

Subsurface Processes

Subsurface processes include eluviation, solution, and lessivation. *Eluviation* (subsurface wash) and *solution* involve the mobilization and movement of material in solution or as exceedingly small individual minerals through the structure and fabric of the regolith or the weathering zone. Tunnels and pipes develop because of these processes. The rates of the processes are not well known, except in limestone terrains. There is increasing evidence that a significant amount of material is removed from the landscape in all environments through these processes, much more than by any other processes. Eluviation, solution, and lessivation act primarily near or at the surface. The main component of change occurs backwards into the slope, and thus slope angles stay the same. Studies in the Sudan have shown that about 60 per cent of material removed from granite areas was removed by solution. Similar figures have also been reported from northern Sweden.

The morphological evidence for eluviation and solution includes the fairly infrequent development of pipes and tunnels (with diameters of a few millimetres to a metre) in the affected areas, showing the removal of soluble mate-rial. The occurrence of these features may be a function of the structure and texture of the regolith or weathering zone. Eluvial-illuvial horizons are another form of evi-dence. These show the leaching of minerals from close to the surface of the soil (eluviation) and their subsequent re-deposition lower down the soil profile (illuviation). In ex-tremely arid areas, evaporation from the surface can cause the capillary rise of groundwater through the regolith and soil, and the removal of a mineral from the subsoil and its deposition close to, or at, the surface (e.g., epsomite, salt, calcium carbonate).

Lessivation is the removal of clay in suspension and its subsequent accumulation downprofile (as in luvisolic soils) or downslope. In the study of the Sudanese granite areas, it was not known whether the material lost from the weathered areas was transported in particulate or colloidal form, but some evidence suggests that the colloidal form was significant.

Two conditions must be met for subsurface processes to occur. First, there has to be sufficient rainfall (continuity being more important than intensity), and second, there must be permeability of the regolith or weathering zone. The minerals in the bedrock, regolith, and soils are impor-tant here because the type and amount of minerals influ-ence the permeability of the material through the type and amount of weathering occurring and the development of the regolith.

The Importance of Slope Processes

It is easy to underestimate the importance of slope processes among the processes of erosion. Some of these occur almost imperceptibly. But they take place along the sides of many valleys and along shorelines, and a large portion of the materials swept out to sea by the world's streams is brought to these water channels through slope processes. Figure 30.14 compares the volume of rock eroded directly by a stream and the volume first moved by mass movement. Even slow, sluggish, meandering streams undercut their banks, causing the collapse of materials into their waters. Rapidly eroding streams in highland areas and streams in deep canyon-like valleys cause much oversteepening and constant collapse along their valley walls. Within these categories there is sometimes more than one type of movement. These movements can be summarized in terms of the rate of downslope movement and the amount of water involved. Figure 30.15 shows

how the different types of slope processes relate to one another with respect to these two parameters.

Why should so much time be spent examining the sliding and flowing earth? A knowledge of slope processes can help in planning and policy-making. It is quite costly to use public money to build public highways in unstable

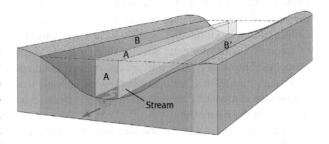

Figure 30.14   Comparison of the amount of rock eroded directly by a stream (**A**) and that first moved to the stream by various types of mass movement (**B, B'**).

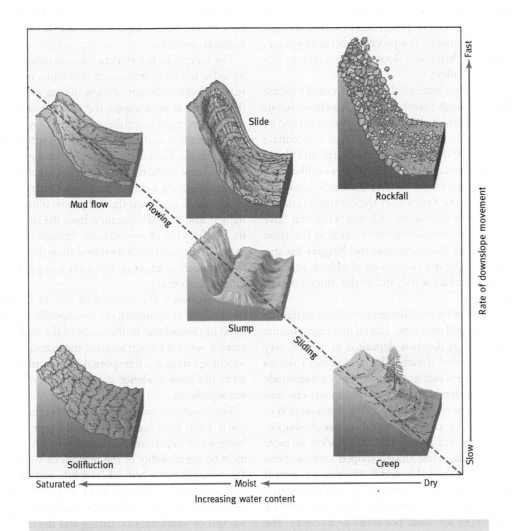

Figure 30.15   Common types of slope processes classified according to rate of movement and water content.

areas (see Figure 30.11). Moreover, many people have little or no regard for the stability of the land and choose to build their houses where the view is spectacular. Some of these residents have had rude awakenings, as Figure 30.16 shows.

Physical geographers are interested in slope processes for other reasons. In sculpting the land surface, these pro-cesses perform the important job of exposing new bedrock to the forces of weathering. By the time the material sags and collapses in a flow or slide, weathering has become much less effective in attacking deeper rock layers. But the slide removes the weathered material. Thus, slope process-es are vitally important in the total complex of erosional processes.

Figure 30.16 Eroding cliffs along the shores of Lake Ontario leave this house hanging precariously over the Scarborough Bluffs. The owners left nearly a year before this photograph was taken.

KEY TERMS

Atterberg limits *page 418*
avalanches *page 418*
creep *page 422*
critical threshold *page 416*
debris torrents *page 426*
drag structures *page 423*
factor of safety *page 416*
gelifluction *page 422*
gullying *page 427*
hillslope process *page 418*
ice wedge *page 423*
ice-wedge cast *page 423*
involution *page 423*
lessivation *page 427*
liquid limit *page 418*
mass movement *page 418*
mudflow *page 424*
peds *page 423*

plasticity index *page 418*
plastic limit *page 418*
rainsplash erosion *page 423*
regolith *page 416*
relaxation *page 415*
rilling *page 427*
shear strength *page 416*
shear stress *page 416*
slope-creating processes *page 418*
slope-modifying processes *page 418*
slump *page 422*
solifluction *page 422*
threshold angle *page 416*
transport-limited slopes *page 418*
true flows *page 424*
wash *page 426*
weathering-limited slopes *page 418*

REVIEW QUESTIONS

1. What is the threshold angle and why is it significant?
2. What fundamental force acts to restrain mass-movement processes?
3. How does creep differ from a flow type of movement?
4. Where (in a tectonic setting) would one expect the highest frequency of large debris and rock avalanches?
5. What is solifluction? How does it differ from gelifluction? In what environment is gelifluction most common?

REFERENCES AND FURTHER READINGS

Allison, R. 1999. *Rock Slopes*. Cambridge, Mass.: Blackwell.

Brabb, E.E., and B.L. Harrod, eds. 1989. *Landslides: Extent and Economic Significance*. Rotterdam: Balkema.

Carson, M., and M. Kirby. 1972. *Hillslope Form and Process*. London/New York: Cambridge Univ. Press.

Couture, R. 2003. *Workshop on Landslide Hazards and Risk Management in Canada*. Ottawa: Geological Survey of Canada Open File Report 4316.

Crozier, M.J. 1986. *Landslides: Causes, Consequences and Environment*. London/New York: Methuen.

Cruden, D.M. 1976. 'Major Rockslides in the Rockies', *Canadian Geotechnical Journal* 13: 8–20.

Eisbacher, G.H. 1979. 'First Order Regionalization of Landslide Characteristics in the Canadian Cordillera', *Geoscience Canada* 6: 69–79.

———— and J.J. Clague. 1984. *Destructive Mass Movements in High Mountains: Hazards and Management*. Ottawa: Geological Survey of Canada Paper 84–16.

Erismann, T.H., and G. Abele. 2001. *Dynamics of Rockslides and Rockfalls*. New York: Springer-Verlag.

Evans, S.G. 2001. 'Landslides', in G.R. Brooks, ed., *A Synthesis of Geological Hazards in Canada*. Ottawa: Geological Survey of Canada Bulletin 548, 43–79.

———— and K.W. Savigny. 1984. 'Landslides in the Vancouver–Fraser Valley–Whistler Region', in J.W.H. Monger, ed., *Geology and Geological Hazards in the Vancouver Region, Southwestern British Columbia*. Ottawa: Geological Survey of Canada Bulletin 481, 251–86.

Hays, W.W., ed. 1981. *Facing Geologic and Hydrologic Hazards*. Washington: US Geological Survey, Professional Paper 1240-B.

Jamieson, B. 2001. 'Snow Avalanches', in G.R. Brooks, ed., *A Synthesis of Geological Hazards in Canada*. Ottawa: Geological Survey of Canada Bulletin 548, 81–100.

Masson, D.G., et al. 2006. 'Submarine Landslides: Processes, Triggers and Hazard Prediction', *Philosophical Transactions of the Royal Society, London* A364, 1845: 2009–39.

Schumm, S.A., and M.P. Mosley, eds. 1973. *Slope Morphology*. Stroudsburg, Penn.: Dowden, Hutchinson and Ross.

Schuster, R.L., and R.J. Krizek, eds. 1978. *Landslides: Analysis and Control*. Washington: National Academy of Sciences.

Selby, M.J. 1982. *Hillslope Materials and Processes*. London/New York: Oxford Univ. Press.

Sharpe, C.F.S. 1960. *Landslides and Related Phenomena: A Study of Mass Movements of Soil and Rock*, 2nd edn. Paterson, NJ; Pageant Books.

Voight, B., ed. 1978. *Rockslides and Avalanches*, 2 vols. Amsterdam: Elsevier.

Young, A. 1975. *Slopes*, 2nd edn. London/New York: Longman.

Zaruba, Q., and V. Mencl. 1969. *Landslides and Their Control*. Amsterdam: Elsevier.

WEB RESOURCES

earthsci.org/processes/geopro/massmov/massmov.html This website provides descriptions, diagrams, and many photographs of landslides, soil creep, debris flow, mudflows and lahars, solifluction, and rockfalls and rockslides.

vulcan.wr.usgs.gov/Projects/MassMovement This US Geological Survey page provides links to a variety of topics relating to the dynamics of mass movements, including the Geological Survey's National Landslide Hazards Program website.

Water in the Lithosphere

Objectives

- To discuss the various paths water may take on and within the surface of the lithosphere.

- To introduce fundamental aspects of river flow.

- To outline basic concepts related to groundwater hydrology.

Water is the essence of life on Earth. Humanity's earliest civilizations arose in the valleys of great rivers. Our ancestors learned to control the seasonal floods of these streams, and irrigation made planned farming possible. We refer to those cultures as *hydraulic civilizations* in recognition of their ability to control and exploit water. Our current dependence on water is no less fundamental. Society's technological progress notwithstanding, water remains the Earth's most critical resource. Human beings can do without oil, coal, or iron, but they cannot survive without water. Thus, the historical geography of human settlement on this planet is in no small part the history of the search for, and use of, water.

The operations of the hydrologic cycle are introduced in Figure 11.6, in the unit that treats the part of the hydrosphere found in the atmosphere (water vapour). In the present unit the focus is on the part of the hydrosphere contained in the lithosphere. In Units 32 to 34 we consider the primary agents of landscape formation. But before water collects in streams, it must travel over or through the surficial layer. Arriving as precipitation (snowfall and rainfall), some of it evaporates. Some of it falls on plants; some of it moistens the upper soil layers; some of it seeps deeper down and collects in underground reservoirs. And part of it runs downslope and collects, first in small channels, then in larger creeks, to become part of the volume of streams.

Water at the Surface

Our inquiry starts with a raindrop that arrives at the Earth's surface. What happens to it depends on the nature and state of the surface. In some cases, raindrops never actually reach the ground; they fall on vegetation and evaporate before they can penetrate the soil. Figure 31.1 shows where this canopy **interception** occurs.

Figure 31.1 Vegetation intercepts a percentage of rainfall. These drops on a few blades of grass do not seem to amount to much, but over a large area such interception can amount to a substantial volume of water that does not reach or saturate the soil.

LINK

The amount of water intercepted by vegetation depends on the structure of the plants involved. In Australia, for example, eucalyptus trees intercept only 2 to 3 per cent of the rain. Hemlock and Douglas fir forests in British Columbia possess a different structure and intercept as much as 40 per cent of the rain. If the rainwater reaches the ground, it can be absorbed by the surface. Such surfaces as concrete roads or granite outcrops that do not permit water to pass through them are said to be *impermeable*. Most natural surfaces absorb a portion of the water that falls on them and are considered *permeable*, although the degree of permeability depends on many factors.

The flow of water into the Earth's surface through the pores (spaces between particles) and openings in the soil mass is called **infiltration**. The infiltration rate depends on several factors: (1) the physical characteristics of the soil, (2) how much moisture is already in the soil, (3) the type and extent of the vegetation cover, (4) the slope of the surface, and (5) the nature and duration of the rainfall. These factors also contribute to a time delay between the start of a rainfall and the start of infiltration.

The most evident characteristics of soil that affect infiltration are its structure and the closeness of the soil particles. For the most part, water can infiltrate more rapidly into coarse, sandy soils than into clay soils. In a much studied valley in Switzerland, forest soil absorbs 100 mm of water in two minutes, but a pasture where cattle graze requires three hours to take in the same amount of water.

A soil that is already wet will allow less infiltration than a dry soil because the soil surface becomes compacted by the rain. The clays in the soil also may swell, closing small openings. Small particles wash into the surface openings, decreasing the porosity, and the existing pores become filled with water and cannot accept any more. Infiltration rates are usually highest in vegetated areas because the vegetation prevents raindrops from compacting the soil, and the roots act to increase the permeability of the surface layer. Moreover, organic litter provides a home for burrowing animals, whose activities further loosen the soil.

The type of vegetation also affects infiltration. The infiltration rate of a bluegrass meadow is decidedly greater than that of a tilled cornfield. Figure 31.2 shows the typical shape of an infiltration curve for two kinds of vegetation. Infiltration rates for both kinds are high at the start of a rainfall event and then decrease over time.

Steep slopes may encourage runoff before water can be absorbed, so the infiltration rate is likely to be somewhat higher on gentler slopes and flat surfaces. The characteristics of local rainfall also are critical to the infiltration rate. Rainfall can vary in intensity, duration, and amount. The *intensity* is the amount of water that falls in a given time. A rainfall intensity of 5 mm per hour is quite heavy; if it kept up for a *duration* of 10 hours, it would produce a total amount of 50 mm of rain.

If the rainstorm has a great enough intensity and duration, it will exceed the infiltration rate. Water begins to accumulate in small puddles and pools. It collects in any

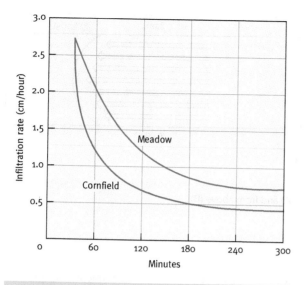

 LINK

Figure 31.2 Infiltration rates for two different vegetated areas. Both show higher rates at the beginning than at the end of the rainfall, but the meadow has higher rates throughout.

hollow on a rough ground surface, detained behind millions of natural micro-dams formed by irregularities in the soil surface, logs, twigs, and heaps of leaves. This situation is called **surface retention**. When there is more rainwater than the small detention hollows can hold, the water flows over the land as surface **runoff** (or *overland flow*). After a short period of detention, any rainfall that does not infiltrate the soil runs off. Thus, as precipitation continues and infiltration rates decrease, runoff rates increase.

Once surface runoff has started, the water continues to flow until it reaches a stream or an area of permeable soil or rock. An area of land on a slope receives all the water that runs off the higher elevations above it. The longer the total flow path is, assuming that the runoff flows across uniform material, the greater the amount of runoff flowing across the area. Therefore, the largest runoff rates occur at the base of a slope, just before the runoff enters a stream. The slope base is where wetter gleisolic or organic soils are found. This emphasizes the need for sound land management practices. If water is needed for raising crops, then the less that runs off the better. Because infiltration and runoff rates are inversely related, runoff depends on all the factors that affect infiltration. By employing appropriate farming techniques, high infiltration rates can be maintained and runoff rates reduced (see Figure 44.1).

LINK Water Flow in Streams

A study of stream flow helps us to make predictions about such matters as pollution and floods. From the smallest flow in a tiny rivulet to the largest flow in a major river, certain general rules apply.

Stream Channels

One fundamental property of a stream channel is its **gradient**, or slope, the difference in elevation between two points along the stream course. Gradients can be measured for the entire course of a stream or over a reach (a short stretch of it). When a gradient is high, the flow of water is very turbulent, as in a mountain stream that has rapids and falls along its channel (Figure 31.3). By contrast, the lower portions of rivers such as the Mackenzie and the Amazon have very low gradients. The Amazon River, for instance, falls only about 6 m over its final 800 km.

 LINK

Figure 31.3 Lower Falls, Gold River, near Alouette Lake, Golden Ears Provincial Park, BC.

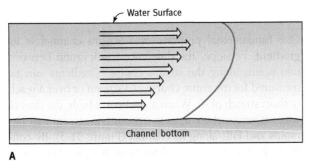
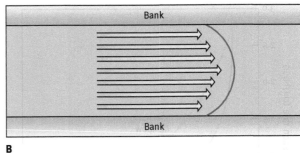

A   **B**

Figure 31.4   Velocity variation in a stream, viewed from the side (**A**) and from above (**B**).

Not all water in a stream channel moves at the same speed, or **velocity**. Water tends to move fastest in the centre of the channel, just below the surface, and slowest close to the bed and banks of the channel, where it encounters roughness and resistance (Figure 31.4). The **discharge (Q)** of a stream is the volume of water passing a given point along the channel (a station) per unit of time. It is measured using the average water velocity (m/s) multiplied by the cross-sectional area (m²). Thus, **Q** (discharge) is measured in m³/s.

In Canada the Water Survey and provincial and territorial agencies maintain gauging stations on numerous streams of all sizes (over 3000 stations). Two types of observations are made at these facilities: (1) water depth and (2) velocity. These data can be used to construct a *rating curve* from which the discharge can be ascertained for a certain flow depth (Figure 31.5).

Long-term records of stream discharge are very important in flood-control strategies and dam construction. Discharge and sediment records indicate how much material the stream can carry downstream in suspension (i.e., kept in the flow by its turbulence and movement). This reflects the stream's effectiveness as an erosional agent. The problem is that data are only available for some streams and in most cases these data cover only the last 50 years or less.

Stream Flow

Measurements of stream flows and sediment loads produce some surprises. For example, some sparkling mountain 'torrents' have lower velocities than the placid lower segments of the Mackenzie River. This happens because water in mountain streams is very turbulent and often flows in circular **eddies**, so that backward movement is almost as great as the forward movement. Only careful measurement can prove the eye wrong. Hydrologists have devised various instruments to obtain some measure of the flow properties of streams. Some of these instruments are designed to be hung from bridges or other structures, and other stations use monitored weirs or culverts. Once installed, they record the behaviour of the stream.

The most important aspect of a stream to be measured is its discharge, from which other properties can be deduced. But discharge varies—by season, by year, and over longer periods. A graph of a stream's discharge over time is called a **hydrograph** (Figure 31.6), and the one shown here records a 10-day period during which the discharge was affected by a storm in Nova Scotia's St Mary River drainage basin. This is only one event in that river's life. The longer the hydrographic record is, the more accurate our knowledge of a stream basin's hydrology.

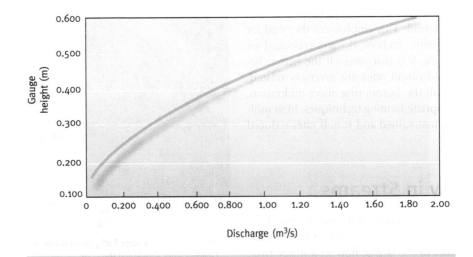

Figure 31.5   A rating curve (stage-discharge) for Sheridan Creek, interior British Columbia.

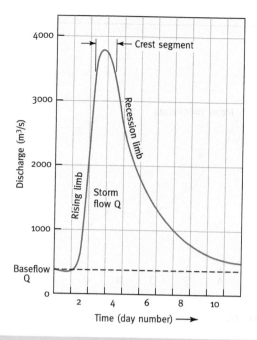

Figure 31.6 Hydrograph for the St Mary River, Nova Scotia, showing the discharge associated with an individual storm.

Seasonal Variations

Stream discharge varies throughout a year because of changes in the amount of rainfall, snowfall, and snowmelt, freezing of the ground surface, and vegetation cover (deciduous vegetation loses its leaves in the fall and cannot transpire during part of the fall, the winter, and part of the spring until leaves grow again). Obviously, such variations differ from year to year, and over the long term as climates change.

Discharge comes from two sources. (1) **Stormflow runoff**, supplied by rainfall or snowmelt (overland flow), is sporadic and occurs only during and just after rainfall or snowmelt. It pulses across the drainage basin surface and brings both water and fine sediment (which it erodes from the ground surface en route) to the stream channel. (2) **Baseflow**, supplied by the slow, constant release of groundwater into the channel through its bed and banks, carries dissolved solids or minerals in solution that were removed from the soil and rocks as the water infiltrated and moved through them.

Figures 31.7–31.10 give some idea of the variation of stream discharge across Canada. Note that the timing of snowmelt (and/or ice melt) varies with temperature, latitude, and altitude. The peak annual flood of these streams also varies. The freshet of the Fraser River at Mission, BC, for example, is in June because it is fed by ice and snowmelt in the Rockies and the central interior of British Columbia, and is not related to conditions at Mission in the Lower Mainland. The Cornelia River is an *ephemeral stream*, which runs only for a few months a year because it is located on Baffin Island, where the melt season arrives later and lasts for a very short period. Alkali Creek in southeastern Alberta is another ephemeral stream (in the semi-arid Palliser's Triangle area). It may flow during the spring melt and in response to summer rainstorms.

Relation of Discharge, Sediment Concentration, and Dissolved Solids

Data are available for the discharge (m³/s), suspended sediment concentration (mg/L), and dissolved solid concentration (mg/L) for many streams in Canada. If these variables (mean monthly figures) are graphed it is possible to see the relationship between them and seasonal changes in the landscape, and also the relationship between the variables.

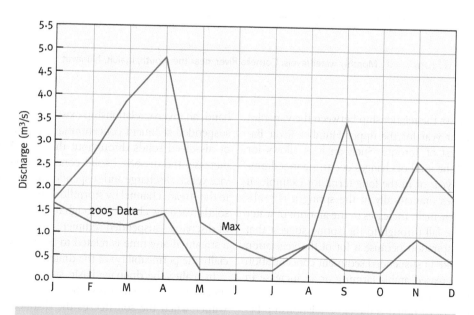

Figure 31.7 Stream discharge, Etobicoke Creek, Brampton, Ontario.

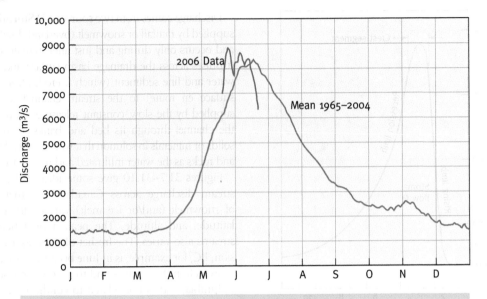

Figure 31.8   Stream discharge, Fraser River, Mission, BC.

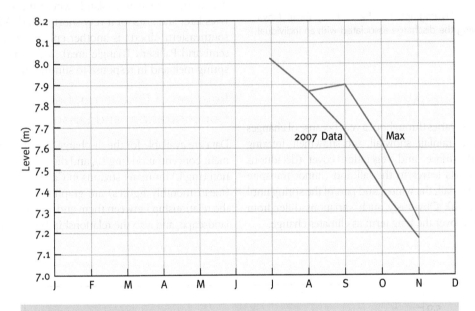

Figure 31.9   Monthly water levels, Cornelia River, near the mouth, Iqaluit, Nunavut.

Figure 31.11 shows the relationship between the variables over one calendar year for the upper Humber River Basin, just northwest of Toronto. Such analysis allows for interpretation of the kind of changes occurring in a drainage basin over a year or in the long term; for example, if discharge increases dramatically in the spring it is probably related to snowmelt. Increases in the amount of water in a stream in the fall through to the spring suggest that there is less transpiration because a lot of the vegetation is dormant. A spike in suspended sediment concentration might suggest increased arable farming or an increase in construction in the basin.

The first thing to be noted is the close relationship between discharge and suspended sediment concentration. These increase and decrease in lockstep. On the other hand, an inverse relationship exists between discharge and suspended sediment concentration and the concentration of dissolved solids throughout the year. As the first two increase, the dissolved solid concentration decreases and vice versa. Discharge and suspended sediment are supplied to the stream channel by stormflow runoff, while dissolved solids reach the channel through the baseflow. The amount of discharge, suspended sediment, and dissolved solids in a stream at any time is related to the character (and especially the permeability) of the drainage basin surface.

In reality, the drainage basin surface is a patchwork of different types of surface with differing permeabilities (in winter when the soil freezes the distinction may not be as pronounced). The permeability of the drainage basin surface is influenced by soil type, vegetation cover (type

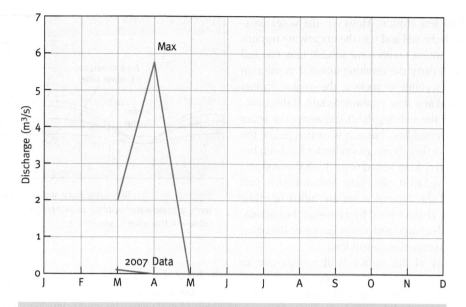

Figure 31.10 Stream discharge, Alkali Creek, near the mouth, Empress, Alberta.

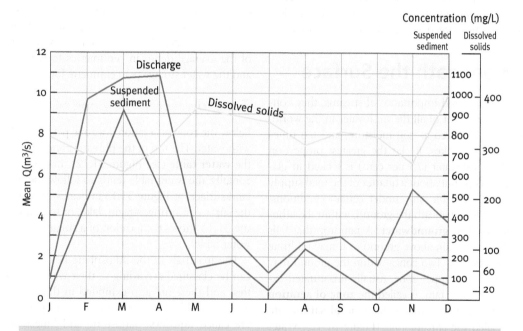

Figure 31.11 Relationship of discharge, suspended sediment concentration, and dissolved solids, Humber River at Elder Mills, Ontario. The data are 30-year means.

and amount), the number of streams, and land use (natural landscape such as forest, agriculture, suburban, urban, etc.), as well as transitory characteristics like soil moisture, the position of the water table, and freezing and thawing of the soil. The character of the precipitation events also is important: the intensity and duration of rainfall, the area affected by rainfall and snowmelt, etc. Some of the above characteristics are fairly permanent while others, such as soil type, change slowly and still others can change rapidly as a result of human-built environments.

Permeability greatly influences how water, sediment, and dissolved solids reach the streams. If the surface is impermeable, most rainfall or snow meltwater will become stormflow (which can have a very short residence time) and run across the soil surface picking up small soil particles. Thus, the stormflow runoff and suspended sediment inputs arrive at the channels at the same time. The input is sporadic and the type of flow regime this leads to is called an ephemeral or *flashy regime* (hence the term 'flash flood'). For most of the time there is little discharge (little sediment transport) but at other times—during and after rainfall or snowmelt—lots of water and suspended sediment are in the streams.

If the surface is permeable more rainfall or meltwater will infiltrate into the soil and less will run off. This means that there will be less erosion. However, the water passing down through the soil and into the underlying regolith and/or rocks will interact with some soluble minerals and weather them and carry the resulting material in solution through the soils, regolith, or rocks to the stream channel where it is released at a slow, continuous rate. If this water is carried through the soils/regolith/rocks above the water table it is called *throughflow*, but if it is carried below the water table it is baseflow. Some groundwater has been below ground for a very long period (over 10,000 years) and is just being released to streams now. Stream basins with a greater input of this type of water are called baseflow regimes. These are characterized by a constant but usually small amount of discharge and a dominance of dissolved solid load over suspended sediment load.

The permeability of the surface is also important in terms of influencing the streams in a stream network. If the surface is impermeable, less water can infiltrate into the ground and more water will have to be evacuated from an area by streams. Consequently, there will be more streams. The reverse is true when the surface is more permeable. More water can infiltrate and travel underground, and less will need to be discharged across the surface by streams.

Water beneath the Surface

Despite the beauty and importance of streams, they contain only 0.03 per cent of all the freshwater in the world. Twice as much is stored as soil moisture, and ten times as much is held in lakes. By far the greatest proportion of the world's freshwater (75 per cent) is locked in glaciers and ice sheets. But about a quarter of the total supply of freshwater is available only under certain conditions. This water is hidden beneath the ground, within the lithosphere, and is called **groundwater**. A raindrop that falls to the Earth may remain above ground or it may infiltrate into the soil and rock. Two zones within the ground may hold this water. The upper zone, usually unsaturated except at times of heavy rain, is called the **zone of aeration** or the *vadose zone*; below this is the **zone of saturation**, sometimes called the *phreatic zone* (Figure 31.12). Water infiltrates into the vadose zone first.

Soil Moisture in the Zone of Aeration

Once rainwater has infiltrated into the soil, it is called *soil moisture*, and any further movement is by processes other than infiltration. The downward movement of water through the pores and spaces in the soil under the influence of gravity, called **percolation**, is the most common method of water movement in a soil. In a contrary motion, described in Unit 44, water may also move upward, like liquid in a straw, through *capillary action*. Moisture also can move around within the soil through evaporation, movement of water vapour, and recondensation onto new surfaces.

The texture and structure of the soil determine the amount of water it can hold. **Field capacity** is the maximum amount of water that a soil can hold by capillary tension against

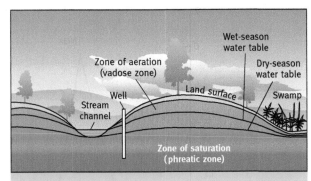

Figure 31.12 Two subsurface water-holding zones. The term *groundwater* applies to water lying below the water table—in the zone of saturation.

the force of gravity. Theoretically, soil moisture can fall to zero. But it takes a lot of drying to reach this limit because a thin film of water clings tenaciously to most soil particles. This *hygroscopic* water is unavailable to plant roots. A more practical lower limit to soil moisture is termed the *wilting point*, and it varies for different soils and crops. Below this point a plant dries out, suffering permanent injury. The total *soil storage capacity* for agricultural purposes is the product of the average depth in centimetres to which roots grow and the water storage per centimetre for that soil type.

Groundwater in the Zone of Saturation

Below the zone of aeration is a zone permanently saturated with water. The top of the phreatic zone is a surface called the **water table** (see Figure 31.12). Instead of lying horizontally, the water table tends to follow the outline of the land surface, as Figure 31.13 indicates. Where it intersects the surface, a spring, stream, lake, or wetland occurs (Figure 31.13 shows the location of a stream in relation to the water table).

The materials of the lithosphere below the water table can be classified according to their water-holding properties, and these are also exhibited in the diagram. Porous and permeable layers that can be at least partially saturated are called **aquifers**. Sandstone and limestone often are good aquifers. Other rock layers, such as mudstone and shale, consist of tightly packed or interlocking particles and, therefore, are usually quite impermeable and resist groundwater infiltration. These are known as **aquicludes** (sometimes called *aquitards*).

An *unconfined aquifer* obtains its water from local infiltration, but a *confined aquifer* exists between aquicludes and often obtains its water from a distant area where the rock layer of the aquifer is exposed at the surface (as shown in the upper right-hand portion of Figure 31.13).

Springs and Wells

In many parts of the world, settlements are located near wells and springs. In such cases, geology directly influences human locational decision-making. Wells can be dug or drilled wherever an aquifer lies below the surface, and in

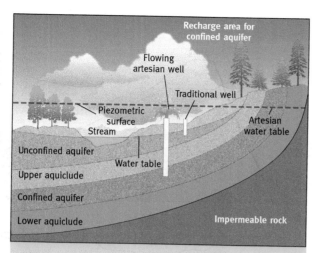

Figure 31.13 Aquifers, aquicludes, and their relationship to the water table and wells.

infiltration by other chemicals. A submersible pump is then installed to raise water to the surface.

The French region of Artois has a confined aquifer whose water supply is recharged from a remote location. Wells sunk into this aquifer produce water that flows to the surface under its own natural pressure (see Figure 31.13). Artois has lent its name to this type of well, and now **artesian wells** are common in many parts of the world, especially Australia, but they do occur in Canada in Saskatchewan (in Dakota sandstone) and southern Ontario. The hydrostatic, or *piezometric*, pressure in artesian wells can sometimes be quite strong because the water table in the aquifer is higher than the ground surface where the well is located (the groundwater has 'a lot of head'). One artesian well dug in the Prairies spouted water over 30 m into the air and had to be plugged with 15 truckloads of rock before it could be brought under control.

Wells sometimes suffer from side effects that limit their use. In some cases the water is withdrawn faster than it can be replaced by water flowing through the aquifer. When this happens, the local water table directly surrounding the well drops, forming a *cone of depression* like that in Figure 31.14A. The amount of the drop in the local water table is called the *drawdown*. When it drops, energy must be used to bring the water to the surface. In addition, salt water can intrude into a well near a coastline. Excessive pumping gradually moves denser, saline sea water (a saline wedge) into the well, as diagrammed in Figure 31.14B. Wells, therefore, must be used with care.

Flowing water that emerges from the ground is called a **spring**. Springs can be formed in a number of ways. Most commonly, an aquiclude stops the downward percolation of water, which is then forced to flow from a hillside, as indicated in Figure 31.15A. Occasionally, as this diagram also shows, the aquiclude leads to the formation of a separate water table, called a **perched water table**, at a higher elevation than the main water table. Sometimes water finds its way through joints in otherwise impermeable rocks, such

most cases springs are formed when an aquifer intersects the surface. In recent years the effect of agricultural runoff on well-water quality has been in the news because of the pollution of groundwater (in artesian wells) and the resulting health hazard for those dependent on the water supply, as occurred in the Walkerton area of southern Ontario in May 2000 when seven people died and hundreds became ill.

There are two kinds of wells—the traditional and the artesian. The *traditional well* is simply a circular opening or drill hole in the ground that penetrates the water table. Water is then drawn or pumped to the surface. Traditional wells usually are sunk below the average level of the water table. The actual level of the water table may vary seasonally and because of droughts or long periods of rainfall. So the deeper the well is sunk below the water table, the less chance there is of the well becoming dry when the water table falls. Most modern wells are drilled, cased in metal or plastic from the surface into the water table to prevent contamination from surface runoff (e.g., road salt) and

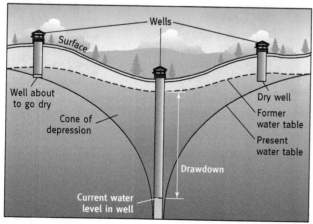

A

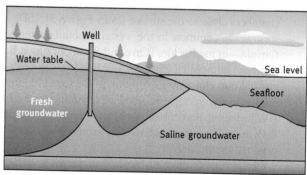

B

Figure 31.14 Potential disadvantages of wells. When water is pumped out faster than it can be replaced, the local water table drops in the form of a cone of depression (**A**). Near a coastline, excessive pumping can lead to the intrusion of seawater into the well (**B**).

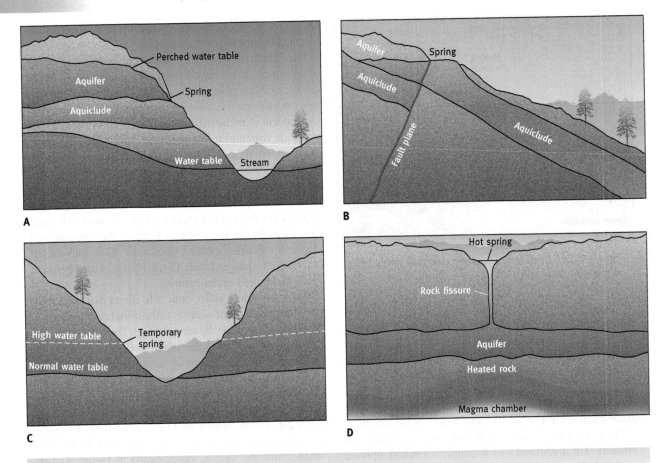

A

B

C

D

Figure 31.15 Conditions leading to the formation of springs.

as granite, and springs form where it reaches the surface. Often, faulting rearranges aquifers and aquicludes so that springs form, as shown in Figure 31.15B. And exceptionally high water tables after long periods of heavy rainfall can occasionally raise the water level high enough to cause temporary springs, as shown in Figure 31.15C.

An interesting variation is the formation of **hot springs**. The water flowing from these has a temperature averaging more than 8°C above the mean air temperature (another of various definitions is a temperature above normal human body temperature, or >37°C). It often comes from springs overlying portions of the Earth's crust that contain magma chambers close to the surface (as in Figure 31.15D). Hot springs are common in the western mountain region of Canada—in the Rockies (Cave and Basin Springs at Banff, Alberta; Fairmont Hot Springs, BC; Liard Hot Springs, BC; and Takhini Hot Springs, Yukon), in the Coast Mountains (Harrison Hot Springs, BC), and in Nahanni National Park, NWT (Rabbit Kettle Hot Springs). Yellowstone National Park in the United States has many geothermal springs and geysers (Figure 31.16).

Geothermal steam can be used to produce electricity. Heated water from hot springs is used to run the Svartsengi geothermal power station, which supplies most of Reykjavik, the capital of Iceland, with electricity. Submarine, mineral-rich hot water springs also occur in spreading zones. These are called **black and white smokers**

Figure 31.16 Old Faithful geyser in Yellowstone National Park, which erupts approximately once an hour. A *geyser* is a hot spring that periodically expels jets of heated water and steam.

(the colour depends on the mineral content of the water coming out of the vents). They are associated with the deposition of mineral-rich smoker chimneys and with *chemotrophic* communities of tube worms (which do not possess mouths or anuses and are basically bags filled with chemotrophic bacteria), crabs, and fish. Most of these creatures are white because they live deep in the ocean, remote from solar energy.

Hot springs containing large quantities of minerals dissolved from the surrounding rocks are sometimes called *mineral springs*, and the mineral water may be used for medicinal purposes. Although it is pleasant to sit in the warm-water bath of a tapped mineral spring, this is one of the less important uses of water. A far more significant human impact is the growing pollution of subsurface water supplies (see 'Perspectives' box).

Lakes

A lake is a body of fresh or salt water of varying size that is completely surrounded by land. Like streams, lakes have drainage basins that supply them with water and sediment. These basins are generally fed by streams. All lakes have one or more forms of outflow: a stream, seepage through the ground, or evaporation. Canada has approximately 60 per cent of the world's lakes. Therefore, it is important to know how they formed and how they function. The study of lakes, lake sediments, and ecosystems is called **limnology**.

Types of Lakes

Lakes can be formed by many natural processes: tectonic rifting (e.g., Okanagan Lake, BC); volcanic activity (caldera

---

Perspectives on the Human Environment

Groundwater Contamination

Residents of highly developed, industrialized countries have long taken it for granted that when they turn on a faucet, safe, potable water will flow from the tap. Throughout most of the rest of the world, however, the available water—particularly groundwater—is usually unfit for human consumption. Although natural dissolved substances make some of this water undrinkable, the more common situation is that these groundwater supplies have become contaminated through the introduction of human, industrial, or agricultural wastes at the surface (e.g., Walkerton, Ontario).

The most common source of water pollution in wells and springs is sewage. Drainage from septic tanks, malfunctioning sewers, privies, and barnyards widely contaminates groundwater. If water contaminated with sewage (coliform) bacteria passes through soil and/or rock with sizable openings, such as coarse gravel or cavity-pocked limestone, it can travel considerable distances while remaining polluted.

Vast quantities of human refuse and industrial waste products are also deposited in shallow basins at the land surface. When such a landfill site reaches its capacity, it is usually sealed within an impermeable membrane, topped by a layer of soil, and then revegetated. (Older landfills, and there are thousands of them, large and small, have simply been abandoned.) Many of the waste products, now buried below ground, are activated by rainwater that percolates downward through the site, carrying away soluble substances. In this manner, harmful chemicals slowly seep into aquifers and contaminate them. The pollutants migrate from landfill sites as plumes of contaminated water, following the regional groundwater flow regime, and they are dispersed at the same rates as the natural flow of subsurface water. Moreover, these effluents are frequently toxic not only to humans but also to plants and animals in the larger biotic environment.

Yet another hazard is posed by toxic chemicals. Each year pesticides and herbicides are sprayed in massive quantities over countless farm fields to improve crop quality and productivity. As is well known, some of these chemicals have been linked to cancers and birth defects in humans; other toxic substances of this type have led to disastrous declines in animal populations. Because of the way in which they are spread, toxic agricultural chemicals can invade the groundwater system beneath huge areas as precipitation flushes them into the soil.

LINK

lakes, such as Crater Lake, Oregon); meteoric impact (Cratere Pingualuit, Ungava, Quebec); migration and abandonment of old channel sections by meandering streams; glacial erosion (e.g., the Great Lakes and many of the lakes in the Canadian Shield and in the Rockies and other alpine areas). Fjord lakes are formed where flooded glacial troughs have been uplifted (or sea level has dropped) and have been cut off from the sea, for example, some of the relic fjords in the Gros Morne area of Newfoundland or some of the valleys in the southwestern area of BC, such as the Pitt River Valley or the Sakinaw Valley on the Sunshine Coast. Proglacial lakes are formed at the margins of glaciers or at the edges of former ice sheets. A good example of the latter is glacial Lake Agassiz, which was an enormous lake ponded up between the ice margin and low escarpments and ridges. This proglacial lake covered a very large area of the Prairies towards the end of the Wisconsinan glaciations. Vestiges of that very extensive lake remain as Lakes Winnipeg and Manitoba.

Lakes also are formed in low-lying areas of periglacial areas over permafrost, and occur in ice sheets and glaciers—about 150 *englacial* lakes are known in Antarctica, the largest of which is Lake Vostock, about the size of Lake Ontario and located 4000 m below the surface of the ice. Underground lakes occur in caves in karst areas. Aeolic lakes form in depressions caused by deflation of sand in arid environments. Of course, there are also many artificial lakes (reservoirs) created by damming streams to provide water for domestic, recreational, industrial, and agricultural uses, irrigation, and the generation of electricity, and to control stream discharge (flood and erosion prevention). Large Canadian examples of reservoirs are Williston Lake, impounded by the W.A.C. Bennett Dam on the Peace River near Hudson's Hope, BC; Lake McNaughton, formed by the Mica Dam on the Columbia

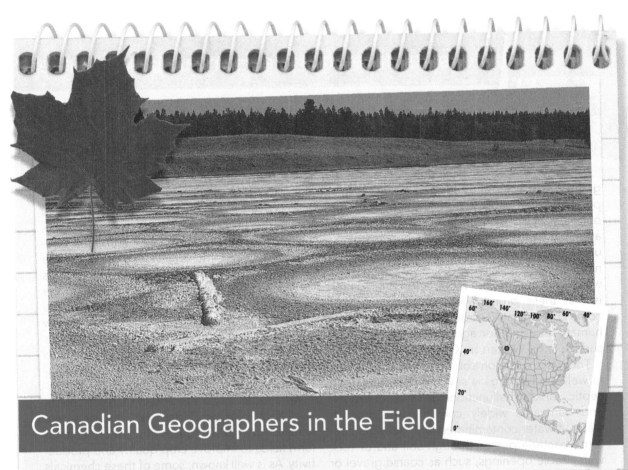

Canadian Geographers in the Field

'*This photo shows unusual patterns in the drying bed of Last Chance Lake, near Clinton, BC. I have been working with an old undergraduate friend, Professor Robin Renault, a geochemist in the Geological Sciences Department at the University of Saskatchewan, on the patterned lakes and travertine mounds of interior BC. We want to find out why certain saline and epsomite lakes dry out to form these patterns while others do not (geochemistry? freezing?).*'

Peter Long is a Pleistocene geomorphologist. He was trained at the University of London in the UK and has been at York University for 22 years.

River north of Revelstoke in southeastern BC; and the Reservoir Manicouagan behind the series of dams on the Rivieres Manicouagan and Outardes (Manic or Manicouagan 1, 2, etc.) built by Hydro-Québec. A number of large reservoirs also have been created in the James Bay region of Quebec as a result of the James Bay hydroelectric project.

Endorheic lakes have no apparent outflows and lose water through evaporation and/or seepage. These are common in arid areas, and many are saline or alkaline. Very large examples of saline lakes are the Aral Sea, Caspian Sea, Dead Sea, and Great Salt Lake. These bodies of water are *hypersaline* and have salinities far in excess of sea water. Smaller endorheic lakes occur throughout the more arid parts of the world, and many of these are *playas*, or lakes that totally evaporate leaving a salt or alkaline (such as epsomite) pan. In Canada they are found in Palliser's Triangle and the central interior of BC.

Classification of Lakes by Nutrient Content

Lakes can be classified in terms of their nutrient content. This is influenced a great deal by the amount of dissolved oxygen in the water, by the pH, and by the amount and type of sediments and dissolved solids entering the lake. Pollutants also are an important input. We can distinguish four types of lakes based on nutrient content:

1. *Oligotrophic lakes* are clear, nutrient-poor bodies of water with a very restricted biota (both in terms of the number and types of organisms).
2. *Mesotrophic lakes* have clear water and an average level of nutrients. Most lakes fall in to this category.
3. *Eutrophic lakes* are nutrient-rich with a profusion of aquatic plants and are subject to algal blooms.
4. *Hypertrophic lakes* are excessively nutrient-rich. Water clarity is lacking and there are many algal blooms because of an excess of nutrients and a decrease in

dissolved oxygen content. This state often arises as a result of runoff from agricultural and livestock operations, industry, or municipal sewerage systems.

Ecological Zones and Stratification

The water column of a lake can be divided into three ecological zones based on the penetration of sunlight. This depends on the clarity or turbidity of the water, which in turn is determined by water density and the amount and size of suspended sediment. (1) The *littoral zone* is the sloped area of the lake bed adjacent to the land and usually has a lot of sunlight penetration. (2) The *photic zone* is an area of open water with abundant sunlight penetration. (3) The *benthic* (or *profundal*) *zone* is a deep-water zone with little sunlight penetration.

As well as having three ecological zones, the water column of a lake is stratified because of the relationship between water temperature and density. This causes the layering or stratification of the lake water. Freshwater is densest at about 4°C at sea level. It is possible to divide the lake water column on the basis of water temperature and density into (1) the *epilimnion*, the top layer of oxygenated water heated by solar energy during the daytime (and summer), which cools down during the night (and winter). In some areas, as in most of Canada, this layer freezes during the coldest months. (2) The *thermocline*, or *metalimnion*, is the transitional middle layer of water that may change depth over the day and/or over the year. (3) The *hypolimnion* is the anoxic bottom layer of the water column (Figure 31.17).

The Movement of Lake Water

The surface of a lake is affected by winds (wind speed, duration, etc.) that can generate wave activity and, in larger lakes such as the Great Lakes, wind-driven currents. The inflow of large amounts of water and sediment from

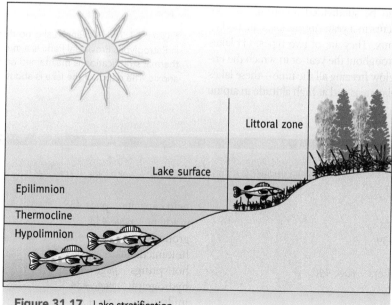

Figure 31.17   Lake stratification.

streams can also affect the circulation of lake water. Wind and differences in air pressure can set up a **seiche** or oscillation of the lake surface (rather like the sloshing of water in a bathtub). This can be shown using the passage of a high-pressure weather system across Lake Ontario as an example. When the high-pressure system is over the southern part of the lake, it depresses that part of the lake surface; winds blow out from the high pressure and the pressure and wave action displace water to the north and the lake level will rise slightly along the north shore of the lake. When the high-pressure system is in the centre of the lake it will cause depression of the water under it and water will be displaced both to the north and south and will cause the lake level to rise along both shores. When the high pressure gets to the north side of the lake it pushes down the water surface there and water is displaced to the south side of the lake. In this way a see-sawing motion is created on the lake surface (or a *seiche* is produced).

The surface movement of the lake water in response to wind is responsible for the mixing or 'turning' of the lake water column (*mixis*) in most lakes. Some lakes do not have this stratification and are composed entirely of an epilimnion layer. These lakes are called *meres*. Lakes can be classified by how frequently mixing occurs.

- In **holomictic lakes** the entire water column is involved in the mixing process.
- **Meromictic lakes** maintain their thermal stratification for extended periods. The bottom of these lakes is anoxic and whatever falls into the basal layers—from pollen to artifacts—is preserved. These lakes are usually pocket-shaped, with a small surface area but a deep basin. The shape precludes wind-generated mixing. Examples in Canada include Pink Lake (Gatineau Park, Quebec), Crawford Lake (Niagara Escarpment near Campbellville, Ontario), McGinnis Lake (Petroglyphs Provincial Park northeast of Peterborough, Ontario), and Mahoney Lake (near Willowbrook in the Okanagan Valley, BC).

Holomictic lakes can be subdivided according to how many times mixing occurs in a year. *Amictic lakes* are bodies of water that do not mix. They are of two types: (1) lakes that are ice-covered throughout the year or in which the entire water column is below freezing all the time—these lakes occur in polar/near polar areas and at high altitude in alpine areas; and (2) deep tropical lakes that do not mix because the water never reaches temperatures where water density is sufficient to cause mixis. There are two kinds of *monomictic lakes*, where mixing occurs once a year. Warm monomictic lakes are usually found in tropical areas. They undergo mixing during a brief period in the hottest part of the year when the thermal stratification of the water column breaks down, while cold monomictic lakes are ice-covered for most of the year and mix during a brief ice-free summer period. *Dimictic lakes* undergo mixing twice a year, usually in spring and fall. *Polymictic lakes* mix several times a year. The mixing is in response to daily temperature changes rather than seasonal changes. Finally, *oligomictic lakes* are mostly tropical. They experience unusual, irregular, and short periods of mixing.

Conclusion

The movement of water on and through the surface of the Earth has important consequences for the erosion, transportation, and deposition of surficial materials. In the following units we highlight the various pathways this water takes, the environmental controls determining their relative magnitudes, and the resultant geomorphic work that is being done. We begin our survey in Unit 32, which explores the processes of stream erosion.

Figure 31.18   McGinnis Lake, north of Norwood, Ontario, in Petroglyphs Provincial Park, is a meromictic lake, in which thermal stratification is maintained and the bottom layer is anoxic. The depth of the lake is about 15 m.

KEY TERMS

aquiclude   *page 438*
aquifer   *page 438*
artesian well   *page 439*
baseflow   *page 435*
black and white smokers   *page 440*
discharge   *page 434*
eddies   *page 434*

field capacity   *page 438*
gradient   *page 433*
groundwater   *page 438*
holomictic lakes   *page 444*
hot springs   *page 440*
hydrograph   *page 434*
infiltration   *page 432*

REVIEW QUESTIONS

1. What general factors influence infiltration characteristics within a soil mass?
2. What is a hydrograph?
3. How does the water table relate to the zones of aeration and saturation?
4. Describe an aquifer and an aquiclude.
5. What is an artesian well?
6. How do meromictic and holomictic lakes differ?

REFERENCES AND FURTHER READINGS

Baldwin, H.L., and C.I. McGuinness. 1963. *A Primer on Groundwater.* Washington: US Geological Survey.

Cech, T.V. 2003. *Water Resources.* New York: Wiley.

Chapelle, F.H. 1997. *The Hidden Sea: Ground Water, Science, and Environmental Realism.* Tucson, Ariz.: Geoscience Press.

Freeze, R.A., and J.A. Cherry. 1979. *Groundwater.* Englewood Cliffs, NJ: Prentice-Hall.

Gleick, P.H. 2000. *The World's Water 2000–2001: The Biennial Report on Freshwater Resources.* Washington: Island Press.

Gregory, K.J., and D.E. Walling. 1998. *Drainage Basins: Form, Process and Management.* Malden, Mass.: Blackwell.

Gurnell, A., and G. Petts, eds. 1996. *River Channels.* New York: Wiley.

Hickin, E.J., ed. 1995. *River Geomorphology.* New York: Wiley.

Leopold, L.B. 1974. *Water: A Primer.* San Francisco: Freeman.

———. 1994. *A View of the River.* Cambridge, Mass.: Harvard Univ. Press.

Lerman, A., et al. eds. 1995. *Physics and Chemistry of Lakes,* 2nd edn. New York: Springer-Verlag.

McAndrews, J.H., and M. Boyko-Diakonow. 1989. 'Pollen Analysis of Varved Sediments at Crawford Lake, Ontario: Evidence of Indian and European Farming', in R.J. Fulton, ed., *Quaternary Geology of Canada and Greenland,* vol. 1. Ottawa: Geological Survey of Canada.

Martin, J.L., and S.C. McCutcheon. 1998. *Hydrodynamics and Transport for Water Quality Modeling.* London: CRC Press.

Mather, J.R. 1984. *Water Resources: Distribution, Use, and Management.* New York: Wiley/Winston.

Maurits La Rivière, J.W. 1989. 'Threats to the World's Water', *Scientific American* (Sept.): 80–94.

Miller, D.H. 1977. *Water at the Surface of the Earth: An Introduction to Ecosystem Hydrodynamics.* New York: Academic Press.

Moore, J.E., and W.E. Wilson, eds. 1998. *Glossary of Hydrology.* Alexandria, Va: American Geological Institute.

O'Sullivan, P.E., and C.S. Reynolds, eds. 2003. *The Lakes Handbook, Volume 1: Limnology and Limnetic Ecology.* Oxford: Blackwell.

Outwater, A. 1996. *Water: A Natural History.* New York: Basic Books.

Pielou, E.C. 1998. *Fresh Water.* Chicago: Univ. of Chicago Press.

Price, M. 1985. *Introducing Ground Water.* London/New York: Chapman and Hall.

 ## WEB RESOURCES

www.dnr.state.mn.us/groundwater/aquifers.html This web page provides basic information about aquifer formation and classification. Each type of aquifer is described in detail, and links are provided to other water resource pages.

www.nps.gov/yell/nature/geothermal This site, created by the National Park Service at Yellowstone, is a tutorial covering the mechanisms of many geothermal features, including hot springs, mud pots, fumaroles, mammoth terraces, and geysers. Photographs are included.

www.nwri.ca This website has links to many useful sites that concentrate on all aspects of water in Canada.

Unit 32

Slopes and Streams

Objectives

- To discuss the processes associated with the erosion of hillslopes.

- To outline the factors influencing the erosional activity of streams and to discuss the mechanisms of stream erosion and sediment transport.

- To characterize the stream as a system and to identify the processes associated with this system.

Streams are one of the most important sculptors of terrestrial landscapes. Elsewhere in Part Four, landscapes carved by glaciers, moulded by the wind, and shaped by waves are discussed. However, none of these erosional agents come close to flowing water as the principal creator of landforms and landscapes on our planet. Even where ice sheets advanced and receded, and where deserts exist today, channelized flowing water plays a major role in modifying the surface.

LINK The Latin word for river is *fluvius*, from which the term *fluvial* is derived, denoting running water. Thus, **fluvial processes** are associated with flowing water, and fluvial landforms and landscapes are produced by streams. Unit 28 notes that streams degrade (erode) and aggrade (deposit). Hence the landscape contains *degradational*, or *erosional*, landforms, created when rock is removed, and *aggradational*, or *depositional*, landforms, resulting from the accumulation of sediment. The Grand Canyon of the Nahanni River in the Northwest Territories and that of the Stikine in northwestern BC are essentially erosional landscapes; the Mackenzie River Delta and the Fraser Delta are an assemblage of depositional landforms. After we have studied fluvial processes, we will examine the landscapes they create.

Erosion and the Hydrologic Cycle

LINK

Unit 11 examines the hydrologic cycle, the global system that carries water from sea to land and back again (see Figure 11.6). This unceasing circulation of water ensures the continuation of fluvial erosion because the water that falls on the elevated landmasses will always flow back towards sea level because of the pull of gravity. As it does so, it carries the products of weathering with it.

Rainfall comes in many different forms, from the steady, gentle rain of a cloudy autumn day to the violent heavy downpour associated with a midsummer afternoon thunderstorm. During a misty drizzle, the soil generally is able to absorb all or most of the water because its **infiltration rate** (the rate at which it is able to absorb water from the surface) is not exceeded. This means that no water collects at the surface. But when rain falls at higher intensities, it may quickly saturate the soil and exceed the infiltration rate, resulting in *runoff* (Ri > Ir). Many small, temporary streamlets form, and such runoff causes erosion.

Large, heavy raindrops dislodge soil particles in a process called *rainsplash erosion*, a form of mass movement (Figure 32.1). Once loosened, these grains are quickly carried away by sheet wash or the streamlets that form during an intense rainstorm. If the surface is flat, much of the loosened soil may be deposited nearby, and the area suffers little net soil loss. But if the exposed soil lies on a slope, rainsplash erosion results in a downslope transfer of fine soil particles. The steeper the slope, the faster this process proceeds. If the rate of erosion, over the long term, exceeds the rate of soil formation, the slope will lose its soil cover

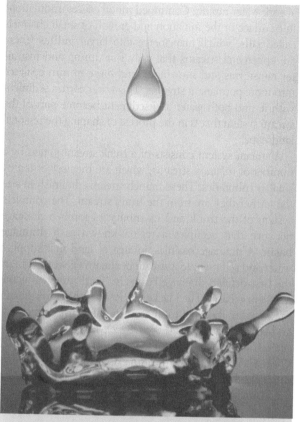

Figure 32.1 Rainsplash erosion. The impact of a drop of water is shown here on a lake surface, but if the drop hits the ground, soil particles are thrown into the air ballistically. If this occurs on a slope, the particles will fall back below their original positions. Cumulatively this process contributes to downslope movement of the uppermost soil surface.

and suffer *denudation* (the reduction in the relief of a landscape resulting from the combined processes of weathering and erosion).

Vegetation plays an important role in restraining erosional forces. Leaves and branches break the fall of raindrops and lessen their erosive impact, and the roots of plants bind the soil and help resist its removal. Leaf litter and grass cover form a cushion between raindrop impact and the soil. Wherever vegetation cover is dense and unbroken, erosion is generally slight. But where natural vegetation is removed to make way for agriculture or construction, or is perhaps decimated by overgrazing or clear-cut logging, accelerated erosion often results (see Figure 43.3).

Streams and Basins

Rain that is not absorbed by the soil runs off as *sheet wash* (*sheet flow*). Sheet wash is a thin layer of water that moves downslope without being confined in a channel. This thin film of water can cause considerable erosion as it removes fine-grained surface materials. Such **sheet erosion** is an important degradational process in certain areas, especially in deserts where the ground is bare and unable to absorb water rapidly. Continued runoff causes undulations in a surface or the initiation and growth of small channels called **rills**, which may merge into larger **gullies** (these are ephemeral streams that only run during and just after rainstorms and snowmelt), and these in turn coalesce into more permanent streams. This water carries sediment with it, and both water and sediment become part of the stream system that is in the process of shaping the regional landscape.

A stream system consists of a *trunk* stream joined by a number of *tributary* streams, which are themselves fed by smaller tributaries. These branch streams diminish in size the farther they are from the trunk stream. The complete system of the trunk and its tributaries forms a drainage network that occupies a region known as a **drainage basin**. A drainage basin is an area of land that supplies water and sediment to a stream or stream network. One of the best-defined drainage basins in North America is the Mackenzie Basin. The Mackenzie River is the trunk stream in the basin; the chief tributaries are the Liard, Arctic Red, and Hare Indian Rivers (Figure 32.2). Two other large tributaries are the Peace River, which drains into Slave and Great Slave Lakes, and the Athabasca River, which flows into Lake Athabasca. Great Slave Lake and Lake Athabasca are major sources of the Mackenzie River.

Streams within a network can be assigned a rank according to their size (this is called *stream numbering* or *morphometry*). The smallest streams are ranked as first-order streams; when two of these streams join, the larger reach of the stream formed by their union ranks as a second-order stream, and so on (Figure 32.3).

A drainage basin is defined by the organization and orientation of water flow. Within it, all streams flow into other streams that ultimately join the trunk stream. The drainage basin supplies runoff and sediment to sustain the stream. A drainage basin is also sometimes referred to as a *watershed*. Adjacent drainage basins are separated from each other by topographical rises called drainage *divides*. One of the most prominent divides in the world is the Continental Divide in western North America, where it follows the spine of the Rocky Mountains (see Figure 36.1B). Water from the eastern slope of the Rocky Mountains in Canada flows across the Prairies and into Hudson Bay (Figure 32.2). Water on the western slope drains into streams that flow into the Pacific Ocean. Farther north, water flows off the Rockies through streams flowing to the Arctic Ocean. Canada has four major drainage basins: the Pacific Basin, the Arctic Basin (of which the Mackenzie Basin is a part), the Hudson Bay Basin, and the Atlantic Basin. A very small portion of southern

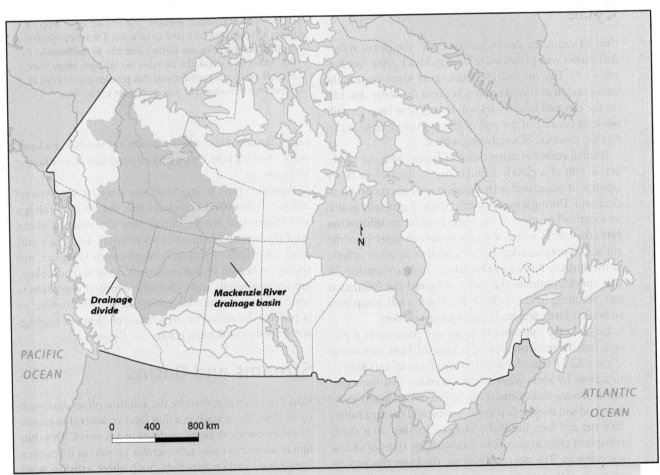

Figure 32.2 The Mackenzie River drainage basin is part of the larger Arctic Basin (see Figure 33.11).

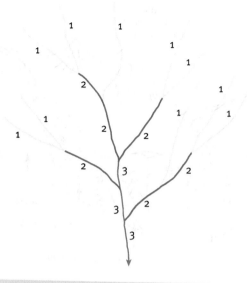

Figure 32.3 A stream-ordering system.

Saskatchewan and Alberta is part of the Gulf of Mexico Basin (see Figure 33.11).

To assess the erosional activity of a stream system in a defined basin, physical geographers take a number of measurements. An obvious one is the quantity of sediment that passes a point on a stream at or near its mouth. The measurement of the total volume of sediment leaving a stream basin in a year is the *sediment yield* (tonnes/yr). But this may not reveal all the erosional work that goes on inside the drainage basin, because some sediment is deposited as **alluvium** at the lower ends of slopes and in the floodplains of streams and thus does not reach the lowest part of the trunk stream.

Another set of measurements identifies every stream segment of the network and the sedimentary load carried by each one. This research has yielded some interesting results. It might be expected, for example, that the larger a drainage basin, the larger the sediment load carried by the streams. But this is not always the case. The vast Amazon Basin of equatorial South America, for instance, is more than six times as large as the basin of India's Ganges River. But its annual sediment load, measured at the Amazon's mouth, is less than one-fifth that of the Ganges. Other comparisons also indicate that basin size and the amount of sediment yield are not reliable indicators of the amount of erosion that occurs within a drainage basin. Most of the erosion in the Amazon Basin occurs through solution. The Amazon's solution load (dissolved solid) is far greater and far more important than its sediment load.

What influences the rate of erosion? Obviously, the amount and type of weathering are major factors. In the Amazon Basin, because of the high temperatures and humidity, chemical weathering is intense and occurs to great depths (>30–50 m plus in places). The amount of precipitation is a factor—more water means more erosion. But the cover of vegetation also plays an important role because it inhibits erosion. The dense canopy of the forests retains a lot of the precipitation and a significant amount of it is

evaporated back into the atmosphere without ever reaching the forest floor. The rainforests in the Amazon Basin undoubtedly help slow down erosion; but as these tropical rainforests are removed—at a prodigious pace, as is explained in Unit 17—the rate of erosion also increases. The *relief* in the drainage basin is important as well. In a basin where the relief is generally low, slopes are less steep, water moves more slowly and allows more infiltration, and erosion is less active than in a basin where the relief is high.

Another factor is the underlying **lithology**, or rock type. More easily eroded sedimentary and metamorphic rocks are degraded much more rapidly than are more competent crystalline rocks. In fact, any factors influencing the permeability of the drainage basin surface also influence erosion rates. More permeable surfaces such as sandy or gravelly soils allow more infiltration. This means that there is less surface erosion, but as the water moves below the surface it interacts with minerals in the soil, sediments, and rocks, and weathers some of this material, putting it into solution (dissolved solids). This groundwater is released at a fairly slow and constant rate to the stream. *Human impact* must also be a factor influencing stream-basin erosion rates. Although human activity can affect the fluvial system in many ways, the usual result is an increased rate of regional degradation (Figure 32.4).

Figure 32.4 The Aswan High Dam, built during the 1960s in the Nile Valley of southern Egypt, is a classic example of human interference in the river erosion process. In this 1988 photo, taken by an astronaut aboard a space shuttle, the area is dominated by a huge reservoir (Lake Nasser) that has filled behind the dam (top centre, where the lake ends). Besides enhancing erosion all around the new lake, the dam has caused increased deposition within the reservoir, as well as an entirely new flow regime in the river below the dam (to the north), all the way from Aswan to the densely populated Nile Delta.

The Stream as a System

The stream is one of the simplest and most easily understood examples of a system that occurs on the Earth's surface (systems are discussed in Unit 1). It is an open system, with both matter and energy flowing through it. The most obvious material flowing through the system is water, entering as precipitation on any part of the drainage basin and leaving by either evapotranspiration or stream discharge.

Energy and Work in a River System

The water in a river generates kinetic energy as it flows downstream. Through the action of the hydrologic cycle (see Figure 11.6)—powered by energy from the Sun—water vapour and, after condensation, liquid water are given potential energy. Any object possesses potential energy by virtue of being raised above the Earth's surface or higher on the surface, and of work having been done against gravity. The motion of water in a stream represents the transformation of potential energy into kinetic energy, the energy of movement. The water uses kinetic energy to transfer itself downstream and carry its load. By the time the water has reached its base level, there is no more potential energy available. At that point, no kinetic energy can be generated, and the stream is unable to do further work as it has reached a state of *entropy*.

Sediment also enters and leaves the fluvial system. Sediment is produced by weathering processes and the various processes of erosion. It is also supplied by the scouring of the stream bed and banks. Its movement through the fluvial system is facilitated by the kinetic energy of the flowing water. The two 'flows', water and sediment, are used to define the behaviour of the river system.

A stream is often characterized as a *steady-state* system—one in which inputs and outputs are constant and equal—at least with regard to water and energy. But this is obviously not the case because the environment is always changing (e.g., one year there is more rainfall, the next less than average rainfall) and therefore streams (and other natural systems) are more correctly said to be in a state of **dynamic equilibrium** rather than in a steady state (Figure 32.5). The major controlling factors relating to streams and other landscape systems are climate, geology, and base level. Physical laws suggest that energy and matter in such a system must move in a particular way. First, there is a tendency for the *least work* to be done. In a stream where all the water starts at the top of one tributary, the least-work profile would be a waterfall straight down to sea level. More practically, the least-work profile would be steep near the head and close to horizontal near the mouth of the stream, as demonstrated in Figure 32.6. It is possible that the sediment carried and deposited by the stream could interfere with or complicate these states.

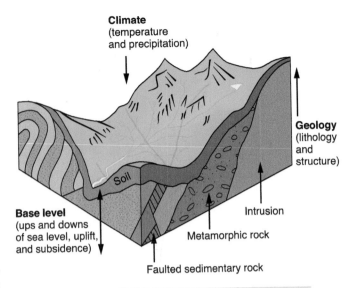

Figure 32.5 The controlling factors of dynamic equilibrium.

Another tendency in a system is for work to be uniformly distributed (*uniform work*). A stream in which this occurred would get wider downstream but have a nearly constant slope, as in the uppermost curve in Figure 32.6. The long profile of a stream in equilibrium is a compromise between the principles of least work and uniform distribution of work, but the actual profile is possible only when the channels are in a material that can be degraded and aggraded. The fact that this profile is indeed typical of many streams suggests that this form represents some sort of equilibrium state. Many of the streams in Canada and in other areas that have been subjected to glaciations do not come close to having this smooth-curved profile and have stepped long profiles. Steps and pools are also common in alpine streams. Streams in the humid tropics also have stepped long profiles with flat sections separated by rapids or waterfalls.

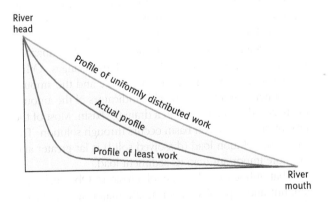

Figure 32.6 Formation of a stream profile as a compromise between the principles of uniformly distributed work and least work. This profile is reached if the material of the river channel is adjustable (i.e., capable of being degraded and aggraded).

Stream Functions and Valley Characteristics

LINK

As streams modify the landscape, they perform numerous functions. These functions can be grouped under three headings: *erosion* (degradation), *transportation* (transfer), and *deposition* (aggradation). Before we examine these processes, let us consider what happens to the river valley itself. A stream is not static—it changes continuously. In fact, one conceptual model used by geographers in the early twentieth century described the life cycle of a river in organic terms, suggesting that it evolved through stages of youth, maturity, and old age. This model has now been disproved.

As the stream develops, the characteristics of its valley change. In the area where the river has its origin, streamlets merge to form the main trunk of the stream. This stream cuts its valley. Over time the 'head' or source of the valley is extended upslope in a process called **headward erosion**. This has the effect of lengthening the stream valley, but it is not the only way a stream's course grows longer. At the other end of the valley, the stream reaches the coast of a sea or a lake and may deposit its sedimentary load in a **delta** (Figure 32.7). As this happens, the stream must flow across its own deltaic deposits, which lengthens the distance to its mouth. And between source and mouth, a stream will develop bends and turns (*meanders*) that make its course longer still. Valley *lengthening*, therefore, affects valleys as the streams within them perform their erosional and depositional functions.

Streams tend to flow more rapidly, even wildly, in mountainous areas (see Figure 31.3). Many streams rise in the mountains and rush downslope in deep valleys. The high velocity of the water, its growing volume, and the sediments being swept along all contribute to valley *deepening*.

Erosion by Streams

Stream erosion takes place in three ways: *hydraulic action*, *abrasion*, and *solution*.

Hydraulic Action   The work of the water itself, as it dislodges and drags away rock material from the stream-channel bed and banks, is referred to as its **hydraulic action**. You can feel the force of the water by wading across a shallow mountain stream. Even in water little more than 30 cm deep, you may have trouble keeping your balance. Large volumes of fast-moving water can break loose sizable material and move it downstream. In its rough-sided channel, the stream develops numerous eddies and swirls that can gouge out potholes and other depressions with the aid of its load.

Abrasion   **Abrasion** refers to the mechanical erosive action of boulders, pebbles, and smaller grains of sediment as they are carried along the stream channel. These fragments dislodge other particles along the stream bed and banks, thereby contributing to the channel deepening and

Figure 32.7   An astronaut's view of the Nile Delta, looking southward from a position over the Mediterranean Sea (bottom). The city of Cairo, Egypt's capital, lies near the junction of the apex of the delta's triangle and the Nile River channel. A small part of the El Faiyum Depression is visible just west (to the right) of the Nile River at the top of the photograph. A portion of the Gulf of Suez, Great Bitter Lake, and the Suez Canal can be seen to the east (left); some cirrus clouds hover near the ancient city of Alexandria near the western point of the delta (far right). The dark colour of the delta itself reflects intensive agriculture, in contrast to the nearly empty desert flanking it. A huge population is concentrated here and, as the image shows, in the lower valley of the Nile beyond.

widening process. Gravel- and sand-sized particles tend to scour the channel bed, wearing it down while eroding the banks. Abrasion and hydraulic action most often function in combination; without abrasive action, hydraulic action would take much longer to erode the stream perimeter. These two processes are important in terms of supplying larger-sized material to the stream. As the stream undercuts the banks and scours the bed, gravel and boulder-grade material are put into the channel.

Solution   In terms of the volume of rock removed, **solution** may be the most important form of erosion by streams in some areas (e.g., in the humid tropics, karst areas, and possibly all areas). It is the process by which certain rocks and minerals are dissolved by water. Limestone, for instance, is eroded not only by hydraulic action and abrasion, but also through solution. Sandstone held together by a calcite matrix will be weakened and removed because the water dissolves the cement. In Unit 35 there is a discussion of the special landscapes formed when solution is the dominant form of erosion in limestone terrain, but they are unusual and develop only under certain environmental conditions.

Transportation by Streams

Erosion, transportation, and deposition go together. The materials loosened by hydraulic action and abrasion, as well as fine-grained suspended sediment supplied by stormflow and dissolved solids supplied by baseflow, are carried downstream. The Hjulstrom Diagram (Figure 32.8) shows the relationship between flow velocity and particle size. It indicates at what velocities certain sizes of material are mobilized or entrained, transported, and deposited. Note that more velocity is needed to mobilize clay and coarser sand particles than medium sand particles when electrochemically bound. Also note that the distance between the entrainment and fall velocity lines decreases with increasing particle size, indicating that a slight change in velocity can cause erosion or deposition. Smaller particles need a high entrainment velocity but fall out of transport (are deposited) at very low flow velocities. Along the way, different transportation processes are dominant. In the mountains, streams carry coarser material (sand and gravel) along in a high-velocity rush of water; in the lower reaches of the stream, slow-moving water is brown- or grey-coloured (turbid) with concentration of fine sediment. Let us now identify the four ways a stream transports its load: *traction, saltation, suspension,* and *solution.*

Traction   **Traction** refers to the sliding or rolling of heavier particles along the stream bed. This is accomplished by hydraulic action, as large pieces of rock are literally rolled or dragged along the stream bed channel (these are also called bed load or channel lag deposits)

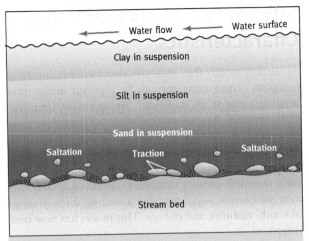

Figure 32.9 Heavier sand and gravel fragments are dragged along the stream bed by traction, while lighter fragments in the bed load advance downstream by saltation. Finer silt and clay particles are carried above in the suspended load, maintained there by the stream's turbulence until the water flow nears a standstill. The finest suspended material is flushed out of the stream system and deposited in a lake or the sea.

(Figure 32.9). Traction (through abrasion, etc.) breaks down larger material into gravel- and sand-sized fragments, which may begin to bounce along the stream bed.

Saltation   The speed of the water lifts these fragments off the riverbed, and they bounce along in a process called **saltation** (from Latin, meaning jump). Saltation, therefore, is a combination of traction and suspension: the particles make contact with the stream bed, but they also are briefly suspended as they move downstream (Figure 32.9). They travel in a ballistic trajectory downstream and hit other particles, putting them into the same kind of motion.

Suspension   Very fine sediment, in the silt- and clay-sized grades, is carried within the stream by a process known as **suspension** (Figure 32.9). When suspension dominates, stream water becomes *turbid,* or muddy, and even when it moves very slowly, it can carry huge amounts of fine sediment. Material in suspension does not make contact with the river bottom except when the water is slowed to a near standstill. The finest suspended material (wash load) is usually completely flushed out of the stream system and is deposited in a lake or the sea.

Solution   As noted earlier, some rock material travels to the stream channel in baseflow dissolved in stream water and is carried downstream in *solution.* The process is not confined to calcium-rich rocks. Numerous other minerals can be partially dissolved, and even a clear mountain stream contains ions of sodium, potassium, and other materials.

Stream Deposition

In combination, these four transportation processes move hundreds of millions of tonnes of earth materials annually

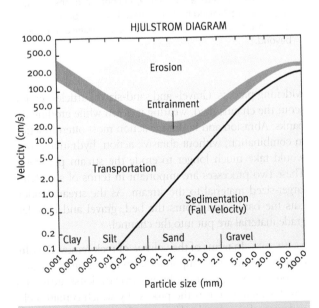

Figure 32.8 The Hjulstrom Diagram shows the relationship between flow velocity and particle size.

from the higher areas of the landmasses towards lower areas, where deposition takes place (as, for example, at the bottom of valleys, in floodplains, and in deltas). In the upper reaches of drainage basins, sediment particles in streams are generally large. These are left behind because they are too large to move. With increasing distance downstream, the particle size decreases. This process is called sorting. This coarse-to-fine sorting can be upset if a stream erodes through coarse sediment along its course. This is common in glaciated areas. Then there is a more complex picture. Along the stream from its source to an area of coarse sediment (an old beach deposit or an esker) the material will progressively become finer, but it will coarsen again and then become fine towards its mouth. There are numerous instances where this happens many times because of the stream cutting through coarser deposits. Aggradational processes dominate in some areas. This depositional work of streams is discussed in Unit 34; but first we need to explore the factors that govern the effectiveness of streams as they erode and transport their loads.

Factors in Stream Erosion

Stream Power

Stream capacity is used to denote the maximum load of sediment that a stream can carry at a given *discharge* (volume of water). It is rather obvious that a stream with a large discharge has a larger capacity than a smaller stream. Another way to measure the erosional effectiveness of a stream is by determining its *competence*, which depends on the velocity (or speed) of water movement. The faster a stream flows, the greater is its ability to move larger material in its channel. A combination of large volume *and* high velocity gives a stream substantial capacity and competence.

The *velocity* of a stream (usually measured in m/s), therefore, is a critical factor in its ability to erode and transport. Flow velocity is related to the size of the stream channel (width and depth). There is a consistent response of these three variables in relation to discharge along a stream channel and between channels:

$$Q = W \times D \times V$$

where Q is discharge (m³/s), W is channel width (m), D is channel depth (m), and V is flow velocity in (m/s). (By multiplying W and D you get the channel cross-sectional area m².)

Width, depth, and velocity vary with discharge but only at a fraction of the rate of discharge change. Many empirical studies have shown that as discharge increases, depth increases at a faster rate than width, while velocity increases at an intermediate rate.

The variation of discharge is very important in terms of channel erosion (which supplies a lot of sediment), sediment transport, and the shape of the stream. Sediment load is proportional to discharge in the following manner:

$$G \, \alpha \, Q^j$$

where G is sediment load in t/yr, α is a symbol meaning proportional to, Q is annual discharge (m³/yr), and j is an empirical constant ranging between 2 and 3. Thus, if annual discharge is 1000 m³/yr, the sediment load will be between 10^6 and 10^9 t/yr. If annual discharge is 10,000 m³/yr, sediment load will be 10^9 to 10^{12} t/yr.

As a rule, the greatest water velocity meanders across the stream channel towards one bank and then the other and is usually associated with the *thalweg*, or low-flow channel (deepest part of the stream). At meander bends the fastest velocities are generally found towards the outer banks. As the water flows from one bend to the next (through the straightaway), the fastest velocity will actually be found close to the midpoint of the stream. Because of friction, the velocity is slowed as the banks and bed are approached. In Figure 32.10 the red line represents the line of maximum velocity (and the thalweg); note that it lies towards the outside of the bends in the channel meander bends. Stream erosion is most active on the outside of those bends, (creating a cut bank or meander or river *cliff*) and enlarging them over time. In this way the channel moves across the floodplain.

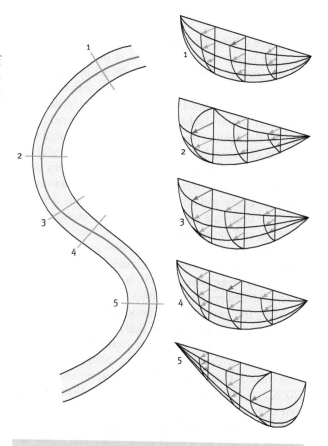

Figure 32.10 Velocity distribution in cross-sections through a meandering, or curving, channel (lengths of arrows indicate relative flow velocities). The zones of highest velocity (red arrows), associated with the thalweg, lie near the surface and towards the middle of the stream where the channel is relatively straight (cross-sections 1 and 4). At meander bends the maximum velocity swings towards the outer bank and lies below the surface (cross-sections 2 and 5).

The *gradient*, or slope, is the key factor in a stream's velocity. Again, this is obvious: a stream plunging down a steep mountain slope has a much higher velocity than a stream of equal volume crossing a coastal plain. What is less obvious, however, is the effect of even a slight change in gradient on the velocity (and thus the erosional power) of a stream. Sometimes the region across which a stream flows is tilted slightly upward by tectonic forces. This may not be very obvious in the landscape, but a stream whose gradient is increased immediately begins to erode its bed with new vigour.

The shape and size of the stream channel also affect velocity and erosional capacity. An open, bowl-shaped, fairly smooth channel cross-section such as those common in cohesive clay- or silt-rich deposits promotes rapid water flow and efficient action. A wide, shallow channel common in streams with granular bank and bed materials (sands and gravels) generates too much friction and reduces both velocity and erosional capacity at low discharges. And a stream channel with irregular sides and a rock-strewn floor also slows water movement.

Stream Floods

Streamflow volume varies through time as a result of changing water inputs from various areas of the drainage basin and the stream's tributaries (areas affected by rainstorms, etc.). Abnormally high rainfall or abrupt seasonal snowmelt can produce a **flood** in the stream system. A flood occurs when stream discharge overflows the channel banks onto the **floodplain.** These floods often result in aggressive scouring of stream beds and banks, the reshaping of the channel, the undercutting of valley sides, and many other consequences. The erosional power of large catastrophic floods is visually striking but mostly temporarily devastating. Such floods are important in terms of erosion, transportation, and the reworking of the floodplain. The floods in the Saguenay region of Quebec (1996) and the Red River Valley of Manitoba (1997) are Canadian examples of the process and devastation caused by large-scale flooding. The massive Mississippi floods of 1993 and of the US Midwest in 2008, the river flooding associated with Hurricanes Katrina, Rita, and Ike along the Gulf Coast of the US (2005 and 2008), and recent floods in the Irrawaddy Delta (Myanmar) caused by Cyclone Nargis (May 2008) and the monsoon-created flooding in southern China and eastern India (2008) also exemplify what flooding can do. All these events were catastrophic floods. In the colder areas of North America and elsewhere, major floods can be caused by ice jams on streams. Ice jams are a major cause of flooding on the Red River (along with spring melt floodwaters from the southern end of the basin in North Dakota moving north and meeting river ice cover in Manitoba) and in other streams all over Canada. Recent major ice jams at the confluence of the Fraser and Nechako Rivers caused the flooding of some of the downtown of Prince George, BC, in 2008.

Overbank flows (smaller-scale floods) occur about every 1.5 to 1.6 years on all types of streams and are nowhere as cataclysmic. Extremely large events, though high in magnitude, are infrequent (50, 100, 150 years). As the flood abates, sediment is put into storage on the lower parts of slopes, in the floodplain, and in in-channel bars.

Discharge below the top of the stream bank is the other important type of flow. These discharges occur 98 to 99 per cent of the time and play a significant role in shaping the stream channel. Most erosion occurs early in the spring before bank vegetation grows and defends the bank. At this point the banks are wet (because of rainfall and/or snowmelt) and therefore heavier and prone to collapse if undercut by the sediment and water flow. Bank material then collapses into the stream and is carried downstream.

Not all floods are exclusively erosional, of course. Streams, particularly in their lower courses, often rise above their average levels and sometimes overflow their channels. During such episodes the streams inundate their floodplains, the low-lying ground adjacent to the stream channel. Fine-grained and mineral-rich overbank deposits (flood muds deposited from slack water on the floodplain) give rise to highly productive soils, often attracting dense human settlement. Although those living on floodplains know the risks involved in living on the low ground near flood-prone streams (see 'Perspectives' box), the fertility of the soils has made that gamble worth taking (Figure 32.11).

Base Levels

We can learn much about the behaviour of streams by studying their longitudinal *profiles*, their downward curve (or stepped profiles) from source to mouth. As a stream erodes and modifies its valley by deepening, widening, and lengthening its channel, it also tends to create a smooth, downstream profile. This does not occur in areas affected by the Pleistocene Ice Age. The profile in these areas is stepped with gently sloping pool areas separated by quite

Figure 32.11 Floodplains have highly fertile soils, which encourage people to undertake the risk of farming and living on them. This is the Red River floodplain in Manitoba.

steep steps (step and pool profile). A critical factor in this process is the stream's **base level**—the level below which a stream cannot erode its bed. When a stream reaches the ocean, its capacity to erode ends (although muddy currents offshore are known to be capable of some degradation). For our purposes, a stream's **absolute base level** is no more than a few metres below sea level. At this terminus, the stream slows down and deposits its sedimentary load.

Some streams, however, do not reach the ocean. A stream that flows into a lake does not relate to the global sea level. The effective base level is the lake level, at whatever altitude it may lie; the lake therefore becomes the stream's **local base level** (Figure 32.12). This also occurs when a reservoir is impounded. Streams flowing into the reservoir tend to aggrade their beds as the water level in the reservoir increases in response to the newly-imposed base level. On occasion, a stream that erodes downward reaches an

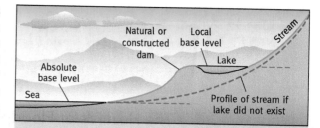

Figure 32.12 Profile of a stream showing its relationship to local and absolute base levels.

especially hard, resistant rock barrier, perhaps in the form of a dyke (see Unit 22). That barrier may keep the stream from developing a fairly smooth profile until the stream has penetrated it. This creates a **temporary base level**, which temporarily limits further upstream channel incision.

Canadian Geographers in the Field

'As an undergraduate research project at Simon Fraser University, I studied the geomorphic impacts of reservoir construction on the sand-bed braided South Saskatchewan River. This photography was taken during a flight with a local pilot from the town of Outlook. As part of my fieldwork for this research, I conducted cross-sectional channel surveys using historic benchmarks installed during the 1960s. Within these cross-sections, which were 500 to 1000 metres wide, sediment was also sampled to characterize downstream changes.'

Roger T.J. Phillips, M.Sc., is a former graduate student at York University who studied meander migration and the Holocene evolution of rivers in southern Ontario. He now works for Aquafor Beech Ltd, a major Canadian engineering and environmental services company in Brampton, Ontario.

Perspectives on the Human Environment

The Hazards of Floodplain Settlement

Episodes of abnormally high stream discharge—known more commonly as floods—can have a major impact on the cultural as well as the physical landscape in a river basin. About one-eighth of the population of the United States now resides in areas of potential flooding. To these people the advantages of living in a flood-prone area outweigh the risks (just as people continue to live on the slopes of active volcanoes and near the San Andreas Fault).

The advantages include the fertility of the soils in these floodplain zones and the flatness of the land. Crops grow bountifully, and the land is easy to farm and develop. The risks, however, are great, and they are not only financial. Recent flood losses in North America have exceeded $1 billion per year, and dozens of human lives are lost annually.

The decision to live on or to avoid a floodplain is not strictly rational. The geographers Gilbert White, Robert Kates, and Ian Burton have shown that human adjustments to the known dangers of flooding do not increase consistently as the risk becomes greater, because people tend to make an optimistic rationalization for continuing to live in a potential flood zone.

Other decisions and trade-offs are associated with floodplain settlement and development.

Floods are natural events, but we sometimes try unnatural methods to prevent their worst effects. Dams and high artificial banks, or *levees*, like those in Figure 32.13 can be built, but such structures sometimes have some unwanted side effects. As was seen with Hurricane Katrina in 2005, levees do not always prevent flooding. Dams, although they help control flooding, can prevent the natural replacement of fertile alluvial soil because the sediment collects behind the dam instead. The Aswan High Dam in Egypt, in the middle Nile Valley (Figure 32.4), holds back sediment that would otherwise be deposited on the highly productive agricultural land in the lower Nile floodplain and delta. Furthermore, artificial levees in floodplains can create a false sense of security.

These levees are seldom designed to cope with the worst possible flood because of the great expense that would entail. There is a tendency to increase the height of levees over time. This restricts the stream to its channel and the stream bed builds up as sediment is deposited. This means the levees have to be built up again, so that in some areas, such as the southern part of the Mississippi River Valley, the stream is actually higher than the floodplain or 'backswamp' areas. When a major flood occurs there is a tendency for the stream water to cut through the

Figure 32.13   Close-up aerial view of the artificial levee system that lines the banks of the lower Mississippi River, here in northeastern Louisiana about 50 km downstream from the riverfront city of Vicksburg in the neighbouring state of Mississippi. Note the service roadway that runs on top of the protective levee, which separates the village of St Joseph and its surrounding farmscape from the often inundated trees that grow along the river's natural banks. This is part of the regional water-control system built by the US Army Corps of Engineers that extends all the way to New Orleans and the delta beyond.

levees in places and find a new lower route on the floodplain. But often, the higher the levee is, the more people will live in the area and the greater the disaster will be when a major flood (such as a '100-year flood' event or bigger) does occur, as happened with Hurricane Katrina. New Orleans and other areas were devastated by the extremely high winds and the flooding, which led to the collapse of some of the levees. Many cities built in backswamp areas, like most of New Orleans, have also unwisely built infrastructure (e.g., subway systems) that is subject to complete inundation when such events occur. Therefore, it is essential for us to have an understanding of floodplains as well as other natural phenomena of the Earth. Otherwise, we cannot make rational decisions about where to live or make the necessary adjustments if we do choose to live in a floodplain.

The Concept of Dynamic Equilibrium

The concept of dynamic equilibrium states that a stream is adjusted to the environment of an area and that any changes to the environment will affect it and the processes going on within it. For example, alteration to the environment could change its flow regime, channel shape, and the kind of sediment it carries. Many factors are involved in the tendency for a stream to attain this equilibrium state, and these factors may be classed as independent, semi-dependent, and dependent (Table 32.1).

Independent factors are those over which the stream has little or no control and to which it must simply adjust. Climate and ultimate base level are good examples. The stream must adjust to its ultimate base level because at this point it no longer has any potential or kinetic energy. The *semi-dependent* factors are partly determined by the three independent factors in Table 32.1, but also, partly, they interact among themselves. The roughness of the stream channel bed and the grain size of the sediment load, for example, interact. The bed roughness is partly determined by the size of the sediment grains and, in turn, partially determines the degree of mixing, or *turbulence*, in the stream. The sediment size generally decreases downstream. Only finer particles remain in suspension in the lower part of the river, where turbulence decreases. Thus, sediment grain size and bed roughness interact via the turbulence factor.

Only one variable in the table appears to be *dependent* on all others, and this is the gradient or slope of the stream. The stream virtually determines this by either depositing or eroding away material as necessary. It was the propensity of a stream to change its slope that first set investigators thinking about the concept of equilibrium. Not until later was it fully realized that many other factors could be involved.

The consensus is that a stream in equilibrium is one in which, over a period of time, stream slope, channel characteristics, and flow volumes are delicately adjusted to provide just the velocity required for the transportation of the load supplied from the drainage basin. As the environment is constantly changing, it is more proper to say that the stream is in a state of dynamic equilibrium. Its diagnostic characteristic is that any change in any of its controlling factors causes a displacement of the equilibrium in a direction that tends to absorb the effect of the change (negative feedback loops). So if a stream was dammed, erosion might occur downstream but ultimately would stop once coarser material was exposed that could not be eroded by the reduced water flow. In some cases deposition might occur.

Not all streams are in equilibrium with the environment, and not all streams in equilibrium assume a smooth longitudinal profile. A newly uplifted tectonic landscape or a recently deglaciated area (e.g., Canada) would present a chaotic deranged drainage system, with streams with long profiles that are not smooth curves. The semi-dependent variables are usually the first to adjust to the process of moving material downstream. It has been argued that a stream usually establishes grade in its lower reaches first, and then the graded condition is slowly extended upstream towards its source. But, because of differences in rock resistance and other factors, it is quite possible for equilibrium to exist in isolated segments of the complete river profile. Many streams in all areas of Canada are in equilibrium with the environmental conditions but exhibit a stepped long profile (step and pool) where rapids or other kinds of *knickpoints* intervene between pools.

Table 32.1 Factors Involved in the Tendency of a Stream to Achieve Equilibrium

Independent	Semi-dependent	Dependent
Climate (Q & sediment load)	Channel width	Slope
Geology (sediment & Q)	Channel depth	
Base level (energy)	Bed roughness	
	Grain size of sediment load	
	Velocity	
	Meander/braid tendency	

Source: Information from A.L. Bloom. *The Surface of the Earth* (Englewood Cliffs, NJ: Prentice-Hall, 1969).

Figure 32.14 Braided stream. This aerial view of the Sunwapta River in Jasper National Park, Alberta, clearly exemplifies braiding, as the streamflow diverges around sand and gravel bars and then converges.

Braided Streams

Braiding is where the channel breaks into many distributaries that diverge around sand and gravel bars and converge again. This usually occurs as flooding decreases. **Braided streams** are characteristic of geomorphologically active environments such as in **proglacial** areas (close to glaciers) and in *periglacial* (or *nival* or snowpack) and arid areas. The reasons are:

1. In such environments stream discharge is extremely variable. In proglacial and periglacial areas, water is frozen as ice or snow for long periods of the year. At the start of the melt season a lot of glacial ice and snow melts, supplying large amounts of runoff to the streams. In arid areas there is minimal rainfall except for very sporadic but high-intensity rainfall. Some arid areas also receive snow or ice melt discharge from neighbouring higher areas.

2. There is an abundance of loose, coarse sediment that is subject to erosion in these areas because of a lack of vegetation cover and soil development, the result of extremely cold or warm temperatures. Therefore, an overabundance of debris supplied to the streams cannot be transported.

3. The gradients (or slopes) that the streams flow down (or across) are quite steep in comparison to the usually shallow slopes associated with floodplain surfaces.

These three factors cause braiding to occur. During the rainy or melting season a lot of water is supplied to the streams. At these times the entire valley bottom becomes flooded and acts as the stream channel. The water is a raging torrent that moves a lot of sediment. As the flood waters abate the water has to find its way around and between piles of sand and gravel deposited as the water loses its power. When viewed from above the bars of sand and gravel make it seem like the stream has been braided, like hair. The granular material makes erosion of the banks very easy, so the stream *distributaries* can migrate across the valley bottom quite rapidly. The buildup of sand and gravel in the valley bottom increases the valley gradient and this adds to the braiding effect. When the supply of water ceases, the valley bottom is left dry and full of granular material. In proglacial and periglacial areas this area is called a valley train or *sandur*. The sediment associated with this process is very different from that carried and deposited by meandering streams with floodplains. Braided streams do not deposit floodplains.

Conclusion

Streams degrade, transport, and aggrade. Here we have studied the processes of stream erosion, and in Units 33 and 34 we examine the products of the work of streams in the landscape. These products range from spectacular canyons and deep gorges to extensive deltaic plains. As we study these landforms, we will learn still more about stream processes.

KEY TERMS

abrasion   *page 451*

absolute base level   *page 455*

alluvium   *page 449*

base level   *page 455*

braided stream   *page 458*

delta   *page 451*

drainage basin   *page 448*

dynamic equilibrium   *page 450*

flood   *page 454*

floodplain   *page 454*

fluvial processes   *page 447*

gullies   *page 448*

REVIEW QUESTIONS

1. How does overflowing water accomplish erosion? What processes are involved?
2. Describe the arrangement of streams within a drainage basin.
3. What factors determine the erosional activity of streams within a drainage basin?
4. Describe the three stream functions.
5. What is the base level, and how is it related to the development of the longitudinal profile?
6. What are the primary independent controls on the development of a river system that is in dynamic equilibrium with environmental conditions?

REFERENCES AND FURTHER READINGS

Allen, P.A. 1997. *Earth Surface Processes.* Malden, Mass.: Blackwell.

Baker, V.R., et al., eds. 1988. *Flood Geomorphology.* New York: Wiley.

Bloom, A.L. 1990. *Geomorphology: A Systematic Analysis of Late Cenozoic Landforms,* 2nd edn. Englewood Cliffs, NJ: Prentice-Hall.

Bridge, J. 2002. *Rivers and Floodplains.* Malden, Mass.: Blackwell.

Brooks, G.R., et al. 2001. 'Floods', in Brooks, *A Synthesis of Geological Hazards in Canada.* Ottawa: Geological Survey of Canada Bulletin 548, 101–43.

Calow, P., and G.E. Petts. 1994. *Rivers Handbook, Vol. 2.* Malden, Mass.: Blackwell.

Clifford, N.J., et al., eds. 1993. *Turbulence: Perspectives on Flow and Sediment Transport.* New York: Wiley.

Gordon, N.D., T.A. McMahon, and B.L. Finlayson. 1992. *Stream Hydrology: An Introduction for Ecologists.* New York: Wiley.

Gregory, K.J., and D.E. Walling. 1995. *Drainage Basins: Form, Process and Management.* Cambridge, Mass.: Blackwell.

Hack, J.T. 1960. 'The Interpretation of Erosional Topography in Humid Temperate Regions', *American Journal of Science* 258-A: 80–97.

Herschy, R.W. 1985. *Streamflow Measurement.* New York: Elsevier.

Kirkby, M.J., ed. 1978. *Hillslope Hydrology.* New York: Wiley.

Knighton, D. 1998. *Fluvial Forms and Processes: A New Perspective.* New York: Oxford Univ. Press.

Laenen, A., and D.A. Dunnette, eds. 1996. *River Quality: Dynamics and Restoration.* Boca Raton, Fla: Lewis.

Leopold, L.B., et al. 1964. *Fluvial Processes in Geomorphology.* San Francisco: Freeman.

Malanson, G.P. 1993. *Riparian Landscapes.* New York: Cambridge Univ. Press.

Moore, J.E., and W.E. Wilson, eds. 1998. *Glossary of Hydrology.* Alexandria, Va: American Geological Institute.

Morisawa, M. 1968. *Streams: Their Dynamics and Morphology.* New York: McGraw-Hill.

Petts, G., and I. Foster. 1985. *Rivers and Landscapes.* London: Edward Arnold.

Schumm, S.A. 1972. *River Morphology.* Stroudsburg, Penn.: Dowden, Hutchinson & Ross.

Smith, D.I., and P. Stopp. 1978. *The River Basin.* New York: Cambridge Univ. Press.

Statham, I. 1977. *Earth Surface Sediment Transport.* London/New York: Oxford Univ. Press.

Ward, R. 1978. *Floods: A Geographical Perspective.* New York: Macmillan.

 ## WEB RESOURCES

gsc.nrcan.gc.ca/floods/ The Geological Survey of Canada's website on floods has information, data, and research about floods in Canada.

www.cwra.org/ The Canadian Water Resources Association has information about the character of floods in different regions of Canada and offers general considerations about floods regarding planning and design.

www.ec.gc.ca/water/en/manage/floodgen/e_floods.htm Freshwater website: floods table of contents; flood links.

www.riverwebmuseums.org/river_facts/river_dynamics This site gives a brief overview of river basin formation and erosional processes, and includes a linked glossary of terms. Photographs and satellite images of river basins are included.

Unit 33

Stream Erosion

Objectives

- To outline the roles of geological structure, lithology, tectonics, and climate in influencing fluvial erosion.

- To introduce terminology to characterize drainage networks and controls on fluvial erosion.

- To briefly consider how landscapes might change or evolve through time in response to stream erosion.

When streams erode the landscape, many processes occur simultaneously. Rock material is removed, transported, processed, and deposited. Stream valleys are excavated. Slope processes are activated. Slopes are being flattened in some places, steepened in others. Long-buried rocks are exhumed, exposed, and eroded. The work of streams endlessly modifies the topography.

The regional landscape—and the individual landforms comprising parts of it—reveals the erosional process or processes that dominate in particular areas. Certain fluvial landforms of desert areas, for example, do not occur in humid environments. Wide, flat floodplains, occupied by meandering stream channels, are not generally found in mountainous areas. Concave slopes and sharp, jagged ridges are more likely to be found in arid areas; round, convex slopes and rounded hilltops reflect moister conditions. It is possible to draw many conclusions about the processes shaping the landscape from simple observational evidence.

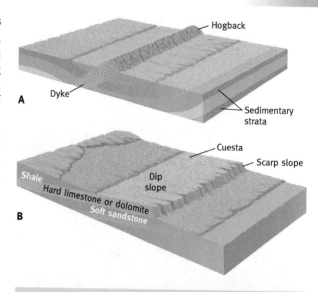

Figure 33.1 Hogback (A) and cuesta (B) landforms. Note that hogbacks dip at a high angle whereas cuestas dip at a low angle. (The cuesta in this drawing is associated with a dry climate.)

Factors Affecting Stream Degradation

Among the many factors influencing fluvial erosion, four have special importance: geological structure, bedrock type (or lithology), tectonic activity, and climate.

Geological Structure

Geological structure refers to features such as synclines, anticlines, domes, and faults that were formed originally by geological processes (see Unit 27). These geological structures are sculpted by streams into characteristic landforms. One of the simplest examples is a landform that results from a high-angle intrusion, a dyke.

Hogbacks and Escarpments   The crystalline rock intrusion of the dyke dips at a high angle and penetrates less-resistant surrounding rocks (Figure 33.1A). Originally this dyke might not have reached the uppermost of the sedimentary rock layers through which it penetrated, but erosion has degraded the countryside and exposed the much harder rock of the dyke. *Geologically*, this tilted structure remains a dyke; *geographically*, it stands out as a prominent, steep-sided ridge called a **hogback**. Stream erosion exposes the differences in resistance between the crystalline rock of the dyke and the sedimentary rocks surrounding it. When ridges like this are eroded and cut through by streams the resulting triangular-shaped remnants are called **flatirons** (Figure 33.2).

Other less prominent ridges may form when a sequence of sedimentary strata of varying hardness lies at a low-angle dip. This is seen in Figure 33.1B, where erosion by streams etches out the least resistant rock strata first. This process is often associated with **uniclinal shifting** of the stream or stream network, which erodes the bedrock

down the dip of the rocks. This leaves a ridge with one fairly steep slope (scarp) and another very gentle one (dip). This landform, known as an **escarpment** or **cuesta**, can be hundreds of kilometres long—for example, the Niagara Escarpment, which forms the edge of the Michigan structural basin, consists of carbonate rocks (limestones and dolostones) and rises to 90–200 m above the shale lowland on which the Greater Toronto conurbation is located. The escarpment stretches from New York State up into Manitoulin Island and then to the lower peninsula of Michigan. The Canadian section of the escarpment is over 750 km long (Niagara Falls to Tobermory, Ontario). A similar feature to this is the Missouri Coteau of the Prairies.

Ridges and Valleys   When structures become more complicated, so do the resulting landforms. The erosion of synclines and adjacent anticlines produces a series of parallel ridges and valleys that reveal the structures below. If the axes of the folds plunge, as is frequently the case, the result is a terrain of zigzag ridges (see Figure 27.13A). Note that the steep face of the resistant layer (numbered 3 on that diagram) faces *inward* on the anticline and *outward* on the syncline, providing us with preliminary evidence of the properties of the folds below the surface. The Appalachian Mountains of the Atlantic Provinces and much of eastern North America provide many examples of this topography (see Figure 27.15).

Domes   In areas where sedimentary strata have been pushed upward to form a dome, stream erosion may produce a characteristic landscape in which the affected layers form a circular pattern, as shown in Figure 33.3. An example of this type of landscape is Isachsen Dome on Ellef Ringnes Island, Nunavut, where the gypsum diapir

Figure 33.2   Flatiron mountains.

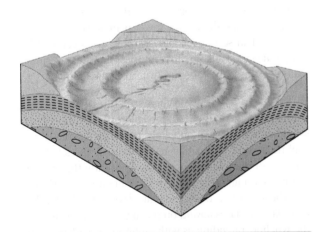

Figure 33.3 Circular cuestas produced by stream erosion of sedimentary rock layers pushed upward to form a structural dome.

core of the dome has already been exposed by erosion but the overlying sedimentary layers (sandstone and shale) still cover its flanks in all directions. As a result, the regional topography consists of a series of concentric cuestas of considerable prominence, separated by persistent valleys.

In some areas not only physical geographic configurations but also the human geographic features reveal the dominance of this concentric pattern: ridges, rivers, roads, and towns all exhibit circular patterns (e.g., in the Black Hills area of South Dakota and Wyoming).

Faults   Faults, too, are exposed and sometimes given relief by stream erosion. Of course, normal and reverse faults create topography by themselves because one block moves upward or downward with respect to the other. But after the faulting episode, stream erosion begins and the fault becomes a geographical as well as a geological feature. In fact, physical geographers distinguish between a **fault scarp** (Figure 33.4A), a **scarp** (cliff) created by geological action without significant erosional change, and a **fault-line scarp**, a scarp that originated as a fault scarp but that has been modified, even displaced, by erosion (Figure 33.4B). And where the geological structures are formed by numerous parallel (*en echelon*) faults, as happens in regions where lithospheric plates are affected by collision movements, the fault-generated terrain is also modified by stream erosion. Even prominent upthrust blocks may be worn down to a reduced relief, and valleys fill with sediment derived from these uplands. The overall effect is to lower the regional relief, as shown in Figure 33.5.

LINK

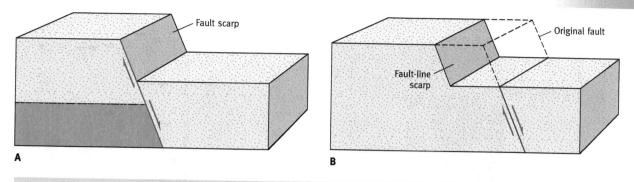

Figure 33.4 A fault scarp (A) originates as a result of geological activity without much erosional modification. A fault-line scarp (B) originates as a fault scarp but then undergoes significant erosional change.

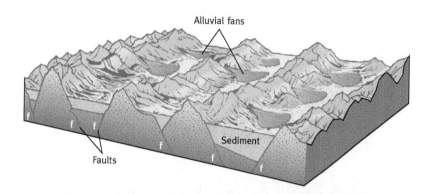

Figure 33.5 The erosion of upthrown blocks leads to the filling of their intervening valleys with sediment. In the interior of British Columbia (e.g., around Ashcroft and Kamloops), parallel faults create a so-called basin-and-range topography in which the fault-formed valleys are filling up with sediment from the ranges. Short streams flowing off the uplands produce alluvial fans—fan-shaped sedimentary landforms where stream velocity is sharply reduced when the streams enter the flat valleys (see Figure 34.1).

Impact and Extrusive Igneous Structures Unit 25 looked at volcanoes as geological phenomena and as landforms. Unit 21 discussed impact cratering. Created by impact cratering or volcanic action, these landforms are quickly modified by stream erosion. Impact craters and extinct or long-dormant volcanic cones reveal their inactivity through numerous, often deep stream-cut valleys carved into their slopes. Eventually, the entire crater structure or volcanic mountain may be worn down. Volcanic cones may leave remnants such as their plugs and radiating dykes (Figure 33.6). Fissure eruptions create hard sills, which may become the cap rocks of plateaus or smaller landforms known as **mesas** and **buttes** (Figure 33.7), although these two landforms may also develop in sedimentary rocks with duricrusts (e.g., caliche or laterite cuirasses) as well.

Intrusive Igneous Structures The sedimentary, fault-dominated, and volcanic structures discussed so far have quite characteristic erosional forms. From topographic and drainage patterns, we can often deduce what lies beneath the surface. But vast areas of the landmasses are underlain by granitic and metamorphic rocks that do not display such regularity. In Part Three we learned that large batholiths formed within the crust have been uplifted and exposed by erosion and that large regions of metamorphic crystalline rocks form the landscapes of the ancient shields. Some batholiths now stand above the surface as dome-shaped mountains, smoothed by weathering and erosion. The great domes, such as Sugarloaf Mountain (Pao de Azucar), that rise above the urban landscape of Brazil's Rio de Janeiro are such products of deep-seated intrusion and subsequent erosion (see Figure 22.6), as is the Stawamus Chief near Squamish, BC, a granite dome rising nearly 705 m above the Howe Sound/Squamish valley bottom, north of Vancouver (Figure 33.8).

Metamorphic Structures Metamorphic rocks often display regional foliation (see Unit 23), and sometimes this

From the Fieldnotes

Figure 33.6 *'Flying to the US west coast from Miami I had a superb view of Ship Rock in New Mexico, a famous geological as well as cultural landmark. It is the 420-m-high remnant of a large volcano that was once active in this now stable area. Dykes radiate outward from the eroding core, marking the dimensions of this extinct giant.'*

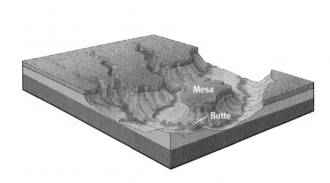

Figure 33.7   Mesa and butte landforms.

Figure 33.8   Stawamus Chief Provincial Park protects the 700-metre massive granite cliffs, the second largest granite monolith in the world, which stands at the southern entrance to Squamish, British Columbia.

tendency to form belts of aligned minerals and structures is reflected in the drainage lines that develop upon them. Some metamorphic rocks, furthermore, are much more resistant than others, so that zones of quartzite, for instance, are likely to stand above softer rocks such as weak slates and schists. Gneiss, on the other hand, is quite hard and often supports uplands reminiscent of those formed on granite batholiths.

Geological structure, therefore, is an important factor in stream erosion, a relationship that cannot be overlooked when human technology attempts to influence river courses (see 'Perspectives' box). It also affects the development of drainage systems. Later we will discover that the actual pattern of drainage lines can reveal the nature of the underlying structural geology.

Perspectives on the Human Environment

LINK

Hurricane Hazel, Regional Flood Control, and Water Management in Ontario

Most of the world's major cities are located on rivers and many of them have seen the results of major flooding. Recent examples include St Louis (1993) and New Orleans (2005). Many attempts have been made to try to 'tame' rivers by attempting to stop their meandering and by controlling their erosive power and flooding. The famous stone walls and embankments that line the Seine in Paris and the Thames in London are testimony to the fair degree of success achieved in some cases. London, however, is not safe even with the added protection of the Thames Barrier and is still threatened because of the combined effects of continued subsidence of the Thames Valley and the North Sea area and the possibility of a very large storm surge and high spring tide occurring at the same time.

Many of the larger cities in Canada have been affected by major flooding. One of the most devastating events was the flooding associated with Hurricane Hazel, which hit the Toronto area in October 1954. It caused the worst flood conditions in Ontario in 200 years.

Hurricane Hazel began as a tropical storm east of the island of Grenada in the Caribbean. It crossed Haiti, killing 1000 and causing a lot of damage. By the time it was approaching the coast of the Carolinas it had become a category 4 hurricane (on the Saffir-Simpson scale), with winds speeds over 240 km/h. As it hit the coastal Carolinas on 14 October, the storm was preceded by a 4.4-m storm surge that destroyed Garden City, South Carolina, leaving only 2 houses (out of 275) habitable. After landfall, the hurricane was soon downgraded to a tropical storm. In the next 12 hours, however, it travelled at extreme speed (and maintained the same intensity)

over the suburbs west of Washington, DC, and through Pennsylvania and New York State. Then it crossed Lake Ontario into southern Ontario. In the US, it killed 100 and caused an estimated $1.5 billion in damage.

At 9:30 a.m. on 15 October the Dominion Weather Office issued a bulletin saying that the intensity of the storm had decreased markedly, that it would pass to the east of Toronto before midnight, and that the main rainfall should end shortly afterwards. The forecasters said that there would be occasional light showers throughout the rest of the night. Winds would increase slightly to 72 to 80 km/h until midnight, then slowly decrease. The outlook for Lake Ontario and Niagara regions and the cities of Toronto and Hamilton was:

Rain tonight. Cloudy with occasional showers Saturday. Little change in temperature. Winds north (64–80 km/h) this evening, decreasing overnight to northwest (48 km/h) on Saturday. Low tonight and high Saturday at Toronto, St Catharines, and Hamilton (7 to 13°C). Outlook for Sunday, cloudy and cool.

Opinions still differ about the accuracy of this forecast and whether it was given in enough time. Few people actually took the warnings seriously. Many lives would have been saved if they had, and property damage would have been much less severe.

In the evening of 15 October over central Pennsylvania the storm re-intensified dramatically (see Figure 33.9), and shortly after it was pounding the Toronto area with winds still at hurricane force of up to 110 km/h; 285 mm of rain fell in 48 hours. Bridges and streets were washed out (over 20 bridges were destroyed

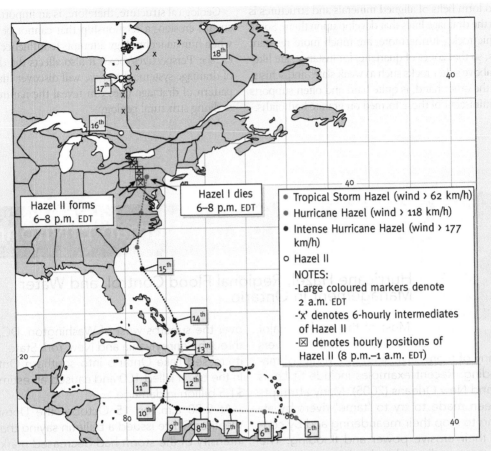

Figure 33.9   The storm track of Hurricane Hazel, 5–18 October 1954.

or damaged beyond repair). Homes and trailers were washed into Lake Ontario. About 4000 people were left homeless (1868 in Toronto) and 81 people were killed in the Greater Toronto area. The total cost of the damages in Canada was estimated at $100 million (about $1 billion in 2000 dollars). The major damage was in the Humber River basin (it affected an area 30,000 km²). The rainfall intensity was 52 mm/hr—by comparison, the heavy rainfall that caused widespread and damaging flooding in the Saguenay region of Quebec in 1996 was 12.7 mm/hr. About 90 per cent of the rain from Hurricane Hazel became runoff because the soils were already filled to capacity as a result of a very wet autumn in southern Ontario. The Humber River rose by six metres (the discharge of the Humber River at Weston, Ontario, on 16 October was 836 m³/s—four times greater than any previously recorded flow) and washed out most of the houses on Raymore Drive in Weston in one hour, killing 32 people.

The devastation and death caused by Hurricane Hazel forced all levels of government in Ontario to work together in an effort to control flooding and manage water resources. The Conservation Authorities Act (Ontario) of 1946 was amended to enable conservation authorities to acquire land for recreational and conservation purposes and to regulate land use to cut down flooding and other risks. The conservation authorities were given three important roles: flood prevention, flood protection, and emergency preparedness and response. The Lands Acquisition program was implemented in 1960 to purchase land for the construction of dams and reservoirs to control flooding and for the creation of conservation areas designed to allow rainfall and snowmelt to infiltrate into the ground. The program was designed to be implemented in three stages:

1. Liability for floodplain lands was transferred to the Metropolitan Toronto and Region Conservation Authority (MTRCA) and the MTRCA was given power to take over land for flood protection works and conservation purposes (2914 ha in total).

2. The Flood Control Program was initiated to build structures to control flooding—dams, reservoirs, major flood channels, erosion control programs, channel improvements, etc.

3. Province-wide floodplain regulations were developed and implemented to control flood zone development and to restrict certain kinds of land use in flood hazard zones (within the 100-year flood limits).

Similar plans were later implemented throughout Ontario. Eighteen tropical storms affected Ontario between Hurricane Hazel and the year 2000, but none was so powerful or caused as much damage and death. It is estimated, however, that a storm of the same size as Hurricane Hazel should hit every 50 years or so. In 2002 and 2004 the downtown area of Peterborough suffered severe flooding caused by rainfall. In August 2005 torrential rainfall (150–200 mm/hr) caused a flash flood in the Black Creek Ravine in North York, Toronto, which washed out a bridge on Finch Avenue West (Figure 33.10) that caused traffic chaos for months, and eroded most of a parking lot at a local library. The storm affected all of southern Ontario and flooded hundreds of basements. The insurance payments totalled over $400 million, making it the most costly storm to have hit the area, but it did not cause widespread flooding throughout the city.

Figure 33.10   The washout of a bridge on Finch Avenue West in Toronto, the result of torrential rains in August 2005.

Bedrock Type (Lithology)

Rock type, for obvious reasons, strongly influences landscape evolution. This is true not only because different rock types have different properties of hardness and resistance against erosion, but also because they exhibit varying capacities to form slopes. A resistant crystalline rock mass, for example, can form and maintain nearly vertical scarps, but weak shales may, under certain circumstances, support a slope angle of not more than 35 degrees.

The bedrock type also influences the sculpting of landforms, such as the zigzag pattern on plunging anticlines and synclines described earlier. If the strata folded into those structures were uniform, then the resulting landscape would not display the variation shown in Figure 27.13. Again, when a fault has the effect of thrusting soft sedimentary rocks upward adjacent to hard crystalline rocks, the weak sedimentary strata will soon yield to erosion and the resulting landscape may *reverse* the geological imprint.

Tectonic Activity

Fluvial erosion is affected significantly by tectonic activity, especially in areas affected by collision plate movement. The landmasses are continuously influenced by the movement of lithospheric plates. Not only are peripheral areas of collision plate contact deformed, but also larger regions of the continents are subject to slight but important warping and tilting. All this has a significant effect on drainage systems and erosional effectiveness. Even a very slight increase in regional 'tilt' can greatly increase a stream's effectiveness. Sometimes the profile of a stream valley indicates that the river has been reinvigorated, that is, its energy increased. This may be the result of several factors, among which tectonic activity is the most obvious. Uplift results in increased potential energy, a greater velocity of streamflow, and enhanced erosional capacity.

LINK Climate

Climate plays a role in the evolution of landscape, but this role remains open to debate. The answer would seem to be obvious: landscapes of humid areas tend to be rounded and dominated by convex slopes, whereas landscapes of arid environments are stark, angular, and dominated by concave slopes. But detailed geomorphological research has not confirmed this contrast—or at least it has not confirmed that climate is the key factor.

Part of our impression, geomorphologists say, has to do with the cloak of vegetation in humid areas, as opposed to the barrenness of arid zones. Strip away this vegetation, they suggest, and the contrast between humid and arid landscapes may be less pronounced than we expect. Moreover, we should take climate change into account. Areas that are humid today were dry just a few thousand years

ago, and vice versa. Elsewhere, glaciers dominated the topography of mountain ranges now being eroded by streams. There are solution caves in arid areas, indicating the presence of much more water than may currently be the case. And there are valleys in high mountains that were gouged out by glacial ice, not streams. Over the long term, therefore, climate certainly plays a role in forging the landscape. But just how climate and hillslopes are related remains a contentious issue.

Drainage Density and Channel Maintenance

The structures and rock types that are sculpted by streams into characteristic landforms strongly influence the drainage patterns that develop on them. The drainage pattern and drainage basins often reveal much about the underlying geology (Figure 33.11). By examining the way a stream system has evolved in a certain area, we can begin to unravel the origins of the regional landscape. Before we study actual drainage patterns, we should acquaint ourselves with the concepts of drainage density and the constant of channel maintenance.

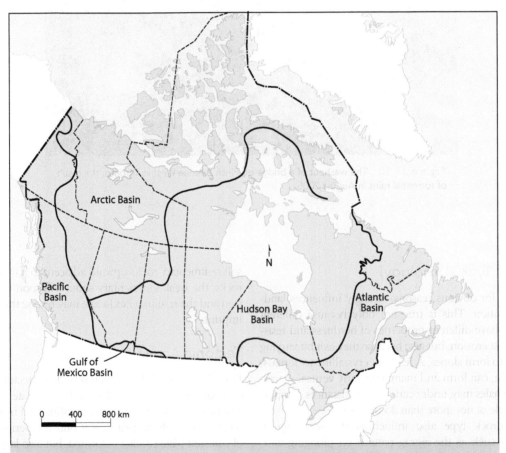

Figure 33.11 Major drainage basins in Canada. The Hudson Bay Basin encompasses the largest land area of Canada, while a small portion of Palliser's Triangle, which is semi-arid in any case, drains to the Gulf of Mexico via upstream tributaries of the Missouri–Mississippi River system. The Mackenzie River drainage basin (Figure 32.2) accounts for much of the drainage in the Arctic Basin.

The effectiveness of a drainage system as an erosional force is directly related to the **drainage density**—the total length of the stream channels per unit area of a drainage basin (km/km²). The higher the drainage density (other things being equal) the greater is the erosional efficiency of the system. More stream channels in an area means that more water is routed across the surface of the drainage basin, more erosion can take place, and more slopes are directly affected by degradation. You might expect the drainage density to be higher in humid areas than in arid locales, so that upland surfaces, virtually unaffected by stream erosion, are more likely to exist in dry than in humid regions. If drainage density is low, there is much less rainfall or more water is being infiltrated into the groundwater system, so fewer streams are necessary. In reality, drainage density is influenced by other factors that affect the surface permeability of a drainage basin besides climate, so this simple generalization is not always accurate.

Drainage density can be stated quantitatively (see above), but it also can be described simply as low, medium, or high. On the windward side of the Coast Mountains in British Columbia, in the path of moist winds, the drainage density is likely to be high; on the leeward side of the mountains, in the rainshadow area where it is more arid, the drainage density will be lower.

The **constant of channel maintenance** (CCM) is the reciprocal of drainage density. It is the area of drainage basin necessary to sustain part or all of a stream (km²/km). In humid temperate areas, such as coastal British Columbia or southern Ontario, CCM is in the order of 1.5–2 km²/km. In more arid areas, such as Arizona or New Mexico, it is approximately 350 km²/km because of less precipitation, greater evapotranspiration, less vegetation cover, and so on.

Drainage Patterns

To see a drainage pattern most clearly, it is best to study a map that shows *only* streams, nothing else. The pattern alone will be useful in later interpretations of structures and rocks.

A **radial drainage** pattern, for instance, shows the drainage of a conical mountain flowing in all directions (Figure 33.12A). It is possible to tell that the drainage in this example flows outward in all directions from the way tributaries join. Except under the most unusual circumstances, tributaries join larger streams at angles of less than 90 degrees, and often at much smaller angles. Radial patterns of the kind shown in Figure 33.12A develop most often on volcanic cones, such as Mount Edziza in northern British Columbia or Mount Price near Garibaldi Lake, near Whistler, BC.

Another highly distinctive drainage type is the **annular drainage** pattern, the kind that develops on domes like Isachsen Dome on Ellef Ringnes Island, Nunavut, or in South Dakota's Black Hills. Here the concentric pattern of valleys is reflected by the positioning of the stream segments, which drain the interior of the excavated dome (Figure 33.12B).

One of the most characteristic patterns is the **trellis drainage** pattern, in which streams seem to flow in only two orientations (Figure 33.12C). This pattern appears very regular and orderly, and often develops on parallel-folded or dipping sedimentary rocks of alternating degrees of competence. The main courses are persistent, but tributaries are short and join the larger streams at right angles.

The **rectangular drainage** pattern (Figure 33.12D) also reveals right-angle contacts between main streams and tributaries, but the pattern is less well developed than in the case of trellis drainage. What the diagram cannot show is that rectangular patterns tend to be confined to smaller areas, where a joint or a fault system dominates the structural geology. Trellis patterns, on the other hand, usually extend over wider areas. This type of pattern is well defined in carboniferous sandstones and salt deposits of northern Nova Scotia around Cobequid Bay and in the Mackenzie Mountains, NWT (Figure 33.13).

The tree-limb-like pattern shown in Figure 33.12E is appropriately termed the **dendritic drainage** pattern because it resembles the branches of a tree. It is the most commonly developed drainage pattern in North America and elsewhere, mainly outside of the parts involved in the Pleistocene Ice Age, and it is typical on extensive batholiths of generally uniform hardness or on flat-lying sedimentary rocks. The entire drainage basin is likely to slope gently in the direction of the flow of the trunk stream. Good examples of this are the streams of the north shore of Lake

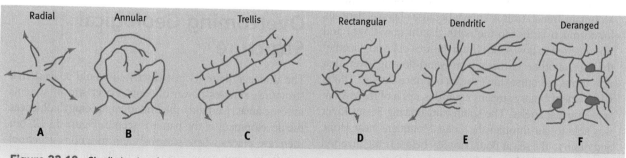

Figure 33.12 Six distinctive drainage patterns. Each provides clues about their underlying geological structures.

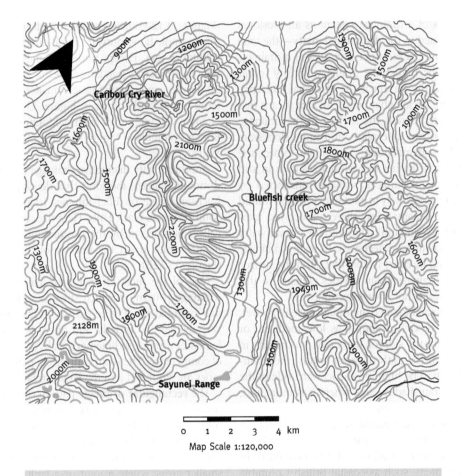

Figure 33.13   Rectangular drainage pattern, Mackenzie Mountains, NWT.

Ontario—Bronte Creek, Oakville Creek, Credit River, Don River, and Rouge River.

A **deranged drainage** pattern (Figure 33.12F) of small stream segments, wetlands, and lakes seemingly arranged independently of bedrock structure occurs on recently deposited glacial debris and is characteristic of many areas of Canada. A **barbed dendritic drainage** pattern (see Figure 33.14) is one where tributaries enter the trunk stream at an obtuse angle. This is caused by drainage diversion or reversal caused by blockage of drainage systems by an ice sheet during the Pleistocene Ice Age. A good example of this is the Fraser and Quesnel Rivers in the central interior of BC. The Fraser originally flowed north through the Rocky Mountain Trench (this is known because of gravel deposits found much farther to the north than it now flows) and was diverted to flow south (from the area of Prince George) through another formerly northward-flowing river that now forms its course downstream of Prince George. This is why some tributary streams enter this reach of the river at very unusual angles. The southward-flowing Fraser River was able to cut through the Coast Mountains near Hope and drain to the sea at Boundary Bay before being diverted north to flow out through Richmond and Delta.

The six drainage patterns shown in Figure 33.12, as well as the barbed dendritic pattern shown in Figure 33.14, are not the only patterns that may be recognized. Other, less common patterns also develop, and some representative names are *convergent* (or *centripetal*) streams flowing into a central basin, *contorted* (disorderly drainage in an area of varied metamorphic rocks), *beaded* or *buttonhole* (streams linking small lakes usually on fairly flat or gently sloping areas), and *parallel* (streams flowing down a steep slope or between elongated landforms). Physical geographers employ this nomenclature to convey the prevalent character of regional drainage systems, often as a first guide to the interpretation of landforms.

Overcoming Geological Structure

The drainage patterns just discussed would suggest that structure exercises powerful control over stream systems in some areas. Certainly the underlying geology influences the development of the patterns seen in Figure 33.12, but there are places where streams seem to ignore structural trends. In some areas, streams actually cut across mountain ranges when they could easily have flowed around them. What lies behind these discordant relationships?

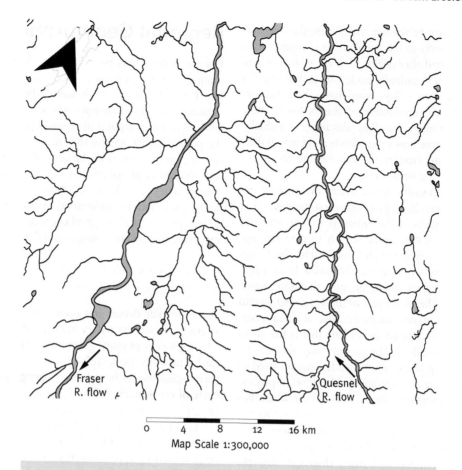

Figure 33.14 Barbed dendritic drainage pattern, Fraser and Quesnel Rivers in British Columbia.

Antecedent Streams

Why do some streams flow through mountain ranges? The ridge through which the river now flows may have been gradually pushed up by tectonic processes. A stream flowing across an area so affected (Figure 33.15A) may have been able to keep pace, eroding downward as rapidly as the ridge was being formed (Figures 33.15B and C). This stream, therefore, predates the ridge and is referred to as an **antecedent stream**.

Stream Capture

One of the most intriguing stream processes involves the diversion or 'capture' of a segment of one stream by another. Also called **stream piracy**, this process diverts water from one channel into another, weakening or even eliminating

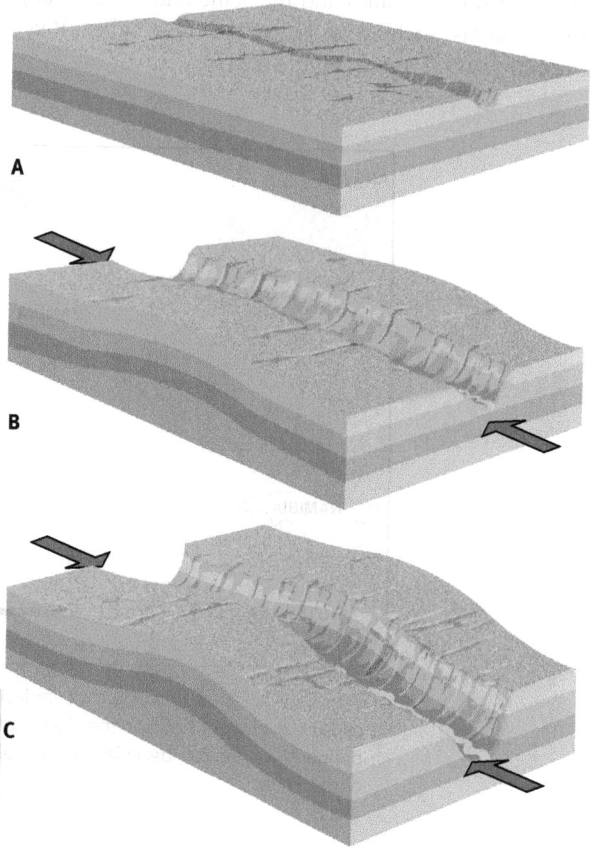

Figure 33.15 Evolution of an antecedent stream, which kept flowing (and eroding downward) as the mountain ridge was being tectonically uplifted across its path. Tectonic forces are shown by the purple arrows.

some stream courses or reaches while strengthening others. The process works as follows. A series of small stream systems is established after deglaciation on an area of uniform rock type. They gradually erode valleys, but some of the streams erode their valleys faster than others, because of differences in the erodability of the bedrock, more stormflow, and/or more baseflow discharge. Gradually, the streams with more flow erode down and back in their valleys by headward erosion and can capture the upper part of a neighbouring stream system.

Sometimes it is possible to see where this process occurred because of an *elbow of capture* or a strange junction between the two parts of the enlarged stream network. This process causes the captor stream to gain the upper reaches of its neighbour and that reach's discharge, while the stream system that was '*beheaded*' loses a section of channel and its discharge, and therefore, some erosive potential. The lower part of the beheaded stream becomes a much smaller stream because of this process (and is called an *underfit* stream or one that is too small to have eroded its valley). The process may also leave a *dry gap* or *wind gap* where the beheaded stream used to flow through a ridge or escarpment. This kind of process may also occur where one stream in flood (or which has aggraded the reaches of its valley) can overflow its basin and cut through a drainage divide into a neighbouring basin and attach itself to the stream network there. This process has happened in many drainage networks all over the world. In Canada it has occurred in the Prairies and in the fairly small drainage systems along the north shore of Lake Ontario. It also occurred in major rivers such the Thames and the Seine and in other large river systems, such as the Kafue and the Zambezi Rivers of south-central Africa (Figure 33.16).

Regional Geomorphology

Physical geographers perform research on landforms and drainage systems, erosional processes, and stream histories. Like other scientists, however, they also want to understand the 'grand design'—the overall shaping of the landscape, the sculpting of regional geomorphology, and the processes that achieve this. At first it would seem that this is merely a matter of the sum of the parts. If the factors affecting erosional efficiency are known (such as those discussed in Units 31 and 32), then surely the evolution of landscape should be understood, shouldn't it? The answer is, not yet. Physical geographers today still debate some very basic issues concerning regional geomorphology.

Ideas about Slopes and Landscape Evolution

One particular debate has been going on for more than a century. It was started by William Morris Davis (1850–1934), pioneer physical geographer and professor at Harvard University from 1879 to 1912. Davis proposed a pedagogical model he called the **geographical cycle**, or **cycle of erosion**. He believed that this cyclical view could be applicable to most landscapes. If the development of certain types of landscapes did not fit this model they were considered to be 'accidents'. Davis considered this cycle to be governed by three variables: geological *structure*, geographical *process*, and time (or *stage*). Every landscape, Davis argued, has an underlying geological structure; it is being acted upon by streams or other erosional processes, and it is at a certain stage of degradation. Davis did not study the geological structure or erosional processes scientifically and concentrated on the stage. A high mountain range was

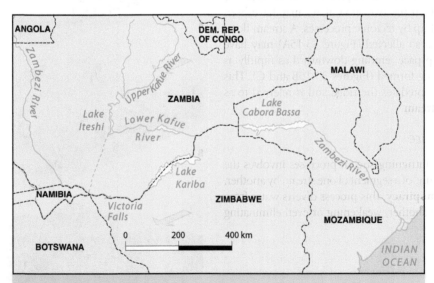

Figure 33.16 Stream piracy enabled the headward-eroding Lower Kafue River to capture the Upper Kafue in the vicinity of Lake Iteshi. Previously, the Upper Kafue River drained into the Zambezi via the (now abandoned) connecting channel, shown by the dashed line.

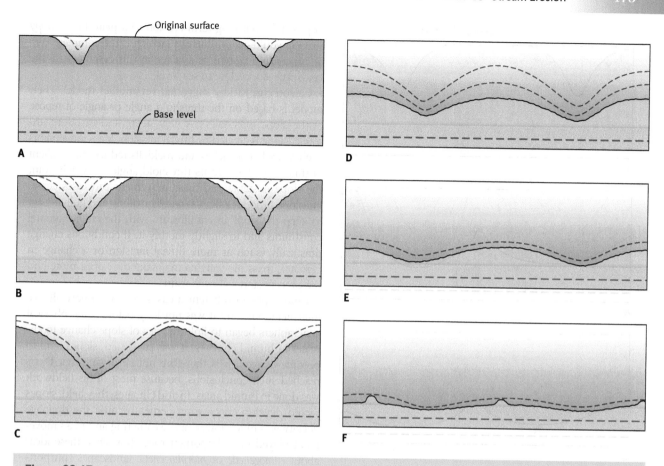

Figure 33.17 Davisian peneplanation model. Streams erode a flat upland area (A), which is gradually transformed into mountainous terrain (B, C). These highlands are subsequently lowered until only the hilly interfluves remain (D, E). Finally these hills are eroded away, leaving the peneplain with a few monadnocks (F).

thought to be in an early stage of development. It would eventually be worn down to a very nearly flat surface, a 'near plain', or **peneplain**. This sequence of events is illustrated in Figure 33.17. In Figures 33.17A and B an upland is being attacked by a network of streams. The upland slopes gradually attain lower angles until the upland is transformed into mountainous terrain (Figure 33.17C). Then the mountains are lowered until they are little more than convex hilly **interfluves** (Figures 33.17D and E). Finally, even these hills are eroded away, leaving a nearly flat plain (peneplain) with a few remnants on it (Figure 33.17F). Davis called the most prominent, not-yet-eroded remnants **monadnocks** (after Mount Monadnock in southern New Hampshire).

In Davis's view, slopes are worn *down*, that is, they become increasingly convex in appearance, and then are flattened. For many years this idea was fairly widely accepted, although many slopes were seen *not* to have a convex form. Nevin Fenneman and Grove Karl Gilbert, in the opening decades of the twentieth century, were among the first to suggest that the Davisian model did not fit all landscapes. European geographers were doubtful of its simplistic view of landscape development. One of these was a friend of Davis's, Walther Penck, who published his doubts (his

book, published posthumously in the 1920s, was not translated into English until the 1950s) and proposed an alternative theory concerning slopes. Penck suggested that slopes retreated backwards and in doing so were replaced by less-steep slopes (slope replacement).

Another theory holds that slopes wear *backward* while maintaining the same angles (by a process called *parallel retreat*). According to a group of scholars, including Alan Wood and Lester C. King, slope retreat is the process whereby highlands are reduced to plains—not peneplains but **pediplains** (the name given to the fairly flat area produced at the foot of the slope as retreat takes place is a **pediment**, so an extensive flattened area is a pediplain). This sequence of events is illustrated in Figure 33.18. Note that the interfluves in this model retain their near-vertical slopes and that the uplands are essentially unaffected until the retreating slopes intersect.

The dynamic equilibrium model is time-independent and suggests that slopes are adjusted to a set of environmental conditions, including climate, base level, geology (solid or superficial), and what processes are occurring at the base of the slope, or slope foot (e.g., undercutting by stream erosion or the sea) (this model was suggested by John T. Hack). The environment is ever-changing, so it is

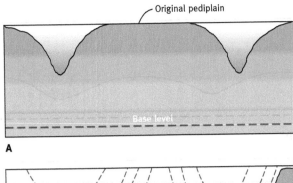

A

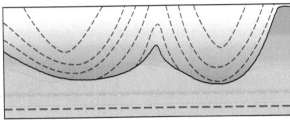

B

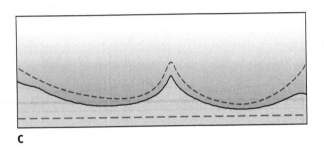

C

Figure 33.18   The pediplanation model, whereby slope retreat reduces highlands to plains. Note that the steep slope angles of the interfluvial uplands are retained throughout the entire erosional sequence.

improbable that long-term erosion to a plain-like *entropy* surface would occur. **Entropy**, which is the complete lack of energy in a system, is a factor in this case because the landscape is too close to sea level.

Carson and Kirkby suggested yet another model. Their model is based on the threshold angle or angle of repose of the slope material(s). A new steep, and therefore unstable, slope is created by fluvial incision. Mass movements such as rock avalanches and rockfalls reduce the gradient of this slope down to its threshold angle, at which point the slope is stable and mass movement processes cease. Hillslope processes such as wash or rilling and gullying act to keep the slope in equilibrium with the environmental constraints and to slightly modify it. If conditions change drastically (such as more fluvial incision or a change in climate), mass movements may take over once more and the process starts all over again.

Landscapes in different areas seem to support all five interpretations, and it was not long before some physical geographers began to link theories of slope change to climate. In humid climates, it was suggested, slopes tend to become convex. It is therefore not surprising that Davis reached such conclusions, because most of his fieldwork was done in humid areas. In arid climates, they held, slopes would develop concave properties because the drainage density was much lower, and weathering and mass movement played more important roles. But when these ideas about *climogenetic* or *morphogenetic* landscapes (purportedly sculpted by geomorphological processes resulting from certain climatic conditions) were put to the test, they failed to account for so many exceptions that they were abandoned. And so the debate about the evolution of landscapes continues.

KEY TERMS

annular drainage   *page 469*
antecedent stream   *page 471*
barbed dendritic drainage   *page 470*
butte   *page 463*
constant of channel maintenance   *page 469*
cycle of erosion (geographical cycle)   *page 472*
dendritic drainage   *page 469*
deranged drainage   *page 470*
drainage density   *page 469*
entropy   *page 474*
escarpment (cuesta)   *page 461*
fault-line scarp   *page 462*
fault scarp   *page 462*
flatirons   *page 461*

geological structure   *page 461*
hogback   *page 461*
interfluve   *page 473*
mesa   *page 463*
monadnock   *page 473*
pediment   *page 473*
pediplain   *page 473*
peneplain   *page 473*
radial drainage   *page 469*
rectangular drainage   *page 469*
scarp   *page 462*
stream piracy   *page 471*
trellis drainage   *page 469*
uniclinal shifting   *page 461*

REVIEW QUESTIONS

1. How can lithology influence stream erosion?
2. What kinds of landforms are most likely to exhibit a radial drainage pattern?
3. Contrast a dendritic drainage pattern with a trellis pattern.
4. How might stream piracy result in the reinvigoration of a stream?
5. Briefly describe the cycle of erosion as envisioned by William Morris Davis.
6. Compare and contrast the Davisian model of slope evolution to the idea of dynamic equilibrium or the threshold angle models.

REFERENCES AND FURTHER READINGS

Allen, P.A. 1997. *Earth Surface Processes*. Malden, Mass.: Blackwell.

Bridge, J. 2002. *Rivers and Floodplains*. Malden, Mass.: Blackwell.

Calow, P., and G.E. Petts. 1994. *Rivers Handbook, Vol. 2*. Malden, Mass.: Blackwell.

Carson, M.A., and M.J. Kirkby. 1972. *Hillslope Form and Process*. Cambridge: Cambridge Univ. Press.

Chorley, R.J., ed. 1971. *Introduction to Fluvial Processes*. London: Methuen.

————— et al. 1984. *Geomorphology*. London/New York: Methuen.

Cumming Cockburn Ltd. 2000. *Hurricane Hazel and Extreme Rainfall in Southern Ontario*. Toronto: Institute of Catastrophic Loss Reduction Research Paper Series No. 9.

Davis, W.M. 1954. *Geographical Essays*. New York: Dover, reprint of 1909 original.

Fenneman, N.M. 1936. 'Cyclic and Non-cyclic Aspects of Erosion', *Geological Society of America Bulletin* 47: 173–86.

Gordon, N.D., T.A. McMahon, and B.L. Finlayson. 1992. *Stream Hydrology: An Introduction for Ecologists*. New York: Wiley.

Gregory, K.J., and D.E. Walling. 1998. *Drainage Basins: Form, Process and Management*. Malden, Mass.: Blackwell.

Gurnell, A., and G. Petts, eds. 1996. *River Channels*. New York: Wiley.

Hack, J.T. 1960. 'The Interpretation of Erosional Topography in Humid Temperate Regions', *American Journal of Science* 258-A: 80–97.

Hickin, E.J., ed. 1995. *River Geomorphology*. New York: Wiley.

Kennedy, B. 1979. *Hurricane Hazel*. Toronto: Macmillan.

King, L.C. 1953. 'Canons of Landscape Evolution', *Geological Society of America Bulletin* 64: 721–52.

————. 1957. 'The Uniformitarian Nature of Hillslopes', *Geological Society of Edinburgh, Transactions* 17: 81–102.

————. 1963. *South African Scenery: A Textbook of Geomorphology*. Edinburgh: Oliver and Boyd.

————. 1967. *Morphology of the Earth*. Edinburgh: Oliver and Boyd.

King, P.B., and S.A. Schumm. 1980. *The Physical Geography of William Morris Davis*. Norwich, UK: GeoBooks.

Knighton, D. 1998. *Fluvial Forms and Processes: A New Perspective*. New York: Oxford Univ. Press.

Leopold, L.B., et al. 1964. *Fluvial Processes in Geomorphology*. San Francisco: Freeman.

Malanson, G.P. 1993. *Riparian Landscapes*. New York: Cambridge Univ. Press.

Mollard, J.D., and J.R. Janes. 1984. *Airphoto Interpretation of the Canadian Landscape*. Ottawa: Department of Energy, Mines and Resources.

Morisawa, M. 1968. *Streams: Their Dynamics and Morphology*. New York: McGraw-Hill.

Penck, W. 1953. *Morphological Analysis of Landforms*. Trans. H. Czech and K.C. Boswell of *Die Morphologische Analyse* (1924). London: Macmillan.

Petts, G., and I. Foster. 1985. *Rivers and Landscapes*. London: Edward Arnold.

Richards, K.S. 1982. *Rivers: Form and Process in Alluvial Channels*. London/New York: Methuen.

Robert, A. 2003. *River Processes: An Introduction to Fluvial Dynamics*. London: Arnold.

Schumm, S.A. 1977. *The Fluvial System*. New York: Wiley.

Wood, A. 1942. 'The Development of Hillside Slopes', *Proceedings of the Geological Association* (London) 53: 128–39.

Worssam, B.C. 1973. *A New Look at River Capture and at the Denudation of the Weald*. Institute of Geological Sciences Report 73/17. London: HMSO.

 ## WEB RESOURCES

archives.cbc.ca/environment/extreme_weather/topics/77/ Information on and video of Hurricane Hazel.

www.acer-acre.org/ClimateChangeCD/frameset.html Section 4.2.1.d of this resource provides images, maps, and text about the capture of a glacial meltwater stream that existed during deglaciation and was captured by Bronte Creek.

www.ec.gc.ca/water/en/manage/floodgen/e_ont.htm Freshwater website about floods and flooding events in Canada, including Hurricane Hazel and the Saguenay floods.

www.Hurricanehazel.ca/ Toronto and Region Conservation Authority site about Hurricane Hazel. Good information and photographs of damage and rescue attempts.

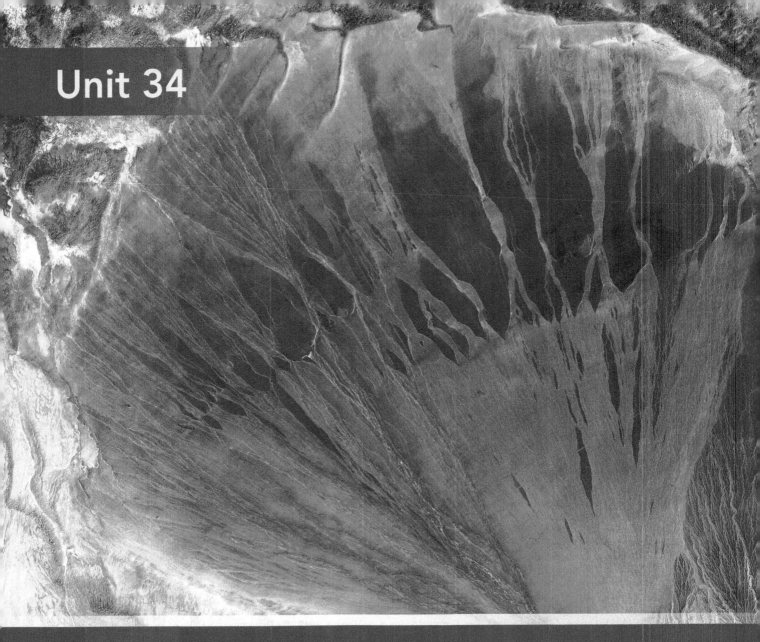

Unit 34

Aggradational Landforms of Streams

Objectives

- To identify the types of landforms built by streams.
- To examine the formation and development of the stream floodplain.
- To investigate the evolution of river deltas.

Unit 33 examined streams as sculptors, carvers, and cutters, and explained how streams degrade and how running water can denude countrysides. This unit focuses on streams as builders. Although the world's streams disgorge hundreds of millions of tonnes of sediment annually into the oceans, part of the transported load does not reach the sea but is laid down in floodplains, in deltas, and elsewhere on land. Whereas the landforms of stream aggradation are not as spectacular as those in high mountains and incised plateaus, they are nevertheless very important. Often the deposits along a stream's lower course reveal the history of the stream's upper course, and can help us unravel the complexities in understanding the development of a regional drainage basin.

Alluvial Fans (Fan Deltas)

In certain areas, especially in arid zones of the world, precipitation is infrequent and streamflow is discontinuous. Rainstorms in such areas or in nearby mountains produce a subsequent rush of water in the valleys, and turbulent, sediment-laden streams flow towards adjacent plains. Emerging from the highlands, the water slows down and deposits its sedimentary load. Much of this water infiltrates the ground, and evaporation removes the remainder. Meanwhile, when the rain has stopped, the stream soon runs dry. A stream that flows intermittently like this is called an *ephemeral stream*.

Ephemeral streams often construct alluvial fans (cones) where they emerge from highland areas. As the term suggests, an **alluvial fan** is a fan-shaped deposit consisting of stream-carried material, located where a mountain stream emerges onto a plain (Figure 34.1). In this situation the stream is not part of the regional drainage basin that ultimately leads to the ocean. Streams that form alluvial fans are unlikely to flow far beyond the edge of the fan. And when the mountain rains are below average, the stream may not even reach the outer margin of its own deposits.

Fan-shaped deposits are not unique to arid areas, although they are best developed there. They can also be found in areas where glaciation has taken place and where streams carry heavy loads of debris to the edges of glacier-steepened mountains. Others are located on the flanks of steep-sided volcanoes. But the typical alluvial fan is primarily an arid landform, a product of stream aggradation (see Unit 40).

LINK

The alluvial fan attains its conical or semicircular shape because the stream that emanates from the often gorge-like mountain valley tends to have an impermanent course on the fan surface. The sediment-clogged water, when it surges from the edge of the upland, quickly slows down, so that it must drop part of its load. Figure 34.2A shows what happens.

As the discharge drops, it exposes **midstream bars**, and water flows around these obstructions. Soon more deposition takes place, and many bars, some submerged, develop. At lower flows the stream divides into many

Figure 34.1 Alluvial fan and basin Keremeos, British Columbia.

smaller channels that intertwine with one another to form a *braided stream*, a process that in certain cases can reach several kilometres in width (Figure 34.2B). Under such conditions, the stream obviously cannot erode a deep valley. In fact, it is flowing on deposits that may build to an elevation above the rest of the fan surface. The next time rains generate a stream surge, the water may seek a different direction.

An alluvial fan, therefore, consists of a series of poorly stratified layers, thickest near the mountain front and progressively thinning outward. The coarsest sediments are normally located nearest the apex of the fan and finer-grained material towards the outer edges. Since the fan lies on bedrock and has layers of greater and lesser permeability, infiltrating water can be contained within it. Many alluvial fans in the southwestern United States and throughout the world are sources of groundwater for permanent settlements.

When environmental conditions exist for alluvial fan development, a mountain front may have not just one or two but dozens of larger and smaller alluvial fans, coalescing across the *pediment* (the smooth, gently sloping bedrock surface that underlies the alluvial cover and extends outward from the foot of the highlands). When this happens,

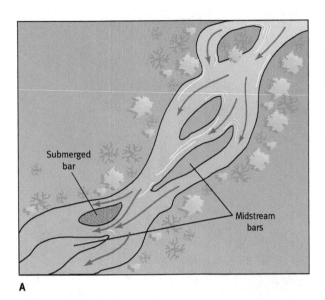

A

B

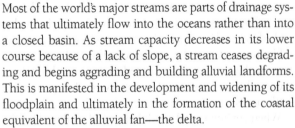

Figure 34.2 Braided streams begin with the deposition of midstream bars as discharge decreases after a flood (A). These obstacles split the stream into many channels as the discharge decreases, widening the stream greatly. Some braided streams can reach widths of 8 km, as is the case with the Brahmaputra River as it flows through northeastern India into neighbouring Bangladesh (B). In this photo, taken from a space shuttle, the Brahmaputra Valley's width is enhanced by flooding associated with the wet monsoon. The river it joins in central Bangladesh at the lower end of its braided segment is the mighty Ganges. Their combined channels flow southward for another 200 km into the Bay of Bengal (upper left corner), crossing the massive compound delta they have built.

the cone shapes of individual adjacent fans may be difficult to distinguish, and the landform is called an *alluvial apron* or a **bajada** (Spanish for slope). Such an assemblage of alluvial fans can exhibit many features. Where streamflow has increased, *arroyos* (gullies) have been cut into the fans, and thus the older upper parts of the fan surface are no longer subject to the shifting stream process described above. These older areas become stable, may support vegetation, and often develop a varnished appearance on the weathered lag gravel surface, which has earned the name *desert pavement* (see Figure 40.2).

Streams to the Sea

Most of the world's major streams are parts of drainage systems that ultimately flow into the oceans rather than into a closed basin. As stream capacity decreases in its lower course because of a lack of slope, a stream ceases degrading and begins aggrading and building alluvial landforms. This is manifested in the development and widening of its floodplain and ultimately in the formation of the coastal equivalent of the alluvial fan—the delta.

The course of the stream exhibits several changes as its depositional function gains strength. While the stream fully occupied its valley upstream, the channel now begins to erode laterally, and for the first time the valley becomes slightly wider than the stream channel. Bends in the stream channel, called **meanders**, are increasingly

evident (Figure 34.3). Erosion occurs on the outside of the bends of these meanders, and deposition on the inside of the bends; in this way the stream migrates across and down its floodplain.

Channel Habit

The channel habit is a term used to describe the *planform* shape of a stream channel. There are many different shapes exhibited by streams. Channel habit is influenced by factors such as:

- the amount and variability of discharge;
- the amount of sediment carried by the stream;
- the type of sediment carried by the stream and in the stream bed and banks (cohesive or granular materials); and
- the channel gradient or slope of the stream channel.

There is a continuum of shapes from straight channels (Figure 34.4), which may be structurally determined but more usually are constructed (e.g., canals are associated with braided environments), through to tortuously meandering (Figure 34.5).

It is possible to separate two distinct types of channel on the basis of shape and related to sediment type:

1. *Suspended load channels* are sinuous channels (sinuosity is over 2:1—e.g., 2.5 km+ of channel length to 1 km of valley length) with gentle slopes. Eighty-five

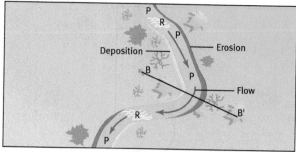

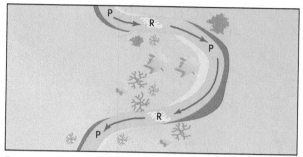

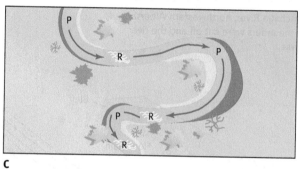

Figure 34.4 Human-constructed straight channel.

Figure 34.3 The development of meanders in a stream caused by differential energy loss over pools and rivers. Pools must lengthen in an attempt to balance the energy loss. (A) A stream bend displays pools and riffles, evidence of deposition on the inside of the bend and erosion on the outside curve. (B) The stream's bends are close to developing meander properties. Erosion on the outside of the now sharper bend (cut bank) is increasing, whereas deposition is occurring on the point bar on the inside. (C) The process has advanced to the meander stage. The stream is building its floodplain; the inside of the meander is a growing point bar. On the outside curve of the meander, erosion is strongest towards the lower part (the southeast in this sketch), resulting in the cross-floodplain down-valley migration of the meander.

per cent of the load carried by these channels is composed of suspended sediment (a large proportion of this is in the silt and clay grades); 15 per cent of the load is coarser bedload. The channels have width:depth ratios greater than 7. They are narrow and deep and occur in cohesive clay and silt bed and bank materials. These types of channels are characterized by meandering.

2. *Bedload channels* are less sinuous (relatively straight). Sinuosity is about 1.5:1. They are associated with

steeper channel slopes. Seventy per cent of the load is bedload while the remaining 30 per cent is suspended sand (no sediment is in the silt-clay range). Width:depth ratios are over 25. These are very wide but shallow channels associated with non-cohesive, granular bed and bank materials. These types of channels are associated with braiding.

Meandering and the Floodplain

Meandering probably develops because of imbalanced energy loss along a stream channel caused by water flow over pools and riffles. All streams have undulating beds (pool and riffle sequences). The shallower parts that may break the surface are the **riffles**; these are characterized by their shallowness, their symmetrical shape, their coarser bed material (gravel, boulders, etc.), and their being slightly wider than the pools. Pools are deeper sections of the bed; they are associated with an asymmetrical section and finer bed materials (fine sand, salt, and clay), and are slightly narrower than the riffles. This means that the same volume of water (discharge) has to get through the areas with larger (pools) and smaller (riffles) cross-sectional areas. For this to be done, the velocity has to increase as water moves from a pool to a riffle (because of the **Venturi effect**) and slow as it goes from a riffle to a pool. The differences in velocity, bed roughness, and turbulence between the two areas mean that more energy is lost over the riffles. To bring the energy loss over the pools up to balance that over the riffles, the pools lengthen, adding more bed and banks, and therefore increasing roughness and causing more energy loss. To lengthen, they have to bend (see Figure 34.3).

When meanders develop in a stream channel, they move in two directions. First, as Figure 34.3 shows, they erode laterally and increase in size; second, they migrate downstream. These two motions, the lateral swing and the downstream shift, have the effect of widening the stream's valley and creating an extensive **floodplain**—the flat, low-lying ground on either side of the stream channel that is inundated during periods of larger discharges. Note that

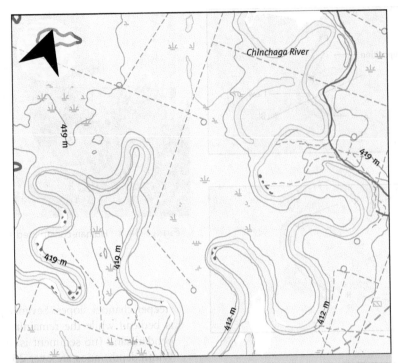

Figure 34.5 Meandering stream: Chinchaga River, northwestern Alberta. Note the oxbow lakes that formed when meanders were cut off and the river sought a straighter, less meandering course.

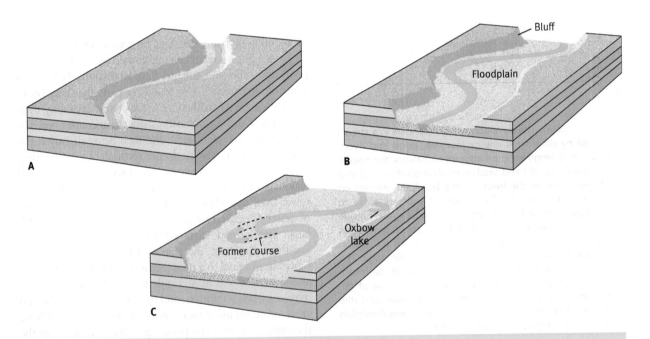

Figure 34.6 Floodplain formation and widening as meanders grow, erode laterally, and migrate downstream.

the channel of the stream still fills almost the entire valley at first (Figure 34.6A), but becomes an ever smaller part of the valley floor as deposition occurs (Figures 34.6B and C). Also, observe that the bottom of the stream channel, swinging back and forth across the valley, may create the base of the floodplain in the underlying bedrock unless it is on a pile of alluvial sediments. But by now the chan-

nel is flanked by deposits laid down by the stream itself. The floodplain is also defined by a very characteristic sequence of sediments (a fining-upward sequence). The coarse material at the base of the sequence is material that was dragged or rolled along the bottom of the stream (bed load). The finer material (sand and gravel) above this was laid down on point bars by slackening floodwaters and at the top of the sequence there is a layer of very fine clay and silt material deposited from pools of slack water on the floodplain surface left as the flood abated.

Figure 34.6C shows the development of two small, crescent-shaped lakes. These are **oxbow lakes**, which form when a meander is cut off, as shown in Figure 34.7. Such *cut-offs* can occur, as seen in the diagram, when the downstream movement of one meander 'catches up' with the lagging movement of the bend immediately below it (Figures 34.7B and C). Another way this can happen is during a flood, when a *meander neck*, such as that shown in Figure 34.7A, can be swept away and the channel is deepened along the course of the dashed lines. When the flood subsides, the new cut-off may be deep enough to have the same effect as in Figure 34.7D, and an oxbow lake, or a slough (a wetland in a partially filled-in oxbow lake), will ultimately form.

The alluvial floodplain is bounded by *bluffs*, cut by the meandering stream (Figure 34.6). Over time the floodplain may become many kilometres wide, and *meander belts* themselves may form giant meanders. As in the case of individual meanders, the entire meander belt tends to move downstream. As a result, a floodplain is full of evidence of previous meanders, meander belts, oxbow lakes, and other features. These are referred to as scars, so that a dried-up oxbow lake becomes a **meander scar**, a place where a meander once existed.

As noted earlier, a floodplain is so named because this plain, between the bluffs, is subject to frequent flooding. Annual floods, during which the river overflows its banks, are a normal part of the floodplain's development. These floods deposit sediments that may build the stream's **natural levees**. (The concept of 'natural' levees remains controversial. There is no real proof that levees occur or began naturally, since humans have worked to protect stream banks from very early on, even in quite 'primitive' societies, and may have initiated levee deposition.) Levees are broad ridges that run along both sides of the channel (Figure 34.8). As the river spills out of its channel, the coarsest material it is carrying is deposited along the levees. When the river contracts after the flood, it stays within its self-generated levees (Figure 34.8C). The levees restrict the amount of flooding. They tend to keep the water and sediment in the channel and therefore over time the bed of the stream and the levees build up an *alluvial ridge* above the general level of the floodplain and well above the lower areas of the floodplain—the *backswamps*. This means that any larger floods could be very catastrophic as the levees might be breached and part of the stream might move off the alluvial ridge and onto the floodplain, flooding vast areas (as in the Hurricane Katrina floods of 2005, the Irrawaddy Delta in Burma [Myanmar] in 2008, the floods in the US Midwest of May and June 2008 [Figure 34.9], and the Philippines flooding caused by Cyclone Fengshen in late June 2008).

Alluvial ridges and levees may also stop a tributary from joining the trunk stream, as is the case with some feeder channels of major rivers such as Mississippi. The prime example of this is the Yazoo River. Because the tributary stream cannot join the trunk stream because it is elevated on the

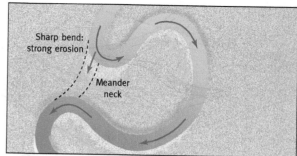

A

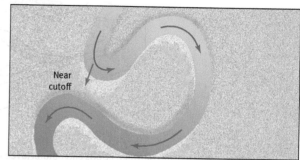

B

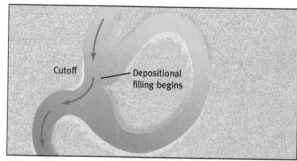

C

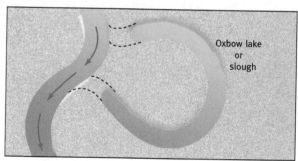

D

Figure 34.7 Formation of an oxbow lake as a result of meander neck cutoff.

alluvial ridge, the feeder stream is forced to flow parallel to the trunk stream for some distance before eventually flowing into it. Such a tributary stream is called a *yazoo stream*.

Infrequently—perhaps once in a century—a stream may experience a flood of such magnitude (50-year, 100-year flood) that its floodplain is greatly modified. Water up to several metres deep may inundate the entire floodplain, destroying submerged levees, eroding bluffs, and disrupting the entire system. These floods have cost millions of

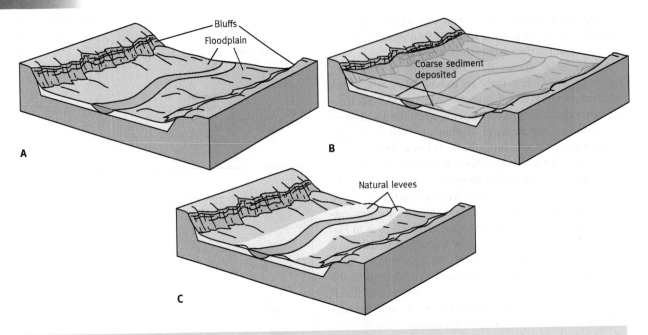

Figure 34.8 Relationship between floods and natural levee development. The river's coarsest deposits are laid down closest to the overflow (B). After repeated flooding, these deposits are built up as levees that contain the stream channel (C).

Figure 34.9 Downtown Cedar Rapids, Iowa, June 2008, after the Cedar River overflowed its banks during major Midwest floods.

lives in the densely populated floodplains of Asia's major streams and cause devastation to thousands of people and to crops in the agricultural lands and cities of the American Midwest. They also occur in the Red River basin of Manitoba, where the damage, too, can be enormous (see 'Perspectives' box). No reinforcement of natural levees or construction of **artificial levees** can withstand the impact of such a powerful 100-year flood.

Terraces

After a flood, a stream returns to pre-flood volume and functions. But what happens in a floodplain if a stream is reinvigorated? Increased volume (through stream capture or longer-term climatic change in the drainage basin), tectonic uplift, or a drop in sea level may increase a meandering stream's capacity to erode.

Perspectives on the Human Environment

The Red River Flood of 1997

The Red River is 877 km long. Its source is near Detroit Station, close to the western border of Minnesota, and it flows north through North Dakota and into Canada at Emerson, Manitoba. Spring melt occurs earlier in the southern part of the basin while the northern reaches of the river are still frozen. This leads to flooding. People living in this area of Manitoba have had to deal with floods since settlement began. The largest flood on the historical record occurred in 1826. Another large flood occurred in 1950, and this led to the construction of the Red River Floodway, familiarly called 'Duff's Ditch' after Dufferin Roblin, the Manitoba premier at the time the floodway was planned and built (it was constructed between 1962 and 1969).

During the spring of 1997, near-record winter snowfalls (up to 250 cm snowpack) occurred in the Red River basin. This amount of snow, together with frozen soils and a rapid spring melt, resulted in extremely extensive flooding in North Dakota and Manitoba. The Red River crested in Winnipeg on 3 May, with a discharge of 3904 m³/s (enough to fill an Olympic-sized swimming pool once every second). Half the flow was diverted past the city by the 47-km-long floodway, which lessened the potential damage. By the next day, floodwaters had covered 1950 km². The floodwaters eventually covered 202,500 ha (or 5 per cent) of Manitoba farmland.

The rising water forced 28,000 Manitobans (including 6000 Winnipeggers) from their homes. Without the floodway it has been estimated that 80 per cent of Winnipeg would have been underwater and about 550,000 city residents would have had to be evacuated. Many hundreds of workers, armed forces, and volunteers worked at sandbagging and helped evacuate people and livestock. Large earth dykes were erected on the southern margin of Winnipeg to stop possible flooding of low-lying neighbourhoods and divert water towards the floodway. Close to 9000 Canadian Armed Forces personnel were involved in 'Operation Assistance'. Their equipment included over 2500 vehicles, 58 watercraft, and 33 aircraft (the aircraft logged over 1500 flight hours).

Losses to dairy farmers alone were estimated to be $1.31 to $2 million; some 2000 cattle and 45,000 laying hens had to be moved out of the path of floodwaters. Whole towns and farms were sandbagged and left as isolated islands in the 'Red Sea' (Figure 34.10). Damages have been estimated at over $815 million. This can be compared with data on the 1950 flood. That disaster had damages of $606 million (in 1997 dollars, and in a time when there was much less built property and property values were a fraction of what they were nearly 50 years later), large sections of the downtown were underwater, and 100,000 people were evacuated.

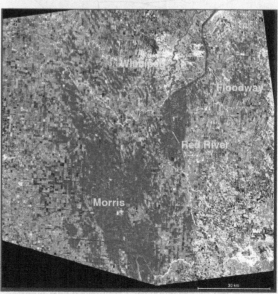

Figure 34.10 These remotely sensed RADARSAT images of the area around Winnipeg show: (A) the normal course of the Red River and (B) the same region after the river spilled over its banks in May 1997.

A stream may cut into its own alluvial deposits (Figure 34.11). For simplicity, levees and other features have been left off the diagram. The stream cuts downward a newly imposed base level from its original level on the floodplain (A) to a new level (B), where it stabilizes and meanders develop. Soon a new floodplain within the older floodplain develops (C), complete with a new set of bounding bluffs.

Remnants of the older floodplain stand above these newer bluffs as **terraces**. These terraces reveal the two-stage evolution of the valley, and may be correlated with other information about the climate, base level, or tectonic uplift in the region involved. The terraces shown in Figure 34.11 are *paired terraces*; that is, they lie at the same elevation on each side of the incised stream. Sometimes terraces are not paired as a result of a combination of valley deepening and lateral (sideways) erosion. This can destroy one side of a set of paired terraces, sometimes making studies of valley history quite difficult. The sequence just outlined is common to streams in southern parts of the US and other areas that were not glaciated.

Terrace deposits in formerly glaciated areas show a sequence of deposits very distinct from those of floodplains. These terraces are characterized by much coarser material, such as large gravels (some as big as watermelons), and they may contain huge ice-rafted blocks weighing many tonnes. The whole sequence appears to be chaotically deposited by a torrentially flowing braided stream supplied with discharge and lots of sediment (glacial material) by deglaciation or a jökulhlaup (glacial burst flood).

Conceivably, the stream could remove all of its alluvial base in the floodplain, leaving a *rock terrace* rather than creating an alluvial terrace. Such a rock terrace, technically, is a degradational landform, but its genesis relates to an earlier phase of floodplain aggradation. Under certain circumstances, such as the uplifting of the land surface above base level, whole meander belts can be incised into hard bedrock from overlying floodplain topography. These incised or **entrenched meanders** can produce some spectacular scenery, as in the canyons of the Fraser and Stikine Rivers in BC (Figure 34.12), the Nahanni River, NWT, the San Juan and Colorado River valleys of southern Utah, and the Grand Canyon of the Yarlung (or Tsangpo) River as it leaves the Tibetan Plateau and cuts through the Himalayas. This gorge was only discovered by outsiders in the 1990s. It is about 250 km long and three times deeper than the Grand Canyon of the Colorado River.

Deltas

About 2500 years ago, the ancient Greek scholar Herodotus, studying the mouth of the Nile River, found that this great stream of northeastern Africa forms a giant fan-shaped deposit where it reaches the Mediterranean Sea. Noting the triangular shape of this area of sedimentation, he called it a **delta** (after the fourth letter of the Greek

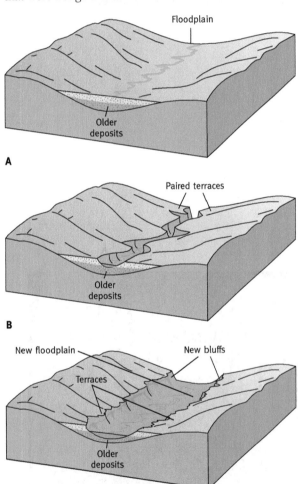

Figure 34.11 Paired terraces emerge as the reinvigorated stream cuts downward into its own floodplain in an area unaffected by glaciation (B). Eventually a new floodplain embedded within the older one develops, bordered by newer bluffs formed by the inner slopes of the paired terraces (C).

Figure 34.12 The Stikine River, with entrenched meanders, cuts through the Stikine Canyon in northwestern British Columbia.

alphabet). Ever since, river-mouth deposits have been called deltas, even when they have a different shape.

Near its mouth a stream comes close to its base level and slows down markedly. Even the finest sediment being carried in suspension is deposited, so that the stream mouth may become clogged. As a result, the stream channel breaks down into smaller channels, which flow over the accumulated sediment. These channels, which begin at the apex of the delta and carry the stream's water in several directions over the surface, are called **distributaries**. Thus, a trunk stream receives *tributaries* in its drainage basin and develops *distributaries* where it forms a delta.

As the map of the Nile Delta (Figure 34.13A) shows, the Nile forms a few prominent distributaries and many smaller ones. When Herodotus did his fieldwork, the Nile Delta was an uninhabited swampy area. Today it is an area of dense rural settlement and intensive cultivation. Control of the Nile's distributaries and land reclamation has made this transformation possible.

The exact form of a delta is determined by: (1) the volume of the stream and the amount of sediment it carries; (2) the configuration of the offshore continental shelf or lake bed near the river mouth; and (3) the strength of marine or lake currents and waves. Many attempts have been made to try to classify deltas. A basic division is based on whether the delta shape is dominated by river, wave, or tidal inputs of sediment and energy. The most appropriate classification for our use is one rooted in the earlier schemes and that

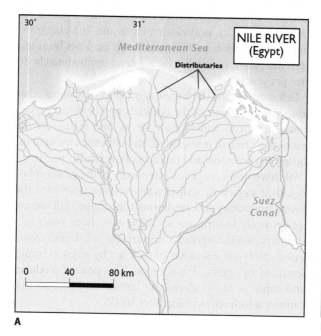

A

B

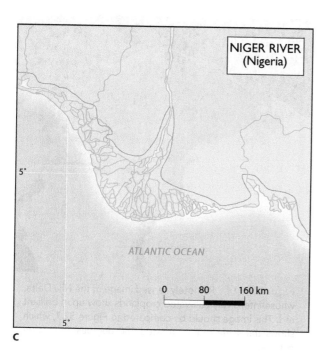

C

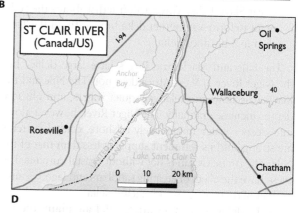

D

Figure 34.13 The spatial form of a delta depends on the quantity of sediment carried by the stream, the configuration of the continental shelf or lake bed beyond the stream mouth, and the power of waves and currents in the sea or lake. The Nile Delta (A) exhibits the classic triangular shape. The Mackenzie (B), exhibiting a birdfoot shape, results from large quantities of sediment carried into quiet water as does the St Clair River Delta (D). The Niger Delta (C) is shaped by strong waves and currents that sweep sediment along the coast.

considers the characteristics of marine and lacustrine deltas in Canada. This classification, which looks at the characteristics of the deltaic sediments and how they were deposited, recognizes four basic types of delta:

1. *Braid deltas.* Braid deltas are composed of sands and gravels and are formed by the building out of sandar into a lake or the sea. Skeiðarársandur in southeastern Iceland is a good example (see Unit 38 and Figure 38.2).

2. *Fan-foreset (or Gilbert-type) deltas.* These are associated with high-energy environments mainly because of steep stream-channel slopes. The top layer of the delta sediments is dominated by gravel, as is the delta front. The lower layers of sediment are sands. These deltas are common in deep-bottomed lakes in mountainous areas. The material is supplied by small steep-gradient streams draining upland basins of limited extent. A prime example is the Lillooet River Delta, BC.

3. *Stable channel-mouth (or fluvial) deltas.* These are the most common type and largest deltas in Canada and elsewhere (such as the Nile). This type includes the 'birdfoot' deltas, as found, for example, at the mouth of the Mississippi River as it enters the Gulf of Mexico. Most deposition takes place in point bars upstream of the delta, and as the channel fills the bars become part of the delta itself. Examples of stable channel-mouth deltas in this country include those of the Peace, Athabaska, Saskatchewan, and Birch Rivers. The Mackenzie, Red, and St Clair Rivers are 'birdfoot deltas' (Figures 34.13B and D).

LINK

4. *Wave-influenced deltas.* Wave-influenced deltas are dominated by well-sorted river-supplied sands formed by wave action. Examples in Canada are the Slave and William River deltas, the latter of which enters Lake Athabasca, and that of the Hay River as it flows into Great Slave Lake. Wave action redistributes the sediment to form a smoother delta front without the 'toes' seen in a birdfoot delta.

The Nile and Mackenzie Rivers have large deltas, but the Niger River of West Africa does not. The Nile and the Mackenzie flow into relatively quiet waters, and offshore depths increase gradually. The Niger River, however, flows into deeper water immediately offshore, coastal currents are strong, and its sediment supply is less than that of the Nile. The Arctic Ocean is not without coastal currents, but these have the effect of creating sandbars and lagoons rather than of destroying the advancing delta.

As the delta grows seaward, the **deltaic plain** (the flat landward portion of the delta) stabilizes. The distributaries of many deltas are dredged and controlled today, affecting the process of formation. In thve case of the Mississippi Delta, for example, many distributaries that would have become blocked by sediment are kept open, creating a birdfoot delta.

The Delta Profile

No two deltas form in exactly the same way, and the process is extremely complicated. The finest deposits to be laid down are the **bottomset beds**. The stream deposits its finest-grained material ahead of the delta, where (it may be assumed in this instance) the water is quiet and such deposition can occur. In the meantime, the stream is adding to the **topset beds** of the delta, the horizontal layers that underlie the deltaic plain. As the delta grows outward, the **foreset beds** are built from the leading edge of the topset beds. Later, the newly accumulated foreset beds will be covered by extended topset beds.

The thickness and the resulting weight of deltaic sediments can depress the coastal crust isostatically, complicating the process of delta development still further. Areas of surrounding coastland, but not part of the delta structure itself, may be affected by such subsidence, with serious consequences. The Mississippi Delta, where it meets the Gulf of Mexico in southeastern Louisiana, is a classic example of this phenomenon, and much land has been lost over the past few decades (at a rate of approximately 80 km^2 per year).

Deltas are among the largest aggradational features related to streams. Some of the boulders and pebbles dragged down mountain valleys now lie as fine grains on the coast—pulverized, transported, and deposited by streams, those great sculptors and builders of the landscape.

We have now completed our survey of the geomorphological processes associated with running water and the fluvial landscapes and landforms they shape. But we are not yet ready to turn our attention away from water as a geomorphological agent. A special case of degradational action involves the removal of rock not by physical breakdown but by chemical dissolution. This process produces landscapes of highly distinctive surface and near-surface features, which are examined in Unit 35.

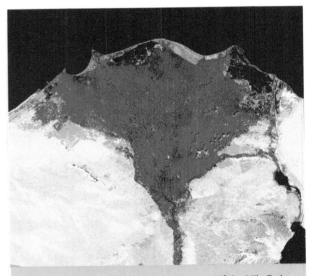

Figure 34.14 Remotely sensed image of the Nile Delta, whose intensively cultivated croplands show up in brilliant red. This image should be compared to Figure 32.7, which shows the same region (rotated 180 degrees) in its true colours.

KEY TERMS

alluvial fan   *page 477*
artificial levee   *page 482*
bajada   *page 477*
bottomset beds   *page 486*
delta   *page 484*
deltaic plain   *page 486*
distributaries   *page 485*

entrenched meander   *page 484*
floodplain   *page 479*
foreset beds   *page 486*
meander   *page 478*
meander scar   *page 481*
midstream bar   *page 477*
natural levee   *page 481*

oxbow lake   *page 481*
riffles   *page 479*
terrace   *page 484*
topset beds   *page 486*
Venturi effect   *page 479*

REVIEW QUESTIONS

1. Describe the circumstances under which alluvial fans form.
2. What are pools and riffles and how do they affect streamflow?
3. How is the process of meandering related to the formation of floodplains?
4. Describe the stages of formation of an oxbow lake.
5. What are stream terraces, and how are they formed?
6. Describe the similarities between alluvial fans and the various types of river deltas.
7. Compare and contrast river terraces found in areas that were glaciated in the Late Cenozoic Ice Age to terraces in unglaciated areas.

REFERENCES AND FURTHER READINGS

Bhattacharya, J.P., and R.G. Walker. 1992. 'Deltas', in R.G. Walker and N.P. James, *Facies Models: Response to Sea Level Change*. St John's: Geological Society of Canada, 157–77.

Bridge, J. 2002. *Rivers and Floodplains*. Malden, Mass.: Blackwell.

Brooks, G.R., et al. 2001. 'Floods', in G.R. Brooks, *A Synthesis of Geological Hazards in Canada*. Ottawa: Geological Survey of Canada Bulletin 548, 101–43.

———— et al. 2003. *Geoscientific Insights into Red River Flood Hazards in Manitoba*. Ottawa: Geological Society of Canada Open File Report 4473.

Calow, P., and G.E. Petts. 1994. *Rivers Handbook, Vol. 2*. Malden, Mass.: Blackwell.

Carling, P.A., and G.E. Petts, eds. 1992. *Lowland Floodplain Rivers: Geomorphological Perspectives*. New York: Wiley.

Chorley, R.J., ed. 1971. *Introduction to Fluvial Processes*. London: Methuen.

de Blij, H.J., ed. 1994. *Nature on the Rampage*. Washington: Smithsonian Institution Press.

Dury, G.H., ed. 1970. *Rivers and River Terraces*. London/New York: Macmillan.

Gordon, N.D., T.A. McMahon, and B.L. Finlayson. 1992. *Stream Hydrology: An Introduction for Ecologists*. New York: Wiley.

Graf, W.L. 1988. *Fluvial Processes in Dryland Rivers*. New York: Springer-Verlag.

Gurnell, A., and G. Petts, eds. 1996. *River Channels*. New York: Wiley.

Hickin, E.J., ed. 1995. *River Geomorphology*. New York: Wiley.

Hoyt, W.G., and W.B. Langbein. 1955. *Floods*. Princeton, NJ: Princeton Univ. Press.

Knighton, D. 1998. *Fluvial Forms and Processes: A New Perspective*. New York: Oxford Univ. Press.

Leopold, L.B., et al. 1964. *Fluvial Processes in Geomorphology*. San Francisco: Freeman.

Malanson, G.P. 1993. *Riparian Landscapes*. New York: Cambridge Univ. Press.

Morisawa, M. 1968. *Streams: Their Dynamics and Morphology*. New York: McGraw-Hill.

Petts, G., and I. Foster. 1985. *Rivers and Landscapes*. London: Edward Arnold.

Rachocki, A.H., and M. Church, eds. 1990. *Alluvial Fans: A Field Approach*. New York: Wiley.

Richards, K.S. 1982. *Rivers: Form and Process in Alluvial Channels*. London/New York: Methuen.

Robert, A. 2003. *River Processes: An Introduction of Fluvial Dynamics*. London: Arnold.

Schumm, S.A. 1977. *The Fluvial System*. New York: Wiley.

Smith, D.G. 1991. 'Canadian Landform Examples—22: Lacustrine Deltas', *Canadian Geographer* 35, 3: 311–16.

Ward, R. 1978. *Floods: A Geographical Perspective*. New York: Macmillan.

 ## WEB RESOURCES

wrgis.wr.usgs.gov/docs/usgsnps/deva/galfan.html The US Geological Survey focuses here on the alluvial fans present in Death Valley National Park, with many colour photographs and links to more information about the region and its accompanying geology. A virtual field trip guides viewers through the park.

www.canadiangeographic.ca/specialfeatures/floods/flood.asp This website has information, maps, photos, and links relating to floods in Canada.

www.usgs.gov/themes/flood.html This US Geological Survey hazards page has links to water resources management by location, El Niño–related flood information, Mississippi and Missouri River data, and other hazard-preparedness information.

Unit 35

Karst Processes and Landforms

Objectives

- To discuss the general environmental conditions that favour the formation of karst landscapes.

- To analyze the landforms characteristic of karst landscapes.

- To relate karst processes to the development of extensive underground cave systems.

Water erodes rocks of all kinds, sculpting the surface into many distinctive landscapes. Under certain special conditions, however, water dissolves soluble rocks and minerals, transporting them away in solution. Water performs this function both at and *below* the surface. When it dissolves rocks beneath the surface, it may remove soluble layers while leaving overlying as well as underlying strata in place. This dissolution process leads to the formation of caves and associated subterranean features.

Caves occur in many areas of the world, and some are so large and spectacular that they have become quite famous. Mammoth Cave, located in west-central Kentucky, is a network of underground chambers and passages totalling over 500 km in length. Carlsbad Caverns in New Mexico has more than 37 km of explored chambers and tunnels. Other major cave systems lie in the Appalachians, the Ozarks, the Canadian Rockies, and the Northwest Territories; they also can be found in many parts of Europe, in China, Australia, Africa, and South America. In a number of places these caves have become popular tourist attractions (see 'Perspectives' box). In short, caves have developed wherever the conditions for their formation were favourable, and such conditions exist, or have existed, in thousands of places beneath the Earth's surface.

Although this unit focuses on caves and other features formed by dissolution, we should note that not all caves are sculpted this way. Caves are also carved by waves along shorelines; they can be created by tectonic movements; and they can even result from large-scale eluviation processes. Here, however, as this unit's title indicates, the focus is on *karst* topography, which is associated with *limestone* and other carbonate rocks such as anhydrite (a crystalline form of calcite), marble, halite, and gypsum. Other caves and caverns, including those formed in other materials, are not karst features.

Archaeologists have discovered that caves were purposely occupied hundreds of thousands of years ago, and some caves contain valuable evidence about their occupants. In the Lascaux Cave in southwestern France, the cave walls were decorated by artists, from whose drawings we can deduce what kinds of animals were hunted and how the inhabitants may have lived. Other caves, such as the Sterkfontein Caves in South Africa, have yielded australopithecine skeletons that have helped anthropologists unlock the secrets of the chain of human evolution. Caves, therefore, are more than mere curiosities to Earth scientists, archaeologists, and spelunkers. They are expressions of a particular set of geomorphic processes that also produce many additional related landforms; they also contain important information about where we have been, as a species, in the past.

LINK

LINK

Karst

Except for its entrance, a cave cannot be seen from the surface. But the processes that form caves also produce visible landforms and, indeed, entire landscapes. If rock

Figure 35.1 A karst window near Willow Creek in the Bruce Peninsula, Ontario.

removal by dissolution can go on beneath the ground, it obviously can also take place at the surface. When this happens, the landscape takes on a distinctive, sometimes unique appearance (Figure 35.1; also see Figure 29.3). Such scenery is called **karst** landscape, a term derived from the Kras Mountain range in Slovenia, located along the border with Croatia and Italy. There, surface streams disappear into subsurface channels, steep-sided and closed depressions dot the countryside, and stark limestone hills crown a seemingly chaotic topography. This terrain extends to the Adriatic coast itself, and where sea and limestone meet, the shore becomes a monument of natural sculpture.

Karst terrain is not always as spectacular as this, but some karst areas are world famous for their angular beauty. Perhaps the most remarkable of all lies in southeastern China, centred on the city of Guilin (see Figure 17.17B). Here the Li River winds its way through a landscape of limestone towers (isolated hills called *feng lin* [pronounced 'funglin'], and hill clusters called *feng cong* ['fungston']) that for millennia has inspired artists and writers. And to the west, in the province of Yunnan, lies another unique manifestation of karst processes, the fantasy-like *shilin* (pronounced 'sherlin') stone forest (Figure 35.2).

Karst terrain is widely distributed across the Earth, occurring on all the continents in hundreds of localities. About 8 per cent of the continental surface is occupied by karst. More than a century ago, in 1893, a Serbian scholar named Jovan Cvijic produced the first comprehensive study of karst processes and landscapes, under the title that translates as *The Karst Phenomenon*. Ever since, the term *karst* has been in use. Cvijic also described and gave names to many landforms resulting from karst processes. However, he was not aware of the numerous places where karst topography also existed, and later

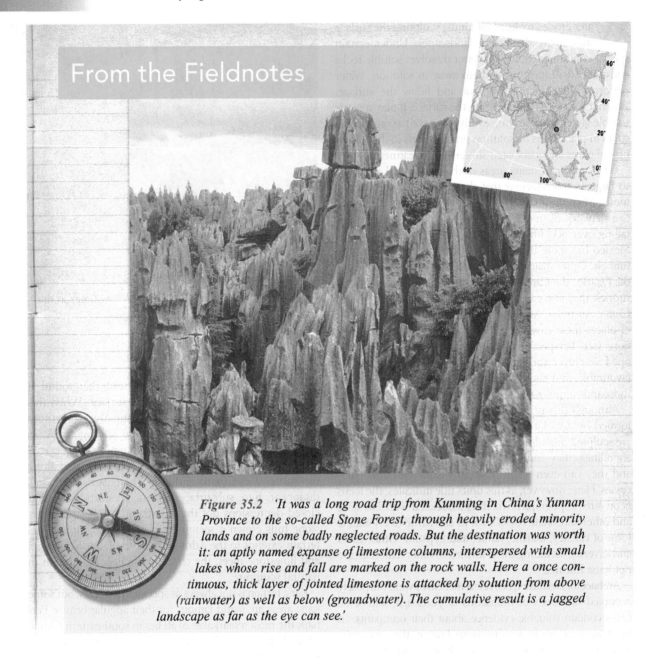

From the Fieldnotes

Figure 35.2 'It was a long road trip from Kunming in China's Yunnan Province to the so-called Stone Forest, through heavily eroded minority lands and on some badly neglected roads. But the destination was worth it: an aptly named expanse of limestone columns, interspersed with small lakes whose rise and fall are marked on the rock walls. Here a once continuous, thick layer of jointed limestone is attacked by solution from above (rainwater) as well as below (groundwater). The cumulative result is a jagged landscape as far as the eye can see.'

additional karst phenomena were identified and named. As these studies progressed, karst geomorphology became an important part of physical geography. In Canada, there are widespread areas of karst (Figure 35.3). In fact, karst is common in all areas of the country outside of the Shield.

Karst Processes

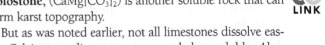

Karst landforms and landscapes are the products of a complex set of geomorphological processes, conditions, and lithology. Karst is essentially a specialized form of fluvial landscape that is strongly influenced by rock type. The major factors affecting its formation include the stratigraphy,

local relief, surface drainage, and groundwater. Karst landscape develops only where certain particularly soluble limestones, rich in calcite ($CaCO_3$), anhydrite, or marble, forms all or part of the stratigraphy. **Dolomite**, or **dolostone**, ($CaMg[CO_3]_2$) is another soluble rock that can form karst topography.

But as was noted earlier, not all limestones dissolve easily. Calcite-poor limestones are much less soluble. Also, where metamorphism has created marble from limestone, dissolution proceeds more slowly. In arid areas, limestone may resist weathering, dissolution, and erosion more than other rocks do, and thus may form ridges and plateaus rather than depressions and caves. Outcrops of carbonate rocks along the coast are usually preserved as headlands because seawater is saturated with calcium carbonate.

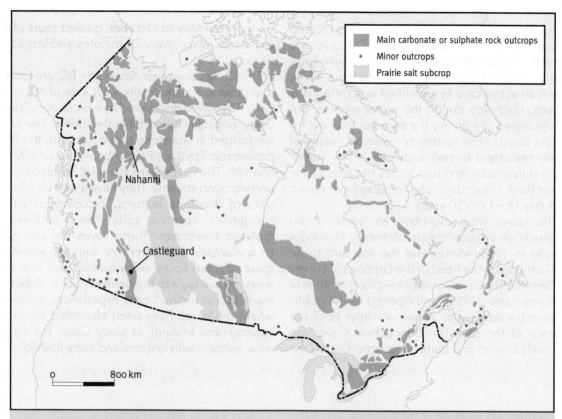

Figure 35.3 Map showing the main carbonate and sulphate rocks in Canada and the location of the Castleguard and Nahanni karst areas.

Perspectives on the Human Environment

Cave Tourism

Caves have been tourist attractions and the focus of commercial enterprise for many years, especially in the United States. Mammoth Cave in south-central Kentucky was commercially mined for the calcium nitrate in guano—to produce gunpowder—during the War of 1812, and for a brief time in the mid-1800s a tuberculosis sanatorium was established inside the cave, presumably because of the cave's 'pure' air. Further east, near Luray, Virginia, in the Shenandoah Valley of north-central Virginia along the Blue Ridge, the proprietor of Luray Caverns in 1901 established a sanatorium for those with respiratory illnesses in a house at the top of the large cave system,

piping air from the cave below into what was claimed to be the first air-conditioned home. Today, these and many other cave systems in the US, some operated by government and some by private enterprise, attract millions of visitors annually.

Many of the larger cave systems with the best-developed speleothems in Canada are in remote areas and not accessible for commercial exploitation. None of the more accessible caves in Canada are anywhere close to the same scale as Mammoth Cave, the largest known cave system in the world, or Carlsbad Caverns of the US. Two more easily accessed cave systems in Canada are located in Eganville, Ontario, and near Ainsworth in southeastern BC.

The Bonnechere Caves in Eganville are located about 130 km northwest of Ottawa. The caves are carved in 500-million-year-old Ordovician limestone. Located close to the Bonnechere River, this is an active cave system filled with torrentially flowing discharge during the winter months, but it is pumped dry during the summer to allow for public access. The system is made up mainly of water-smoothed tunnels with only a few stalactites, stalagmites, and rock icicles because of the water flow. These dripstone features have grown at a rate of ~1 cm/50 years.

The caves were identified as 'subterranean channels' on a map of the area drawn by Alexander Murray in 1853. Murray was the assistant to Sir William Logan, the head of the Geological Survey of Canada. The caves were not explored until over 100 years later (1955), and opened to the public later in the same year. A few sinkholes pock the surface of the site. The Bonnechere Caves are privately owned and quite accessible. During the period from May to October, guided tours of the caves take place every 20 minutes and last about an hour.

The Cody Caves near Ainsworth, BC, are located in a provincial park on the west side of Kootenay Lake. They were discovered by a prospector (Henry Cody, originally from PEI) in the 1890s. The caves are formed in limestone that dates from the Neoproterozoic Era (Late Precambrian), about 600 million YBP. The caves were sculpted by glacially fed underground streams. They have a well-developed suite of dripstone features, including stalactites, stalagmites, columns, soda straws, and various types of flowstones. These caves are accessible to spelunkers and adventure tourists, adventure tours of three hours are available, and one-hour tours are available to the general public. Unlike the many tourist-focused cave experiences in the US, where the caves have been electrified for better viewing (and footing), at Cody Caves the visitors wear helmets with lanterns and carry flashlights.

The texture and structure of the limestone also influence the dissolution process. Greater permeability allows a greater water flow through joints, faults, and fissures (conduit flow). The higher the porosity (water-holding capacity) of the rock, the more susceptible it is to diffusion of water through its pores or voids (diffusion flow). As flow increases in either case, there is more dissolution and removal and therefore an increasing rate of erosion.

The Role of Water

Even when the lithology and stratigraphy are suitable, karst topography may not fully develop unless other conditions also prevail. The most important of these are water and drainage. In karst areas, three kinds of water movement contribute to erosion: (1) surface streams, (2) underground drainage flows, and (3) groundwater. Surface streams may be poorly developed in karst terrain, but they supply the underground system. The underground network of interconnected channels is the most important agent of dissolution. The fluctuations of groundwater and the water table also influence karst processes.

Together these waters, moving across and through carbonate rocks, create karst landforms. But the dissolution process is not uniform. There are three solution processes at work:

1. *Dissociation.* Anhydrite, halite, and gypsum dissociate in the presence of water. Gypsum, for example, dissolves until the gypsum concentration reaches 2500 mg/L (at 25°C). At this point precipitation starts.
2. *Solution.* Rainwater absorbs atmospheric gases as it passes through the atmosphere, so that water (H_2O)

plus a small quantity of carbon dioxide (CO_2) combine to become a weak acid (carbonic acid [H_2CO_3]). In this form, and depending on its acidity, rainwater becomes an effective solvent for limestone and dolostone. The mixing of waters with different CO_2 contents causes more corrosion. The mixing of CO_2-rich water with CO_2-poor seawater or saline groundwater forms brackish water undersaturated with calcite and is more aggressively erosive.

3. *Sulphidic weathering.* Recent studies have shown that some cave formation occurs because of the presence of sulphidic bacteria; these bacteria produce sulphuric acid, which dissolves the limestone (resulting in **sulphidic caves**). The bacteria occur as floating rafts on the water surface or as **biofilm** on the rock surface. Many caves are now being studied to see if they were developed by sulphidic bacteria.

Another factor relates to the soil and vegetation present in a karst area. They contribute to the presence of carbon dioxide, which is critical to the karstification process. More carbon dioxide dissolves into water in the soil because it is released during the decomposition of dead plants. Therefore, if soil water seeps into underground channels, it will increase the acidity of the water in those channels and thus the water's capacity to dissolve limestone. This helps to explain why more fully developed karst topography is found in warmer as well as moister climatic regions. Higher temperatures promote biogenic action, and this in turn enhances the effectiveness of the available water (in the form of carbonic acid) as an agent of erosion.

Rates of Erosion

Erosion rates are influenced by the amount and temperature of the water and the amount of carbonic acid available. When waters are saturated with carbonic acid, greater amounts of solution can take place. The rates vary from less than 5 m³/km²/yr in polar and arid areas to well over 100 m³/km²/yr in the hot, humid tropics (see Unit 29 for more on solution).

Relief

The formation of karst landscape is further promoted when the area of limestone and/or dolomite strata affected lies under at least moderate relief. Where the surface is flat or nearly so, and where surface streams have not succeeded in creating some local relief, underground drainage and dissolution are slowed, and karst formation is inhibited. Research has shown that in this respect, at least, surface and subsurface streams have something in common.

Increasing water velocity at the surface increases a stream's capacity to carry loads and perform erosion. Below the surface, water in tunnels also retains its erosional capacity longer if it moves rapidly, and loses it if it is slowed down. Sluggishly moving water soon becomes saturated with dissolved calcium and thereby loses its capacity to dissolve more of it. Dipping strata plus moderate relief combine to favour speedy subsurface water movement. Another condition favouring dissolution is the substantial uplift of the affected area. This allows underground streams to descend from one level to the next. Many cave networks lie on several levels, indicating that uplift and/or dropping water tables played a role in the evolution of the system (Figure 35.4).

Small-scale Surface Features

These can occur on bare carbonate rock surfaces (bare or exposed karst) or under a thin cover of soil or organic material (covered or mantled karst). There is some evidence that soil acids may enhance the weathering process. These small features include solution pits, which are circular, elliptical, or highly irregular in planform and have rounded or tapering floors in bedrock or fill and are over 1 cm in diameter. *Karren* (grooves and runnels), usually a few metres in length, a few centimetres wide, and only a few centimetres deep, develop along joints or cracks and fissures by solution weathering. Where there is a dense distribution of these features over a surface it is called *lapiès* or *limestone pavement* (see Figure 29.3). Good examples of lapiès occur on Anticosti Island in the Gulf of St Lawrence and on the Niagara Escarpment on the Bruce Peninsula in southern Ontario, while smaller outcrops are found near Hamilton, Ontario, and Montreal. The Eramosa karst area in Hamilton (also on the Niagara Escarpment) has all the essential elements of a karstic area—soil pipes, suffusion dolines, overflow sinks, dry valleys, disappearing streams, and a 335-metre-long cave. An extensive subsurface lapis occurs under glacial Lake Agassiz sediments in the Winnipeg area of southern Manitoba (about 3500 km²). Lapiès are made up of intersecting karren (or grykes) that separate intact blocks of limestone (clints). Limestone felsenmeer produced by freeze–thaw weathering is widespread over carbonate rock outcrops in northern Canada.

Groundwater

A number of groundwater zones are recognized by karst scientists:

- soil zone or water in the soil;
- an aerated vadose or recharge zone above the water table;
- an epikarstic zone that occurs close to the water table and is influenced by its fluctuations; and
- the phreatic zone below the water table (see Unit 31).

Below the water table, porous rock is saturated, its pores and other open spaces occupied by water. The water table fluctuates seasonally, and rises and falls locally after rainstorms and during prolonged dry periods. But karst conditions are different because the rocks in limestone areas are soluble. Thus, the groundwater does more than simply occupy openings: in the form of weak carbonic acid, it contributes to underground weathering and erosion by changing the calcium carbonate in limestone into calcium bicarbonate, which is removed in solution. Studies have shown that karst areas contain *perched aquifers*, pockets of groundwater situated above the level of the local water table. Water in these perched aquifers is confined, just like water under artesian conditions, and sometimes it emerges in natural springs (see Figure 31.15A).

By tracing the movement of water in underground drainage networks, scientists have made significant discoveries about cave systems. One way to accomplish this is by putting dyes in surface water where it disappears below the ground, and then to check for the appearance of the coloured water in certain accessible cave locations and at springs. This research has indicated that a cave-riddled

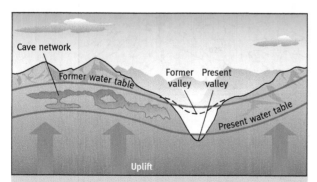

Figure 35.4 Cave network formed by water that entered limestone fractures and enlarged them below the (former) water table. When that water table dropped—due partly to uplift and partly to the nearby stream's deepening of its valley—the cave system filled with air.

karst area may have several separate, rather than interconnected, underground drainage systems.

In a single karst area, therefore, there may be as many as half a dozen subsurface drainage systems, functioning at different levels but not linked to one another. This means that an extensive cave system in a honeycombed mountain may have many tunnels leading inward from the entrance, but there are other tunnels that are not directly accessible above as well as below. Water entering the subsurface from one location on the surface becomes part of one underground system, whereas water from another ground-level location joins a different and separate network below.

Karst Landforms and Landscapes

Two types of karst have been distinguished. (1) **Holokarst** is characterized by an array of closed surface depressions where water is routed underground. (2) **Fluviokarst**, which is more common, is characterized by water flowing across the surface. In these instances, karstic processes have been superimposed on a pre-existing fluvial landscape.

A topographic map of a karst area such as that found in Wood Buffalo National Park quickly reveals the unusual character of relief and drainage (Figure 35.5). It seems that all

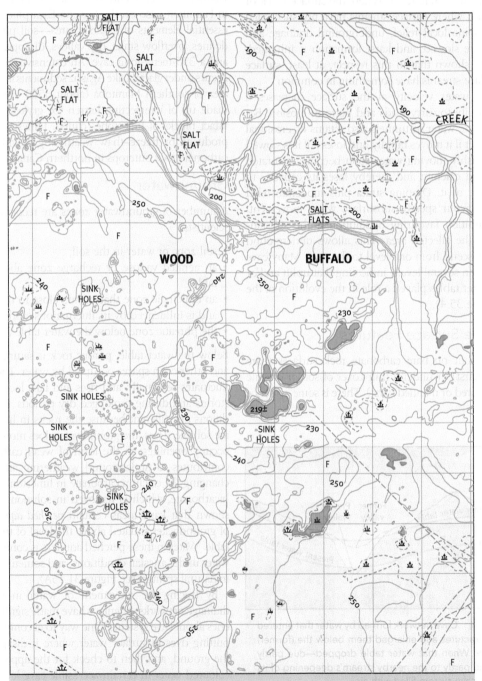

Figure 35.5 Karst area in Wood Buffalo National Park in Alberta. The salt flats seen to the north are a result of the underlying halite (salt) deposits. The sinkholes (dolines) are developed in limestone and have collapsed because of the solution of the underlying halite and gypsum deposits.

the rules learned so far from other areas are broken. Surface streams are interrupted and stop (or shrink) in mid-valley. Contour lines reveal basins without outlets and without streams entering or leaving them. Steep-sided hills rise from flat plains without displaying familiar slope characteristics.

Close examination of maps reveals the clear signature of karst topography, but it is not the same everywhere. Geomorphologists identify four types of karst landscape: alpine, temperate, tropical, and Caribbean.

1. **Alpine karst** is found at high altitude. It is characterized by *sinks*, or *sinkholes*, and *karren* above the treeline. The sinks drain into deep cave systems. This type of karst is common in parts of the Rocky Mountains and on Vancouver Island. Castleguard Cave in Banff National Park, Alberta, is the best example of subglacial karst in the world. It is an extensive cave system (20,357 m of passages surveyed as of 2007, 384 m deep at its deepest) developed in carbonate rocks on the south side of the Columbia Icefield under Castleguard Mountain. Ice blocks the termination of the passage system and meltwater feeds through the cave to springs in Castleguard Meadows. The cave system is flooded by meltwater during the spring. It is also affected by occasional jökulhlaups. Ultimately, the water flows into the North Saskatchewan River. The deepest cave in Canada is Arctomys Cave (536 m deep—the deepest cave north of Mexico—and 3496 m long), located in the Rockies about 150 km northwest of Castleguard Meadows in Mount Robson Provincial Park, BC. Its name is taken from the scientific name for the woodchuck, or groundhog (*Arctomys monax*). Alpine karst is also well developed in the Crowsnest Pass area of the southern Alberta–BC border region.

2. **Temperate karst**, of which the 'type' area in Slovenia and Croatia is an outstanding example, forms more slowly than tropical karst. Disappearing streams, jagged rock masses, solution depressions, and extensive cave networks mark temperate karst (Figure 35.6).

3. **Tropical karst** develops rapidly as a result of the higher amounts of rainfall and humidity, biogenic action, and organic acids in the soil and thus the subsurface water. Steep-sided hills tend to be vegetation-covered, and solution features are larger than in temperate karst landscapes.

4. **Caribbean karst** is a special case found only in a few locations. In the type area of central Florida, nearly flat-lying limestones are eroded underground, although they lie barely above sea level. Water comes from the hill country to the north, seeps through the limestones, and leaves the system through offshore submarine springs. This situation also exists in Mexico's Yucatán Peninsula. There, as in Florida, the roofs of the subsurface conduits have in many places collapsed, creating those characteristic depressions (sinks) in the ground.

Disappearing Streams and Sinkholes

Where a surface stream flowing along a blind valley (a valley that begins and ends abruptly) 'disappears', flowing into an underground channel, the place of descent is called a sink, sinkhole, swallet, or *swallow hole* (Figure 35.6, top left). This may occur at a fault or an enlarged joint that has been widened by dissolution and leads to a subsurface drainage system. Interrupted drainage of this sort is a general indicator of karst conditions. Another common karst landform is the surface depression, ranging in size from small hollows to larger basins called **dolines** (Figure 35.7). Dolines are important diagnostic features of karstification. They may have an ephemeral or permanent lake at the bottom or be dry. The size of these features ranges from 10 m to 1 km in length and/or width. The dominant process of formation, as noted, is dissolution. Depressions also can form from the collapse of part of the roof of an underground stream conduit. Logically, the former are referred to as solution or suffusion dolines or sinkholes and the latter as collapse dolines or sinkholes (see Figure 35.6).

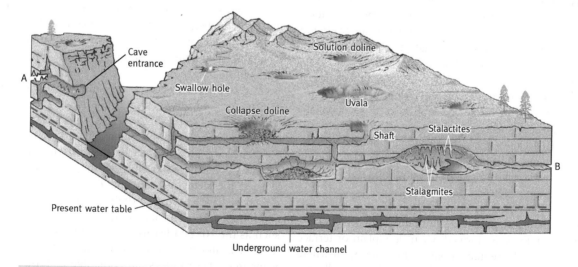

Figure 35.6 Surface and underground features of temperate karst. When the groundwater table was higher, the solution features at levels **A** and **B** formed. Now the water table is lower and solution proceeds. A new cave network will form when the next drop in the water table occurs.

Figure 35.7 Montezuma's Well, southwestern US, is a large natural limestone sinkhole that has filled with water.

Solution (suffusion) dolines (Figure 35.6, top right) range in size from a bathtub to a football stadium. A single area of karst topography may contain tens of thousands of them, some old and established, others just starting to form. Their relative location probably has to do with the configuration of the terrain when karstification began; low-lying places became solution hollows first. These subsequently expanded, and others formed as the surface was lowered overall. In cross-section (see doline at front edge centre of Figure 35.6), solution hollows resemble funnels, with water seeping down the sides to the approximate centre of the basin. There a *shaft* leads downward, and the water joins the regional groundwater (or subsurface conduit) through this outlet.

Collapse dolines (Figure 35.6, left front corner) are created by the collapse or failure of the roof or overlying material of a cave, cavern, or underground channel. The dissolution process also created these subsurface tunnels, so even a collapse sinkhole ultimately owes its origin to the dissolution process. Physical geographers distinguish between a *collapse sink*, in which the rock ceiling of the sinkhole collapses into the underground solution hole, and a *suffusion sink*, created when an overlying layer of unconsolidated material is left unsupported. Where such loose material lies on top of limestone strata affected by the karst process, lower parts of this material are drawn downward into the enlarging karst joints. This creates a void in the lower stratum of this unconsolidated layer, and when the void becomes large, it will collapse. That can happen quite suddenly, unlike the slow development of solution sinkholes. Obviously, building in a zone of collapse or suffusion sinkholes can be a hazardous proposition.

Two other types of dolines occur but are less common—alluvial dolines and solution subsidence pockets. Alluvial dolines are formed when floodplain or terrace sediments collapse into a doline. The latter occur where overlying rock beds or non-alluvial sediment collapses into the doline because of the removal of underlying

support. These both leave small depressions at the surface or may not even show any sign of the collapse because of in-filling.

The frequency of dolines can be over 500/km² in parts of Canada. Thousands of these occur in southern Canada. In western Newfoundland and in Nova Scotia they occur on gypsum while on Vancouver Island they have developed in limestone. Some of the most spectacular examples occur in Wood Buffalo National Park and to the west of Great Bear Lake, where limestone and dolostone layers have collapsed into the underlying gypsum of halite beds to create dolines, karst streets, and poljes. The development of dolines in gypsum is much more rapid than in limestone and is a major geological hazard in parts of Nova Scotia and Newfoundland.

Dolines usually occur in clusters or along lines, and as they develop and grow they can join up to become a larger feature called an **uvala** (Figure 35.6, centre). Uvalas can reach a length of or have a diameter of more than 1.5 km. Some have rough, uneven floors that are dry and vegetated; others are filled with water and form scenic lakes.

Still larger depressions caused by the coalescence of uvalas are called *poljes*. A polje (also called a karst window or pocket valley) is a fairly small steep-sided valley a few hundreds of metres wide and about 1 to 2 km long. It usually has a stream (either ephemeral or permanent) flowing along it since its bottom is impermeable because of sediment deposited on the top of the limestone bed or because the bottom is the aquiclude rock bed underlying the limestone. The stream issues from a spring at the head of the polje and disappears into a *ponor* or cave entrance in the limestone at the other end of the valley. Natural arches are often found in both uvalas and poljes. These are remnants of the cave roofs. A good example of a polje is the Medicine Lake Valley in Jasper National Park. During the summer melt season the Maligne River discharges water into the polje and forms an ephemeral lake—Medicine Lake (at its maximum size: 9 km long, 1 km wide, and 30 m deep). In winter when there is little stream flow the lake dries up to form a series of small doline ponds. The water that filled the lake is discharged by about 60 springs in the floor of the Maligne Canyon about 16 km to the northwest. The combined discharge from these springs in the fall of the year is approximately 65 m³/s.

Long and narrow depressions caused by the collapse of underground passages or conduits are called *bogaz forms* or *karst streets* (or corridors). Such features can be seen in Wood Buffalo National Park and in the South Nahanni karst areas. Larger linear forms are called dry valleys. When the water table was higher or areas were affected by permafrost, streams cut these valleys, but they now have subsurface drainage. These features are common on the dip and scarp slope of escarpments such as the Niagara Escarpment. In England, such valleys on chalklands are called coombes (Figure 35.8). Sometimes these valleys are gorge-like or form proper gorges.

Figure 35.8 Coombe in the Chiltern Hills, UK.

Figure 35.9 Pinnacle karst in Borneo Sarawak National Park, Malaysia.

Studies of doline terrain indicate that this kind of karst landscape develops best where the environment is humid, so that there is plenty of water to sustain the underground drainage system. It also appears that the rise and fall of the water table may have something to do with the distribution of collapse dolines. Where groundwater levels rise and fall rapidly and substantially, this process seems to trigger more frequent collapses.

Karst Towers

LINK

If dolines or sinkholes are the signature landform of temperate karst areas, then the dominant feature in tropical karst regions is the *tower*. Towers are also called *mogotes* (karst inselbergs). They are generally found in association with fairly flat alluvial areas. A **tower** is a fairly steep-sided hill that rises above a surface that may or may not be pocked with solution depressions. Even when many such dolines are also present, the towers, sometimes hundreds of metres tall, dominate the landscape. If the sides of the hills are almost vertical they are called cones. In tropical karst zones, the contrast between towers and depressions is so sharp that the whole scene is referred to as **cockpit karst**, the term *cockpit* referring to the irregular, steep-sided, star-shaped dolines between the towers. The shape is due to the centripetal internal drainage system that flows off the tower areas.

Tropical karst, studded with these towers, is found in such locales as Puerto Rico, Jamaica, Cuba, and Vietnam. Exactly what determines the location and distribution of the towers is still uncertain. The towers are remnants of a thick bedrock sequence consisting of limestone and/or dolomite layers. Before the karst topography developed, and following regional uplift (or the lowering of the sea level), the original surface presumably developed a soil cover and plants took hold. This initial pattern of soil and vegetation (thick and well developed in some places, thin and sparse in others) probably was determined by the original terrain.

Where the surface was low, moisture collected and soil soon formed, but higher places stayed barren. Eventually these higher places became the tops of karst towers as the intervening hollows grew ever deeper. China's tower karst in the Guilin area and shilin (or stone forest, pinnacle karst) (Figure 35.2) may have originated in this way, although fluctuating groundwater also was a factor in the process. In fact, some of the pinnacles in the Stone Forest still rise over 25 m from lakes whose levels vary seasonally. Similar areas of smaller-scale pinnacle karst also occur in central Madagascar and Malaysia (Figure 35.9).

Karst and Caves

In this section, we examine caves in more detail. Technically, a **cave** is any substantial opening in bedrock that leads to an interior open space. The word 'substantial' here has a human connotation: it is generally agreed that a cave, in order to be called a cave, must be large enough for an average-sized adult person to enter. The terminology applied to caves changes with their size—richly decorated (i.e., with lots of **speleothems** or unique cave features) medium-sized caves are called 'grottos', larger features are termed 'rooms', while the biggest caves are 'chambers'. Thus, even a vacated swallow hole, where a stream once flowed into an underground channel, is a cave. This is one way a *cave shaft* (or *aven*) forms, and many unsuspecting animals and people have fallen into such vertical cave entrances. Caves can be defined on the basis of running water. They are either *active caves* with flowing streams or *inactive caves*, which are streamless.

Cave Development

Caves are formed in four principal ways:

1. by the corrosive action of aggressive recharge (or vadose or ephiphreatic) water above the water table (vadose caves);

2. by the deep circulation of phreatic water below the water table (phreatic caves);
3. at the water table or in the shallow phreatic zone associated with the fluctuations of the water table (epikarstic caves); and
4. by sulphidic bacterial action (sulphidic caves).

The development of cave systems is influenced by a number of factors, including the structure and lithology of the rocks, the flow of groundwater, and chemical kinetics.

Vadose and phreatic caves differ morphologically. Vadose caves are formed by the gravitational flow of recharge water above the water table. This usually occurs down the steepest routes—joints, fissures, etc. Because of this, the cave passages are dominated by deep canyon-like conduits and avens (or shafts). The passages tend to be independent and converge only when forced to by rock properties such as dip, fissure, or jointing pattern. Phreatic caves, on the other hand, are dominated by tubes or conduits, which tend to develop along hydraulically efficient paths in the rock. The passages converge and very few are consistent with the trends of joints or fissures in the rock. The cave passages are highly irregular in terms of elevation and may form 'loops' that descend well below the water table and rise to it again, and may even go above the water table.

In all cases, the development of caves depends on time. Studies have tended to separate the development into early and late phases based on size, connectedness, and elaborateness of the cave decorations (speleothems). The transition between the two phases occurs at different times in individual caves but varies between about 10,000 and 100,000 years.

Cave Features

A fully developed cave consists of an entrance (portal or shaft) and one or more chambers, passages, and terminations. A *termination*, in accordance with the above anthropocentric definition, marks the place beyond which a person cannot crawl any farther along an underground passage or conduit. Passages in a fully developed cave system form a network of interconnected conduits. The pattern of this network depends on the lithology, structure, faulting, and jointing of the bedrock sequence. It may consist of one major subsurface artery (the *linear form*); it may look like the branches of a tree (*dendritic* or *branchwork forms*); or, if block jointing is well developed, it may have an *angulate* (right-angle, stepped) form. As well as simple forms there are *mazes* or more complex forms of various types with closed loops of systems of passages. These include:

1. network maze forms, which are guided by joint patterns or faults and appear trellis-like when looked at from above;
2. anastomizing mazes in which the passages bifurcate and rejoin again and again; and

3. spongework mazes, which look like some areas have developed randomly by suffusion while others are fault or structurally guided, and they have all grown together to form a system.

Given the complexity of karst features, various other, more detailed models have been developed, accounting also for the overall structure of the mazes of caves, caverns, and conduits.

Where passages grow exceptionally large, rooms or chambers develop. These chambers, some with the dimensions of a large hall, contain many fascinating forms. Lakes stand in some of these chambers, and some have populations of fish or amphibians specific to that particular cave lake (Figure 35.10). Drops of water falling from the ceiling create eerie musical echoes in the dark void. Streams may even flow through them, with the magnified sound of a waterfall.

Dripping water that is saturated with calcium carbonate ($CaCO_3$) precipitates its calcite in the form of the mineral *travertine*. This water, entering the cave, contains calcium bicarbonate. If the air in the cave contains less carbon dioxide than it could, i.e., more carbon dioxide can be added to the cave air before it is saturated and begins to precipitate, then there will be excess carbon dioxide in the water solution dripping from the cave ceiling or wall. This results in the degassing of some carbon

Figure 35.10 A cave lake, with stalactites: Lake Cave, Margaret River area, southwestern West Australia, about 270 km south of Perth.

Figure 35.11 Soda straws, or cave straws.

dioxide from the water solution to the air, which means, of course, that some of the calcium bicarbonate that contains the carbon dioxide will have to chemically revert to calcium carbonate. When this happens, the form of $CaCO_3$ that is deposited is *not* calcite but *travertine* (or *tufa*) dripstone or flowstone, a less soluble form of limestone. Travertine forms various types of speleothems or cave decorations.

This process leaves dripstone as icicle-like **stalactites** hanging from the ceiling and **stalagmites** standing, sentinel-like, on the floor. Very long and exceptionally thin stalactites that are cylindrical in shape are called *soda straws* (Figure 35.11), while similar features with branch-like or spiral projections are known as *helictites*. Stalagmites can be a variety of shapes ranging from very thin (broomsticks) to very convoluted and weirdly shaped (totem poles). Small, still-forming stalactites or oozing roof pendants in sulphidic caves are known as *snoticles* or *snotties*. These white, opposing pinnacles can become several metres tall and often coalesce to form **columns**. Elaborate and complex stalactites are called chandeliers. They have been compared to the pipes of a huge organ and have also been perceived as the teeth of a lurking giant.

Flowstone can form thin wavy sheet-like deposits on cave walls or floors called 'curtains' or 'draperies'. If these forms are variegated (stained other colours by iron or other minerals) they are termed 'bacon'. Flowstone also forms below springs or seeps where it can create a step-like mound (stone waterfalls) over which the water flows. It forms *gours*, or rimstone dams, which can pond back shallow 'steps' of water. Travertine also forms below surface springs and seeps. Other features found in caves are erosional- or weathering-related rather than depositional. These are called *speleogens* and include pillars, scallops, bonework, and boxwork etched out by erosion. Much smaller cave features are the various concretions of crystals that form, such as cave pearls, flower-like aragonite crystals or anthodites, moonmilk, and frostwork.

Some caves, cave passages, and conduits are partially or totally filled-in with sediments (cave fill) of various types that have been brought down from the surface or brought in from other caves by subsurface streams. Cave and passageway floors can also have accumulations of bird and/or bat droppings, or *guano*, which can necessitate the wearing of masks or breathing apparatus because of its toxic and/or fine-grained nature.

Cave Networks

To physical geographers, however, caves present other mysteries. In 1988 divers for the first time penetrated the water-filled tunnels of a cave system beneath northern Florida's Woodville Karst Plain near Tallahassee. They entered a sinkhole lake and followed a flooded passage, using battery-powered motors and floodlights. The passage went 75 m below the surface, and they followed it for more than 2.5 km until they saw daylight above and returned to the surface through another doline. The cave passages, they reported, were as much as 30 m wide, but also narrowed considerably. They saw side passages joining the main conduit, and realized that they were seeing only a fraction of a very large and unmapped network. These Florida cave systems, now below sea level and filled with water, were formed more than 35 million years ago during a period of lower sea level.

Much remains to be learned about caves. Their formation is generally understood, but many details remain unclear. How important is abrasion by underground streams? What role does groundwater play? How do the underground processes combine to produce such extensive cave systems? What happens when those systems are submerged? As yet there is no general agreement on such issues, which proves that physical geography still holds some dark secrets.

Karst terrain and associated caves are widely distributed across the Earth. Some of the world's most impressive karst regions are only now becoming known and understood (such as the karst structures of Australia's Kimberley region in the northern part of West Australia). Karst topography has been submerged by coastal subsidence, and it also has been uplifted into high mountains. There is karst terrain under Canadian glaciers (e.g., the Upper Castleguard cave system under the Columbia Icefields in the Rockies) and on frigid Andean slopes in South America. Sometimes karst landforms occur where solution is not an important contemporary process—for example, in semi-arid New Mexico. Thus the map of karst and cave distribution contains valuable evidence for climatic as well as geologic change. The geomorphological signature of karst is indeed one of the most distinctive elements in the global environmental mosaic. Recent studies indicating possible sulphidic bacterial action linked to karst processes have reawakened interest in the subject.

KEY TERMS

REVIEW QUESTIONS

1. Which rock types are prone to karst development?
2. Describe the general climatic conditions that favour karst development.
3. What chemical weathering process is instrumental in the development of karst landscapes?
4. What is the difference between temperate and tropical karst?
5. How do towers form in karst regions?
6. Discuss the difference between limestone dissolution by solution and the action of sulphidic bacteria.

REFERENCES AND FURTHER READINGS

Beck, B.F., ed. 1989. *Engineering and Environmental Impacts of Sinkholes.* Rotterdam: Balkema.

———— and W.L. Wilson, eds. 1987. *Karst Hydrogeology: Engineering and Environmental Applications.* Rotterdam: Balkema.

Focus. 1998. 'Living with and Teaching about Karst: Special Theme Section', (Summer/Fall): 13–27.

Ford, D.C. 1983. 'Effects of Glaciations upon Karst Aquifers in Canada', *Journal of Hydrology* 61: 177–80.

————. 1983. 'Alpine Karst Systems at Crowsnest Pass, Alberta–British Columbia, Canada', *Journal of Hydrology* 61: 187–92.

————. 1987. 'Effects of Glaciations and Permafrost upon the Development of Karst in Canada', *Earth Surface Processes and Landforms* 12: 507–21.

————. 1998. 'Perspectives in Karst Hydrology and Cavern Genesis', in A.N. Palmer et al., eds, *Karst Modeling: Speleogenesis and Evolution of Karst Aquifers.* Charles Town, WV: Karst Waters Institute, Special Publication 5.

———— and P.W. Williams. 1989. *Karst Geomorphology and Hydrology.* Winchester, Mass.: Unwin Hyman.

Gillieson, D. 1996. *Caves: Processes, Development and Management.* Malden, Mass.: Blackwell.

Gunn, J., ed. 2003. *Encyclopedia of Caves and Karst Science.* London/New York: Routledge.

Herak, M., and V.T. Springfield. 1977. *Karst Regions of the Northern Hemisphere.* Amsterdam: Elsevier.

Jakucs, L. 1977. *Morphogenetics of Karst Regions.* New York: Wiley/Halsted.

Jennings, J.N. 1985. *Karst Geomorphology.* New York: Blackwell.

Karolyi, M.S., and D.C. Ford. 1983. 'The Goose Arm Karst, Newfoundland, Canada', *Journal of Hydrology* 61: 181–5.

Lafleur, R.G. 1984. *Groundwater as a Geomorphic Agent.* Winchester, Mass.: Allen & Unwin.

Ritter, D.F., et al. 1995. *Process Geomorphology*, 3rd edn. Dubuque, Iowa: W.C. Brown.

Roberge, J., and D.C. Ford. 1983. 'The Upper Salmon River Karst, Anticosti Island, Quebec, Canada', *Journal of Hydrology* 61: 159–62.

Smart, C.C., and D.C. Ford. 1983. 'The Castleguard Karst, Main Ranges, Canadian Rocky Mountains', *Journal of Hydrology* 61: 193–7.

Sweeting, M.M. 1972. *Karst Landforms.* New York: Columbia Univ. Press.

————. 1981. *Karst Geomorphology.* Stroudsburg, Penn.: Dowden, Hutchinson & Ross.

Trenhaile, A.S. 1998. *Geomorphology: A Canadian Perspective.* Toronto: Oxford Univ. Press.

Trudgill, S.A. 1986. *Limestone Geomorphology.* London/New York: Longman.

Veni, G., et al. 2001. *Living with Karst: A Fragile Foundation.* Alexandria, Va: American Geological Institute.

White, W.B. 1988. *Geomorphology and Hydrology of Karst Terrains.* New York: Oxford Univ. Press.

———— et al. 1995. 'Karst Lands', *American Scientist* 83: 448–59.

WEB RESOURCES

conservationhamilton.ca/parks/visit/eramosa.asp Here you will find information and maps concerning the Eramosa karst area.

speleogenesis.info This page is run by the Commission on Karst Hydrology and Speleogenesis of the International Speleological and Karst Commission of the International Geographical Union. It has lots of information about terms and processes and a very comprehensive bibliography and archive of material on the subject.

www.cancaver.ca The website of the Canadian Cave and Karst Information Server has lots of information about caves, cave research, and so on; it includes a bibliography of Canadian publications.

www.goodearthgraphics.com/virtcave This page is called the 'virtual cave' and provides a stunning photographic tour of solution caves, lava tube caves, sea caves, and erosional caves. Cave maps are provided as well as links to the National Speleological Society and US show caves directory.

www.staff.amu.edu.pl/~sgp/spec/linkk.html The karst link page provides a comprehensive listing of all websites related to karst topography. Varying levels of technicality are available, and the page is subdivided by world regional areas.

Unit 36

Glacial Degradation and Aggradation

Objectives

- To discuss the different categories of glaciers.
- To give a brief history of how glaciation has influenced the Earth's surface.
- To outline how glaciers form, move, and erode the landscape.

In this unit and in Units 37 and 38 we address various aspects of the cryosphere, one of the five major components of the Earth System (see Figure 2.1). The **cryosphere** consists of all the forms of frozen water that exist above, on, and just below the Earth's surface. It includes all types of glaciers, snow cover, ice floating atop water bodies, and permanently frozen ground (permafrost). The focus here will be on glaciers as powerful agents of landscape modification in high-latitude and high-altitude regions, where they create an array of distinctive degradational and aggradational landforms. Beyond their geomorphological role, as seen in Unit 18, glaciers are also of interest to physical geographers because they provide valuable evidence in the study of environmental dynamics. This includes information about past and present climate change, the evolving composition and temperature patterns of the atmosphere, volcanic eruptions, and the rise and fall of the global sea level.

A **glacier** is a body of ice, formed on land and in motion. This motion is not readily apparent over short time periods, however, and to an observer glaciers appear to be mere accumulations of ice, snow, and rock debris. Yet glaciers do move, and they steadily erode their valleys. Scientists realized this centuries ago, and in the Swiss Alps they calculated glacial movement by putting stakes in the ice and in the rock on the sides of the valley and measuring the annual downslope advance or retreat of the ice. But just how mountain glaciers move and how they modify the landscape below (Figure 36.1) continues to be a subject of

From the Fieldnotes

Figure 36.1 *'Flying over glaciated terrain suggests how the planet changes as climatic cycles run their course. When mountain glaciers develop over an area originally sculpted by rivers, they bury most of the terrain and fill the valleys with ice, leaving only the crests and peaks of ranges and mountains protruding above, as you can imagine from a view over a section of the Alaska Range (A). When the glaciers have melted away (and they may even melt from the Alaska Range), the exposed topography reveals their work in a variety of landforms, including their steep-sided valleys, jagged mountain peaks, and sharp-edged ridges (B). This photo was taken over a part of Colorado's southern Rocky Mountains, where most of the once prevailing ice has melted away in the warmth of the current interval.'*

debate and ongoing research. In many ways glaciers and glacial activity are more difficult to understand than rivers because of the difficulty in observing processes within and beneath the flowing ice.

The glaciers of Canada's Rockies and Coast Mountains and of Switzerland's Alps are **mountain (alpine) glaciers**. These glaciers are confined in valleys that usually have steep slopes (they are sometimes called *valley glaciers*). However, not all glaciers occur in valleys. Some glaciers consist of huge masses of ice that are not confined to valleys but that bury whole landscapes beneath them. These glaciers are called **continental glaciers**, ice sheets, or icecaps. Antarctica (a continent nearly twice as large as Australia) is almost completely covered by a vast icecap, and so is Greenland, the world's largest island. Continental glaciers move, but generally even more slowly than mountain glaciers. Accordingly, they conform to our definition: they are bodies of ice and they exhibit motion.

Glaciers of the Past

As noted in Unit 18, the Earth has periodically experienced ice ages. An **ice age** is an interval of geological time during which the Earth's average atmospheric temperature was lowered, resulting in the expansion of glacial ice in high latitudes and the growth of glaciers at high altitudes in lower latitudes. During an ice age, which may endure for millions of years, stages of global cooling alternate with stages of warming. As a result, glacial ice expands (advances) and contracts (recedes) over periods measured in tens or hundreds of thousands of years.

A cooling period, during which the ice expands, is known as a **glaciation**. During such a time, ice sheets become continental in size and gain many hundreds or even thousands of metres in thickness. At the same time, mountain valleys fill with glacial ice, often replacing streams that formerly flowed there. After the cooling period has reached its peak and the glaciers have expanded as far as they can, the climate begins to warm up. Now the glaciers start melting and receding in a phase known as **deglaciation**. After deglaciation, the global climate may stabilize for some tens of thousands of years as the Earth awaits a new cooling episode. This interval between the most recent deglaciation and the onset of the next glaciation is referred to as an **interglacial** (~10–15,000 years).

LINK

The Earth today is comparatively warm, glaciers have withdrawn to the coldest of the polar (and mountainous) regions, and areas once covered by continental ice sheets are dominated by other geomorphological processes. In other words, we are presently experiencing an interglacial. Just 12,000 to 15,000 years ago, however, Canada was almost entirely covered by continental glaciers (about 97 per cent) and these ice sheets reached as far south as the Great Lakes and beyond. Over the past 10 millennia, the Earth has warmed up and the glaciers have receded—but the present interglacial is unlike any other this planet

has witnessed. During the interglacial now in progress, the world's human population has grown explosively. Geologically, these last 10,000 years constitute the Holocene Epoch (see Figure 28.7). Geographically, the Holocene has witnessed the transformation of the planet—not only by climatic change but also by human activity.

The present interglacial is unprecedented because, for the first time in the Earth's history, humans have become an agent of major environmental change. On the basis of what is known about the patterns of previous glaciations and interglacials, it may be assumed that another cooling episode lies ahead and that the glaciers will once again expand and advance. But human interference in the composition of the atmosphere may affect the course of events. Many scientists now warn of the human contribution to the intensification of the atmosphere's greenhouse effect. This will lead to further warming of the Earth, thereby causing additional melting of ice in polar and high-mountain regions, a rise in the global sea level, and widespread flooding of low-lying areas. It has recently been suggested by some of the world's leading researchers that the North Pole has a more than 50/50 chance of being ice-free during the summer of 2013. These are much worse odds than many models have predicted (a 1 in 70 chance in the next decade). Continued climatic change may also contribute to a sudden 'trigger effect' when the next glaciation occurs, again with an unpredictable impact, for pollen evidence from previous interglacials shows climate warming occurring before the onset of a glaciation.

The most recent ice age is often called the *Pleistocene Ice Age* because it has seemed to coincide almost exactly with the Pleistocene Epoch of the Cenozoic Era (see the geologic time scale, Figure 28.7). But geologists now know that this ice age began during the Pliocene Epoch, the epoch preceding the Pleistocene, probably between 2.5 and 3 million years ago. In fact, there is evidence of even earlier cooling.

The Pleistocene Ice Age is only the latest in a series of such events in the Earth's environmental history. For example, there is no longer any doubt that the great continent of Gondwanaland (see Unit 24) experienced an ice age before it broke apart. During the Permian Period of the Palaeozoic Era, the Dwyka Ice Age spread great ice sheets over the polar regions of Gondwanaland. More than 250 million years ago, these continental glaciers left ample evidence of their activity. When Gondwanaland split apart, its several fragments (Africa, South America, India, Australia, Antarctica) all carried this evidence in their landscapes and underlying rock strata. When geologists discovered this evidence, they had a major clue to the former existence of Gondwanaland—as well as its polar orientation during Permian times. Moreover, much older rocks from West Africa indicate an even earlier ice age dating probably to the Silurian Period about 420 million years ago. Ice ages, therefore, have affected our planet repeatedly (see 'Perspectives' box).

When we study glaciers, present or past, it is important to remember their significant connections to global environments. Even today, when the ice is of comparatively limited areal extent, the glaciers of Greenland and Antarctica influence the radiation and heat balances of the planet. Continental ice sheets contain huge volumes of freshwater and thereby affect the global water balance as well. When a glaciation begins, precipitation in the form of snow is compacted into glacial ice. Therefore it is not returned to the oceans (recall the hydrologic cycle diagrammed in Figure 11.6), so that the sea level drops by as much as 100 m and continental shelves are exposed as the glaciation proceeds.

Later, when deglaciation begins, the melting glaciers yield their large volumes of water and the sea level rises again. Thus, glaciation and deglaciation are accompanied, in turn, by falling and rising sea levels. During an interglacial such as the present one, continental shelves are inundated. When the glaciers expand again, the flooded continental shelves will be exposed once more. Taking the long view of the future occupation of the Earth by humankind, it is therefore true that land lost in the high latitudes to glacial advance will be partly compensated for by land exposed by the drop in global sea level at lower, unglaciated latitudes.

Perspectives on the Human Environment

What Causes Ice Ages?

It is known that the Earth has experienced repeated glaciations. The Pleistocene Ice Age is only the most recent. When Gondwanaland was still a huge continent, it experienced a prolonged glacial age (the Dwyka Glaciation), and there is evidence of still earlier ice ages (e.g., the Proterozoic **'Snowball Earth'**). Much is known, too, about ice sheets and mountain glaciers, and their erosional and depositional work. But scientists remain unsure about the causes behind these events. Why are the glacial ages periodic? Do they come at regular intervals? Are they caused by terrestrial conditions, or are they the result of conditions in the solar system and planetary orbits? Several theories have been formulated to account for what we know about ice ages, but none has yet gained general acceptance.

One theory attributes ice ages to *plate tectonics*. This theory holds that when landmasses are moved into the polar latitudes through plate tectonics, their elevation, combined with polar coldness, generates ice sheets—like Antarctica's today. But what is known about past movements of landmasses does not completely support this idea. Nor does it explain why ice ages are marked by alternating periods of cooling (glaciations) and warming (interglacials).

A second theory links ice ages to *crustal bulging* resulting from plate collisions. The Pleistocene Ice Age, for example, is thought to have its origins in the vertical uplift of Asia's Himalayas and the adjacent Tibetan Plateau over the past

20 million years, and the contemporaneous uplift of North America's Sierra Nevada and southern Rocky Mountain ranges. These raised crustal segments, it is argued, would interfere with jet streams and other atmospheric windflows, combining the coldness from the elevation with a latitudinal shift of air circulation, thereby creating hemispheric cooling. A problem here is the absence of such a landmass-generated cooling in the Southern Hemisphere, except in the case of Antarctica—which can be explained by other means.

Yet another theory relates glaciations to episodes of *volcanic activity*. Certain periods in Earth history have been marked by intense volcanism. The dust and chemicals spewed into the atmosphere might, according to this hypothesis, interfere with solar radiation to such an extent that the volcanically derived dust and chemical aerosols cool the surface sufficiently to trigger a glaciation.

Still another set of theories attributes glacial cooling to *changes in the Earth's atmosphere and hydrosphere*. Fluctuations in carbon dioxide in the atmosphere could cause alternating warming (intensified greenhouse conditions) and cooling. When global vegetation is abundant, more carbon dioxide is consumed and its presence in the atmosphere is reduced. This would lead to cooling and glacial conditions; but when the vegetation dies, more carbon dioxide is released into the atmosphere and greenhouse warming resumes. One problem with this idea, however, is that evidence for the short-term vegetation changes required for the model is lacking.

LINK

Theory building also focuses on changes in *oceanic circulation*, which are postulated to be controlled by the tectonic movement of continents. Some scientists believe that the inflow of warm Atlantic water into the basin of the Arctic Ocean would melt part of that ocean's ice cover, thereby releasing moisture for snow-bearing air masses. Huge amounts of snow would then accumulate in high-latitude North America and Eurasia—just where the great continental glaciers of the Pleistocene formed. At present, with Greenland and North America located as they are, warm Atlantic water cannot enter the Arctic Basin in large quantity. Thus the Arctic Ocean remains frozen most of the time, and the supply of snow is much reduced. The obvious problem with this theory is that it fails to explain the rapid alternations between glaciations and interglacials.

Additional theories look beyond the Earth and suggest that Earth–Sun relationships and planetary orbits (**Milankovitch forcing**) are ultimately responsible for ice ages (as noted in Unit 18). Over many millions of years, the distance from the Earth to the Sun during orbits changes slightly. Moreover, the angle of the Earth's axis to the plane of the ecliptic also undergoes some variation. In combination, these changes affect the amount of solar radiation received by all areas on the Earth's surface. Data from various sources now suggest that this may be the fundamental cause of ice ages, including the short-term advances and withdrawals of the ice of the Pleistocene. Therefore, the intensity and the duration of each global ice age probably are determined by orbital variation, plus some of the conditions on which other theories are based.

The Formation of Glaciers

Glaciers consist of ice, and this ice is formed from compacted, recrystallized snow. But not all snow, not even in mountainous areas, becomes part of a glacier. In a high mountain area such as the Rocky Mountains, there is a **snow line**, a line above which snow remains on the ground throughout the year. Below this snow line the winter's accumulation of snow melts during the next summer, and none of it is transformed into ice. But above the snow line—also known as the *firn line*—the snowpack thickens over time. Some permanent snow survives the summer and contributes to the growing thickness of the snowpack. Where summer snow loss is less than winter gain, conditions favourable to the formation of glacial ice exist.

Snow is converted into ice in stages. Newly fallen snowflakes are light and delicately structured crystals. A layer of freshly fallen snow generally has a low density. Some melting of the outer 'points' of the crystals may take place, changing them into irregular but more spherical grains (Figure 36.2A), or a later snowfall might compress the layer below it, packing the crystals more tightly together and destroying their original structure. These changes in snowflake structure have the effect of increasing the density of the lower layer and reducing its open spaces, or porosity. In areas where periodic melting occurs, fluffy snow can be converted into dense granular snow in a matter of days.

But this first stage does not yet yield glacial ice. The granular, compacted snow—called **firn**—undergoes further compression and recrystallization (Figure 36.2B). That takes time, more time in cold polar areas than in moister temperate zones. This is so because in the temperate areas, where melting occurs, percolating meltwater fills the remaining pore spaces, refreezes there, and adds to the weight of the snowpack. Glaciologists calculate that

the transformation from firn to ice in temperate areas may require less than 50 years. In polar areas, it may take 10 times as long. This means that a snowpack in temperate areas needs to be less thick to be converted into glacial ice.

A glacier in coastal northwestern British Columbia may need a firn less than 15 m deep for ice to form. On the other hand, in the colder and drier Antarctic, 100 m of firn

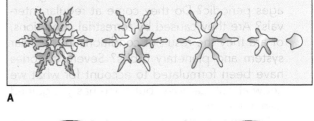

A

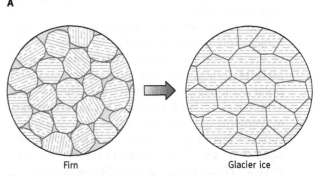

Firn   Glacier ice

B

Figure 36.2 The transformation of a snowflake into a granule of old snow (firn) can take several weeks as the outer 'points' of the crystal melt (A). The conversion of firn into glacier ice takes decades, even centuries, in the coldest climates as recrystallization and further compression slowly squeeze out the open spaces between individual granules (B).

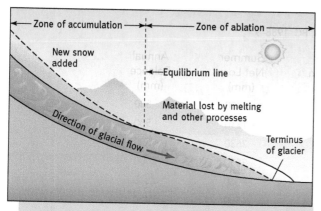

Figure 36.3 A glacier is an open system, with new snow added in its upper zone of accumulation and material lost in its lower ablation zone.

would be required to produce glacier ice of the same density. Such data are useful in determining the age of the great ice sheets. Snow accumulation on the Antarctic ice sheet is very slow, but the firn is of enormous depth. Obviously, this continental glacier required a long time (probably several million years) to achieve its present dimensions.

The Glacier as a System

A glacier is an open system, as shown in Figure 36.3. If the glacier is in equilibrium, it will gain as much matter in the form of precipitation in its **accumulation zone** (or **névé**) as it loses through various processes in its **ablation zone**. These are separated by the equilibrium line. The term *ablation* denotes all forms of loss at a glacier's lower end. Material is moved continuously downslope from the accumulation zone to the ablation zone.

In this system, therefore, matter enters in the solid state as snow, undergoes two changes (to granular and then to crystalline form), and leaves the system in a liquid or vaporized state. Under conditions of equilibrium, a glacier neither grows nor shrinks. But equilibrium conditions rarely exist, and never occur over a long period of time. Glaciers therefore tend to fluctuate in size, especially in the ablation zone. When the *mass balance*—the gains and losses of matter in the system—is positive, the glacier thickens and advances, and its leading edge is steep and icy. When the balance is negative, the glacier thins and recedes, and its front end becomes less pronounced and is marked by grey melting ice covered by melted-out rock debris. Currently, many glaciers are undergoing rapid melting related to climate change and have markedly negative mass balances.

Glacial Mass Balance

The **mass balance** of a glacier is closely related to local energy balances. This mass balance, or budget, defines the relationship between the gain and loss of ice mass. The net gains usually occur in the upper parts of the glacier (the

névé). Net losses usually take place in the ablation zone. The **equilibrium line** separates the accumulation zone from the ablation zone. At present, many glaciers are losing mass and the upglacier movement of their equilibrium lines can be seen. If they gain mass in the future the reverse will take place. The balance is measured over one balance year starting with the onset of winter and culminating at the end of the next summer. Data can be amassed over many years and then is drawn together as a *mass balance series*. Accumulation of mass occurs through processes such as snowfall and rainfall and the refreezing of meltwater that is on, in, or under the ice. Major inputs result from windblown snow and snow avalanches off surrounding slopes.

The losses, as noted above, occur in the lower parts of the glacier (in the ablation zone) through the following processes:

1. Melting (a phase change of water from solid to liquid)
2. Evaporation (a phase change from liquid to gas)
3. Sublimation (a phase change from solid to gas)
4. Wind erosion
5. Wasting (on land) or calving (tidewater glaciers or glaciers terminating in lakes). Calving is a major output, e.g., the Rinks Isbrae (outflow glacier) on the central west coast of Greenland loses an estimated 500 million tonnes of ice in a few minutes once every two weeks during the summer melt season. This amounts to between 10.7 and 16.7 km³/yr of ice loss. A larger neighbouring glacier (Jakobshaven Isbrae) loses 26–44 km³/yr by calving. About 10,000 to 15,000 icebergs of various sizes calve off from the Greenland icecap every year. In Antarctica, one tabular iceberg that broke off the shelf of the Antarctic Ice Sheet in November 1987 was about 1000 km² (larger than Prince Edward Island). An iceberg that broke away in 1956 was estimated to be approximately 31,000 km²—twice as big as Belgium.

Ice and debris move through a glacier at all times, whether there is a positive or negative balance. Table 36.1 shows the mass balance of the Sentinel Glacier in British Columbia's Coast Mountains, near Garibaldi, BC (Figure 36.4), for one balance year.

There is a lag between a change in mass balance and a response (advance or retreat) seen at the snout of the ice. The average lag for valley glaciers is 3–30 years. The Athabasca Glacier, a huge tongue of ice flowing out of the Columbia Icefields, has a lag of about 100 years, while the huge outlet glaciers of Antarctica and Greenland are estimated to have lags of about 5000 years.

Glacial Movement and Erosion

It is certainly true that glacier movement, even in high-relief mountain zones, is not as rapid as streamflow. But the erosional power of glaciers is enormous. When mountain glaciers have melted away and vacated their valleys, they

Table 36.1   Mass Balance of the Sentinel Glacier, BC, 1988–9

Altitude Zone (m)	Area (km²)	Winter Net Gain (mm)	Summer Net Loss (mm)	Annual Balance (mm)
>2100	0.033	2250	−1700	550
2000–2100	0.345	2390	−1810	580
1900–2000	0.479	2330	−2630	−300
1800–1900	0.515	2050	−3450	−1400
1700–1800	0.287	1770	−4060	−2300
<1700	0.084	1750	−4500	−2750
Summary	1.743	2137	−3018	−882

Note: All balance values in mm (water equivalent).
Source: Data from Haeberli and Hoelzle (1993).

Figure 36.4   Sentinel Glacier in the Coast Mountains of British Columbia.

leave exposed some of the world's most spectacular scenery (Figure 36.5). Valley sides are sheer; waterfalls plunge hundreds of metres onto flat, wide valley floors. Whole mountainside spurs, once rounded by a meandering stream before the glacier occupied its valley, are sheared off as if by a giant knife, as the ice straightened and smoothed the valley's course. Lakes are formed behind natural dams made from glacial and rock avalanche debris. Angular peaks and ridges rise above the landscape. The glaciers may be gone, but the landscape bears the dramatic imprint of their work.

Temperature and Glacial Erosion

Observations of the contact plane between ice and bedrock—where erosion takes place—are difficult to make, and movement within various parts of the glacier cannot be easily measured. Temperature is a critical factor in glacial movement, erosion, transport, and deposition. Indeed, the temperature of the ice at the base of a mountain glacier or an ice sheet, together with the melting point of the ice, may be the most important factor of all in that glacier's capacity to erode its valley.

The temperature of glacial ice does not decrease steadily with depth. Various factors, including the pressure exerted by the weight of the ice and the temperature in the bedrock below, affect the temperature of the lowest ice layers, the **basal ice**. When the basal ice is close to or at the melting temperature (as is the case with **wet-based [temperate] ice**, which can reach pressure melting point), the glacier moves faster, erodes more effectively, and transports a larger sedimentary load than when the basal ice is cold (cold, or polar, ice). Debris can be added to the base of the ice and transported there by a process called **regelation** (which involves melting, entrainment, movement, and refreezing). **Cold ice** is frozen to its bed and cannot move. The strength of the ice–rock interface is much greater than between ice and ice. Movement does occur, however, because ice above the basal layers shears over the stationary bottom layers. Mountain glaciers in temperate zones, therefore, erode more strongly than similar glaciers in very cold polar areas, where the temperature of the basal ice is much lower, but many glaciers are **polythermal**, having both wet-based areas where the ice is thicker and cold areas where there is thinner ice. This is important in terms of how the ice moves and also how water and debris get into the ice. Continental icecaps such as those covering Greenland and Antarctica are of massive dimensions, but

From the Fieldnotes

Figure 36.5 *'The magnificent scenery of Yosemite National Park in California's Sierra Nevada was sculpted by streams and glaciers. Half Dome (right) seems to have been halved by a powerful glacier coming down the U-shaped valley it overlooks, but scientists are not unanimous on this point.'*

their movement is very slow. Their erosional work, compared to their size, is much less effective than that of lower-latitude mountain glaciers because of the exceedingly low atmospheric temperatures. The interplay of cold ice and wet-based ice in a glacier is very important. Where wet-based ice pulls away from cold-based ice, crevasses form (extension flow). These allow material and water on the surface to enter the glacier and become englacial or subglacial materials. Wet-based ice moves faster than cold-based sections because it is often floating on a thin film of basal meltwater. The wet-based ice moves faster and shears over the slower cold-based section (compression). The shear zones formed in this way bring basal debris into the ice from the base of the glacier (Figure 36.6).

The Movement of Ice

Glaciers move slowly. The great continental icecaps move as little as 2 to 3 cm per day, and even some cold-area mountain glaciers move just a few centimetres daily. In a rapidly moving alpine glacier, the daily advance may amount to as much as 4 or 5 m or even more. Occasionally, a mountain glacier develops a **surge**, a rapid movement of as much as one metre per hour or more, sustained over a period of months, producing an advance of several kilometres in one season. Surges are caused by the damming up of the glacier's internal plumbing system. Water builds up under the ice and lubricates movement. Surges end when the dam breaks and the water gushes out in a glacial burst flood, or jökulhlaup (see Unit 38).

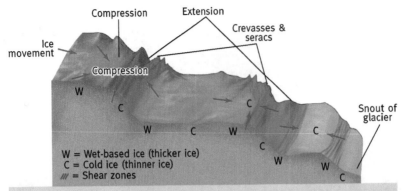

Figure 36.6 Glacial extension, compression, crevasses, shear zones, and thermal regime. Wet-based ice shears over cold ice, eroding material at the base, and debris is brought up into the ice. Crevasses allow surface meltwater and debris to get down into the ice.

A profile through the centre of a mountain glacier reveals that its upper layer consists of rigid, brittle ice that is often cut by large cracks called **crevasses**; below this rigid layer, the ice takes on the properties of a plastic material (Figure 36.7). The masses of ice between the crevasses are called *seracs*. When the glacier moves downslope, its centre advances more rapidly and the sides more slowly because of freezing to the valley sides or friction and roughness (Figure 36.8). In vertical cross-section, the upper surface moves fastest while the basal ice moves more slowly. The Victoria Glacier (which feeds into Lake Louise, Alberta) has a flow velocity of about 40 m/yr (11 cm/day) at the surface near its centre. At its margins along the valley wall the rate of flow is less than 23 m/yr and near its snout the velocity drops to about 15 m/yr. There are different types of flow related to the phenomenon. The most common types are:

1. *Parabolic flow.* The centre of the glacier moves faster than the margins. This type of flow is characteristic of glaciers in the Alps.

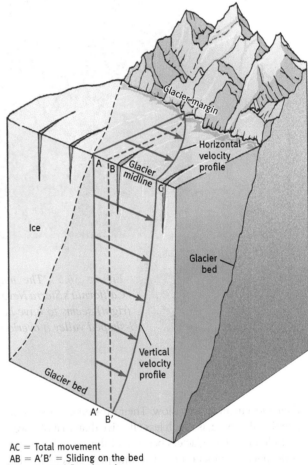

AC = Total movement
AB = A′B′ = Sliding on the bed
BC = Internal flow (creep)

Figure 36.8 Differential movement rates within an advancing glacier. Vertically, the upper surface moves fastest and the basal ice slowest. Horizontally, the centre moves fastest and the sides move slowest.

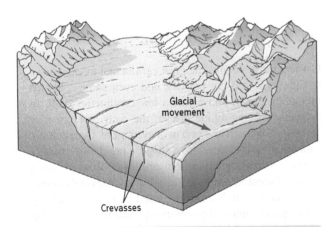

Figure 36.7 A glacier's brittle upper layers are studded with large crevasses. Down below, plastic flow predominates.

2. *Plug flow.* The marginal ice is immobile, but there is flow in the centre of the glacier and there is a rapid transition between the immobile and moving

ice. This causes the ice to fracture and produces many crevasses. This type of flow is seen in many Himalayan glaciers.

3. *U-shaped (or intermediate) flow*. This is intermediate between the other two flow types. This type of flow also produces a lot of crevasses. A good example of this type of flow is the Saskatchewan Glacier in the Columbia Icefields.

Glaciers move in two different ways. The first, called **ice creep**, involves the internal deformation of the ice, with crystals slipping over one another as a result of the downslope movement just described. This occurs in both wet-based and cold ice, and is a consequence of weight, slope, and gravity. The second flow mechanism, called **basal (peripheral) sliding**, is the movement of the entire glacier over the rocks below it. This process only occurs in wet-based ice, and it directly involves the glacier's erosional work. It is generally conceded that glacial sliding is enhanced by the existence of a thin film of water between the basal ice and the bedrock floor. This film of pressurized water is just millimetres thick and is probably discontinuous. But it is enough to lubricate the contact plane between glacier and bedrock, and speeds the glacier's movement downslope.

Dynamic Classification of Glaciers

Glacial activity is influenced by the thermal regime of the ice and is closely associated with the glacial mass balance. Using examples from the lee side of the Columbia Icefield in Alberta, it is possible to classify glaciers, on the basis of ice supply and movement, into the following categories:

1. *Active ice*. This is fed by a continuous supply of ice from a névé. Outlet glaciers such as the Athabasca Glacier are of this type (Figure 36.9).
2. *Passive (or inactive) ice*. This is fed by a discontinuous supply of ice from the icefield because of a restricted area of ice falls, or it is reliant on snow avalanches for ice supply. This type of ice is very common on the lee side of mountain ranges. Good examples are the Dome and Stutfield Glaciers (Figure 36.10).
3. *Dead ice*. This is where a glacier is no longer receiving ice from the névé or part of a glacier is cut off from the rest of the ice mass by shear zones. The movement of dead ice, such as the Kitchener Glacier in the Columbia Icefields, depends solely on the slope of the glacial valley.

Glacial Erosion

Erosion by glaciers can take place through **plucking** (also called *quarrying*), a complicated process in which the properties of the bedrock (rather than the transported rock debris) are most significant. In plucking, blocks or fragments of bedrock beneath the glacier are pulled from the bed as the ice moves forward. Glacial erosion also can occur by **abrasion**, the scraping process produced by the

Figure 36.9 The Athabasca Glacier in Alberta.

Figure 36.10 The Stutfield Glacier in the Rocky Mountains of Alberta.

impact of rock debris carried in the ice upon the bedrock below. Despite its appearance, ice is not a hard substance; on the Mohs Hardness Scale (see Table 22.1) it would rate only about 1.5. Thus, ice by itself cannot be an effective erosional agent. Abrasion, therefore, must be performed by the rock fragments being dragged along the bedrock floor (and the submerged valley sides) by the moving ice.

Abrasion   Some of these rock fragments are, of course, quite 'soft' themselves and do not have much effect on glacial erosion. This softer material is soon pulverized and becomes part of the dark zones within the ice visible on the glacier's surface (**ogives,** or dirt bands). Harder fragments, however, do have a powerful impact on the bedrock floor and valley sides beneath the glacier. The enormous weight of the glacier pushes a boulder downward while dragging it along, and this combination can create rapid degradation. Other factors also come into play: the rate of movement of the glacier, the temperature of the basal ice, and the character of the underlying bedrock.

How fast do glaciers degrade? Various studies have been undertaken, but it is not possible to generalize from these. In one area of temperate-zone glaciers, average erosional rates ranged up to 5 mm per year, but in another area a rate nearly seven times as high was recorded. The effectiveness of the abrasion process is quite variable. Abrasion can produce several telltale features in the landscape. When the abrading debris consists of fine but 'hard' particles (quartz grains, for instance) and the underlying bedrock also is quite hard, abrasion produces a polished surface that looks as though the bedrock has been sandpapered. But when the rock fragments are larger, the underlying surface may be scratched quite deeply. These scratches, made as the boulder or pebble was dragged along the floor, are called glacial **striations.** They often are metres long and centimetres (but more often millimetres) deep. They can be useful indicators of the direction of ice movement where the topography provides few clues, because striations tend to lie parallel to the direction of ice movement.

Plucking   Plucking, a process diagrammed in Figure 36.11, also leaves evidence in the landscape. One of the most common landforms associated with glacial plucking is the *roche moutonnée* (Figure 36.12). This asymmetrical bedrock mound appears to result from abrasion on the upglacier side and plucking on the leeward side. A complicated process allows the glacier to quarry this leeward side, lifting out and carrying away loosened parts of the feature. Studies suggest that jointing in the bedrock and, probably, frost-caused fracturing contribute to the glacier's ability to 'pluck' the leeside of the hill over which it passes. Other evidence suggests that the leeside is affected by frost wedging in a **subglacial cavity,** which forms as the ice goes over the obstruction. Whatever the nature of the process, *roches moutonnées,* like striations, help us reconstruct the path of the glacier. *Roches moutonnées,* the largest features observed forming under a glacier, range in size from a few tens of metres to a few hundred metres in length and can be up to several tens of metres in height. They are quite common in some areas of Canada; many can be seen in road cuts along major highways that run across the Shield.

As in the case of streams, glaciers deposit (aggrade) as they erode (degrade). The degradation of their source areas is matched by aggradation at their terminal edges. Like rivers, glaciers process the sedimentary loads they carry;

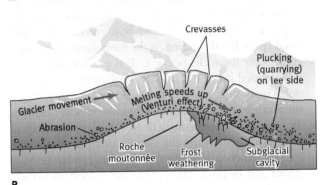

Figure 36.11   Plucking occurs when glacial-bed rock fragments are torn loose (by ice freezing into cracks that are subsequently enlarged by wedging), rotated upward, and carried away downslope embedded in the basal ice flow (A). Larger mound-like landforms, called *roches moutonnées,* are also created by this process, with the plucking found on the leeward side (B).

Figure 36.12   A *roche moutonnée* in the Abitibi region of western Quebec. Note the striations on the surface of this bedrock, which indicate the direction in which the glacial ice sheet was moving.

but unlike rivers, fragments of hard rock that have taken the long trip encased in glacial ice appear at the glacier's end as angular boulders. The debris carried downslope by alpine glaciers tends to concentrate in certain zones of the glacier and appears on the surface as a series of parallel bands (active lateral and medial moraines). Once deposited,

LINK

this material leaves no doubt as to its origin: rounded fragments are a sign of fluvial action, whereas angular fragments signify the work of ice. Continental glaciers, too, degrade their source areas and aggrade where their advance is slowed or stopped. Much of the topography of the area of the Great Lakes and the surrounding areas is underlain by glacial debris scoured by continental ice sheets from the Canadian Shield and deposited to the south. The next unit deals with the landforms and landscapes created by the great ice sheets of the past.

KEY TERMS

ablation zone   *page 507*
abrasion   *page 511*
accumulation zone   *page 507*
basal ice   *page 508*
basal (peripheral) sliding   *page 511*
cold ice   *page 508*
continental glacier   *page 504*
crevasse   *page 510*
cryosphere   *page 503*
deglaciation   *page 504*
equilibrium line   *page 507*

firn   *page 506*
glacial surge   *page 509*
glaciation   *page 504*
glacier   *page 503*
ice age   *page 505*
ice creep   *page 511*
interglacial   *page 504*
mass balance   *page 507*
Milankovitch forcing   *page 506*
mountain (alpine) glacier   *page 504*
névé   *page 507*

ogive   *page 512*
polythermal ice   *page 508*
plucking   *page 511*
regelation   *page 508*
roche moutonnée   *page 512*
'Snowball Earth'   *page 505*
snow line   *page 506*
striations   *page 512*
subglacial cavity   *page 512*
wet-based (temperate) ice   *page 508*

REVIEW QUESTIONS

1. Where do continental glaciers presently exist?
2. What is meant by the term *Late Cenozoic Ice Age*?
3. How does snow become transformed into glacial ice?

4. Describe how the mass balance of a glacier controls the glacier's movement.
5. How is a *roche moutonnée* formed?

REFERENCES AND FURTHER READINGS

Andrews, J.T. 1975. *Glacial Systems: An Approach to Glaciers and Their Environments.* North Scituate, Mass.: Duxbury Press.

Benn, D.I., and D.J.A. Evans. 1998. *Glaciers and Glaciation.* New York: Oxford Univ. Press.

Broecker, W.S., and G.H. Denton. 1990. 'What Drives Glacial Cycles?', *Scientific American* (Jan.): 39–45.

Embleton, C., and C.A.M. King. 1975. *Glacial Geomorphology.* London: Edward Arnold.

Evans, R. 1996. *The Geography of Glaciers.* New York: Wiley.

Eyles, N., ed. 1983. *Glacial Geology: An Introduction to Engineers and Earth Scientists.* New York: Pergamon.

Haeberli, W., and M. Hoelzle. 1993. *Fluctuations of Glaciers: 1985–1990,* vol. 6. Paris: IAHS/UNEP/UNESCO.

———— and C.C. Wallen. 1996. *Glaciers and the Environment.* Nairobi: United Nations Environmental Program.

Hambrey, M., and J. Alean. 1994. *Glaciers.* New York: Cambridge Univ. Press.

Hughes, T.J. 1998. *Ice Sheets.* New York: Oxford Univ. Press.

Imbrie, J., and K.P. Imbrie. 1979. *Ice Ages: Solving the Mystery.* Short Hills, NJ: Enslow.

John, B.S. 1977. *The Ice Age: Past and Present.* London: Collins.

Matsch, C.L. 1976. *North America and the Great Ice Age.* New York: McGraw-Hill.

Post, A., and E.R. Lachapelle. 1971. *Glacier Ice.* Seattle: The Mountaineers.

Sharp, R.P. 1988. *Living Ice: Understanding Glaciers and Glaciation.* London/New York: Cambridge Univ. Press.

Sugden, D.E., and B.S. John. 1976. *Glaciers and Landscape: A Geomorphological Approach.* London: Edward Arnold.

Williams, R.S., Jr. 1986. 'Glaciers and Glacial Landforms', in N.M. Short and R.W. Blair Jr, eds, *Geomorphology from Space: A Global Overview of Regional Landforms.* Washington: NASA, Special Publication SP-486, 54–77.

———— and D.K. Hall. 1993. 'Glaciers', in R.J. Gurney, J.L. Foster, and C.L. Parkinson, eds, *Atlas of Earth Observations Related to Global Change.* New York: Cambridge Univ. Press, 114–23.

WEB RESOURCES

nrmsc.usgs.gov/research/glaciers.htm This page describes glacier monitoring techniques and data for Glacier National Park in the US.

Unit 37

Landforms and Landscapes of Continental Ice Sheets and Mountain Glaciers

Objectives

- To delineate contemporary continental ice sheets and define their former extent during the Pleistocene Ice Age.

- To identify the typical deposits and landforms produced by continental ice sheets.

- To examine the current distribution of mountain glaciers and to comment on the Pleistocene extent of these glaciers.

- To discuss the landforms produced by mountain glacier erosion and deposition.

During an ice age the Earth's surface is transformed. Great ice sheets form over landmasses situated at high latitudes. Whole regions are submerged under ice—mountains, plateaus, plains, and all. The weight of the ice, which may reach a thickness of more than 3000 m, pushes the underlying crustal bedrock downward isostatically (see Unit 24). So much water is converted into snow (and subsequently into glacial ice) that the sea level can drop more than 100 m. Large areas of continental shelf are exposed, coastlines are relocated accordingly, and continental outlines change shape. As the ice sheets expand, thereby expanding the region of polar-type temperatures, global climatic zones are compressed towards the lower latitudes. Mid-latitude lands that were previously temperate become cold, barren, and subpolar in character; vegetation shifts equatorward.

The global climate during the Cenozoic Era was generally mild until the onset of the Pleistocene Ice Age. Before the ice age began, even Antarctica was mostly ice-free; on high mountains, streams—not glaciers—sculpted the landscape. The landforms associated with stream erosion and deposition also characterized such major mountain ranges as the Rockies, Alps, Andes, and even the Himalayas. Hilltops displayed rounded forms, valleys were eroded by meandering streams, and most tributary junctions were structurally concurrent. The mountain regions of the world looked much like parts of today's Appalachian Mountains, the Atlas Mountains of northwestern Africa, or the Great Dividing Range of eastern Australia, except that higher relief generally prevailed.

When the first cooling episode occurred and the altitude of the snow line dropped, the formation of glaciers began. The Antarctic ice sheet probably was the first continental ice mass to develop because of Antarctica's polar location and its high overall elevation. Gradually, on the other continents, permanent ice formed on higher mountain slopes. Snow accumulated above the firn line, and *alpine glaciers* flowed down the high valleys.

These glaciers occupied valleys first carved by rivers, and glacial erosion replaced stream erosion. Permanent ice appeared on high mountains even in equatorial areas, and the Earth was indeed transformed. This unit focuses on glaciers that form on mountains and erode and deposit material in these alpine settings. These glaciers differ from the ice sheets of continental glaciation in that they are generally confined to valleys, and their behaviour is influenced by the topography they inhabit. In other respects, they are quite similar to continental icecaps and ice sheets.

Contemporary Ice Cover

On a global scale, contemporary ice action (erosion, transport, and deposition) is areally insignificant because less than 10 per cent of the continental area is covered by ice. Almost all of this is in Antarctica and Greenland.

The Antarctic Icecap

The present climate is relatively warm compared to the atmospheric conditions of the past few million years, and glaciers have receded from many areas and, increasingly, are doing so as a consequence of global warming. But two large **icecaps** persist to this day—in Antarctica and Greenland (Kalaallit Nunaat). An icecap is a dome-shaped mass of ice that covers a large area of land.

The **Antarctic Icecap**, which began forming about 40 million years ago, has existed throughout the entire Late Cenozoic Era and is unlikely to melt entirely in Holocene times. This ice mass allows us to measure and observe the properties of continental-scale glaciers and to better understand how they affected the now deglaciated areas of the Northern Hemisphere. The Antarctic Icecap (Figure 37.1) is of a size comparable to that of the **Laurentide Ice Sheet** that covered Canada and the northern United States repeatedly during the Pleistocene Ice Age. The Antarctic Icecap covers an area of more than 13 million km^2, constituting almost 9 per cent of the 'land' area of the globe.

Beneath this great glacier lies an entire continental landmass, including an Andes-sized mountain range and a vast plateau. In places on top of this plateau—particularly the region to the right of the South Pole in Figure 37.1—the

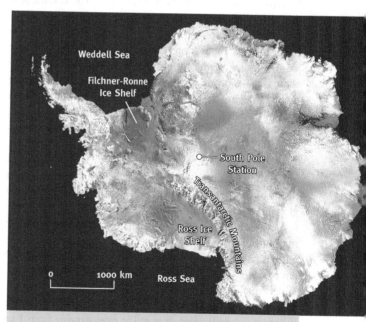

Figure 37.1 Infrared satellite image of Antarctica in its standard orientation, with the Antarctic Peninsula extending northwest towards South America. Snow is represented in white, ice in blue, and nunataks in black (the girdling Southern Ocean also appears in black). The mostly buried Transantarctic Mountains can be observed extending across the continent from the landward end of the Antarctic Peninsula. The huge bay to the east of the peninsula is the Weddell Sea, and the blue area at the apex of that sea is the Filchner-Ronne Ice Shelf. The Ross Ice Shelf directly across from the Filchner-Ronne, flanking the Transantarctic Mountains, is even larger.

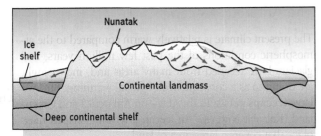

Figure 37.2   The Antarctic Icecap forms a gigantic dome that depresses the landmass below. In a few places mountain peaks (nunataks) rise above the icecap. Outlet glaciers flow off the icecap into the sea. Vertical scale is markedly exaggerated.

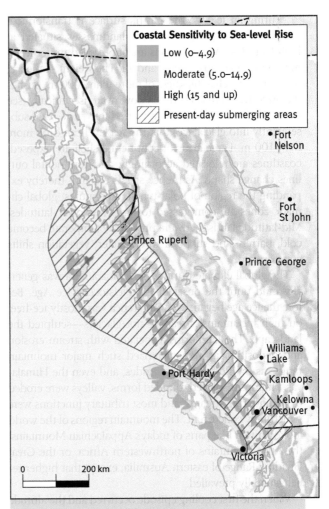

Figure 37.3   Effects of a 0.09–0.88-m rise in sea level on British Columbia, showing coastal zones and some of the major cities that would be affected.

ice is more than 4000 m thick. A few of the highest mountain peaks protrude through the ice and snow; such exposed tips are called **nunataks**. Except for the outer parts of the Antarctic Peninsula, the Antarctic Icecap prevails from coast to coast. In schematic profile it looks like a giant dome, resting on the landmass below (Figure 37.2). Because of this great ice accumulation, Antarctica has the highest average altitude of all the continents.

Volume and Weight of the Icecap   The volume and the weight of the Antarctic Icecap are perhaps best illustrated by the following data. About 65 per cent of all the freshwater on Earth is presently locked up in the Antarctic ice. If this ice melted, the global sea level would rise by some 0.09–0.88 m and possibly more, thereby drowning many low-lying areas (the effects such a rise would have on coastal British Columbia are shown in Figure 37.3). The weight of the Antarctic Icecap is so great that the landmass below it has sunk isostatically by an estimated 600 m. Thus, if the ice were to melt, the Antarctic landmass would rebound upward exceptionally slowly by about 600 m as a result of the removal of this load, further contributing to global sea-level rise.

At present the Antarctic icecap experiences very little mass input in the interior zone of accumulation. Average annual snowfall in the interior amounts to less than 10 cm of water equivalent (melted water from ice and snow), which qualifies this region as a desert. But over this vast area, even that meagre amount of snow is sufficient to keep the great icecap flowing outward at rates varying from 1 to 30 m per year.

Features of the Antarctic Icecap   The Antarctic Icecap exhibits several features that are useful in the study of other, extinct continental glaciers. One of these is the division of the ice dome into **flow regimes** (Figure 37.4). The ice does not move outward in a simple radial manner. Rather, it flows seaward in several discrete regions, each of which has its own ice supply basin (névé) or catchment area and its own rates of snow accumulation, ice formation, and velocity.

Another interesting feature of the ice sheet is its behaviour in Antarctica's marginal areas. Here the ice thins out, and the underlying topography plays a much more important role than it does under the thicker ice of the continental interior. In places the ice sheet fans out into valley glaciers and *ice tongues* (outlet glaciers that extend into the sea). These marginal glaciers are fed in part by the icecap and in larger part by heavy snows falling on their local basin areas. As a result, they move faster than the main body of the icecap. Moreover, recent research suggests volcanism is a factor here as well: volcanic activity beneath the ice produces ground warmth that melts sufficient basal ice to keep the marginal glaciers flowing seaward atop a slippery layer of meltwater and mud.

Still another feature of the Antarctic Icecap is the formation of **ice shelves**. These are floating extensions of the main icecap, which remain attached to the continental ice as they protrude from land into the frigid seawater (see far left edge of Figure 37.2). Antarctica presently

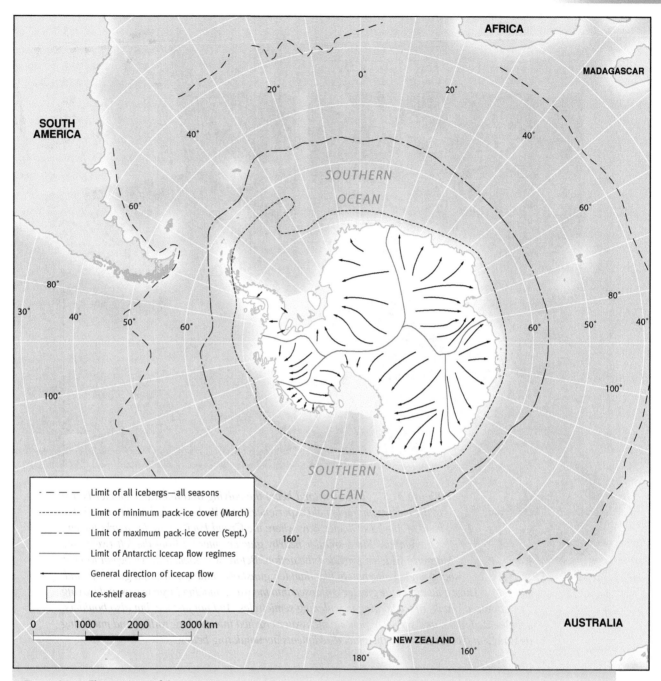

Figure 37.4 Flow regimes of the Antarctic Icecap and ice limits in the surrounding Southern Ocean.

has two prominent ice shelves—the Ross Ice Shelf in the Ross Sea and the Filchner-Ronne Ice Shelf in the Weddell Sea (shown in Figure 37.1)—plus many smaller ice shelves. The Ross Ice Shelf has an area of 535,000 km² and is under half the size of Ontario; the Filchner-Ronne Ice Shelf is nearly 400,000 km², just under the size of Newfoundland and Labrador. The thickness of the ice in these shelves declines with distance from the mainland. At the coast, the Ross Ice Shelf is 300 m thick; at its seaward edge, about 600 km from shore, thickness is reduced to about 180 m. At this outer edge the ice

shelves break up into huge tabular icebergs and smaller pieces (Figure 37.5) in a process called **calving** (which is a form of ablation). These flat-topped icebergs generally range in size from a few hundred metres to about 35 km across, although some are several times larger. For example, in 1956 one was sighted that was about 333 km in length and 90 km wide (20,092.8 km²). Very large icebergs have broken off Antarctica recently, too.

The tabular iceberg is characteristic of Antarctic waters. Icebergs (which are formed from freshwater ice), whatever their appearance or origin, have a slightly lower density

Figure 37.5 'To watch (and hear) the calving of a tidewater glacier is one of the most memorable field experiences ever. We had sailed north towards the head of Alaska's Glacier Bay, where the Grand Pacific Glacier marks the end of navigation. But a smaller nearby glacier entering from the left (west), the Margerie Glacier, provided the action. Before we reached it, we began to hear what sounded alternately like thunder, gunshots, loud groans, and gusts of wind. Huge columns of the glacier collapsed into the water, making large waves and leaving car-sized chunks of ice floating in widening semicircles. And not just ice, but also boulders, pebble-sized rocks, and surges of pent-up meltwater crashed into the bay, roiling and muddying its waters and contributing to the glacial sediments accumulating below.'

than the saline cold water in which they float. Only about one-sixth of the mass of an iceberg appears above the water. A peaked iceberg in northern waters may have an underwater base extending far beyond its exposed form, and many ships have collided with icebergs that still appeared to be a safe distance away.

Surrounding the great Antarctic Icecap and its zone of tabular icebergs lies a zone of floating sea ice that mostly covers the water's surface. This **pack ice** (see Figure 37.4) does not derive from the ice sheet: it forms from the freezing of salt water in the adjacent Southern Ocean. Dur-ing the winter the belt of pack ice thickens and spreads. Thus, from March to November Antarctica lies encircled by a nearly solid zone of floating ice, so wide that it nearly doubles the 'size' of the continent. There are permanently open areas of water—polynyas—in the pack ice in the Antarctic and Arctic. These are associated with rich mam-mal faunas (seals, walruses, whales). After November the pack ice surrounding Antarctica rapidly breaks up, and *leads*, or channels of open water, form through it, allow-ing ships carrying supplies and equipment to reach the continent's coastal research stations.

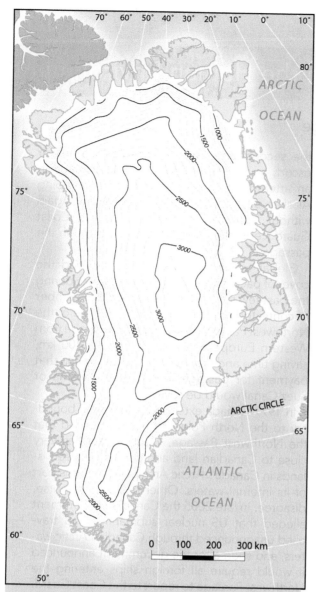

Figure 37.6 The Greenland Icecap, which is one-eighth the size of the Antarctic Icecap. Ice thickness contours are given in metres.

Figure 37.7 Floating (and solid) pack ice fills most of the Arctic Ocean for much of the year. The cracks and pressure ridges reflect the crushing and breaking that take place in this constantly churning surface, which is being monitored closely to determine the effects of global warming. By 2008, satellite imagery for August showed an increasingly vast amount of open Arctic water.

The Greenland Icecap

In total area, the **Greenland Icecap** is about one-eighth as large as Antarctica's continental ice mass, covering about 1.7 million km² of surface (Figure 37.6). Indeed, this icecap creates most of the surface of Greenland, the largest of all the world's islands. But in terms of volume, the Greenland Icecap is less important, and it contains only about 11 per cent of the world's freshwater supply. Like the Antarctic Icecap, Greenland's ice mass exhibits the shape of a dome, reaching its highest elevation (over 3000 m) in the east-central part of the island. From there the surface drops quite rapidly towards the coasts, where the thickness of the ice is reduced to 150 m and even less.

The icecap also leaves about 19 per cent of Greenland uncovered, which is nearly 10 times proportionally more than in Antarctica. It appears to have been quite stable until recently, with ablation in the coastal zone approximating the accumulation in the interior, but this has changed in response to continued global warming and the balance has been upset.

There are no ice shelves here comparable to those of the Antarctic ice sheet. Indeed, the only ice-shelf feature in the Arctic lies not in Greenland but along the northern coast of adjacent Ellesmere Island, Nunavut, to the northwest. Where the Greenland Icecap reaches the edge of the ocean, it extends seaward in valley outlet glaciers. From these, large masses of ice calve and float as icebergs into the Arctic and North Atlantic Oceans.

Age of the Present Ice Sheets

The Antarctic and Greenland Icecaps have survived the warm interglacial of the Holocene so far. But were they permanent throughout the present ice age? How old are they? These questions can now be answered because new research methods have been developed to solve the problems of ice-age chronology. As in the case of plate tectonics and crustal spreading, the oceans provided crucial evidence.

LINK

Perspectives on the Human Environment

The Northwest Passage

Following the discovery in 1520 of the Strait of Magellan at the southern end of South America, many European explorers were convinced that a similar northern route connecting the Atlantic and Pacific Oceans could be found. For centuries the search for the Northwest Passage was a major aim. Many of the adventurers who traversed Canada by land or sea were looking for this route.

As early as 1576 Sir Humphrey Gilbert, half-brother of Sir Walter Raleigh, had written about the benefit of such a route to trade with the Far East in his *A Discourse of a Discovery for a New Passage to Cataia*. (Cataia, or Cathay, was a common name for China in medieval and Renaissance Europe.) And many men and ships tried to find the passage. All failed until the mid-nineteenth century, when Commander Robert McClure of the Royal Navy found one of the various routes through the Canadian Arctic Archipelago while searching for Sir John Franklin's lost expedition. The first full navigation of the route from east to west was achieved by Norwegian explorer Roald Amundsen in his sloop *Gjoa* (pronounced 'Jo') in 1903–6. The RCMP ship *St Roch* (under Sergeant Henry Larson) later traversed the route from Vancouver to Halifax in 1940–2. In these cases the explorers wintered over in the Arctic pack ice, and this pack ice prevented any regular year-round or even seasonal shipping until recently, although in 1969 and again in 1970 the American tanker SS *Manhattan* transited the Northwest Passage, the second time with a Canadian icebreaker escort, and sustained considerable damage in an attempt to prove the viability of shipping Alaskan oil across the top of the globe. Again without Canadian permission, the US Coast Guard icebreaker *Polar Sea* busted through the passage in 1985.

Global warming, however, has reduced the cover of pack ice and created open water during the past few summers. This has led to a number of contested sovereignty claims, and use of the Northwest Passage also would cut a voyage from Western Europe to Japan by about 7400 km, saving time and money. It would also mean that payment for passage through the Panama or Suez Canal would be saved.

In 1977 Canada extended its northern boundary to the North Pole and has maintained that the Northwest Passage, which in fact lies very close to Canadian land and passes between islands in Canada's Arctic Archipelago, forms part of its internal waters. Other nations, of course, disagree. In late 2005 the Canadian government alleged that US nuclear submarines had travelled unannounced through Canadian Arctic waters, and soon after the government announced it would require all foreign ships entering the Northwest Passage to report to the Coast Guard. In August and September 2007 the government announced plans to build eight new icebreaker/patrol ships and to establish a greater military presence in the Far North, with a training centre at Resolute Bay and a deepwater naval station at Nanisivik on the northern tip of Baffin Island.

Episodes of cooling and warming occur during an ice age, and these stages are recorded by the microorganisms (foraminifera) that become part of the deep-sea sediments. These tiny organisms lived at the surface of the sea, like plankton, then died and sank to the ocean floor. Cores of such sediments, obtained by deep-sea drilling, now allow geologists and marine scientists to study the sequence and length of ice-age glaciations, analyze paleomagnetic data, and search for the presence of certain isotopes of oxygen in proportions that reveal the times of arrival of meltwater and the removal of seawater during the successive deglaciations and glaciations.

In combination, these data sources have produced evidence that the present ice age began well before the onset of the Pleistocene Epoch 1.8 million years ago. According to the scientists engaged in this research, there have been more than 30 glaciations since the ice age

LINK

began. Glaciations appear to occur, on average, 90,000 to 100,000 years apart. Within individual glaciations, there are fluctuations when the advancing ice stalls or temporarily recedes before resuming its forward progress.

As for the Antarctic Icecap, the evidence indicates that cooling and ice formation in Antarctica began about 40 million years ago, long before the Pleistocene Epoch commenced. This great continental ice mass grew slowly at first and probably reached its full extent (somewhat larger than its present size) about 3.5 million years ago. It has survived all of the interglacials of the Pleistocene Ice Age,

but will it survive the warming atmospheric conditions of the Holocene?

North America's Glaciation: The Final Four (and Probably Many More?)

Before the days of deep-sea drilling and oxygen-isotope analysis, researchers had to rely on stratigraphic evidence to unravel the complicated glacial past. By mapping the

Canadian Geographers in the Field

'The shorelines of the Great Lakes are superb outdoor laboratory sites for fieldwork investigations. This site near Port Burwell, southern Ontario, on the north shore of Lake Erie reveals a complex stratigraphy of upper glaciolacustrine laminated muds; below that are glaciofluvial sands and gravels and subglacial lodgement, and waterlain tills in the lower half of the photograph. In a single exposure, therefore, one can find all the needed evidence of the late Wisconsinan Laurentide Ice Sheet glaciation and associated retreat sediments related to ice marginal proglacial sedimentation, first within a shallow near ice-marginal proglacial zone, then, at the top of the section, within an increasingly deeper glacial lake environment.'

John Menzies, B.Sc., Ph.D., P.Geo., is Professor of Geography and Earth Sciences at Brock University.

surface geology and constructing cross-sections, they tried to determine the succession of glaciations and interglacials. Dating these in absolute terms was not yet possible, so chronologies were based on what was known about the rates of accumulation of glacial deposits, on the depth of soils that developed between glacial episodes, and on related data. In part, certain assumptions were made that the Alpine chronology in Europe could be used in North America.

Under these circumstances, this field research achieved some remarkably good results. Alpine glaciologists Albrecht Penck and Edouard Bruckner identified four major phases of glaciation (more recent studies have shown that Penck and Bruckner's study was flawed). Thus it was assumed that the Pleistocene glaciation was a four-stage sequence, involving a total period variously estimated to have lasted from 0.5 to 1.5 million years. In North America it was assumed (because of Penck and Bruckner's model) that there were four major advances of the Laurentide Ice Sheet, of which the **Wisconsinan glaciation** was the most recent (Table 37.1).

The current state of knowledge is that these four glaciations actually represent the last of the more than 30 glacial episodes of the Pleistocene Ice Age. It is also now understood that the glacial and interglacial periods were complex. For example, the Wisconsinan period consisted of two major advances, not just one—the Early and the Late Wisconsinan stadials separated by an *interstadial*. In Europe, the Mindel glaciation is now called the Mindel Complex because there is evidence of repeated glacial advances. The pre-Günz (pre-Nebraskan) glaciation also is now recognized. Nonetheless the four-stage sequence (Table 37.1) was a remarkable approximation, given that it was based on evidence that existed only in Alpine Europe. The last phases of glaciation form the record of perhaps the last 400,000 to 450,000 years of the Late Cenozoic's 3 million years of rhythmic global warming and cooling.

When the technique of radiocarbon dating of carbon-bearing substances in the most recent (Wisconsinan)

glacial deposits became possible, the story of the last pre-Holocene deglaciation emerged. The final advance of the Wisconsinan ice was so rapid in some areas that the leading edge of the ice sheet toppled trees and encased them. When deglaciation began, these tree trunks were deposited along with the glacier's rock debris. Radiocarbon dating revealed the year when they were engulfed by the ice. This was about 12,000 years ago, so the final deglaciation that led directly to the present Holocene interglacial has lasted barely 10 millennia.

Landscapes of Continental Ice Sheets

Unit 36 dealt with the ways glaciers erode and described two kinds of degradational features—polished and striated surfaces, and *roches moutonnées*. These landforms are neither prominent nor very common. But ice sheets do create extensive landscapes of degradation. They acquire their enormous sedimentary load by scouring huge parts of their source areas clear of soil, regolith, and loosened rock. Sometimes where the underlying topography has valleys roughly parallel to the direction of ice movement, a continental glacier can even behave like a mountain glacier, deepening and widening such valleys. In southern Ontario and the Finger Lakes region of upstate New York (Figure 37.8) subglacial tunnel valleys occurred.

More often, when a continental glacier melts away, what is left is a vast ice-scoured plain marked by depressions, which are filled with water where the ice sheet did its gouging and scouring. Much of the surface of the Canadian Shield and Northern Europe's Scandinavian Shield (see Figure 20.12) display such landforms. Erosion has created extensive continental-glacier landscapes.

Aggradational Landforms of Ice Sheets

A continental ice sheet transports huge amounts of rock debris as it thickens and expands, scouring and sculpting the surface beneath it. When the Laurentide Ice Sheet moved from the hard crystalline rocks of the Canadian Shield to the softer rocks of adjacent areas, its sedimentary load increased even more. If we were able to take a view in profile of such a sediment-charged glacier, we would note that the sediment **subglacial** load is carried near the bed of the glacier. Other material would be carried in (englacially) or on the top of the ice (**supraglacially**). Some of the rock material would be fine-grained, but much of the load would be pebble and boulder-sized or even larger. Laden with all this debris, the ice sheet edged forward, depositing some of its load in places along the way and eroding material elsewhere.

Table 37.1 Four North American Pleistocene Glaciations and Their Alpine Equivalents

North America	Interglacial	Alpine
	Holocene	
Wisconsinan	Late	Würm
	Early	
	Sangamonian	
Illinoisan		Riss
	Yarmouthian	
Kansan Complex		Mindel Complex
	Aftonian	
Nebraskan (pre-Nebraskan)		Günz (pre-Günz)

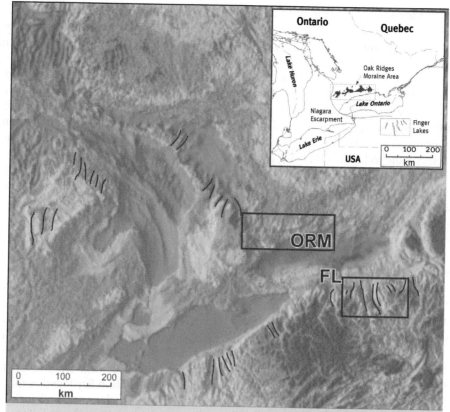

Figure 37.8 Satellite view of the Oak Ridges Moraine in southern Ontario. The moraine was created by glaciation and acts as a ground and surface water reserve. It extends for 160 km between the Niagara Escarpment and the eastern end of Rice Lake.

Glacial Processes

There is a very complex mix of transportational and depositional environments associated with glaciations. Glacial deposits include a wide range of materials, including *tills, loess and coversands, varved lake sediments,* and *outwash sands and gravels.* While **tills** are ice deposits, the other sediments are essentially aeolian or aqueous suspended and traction deposits. It is possible to separate glacial deposits into three groups based on a number of characteristics related to their mode of deposition, as shown in Table 37.2.

These groups of deposits often occur interbedded because of the complexity of the glacial deposition process and because of the fluctuations of the ice front over time. Fluvioglacial and windborne deposits will be discussed in Unit 38.

Basal and Ablation Tills

When deglaciation begins, deposition occurs in many ways depending on whether the material is carried in and under the ice or on top of the ice. Solid material carried at the base of the glacier is deposited as **basal (lodgement)**

Table 37.2 Categorization of Glacial Deposits

Waterlain Deposits (deposited by running water or in glacial lakes)	Windlain Deposits (deposited by the wind)	Ice Deposits (dumped as glacial ice melts)
Bedded	Bedded	Unbedded
Sorted	Sorted (diminish in size and depth with distance from source)	Unsorted
Rounded	Rounded	Mix of angular and rounded
Restricted calibre (sands and gravels)	Restricted calibre (clays to sands)	A very wide range of grain sizes from clays to immensely large masses (e.g., *schollen*: village-sized masses of sediments found in tills of the North German Plain)

till, which consists of fragments ranging in size from fine clay particles to extremely large rocks the size of buses and large masses of frozen sediments. (Compacted and lithified into *tillite*, till provides evidence for the existence of glaciers hundreds of millions of years ago.) The base of the ice is a mosaic of many different depositional environments and many processes are responsible for till deposition. **Ablation till** is composed of debris riding along on the top of the ice or melted out of ogives or dirt bands as the ice melts. Another more technical term being increasingly used for till material is **diamicton** (a sediment composed of a wide range of sizes from very fine to very large). Table 37.3 classifies glacial tills.

Basal till can be deposited in a number of ways depending on the mass, the thermal regime, and the mobility of the ice, as well as on the permeability of the ground. The process of deposition results from very localized subglacial conditions that govern the flow of till and its relation to the ice, e.g., subglacial cavities, the collapse of cavity roofs, deposition around obstacles, etc.

There are two main forms of subglacial deposition. (1) A '*plastering-on*' process occurs when the frictional stress on the basal layer of ice/till/meltwater exceeds the motive force imparted by the ice. This involves a *thixotropic* process similar to that seen in non-drip paint. The material flows when under pressure but is deposited when the pressure is decreased. (2) The *melt out* of debris also occurs from the basal ice, especially in dead or stagnant (cut off from the ice supply) ice. The ice melts from around the debris layer, leaving a film of debris and interstitial ice that eventually melts away.

Both forms of subglacial deposition are characterized by a collection of highly angular clasts and rounded pebbles (derived from older stream or beach deposits) of many different sizes mixed into a fine-grained matrix. The clay matrix is clearly a product of a number of processes. It is dominated by pulverized silica formed by glacial milling (or Cenozoic deep weathering). There is no down-glacier sorting. Fine and coarse material are common throughout the deposits. Fine material is possibly added by continual reworking of the debris and comminution. The fine material seems to be supplied in part by more erodible rock types such as limestones, sandstones, and shales or by weathered rocks. The coarser material supplied by 'softer' rock outcrops is soon broken down to sand and finer material. This seems to suggest that abrasion of the debris takes place in the glacier. The fine material is abundantly present in tills and meltwater deposits (e.g., the 'rock flour' seen in meltwater streams).

Basal Till

Basal till is loaded or compacted because of pressure from the overlying ice mass. The origin of the material forming the till has garnered a lot of discussion over the years. In the past a lot of emphasis was placed on far-travelled (erratic or exotic) material from beyond the immediate area, for example, pebbles of rock types found in the Canadian Shield around Hudson Bay found in tills in southern Ontario. Erratic material occurs in all grain sizes from clay to immense boulders. These far-travelled rock types do not form the bulk (and maybe not the most significant part) of the deposit. In many cases it is difficult to separate and distinguish the till material from subjacent rock types unless there is an intervening bed of sand or gravel. Most of the till material is locally derived. The Halton till (Late Wisconsinan) in Mississauga (just west of Toronto) is an example. The local derivation of the till is seen in its colour. Over the Georgian Bay shale found in the north and east of the city the till is grey- or olive-coloured (the same colour as the bedrock). To the west the till is reddish-brown over the Queenston (red shale) Formation. The local derivation can also be seen by looking at two till deposits in the Toronto area (Table 37.4).

A study of heavy minerals in southern Ontario tills found a wide range of erratic Precambrian material (7.5 per cent to 52.5 per cent). The highest percentage of erratic material occurred between 24 and 64 km south of the geological boundary between the Canadian Shield and Paleozoic sedimentary rocks. The ice sheet obviously moved south across the boundary and deposited most of the Shield rock material soon after. Most tills in southern Ontario had less than 15 per cent Precambrian material. The same study also found 5–20 per cent of pebble samples in all the tills studied were of Precambrian origin (most in the 10–15 per cent range). In most cases the sand and coarse silt fractions were richer in erratic material than the pebbles. It could be that this finer exotic material was derived from the breakdown of Precambrian pebbles in transit (or from preglacial deep weathering of the Shield rocks). A lot of Precambrian material could have been incorporated in the till from the erosion of earlier tills, gravels, and sands of various types.

Table 37.3 The Characteristics of Glacial Tills

Basal Till	Ablation Till
Compacted or loaded	Not compacted or loaded
Looks very much like the subjacent rocks	Appearance not applicable Looks different from local rocks
Higher percentage of fine material	Lower percentage of fine material
Thick (sometimes well over 5 m) and generally of uniform thickness (except near snout of glacier)	Thickness varies (up to 6–7 m deep)
Till fabric orientation, i.e., pebbles oriented in direction of rolling at the base of the ice or left by ice melt as they were moving up shear zones within the ice	No till fabric orientation
	Often separated from basal till by a bed of sand and/or gravel

Table 37.4 Composition of the Clasts in Some Toronto Area Tills: Local and Far-Travelled Deposits

Till	Clast Rock Types (%)			
	Limestone (local)	Dolostone (local)	Shale (local)	Precambrian (from the Canadian Shield)
York Till (Illinoian Glaciation)	22	–	75	3
Sunnybrook Drift* (Wisconsinan Glaciation)	45	12	26	17

*The Sunnybrook Drift may not be a true till. It could be a glaciolacustrine deposit laid down by icebergs in an earlier phase of Lake Ontario. The higher percentage of erratic material in it could be a function of their derivation from older rocks or deposits.

Source: Karrow (1967).

Emphasis has been placed on larger exotic material. It has also been placed on igneous material because it is easier to find the provenance and trace any changes. The character of the erratic material might be of more use to distinguish tills with limestone pebbles from those with high igneous rock pebble content or to distinguish till material from pebble-less bedrock.

In broad terms, the composition of a till reflects the geology of the drainage basin or the immediate area, as shown in Table 37.5. The percentage of each rock type in a till is a function of the way in which that rock type breaks down into pebbles/clasts or fine materials. Of course, very large blocks of rock and masses of frozen sediments can be transported in tills. These *schollen* can have dimensions that exceed 1 km × 1 km × 100 m in depth. Shales reduce very quickly to silts and clays. Limestone weathers by solution, producing very little fine material. Granite and other igneous and metamorphic rocks remain as pebbles or break down to sands and gravels.

The clast material is often very angular, tending to sub-angular. It may become subrounded with distance of travel. One study has shown that about 97 per cent of clasts in a till were disc- or rod-shaped; 75 per cent were discoidal. The degree of rounding is nowhere near that of fluvial or fluvioglacial pebbles. Obviously, some rounded pebbles do occur in some tills because of incorporation from bedrock, fluvial, fluvioglacial, or beach sources. Internal tectonics is seen in tills. Folding and faulting are caused by ice push

over existing till material, differential melting under the ice, the pressure of ice on the active till layer beneath, and isostatic recovery. The response of any till to stress varies with its texture. The effects of interstitial water in clays in till is insignificant, although it can cause structural collapse in sand and gravel materials.

The thickness of till layers is quite diagnostic. For example, in the Toronto area various tills can be easily separated on this basis (Table 37.6).

Over a long period of repeated ice advances and recessions, glacial drift can become very thick, completely burying the underlying bedrock topography. Large areas of the Canadian Prairies, southern Ontario, and the US Midwest are covered by glacial deposits of varying thickness. Some 30 m below the present surface in such areas lies a very different buried landscape, covered now by glacial sediments accumulated during repeated glaciations and deglaciations. Some areas of glacial drift deposits are even thicker, reaching a depth of 60 m; but some areas, notably the part of southwestern Wisconsin known as the **Driftless Area**, were bypassed by the ice sheets and exhibit a rather different landscape. The Driftless Area, which covers ~42,000 km², is also known as the Paleozoic Plateau region. The bedrock is not covered by any glacial tills (hence the name). The rivers are deeply incised into this landscape and there is ample evidence of catastrophic flooding

LINK

Table 37.5 Comparison of Rock Type of Till Pebbles to Geology of the Immediate Area (%), Dartmoor, UK

Rock Type	Till Pebbles	Area
Granite	78.3	82.0
Basic intrusive	8.2	9.6
Metamorphic	9.1	4.4
Quartzite	4.0	2.6
Limestone	0.4	1.4
	100	100

Source: C.P. Green, personal communication, 1973.

Table 37.6 Till Thickness, Toronto Area Tills, North German Plain, and Ohio

Till	Thickness (m)
Halton/Leaside Till	12–15.5
Meadowcliffe Till*	0.80
Sunnybrook Drift*	3.9
York Till (Illinoian Gaciation)	1.8–2.0
North German Plain	58
Ohio	29

*May not be true tills but glaciolacustrine deposits.

Sources: Dreimanis (1961); Karrow (1967).

Table 37.7 Till Matrices, Toronto Area

Till	Matrix Grain Size		
	% Sand	% Silt	% Clay
Halton/Leaside Till	47	33	20
Meadowcliffe Till*	11	35	54
Sunnybrook Drift*	18	37	45
York Till	47	23	30

*May not be true tills but glaciolacustrine deposits.

Sources: Dreimanis (1961); Karrow (1967).

associated with the emptying of Glacial Lake Agassiz on numerous occasions.

Basal tills have an unsorted texture. The grain size distribution of the till matrix is useful in distinguishing different tills. Again, using examples from the Toronto area, Table 37.7 shows the notable distinctions in till matrix of different tills.

The orientation and dip of clasts or pebbles is characteristic of basal tills, which are melted out in situ and are undisturbed. This was first noted about 1860 and discussed in the 1880s. The movement of the depositing ice imparts the orientation and dip of the clasts. Studies have shown that two-thirds of the pebbles have an up-glacier or up-ice dip (one-third have long axes dipping at less than 10°). About 30 per cent have down-glacier or down-ice dips, and roughly 10 per cent are oriented transverse to the ice flow. This considerable scatter occurs because of different clast shapes and sizes and different modes of transport in or under the ice. Pebbles with long axes parallel to ice flow may have slid along shear zones in the ice. Those with long axes transverse to the flow probably rolled along the base of the ice or up shear zones. The dip and orientation may be related to the position of the material in shear zones at the time of deglaciation/melting. Parallel orientation may be due to free-flowing ice, while the transverse pebbles may be related to terminal areas of the ice where wet-based ice was shearing over cold-based (dead) ice.

Ablation Till

Ablation tills are not compacted because they formed from supraglacial material. It is, however, possible that some may have been loaded by ice cover in a subsequent glacial advance. Ablation till has a lower percentage of fine-grained material than basal till. Ablation tills have 25–30 per cent clay in their matrices while basal tills have around 50 per cent. This is because much of the finer material has been washed out by meltwater on the ice surface, while the coarser material has been left. Ablation till is characterized by many striated pebbles. The thickness of the till is quite variable because of slumping and other processes on the surface of the melting ice. It is usually 6–7 m deep. Till fabric orientation is completely messed up because of slumping and slippage over the ice surface and post-depositional deformation. Ablation till is often

separated from basal till by a bed of englacial fluvioglacial sands and gravels.

Geoffrey Boulton and others have argued that the thermal regime of the ice is very important to deposition. Four different subglacial thermal regimes, all of which can occur within one glacier, have been identified:

1. *Basal temperatures favouring a dominance of melting.* In this environment the lodgement of till occurs where frictional drag of the ground surface exceeds the tractive force of the ice. Meltwater at the base of the ice impedes deposition except where there is permeable bedrock. Deposition occurs around small-scale obstacles. These could grow into drumlins (see Unit 38) or, if the process continues, could lead to till sheet formation.

2. *Basal temperatures favouring both freezing and melting.* This is much the same as with a dominance of melting, except there is intermittent freezing or freezing during the winter, which can slow down the processes described above.

3. *Basal temperatures favouring freezing to the subglacial surface.* Ice moving from a temperate (wet-based) environment to a cold base favours erosion because basal material is taken up into shear zones to become englacial or even supraglacial debris, where it will become ablation till or flow till. The basal conditions are not effective in terms of erosion unless any bedrock obstacles are large enough to project into the shear zone. Cold ice is essentially protective but is of prime importance to the creation of shear zones as temperate ice overrides the stationary cold (dead) ice.

4. *Temperatures favouring melting throughout the ice.* If melting dominates throughout the ice the volume of potential till material in the ice may be quite small. This is because less shearing will have occurred because of a lack of basal freezing (cold ice). There is usually some distance between the terminal moraine and other depositional features such as drumlins. This might be linked to the distribution of basal temperature regimes (see Figure 37.9).

The implications of the above are that subglacial conditions are extremely complex and depend on the subglacial thermal regime and the permeability of the subglacial surface.

The dominant aggradational landscape of continental glaciation, therefore, is a flat to undulating plain underlain by heterogeneous material. This landscape is often studded with erratic boulders that were transported far from their source area by the ice sheets.

Moraines

Ice-sheet topography, however, is not always of low relief. Continental ice sheets carry large loads of rock debris in and on their snouts and even push mounds of such debris ahead of them as they advance like a bulldozer (Figure 37.10A). When progress stops, this material is left as a

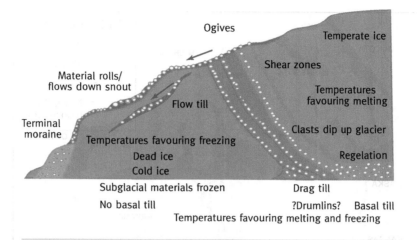

Figure 37.9 Glacier temperature regime. (After Boulton, 1972)

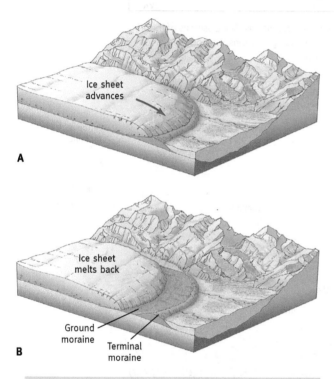

Figure 37.10 A terminal moraine is formed from bull-dozed debris at an advancing ice sheet's front edge and from meltout material falling down the front of the ice (A). When forward glacial movement ends, this debris remains as a ridge after the ice melts back (B).

curving irregular ridge, marking the outline of the farthest extent of the ice lobe (Figure 37.10B). Material also slumps and slides down the snout of the ice and is added to the mix. Such a ridge is called a **terminal moraine**, and many such moraines can be mapped in Canada and the north-central United States. From the properties of the glacial sediments and the positions and relationships of the terminal moraines, geomorphologists have been able to reconstruct and map the glaciations shown by these margins

(Figure 37.11). Many moraines contain mixtures of glacial, fluvioglacial, and lake deposits (e.g., Oak Ridges [Kame] Moraine of southern Ontario).

The term **moraine** is applied to many kinds of glacial features—even material still being carried on a mountain glacier is referred to as *active* moraine. In all glaciers, a *terminal moraine* is distinguished from a **recessional moraine** (see Figure 37.12). A terminal moraine marks the farthest advance of the ice, but a recessional moraine develops when an already receding glacier becomes temporarily stationary. Thus, a receding glacier can form several recessional moraines, but it will leave only one terminal moraine. The term *moraine* also is applied to that extensive blanket of till that is laid down at the base of a melting ice sheet (Figure 37.10B). In this case it is called a **ground moraine** (also known as basal till).

Mountain Glaciers

Above we noted that two large icecaps survive to the present (the Antarctic and Greenland Icecaps) and that several other major continental glaciers and icecaps wasted away with the onset of the Holocene interglacial. Mountain glaciers, too, were larger and much more prevalent before the current interglacial began. Many mountain glaciers melted away and vacated their valleys as the firn line rose and ice formation in their source areas diminished or ceased. But despite the warmth of the present global climate, numerous mountain glaciers endure. Some have not disappeared, but have receded up their formerly occupied valleys, leaving abundant evidence of their earlier advances. This has been especially the case in the last 10–20 years because of global warming. Many glaciers are losing mass at great rates.

Global Distribution

Every major landmass on Earth except Australia contains alpine glaciers. It has been estimated that there are

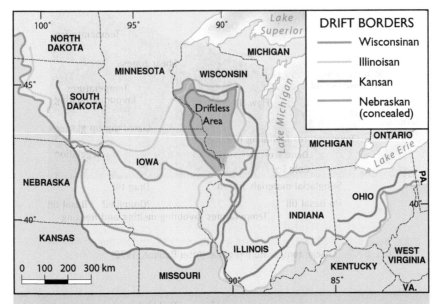

Figure 37.11 Drift margins of the north-central United States. The positions of these terminal moraines indicate that in each of the final four glaciations the continental ice sheet reached a different line of maximum advance.

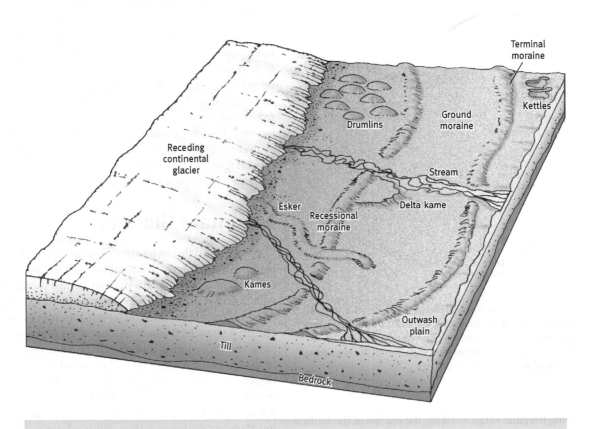

Figure 37.12 Some aggradational landforms associated with a receding ice sheet.

as many as 150,000 individual mountain glaciers in the world today, ranging in size from huge bodies to small narrow ribbons of ice. One of the largest mountain glaciers lies in Antarctica's Queen Maud Mountains, where it feeds the continental icecap. This is the Beardmore Glacier, and it remains a mountain glacier for more than 200 km before it merges into the Antarctic Icecap. The Beardmore Glacier is as much as 40 km wide, vastly larger

Figure 37.13 Peyto Glacier, part of the Wapta Icefield in the Canadian Rockies and about 90 km northwest of Banff, has retreated significantly in recent decades.

Figure 37.14 Peyto Lake, with the characteristic aquamarine colour of alpine glacier-fed lakes, which results from glacial rock flour in the lake, is fed by meltwater from Peyto Glacier, about 5 km north (left in the photograph) of the lake.

than anything seen in the Canadian Rockies, Alaska, or the European Alps.

The remote Beardmore Glacier has been observed by comparatively few people, but other glaciers lie in more accessible areas. Cruise ships visit the Alaskan glaciers where they enter the Gulf of Alaska, and tourists can see active mountain glaciers from the Icefields Parkway in the Canadian Rockies and from their cable-car gondolas or from roads in the French and Swiss Alps. Landscapes produced by alpine glaciation are among our most dramatic and underscore the significance of ice in shaping the surface of the Earth.

North America   Many alpine glaciers lie on the islands that encircle the Arctic Ocean, such as Spitsbergen, Ellesmere Island, and Novaya Zemlya. In North America major clusters of mountain glaciers lie in southeastern Alaska, the Yukon Territory, and the Coast Mountains of British Columbia, and in the Canadian Rocky Mountains along the Alberta–British Columbia border (Figure 37.13).

Equatorward of 50°N latitude, glacier formation becomes less common. The South Cascade Glacier near Mount Rainier in western Washington State is an example of a temperate glacier in a moist maritime environment, where abundant orographic snowfall sustains a glacier despite relatively high summer temperatures. In Colorado, where there is much less snowfall in the Rockies, strong winds create high-elevation snowdrifts deep enough to produce ice formation and maintain small remnant glaciers.

In Canada, the Athabasca Glacier reached its neoglacial maximum in the 1860s. It has retreated over 1.5 km since 1870. The rate of retreat has increased dramatically over the years. Between 1870 and 1938 it was 7.6 m/yr; over the 1938–50 period it retreated 23.33 m/yr; and from 1950 to 1977 its retreat averaged 25.9 m/yr. Since 1980 there have been no consistent studies of retreat. There is an

indication that between 1992 (the last dated plaque) and 2002 it retreated 200 m. But many websites and articles suggest that the rate has increased recently. The neighbouring Saskatchewan Glacier has retreated even more drastically over the same period, but there are no firm data on the rate of retreat. With retreat it has lost a lot of mass. The Peyto Glacier reached its neoglacial maximum in 1840 and has retreated dramatically recently. Since 1966 it has retreated about 800 m and lost 25 per cent of its volume (Figures 37.13 and 37.14).

South America   In South America there are large mountain glaciers in the southern Andes of Chile. These begin just south of latitude 45°S (about the latitude of Montreal in the Northern Hemisphere) and become progressively larger at higher latitudes. At the Strait of Magellan, where the South American mainland ends, glacial ice reaches the sea. As the world map shows, the Antarctic Peninsula reaches towards South America, but much of this peninsula is not covered by the Antarctic Icecap. However, large mountain glaciers descend from the highland backbone of the peninsula (an extension of the Andes Mountains) towards the coasts.

Africa   Africa has high mountains in the far northwest (the Atlas massif) and south (the Drakensberg), but neither of these ranges carries glaciers, although they do receive winter snows. Almost all of Africa's glaciers lie on two soaring volcanoes near the Equator: Mount Kilimanjaro (5861 m) and Mount Kenya (5199 m). Glaciers descend from near the summits of both mountains, and on Mount Kilimanjaro they reach as far down as 4400 m on the south side (see Figure 17.33). There are a dozen small glaciers on Mount Kenya, two of which are still quite substantial, although, like the others, they are receding. Recent studies indicate that the ice cover on both mountains has decreased enormously over the last century. Mount Kilimanjaro has lost 82 per cent of its ice cover since 1912. About one-third of this loss has taken place over the last 12–15 years. If ice loss continues at the same rate the mountain will be ice free by 2025. The largest glacier on Mount Kenya (Lewis Glacier) has decreased in size by 92 per cent over the last 100 years and between 1987 and 2000 the whole mountain lost 39 per cent of its ice cover.

Australia and New Zealand   Australia's mountains are too low to support glaciers, but higher latitude, higher elevation, and greater precipitation combine to sustain large valley glaciers on the South Island of New Zealand. The Southern Alps, the mountain backbone of this island, reach their highest point in Mount Cook (3764 m). In the vicinity of Mount Cook lie another 15 mountains over 3000 m high. The entire mountain range was covered by an icecap in glacial times, and several major glaciers survive in the area of Mount Cook. Among the best known are the Franz Josef Glacier and the Fox Glacier. The Fox Glacier is receding quite rapidly, and its withdrawal is marked by signposts in its lower valley along the road leading to the present glacial margin (Figure 37.15).

Europe   Most of the world's mountain glaciers lie in two major clusters on the Eurasian landmass. Of these

From the Fieldnotes

Figure 37.15 'The Fox Glacier flows westward off New Zealand's Southern Alps. There was a time when this glacier surged into the forested lowlands near the coast, cutting down trees like matchsticks; but today you can walk up a vacated valley to its receding face. The glacier's recession has been monitored for decades, and signposts in the valley mark where it stood years ago. Global warming, reduced snowfall in its catchment area, and possibly other factors as well combine to stagnate this once aggressive glacier. Today morainal deposits in a wide, U-shaped valley evince the Fox Glacier's former power, but the glacier itself is covered by rock rubble, and meltwater streams emanate from its base, feeding small lakes downvalley.'

two, the European Alps are undoubtedly the most famous, and the south-central Asian zone is by far the largest. Much of what is known about the degradational and aggradational work of glaciers was learned through research performed in the European Alps. Europe's Alps extend in a broad arc from southeastern France through the area of the Swiss–Italian border into central Austria (Figure 37.16). Mont Blanc, 4807 m high, is the tallest peak, but several other mountains exceed 4000 m. Active glaciers abound in the Alps, and virtually every erosional and depositional landform associated with glaciation is found there. From the deposits left by the repeatedly advancing glaciers, European scientists deduced the glacial sequence presented in Table 37.1.

Asia The glacial topography of the European Alps is dwarfed, however, by the vast expanse of glacial landscape that extends across the soaring highlands of south-central Asia from Afghanistan to southwestern China

(Figure 37.17). This region was the site of one of the Late Cenozoic's largest icecaps, and tens of thousands of residual glaciers now provide testimony of that phenomenon. The glacial landscape extends from northeastern Afghanistan along the length and breadth of the highlands, marking the boundary between the Eurasian and Indian Plates (see Figure 24.2).

Many of the world's highest mountains—including the tallest of all, Nepal's Mount Everest (Saganatha to Nepalis; Chomuolungma to Tibetans), 8850 m high—lie in this zone. Much of the region still remains buried under ice and snow, and many of the mountain glaciers here are hundreds of metres thick and many kilometres wide. Maximum development occurs in the Himalayan–Tibetan area (Figure 37.17). Vast as the ice and snow cover is, however, there is abundant evidence that here, too, the glaciers have receded during the Holocene: glacial topography and glacial deposits extend far beyond the margins of the present ice.

Figure 37.16 Central Europe's Alps form a gigantic crescent of spectacular mountain ranges. The large lowland they frame just to their south is northern Italy's Po Plain. The Italian peninsula, with its Apennine Mountains backbone, extends seaward from the southern margin of the Po Valley.

Figure 37.17 A space-shuttle view of the Himalayas, looking westward from a point above the easternmost part of India's Ganges Plain. With the Tibetan Plateau to the north (right), they constitute the Earth's most prominent highland zone.

Isolated Remnant Glaciers In addition to the Earth's notable clusters of alpine glaciers, there are isolated glaciers in some places, such as the high-elevation glaciers of equatorial East Africa; similar glacier development also occurs on the highest slopes of the Andes Mountains in tropical-latitude Ecuador and Peru. Remnant glaciers also exist in northern Norway, where latitude, not altitude, supports them. Mount Elbrus, the highest peak in the Caucasus Mountains (between the Black and Caspian Seas along Russia's southern flank), reaches 5642 m and carries several small glaciers. All of these glaciers are surrounded by evidence that they, too, are remnants of larger ones that existed in the past.

Degradational Landforms of Mountain Glaciers

There is no mistaking a landscape sculpted by mountain glaciers, even long after the glaciers have melted away. Mountains, ridges, valleys, and deposits all bear the stamp of the glaciers' erosional or depositional work. Before examining the major landforms created by glacial action, we should review the nature of alpine glaciers' mass balance as well as their appearance and general morphology. The zones of mass accumulation of these glaciers lie on high mountain slopes. There, snow is compacted into ice, and the ice moves downhill under the force of gravity, assisted by basal lubrication in wet-based ice, to occupy valleys formed earlier by stream erosion or other processes. Unlike the surface of an ice sheet, which tends to be snow-white or ice-blue, the surface of a mountain glacier normally is streaked or entirely covered by rock debris.

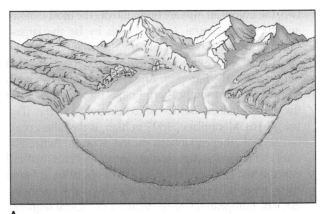

A

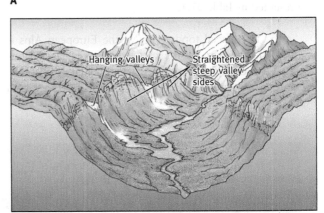

B

C

Figure 37.18 Evolution of a glacial trough. Diagram (A) shows the stage of peak glaciation, with the U-shaped trough gouged out by the trunk glacier that is advancing towards the viewer. When the valley glacier has melted away, truncated spurs and hanging valleys are readily apparent (B). If the glacial trough is near the coast and has been deepened below (rising) sea level, it will become inundated and a fjord will form (C). (After Arthur N. Strahler, copyright Arthur N. Strahler)

Glacial Valleys

A mountain glacier, when it occupies a river valley, immediately begins to change the cross-section and profile of that valley. Glaciers work to widen as well as deepen their valleys, and the typical cross-section of a glacial valley is catenary or U-shaped (Figure 37.18). The U-shaped glacial valley, or **glacial trough**, is one of the most characteristic of the glacial landforms.

Maps and aerial photographs of glacial troughs also reveal other properties of these valleys: they are characterized by straight steep sides. Glaciers are powerful erosional agents that can destroy obstacles in their paths. As a result, many mountainside slopes *around* which rivers once flowed are sheared off by glaciers, thereby straightening the valley course. Such straightened steep slopes (**truncated spurs**) are further evidence of glacial action left in the landscape after the glaciers have melted away (Figure 37.18B).

LINK

When a stream is joined by a tributary, the water surface of both streams is at the same level and the floors of the two valleys tend to be concordant as well. In other words, there is no sharp break between the floor of the main stream valley and that of the tributary valley. But when a smaller glacier joins a larger one, the base of the tributary glacier is not nearly as low, nor the valley as deep, as that of the larger trunk glacier. Their ice surfaces will be at about the same level (as shown in Figure 37.18A), but their bedrock floors are discordant, sometimes by hundreds of metres. When both glaciers melt away, the valley of the tributary glacier, as viewed from the floor of the main glacier, seems to 'hang' high above. Such a discordant junction is appropriately called a **hanging valley** or hanging trough (Figure 37.18B), still another sure sign of the landscape's glacial history. A hanging valley is often graced by a scenic waterfall where the stream now occupying the tributary glacier's valley cascades down the steep valley sides of the main trough.

High-Mountain Landforms

Above the 'trim line' of the glaciated valleys (the highest points affected by glacial erosion), the landscape is generally more rounded and is much like it must have been in preglacial times. This area is called an **alp**. In some mountains the source areas of the glaciers occur above the glacial valleys. There the landscape is also transformed. The series of three block diagrams in Figure 37.19 suggests a possible sequence of events. Initially the landscape consists of rounded ridges and peaks (Figure 37.19A). With the onset of glaciation, deep snow accumulations form on the higher slopes, and the ice subsequently thickens. The ice moves downslope under gravity, and glacial erosion begins (Figure 37.19B).

In the upper area of continuous snow accumulation, the ice hollows out shallow basins, which become the glacier's source area. Not only does the ice excavate such basins, but frost wedging on the walls above them, plus undercutting by headward erosion, also creates distinctive, amphitheatre-like landforms, which are referred to as **cirques** (Figure 37.19C). A cirque is a bowl-shaped, steep-sided depression in the bedrock with a gently sloping floor; many are overdeepened and have a bedrock lip. Two, three, or even more cirques may develop near the top of a mountain. The development of cirques

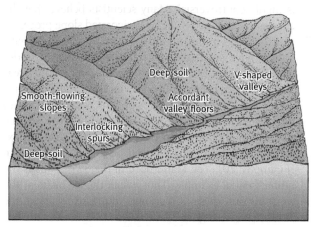

A   BEFORE GLACIATION

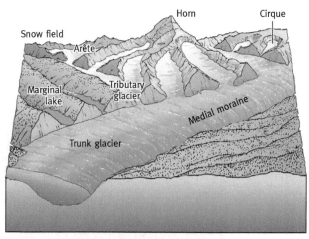

B   DURING GLACIATION

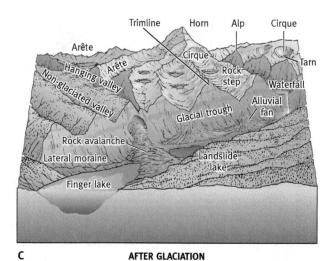

C   AFTER GLACIATION

Figure 37.19 A possible sequence showing the transformation of a mountain landscape by alpine glaciation. Note how the initial rounded ridges and peaks are sculpted into a much sharper-edged topography by frost wedging and glacial erosion.

LINK

is highly controversial. Many scientists believe that the cirques are enlarged more by invigorated slope processes in a cold environment rather than by glacial activity. Others have suggested that cirques could form under large ice sheets that once covered the mountain areas and have later been modified by local ice and slope processes. As the headward erosion proceeds, the cirques intersect, at which point nothing remains of the original rounded mountaintop in the centre of the diagram except a steep-sided, sharp-edged peak known as a **horn** (Figure 37.20). The Matterhorn in the Swiss Alps is the quintessential example. Thus, when the ice melts or the ice thins out, these horns tower impressively above the landscape (see Figure 37.19C).

Other dramatic elements of alpine glacial topography are shown in Figure 37.19C. One such element is the large number of razor-sharp, often jagged ridges that rise above the ice-containing troughs. These ridges often separate adjacent glaciers, cirques, or glacial valleys and are known as **arêtes**. They can develop when two or more large cirques intersect, and form from erosion and frost wedging on the two steep slopes on either side of the ridge.

Another major feature occurs as the glaciers move downslope. They not only straighten their courses, but they also create step-like profiles (valleys emanating forward below the horn in the centre of Figure 37.19C). Such landforms result from a combination of factors. One relates to the differential resistance of various rocks over which the glacier passes. The jointing of the bedrock (and therefore its susceptibility to frost wedging, etc.) also affects this process. In the postglacial landscape, **rock steps** reveal the local effects of such glacial erosion. (Interestingly, stepped long profiles are characteristic of both tropical streams and streams in once glaciated areas, such as Canada.)

From the Fieldnotes

Figure 37.20 '*Boarded a two-seater airplane to fly from the airstrip at Whataroa (on New Zealand's South Island) up the Franz Josef Glacier towards the Mount Cook area in the Southern Alps. This scenery seems even more spectacular than the "real" Alps. How I wish that I could have my whole physical geography class with me here—what a matchless laboratory! This view of a basin-shaped, snow-accumulating, ice-generating cirque also reveals a developing* horn *(right background) and a sharp-edged* arête *(left foreground).*'

Lakes

As in the case of continental glaciers, depressions gouged by alpine glaciers are filled by water during interglacials such as the present period. Where the climate is warm enough so that even high-altitude cirques are no longer filled with snow, small circular lakes are found on the floors of the cirque basins. These lakes, dammed up behind the 'lip' of the cirque, are known as **tarns** (one is labelled in the upper far right of Figure 37.19C). Sometimes the floors of cirque basins have wetlands or bogs rather than lakes. Lakes also may form on the rock steps previously described, as again shown in those three valleys below the horn in the central portion of Figure 37.19C. Some of these lakes are impounded by slope failure debris or by moraines. There may be a sequence of lakes separated by streams with rapids and waterfalls (as the stream tumbles down a step). From above, the drainage looks like a section of a bead necklace. The largest lakes fill substantial parts of glacial troughs, as the lower left of the diagram shows. Such lakes may be several kilometres wide and 50 km or more long and are called **finger lakes**. Some of the world's most scenic lakes, from the Rockies, the Swiss Alps, and the Southern Alps of New Zealand, owe their origins to glacial erosion.

Fjords

Among the most spectacular landforms associated with glacial erosion are fjords. A **fjord** is a narrow, steep-sided, elongated estuary (drowned river mouth) formed from a glacial trough inundated by seawater (see Figure 37.18C). Many fjords have been flooded by rise in sea level during the early part of the Holocene. During glaciations many glaciers reach the ocean. Ice has a density about five-sixths that of seawater, so a glacier reaching the ocean can continue to erode a valley many metres below sea level. Thus, vigorously eroding glaciers created seaward troughs. Fjords developed mainly in places where glaciated mountains are near a coastline, such as in British Columbia, parts of Nova Scotia and Newfoundland (Figure 37.21), southern Alaska, and western Norway. Other famous and scenic fjords lie along the southwestern coasts of Chile and on New Zealand's South Island.

Aggradational Landforms of Mountain Glaciers

As components of scenery, the depositional landforms of alpine glaciers are no match for the erosional features just discussed and illustrated. Some of the debris carried downslope is ground into particles so fine that this is called **rock flour**, and when the glacier melts and deposits this rock flour, much of it is blown away by the wind or is carried away by streams and ends up in lakes, giving the water an aquamarine colour, as in Moraine Lake, Peyto

Figure 37.21 This freshwater fjord at Western Brook Pond, Gros Morne National Park, Newfoundland, was cut off from the sea after the last ice age.

Lake, and other lakes in the Rockies. Larger fragments, as in the case of continental glaciers, are deposited at the (stalled) edge of the advancing glacier as *terminal moraines*. Again, as with continental glaciers, stationary periods during a glacier's retreat are marked by *recessional moraines* (see Figure 37.12). Terminal and recessional moraines lie as low ridges across the valley floor. These mounds can form dams that impound meltwater, creating permanent or temporary glacial lakes and associated glaciofluvial features (see Unit 38).

Moraines

Debris carried by an alpine glacier comes not only from the valley floor it erodes but also from slope processes on the valley sides above the glacial ice. Frost wedging, the repeated freezing and thawing of water in rock cracks and joints, loosens pieces of bedrock (see Figure 29.8). These fall onto the glacier's surface along the margins of the ice, where they become part of bands of debris called **moraines** (the same term used in relation to ice sheets, discussed above, but with a somewhat different meaning here). The vigorously eroding glacier also tends to undercut its valley sides so that mass movement contributes additional material to the glacial surface.

Material that falls from the valley wall first becomes part of the glacier's **lateral moraines**, the moraines situated along the edges of the ice (Figure 37.22). When a trunk glacier is joined by a substantial tributary glacier or dams another glacier, their lateral moraines join to become a **medial moraine**, which is situated away from the glacier's edges. This pattern may be repeated several times as additional tributary glaciers enter the trunk glacier.

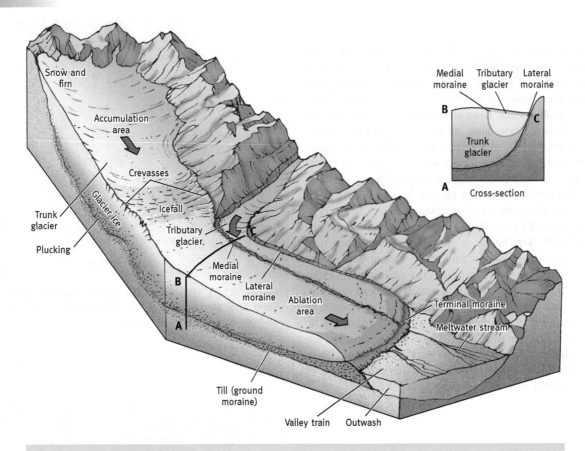

Figure 37.22   Cutaway view of a valley glacier and one of its tributaries, showing depositional features. Note the positions of the lateral, medial, and terminal moraines. When the glacier recedes, the till on the valley floor behind the terminal moraine is left behind as a ground moraine.

Furthermore, as shown in Figure 37.22, erosion at the base of the valley glacier creates till or **ground moraine** (in this case the term has the same connotation as for ice sheets). The ground moraine is exposed on the floor of the glacial trough as the ice recedes, and is thickened by the deposition of the contents of the melting, debris-laden glacier. Recession of the valley glacier will also result in the deposition of the lateral and medial moraines, which form irregular ridges and mounds of unsorted material.

Postglacial Landscape Change

Stream action begins to modify the aggradational landforms in glacial troughs as soon as the glaciers vacate them. When meltwater starts to fill the valley floor with deposits derived from the morainal material left behind, the new deposit is known as a sandur (plural sandar) or valley train (Figure 37.22). Modification of the glacial deposits (not the bedrock topography) usually is quite rapid (paraglacial erosion). Glacial lakes are drained,

material is sorted and redistributed fluvioglacially, and vegetation recovers.

Glacial topography is scenic, and it attracts countless sightseers and tourists to ski lodges and other highland resorts. But as the foregoing has made clear, glaciated areas are not stable. The glaciers retreated from valleys with oversteepened walls. Frost wedging loosened huge quantities of rock, much of it perched precariously on steep slopes. Snow accumulations can lead to avalanches that would be harmless in remote terrain, but are often fatal when humans populate these landscapes. Mass movements of various kinds form a significant natural hazard in alpine-glaciated regions, as the large rock avalanche and its dammed lake suggest in the lower central portion of Figure 37.19C. Many of the slopes in the Rockies and Coast Mountains and in other alpine areas are undergoing *relaxation* to today's conditions—the ice that once kept the slopes up has gone and so there are lots of slope failures that produce talus, or scree, slopes and reduce these unstable oversteepened slope angles.

Canadian Geographers in the Field

'This photo shows a large igneous glacial erratic, near Rio Grande, northern Tierra del Fuego, Argentina. This erratic was transported eastward from the Darwin Mountains in Chile. Although there are no other glacial landform features on the landscape, the presence of this erratic indicates that the area was glaciated. By dating the buildup of cosmogenic radioisotopes on the surface, resulting from bombardment by solar insolation, the time of glacial deposition can be determined. This technique is essentially analogous to looking at a suntan; we are determining how long the erratic has been exposed to solar insolation. Weathering is extremely slow in the dry climate of northern Tierra del Fuego.'

Norm Catto is Professor of Geography, Memorial University.

KEY TERMS

ablation till   *page 524*
alp   *page 533*
Antarctic Icecap   *page 515*
arête   *page 534*
basal (lodgement) till   *page 523*
calving   *page 517*

cirque   *page 533*
diamicton   *page 524*
Driftless Area   *page 525*
finger lakes   *page 535*
fjord   *page 535*
flow regime   *page 516*

glacial trough   *page 533*
Greenland Icecap   *page 519*
ground moraine   *page 527*
hanging valley   *page 533*
horn   *page 534*
icecap   *page 515*

REVIEW QUESTIONS

1. What is the approximate size (area and thickness) of the Antarctic Icecap?

2. Name the three northern hemisphere Pleistocene ice sheets and their major geographic dimensions.

3. What is the difference between tills, moraines, and erratics?

4. What is the difference between basal and ablation tills in terms of origin and deposition?

5. What are the two regions that contain the greatest concentration of mountain glaciers?

6. In what way does a glacial trough differ in shape from a stream valley?

7. What is a hanging valley and how does it form?

8. What is a fjord and how is it formed?

REFERENCES AND FURTHER READINGS

Benn, D.I., and D.J.A. Evans. 1998. *Glaciers and Glaciation*. New York: Oxford Univ. Press.

Bird, J.B. 1980. *The Natural Landscapes of Canada: A Study of Regional Earth Science*, 2nd edn. Toronto: Wiley.

Boulton, G.S. 1972. 'Modern Arctic Glaciers as Depositional Models for Former Ice Sheets', *Journal of the Geological Society* (London) 128: 361–93.

————. 1972. 'The Role of Thermal Regime in Glacial Sedimentation', in R.J. Price and D.E. Sugden, eds, *Polar Geomorphology*. London: Institute of British Geographers Special Publication 4, 1–19.

Chapman, L.J., and D.F. Putnam. 1984. *The Physiography of Southern Ontario*. Toronto: Government of Ontario, Ontario Geological Survey Special Vol. 2.

Crossley, L. 1995. *Explore Antarctica*. New York: Cambridge Univ. Press.

Cullen, N.J., et al. 2006. 'Kilimanjaro Glaciers: Recent Aerial Extent from Satellite Data and New Interpretation of 20th Century Retreat Rates', *Geophysical Research Letters* 33, L16502, doi:10.1029/2006GL027084.

Dreimanis, A. 1961. 'Tills of Southern Ontario', in R.F. Legget, ed., *Soils in Canada*. Royal Society of Canada Special Publication 3. Toronto: Univ. of Toronto Press, 80–96.

Drewry, D. 1986. *Glacial Geological Processes*. London: Edward Arnold.

Embleton, C., and C.A.M. King. 1975. *Glacial Geomorphology*. London: Edward Arnold.

Evans, R. 1996. *The Geography of Glaciers*. New York: Wiley.

Eyles, C.H., N. Eyles, and T.E. Day. 1983. 'Sedimentologic and Paleomagnetic Characteristics of Glaciomarine Diamict Assemblages at Scarborough Bluffs, Ontario, Canada', in E.B. Evenson, R. Rabassa, and C. Shluchter, eds, *Tills and Related Sediments*. Rotterdam: A.A. Balkema, 23–45.

Fitzgerald, D.M., and P.S. Rosen, eds. 1987. *Glaciated Coasts*. Orlando, Fla: Academic Press.

Hambrey, M., and J. Alean. 1992. *Glaciers*. New York: Cambridge Univ. Press.

Hughes, T.J. 1998. *Ice Sheets*. New York: Oxford Univ. Press.

Ives, J.D., ed. 1994. *Mountains*. Emmaus, Penn.: Rodale Press.

Karrow, P.F. 1967. *Pleistocene Geology of the Scarborough Area*. Ontario Department of Mines Geological Report 46. Toronto: Ontario Department of Mines.

Long, P. 2002. 'Geomorphic Journey: Evolution of the Mississauga Landscape', in F.A. Dieterman, ed., *Mississauga: The First 10,000 Years*. Toronto: East End Books and Mississauga Heritage Foundation, 3–17.

Matsch, C.L. 1976. *North America and the Great Ice Age*. New York: McGraw-Hill.

Ouma, Y.O., and R. Tateishi. 2005. 'Optical Satellite-Sensor Band Monitoring of Ice Coverage Fluctuations on Mt Kenya 1987–2000', *International Journal of Environmental Studies* 62, 6: 663–75.

Owne, L.A., et al. 1998. *Polar and Alpine Geomorphology*. Malden, Mass.: Blackwell.

Paterson, W.S.B. 1981. *The Physics of Glaciers*, 2nd edn. Elmsford, NY: Pergamon.

Penck, A., and E. Bruckner. 1909. *Die Alpen in Eiszeitalter* (The Alps in the Ice Age). Leipzig.

Pielou, E.C. 1991. *After the Ice Age: The Return of Life to Glaciated North America*. Chicago: Univ. of Chicago Press.

Post, A., and E.R. Lachapelle. 1971. *Glacier Ice*. Seattle: The Mountaineers.

Price, L.W. 1981. *Mountains and Man: A Study of Process and Environment*. Berkeley: Univ. of California Press.

Roberts, N. 1998. *The Holocene*, 2nd edn. Malden, Mass.: Blackwell.

Ryder, J.M. 1981. 'Geomorphology of the Southern Part of the Coast Mountains of British Columbia', *Zeitschrift für Geomorphologie* Supplementband 37: 120–47.

————. 1998. *Geomorphological Processes in the Alpine Areas of Canada*. Ottawa: Geological Survey of Canada Bulletin 524.

Sugden, D.E.. 1982. *Arctic and Antarctic: A Modern Geographical Synthesis*. Totowa, NJ: Rowman & Littlefield.

———— and B.S. John. 1976. *Glaciers and Landscape: A Geomorphological Approach*. New York: Wiley.

Syvitski, J.P.M., et al. 1987. *Fjords: Processes and Products*. New York/Berlin: Springer-Verlag.

Teller, J.T., et al. 2002. 'Freshwater Outbursts from Glacial Lake Agassiz and Their Role in Climate Change during the Last Deglaciation', *Quaternary Science Reviews* 21, 8–9: 879–87.

Theakstone, W.H., et al. 1994. *Glaciers and Environmental Change*. Sevenoaks, UK: Edward Arnold.

Titus, J.G., and C. Richman. 2001. 'Maps of Lands Vulnerable to Sea Level Rise in the US', *Climate Research* 18, 3: 205–28.

Trenhaile, A.S. 1998. *Geomorphology: A Canadian Perspective*. Toronto: Oxford Univ. Press.

Williams, R.S., Jr, and D.K. Hall. 1993. 'Glaciers', in R.J. Gurney, J.L. Foster, and C.L. Parkinson, eds, *Atlas of Earth Observations Related to Global Change*. New York: Cambridge Univ. Press, 114–23.

———— and J.G. Ferrigno. 1991. 'Cold Beauty: Rivers of Ice', *Earth Magazine* (Jan.): 42–9.

———— and J.G. Ferrigno, eds. 1988. *Satellite Image Atlas of Glaciers of the World*. Reston, Va: US Geological Survey, Professional Paper 1386 A-K.

Wilson, R.C.L., S.A. Drury, and J.A. Chapman, eds. 2000. *The Great Ice Age: Climate Change and Life*. London/New York: Routledge.

 WEB RESOURCES

atlas.gc.ca/site/english/maps/climatechange/potentialimpacts/coastalsensitivitysealevelrise Maps of coastal sensitivity to sea-level rise for all coasts of Canada.

tapestry.usgs.gov/features/39moraines.html This US Geological Survey page is devoted to recessional moraines and places subsequent landform formation on a geologic timeline. There are links to the Pleistocene ice sheet and various geological epochs.

www.geocities.com/goodlordtom/prehistory.html This page focuses on aggradational landform building, including the prehistory of Switzerland and the formation of the Alps. Colour graphics and photographs illustrate the process.

www.virtualmuseum.ca/Exhibitions/Fjord/english/f_formation_e.html This page describes formation of the Saguenay fjord in Canada, and has detailed graphics of the formation process.

Unit 38

Fluvioglacial Processes, Deposits, and Landforms

Objectives

- To understand the importance of erosion and deposition caused by meltwater.

- To recognize the impact of meltwater floods on the landscape.

- To appreciate the impact of large discharges of meltwater on the climate.

LINK

Fluvioglacial processes relate to meltwater streams flowing on, in, and under glacial ice and emerging from the margins of a glacier or an ice sheet. The processes involved are very much the same as those seen in the fluvial environment in regard to erosion, transport and deposition, channel slope, and channel plan (fluvioglacial channels are usually braided). But different factors control the pattern of activity. These involve:

- the seasonal and diurnal freezing and melting of glacial ice;
- the damming of waters and bursting of ice and/or sediment dams in the glacial meltwater plumbing system (on, in, and under the ice);
- the buildup of water in cavities in glacial ice caused by excessive melting, a result of increased temperature or rainfall, or of geothermal or volcanic heat; and
- the ponding of meltwater on the sandur or on the valley bottom and breaching of moraine or other types of dams.

All of these factors increase the volume of water in supraglacial, englacial, and/or subglacial meltwater tunnels and in proglacial streams and lakes at various points in the year. Some glaciers and icecaps are (as, presumably, ice sheets were) subject to periodic and catastrophic glacial burst floods, or **jökulhlaups** (or debâcles). A massive jökulhlaup was triggered by a volcanic eruption under the Vatnajökull Icefield in Iceland in 1996. The flood lasted for about 15 hours and its peak discharge was about 55,000 m³/s. This event caused the complete reworking of the Skeiðarársandur and moved and deposited an immense amount of sediment. Film of the event shows stone blocks of 500 tonnes and greater being rolled in the flow and ice-rafted in the flood.

Evidence of Fluvioglacial
 # Erosion
LINK

At the smallest scale of fluvioglacial erosion are forms called plastic moulding features. These occur where the bedrock surface has been smoothed by the passage of meltwater under hydrostatic pressure under the ice mass. These features suggest that meltwater is capable of a high degree of smoothing, fluting, and channelling of a surface because of the very high water velocities and turbulence associated with meltwater flowing under a glacier. The implosion of air bubbles in the turbulent flow causes shock waves in the bed of fluvioglacial channels. These shock waves can aid erosion and can cause the rapid erosion of surfaces of considerable size in subglacial channels. Added to this, the large sediment load (sands and fine gravels) carried by the streams is erosive and smoothing, rather like sandpaper or emery cloth. This smoothing is evidence for the existence of subglacial meltwater flow and streams. The smoothing is often associated with gouges and other markings made by the sediment carried by the water.

Larger-scale evidence is afforded by channels associated with the ice margins. Two types of channels can be distinguished:

1. Meltwater channels (chutes) are intimately associated with the ice and ice margin. These include tunnel valleys and channels associated with esker deposits.
2. Spillways are related to relic proglacial lakes, and are not immediately related to the ice margin.

The form of the meltwater channels and their position in the landscape distinguish them from fluvially eroded channels. Sometimes they have an anomalous relationship to the fluvial system and the post-glacial relief as a whole. Often, these channels may run obliquely to the contours of the land or cut across them, and many of these channels have caused the dissection of glacial valleys and bear no relation to the pre-existing relief. These chutes can occur more or less parallel to each other but in other cases their arrangement is extremely complex. Some of the chute channels have an abrupt termination, indicating that meltwater streams flowed off the ice and onto the bedrock of the valley sides in places when ice filled the valley. In some cases the ice acted much the same way as rock, and hence the very extraordinary positions of some of the channels once the ice is gone.

Tunnel valleys or channels can be cut in sediment and/or bedrock. Unlike fluvial valleys, they are trough-shaped with steep terminations at both ends. They seem to form subglacially where meltwater under hydrostatic pressure (and with a considerable load of sediment) cuts down into the sediments or bedrock at the glacier bed. There are examples of tunnel valleys in the Great Lakes area (e.g., the Dundas Valley, found north of and running north–south under parts of the Oak Ridges Moraine; some bedrock valleys of streams in the Toronto area; and bedrock valleys in the Finger Lakes area of New York State). The tunnel valleys under the Oak Ridges Moraine are of considerable size—up to 5 km wide, 40 km long, and over 100 m deep.

The Origin of the Meltwater Channels

Meltwater channels could have been developed by superimposition, or the streams were gradually let down from on top of or within the ice as the ice melted (which would explain the anomalous terminations and undulating long profiles of channels), or by subglacial formation (hard to distinguish from fluvial channels except where they have uphill sections). It is likely (from observations of contemporary glaciers and from inference) that several meltwater channels were active at one time at different points along the ice margins, some ice-marginal, some englacial, and some subglacial. The older literature believed that these features were all ice-marginal and therefore a chronology of ice melt could be based on the position of these channels.

Spillway Channels

Spillway channels were carved out by the overflow or breaching of **proglacial lakes**. Therefore, they were not intimately linked to the ice margin and could be tens or hundreds of kilometres away from the ice front. These spillways developed as meltwater in proglacial lakes that broke through or discharged over low points (cols) in moraine ridges or other ridges (e.g., escarpments), or resulted when ice dams were breached or burst open from the pressure of meltwaters.

The older literature, spanning the years of about 1900 to 1940, emphasized the existence of extensive proglacial lakes in Europe and North America to account for fairly flat terrain or the reversal or diversion of drainage. Many of these lakes were 'theoretical', however, in that there was no evidence in the form of sediments or features such as bluffs, beaches, or deltas to suggest the existence of a lake. Nonetheless, there is evidence for large proglacial lakes in many parts of North America (e.g., Lake Agassiz, Lake Missoula) and for various high-stand phases of the Great Lakes. Lakes were impounded in areas of the Prairies and in valleys in the interior of BC. Today, proglacial lakes tend to be rather small, but a number of quite large lakes are impounded by the Barnes Icecap on Baffin Island. Conn and Beiler Lakes are the largest of these (Figure 38.1).

In many cases, the ice margins of proglacial lakes may have been composed of active, wet-based (permeable) thick ice that would have permitted water to drain through the ice or drain back under the ice rather than impound a lake. Present-day proglacial lakes are always associated with lake sediments, beaches, bluffs, and/or deltaic accumulations. Where meltwater is intimately related to the ice margin, unique depositional features occur. These are called eskers and kames.

LINK

Meltwater

LINK

Meltwater discharge from glaciers and ice sheets varies in two ways: diurnally and seasonally. Diurnal fluctuations reflect air temperature and the pattern of daily ice ablation. Discharge is usually low in the early morning and rises to a maximum in the late afternoon or early evening. This variation is suppressed during the winter but increases towards late summer when the daily ablation rate reaches its maximum. Seasonal variations also are dramatic. They reflect the importance of two factors: the seasonality of ablation, and the seasonal development of the (wet-based) glacier's internal drainage (or plumbing) system.

Seasonal Drainage Development and Discharge from Ice

LINK

It is possible to trace drainage and discharge through the various seasons:

1. *Spring melt*. Ablation of the winter snow cover begins on the glacier surface. Consequently, water pressure starts to build up in the glacier. In front of the glacier the ice covering proglacial lakes and/or streams (*aufeis*) starts to break up and there is the rapid melting of winter snow.
2. *Late spring melt*. Ablation of the winter snow is well advanced on the glacier. There is rising discharge in all meltwater channels, tunnels, and pipes. The conduits grow in size and the internal drainage system develops. The amount of water within the glacier

Figure 38.1 Terra MODIS image of the Barnes Icecap, Baffin Island, showing several proglacial lakes, the largest of which are Conn and Bieler Lakes.

exceeds the ability of the drainage network to discharge it. This may cause the glacier to surge as water builds up under the ice. Discharge from the glacier steadily increases into the proglacial stream system.

3. *Early summer*. Much of the stored water in the glacier is released as the development of a well-integrated plumbing system in and under the ice takes place. The daily discharge exceeds the amount of daily melting and in the course of a few weeks the drainage system of the glacier releases a vast majority of its total annual discharge ('nival flood').

4. *Late summer*. The glacier plumbing system has reached its optimum efficiency. All the stored meltwater has been discharged so that the daily discharge is equal to the daily ablation. Water pressure in the glacier is usually close to, or at, a minimum.

5. *Autumn*. The end of the melt season means a drastic drop in discharge. The internal drainage system in the ice begins to collapse as meltwater flow drops and tunnels and pipes close up due to pressure of the ice mass and ice deformation. Only a few major arteries contain enough flow to remain open.

6. *Winter*. The amount and timing of the closing down of the plumbing system in and under the glacier depend on the climate and the severity of the winter. Most meltwater discharge (if any) occurs because of internal melting, or in some cases geothermal or volcanic heat at the base of the ice. The degree of the collapse of the drainage system is highly variable from year to year because of temperature differences and other factors.

In some glaciers the pattern of daily and seasonally changing discharges is interrupted by catastrophic events called *jökulhlaups* (glacial burst floods, megafloods, dumping, or debâcles). These are very high-magnitude events, often several orders of magnitude greater than the normal peak floods. They may occur in one of four ways:

1. Intense melting and/or rainfall.
2. Enlargement of the pre-existing glacier plumbing network under an ice dam because of an increase of meltwater flow, which is caused by the passage of supercooled water.
3. Subglacial geothermal or volcanic activity, as in the case of the Gjalp event of 1996 in Iceland.
4. The catastrophic drainage of ice-dammed or moraine-dammed lakes resulting from: a thinning ice dam (caused by undermining by supercooled water or surface melting); water pressure floating the ice dam; an earthquake cracking the ice dam; or the friction of overflowing water melting an ice dam or overflowing water cutting through a moraine dam.

Eighty-three per cent of the world's subglacial eruptions occur in Iceland and all of these cause the catastrophic melting of basal ice and consequently flooding. Jökulhlaups affect the three major streams draining across the Skeiðarársandur, the largest sandur in

Figure 38.2 Satellite photo of Iceland's Vatnajökull Icecap, which covers about 8000 km² and, at its thickest, is 950–1000 m. Skeiðarársandur is the dark area to the south (below) the icecap. The sandur is subject to many jökulhlaups from a subglacial lake called Grimsvötn.

Iceland (about 1300 km²). It is located in southeastern Iceland. The meltwater streams supplied by melting ice in this area are the most studied *jökulsas*. These events occur because of meltwater building up to form an immense subglacial lake in a large (6 × 8 km) caldera (Grimsvötn or Sviagigar). The meltwater is created by surface melting (25 per cent) and by geothermal and volcanic heat (75 per cent), as in the Gjalp event of 1996. As the lake level rises it lifts the Vatnajökull Icecap (Figure 38.2) up slightly and allows the meltwater to flow along a 50-km-long subglacial tunnel system that connects the lake to the sandur. The meltwater takes about five to six years to build up to a point where it can float the icecap and cause the flooding. The volume of the caldera lake is ~3.5 km³, and if this is exceeded flooding occurs. The buildup of water under the ice is usually accompanied by a glacial surge. It takes 10 hours for meltwater to travel through the subglacial tunnel system from Grimsvötn to the sandur. At the snout of the ice the water rises up almost vertically to the sandur surface. The average discharge during the jökulhlaups is between 3.0 and 3.5 km³ but much larger events have occurred; a 1922 flood had a discharge of approximately 7.1 km³, while the 1996 Gjalp flood was 3.2 km³. The Gjalp flood was four to five times greater than the magnitude of the Mississippi floods of 1993 that devastated the US Midwest.

Many glaciers and glacially related lakes in the Rockies and the Coast Mountains of BC are subject to this process. The hydrographs for jökulhlaups are very unusual (see Figure 38.3).

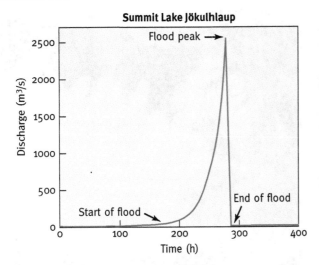

Figure 38.3 Typical hydrograph of a jökulhlaup, Summit Lake, BC.

Figure 38.5 The Norwood Esker forms a ridge on both sides of Highway 7 near Norwood, to the east of Peterborough, Ontario. Aggregate companies utilize the esker for sand and gravel for the construction industry.

Fluvioglacial Landforms

Eskers

Eskers are long sinuous mounds of sands and gravels mainly deposited by supraglacial, englacial, and subglacial meltwater streams. Frequently, lake sediments are part of these features. They may exhibit braiding and esker 'ox-bows' (Figure 38.4). The crests of many eskers undulate and some features exhibit 'beading' in planview (i.e., seen from above as on a map or in plan). Eskers can be related to meltwater channels in a number of ways—they are found within meltwater channels or as continuations of them. Some eskers are very large: more or less continuous features several hundreds of km long, up to about 0.5 km wide, and between 40 and 50 m high. There are many eskers in southern Ontario, including the Brampton Esker (~2.5 km long). Numerous eskers are found in the area surrounding Peterborough (Figures 38.5 and 38.6): the Norwood Esker, east of Peterborough, extends 32 km; the Codrington Esker, southeast of Peterborough and north of Brighton, is over 65 km in length. One of the longest eskers in northern Ontario is 249 km long and is located between Cochrane and Kirkland Lake. The Munro Esker (also in northern

Ontario) is 250 km long and about 5 km wide. The Thelon Esker of the NWT–Nunavut is 800 km long.

Small esker features have been seen developing at the limits of modern glaciers but these are only about 10 m long, a few metres high, and are often ice-cored. Eskers are commonly found within the terminal moraine, sometimes extending over drumlinized areas. The materials forming them are coarse sands and gravels with boulders up to 1.25 m in diameter. The material is sub-rounded. The gravels are usually imbricated with an upstream dip. The fabric may be confused at the margins because of slumping and collapse. This is caused by the removal of the support of the ice channel or tunnel ice walls as melting took place or as the ice core of the feature melted. No satisfactory observations of the formation process have been undertaken. The development of eskers seems to takes place in a number of ways:

1. The form of the features suggests that they developed as englacial or subglacial sands and gravels that infilled pipes or tunnels (conduits) in dead ice (like many of the eskers in south-central Ontario).
2. Some occur on water-worn surfaces that run uphill, which also suggests they were deposited by water under hydrostatic pressure and therefore have a subglacial origin.
3. There is an accordance of esker summits in some areas that seems to suggest the influence of a water table within the ice mass.
4. Other eskers seem to suggest that formation occurred in channels between masses of dead ice.
5. Small-scale eskers have been observed developing as deltas of meltwater streams flowing into proglacial lakes in Canada and Norway. Such development is related to the melting-back of the ice front, and could account for the 'beaded' planform shape of some eskers. Many of these features are ice-cored and subsequently collapse as the ice melts. The deltaic origin would account for the lacustrine deposits found in many eskers (e.g., the Codrington Esker north of Brighton, Ontario).

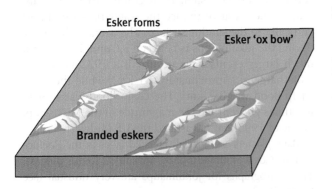

Figure 38.4 Esker forms: 'oxbow' and braiding.

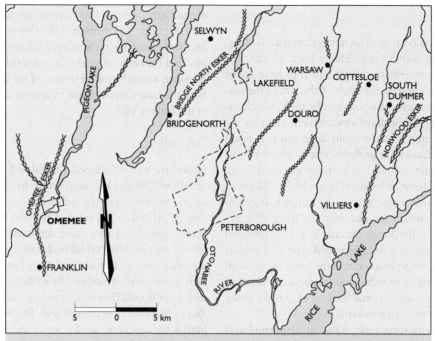

Figure 38.6 Eskers in the Peterborough, Ontario, area are principally oriented in the direction of the ice flow and meltwater flow of Pleistocene glaciation.

Canadian Geographers in the Field

'While mapping the bedrock geology north of Yellowknife, Northwest Territories, for the Geological Survey of Canada, my field crew and I set up camp on this small beach derived from the esker immediately behind it. This area has become famous since the discovery of diamonds in the Lac de Gras area just to the east. The eskers were deposited from rivers flowing below glaciers covering the area during the Late Wisconsinan glaciation that receded in this area about 8000–10,000 years ago. Geologists found minerals associated with diamonds in the eskers and followed the eskers back to find the diamond deposits, which today make Canada one of the largest diamond producers.'

Blair Hrabi has a B.Sc. (McMaster University) and M.Sc. (Queen's University) in geology and studies the geochemical composition of volcanic rocks and the structural evolution of Precambrian rocks in the Canadian Shield. He is now a senior geologist at SRK Consulting Engineers & Scientists, Toronto.

Kames

The term **kame** has been used for any accumulation of fluvioglacial material without any definite linear extent. The margins of kames are usually quite steep. They have slopes of 30 to 40° depending on the angle of the rest of the material. Many kames are cut across by channels, which indicate a changing depositional environment close to the ice front. Some kame forms are quite large and may reach 10 m in height. Kames are probably responsible for most of the sandur material found in formerly glaciated areas. Many eskers terminate in kames (Figure 38.7A). Much of the material is fairly coarse and locally derived. It exhibits variations that reflect the changing discharge of water and load. Much of the kame material is poorly rounded and unsorted, suggesting a disorganized type of transport and deposition. Contortions occur in the kame fabric, with some kames having large subsidence depressions (kettles) caused by the post-depositional melting of chunks of ice incorporated into the kame material.

The kame and kettle topography is also called **thermokarst** because it looks somewhat like the result of solution subsidence or pitted topography. Lakes or wetlands are often found in kettles (kettle lakes or kettle bogs). The incorporation of blocks of ice into the kame material suggests that kames have an ice-marginal or possibly subglacial origin. The most probable explanation is that they represent sands and gravels that melted out of the ice (ablation till material) and slid and sludged down the margin of the ice, creating cones or ramparts of material as the ice front melted down and retreated. The Oak Ridges (Interlobate) Moraine

of southern Ontario (160 km long, up to 20 km wide, with the crest over 300 m above Lake Ontario) is considered to be a kame moraine rather than a terminal moraine. It accumulated between tongues of southward-flowing Late Wisconsinan ice and another tongue of ice flowing northwards from the Lake Ontario basin (responsible for the deposition of the Halton Till).

Drumlins

Drumlins are oval-shaped streamlined hills (steep on the up-glacier end and less steep on the lee end), which are also called 'whalebacks'. They are one of the most controversial features related to glaciation. Until about 20 years ago scientists agreed that they were deposited and formed as ice moved over and shaped till and other materials. Many geomorphologists in Canada and elsewhere now believe they were formed and streamlined by erosion caused by subglacial meltwater floods. Drumlins appear to occur beneath the Oak Ridges Moraine at its eastern end. Drumlins can be formed from a bedrock core, sandur sands and gravels, till, or mixtures of these elements. Some drumlins have bedrock at one end and sands and gravels or till at the other. In all cases they have a veneer of ablation till, rather like chocolate covering different kinds of nuts or candy. The size varies considerably from 0.1 to 8 km in length, 50 m to 2 km wide, and 5 to 30 m high. The size is fairly uniform within individual fields, or swarms, as is the spacing. It has been noted that drumlins at the bottom of valleys tend to be more elongated.

Drumlin fields are found all over Canada, but especially in Nova Scotia, the Thelon Plain of Nunavut and the

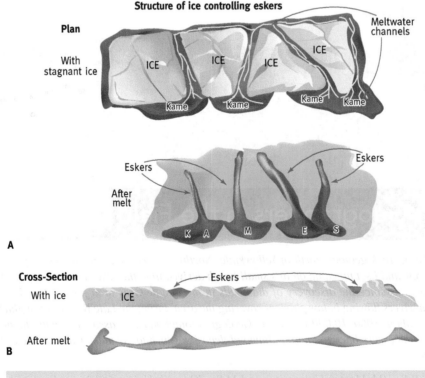

Figure 38.7 Plan and cross-section views of esker and kame formation.

Canadian Geographers in the Field

'My passion for physical geography began with an interest in glacial landforms. This is an aerial photograph of one of the many drumlins in the Lunenburg drumlin field, on the southeastern shore of Nova Scotia. I ended up writing my undergraduate thesis on the morphological properties of the drumlins in the "field". I think I was really interested in these features because, at the time, there was a lot of debate surrounding the specific processes of their formation. These features are sometimes difficult to distinguish from the ground, but from a bird's eye view you can see the moulding effect of the glacial ice. Many important cultural features, such as Citadel Hill in Halifax, are situated atop drumlins.'

Cathy Conrad is Chair of the Department of Geography at Saint Mary's University and the Founder and Research Coordinator of the Community-Based Environmental Monitoring Network.

Northwest Territories, Labrador and northern Quebec, Alberta and the other Prairie provinces, and southern Ontario. In Ontario, there are large drumlin fields in the Peterborough area (about 10,000 drumlins in a 900 km² area, with 6–8 drumlins/km²), near Guelph and Kitchener–Waterloo, around Caledonia and Woodstock, in Grey–Bruce, and around Walkerton and Palmerston. They also are found in eastern Ontario between the Ottawa Valley and the St Lawrence. Recent studies have also found them on the beds of Lakes Simcoe and Ontario.

Sandur Material

Sandur, as in Skeiðarársandur, the large Icelandic outwash plain (Figure 38.2), is the term now applied to the outwash plains of ice sheets or icecaps and valley trains of alpine glaciers. Sandar (the plural of sandur) are the products of fluvioglacial outwash and meltwater. They have a fairly smooth topography and generally occur downstream of dead-ice topography (e.g., moraines, kames, and kettles). The gradient of the sandur surface is quite steep in comparison to that of a floodplain (20–30 m/km versus 7–10 m/km). Braided streams occur as a result of the variable discharges related to the ice front and to the plethora of loose materials. Depositional conditions vary widely because of daily and seasonal fluctuations of discharge, the ponding of meltwater behind moraine dams, and breaching of these features as the meltwater builds up and overflows (jökulhlaups). During major floods the whole sandur surface essentially becomes the riverbed. When the floods subside the sediment load is deposited and water flow is diverted around these mounds of sands

Perspectives on the Human Environment

Iceland and Fluvioglacial Research

Iceland is a major research site for many kinds of physical geographical and geological studies—fluvial, glacial, coastal, volcanic, tectonic, aeolian, and fluvioglacial processes and landforms. There are a number of reasons for this. Obviously, Iceland has a very diverse and active terrain with a plethora of these processes and features, and these are in pristine condition because of the sparse population: 64 per cent, or about 200,000, of the nation's population of 302,169 (in 2008) live in the greater Reykjavik area. The island is small and research sites can be easily accessed from the island's ring road (Route 1, also known as Hringvegur). Small groups can readily undertake research. In addition, there is a lot of local knowledge, from the local population, from Icelandic scientists, and from previous studies by foreigners. This allows for follow-up studies. Iceland's copious historical records and archives can be used to find out about physical geographical events and conditions in the past, such as volcanic eruptions, floods, and climatic conditions.

In addition, Iceland has become a favourite location for undergraduate field trips for many European universities and has been a focal point for generations of thesis writers. Also, earlier generations of Icelandic geographers and geologists had to go abroad to complete higher degrees and established ties with many universities in Norway, Sweden, Denmark, Britain, Germany, and the US and Canada. Once these relationships were established, research 'chains' have handed down sites or projects from one generation of Earth scientists to the next.

and gravels, causing the braiding. Braiding is not the only response to changing discharges. Because of variations of flow and sediment load aggradation, erosion of the sandur surface can occur to produce terraces. In the proglacial landscape these features can be superimposed on isostatic or eustatic terrace features.

One of the main characteristics of sandar is the down-sandur sorting and fining of material, which occurs fairly rapidly. This can be complicated by the existence of a number of ice fronts as the ice retreats. The sandur surface also can be complicated and cut up by thermokarst and resemble dead-ice topography, but a useful parameter to distinguish them is the degree of sorting of the sandur material.

The Relationship of the Features to the Glacier Regime

The extreme complexity of the fluvioglacial landscape is a result of the dynamic environment responsible for its formation. It is the outcome of melting ice margins, variable discharges, and loads over a considerable time span. One question that remains is whether the accumulation of the material is most rapid when the ice is advancing or retreating, when there is an abundance of meltwater. Some recent studies of marginal fluctuations of glaciers in Iceland (see 'Perspectives' box) suggest that aggradation is associated with periods of stability or when the glaciers are advancing, while incision into the deposits occurs when the glaciers are melting and retreating and more meltwater is being produced.

Glacial Lakes

Glacial lakes are of great importance and interest in the study of glaciated landscapes. In addition to the lakes formed in depressions sculpted at the bottom of continental glaciers, lakes also formed when glacial deposits blocked the path of outflowing meltwater at the leading edge of ice sheets. Such dammed-up lakes formed during the recession of valley glaciers as well as of continental ice sheets. These lakes, born on the margins of melting ice (proglacial lakes), contain sediments that are layered in a characteristic pattern.

A cross-section of such lake-bottom sediments reveals pairs of layers: each pair consists of a light-coloured band of silt and a dark-coloured band of clay. Together these two bands represent one year's deposition. The coarser silt was washed into the lake during the summer, when the ice was melting and sediment entered the lake in quantity; this material settled quickly on the lake floor. During the ensuing winter the lake surface froze and no meltwater or new sediment arrived. But finer material, still in suspension, now settled slowly on top of the silt. This finer material

LINK

consisted of clay particles and organic matter, which created the dark band.

The paired layers, one light and one dark, each constitute a **varve**. By counting varves, glaciologists can calculate the lifespan of a glacial lake, much as tree rings can be used to date the age of a tree. Elaborate systems of correlations have been developed to extend the varve counts from lake to lake. Such research has made an important contribution to early estimates of the timing of glacial movements.

Glacial and Pluvial Lakes and Megafloods

Glacial Lake Agassiz   Glacial Lake Agassiz formed 11,500 years ago from the meltwaters of the Wisconsinan Laurentide Ice Sheet, covering northern Ontario, Manitoba, and Saskatchewan. At its maximum size it extended over 500,000 km² of these areas and parts of North Dakota and Minnesota. It was the largest lake in North America during the deglaciation. The lake lasted for 4500 years, its level rising and falling a number of times. These changes were related to advances and retreats of the ice front and the opening and closing of various spillway channels. At some points, water from the lake was discharged to the south, through the Mississippi River system to the Gulf of Mexico. At other times, the lake discharged water through the Great Lakes–St Lawrence system to the Atlantic Ocean, and at still other times it discharged to the north (Hudson Bay and into the Arctic Ocean). These outpourings of cold meltwater into the oceans that influence or change the thermohaline circulation system are called Heinrich Events.

During this period three large cooling events in the Northern Hemisphere occurred, each following closely after the largest outbursts of water from Lake Agassiz. The cooling events can be summed up as follows:

1. *The Younger Dryas* (a readvance of ice sheets in Europe during deglaciation). This cooling event was preceded by a discharge of 9500 km³ of cold water from the interior of North America to the North Atlantic.
2. *The Pre-Boreal Oscillation.* This was preceded by two outbursts of lake water to the Atlantic (9300 km³ and 5900 km³).
3. *The '8.2 k cold event'.* This cooling event was preceded by the largest outburst (163,000 km³) through the Great Lakes–St Lawrence system.

LINK

These massive discharges of cold water have been calculated by the area of the lake and depth of water estimated from dated beach features, sediments, and the like. Such large discharges inhibited the thermohaline circulation system in the North Atlantic and provided triggers that brought about changes in ocean circulation; these changes, in turn, caused a widespread drop in temperature in Western Europe and as far as the Middle East.

Glacial Lake Bonneville   As the map of the maximum extent of the Laurentide Ice Sheet and its adjoining

Rocky Mountain Icecap indicates, the continental glacier never reached as far as Utah, Nevada, Oregon, or California. Still, the glaciations had far-reaching effects there. Today the basins in this area of the Far West are arid. During the glaciations, however, precipitation in this region was substantially higher than at present, and more than 100 lakes, known as **pluvial lakes**, developed as a result (Figure 38.8).

The largest of them, Lake Bonneville, was the forerunner of Utah's Great Salt Lake. Glacial Lake Bonneville at one stage was about as large as Lake Michigan is now. It reached a maximum depth of 300 m and overflowed northward through Idaho into the Snake and Columbia Rivers. Although Glacial Lake Bonneville has now shrunk into the Great Salt Lake, its former shorelines still can be seen on the slopes of the mountains that encircled it. Today, only a few of these pluvial lakes contain water, and this water is saline; the Great Salt Lake is the largest of them. The other pluvial lakes have evaporated away, leaving only geomorphological and sedimentological evidence of their former existence.

The Great Lakes and Their Evolution

The Great Lakes owe their origin to the Pleistocene ice sheets. The area occupied by the present six (including Lake St Clair, which, with the St Clair River, connects Lakes Huron and Erie) Great Lakes (the largest cluster of freshwater lakes in the world) was probably an area at a

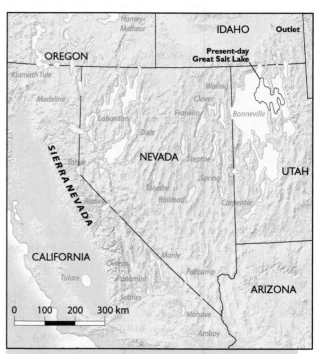

Figure 38.8 Pluvial lakes of the US Far West during the glaciation stage. Blue dashed lines represent overflow channels.

low elevation and of low relief drained by a large stream network when the glaciers advanced over it. The ice excavated a set of shallow but very extensive basins early on in the ice age. When the ice receded, deposits left along its leading edge blocked the outflow of meltwater southward except through a few channels, and the first stage in the evolution of the Great Lakes began.

The major outlet to the south led from near the southern end of present-day Lake Michigan across Illinois into the Mississippi River (Figure 38.9, route 5). What began as a set of separate, marginal lakes that linked up sporadically with Glacial Lake Agassiz grew into an interconnected group of major water bodies. Not only was their overflow channelled southward into the Mississippi Basin, but they also drained eastward into the Hudson via Rome, NY (route 14), and the St Lawrence Valley (routes 12 and 13).

The Great Lakes reached their maximum extent in the early part of the Holocene interglacial, when Lake Huron far exceeded its present size and flowed through the Ottawa River into the St Lawrence Valley (Figure 38.9, route 12). Then, with the meltwater sources gone, the lakes began to shrink. Lowered water level closed the Lake Michigan outflow; crustal rebound closed the Ottawa River exit. But the lakes continued to flow into each other, and the St Lawrence River and its estuary eventually became the only outlet for Great Lakes water (Figure 38.9, route 13). At certain points in time, large quantities of meltwater from the deglaciation of the Prairies funnelled through the Lake Agassiz–Great Lakes system into the North Atlantic—related to the onset of the **Younger Dryas** glaciation in Europe.

The future of the Great Lakes is uncertain. The lowering of the lake levels exposed large areas of fertile soils, and these lakeshore zones now constitute one of the continent's most densely populated areas. Major cities have evolved on the shores of the Great Lakes, including Chicago, Cleveland, and Toronto. Urban and agricultural pollution have had a severe impact on the lakes, and Lake Erie in particular has been gravely threatened in recent decades. In the meantime, the lake levels are kept up by the considerable precipitation received in the region. Over the longer term, however, continued crustal rebound at the outlet of Lake Ontario, which is rising more than is the western end of the lake following the recession of the Wisconsinan ice, plus a changing water budget will continue to modify the map of the Great Lakes and their drainage basin.

The Missoula Flood and the Channelled Scablands

The **Channelled Scablands** (or Palouse area) of eastern Washington state has some very unusual landscapes. The area has a weird drainage pattern with **underfit streams** (i.e., streams too small to have cut the valleys in which they are situated) and many dry valleys or coulees, huge rectangular valleys, and gorges with immense

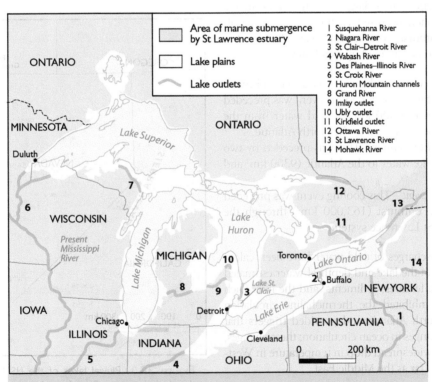

Figure 38.9 Lake plains (former lake bottoms) of the late Pleistocene Great Lakes and major outlets used by these lakes during their evolution into the present-day Great Lakes.

dry waterfalls cut into basalt bedrock. About 65 m of soil and sediment have been stripped off in many areas and formed into giant ripples in others. There are mammoth bars of grapefruit-sized gravels, huge potholes or 'kolks' (which were the reason for the name 'Scablands'), and immense erratic blocks weighing up to 250–300 tonnes. J. Harlen Bretz, a young University of Chicago geologist, studied this area beginning in the 1920s and suggested that the bizarre landforms of this area had been caused by an enormous flood, but he did not know where the water had come from. Another scientist, J.T. Pardee, was studying the area around Missoula, Montana, at about the same time. He found evidence of an immense proglacial lake that left relic shorelines cut in hillsides, large water-laid sand dunes (~30 m high and tens of metres between crests), and other strange features that he could not account for. Later, these two pieces of information were put together to account for what has become known as the Missoula (or Spokane) Flood (see Table 38.1).

Sometime between 16,000 and 12,000 years before the present a lobe of ice (the Purcell Lobe) moved down into the Idaho area and blocked the Clark Fork River. This ice dam was 762 m high. It ponded up a massive proglacial lake (Figure 38.10). This lake (Lake Missoula) was one and a half times the area of PEI. The water pressure behind the ice dam and undermining of the dam by the seepage of super-cooled water in cracks in the ice barrier caused the dam to fail and water poured out of the lake and was responsible for creating all of the features enumerated above. After leaving the lake the water spread out and eroded and deposited the unusual landforms. The Grand Coulee is a great example of the scale of the features. It is dry valley with a relic waterfall. The coulee is 80 km long, 10 km wide, and 274 m high. Dry Falls is 107 m high (Horseshoe Falls, the Canadian part of Niagara Falls, is 53 m high) and 4.8 km wide (~6 × the width of the Horseshoe Falls). While the water depth and water flow velocity over the Horseshoe Falls is about 3 m and 32 km/h respectively, the water depth and flow over Dry Falls was orders of magnitude greater. It is estimated that during the flood the difference between the elevation of the water level above and below the falls was probably 10–20 m. It took the floodwaters about 24 hours to get to the Pacific Ocean. The kolks or scabs were excavated by immense eddies in the floodwaters, possibly armed with large load material. The huge erratic blocks were either tumbled along in the flow of water or ice-rafted. The flood cut a large valley into the edge of the continental shelf.

There have been many ideas about the number of these flood events over the years. At first only one flood was envisaged, then Bretz estimated that six floods had occurred. Later studies have shown that there could have been 85 or more of these events as the ice dam reformed, the lake filled, and the ice dam failed over and over again. Some scientists believe that the flow from Lake Missoula was enhanced by subglacial floodwaters flowing out from the Cordilleran Ice Sheet.

The idea of immense jökulhlaups generated by supraglacial, englacial, and subglacial flows and by dumping of proglacial meltwater has been suggested by many recent studies in Canada, the US, Siberia, and Europe. It has even been suggested that the Straits of Dover separating Britain from France were cut through by such an event.

Fluvioglacial processes have been and are a very important feature of the landscape and may have been responsible for many small and large features seen in our everyday lives. These processes are not to be underestimated or relegated to a postscript of glaciation.

Table 38.1 Estimated Data for Proglacial Lake Missoula and the Missoula Flood

	Dimensions	Remarks
Lake Missoula		
Height of ice dam	762 m	1.3 × the height of the CN Tower
Depth	610 m	~56.5 m higher than the CN Tower
Area	7770 km²	~1.5 × the size of PEI (5660 km²)
Volume	2083 km³	~ the total volume of Lakes Erie and Ontario
Sand dunes (Camas Prairie)	11 m high, crest to crest; spacing >152 m; area of Prairie: 16 km²; flood velocity: 85 km/h	
Missoula Flood		
Travel length	842 km	~ distance from Montreal to Fredericton (850 km) or Toronto to Quebec City (800 km)
Area covered	41,440 km²	~75 per cent of the area of Nova Scotia
Height	244 m	~2.6 × the height of the Peace Tower
Maximum flow rate/ discharge	40 km³/h 17 million m³/s	A rate that would empty Lake Erie in 8 hours
		The discharge was >350 × that of the peak of the Mississippi floods of 1993

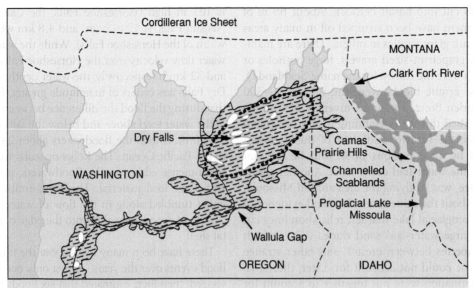

Figure 38.10   Proglacial Lake Missoula and the Missoula Flood.

KEY TERMS

Channelled Scablands   *page 550*
drumlin   *page 546*
esker   *page 544*
fluvioglacial processes   *page 541*
jökulhlaup   *page 541*
kame   *page 546*
pluvial lakes   *page 549*

proglacial lake   *page 541*
sandur   *page 547*
spillway channels   *page 541*
thermokarst   *page 546*
underfit streams   *page 550*
varves   *page 549*
Younger Dryas   *page 550*

REVIEW QUESTIONS

1. What are the differences between glacial and fluvioglacial materials?

2. What are the major controls of fluvioglacial discharges and sediment?

3. What is the difference between eskers, kames, and drumlins?

4. How are jökulhlaups generated and why are they so important?

5. What kind of evidence can be used to support the idea of megafloods?

REFERENCES AND FURTHER READINGS

Baker, V.R. 2002. 'The Study of Superfloods', *Science* 295: 2379–80.

——. 2007. 'Greatest Floods and Largest Rivers', in A. Gupta, ed., *Large Rivers*. New York: Wiley.

—— et al. 1981. *Catastrophic Flooding: The Origin of the Channeled Scablands*. Benchmark Papers in Geology 55. Stroudsburg, Penn.: Dowden, Hutchinson & Ross.

—— et al. 1993. 'Paleohydrology of Late Pleistocene Superflooding, Altay Mountains, Siberia', *Science* 259: 348–50.

Barnett, P.J., et al. 1998. 'On the Origin of the Oak Ridges Moraine', *Canadian Journal of Earth Sciences* 35, 10: 1152–67.

Bjornsson, H. 1977. 'The Cause of Jökulhlaups in the Skaftá River, Vatnajökull', *Jökull* 27: 71–8.

——. 1998. 'Hydrological Characteristics of Drainage System beneath a Surging Glacier', *Nature* 395: 771–4.

Boyce, J.I., and N. Eyles. 1991. 'Drumlins Formed by Deforming Till Streams below the Laurentide Ice Sheet', *Geology* 19: 787–90.

Brandsdóttir, B. 1984. 'Seismic Activity in Vatnajökull in 1900–1982, with Special Reference to Skeiðaráhlaups, Skaftáhlaups and Volcanic Activity', *Jökull* 34: 141–50.

Branson, J., et al. 1996. *Global Continental Changes: The Context of Palaeohydrology*. Geological Society of London Special Publication 115. London: Geological Society.

Brennand, T.A. 1994. 'Macroforms, Large Bedforms and Rhythmic Sedimentary Sequences in Subglacial Eskers, South-central Ontario: Implications for Esker Genesis and Meltwater Regime', *Sedimentary Geology* 91, 4: 9–55.

———. 2000. 'Deglacial Meltwater Drainage and Glaciodynamics: Inferences from Laurentide Eskers, Canada', *Geomorphology* 32, 3 and 4: 263–93.

——— and J. Shaw. 1994. 'Tunnel Channels and Associated Landforms: Their Implication for Ice Sheet Hydrology', *Canadian Journal of Earth Sciences* 31: 502–22.

Bretz, J.H. 1923. 'The Channeled Scabland of the Columbia Plateau', *Journal of Geology* 31: 617–49.

———. 1927. 'Channeled Scabland and the Spokane Flood', *Washington Academy of Sciences Journal* 17: 200–11.

Chapman, L.J., and D.F. Putnam. 1984. *The Physiography of Southern Ontario*. Ontario Geological Survey, Special Publication 2. Toronto: Ontario Ministry of Natural Resources.

Church, M.A. 1972. *Baffin Island Sandurs: A Study of Arctic Fluvial Processes*. Geological Survey of Canada, Bulletin 216. Ottawa: Canada Energy, Mines and Resources.

Clague, J. 1987. 'Catastrophic Outburst Floods', *Geos* 16, 2: 18–21.

Cofaigh, C.O. 1996. 'Tunnel Valley Genesis', *Progress in Physical Geography* 20, 1: 1–19.

Embleton, C., and C.A.M. King. 1975. *Periglacial Geomorphology*. London: Edward Arnold.

Eyles, N. 2002. *Ontario Rocks: Three Billion Years of Environmental Change*. Markham, Ont.: Fitzhenry & Whiteside.

———. 2006. 'The Role of Meltwater in Glacial Processes', *Sedimentary Geology* 190, 1–4: 257–68.

Gaidos, E., et al. 2004. 'A Viable Microbial Community in a Subglacial Volcanic Crater Lake, Iceland', *Astrobiology* 4, 3: 327–44.

Gilbert, R., ed. 1994. *A Field Guide to the Glacial and Postglacial Landscape of Southeastern Ontario and Part of Quebec*. Geological Survey of Canada, Bulletin 453. Ottawa: Canada Energy, Mines and Resources.

Glasser, N.F., and M.R. Bennett. 2004. 'Glacial Erosion Landforms: Origin and Significance for Palaeoglaciology', *Progress in Physical Geography* 28, 1: 43–75.

Grove, J.M. 1987. 'Glacier Fluctuations and Hazards', *Geographical Journal* 153, 3: 351–67.

Gudmundsson, M.T., et al. 1993. 'Changes in Jökulhlaup Sizes in Grimsvotn, Vatnajökull, Iceland, 1934–1991, Deduced from in-situ Measurements of Subglacial Lake Volume', *Journal of Glaciology* 41, 138: 263–72.

Gupta, S., et al. 2007. 'Catastrophic Flooding Origin of Shelf Valley Systems in the English Channel', *Nature* 448, 7151: 342–5.

Kerr, M., and N. Eyles. 2005. 'Origin of Drumlins on the Floor of Lake Ontario and in Upper New York State', *Sedimentary Geology* 193, 1–4: 7–20.

Knudsen, O., et al. 2001. 'Changes in the Gígjukvísl River Channel during the November 1996 Jökulhlaup, Skeiðarársandur, Iceland', *Jökull* 50: 19–32.

Magilligan, F.J., et al. 2002. 'Geomorphic Effectiveness, Sandur Development, and the Pattern of Landscape Response during Jökulhlaups, Skeiðarársandur, Southeastern Iceland', *Geomorphology* 44: 95–113.

Malde, H.E. 1968. *The Catastrophic Late Pleistocene Bonneville Flood in the Snake River Plain, Idaho*. USGS Professional Paper 596. Washington: US Government Printing Office.

Marren, P.M. 2002. 'Glacier Margin Fluctuations, Skaftáfellsjökull, Iceland: Implications for Sandur Evolution', *Boreas* 31, 1: 75–81.

Martini, I.P., et al., eds. 2002. *Flood and Megaflood Processes and Deposits: Recent and Ancient Examples*. International Association of Sedimentologists Special Publication 32. Oxford: Blackwell Science.

Menzies, J., and J. Rose. 1987. *Drumlin Symposium*. Rotterdam: Balkema.

O'Connor, J.E. 1993. *Hydrology, Hydraulics and Geomorphology of the Bonneville Flood*. Geological Society of America Special Paper 274. Boulder, Colo.: Geological Society of America.

Pardee, J.T. 1910. 'The Glacial Lake Missoula', *Journal of Geology* 8: 376–86.

Preece, R.C., ed. 1995. *Island Britain: A Quaternary Perspective*. Geological Society of London Special Publication. London: Geological Society.

Rudoy, A.N. 2002. 'Glacier-dammed Lakes and Geological Work of Megafloods in the Late Pleistocene, Southern Siberia, Altai Mountains', *Quaternary International* 87: 119–40.

Saunderson, H.C. 1975. 'A Comparison of Empirical and Theoretical Frequency Distributions in Two-dimensional Palaeocurrent Data from the Brampton Esker and Associated Sediments', *Geografiska Annaler* 57A, 3 and 4: 189–200.

Sharpe, D.R., et al. 2002. 'The Need for Basin Analysis in Regional Hydrogeological Studies: Oak Ridges Moraine, Southern Ontario', *Geoscience Canada* 29, 1: 3–20.

Shaw, J.A. 1994. 'A Qualitative View of Sub-Ice-Sheet Landscape Evolution', *Progress in Physical Geography* 18, 2: 159–84.

———. 2002. 'The Meltwater Hypothesis for Subglacial Bedforms', *Quaternary International* 90: 5–22.

——— and D.R. Sharpe. 1987. 'Drumlin Formation by Subglacial Meltwater Erosion', *Canadian Journal of Earth Sciences* 24: 2316–22.

Thorarinsson, S. 1939. 'The Ice-dammed Lakes of Iceland with particular reference to Their Value as Indicators of Glacier Oscillations', *Geografiska Annaler* 21: 216–42.

Todd, B.J., et al. 2008. 'Quaternary Features beneath Lake Simcoe: Drumlins, Tunnel Channels and Records of Proglacial and Postglacial Closed Lakes', *Journal of Paleolimnology* 39, 3: 361–80.

Worsley, P. 1998. 'Iceland: Contrasting Skeidarár Mega-flood Hydrographs', *Geology Today* 3, 3: 97–9.

 ## WEB RESOURCES

(There are many websites about the Missoula Flood and other megafloods. Caution should be taken because some are creationist in outlook. The Canadian Geological Survey and the US Geological Survey provide good coverage of fluvioglacial landforms, etc., on their websites. The Icelandic Meteorological Agency and other Icelandic sites have a great deal of information about grimsvötn and jökulhlaups related to other icecaps and volcanic eruptions.)

bridgenorthesker.ca/ Webpage of a former graduate student (Glenn Jackson) at Trent University about his study concerning an esker in southern Ontario. Good photographs and information.

www.mines.edu/academic/geology/faculty/klee Website of an emeritus professor of geology with information about the Bonneville and Missoula floods.

Unit 39

Periglacial Environments and Landscapes

Objectives

- To discuss the unique landscapes that develop under near-glacial conditions at high latitudes and high altitudes.

- To highlight the important weathering and mass-movement processes that shape periglacial landscapes.

The Earth is undergoing an interglacial at present; yet, large regions of the world are anything but warm, even during the summer. Figure 16.2 shows the large expanses of existing **Dfc**, **Dfd**, and **E** climates. Conditions in these high-latitude regions are nearly, but not quite, glacial. The technical term for such environments is **periglacial**—on the perimeter of glaciation. In this unit we study the processes and landforms that characterize periglacial areas.

LINK

Periglacial zones today occupy high polar and subpolar latitudes, almost exclusively in the Northern Hemisphere. No periglacial environments exist in southern Africa or in Australia, although the highlands of Tasmania (off the southeastern coast of Australia) show evidence of recent periglacial conditions. Only small areas of southernmost South America (most notably the island of Tierra del Fuego) and the Antarctic Peninsula exhibit periglacial conditions. Accordingly, this unit deals almost exclusively with the Northern Hemisphere. Nonetheless, it is estimated that as much as one-quarter of the entire land surface of the Earth is dominated by periglacial conditions, and this alone should persuade us to learn more about these cold environments.

In the past, periglacial conditions migrated into the middle latitudes when Pleistocene ice sheets expanded. When the Wisconsinan ice sheets covered much of northern North America, periglacial conditions extended far to the south, where the landscape still bears the imprints. This reminds us that the Earth's comfortable living space during the next glaciation will be much smaller than the land area not actually covered by ice. Periglacial conditions, extending in a wide belt from the margin of the ice, will restrict the ecumene even more (see 'Perspectives' box).

Periglacial Processes

Periglacial processes can be separated into three types: (1) those related to climate—pergelation (creation of permafrost or related to permafrost), ground ice, freeze–thaw activity, nivation (processes related to snowpack development and melting such as wash), solifluction/gelifluction; (2) periglacial and proglacial processes *distal* (at distance) to the ice that are related to the presence of ice masses or glaciers, which act as reservoirs for water and sediment; and (3) the processes related to ice masses or glaciers that are *proximal* (close to) to the ice. Unit 38 focused on proglacial processes that are proximal to ice; here we deal with those at distance from the ice and with climate-related processes.

LINK

The term *periglacial* was introduced early in the twentieth century to describe the climate and environment close to the margins of the Pleistocene ice sheets and later was applied to near-polar conditions. The term was used generally and vaguely and remained ill-defined until after World War II. In 1950 an attempt was made by Peltier to define a periglacial morphogenetic region based on mean annual temperature and precipitation. The mean temperature range was $-15°C$ to $-1°C$; mean precipitation: 120–1400 mm/yr. It was described as an area with strong mass movements and occasional strong winds. Running water was assumed to be relatively unimportant. The definition also stated that over time the areas subjected to these conditions had changed (because of the ice age).

Perspectives on the Human Environment

Humans and the Periglacial Environment

Cold and inhospitable as periglacial environments are, people have lived in and migrated through these regions for many thousands of years. Those who stayed there adapted to the difficult conditions. The Inuit, best known of the Arctic peoples, skilfully exploited the environment's opportunities on both land and sea. Their numbers remained small, their social organization was comparatively simple, and their impact on the fragile periglacial domain was very slight.

But the recent invasion of technologically advanced societies, driven by the search for resources, generated new and major problems and threatened local environments as never before. Examples are the Klondike gold rush of the late 1890s and a number of World War II developments, including the Alcan (Alaska–Canada) Highway (Figure 39.1), the building of airfields to supply matériel to the Russian allies

(Northern Staging Route), and the short-lived Canol oil pipeline from Norman Wells, NWT, to a refinery at Whitehorse, Yukon, and then to Fairbanks, Alaska. Barely a decade later, the Distant Early Warning Line (DEW Line) to detect Soviet-era planes and missiles stretched across Canada at the 70th parallel and the Mid-Canada Line served the same purpose along the 55th parallel, both completed in 1957. In the 1950s, too, the government first experimented with permanent settlements for the Inuit, and 20 years later the Mackenzie Valley Pipeline Inquiry of 1974–7 gained wide media coverage and brought a new awareness of Canada's Far North and people to those living in southern Canada. The catastrophic 1989 *Exxon Valdez* oil spill in Prince William Sound, Alaska, underscored the possible results of this kind of intervention in periglacial environments (Figure 39.2). The periglacial environment poses engineering, construction, and maintenance problems unknown in warmer regions. Most buildings have to be built on stilts or special types of foundations to decrease permafrost degradation. Despite the arrival of modern technology in the Subarctic, however, population numbers remain low. Nevertheless, the impact of the new era is felt throughout the region in the form of frontier towns and highways, dia-mond and other mines, oil facilities, and military installations.

The periglacial world is a landscape of recent glaciation, of scoured bedrock, of basins and lakes, of thin and rocky soil, of muskeg and of scattered fluvioglacial deposits such as kames, eskers, and drumlins. Winter is protracted and bitter; nights are frigid and long. Summer is short and cool, depending on latitude and exposure. The surface is frozen half the year or more, but when the accumulated snow melts, the ground is saturated. Plants, animals, and indigenous peoples have adapted to a combination of environmental conditions that are delicately balanced and so easily disturbed.

This area has been and will continue to be affected by global warming. As the climate changes, the permafrost is melting, making slopes unstable and soils impossible to traverse. The wet soils are emitting more methane and carbon dioxide into the atmosphere, increasing greenhouse gases; lake and river ice is no longer thick enough in places to allow for ice roads and therefore supplies are more difficult to transport to the northern communities; sea ice is forming later and there is much less of it. The timing and the lack of sea-ice formation cause problems for polar bear populations in some areas, and for the Inuit who rely on the sea ice to hunt for seals and other animals.

LINK

Figure 39.1   Construction work on the Alaska Highway during World War II.

Figure 39.2 North America's most serious high-latitude environmental disaster to date: the fully loaded *Exxon Valdez* disgorging some 42 million litres of crude oil into Prince William Sound, Alaska, shortly after the supertanker ran aground on 24 March 1989. A major study in 2001 revealed that oil contamination still plagued the Sound's shoreline, and the after-effects of this ecological tragedy are likely to linger for decades to come.

Permafrost

Reports of ground ice and frozen ground go back to the early nineteenth century and earlier. Frozen mammoth carcasses were found melting out from stream banks in Siberia by many explorers. In fact, the economy of czarist Russia was kept afloat partly by export of ivory from this source for the production of jewellery, billiard balls, and piano keys. Later, gold rushes along the Klondike River in Yukon and in Alaska and the building of towns like

Dawson City, as well as the construction of the Trans-Siberian Railway, showed that permafrost was widespread and very difficult to mine through and build on.

Defining the exact environmental limits of periglacial regions is not a simple matter of drawing definite lines across a map. Perhaps the most practical way to delimit periglacial conditions is based on a phenomenon unique to these regions—**permafrost**, or perennially frozen ground (frozen for more than two years). Much of the permafrost is a remnant of the Pleistocene glaciations. In periglacial zones, the ground (soil as well as rock) below the surface layer is permanently frozen. What this means, of course, is that all the water in this subsurface layer is frozen. The permafrost layer (Figure 39.3) normally begins between 15 cm and 5 m below the surface.

The upper surface of the permafrost is called the *permafrost table*. The soil above the permafrost table is subject to annual freezing and thawing. This is the *active layer*, or **talik**; it is thickest in the Subarctic region and becomes thinner both poleward and southward. The thickness of the active layer is a function of:

1. air temperature;
2. exposure;
3. aspect;
4. insulation by snow or vegetation cover; and
5. soil heat conductivity (how the soil heats up, how it transfers heat downprofile, and how it loses heat).

Below the permafrost table the frozen ground can be very deep. In North America it averages around 300 m, but in the heart of high-latitude Eurasia permafrost depths of more than 1200 m have been measured. Like a growing glacier, the permafrost would keep thickening season after

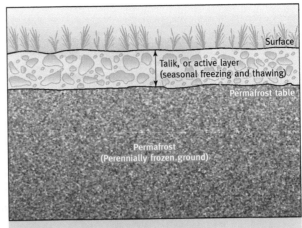

Figure 39.3 The talik, or subsurface active layer, and permafrost layers characteristic of periglacial zones. Note how the upper active layer contains ice-fractured rock fragments of varying size that have been deposited in the soil as frost wedging in the harsh environment above constantly breaks down boulders and pebbles.

season, except that heat from the Earth's interior eventually limits this process.

The distribution of permafrost in the Northern Hemisphere is mapped in Figure 39.4. Note that the map first differentiates between *continuous permafrost*, located in northernmost Canada, and *discontinuous permafrost*, found as far south as the latitude of James Bay. Continuous permafrost, as the term implies, is thick and unbroken, thinning somewhat only under lakes or wide rivers. Discontinuous permafrost is generally thinner and contains unfrozen gaps (also called *talik*).

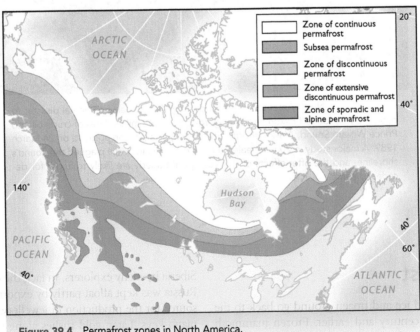

Figure 39.4 Permafrost zones in North America.

Also shown on the map are lower-latitude areas of *sporadic permafrost*. Sporadic alpine permafrost zones mostly occur at high elevations in mountains such as the Rockies, and are remnants of the permafrost of glacial times.

The map of world vegetation (see Figure 47.1) indicates that a certain correspondence exists between the boundary separating continuous and discontinuous permafrost and the treeline that delimits tundra from forest vegetation. While it is not clear whether the vegetation influences the properties of the permafrost or vice versa, it is clear that many factors, including not only vegetation but also precipitation and temperature regimes, affect permafrost development and persistence.

Ground Ice

Most ground ice exists in permafrost areas (both continuous and discontinuous zones). It ranges in size from ice filling pores in the soil to masses of clear ice of 30 m or more across. Many scientists have described the various types of ice found in periglacial environments, and various features are associated with and unique to ground ice.

- *Involutions*. These are deformed layers where the boundaries between the various beds are undulating, tongue-shaped, or flame-like. They result from cryoturbation, i.e., the mixing and churning of the ground caused by differential freezing and thawing of soil material or sediments, such as silts and clays versus sands and gravels.
- *Earth and turf hummocks*. These are small hills or mounds forced up by the growth of ice lenses in the ground. These include *palsas* (in organic terrain) and possibly *mima mounds*. Mima mounds are very regular in size, shape, and spacing. The type site, from which the term comes, is the Mima Prairie just south of Olympia, Washington. They are found in the western US and western Canada, and though they have been studied for over 150 years, no commonly accepted theory (and there are about 100 different ideas as to their origin) accounts for them. Some researchers think they developed because of ground freezing and thawing and ground ice growth, some because of earthquake activity, and some others because of pocket gopher activity.
- *Pingos* (see below).
- *Oriented thaw lakes*. These roughly oval lakes are oriented parallel to the prevailing wind direction. The shape is affected by wind-generated waves undercutting the frozen banks. They are formed by the melting of permafrost or ground ice and may take 500–1500 years to form. The rate of bank undercutting is 5–20 cm/yr. They are often associated with pingos.
- *Thermokarst*. These are areas, as we saw in Unit 38, where ground ice or permafrost has melted and created depressions (often water-filled) that look like landforms related to limestone solution.

Geomorphological Processes in Periglacial Environments

The modification of the landscape in periglacial zones takes place in ways that differ from other regions, because freezing and thawing and mass movements play such dominant roles. Water, when changing phases from the liquid to the frozen state, is an important force. When a permanently frozen layer exists below the surface, water cannot drain downward; therefore it often saturates the active layer. In this upper stratum, boulders are shattered by frost, and fragments are constantly moved by freezing and thawing and the force of gravity. This results in landforms that are unique to periglacial areas.

Frost Action

The key disintegrative combination in periglacial environments is the amount of water in soil and rock and the freezing and thawing of that water. **Frost wedging** or *shattering* occurs when the stress created by the freezing of water into ice becomes greater than the cohesive strength of the rock containing it. Research has proven that the more water a rock contains, the greater the power of frost wedging. For instance, porous sedimentary rocks containing water will shatter more rapidly than less porous rocks. Joints and cracks in non-porous crystalline rocks are zones of weakness that are exploited by frost shattering (see Figure 29.8). Frost wedging is capable of dislodging boulders from cliffs, of splintering boulders into angular pebbles, of cracking pebbles into gravel-sized fragments, and of reducing gravel to sand and even finer particles. Thus, the active layer consists of a mixture of ice-fractured fragments of all sizes (Figure 39.3).

Ice growth in the crack of a rock or boulder can reach a theoretical maximum force of ~2100 kg/cm². This is 10 times the maximum pressure limits of the strongest rocks. Blocks, gravel, and finer material may have also persisted in the environment from previous glaciations and interglacial periods. Freezing generally occurs in open wedge-shaped cracks.

Freeze–thaw is related to ground temperature variations rather than air temperature, and ground temperature is influenced by several variables, including:

1. the amount of insolation;
2. the presence of water, ice, or snow;
3. the absorption of heat; and
4. longwave emission.

Slopes in the sun tend to melt before air temperatures increase appreciably. Alternate periods of sun and cloud can cause freeze–thaw activity.

The abundance of apparently frost-riven rocks in the environment may be related more to processes active during the Pleistocene rather than to present processes. Other forms of weathering, such as solution and chelation, may be just as (or more) important. Chemical changes such as oxidation and hydration have been seen in rocks in many Subarctic environments. One study estimated that solution amounted to 26 tonnes/km²/yr in northern Sweden. There is also a lot of evidence for pre-glacial deep weathering in some areas—tors, block fields, and saprolite.

The surface layer of the ground is often characterized by the sorting of fragments by size. This sorting is done by repeated freezing and thawing of the talik and produces a phenomenon called *patterned ground* (see Figure 39.9). Once rock fragments have been loosened by frost wedging, they are moved by frost heaving. **Frost heaving** causes vertical (upward) displacement when the formation of ice in the ground expands the total mass. Large fragments are moved upward a greater distance than smaller ones, so that the surface sometimes seems studded with small boulders rising above the ground (Figure 39.5). The same frost heaving that moves boulders upward also pushes concrete blocks, road segments, posts, poles, and other artificial fixtures out of the ground (see Figure 17.26).

In addition to frost heaving, other processes move material horizontally. One of these processes is **frost thrusting**. The mechanics of this process are not well understood, but there can be no question that it moves rock fragments horizontally within the active layer. Another process is **frost creep**, the movement of particles in the talik under the influence of gravity (Figure 39.6). Rock brought to the surface by frost heaving will move downward through the sodden talik and downslope during the thawing phase. Frost wedging, frost heaving, and frost creep combine to produce some remarkable landforms.

Figure 39.5 The effects of frost heaving—as boulders under the ground are thrust upward—can be seen on the tundra in Kootenay, British Columbia.

Slope Forms and Processes

Slopes are related to the threshold angle of the bedrock and slope deposits (scree or talus ramparts and cones). The slopes are cliff pediments with slope deposits obscuring their lower parts. Two types of slopes and slope processes have been recognized:

1. Slopes affected by rapid sporadic movements such as rockfalls, rock topples, and mud and debris flows.
2. Slopes affected by slower sporadic movements, such as solifluction or talus creep.

Solifluction (also known as **gelifluction**) is a form of soil creep, the slow flowage of saturated soil. The upper horizons of cryosolic soils (talik) in permafrost areas are often saturated because water cannot drain below the permafrost table. In the warm season such saturated soil begins to move as a mass, even when the slope angle is low (Figure 39.7). The texture of the soil is important, because highly permeable materials such as gravel and sand are not likely to move by solifluction whereas silt-laden soils move quite freely because they do not drain.

Periglacial areas are cold, but they are not without vegetation, which plays a significant role in stabilizing the talik and in impeding solifluction. Solifluction sheets or lobes may form in this way. Looked at in planview and in section a solifluction lobe is lingual, or tongue-shaped. From the side it looks somewhat like a teardrop, with the wide part downslope. The front of the lobe is often covered by turf or stones. In planview these resemble a garland and are therefore called *turf* or *stone garlands*. As solifluction occurs the mass of soil slowly flows downslope and water gradually drains out of it. This causes slopewash on the lower parts of the slope. The loss of water causes the solifluction lobe to gradually stop as it loses weight and lubrication. The processes of solifluction and slopewash produce a diagnostic sequence of stone layers separated by fine soil material seen on the lower parts of many slopes (*grezes litees*).

Again, human intervention can have devastating effects. When the protective vegetative cover (whether tundra or forest) is removed, binding roots are destroyed, summer thawing reaches a greater depth, and more of the active layer is destabilized. Recovery, in fact, may not occur at all, even after the damaged area is vacated. Periglacial ecologies are particularly fragile.

Stream Action and Valley Development

Stream action is governed by ice and snow melt in the immediate neighbourhood and possibly upstream. The production of glacial and snowpack meltwater is the main influence on discharge, which exhibits irregular and sudden fluctuations. No flow occurs during the winter except in major exotic rivers with their headwaters in other environments. In these streams, flow may occur under a deep ice cover. During spring and early summer (breakup and just after) there are major snow- and/or glacier-fed floods that

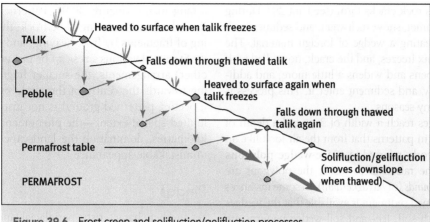

Figure 39.6   Frost creep and solifluction/gelifluction processes.

Figure 39.7   The talik, or active layer, above the permafrost, frozen in winter but thawed and very wet in summer. Even where slope angles are low, the whole active layer may move slowly downslope. While younger vegetation may not yet reflect this, older trees may lean as a result of this solifluction process.

cause much erosion and transport of debris. Because of the widely fluctuating discharges and the plethora of loose debris, braided streams are very common. The aggradation of stream beds occurs because of debris storage between major discharge events. Three different types of discharge are common: (1) glacially fed; (2) snowmelt-fed (nival); and (3) jökulhlaup (caused by catastrophic meltwater release from a glacier or a moraine dam breach).

The Mecham River, near Resolute, Cornwallis Island, Nunavut, is a good example of such a nival periglacial stream. The Mecham remains frozen until the latter part of June. At that time there is a gradual start of water flow, which grows quickly to a peak discharge of 3.00–7.20 m³/day by early July. Flow then diminishes to less than 1 m³/day by the third week in July. The discharge remains at around this level until freeze-up around 20 September. Eighty per cent of the annual flow and sediment transport occurs in the ten-day period of maximum discharge.

Asymmetrical Valley Development   The asymmetrical development of west–east valleys in periglacial areas is also seen in valleys in the Rocky Mountains and Alps. This asymmetry is influenced by aspect. Less freeze–thaw activity and solifluction occurs on shaded north-facing slopes than on the south-facing slopes that receive more direct solar energy. Thus, the north-facing slopes retain their initial steepness while the south-facing slope angles are decreased. Also, slope processes on the south-facing slopes tend to push the streams up against the north-facing slopes. This undercuts the slopes and helps to maintain steeper angles.

Aeolian Processes   Wind erosion and deposition are important in periglacial regions because such areas often lack moisture and vegetation cover. Erosion creates deflation pavements where the finer material is blown away, leaving coarser material at the surface, much like in hot desert areas. Wind-shaped pebbles occur (ventifacts) on the pavement surfaces. Silt and sand are eroded, transported, sorted, and deposited by the wind to form cold loess and coversand deposits.

Landforms of Periglacial Regions

Landforms in periglacial regions are not as dramatic or spectacular as those of mountain-glaciated areas. They are nonetheless quite distinctive, resulting from a combination of frost action and slope processes. The geomorphological features thus produced often take the form of special patterns that appear to be the result of intentional design.

Ice Wedges

One of these remarkable shapes is created by *ice wedges*. During the frigid Arctic winter, the ground in the active layer (and even the upper permafrost) becomes so cold that it cracks, much as rock cracks form (see Unit 29). During the following summer, snow, meltwater, and sediment will fill this crack, creating a wedge of foreign material. The next winter the mix freezes, and the crack, now filled with the ice wedge, opens and widens a little more, and additional water, snow, and sediment enter it. This process is repeated over many seasons.

Some ice wedges reach a width of 3 m and a depth of 30 m. They align in patterns that from the air look like an interlocking network, referred to as **ice-wedge polygons** (Figure 39.8). The raised areas inside the polygons are called *cemetery mounds* (or *baydzherakhi*). In some instances so much fine-grained sediment is available that the wedges become filled with soil. Ice- and soil-wedge patterns are typical of permafrost zones, and when climatic conditions change, they remain imprinted on the landscape. They form a major element of patterned ground, and the size of these polygons is related to a number of factors:

LINK

1. *Altitude*. The polygons get smaller with increasing altitude.
2. *Soil depth*. The polygons get smaller as soil depth decreases.
3. *Stone size*. Generally, larger stones mean larger polygons.
4. *Stage of development*. Polygons grow larger as they develop.

Patterned Ground

Another characteristic feature of periglacial regions is patterned ground. **Patterned ground** consists of rock and soil debris shaped or sorted in such a manner that designs are formed on the surface resembling rings, polygons, lines, and other repeatedly regular arrangements (Figure 39.9). Patterned ground results from the frost shattering of bedrock, the lifting and sorting of fragments by frost heaving, and the force of gravity. Stones of various sizes can be moved into circular (or other) arrangements, the smaller fragments accumulating towards the centre of the circle or polygon. When it occurs, patterned ground is not just a local feature of limited spatial extent—the phenomenon can persist for kilometres, dominating the landscape and giving it an unmistakable appearance.

Pingos

Yet another characteristic periglacial landform is a mound called a pingo. **Pingo** is the Inuit word for hill. They are also called ground ice mounds. Permafrost conditions are a prerequisite for the formation of these mounds, which are round or elliptical at the base and can grow quite large. While many are comparatively small and occur in clusters of hundreds, some isolated pingos are as large as

Figure 39.9 Ground-level view of a plain filled with rock debris sorted into myriad stone circles 3 to 5 m in diameter. This striking example of patterned ground was photographed in western Spitsbergen, part of the Arctic Ocean's Svalbard island chain, which belongs to Norway.

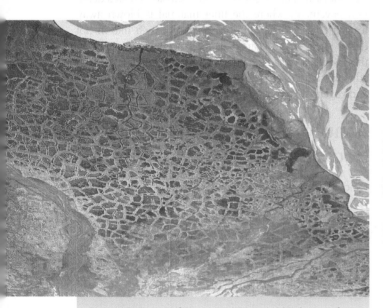

Figure 39.8 View from an airplane over a landscape of ice-wedge polygons in the Canadian Arctic.

600 m in diameter and 60 m high (Figure 39.10). The core of a pingo is made of ice, not rock or soil. Most pingos are found in the Mackenzie Delta, NWT. Pingos are associated with shallow lakes oriented in the direction of the prevailing winds, which cause waves that erode the downwind ends of the lakes. Many pingos have broken tops that expose the icy core. Some have pools in their broken tops during the melt season.

Pingos are believed to form from drained lakes where the permafrost table rises to the surface and bulges upward. As it does so, the saturated overlying lake sediments also are frozen and remain atop the bulging ice. Eventually only this uppermost active zone remains free of permanent ice and may sustain vegetation, even trees. In some northern communities, the inhabitants burrow into the sides of pingos and use them as natural food freezers. Pingos are unique to periglacial environments, and thus they are indisputable evidence of former periglacial conditions if they are found as 'fossil pingos' in now temperate zones.

Such fossil pingos show collapsed features because their icy cores have long since melted. What remains in the landscape is a low circular mound, the remains of the soils of the active layer. Fossil pingos have been found in northern Illinois and in parts of Europe, proof that periglacial conditions prevailed there when the Pleistocene ice sheets lay farther north.

Boulder Fields

Although streams do flow through periglacial areas (the northward-flowing streams in the Northwest Territories and Siberia, for example), they do not create distinctive landforms.

The main mover of loosened material in periglacial zones is *gravity*. Gravity does more than move material in the active layer. In areas of substantial relief, where there are bare bedrock surfaces, large boulders pried off the rock faces by frost wedging are moved into boulder fields. **Boulder fields** (rock sea, felsenmeer) are what the name implies: slopes covered by blocky pieces of rock covering a large area (see Figure 39.11).

The boulders or blocks (angular stones) that make up boulder fields are large, as much as 1 to 3 m in diameter. They are loosened from bedrock slopes, cliffs, or other exposed surfaces by frost action, but then gravity takes over. When they are moved downslope, they accumulate in fields as large as 100 m wide and over 1 km long. Exactly how movement takes place is still being investigated. Apparently it does not occur in a single rock avalanche; there is evidence that slow downslope progress continues, the speed related to the angle of the slope against which the boulder field lies. Boulder fields are also found around tors (forming *clitter*).

Boulder fields can also be quite deep, and some have been measured to be 20 m in thickness. Another interesting aspect is that the long axes of the boulders tend to be lined up approximately parallel to each other, indicating that some sorting does take place. Some geomorphologists believe that movement may have been aided by a matrix of finer material between the boulders, so that the whole mass was capable of being saturated, thereby facilitating movement. Later, the finer material was eroded away. Others suggest that ice may have filled the openings between the boulders, so that the blocks originally moved as a **rock glacier**.

Whatever the answer, boulder fields are known to occur in periglacial areas and in cold mountainous zones above the timber line. They clearly result from the combination of frost action and slope process, and although the mechanisms may not be clearly understood, they do provide evidence that near-glacial conditions once prevailed where they exist. We might expect that the Driftless Area of Wisconsin, which escaped glacierization, ought to be a likely locale in which to find a boulder field. Not surprisingly, this type of landform does indeed occur there.

Figure 39.10 This prominent pingo, located in the Mackenzie River Delta in northwesternmost Canada, certainly ranks in the largest size category exhibited by these periglacial landforms.

Figure 39.11 A boulder field on Melville Island, Nunavut, with a *roche moutennée* in the foreground.

Canadian Geographers in the Field

'This vegetation sampling fieldwork was undertaken in the summer of 2001, in the middle of Boothia Peninsula, Nunavut (near Sanagak Lake and north of the community of Taloyoak). We were estimating percentage cover of plant functional types to characterize different tundra vegetation communities, and attempt to link them to Landsat ETM 7 satellite imagery and IKONOS imagery. The percentage of tundra vegetation cover was estimated visually, within a 50 cm × 50 cm quadrat. The 10 cm red and white divisions were augmented by a grid of string to aid in estimating the relative abundance of each plant functional type (i.e., graminoids, forbs, shrubs, and mosses). Along with percentage cover estimates, we collected biomass samples and spectral samples to help characterize tundra vegetation productivity and spectral characteristics (also to help link to satellite imagery).'

Gita J. Laidler is an assistant professor in the Department of Geography and Environmental Studies at Carleton University. She is studying environmental/cultural geography, exploring the importance and uses of Arctic sea ice from Inuit and scientific perspectives.

Muskeg (Organic) Terrain

Muskeg (Algonquian for 'grassy bog') is used to describe acidic wet organic terrain in Subarctic and boreal areas closely associated with permafrost and ground ice. It is estimated that Canada has over 1.2 million km² of muskeg (more than any other country). **Muskeg** is actually classified as a *mire*. It is also called peatland or bogland. It northern Russia it is known as *boloto*. Muskeg includes peat bogs, swamps, tundra, and forest floors. It is composed of the following layers: a surface mat of mosses, sedges, and/or grasses with or without shrubs and trees over a subsurface layer of peat and fossilized plant debris (peat and muck). One of the most important types of vegetation is sphagnum moss, which can hold 10 to 15 times its weight in water. It is often associated with stunted trees such as willows, poplars, shore pine, and spruce, which grow at a rate of about 25 cm per 300–400 years. These areas are nutrient-poor and have some species of carnivorous plants—because of the lack of soil nutrients the plants get more nutrients by carnivory (eating flies, etc.).

Muskeg freezes during the winter and thaws in the spring. It is trafficable when frozen but very difficult to cross when thawed unless specialized vehicles with tracks or large wheels are used. The permafrost table stops any percolation of water into the underlying ground so there is perched groundwater and the water table is close to, or at, the surface. There are many stories of heavy equipment—bulldozers, dump trucks, and even locomotive engines—sinking into the morass during the melt season. During the summer, muskeg degasses (burps) methane and carbon dioxide into the atmosphere. Muskeg can reach a thickness of more than 30 m, depending on the underlying topography. Construction on muskeg terrain is very difficult. The organic material has to be dug out down to the bedrock or sediment surface and replaced with gravel before building can occur. Roads across this terrain are either seasonal, i.e., winter snow or ice roads (Figure 39.12) or corduroy roads built up by a layer

of geotextile below, a layer of logs, and capped by clay or another stable material, hence the name.

Resource Development in Periglacial Environments

Periglacial environments and landscapes are experienced by a very small minority of the Earth's population. Our general understanding of these landforms and landscapes is based mainly on what we have learned in the temperate and tropical areas of the world. But now, in our search for fossil-fuel and mineral resources to satisfy the requirements of the developed countries, permafrost makes mining very difficult, and we are invading a realm well known to its indigenous peoples but little understood by outsiders. It is a realm of migrating caribou and reindeer, of muskox and wolves, of huge flocks of migratory birds and dense swarms of insects in summer. The landscape is one of unfamiliar forms and plants, of mosses and lichens, of needle-leaf evergreen trees, and of large patches of barren ground.

So far the modern invasion is limited. The realm is vast, and the invaders are few. But radioactive fallout from the 1986 Chernobyl disaster in Soviet Ukraine poisoned the reindeer of Scandinavia's Sámi (Lapps), and caribou migration has been adversely affected by Alaska's oil pipelines and other developments since 1970. New economic realities have changed Inuit ways of life. And for all their engineering prowess, developers can never be certain that their impact on Subarctic environments will be as they predict. Like Antarctica, the periglacial realm lies open, vulnerable, and fragile in a world of burgeoning demand for what it may contain.

The remote location of most periglacial environments has also severely limited their scientific study. We have repeatedly pointed out knowledge gaps concerning the exact nature of the geomorphic processes operating in these regions. As interest in these regions continues to grow, especially in regard to the effects of climate change, there will be an expansion of research efforts to better understand this vast, but still superficially explained, landscape.

Figure 39.12 A winter ice road from Yellowknife, NWT, allows for the transport of fuel, supplies, and heavy equipment to the diamond mines to the north and east, as well as to the Lupin gold mine just across the territorial border in Nunavut. During the summer season, the muskeg is an impassable morass and supplies and workers can be transported only by air or river.

KEY TERMS

REVIEW QUESTIONS

1. Define the term *periglacial* and describe the general spatial distribution of these environments.
2. Which Köppen climatic zones favour the development of periglacial landscapes?
3. Describe permafrost. How is it instrumental in the process of solifluction?
4. How do patterned ground and ice-wedge polygons form?
5. How does the existence of 'fossil pingos' help in the reconstruction of climatic conditions?

REFERENCES AND FURTHER READINGS

Benn, D.I., and D.J.A. Evans. 1998. *Glaciers and Glaciation*. New York: Oxford Univ. Press.

Bone, R.M. 2009. *The Canadian North: Issues and Challenges*, 3rd edn. Toronto: Oxford Univ. Press.

Brown, R.J.E. 1970. *Permafrost in Canada*. Toronto: Univ. of Toronto Press.

Clark, M.J., ed. 1988. *Recent Advances in Periglacial Geomorphology*. New York: Wiley.

Dixon, J.C., and A.D. Abrahams, eds. 1992. *Periglacial Geomorphology*. New York: Wiley.

Drewry, D. 1986. *Glacial Geologic Processes*. London: Edward Arnold.

Embleton, C., and C.A.M. King. 1975. *Periglacial Geomorphology*, 2nd edn. New York: Wiley/Halsted.

Evans, D.J.A., ed. 1996. *Cold Climate Landforms*. New York: Wiley.

Fountain, H. 2003. 'For Patterned Stone and Soil, the Earth Moved', *New York Times*, 21 Jan., D3.

French, H.M. 1996. *The Periglacial Environment*, 2nd edn. London/New York: Longman.

Harris, S.A. 1986. *The Permafrost Environment*. Totowa, NJ: Rowman & Littlefield.

Hewitt, K., et al., eds. 2002. *Landscapes of Transition: Landform Assemblages and Transformations in Cold Regions*. Dordrecht: Kluwer.

King, C.A.M., ed. 1976. *Periglacial Processes*. Stroudsburg, Penn.: Dowden, Hutchinson & Ross.

Krantz, W.B., et al. 1988. 'Patterned Ground', *Scientific American* (Dec.): 68–76.

Macfarlane, I.C., ed. 1969. *Muskeg Engineering Handbook*. National Research Council Associate Committee on Geotechnical Research, Muskeg Subcommittee. Toronto: Univ. of Toronto Press.

Mathews, J.A. 1992. *The Ecology of Recently-Deglaciated Terrain: A Geoecological Approach to Glacier Forelands*. London/New York: Cambridge Univ. Press.

Owen, L.A., et al. 1998. *Polar and Alpine Geomorphology*. Malden, Mass.: Blackwell.

Peltier, L.C. 1950. 'The Geographic Cycle in Periglacial Regions', *Annals, American Association of Geographers* 40: 214–36.

Pielou, E.C. 1994. *A Naturalist's Guide to the Arctic*. Chicago: Univ. of Chicago Press.

Price, L.W. 1972. *The Periglacial Environment, Permafrost, and Man*. Washington: Association of American Geographers, Commission on College Geography, Resource Paper 14.

Price, R.J. 1972. *Glacial and Fluvioglacial Landforms*. Edinburgh: Oliver & Boyd.

Radforth, N.W. 1952. 'Suggested Classification of Muskeg for the Engineer', *Engineering Journal* 35, 11: 1199–1210.

———— and C.O. Brawner. 1977. *Muskeg and the Northern Environment in Canada*. Toronto: Univ. of Toronto Press.

Schneider, K. 1994. 'In Aftermath of Oil Spill, Alaskan Sound Is Altered', *New York Times*, 7 July, A1, A9.

Shoop, S.A. 1993. *Terrain Characterization for Trafficability*. Office of the Chief Engineers. Washington: US Army Cold Regions Research and Engineering Lab. Also available online.

Smith, S.L., et al. 2001. 'Permafrost in Canada, a Challenge to Northern Development', in G.R. Brook, *A Synthesis of Geological Hazards in Canada*. Ottawa: Geological Survey of Canada Bulletin 548, 241–64.

Sugden, D.E., and B.S. John. 1976. *Glaciers and Landscape: A Geomorphological Approach*. New York: Wiley.

Washburn, A.L. 1973. *Periglacial Processes and Environments*. London: Edward Arnold.

Williams, P.J., and M.W. Smith. 1989. *The Frozen Earth: Fundamentals of Geocryology*. London/New York: Cambridge Univ. Press.

 WEB RESOURCES

atlas.gc.ca/site/english/maps/environment/land/permafrost Map of permafrost zones in Canada.

gsc.nrcan.gc.ca/permafrost/index_e.php This Geological Survey of Canada permafrost website has lots of information, data, research, and links.

www.fakr.noaa.gov/oil/default.htm The National Marine Fisheries Service of the National Oceanic and Atmospheric Administration in the

US provides impact and restoration data for the region affected by the *Exxon Valdez* oil spill of 1989. The Gulf Ecosystem Monitoring (GEM) Program continues to provide information about resource development in this periglacial environment.

Arid Environments and Wind as a Geomorphological Agent

Objectives

- To examine the characteristics of and geomorphological processes in arid environments.

- To examine the mechanisms of wind erosion and the landforms produced by this process.

- To relate various types of sand dunes to environmental controls.

- To note the importance and environmental significance of loess.

Arid Environments

LINK

Aridity is defined by a negative water balance. This occurs because the amount of precipitation is less than **potential evaporation** (the amount of water evapotranspired if there was a never-ending water supply). Polar deserts and cold deserts such as the Gobi Desert of Mongolia and northern China are common but have not been studied. Processes in polar and cold deserts may vary from those seen in hot deserts. Some landforms in both may appear similar but may result from different processes.

Arid areas can be classified as extremely arid, arid, and semi-arid. Extremely arid areas include the central parts of the Sahara Desert, the Atacama Desert in Chile, and parts of the Namib Desert of Namibia and southwest Angola. These areas make up about 4 per cent of the Earth's continental area and have nearly 12 months of the year without rainfall. Indeed, in parts of the Atacama Desert no rainfall has ever been recorded. The second category—arid areas—comprise about 15 per cent of the continental area and semi-arid regions cover another 14 per cent of the Earth's land surface.

Nearly all hot arid areas occur between about 15° and 25° latitude north and south of the Equator (in the Tropics). The largest region is the Sahara–Arabia–Iran–Thar desert belt of North Africa and southern Asia. There are also the deserts in central Australia, the US Southwest, and the Sonoran Desert of Mexico, as well as the Atacama Desert and Namib Desert, mentioned above. Cold deserts include Antarctica, the Arctic-Greenland area, and the Gobi Desert. The Carcross Desert (2.6 km²), 74 km south of Whitehorse, Yukon, is in a rain shadow area but precipitation data (over 500 mm/yr) indicate that it cannot be classified as a true desert (Figure 40.1). The Błędów Desert in Poland has developed since medieval times because of mining and poor land use and is, like the Carcross area, not a true desert but an area of sand dunes. There are many sand dune areas throughout Canada. As well, semi-arid areas are found in Canada in Palliser's Triangle of southern Alberta, southern Saskatchewan, and southwestern Manitoba, and in some areas of the central interior of BC.

Deserts are defined as having a rainfall of less than 250 mm/yr. Extremely arid areas such as the Atacama Desert and parts of the Namib Desert have less than 50 mm of precipitation in a year. Some weather stations in these areas have not recorded rainfall in 50 to 75 years. In the Egyptian Desert there are stations with a mean annual rainfall of 0.5 mm. Such areas have very infrequent heavy rainstorms that break the drought. An example is Wadi Halfa, just inside the northern border of Sudan.

Temperature Variations

There is a wide variation in annual and diurnal temperatures in hot and cold deserts. Coastal deserts have smaller ranges than inland areas. Inland sites have much greater temperature extremes. Maximum temperatures in the

Figure 40.1 The Carcross Desert, known as the world's smallest 'desert', is formed from sandy lake-bottom sediment from an earlier glacial era. Strong winds maintain active dune formation and movement, but the level of precipitation in this area means that it is not a true desert.

shade in hot deserts can reach over 50°C. Temperatures may remain above 35°C for many days consecutively.

- Extremely arid areas such as the Atacama Desert have air temperatures over 32°C for months on end. The maximum daytime temperatures are in the range of 42–48°C. The coolest months have temperatures between 15 and 20°C.
- Wadi Halfa is in an arid area. The very hot period has temperatures in the 32–35°C range. The maximum daytime temperatures are 43°C to 48°C. The coolest months are December and January, when temperatures are 15°C to 20°C.
- Kayes (Mali) is in a sub-arid area. The hottest period is from November to January. The temperatures at this time reach 30–33°C. The coolest period (April–May) has temperatures ranging from 12°C to 15°C. The wet season occurs between June and August because the Intertropical Convergence Zone moves northward at this time.

At night temperatures in deserts may fall below 10°C because of usually cloudless skies, which allow the rapid loss of longwave radiation from the desert surfaces. Ground surface temperatures have greater ranges than air temperatures. Sand and rock surfaces can reach 82°C or more during the day and have temperature ranges of about 50°C. Sand and bedrock surfaces can be so hot during the day that it is impossible to walk on them in bare feet or in thin-soled shoes.

Types of Deserts and Their Causes

Deserts result from various factors:

1. *Trade-wind deserts*. These are caused by atmospheric high pressure cells that block cloud and moisture-carrying low pressure (depressional) weather systems. Examples are the Sahara–Arabia–Iran–Thar desert belt, central Australia, and the Namib Desert.
2. *Rain shadow deserts*. Orographic conditions block rain-carrying weather systems. Examples are the deserts of the southwestern US and northwestern Mexico.
3. *Coastal deserts*. Cold oceanic currents limit evaporative moisture loading of weather systems. An example is the Atacama Desert.
4. *Global circulation deserts*. These are caused by continentality (distance from the sea and extremes of temperature and pressure systems), with low pressure at the surface because of surface heating and high pressure above. An example of this type of desert is the Taklamakan Desert of western China.
5. *Polar or cold deserts*. These are caused by extremely low temperatures that limit the ability of the air to hold moisture. Examples are the Antarctic and Arctic-Greenland deserts and Asia's Gobi Desert.

Any one of the above reasons can dominate or two or more factors can work together to cause aridity.

Desert Landscapes

As stated above, arid and semi-arid areas cover about 33 per cent of the continental surfaces. Hot deserts are associated with three main sedimentary environments:

1. Alluvial fans and ephemeral streams
2. Inland *sabkhas* or *playas* (sedimentary silt and sand along with salts in flat basins)
3. Sandy deserts (*sand seas* or *ergs*).

Much of the desert areas are composed of: (1) eroding mountains and uplands (about 40 per cent of the total world desert area); (2) stony deserts associated with erosion rather than deposition (about 10–20 per cent); (3) sandy surfaces (about 20 per cent). The deserts of southwestern North America are not typical of the deserts in the rest of the world. In America, alluvial fans are more important (about 30 per cent of area) and sandy deserts are less important (less than 1 per cent) compared to deserts on other continents.

Geomorphological Processes and Desert Landforms

Geomorphological processes in desert areas are particularly sensitive to climatic conditions and climatic changes. There are a variety of topographic settings from mountains to basins of different types, as well as many relic landforms and deposits.

Weathering

The water deficit limits the development of vegetation cover and the amount of chemical weathering in extremely arid areas. Water is in greater abundance in semi-arid regions, and therefore weathering and soil development are more pronounced. Although arid and semi-arid environments have been closely associated with physical weathering processes, chemical weathering is probably as important if not more so in some situations, e.g., in the development of weathering pits, or *tafoni*, which develop on bare rock surfaces and are caused by water (from night cooling and dew production in interior sites and fog or mist in coastal deserts) that concentrates in depressional areas of irregular surfaces.

The most important weathering processes are **salt crystal (salt burst) hydration** (halioclasty) and *thermal expansion and contraction*. The water for the hydration of salt crystals is supplied by dew or fog. Salt weathering is very important in arid and semi-arid areas. Evaporites such as glauberite or sodium calcium sulphate—$Na_2Ca(SO_4)_2$—and natrinite (sodium nitrate, or Chile saltpetre—$NaNo_3$—which was commonly used as a fertilizer and to make explosives) are two good examples of this process. They may expand by 300 per cent when hydrated.

Crust Development

The development of indurated crusts, or cuirasses (or duricrusts) is significant in arid areas. There are many kinds of crusts—laterite (iron-rich), bauxite (aluminum-rich), silcrete (silica-rich), caliches (calcium-rich), and gypcretes (gypsum-rich). These may cap more readily eroded materials and protect them from erosion, much like a basalt caprock, to form plateaus, mesas, buttes, columns, or pillars. Some crusts develop because of long-standing intense weathering and the removal of other weatherable minerals (e.g., laterite and bauxite), while others form because of evaporation and the capillary-rise of mineral-rich groundwater towards the surface (silcrete, caliche, and gypcrete).

Lag Surfaces

Lag surfaces are called **desert pavement** in the US, stone or debris mantles and gibber in Australia, gobi in central Asia, and hamada, reg, or serir on the Arabian Peninsula (Figure 40.2). They are associated with alluvial fans and their deposits. Lag surfaces are formed

Figure 40.2 An extensive area of desert pavement covers the surface of a section of Signal Park in Arizona's Kofa National Wildlife Refuge.

by wind deflation and the winnowing process. Vertical sorting of the heavier pebble material left behind by the wind is characteristic. The coarser material is found on the surface with finer material below. The coarser clasts move up through and out of the finer material because of continued wetting and drying and expansion and contraction of the finer material. *Desert varnish*, a minor weathering product, commonly forms a thin crust (about 10–30 μm thick) of iron or manganese oxide over the lag surface gravels. The crust is black and shiny. It is a residue left by migrating mineralized water moving up through the lag deposits, and is concentrated on the surface of the clasts as evaporation takes place and also because of cyanobacterial action.

Streams in Deserts

Streams are not generally associated with deserts but they do play an important role in shaping the landscape. There are two types of streams in desert environments: *ephemeral streams* and *perennial exotic streams*.

Ephemeral and Perennial Streams

To create surface runoff in deserts precipitation must be intense, and this only occurs sporadically. Consequently, most desert streams are **ephemeral streams**, only flowing for short periods in response to irregularly episodic rainfalls that occur several times a year. As such, the streams are in flood whenever this occurs. A number of factors are important in terms of maximizing runoff. (1) The desert surface is often composed of clay and silt particles that slow down infiltration and increase runoff. (2) Many areas are cemented by various types of crusts. (3) Vegetation cover is sparse so interception and storage are limited.

All these factors lead to the rapid conversion of overland flow into discharge and flash flooding of short duration (1 to 5 hours). The hydrographs for such streams exhibit a near-vertical rising limb, which may peak between 10 and 30 minutes after the beginning of the flow. A wall of water (a bore) rushes down the dry channel (southwestern US: **arroyo**, or gully). The velocity of the bore increases downstream until it reaches a point where it starts losing water to evaporation or infiltration. The floors of the dry channels are often choked by debris in storage from previous flash floods. This is easily picked up by the water. This means that the sediment loads of these streams can be enormous and make them look more like mudflows than streams. After a certain point discharge decreases downstream (which is the opposite of temperate and humid tropical streams) because:

1. Water sinks rapidly into the porous debris that forms the floors of the channels and adds to groundwater recharge. Such seepage losses make the flow more viscous and mudflow-like.
2. The localized nature of desert rainfall means that as flow occurs down the channels it is not augmented by inflow from tributary streams.
3. Evaporation from the basin surface and the surface of the flowing stream is very high because of the high temperatures and the lack of atmospheric humidity.

Ultimately the flow of water may stop completely as a result of such losses. The sediment load is dumped, to await the next period of flow.

Arroyos, or gullies, usually occur in the bottoms of or lead out from **box canyons** (also called gulches or dry washes in the US or **wadis** in the Middle East). The floor of the box canyons cannot usually be separated into channel and floodplain areas because the bottoms are formed by continuous sheets of sediments between the rock walls (Figures 40.3 and 40.4). The sediments at the bottoms of the canyons are subject to total remodelling by sheetwash process during the next rainfall event. Historical records show that the canyon bottoms in the southwestern US were not cut into by arroyos during the early nineteenth century. Many are now occupied by steep-walled arroyos. These channels have been studied extensively. They often show repeated episodes of cut and fill of alluvial deposits. Long-term changes appear to be related to climatic and land-use changes. Entrenchment of many of the arroyos began with European settlement and reached a peak between 1865 and 1915. The reasons for the arroyo entrenchment seem to differ in different areas but are likely related to human-caused reduction of infiltration and decrease in vegetation cover in the surrounding environment. These changes can result in either or both of increased flow velocity of these ephemeral streams or their increased capability of eroding the canyon floors.

Figure 40.3 Arroyo (wadi) in Tamanguillet, Mali. Arroyos, with their intermittent flash floods, can cut into the valley floor by over 20 m and often are wider than 50 m.

Figure 40.4 Box canyon, with scrub smoke trees, in the Rodman Mountains of the Mojave Desert in southern California.

The volume of stream-transported material is dependent on the rainfall. In general, however, ephemeral streams in arid regions have high *specific yields* compared with those seen in humid areas. As rainfall totals increase, more sediment is eroded and transported. A peak is reached at precipitation figures around 250–300 mm/yr (the geomorphologically optimum value). In wetter areas the sediment yield declines because vegetation cover increases and reduces the effectiveness of rainsplash erosion and overland flow.

Perennial exotic streams, or *exoreic streams,* have a continuous water flow throughout the year because their sources are outside of the desert area. Examples include the Nile, Colorado, Niger, and Indus Rivers. These streams supply recharge to the desert groundwater systems.

Desert Lakes

Not all desert streams disappear because of evaporation and infiltration as they flow down-channel. In many areas ephemeral streams feed into desert basins with pediments. Lakes, inland sabkhas, or playas (also called *salinas, bolsons, chotts*) are fed by these internal drainage (endorheic) systems. The lakes may dry up to leave salt flats. Some lakes are permanent, e.g., the Dead Sea in the Middle East, the Great Salt Lake in Utah (a remnant of the much more extensive Pleistocene *pluvial* Lake Bonneville), and Lake Natron and other lakes associated with the East African Great Rift Valley. The only outlet from these lakes is by evaporation; as this takes place brine concentration increases. These lakes have a much higher salt content than seawater: Dead Sea, 225,000 parts per million; Great Salt Lake, 200,000 ppm; seawater, average of about 35,000 ppm. Halite, glauberite, epsomite, trona, natron, nitratine, and gypsum are commonly precipitated by the brine concentration process as the ephemeral lakes dry up.

Alluvial Fans

Where box canyons emerge from upland areas onto the pediment surface, the abrupt change causes sediment to build up a large, low-angled cone of debris (alluvial fan). These often measure up to 10 km across and have slope angles of less than 10°. They are gently concave. Alluvial fans occur in other areas but are best developed in arid areas. These fans often coalesce or overlap to form an apron of sediment (a *bajada*) around the edge of the basin. Depositional areas shift rapidly across these features producing *segmented fans*. The upper parts of the fans are often entrenched. Like arroyos, sedimentation and erosion depend on seasonal and longer-scale climatic changes, the intensity of individual storms, and the lack of a vegetation cover. Fans are often found where seepage losses are so great that the flow from the canyon comes to a halt and the major form of deposition is by mudflow. The lower parts of the fans are usually composed of finer sediments and may develop integrated dendritic channel networks that carry away rainfall received by the fans. The size of the fans is related to the size of the canyon drainage basin.

Figure 40.5 presents a schematic drawing of an alluvial fan system.

Slope Processes and Pediments

The relationship of slopes to bedrock can be seen clearly in desert environments because of the lack of both soils and vegetation cover. The cliff–pediment form is seen everywhere.

Slopes are the primary source of all debris in arid and semi-arid areas. They are affected by climatic changes and tectonics working through changes in discharges and sediment yields off the slopes. The amount of moisture available to the slopes decreased during the

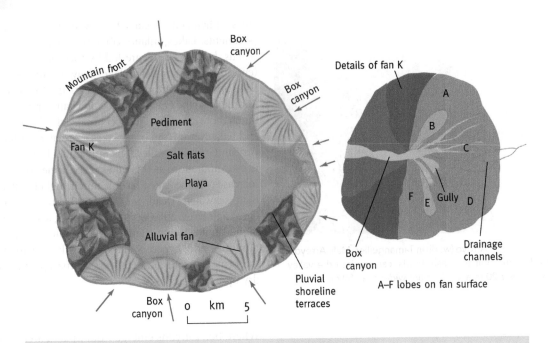

Figure 40.5 Model of a playa lake basin and alluvial fan system. (After Cooke and Doornkamp, 1990)

Pleistocene–Holocene transition in many areas and caused major changes:

1. Temperatures increased and/or precipitation decreased, leading to a reduction in vegetation cover and an increase in runoff and soil erosion. The decrease in soil depth also added to the decrease in vegetation cover.
2. The decrease in vegetation cover decreased infiltration (which in turn added to the decrease in vegetation).
3. Increased erosion decreased the average depth of soils and increased the area of impermeable surfaces, which caused an increase in runoff and erosion.

Rapid erosion of the soil cover of the upper slopes resulted, so that now there are sudden but infrequent stream discharges and low sediment yields.

The features of the pediment have been studied by many geomorphologists, and definitions and understandings vary. Essentially, however, the low-angled slopes (between 0 and 11°) of these bedrock surfaces underlying alluvial fans at the base of mountains and highlands are usually mantled with debris. Pediments associated with fault scarps are slightly more inclined, and pediments vary widely in size, from less than 1 km² to over 620 km² (mean value: about 100 km²). The size of the pediment or exposed bedrock seems to be linked to the size of the drainage basin that supplies runoff and debris to it.

Aeolian Processes, Deposits, and Landforms

The role of **aeolian** (wind-related) processes in shaping the Earth's surface, both in arid regions and elsewhere, has been the subject of ongoing debate among geomorphologists.

Whereas the effects of running water, flowing ice, and coastal wave action are generally obvious, the role of wind as a geomorphic agent is usually more subtle and difficult to measure. In hot and cold arid landscapes with little vegetation, wind redistribution of material weathered at the surface takes the form of sand dunes, the morphology of which is controlled by aspects of the local windflow pattern and its strength.

In general, as conditions become more humid, the stabilization of the surface by vegetation diminishes the role of the wind, and other processes become more important in shaping the physical landscape. Complicating this simple assessment is the realization that much of the Earth's surface bears the signature of processes that are no longer operating. There is no question that aeolian processes have had an important influence on the landscapes of various regions during previous climatic regimes. Furthermore, human activities often destabilize the surface vegetation, and in some areas aeolian processes are even becoming more significant.

Aeolian processes, deposits, and landforms occur in many different environments. Besides hot arid and semi-arid areas, periglacial (cold arid), fluvioglacial, and coastal landscapes show the effects of wind. In fact, arid environments in the subtropics are less windy than the temperate zone but aeolian deposits and landforms are common in areas with less than 200–300 mm/yr rainfall. The lack of vegetation cover in all these areas means that there is no vegetation canopy buffer to reduce wind velocities and no binding of the soil surface and topsoil by humus, root systems, or plant litter. This enables large volumes of sand to be mobilized and moved by the wind. Strong prevailing winds and desert storms are spectacular and are extremely efficient at moving sand and smaller

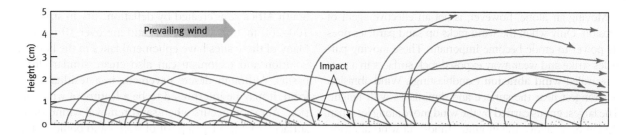

Figure 40.6 Wind causes movement of coarse sand grains by saltation. Impacted grains bounce into the air and are carried ballistically by the wind as gravity pulls them back to the loose sand surface where they impact other particles, repeating the process (reptation).

materials, but generally they occur for very short periods. Lower wind speeds are probably responsible for moving the greatest volume of sand, silt, and clay in all these different environments.

Sand Mobilization and Movement

Sand (and silt and clay) grains are set in motion (1) by strong shear forces as the wind blowing over the surface equals or exceeds the fluid threshold holding the grains to the surface and (2) by ballistic impact from other grains exceeding the impact threshold.

Smaller grains need a higher fluid threshold to put them in motion because they create an aerodynamically smooth surface and are more cohesive. The larger sand grains sitting on the surface create turbulence in the airflow that lifts the grains and entrains them. The impact of mobile grains can entrain material at lower wind speeds and causes sudden movement or bouncing (*saltation*). Particles are lifted almost vertically into the faster wind above the surface and are then transported downwind (saltated) along a trajectory sloping at 6–12°. As the saltating grains impact the surface they entrain other particles. Impact with grains on the surface too large to be saltated causes them to creep (roll or slide) or make short bounces (*reptation*) across the surface. One impacting grain can cause a number of grains to start bouncing. Many impacting grains can cause mass bouncing and cause a *reptating population* of particles (Figure 40.6). Sandstorms are the most extreme form of saltation (Figure 40.7). In contrast to dust storms, which can reach a high altitude and in which suspension is the major process (see Figure 43.8), sandstorms are confined to the lower layers of moving air, and saltation is the dominant mode of movement.

Most mobile sand lies in the range between 0.20 and 0.45 mm. Finer and coarser material is generally left behind to form a lag deposit with a bimodal grain size distribution (mix of small and large). Aeolian deposits are well-sorted and unimodal. Windblown glacial or desert silt and fine sand (*loess*) also occurs, as does aeolian clay, or *parna*. Wind also moves larger rock fragments by actually rolling or pushing them along the surface in a process called **surface creep** (rolling or sliding). Pebbles and even small boulders of considerable weight can be moved by strong windstorms.

Wind Erosion

In order for wind to be an aggradational agent, it must also be able to erode—to degrade the surface. As in the case of water erosion, the speed of the wind is of primary importance. The higher the velocity of the moving air, the greater is the wind's degradational power. Wind direction also influences the cumulative effect of wind erosion: when the wind blows fairly constantly in the same direction, it erodes more rapidly than it would otherwise.

Figure 40.7 A sandstorm bears down on a settlement in Arizona. Overgrazing and general overuse of land in fragile ecosystems generate conditions like this. Much of West Africa's Sahel suffers from recurrent sandstorms, as does East Asia.

Moving air alone, however, is not an effective agent of erosion. Only when the wind picks up sand particles does its power to erode become important. These moving particles strike and wear away exposed rock surfaces in a process called **wind abrasion** (sandblasting). Wind abrasion is strongest near the surface and diminishes with height. The largest grains carried by the wind move along less than 20 cm or so above the ground. Almost all wind abrasion takes place within 2 m of the ground surface.

Degradational Landforms

When the wind sweeps along a surface and carries away the finest particles, the process is called **deflation**. The results of the deflation process can be seen in desert areas today, because the arid landscape often includes shallow basins without outlets (Figure 40.8). These basins lie in rows parallel to the prevailing wind direction. They begin as small local hollows that are continuously enlarged as the wind removes freshly weathered particles. Eventually these basins grow quite large (to hundreds of square kilometres in area), and other processes may reinforce their growth.

Not many landforms can be attributed exclusively to wind erosion. The **deflation hollows** just described as desert basins created by wind erosion undoubtedly result from erosion by moving air (e.g., Qattara Depression in northwestern Egypt). Where wind has removed finely textured material (an estimate is that up to 3000 km³ of sand was removed from this area in Egypt), a surface concentration of closely packed pebbles (lag deposit) is left behind as desert pavement (Figure 40.2). In

South Africa *pans* created by deflation vary in size from 100–200 m² to over 300 km² and are over 10 m deep. Many of these sites have ephemeral lakes in the bottom. Solution and tectonism can also create similar closed basins. Although desert pavement is a residual landform, it may be interpreted to be a feature of wind erosion. Abrasion occurs when sand removal winnows the surface, leaving a lag deposit of stones and boulders that becomes concentrated as the surface is lowered. Sand movement abrades facets and pits into the exposed faces of pebbles on the surface of the pavements, creating *ventifacts* (from the French for *wind*). Changes in wind direction or toppling of the pebbles may produce several faceted surfaces on one clast. The sand can also abrade larger landforms. The ideal flux of sand for abrasion is about 1.0 g/cm²/s. If it is larger, material bounces off targets and buffers the process. Abrasion can erode areas of less-resistant rocks and leave upstanding pinnacles with sculpted shapes or elongated forms under more resistant caprocks, such as basalt, or a crust. These are commonly called hoodoos.

The most common product of wind abrasion is the **yardang** (Figure 40.9). Yardangs are low aerodynamic ridges that form parallel to the prevailing wind direction in uniform rock types. They tend to develop in dry sandy areas affected by strong winds, especially where the bedrock is fairly soft and unprotected by vegetation. The yardangs are separated by troughs that are scooped out and smoothed to a polished-looking surface by wind abrasion. The yardangs are rock outcrops that are shaped like the inverted keels of ships with their wider ends upwind and the sharper ends downwind. The size varies

Figure 40.8 Wind action is the second most powerful degradational force in desert areas, shaping the landscape in some places. Here the floor of Golden Canyon in California's Death Valley is being shaped by deflation.

Figure 40.9   The striking topography of a zone of yardangs dominates the foreground and centre of this photo. This locale is near Minab, a coastal town on the Persian Gulf's Strait of Hormuz in southeastern Iran.

from metres to kilometres in length, they can range up to many kilometres wide, and they usually are less than 200 m high. The length:width ratio ranges from 3:1 to 10:1. They often occur in groups or *fleets*. Large-scale yardangs (megayardangs) can be tens of kilometres long; and yardangs hundreds of metres high have been found in the central parts of the Sahara and on Mars.

Aggradational Landforms

It is important to remember that wind action is not confined to deserts or semi-arid steppelands. Wind also has erosional functions in glacial and periglacial zones, in savannas and humid mid-latitude grasslands, and in other areas as well. During a severe windstorm in England in 1987, for example, an estimated 1 million trees were toppled.

Nevertheless, wind does its most effective work in dry environments. Some deserts and semi-deserts are dominated by aeolian processes, and the landforms and landscapes of wind action are best developed in North Africa's Sahara, Southwest Asia's Arabian Desert, the Great Sandy Desert of Australia, and the Earth's other extensive dry-lands. But even in these desert areas, the landforms typically associated with aeolian deposition are confined to relatively small sections of the desert. Where sand accumulations are large and extensive, there may still not be any prominent aeolian landforms. Over large expanses of sandy desert landscape, the dominant feature is the **erg**, or *sand sea*. Over 95 per cent of all aeolian sand is found in these sand seas. Wind directions may vary seasonally to such an extent that there is no dominantly prevailing airflow, so the sand is continuously moved about, but normally the predominant winds cross the ergs in more or less parallel lines.

The main reason for the accumulation of sand in ergs seems to be:

1. The presence of a depression.
2. The presence of a moist surface or scattered vegetation (or both) to trap the sand.
3. The trapping action that dunes have on moving sand once accumulation has begun.

The landscape in such places takes on an undulating (gently rolling) appearance. The surface of the sand may be formed into *ripples* by saltation and surface creep, but otherwise the topography is unremarkable.

Sand Dunes

The landform most commonly associated with wind deposition is the dune. A **dune** is an accumulation of sand that is shaped by wind action. This definition is clear and concise, but when you look at an aerial image of a dune landscape, it is clear why the many dune formations are difficult to interpret. Dunes come in many shapes and sizes: as straight or curving ridges, as quarter-moon-shaped crescents, as irregular mounds, and more. Physical geographers are interested in three aspects of dunes: (1) whether or not they are stable; (2) what their shape or form is; (3) how they are arranged in the landscape.

Dunes in sandy desert areas normally support no vegetation. The wind modifies them continually, removing sand from the windward side and depositing it on the leeward side (Figure 40.11). This has the effect of moving the dune across the landscape, so that the dune is unstable, or *active*. Over time, however, dunes may migrate into moister areas on the desert margin, or a climate change may affect a dune area. Then plants will take hold, and the vegetation will slow or even halt the dune's movement; in such instances a dune is described as stable, or *fixed*. Dunes close to the coast (see 'Perspectives' box) may be fixed by the growth of grasses, e.g., marram grass.

Dune Features

Every dune has a profile, a cross-section that reveals much about its history. This profile consists of three elements: the windward slope, or **backslope**; the top, or crest; and the leeward slope, or **slip face**. As Figure 40.11 shows, the windward slope has a lower angle than the leeward slope. The wind drives the sand grains up the length of

Perspectives on the Human Environment

Sand, Dunes, and the Game of Golf

The game of golf, generally believed to have had its origins along the North Sea coast of Scotland in the fifteenth century, owes its birth to the dune-filled landscape of this part of the British Isles (Figure 40.10). The first bunkers (sand traps) on the early links courses of Scotland were created by aeolian processes, and the steep bunker faces were enlarged by sheep digging into the slip faces of dunes to find shelter from the winds off the North Sea and the North Channel. One bunker on the Royal Troon links course, on the North Channel between Scotland and Northern Ireland, proved so deep that a Canadian brigade commander, in night-time training with his men just prior to shipping out for the invasion of Sicily during World War II, lost radio communications with his superior officer for several hours.

The sandy soil of coastal Scotland also meant that the links courses, despite being set in a moist and often rainy maritime environment, had excellent drainage and the Scottish golfers could play despite the weather, unlike

Figure 40.10   The 'Postage Stamp', the eighth hole at Royal Troon, is among the most widely known and acclaimed short holes in all of golf. The small green, from which the name of the hole derives, was created simply by flattening out a dune, with the rest of the landscape left as it had been formed by the aggradational forces of winds off the Firth of Clyde. Interestingly, the hole was originally named 'Ailsa', for Ailsa Craig, a granitic island visible from the tee that rises to 338 m in the Firth of Clyde and is formed entirely of the plug of an extinct volcano. In earlier years, Ailsa was quarried to make curling stones.

the over-watered parkland golf courses of inland North America, where a rainstorm can quickly flood low-lying areas and golf balls can disappear into the mud. For this reason, and for the visual and participatory aesthetics of golf courses built on links-style landscapes, when golf migrated beyond Scotland and the British Isles many of the first and best courses were built on coastal and inland dune lands in Australia and in North America. And when they weren't, course designers and builders imported many tonnes of sand to create bunkers. Today, golf course architects seek dune lands for designing and building championship and resort courses, from the coastal dunes of Prince Edward Island to the high dunes along the rugged Oregon coast. Many of the best new courses, such as Prairie Dunes near Hutchinson, Kansas; Whistling Straits, on Lake Michigan in Wisconsin; Bandon Dunes in Oregon; Pine Barrens at World Woods and The Dunes in the sand belt of central Florida; and the Ocean Course at Kiawah Island, a barrier island along the South Carolina coast, have been established on lands evocative of golf's origins along the Scottish coast.

the backslope, pushes them over the crest, and lets them drop on the slip face, on which they may fail or slip down. Thus a dune has a degradational and an aggradational side, and the prevailing wind can be determined from the dune profile. The backslope of the dune can maintain angles of between 10° and 15° while the leeside slip face has angles of 33° +/− 1°.

Aeolian Bedforms

Given these conditions, it might be assumed that loose sand influenced by prevailing wind will be arranged into one dominant landform. That is not the case. Four scales of aeolian dunes or bedforms are recognized:

1. *Ripples or ripple ridges*. These small-scale features (a few centimetres wide and high) are flatter than those seen in water and have more rounded crests.
2. *Meso-dunes*. These features are up to 10 m across and a few metres high.
3. *Transverse and longitudinal dunes*. These are tens of metres across and 10–100 m high.
4. *Complex pyramidal dunes*. These are 20–450 m high.

Dunes develop various forms, and the exact origin of some of them is not completely understood. The rates of dune migration increase during drier periods by 5–10 per cent and more because of the decrease in vegetation stabilization. It seems that large dune complexes modify the local wind patterns by topographic deflection and as a result of the extreme heating of the sand surface. Sand dunes cover about 0.27 per cent of the Canadian landscape. Forty-five per cent of this area is in Alberta, 36 per cent in Saskatchewan, and 10 per cent is in Manitoba. Only 2.5 per cent of this area has active dunes. Most of them have been stabilized by vegetation cover, which has been developed by the natural succession process. Some areas have been planted by humans. It has been estimated that 95 per cent of dune sand in Canada is found in one area of the Prairies—the Athabasca sand dunefield (385 km²), south of Lake Athabasca in Saskatchewan.

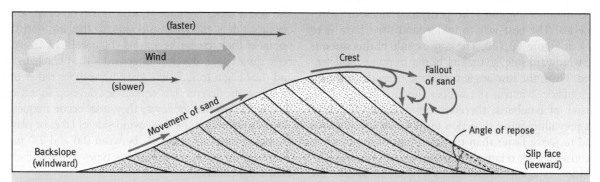

Figure 40.11 Cross-section of an active sand dune that is migrating from left to right. The lower-angle, windward backslope is the degradational side of the dune, with surface sand grains pushed upward towards the crest. The steeper, leeward slip face is the aggradational component of the dune, where wind-driven sand is deposited. The accumulation of sand grains on the advancing slip face produces strata inside the dune, much like the foreset beds in a delta.

Ripples   Ripples are the smallest bedforms that develop. They are formed by saltation. They are initiated by surface irregularities or moisture differences over a surface. Such irregularities cause saltation to occur from the windward slope, and once ripples form, saltation from the windward slopes spreads the newly created forms downwind.

Meso-Dunes and Dunes   Dunes are larger than ripples. The simplest dune forms are small **transverse dunes** (or asymmetrical ridges). Transverse dunes are usually straight or slightly curved and positioned at right angles to the prevailing wind (Figure 40.12A). These dunes look like extremely large ripples on the landscape. Indeed, transverse dunes often mark ergs, giving the topography the look of a sandy sea complete with 'wave crests'. Transverse dunes develop when local topographic or climatic disturbances produce a wave motion in the air stream. When faster air flow dips towards the surface, erosion takes place. Deposition builds the dune in the low velocity zone beneath the crests. The shape, once formed, affects the airflow and small back eddies develop to the lee of the **dune crest**. Grains saltate or creep up the windward side of the dune and avalanche down the slip face. The migration rates for this type of dune are typically 1.2–3.6 m/yr. Transverse dunes are often found associated with parabolic dunes in the dunefields of the Canadian Prairies and are also prominent along sandy beaches on the coastlines of western and eastern Canada and along the shores of the Great Lakes at locations such as Sandbanks and Pinery Provincial Parks and Wasaga and Sauble Beaches in Ontario.

Barchans   Other dune types also form at right angles to the windflow, but their sides begin to adjust to the wind and become rounded or crescent-shaped, as is the case with barchans and parabolic dunes. This is especially true where the sand supply is limited, as is the case around the edges of the ergs. **Barchans** are the quintessential dunes seen in many 'desert' movies, probably because they are quite common in the deserts of the southwestern US. They are relatively common in most deserts and quite common along coastal areas and in contemporary and relic periglacial areas in North America. The best way to understand their form is to look at Figure 40.12B. The convex side of this dune is the windward side, so that its 'horns' or points lie *downwind*. Thus, the low-angle backslope faces the wind on the outside, whereas the steeper slip face lies inside. A cluster of barchans, therefore, immediately indicates the prevailing wind direction in its locality. The horns tend to move faster than the main part of the barchan because of their relatively smaller volumes of sand. Deposition is again controlled by vegetation and/or the presence of moist surfaces. These dunes move at rates of 2 to 3 m/yr. In the Mojave Desert rates occur up to 15 m/yr, while in coastal Peru rates of 17–47 m/yr have been recorded.

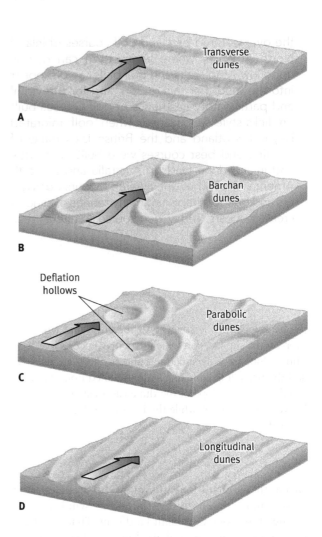

LINK

Figure 40.12 The four most common types of sand dunes. In each diagram the prevailing wind direction is indicated by the arrow. Note that longitudinal dunes lie parallel to the prevailing wind, whereas the others form at right angles to it.

Parabolic Dunes   Not all dunes with a crescent shape are barchans, however. A **parabolic dune**, or *lunette dune*, also has a crescent shape, but in this type of dune the concave side is the windward side, so that the 'horns' or points of the crescent lie *upwind* (Figure 40.12 C). Parabolic dunes often develop longer sides than barchans do, and they begin to look like giant horseshoes rather than crescents. In deserts they sometimes develop in association with deflation hollows; they also occur frequently along coastlines on the downwind side of lakes or playas. Migration rates are generally between 0.6 and 2.0 m/yr. These are the most common dune types in the Canadian Prairie dunefields.

If the wind direction changes with the season or if there is no prevailing wind direction, more complex dunes form. Often barchans and parabolic dunes can be blown out and change into long, narrow longitudinal (seif) dunes.

Longitudinal Dunes   **Longitudinal dunes** (also known as linear dunes or *seifs*, after the Arabic word for 'sword'), like transverse dunes, form lengthy, narrow, sinuous sand ridges, but they lie *parallel* to the prevailing wind direction (Figure 40.12D), not perpendicular to it. It has been suggested that when the sand supply is plentiful, as in an erg, transverse dunes will develop, but that when the sand availability is limited, longitudinal dunes develop. The swales between the dunes are swept by vortices to maintain the dune form. These dunes are associated with great thicknesses of sand and occur in the central parts of ergs and form large dune systems parallel to the dominant wind direction (called mega-dunes or *draa*).

Draa can cover very large areas, such as the Rub-al-Khali in Arabia. This is an extremely arid area. In this region the longitudinal dunes often have Y-shaped junctions where they have been connected to one another by *silks* or *link seifs*, smaller 'fish-scale' dunes formed by the swirling action of the wind. Between Adelaide on the coast of South Australia and Alice Springs in the heart of the continent, an entire landscape looks like corrugated cardboard. Here, thousands of longitudinal dunes over 3 m high, with many as tall as 20 m, extend continuously for as far as 100 km.

Complex Dunes   If wind direction is changeable, two trends of dunes can meet and the patterns interfere to form *star-shaped dunes*, or *rhourds*. Some dunes form around rock outcrops or individual trees or groups of trees rather like snowdrifts. Dunes can also form behind objects (*nebkhas*, or coppice dunes). Other dunes may even 'climb up' ridges or escarpments and fall down the other side. They may form against steep cliffs where the wind is funnelled and vortices sweep the sand into *echo dunes*. These can reach up to 300 m high.

Zibars   Many ergs or interdune areas are characterized by low rolling dunes without slip faces. The maximum relief of these features is 10 m with dune spacing of 50–400 m. These areas are called *zibars*. These typically are composed of coarser sand and occur on the upwind margins of ergs. Small dunes of this type in the Namib Desert move at rates of around 4 m/yr.

Dune Landscape Research

These are just some of the many dune shapes and forms that have been classified and whose origins are understood. Many others remain to be studied. Research on present-day dune landscapes—in deserts, in periglacial areas, and along coasts—also contributes to the interpretation of the past because dunes offer clues about climate change. Certain areas where dunes now lie are no longer arid or periglacial, and the dune landscape has become fixed (Figure 40.13)—for example, Hillsburgh Sandhills in the Orangeville area of southern Ontario,

in the approximately 120 dunefields in the Prairie provinces (including the Carberry–Brandon and Oak Lake Sandhills of Manitoba), and in Quebec. Some relic areas such as the Yukon's Carcross Desert are still active, however, because of strong prevailing winds. Only the margins and some depressional areas of this sand spread have been invaded by plants such as sage, dwarf aspens, and kinnikinnik (*Arctostaphylos uva-ursi*). From the morphology of the dunes, however, conclusions may be drawn about earlier climates not only in general terms but, more specifically, about wind directions and velocities as well.

Another reason to know as much as we can about wind erosion and dune formation is immediate and practical. As explained in Units 17 and 44, *desertification* has become a global problem. There even are places along desert margins where advancing dunes are overtaking inhabited land. By understanding how dunes migrate and how wind action drives them, we are in a better position to develop ways to stabilize them and to halt their progress (see Figure 17.12).

Loess and Coversands

Perhaps the most impressive evidence of the capacity of wind to modify the landscape comes from ice-age times. As described in Units 37 and 38, glacial processes are associated with tremendous quantities of fine-textured sediment, and such material became part of the extensive sandur deposits formed during glacial recession. Strong winds, which were common in periglacial environments during the Pleistocene, carried away huge quantities of these fine particles to the south of the ice margins. At times the sandar must have looked like the dust storm depicted in Figure 43.8, as vast clouds of dust darkened the skies and obscured the Sun. Because prevailing winds were fairly steady, much of the dust moved in specific directions. When the air motion eventually subsided, the fine-grained dust was deposited on the ground, sometimes hundreds of kilometres from its source. In this way, sedimentary deposits called **loess** (pronounced 'lerss') accumulated (in this case, *periglacial*, or *cold, loess*). Dust storms originating from hot deserts can distribute *hot* (or *desert*) *loess*.

While vast areas of loess deposits are among the richest agricultural lands on Earth, coversands, another wind-blown deposit, are of less significance. These are periglacial aeolian sands that cover areas on the upwind side of loess accumulations. They are very common in Europe and in many parts of the US and Canada, including the Prairies, Ontario, and Quebec. They include such areas as the Carberry–Brandon region of Manitoba and Yukon's tiny Carcross Desert. The same features seen in hot deserts, e.g., dunes, can be seen in many of these areas.

Figure 40.13   Coastal dune on the west coast of Australia, about 160 km north of Perth. When the coastal location brings some moisture to the environment, vegetation can spread on the sandy surface and anchor the dune.

Distribution of Loess Deposits

Loess was laid down in many areas south of the ice sheets in the Northern Hemisphere, and it also occurs in the Southern Hemisphere (Figure 40.14). Loess covers about 10 per cent of the continental surface and influences a far greater area where small amounts of loess are incorporated in pre-existing topsoils. In North America the most prominent loess deposits extend from the Great Plains to the lowlands of the Mississippi, Ohio, and Missouri River Basins (Figure 40.15). As this map shows, some of the thickest deposits lie in Nebraska and Iowa, where as much as 60 m of loess has buried the underlying topography. Most of these loess deposits, however, are between 1 m and 30 m thick. Streams eroded the area after the loess was deposited, and the loess deposits can be seen in the walls of many river valleys. Another major area of loess deposition was the Columbia Plateau in the Pacific Northwest, near where the states of Washington, Oregon, and Idaho meet (Figure 40.15). Loess blankets tend to diminish away from the source and grain size tends to decrease in the same direction. Thin and discontinuous loess is found in many places around these areas, and around all this there is a region where a loess component is found in the soils.

Grain size is related to the distance travelled, with finer grains travelling further, which in turn is related to a constant wind velocity and the settling velocity of the silt and fine sand grains. These factors lead to a vertical and horizontal sorting of the material. Loess can be carried over hundreds of kilometres and deposited over vast areas.

As the world map (Figure 40.14) shows, loess deposits are even more extensive in Eurasia than in North America. Loess was first identified in the Rhine Valley as long ago as 1821, which is how it got its name (German for 'loose'). It also exists in France's Paris Basin, in the Danube Valley of Eastern Europe, and in large areas of southern and central Russia. Many different kinds of loess are recognized in Central Europe: slope loess, fluvial loess, etc. But the thickest loess accumulations are in Asia, especially in east-central China. These were first described by the German geographer Ferdinand, Baron von Richthofen (uncle of Manfred, Baron von Richthofen—'The Red Baron', the famous World War I fighter pilot) in the 1880s, who suggested that they were carried and laid down by aeolian action.

Almost the entire surface of the North China Plain consists of loess, and to the west, in the hilly middle basin of the Huang He (Yellow River), is an even thicker loess deposit. In fact, the Chinese call this region the Loess Plateau, and here the loess averages 75 m in thickness and in some places, such as Lauzou in central China, it can reach over 300 m (Figure 40.17).

Loess also occurs over a sizable area of southern South America, including Argentina's agriculturally productive pampas area. Other smaller deposits of loess (as well as loess-like sediments) have been found elsewhere in the Southern

LINK

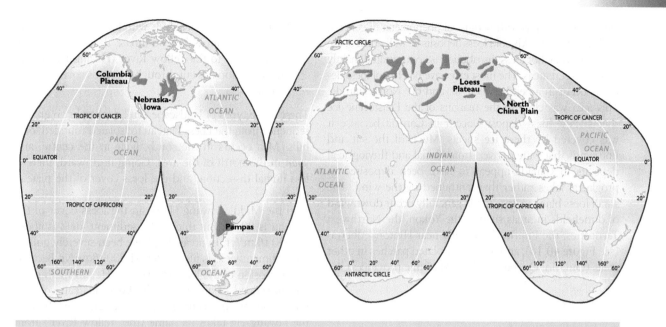

Figure 40.14 Major loess deposits of the world.

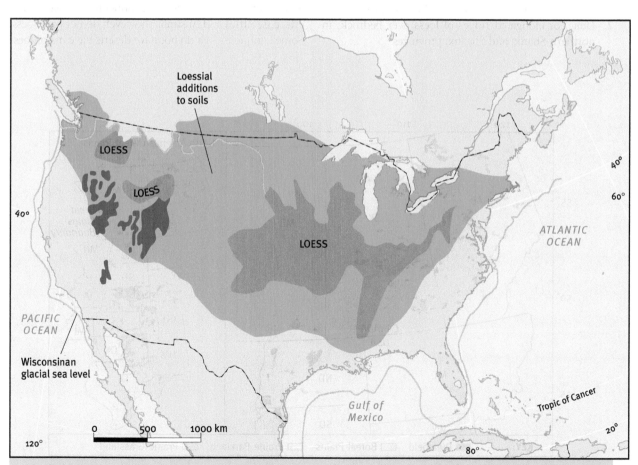

Figure 40.15 Loess regions of North America, highlighting the major deposits of the east-central Great Plains, the Mississippi Valley, and the Pacific Northwest.

Hemisphere. But as with periglacial phenomena in general, the bulk of the world's cold loess deposits lie well north of the Equator, while hot loess distribution is concentrated mainly around desert areas. The most extensive patches of loess deposits occur in a belt between 40° and 60° North latitude. This area was close to the margins of the Pleistocene ice sheets. Few loess deposits occur in Canada because it was covered by these ice sheets. Much of the silt and fine sands that were derived from glacial and fluvioglacial deposits in Canada appear to have been deposited in proglacial lakes rather than entrained by the wind. The small loess blankets in Canada generally occur downwind of dunefields in areas such as the Yukon, the Northwest Territories, the Prairies (especially near Hinton, Alberta) (see Figure 40.16), and in small, isolated patches in other areas (Ontario, Quebec, and the Maritime provinces).

Context

Loess tends to fill in depressions and not to form constructional features. It can maintain a uniform thickness or it wedges out downwind. In China, loess can be found in three distinct contexts:

1. *Yuan*, or flat to gently rolling loess plateau with about 200 m of loess over bedrock. This occurs in the south of Shanxi and the western part of Gansu provinces.
2. *Liang*, or elongated ridges of loess over bedrock, in northern Shanxi and Shaanxi provinces.

3. *Mao*, or hemispherical hills with loess caps. These occur in Liang areas but dominate the topography of Shanxi close to the Yellow River (Hwang He) where fluvial erosion has cut through the loess cover into the bedrock.

These three types of landscape can be taken as an erosive sequence from the Loess Plateau to isolated rounded loess hills. *Mao* occurs in the south, *liang* in the centre, and *yuan* in the north of the area. Going northward, there is less fluvial dissection, and the loess cover of the plateau thins.

In the Middle Hwang He basin the loess cover of the plateau is 80–120 m thick. The sediment yield is about 10,000 t/km²/yr. In areas that have been severely gullied the sediment yield is just under 34,500 t/km²/yr. Because of the erosion of the loess the Hwang He has the highest sediment load of any river. The Loess Plateau contributes about 92 per cent of the silt to the river. In fact, the Hwang He takes its name (the 'Yellow River') from the colour, a consequence of carrying so much loessial material.

Sources and Deposition of Loess

LINK

The main source areas for hot and cold loesses are deserts and periglacial sandar. Some continents with large deserts, e.g., Africa and Australia, however, do not have loess. Some continents that do not have deserts have major loess

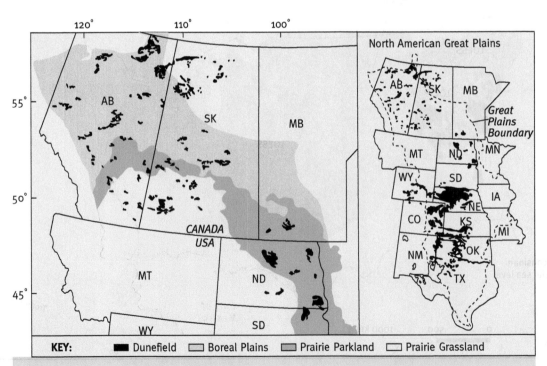

Figure 40.16 Great Plains dunefields. The map on the left shows the three main ecological regions and the occurrences of dunefields on the northern Great Plains. (From Hugenholtz and Wolfe, 2005)

deposits derived from periglacial sources, especially sandar surfaces where silt and fine sand were winnowed prior to the surfaces being stabilized by vegetation. The supply of sediment in such areas was replenished by flooding of proglacial streams.

The absence of loess in areas around deserts is a function of the lack of suitable source rocks and/or dust-trapping surfaces such as moist soil or vegetated surfaces. Sahara dust is blown north into Europe and across the Atlantic into South America by the *Harmattan* wind, a part of the northeast trade wind system that carries the Saharan dust plume to Brazil. These are major inputs of soil nutrients in both cases. It has also been suggested that Saharan and Sahelian dust (which has increased because of desertification) may be partially responsible for the increase in asthma and allergies seen in the US and Canada over the last 20 years. Short-term outbreaks of north Saharan dust are transported to Europe by the *Sirocco* or *Garmsil* winds.

An estimated 500 million tonnes of dust are transported by the wind on Earth each year. Severe storms may account for most of the transport, e.g., a 1935 dust storm over the interior plains of the US is estimated to have caused about 5 million tonnes of dust to be suspended in the air over a 78 km² area near Wichita, Kansas. The same storm caused at least 300 tonnes/km² of dust deposition in Lincoln, Nebraska. Several factors cause loess deposition:

1. Wind velocity and turbulence decrease.
2. Particles are 'captured' on rough, moist, or electrically charged surfaces.
3. Dust particles become charged and form aggregates that are too heavy to be entrained and are therefore deposited.
4. Particles are washed back to the surface by precipitation.

Properties of Loess

Ever since loess was first identified, the origins of its various deposits have been debated. Is loess really a wind-borne sediment, or did water also play an aggradational role? The answer seems to be that loess is indeed a product of wind transportation and deposition. The deposits do not form landforms but blanket the terrain below, filling valleys and covering hilltops in ways that fluvial deposits do not.

Certainly there is no argument about the interest in and importance of loess. If you compare the maps of loess deposits, agricultural productivity, and population distribution, you will see that some of the world's most fertile areas—and some great human agglomerations—lie in loess regions. In the United States the loess of Iowa and Illinois yields massive harvests of corn, soybeans, and other crops. In the drier Great Plains farther west, the wheat of Kansas and Nebraska also comes from loess-derived soils. In terms of population size and density, however, nothing on Earth matches the great human cluster centred on the North China Plain, supported by vast wheat fields on fertile loess-based soils. The most productive farmlands of Russia and Ukraine, too, occur on loess.

Just what makes loess such an unusual sediment? It consists of silt-sized quartz particles along with feldspars, carbonates, clays, and other minerals. Loess contains the whole range of minerals derived from ground-up bedrock, which are in forms that can easily be absorbed by plants. Moreover, its fertility is not confined to an upper layer; loess is fertile all the way down its profile. Scrape off the top horizon, and lower layers of it will support plants just as well. But there is more to it.

Technically, loess is described as a fine-grained, unstratified, homogeneous, highly porous deposit. After deposition, compaction causes slight shrinkage in the mass, so that vertical passages develop. These vertical passages may take the form of capillaries or may resemble the joints found in harder sedimentary rocks (see Unit 23). Water, seeping down through the loess, dissolves some of its mineral matter and redeposits it lower down, thereby strengthening the walls of capillaries and cleavages. These processes combine to give loess a capacity to stand in upright walls and columns, and to resist collapse when it is excavated.

These qualities (fertility, vertical strength) are on display in what must be the world's most interesting loess region, China's Loess Plateau (Figure 40.17). This region is neither as large nor as populous as the great North China Plain, having more relief and less water. But here loess is more than fertile soil—loess also serves as living quarters. Millions of families still live in caves excavated out of the loess.

In stream valleys, against hillsides, and in the walls of deep road cuts, the local inhabitants have excavated the loess to create dwellings that are sometimes large and elaborate. The entrances to these underground living quarters are sometimes ornately decorated, but in fact they are caves. As long as the region remains geologically stable, the millions of people dwelling underground are safe. But whereas loess withstands erosion and has vertical strength, it collapses when shaken. In 1920 a severe earthquake struck the Loess Plateau, and an estimated 180,000 people lost their lives, most of them buried inside their caved-in homes.

Periglacial loess deposits leave no doubt that wind erosion has played a major role in shaping the postglacial landscape. But loess and loess-like deposits also are found in areas far from glaciers, for example, near mid-latitude deserts (hot or desert loess). There, winds have laid down accumulations of fine-grained material derived from the dry, dusty desert surface. Some other loess-like deposits may in fact be the work of water, not wind. The great loess deposits of Eurasia and North America, however, confirm the role of wind as a major aggradational agent.

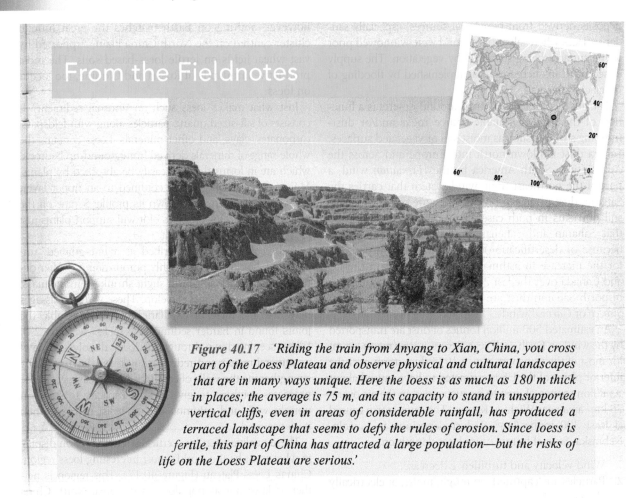

From the Fieldnotes

Figure 40.17 *'Riding the train from Anyang to Xian, China, you cross part of the Loess Plateau and observe physical and cultural landscapes that are in many ways unique. Here the loess is as much as 180 m thick in places; the average is 75 m, and its capacity to stand in unsupported vertical cliffs, even in areas of considerable rainfall, has produced a terraced landscape that seems to defy the rules of erosion. Since loess is fertile, this part of China has attracted a large population—but the risks of life on the Loess Plateau are serious.'*

The 'Loess Problem'

While loess is an aeolian deposit, loess-like materials can be formed or deposited by a wide range of processes—weathering, mass movement, wash, and fluvial action. This has been realized in Europe for a long time, where many loess types are recognized. Such deposits are the brickearths (used for making bricks) that cap many of the terraces that occur in 'flights' on the sides of the Thames Valley, England. Some scientists believe that these deposits are true loesses and were blown in from somewhere in the North Sea Basin during the last glaciation. But it is quite possible that these materials were formed by more localized processes, from reworked loess (or loess deposited by slope or fluvial processes), or they may be derived from other sources, such as local rock outcrops.

Some brickearths found close to outcrops of London Clay look exactly like London Clay while others found near exposures of Thanet sand look exactly like that rock type.

Heavy mineral and grain size studies indicate that these rock types were the sources of much of the deposit and that it was probably soliflucted material. East of London the brickearth deposits are much deeper and contain both fluvial mollusc shell fossils and a wide variety of mammal bones. From the stratigraphy and the contained fossils, it is believed that these deposits were likely laid down in a river or on a floodplain. It is possible that a small amount of wind-blown material was added during deposition but most of the deposit seems to be locally derived. In North America, all loess is assumed to be aeolian and no other sources and depositional environments have been investigated.

There is also controversy about whether the clays and calcium carbonate found in loess are due to the weathering of the original mass or a consequence of soil development in the deposit. Loess is associated with paleosols, secondary calcium carbonate concretions, and krotovinas (in-filled animal and/or root tunnels).

KEY TERMS

aeolian   *page 572*
arroyo   *page 570*
backslope   *page 576*
barchan   *page 578*
box canyon   *page 570*
deflation   *page 574*
deflation hollow   *page 574*
desert pavement   *page 569*
dune   *page 576*
dune crest   *page 578*
ephemeral stream   *page 570*
erg   *page 575*

loess   *page 579*
longitudinal dune   *page 579*
parabolic dune   *page 578*
perennial exotic stream   *page 571*
potential evaporation   *page 568*
salt crystal (salt burst) hydration   *page 569*
slip face   *page 576*
surface creep   *page 573*
transverse dune   *page 578*
wadi   *page 570*
wind abrasion   *page 574*
yardang   *page 574*

REVIEW QUESTIONS

1. Describe the vertical limits of wind erosion.
2. Describe the typical sand-dune profile and how the prevailing wind direction might be deduced from it.
3. Describe and differentiate among barchan, parabolic, longitudinal, and transverse dunes.
4. What is loess? Describe its major physical properties.
5. How have the thick loess deposits in North America accumulated?

REFERENCES AND FURTHER READINGS

Abouguenda, Z.M., and W.W. Sawchyn, eds. 1980. *The Athabasca Sand Dunes of Saskatchewan: An Interdisciplinary Study*. Regina: Saskatchwan Research Council Report, C-805-0-4-E-80.

Abrahams, A.D., and A.J. Parsons, eds. 1995. *Geomorphology of Desert Environments*. New York: Chapman & Hall.

Bagnold, R.A. 1971. *Physics of Blown Sand and Desert Dunes*, 2nd edn. London: Methuen.

Bélanger, S., and L. Filion. 2006. 'Niveo-aeolian Sand Deposition in Subarctic Dunes, Eastern Coast of Hudson Bay, Quebec, Canada', *Journal of Quaternary Science* 61: 27–31.

Brookfield, M.E., and T.S. Ahlbrandt, eds. 1983. *Eolian Sediments and Processes*. Amsterdam: Elsevier.

Cooke, R.U., and J.C. Doornkamp. 1990. *Geomorphology in Environmental Management*, 2nd edn. Oxford: Oxford Univ. Press.

———, A. Warren, and A.S. Goudie. 1992. *Desert Geomorphology*. Bristol, Penn.: Taylor & Francis.

Côte, D., J.-M.M. Dubois, and L. Nadeau. 1990. 'Les dunes du Quebec meridional: contribution à l'etude de vents doumants duvant l'Holocene', *Canadian Geographer* 34: 49–62.

David, P.P. 1977. *Sand Dune Occurrences of Canada*. Indian and Northern Plains, Contract no. 79-230 Report. Ottawa: National Parks Branch, 1977.

———. 1979. 'Sand Dunes in Canada', *Geos* 8: 12–14.

———. 1981. 'Stabilized Dune Ridges in Northern Saskatchewan', *Canadian Journal of Earth Sciences* 18: 286–310.

Goudie, A.S., and A. Watson. 1990. *Desert Geomorphology*. London: Macmillan.

Graham, H. 1987. *Citizen and Soldier: The Memoirs of Lieutenant-General Howard Graham*. Toronto: McClelland & Stewart.

Halsey, L.A., et al. 1990. 'Sedimentology and Development of Parabolic Dunes, Grand Prairie Dune Field, Alberta', *Canadian Journal of Earth Sciences* 27: 1762–72.

'Holocene Dune Activity and Drought and Aridity'. 2002. Special sections in *Géographie physique et Quarternaire* 56, 2–3: 191–259.

Hugenholtz, C.H., and S.A. Wolfe. 2005. 'Recent Stabilization of Active Sand Dunes on the Canadian Prairies and Relation to Recent Climate Changes', *Geomorphology* 68: 131–47.

——— and ———. 2005. 'Biomorphic Model of Dunefield Activation and Stabilization on the Northern Great Plains', *Geomorphology* 70: 53–70.

Lancaster, N. 1995. *The Geomorphology of Desert Dunes*. London/New York: Routledge.

Leighton, M.M., and H.B. Willman. 1950. 'Loess Formations of the Mississippi Valley', *Journal of Geology* 58: 599–623.

Leopold, L.B., W.W. Emmett, and R.M. Myrick. 1966. 'Channel and Hillslope Processes in a Semiarid Area, New Mexico', in *Erosion and Sedimentation in a Semiarid Environment*. USGS Prof. Paper 352-G. Washington: US Government Printing Office, 193–252.

Livingstone, I., and A. Warren. 1996. *Aeolian Geomorphology: An Introduction*, 2nd edn. London/New York: Longman.

Marbutt, J.A. 1977. *Desert Landforms*. Cambridge, Mass.: MIT Press.

Marcus, M.G., and A.J. Brazel. 1992. 'Summer Dust Storms in the Arizona Desert', in D.G. Janelle, ed., *Geographical Snapshots of North America*. New York: Guilford Press, 411–15.

Mares, M.A. 2002. *A Desert Calling: Life in a Forbidding Landscape*. Cambridge, Mass.: Harvard Univ. Press.

Muhs, D.R., and E.A. Bettis III. 2003. 'Quaternary Loess-Palaeosol Sequences as Examples of Climate Driven Extremes', in M.A. Chan and A.W. Archer, eds, *Extreme Depositional Environments: Mega End Members in Geologic Time*. Spec. Paper 370. Boulder, Colo.: Geological Society of America.

Odynsky, W. 1958. 'U-shaped Dunes and Effective Wind Directions in Alberta', *Canadian Journal of Soil Science* 38: 56–62.

Pissart, A., et al. 1977. 'Dépôts et phénomènes éoliens sur l'île de Banks, Territoires du Nord-Ouest, Canada', *Canadian Journal of Earth Sciences* 14: 2462–80.

Pye, K. 1987. *Aeolian Dust and Dust Deposits*. London, Academic Press.

——— and H. Tsoar. 1990. *Aeolian Sand and Sand Dunes*. Winchester, Mass.: Unwin Hyman Academic.

Siever, R. 1988. *Sand*. New York: Scientific American Library.

Tchakerian, V.P., ed. 1994. *Desert Aeolian Processes*. New York: Chapman & Hall.

Thomas, D.S.G. 1989. *Arid Zone Geomorphology*. London: Belhaven Press.

Tsoar, H. 2001. 'Types of Aeolian Sand Dunes and Their Formation', in N.J. Balmforth et al., eds, *Geomorphological Fluid Mechanics*. Lecture Notes in Physics, vol. 582. Berlin and Heidelberg: Springer-Verlag.

Walker, A.S. 2000. *Deserts: Geology and Resources*. Reston, Va: U.S. Geological Survey.

Ward-Thomas, P., cont. ed. 1988. *The World Atlas of Golf*, new edn. London: Mitchell Beazley.

Wolfe, S.A., G.R. Brooks, et al. 2001. *A Synthesis of Geological Hazards in Canada*. Ottawa: Geological Survey of Canada, Bulletin 548, 231–40.

——— et al. 2002. 'Holocene Eolian Activity in South-Central Saskatchewan and the Southern Canadian Prairies', *Géographie physique et Quaternaire* 56, 2–3: 215–27.

——— et al. 2004. 'Relict Late Wisconsinan Dune Fields of the Northern Great Plains, Canada', *Géographie phyique et Quaternaire* 58, 2–3: 323–36.

 WEB RESOURCES

pubs.usgs.gov/gip/deserts/dunes Five types of sand dunes are discussed on this USGS page, including crescentic, linear, star, dome, and parabolic dunes. Colour photographs accompany each description.

www.weru.ksu.edu The USDA, in co-operation with Kansas State University, presents this wind erosion research unit website. Wind erosion consequences and simulations are discussed, and a multimedia archive is available. Links to other wind erosion sites are listed.

Unit 41

Coastal Processes

Objectives

- To establish the importance of coastal zones as areas of interaction between physical processes and human settlement.

- To examine the physical properties of waves and their significance in the operation of coastal processes.

- To discuss other sources of energy in the coastal zone and their erosional and depositional significance.

Some of the world's most spectacular scenery lies along the coasts of the continents. Sheer cliffs tower over surging waves. Curving beaches are fringed by steep-sided headlands. Magnificent bays lie flanked by lofty mountains. Great rivers disgorge into the open ocean. Glaciers slide and calve into the water. Coastlines are shaped by many forces: by waves from the sea, by rivers emptying from land, by ice, even by wind. Rising and falling sea levels, tides and currents, and tectonic forces all contribute to the development of coastal topography. The complexity and variety of coastal landforms and landscapes are the result.

Our interest in coastal processes stems from two considerations. On the one hand, we seek to understand how coastal landscapes are created and what processes are presently operating in these zones of interface between land and sea. The other motivation is more practical, stemming from the fact that coastlines are probably the most intensively used landscapes for a variety of human activities such as trade, industry, power generation, sewage and garbage disposal, recreation, and wildlife conservation. In such heavily developed areas, coastal processes can have very significant consequences. Our ability to manage these landscapes successfully rests on our knowledge of the environmental processes operating within them.

Coasts and Shores

In this unit and in Unit 42 we study the **littoral zone**, where land meets sea. In physical geography the term **coast** refers in a general sense to the strip of land and sea or lake where the various coastal processes combine to create characteristic landscapes, ranging from dunes and beaches to islands and lagoons. The term **shore** has a more specific meaning and denotes the narrower belt of land bordering a body of water (the most seaward or lakeward portion of a coast). A *shoreline* is the actual contact border between water and land. Thus we often refer to a coastal landscape, of which the shoreline is but one part.

Coastal areas have special problems. Sometimes beaches must be closed because harmful waste materials dumped into the sea or lake are washed onto them. Some popular beaches become ever narrower and must be protected by jetties or groynes, or they will wash away. Parts of shores are threatened by urban pollution, and their wildlife is endangered. Overcrowding and expansion of waterfront towns and cities imperil local ecologies.

Most of the time, however, people seem to be unaware of these happenings because the changes tend to be slow, not dramatic. The beaches visited year after year look pretty much the same. The strip of beachfront hotels and motels is lengthening, but gradually. Less obvious are the connections among the many processes at work in coastal zones. When coastal authorities dredge the outlet of a port, build a series of jetties, construct a breakwater, or flatten a dune, the consequences may be far-reaching. Beach erosion may slow down in one place but speed up in another. The offshore turbidity (muddiness) of

the water may change, affecting reef life. Coastal zones, therefore, are not only scenic and attractive; their landforms and landscapes result from the complex interaction of many processes.

Currents and Waves

Unit 10 discussed the thermohaline circulation or the 'global conveyor belt' of the ocean. This is driven by differences in the temperature and salinity of seawater, which affects its density. Each ocean basin also has its own circulation system based on the same variables and modified by tidal patterns, wind systems, and the shape of the ocean basins and the morphology of the ocean bed and continental shelves. Such closed or nearly closed horizontal circulation systems in the oceans (they also occur in lakes) are called **gyres**. *Tidal currents* usually dominate the water flow patterns in coastal areas (see 'Perspectives' box). These are generated in response to the rise and fall of the **tide** around hubs in the ocean called **amphidromic points** (also called *cotidal points*), which are related to the Coriolis effect. At these points the tidal range is negligible (Figure 41.1). The distance of an amphidromic point from a coastline and the shape of the coast (whether fairly straight or deeply indented) determines the tidal range.

Secondary currents are caused by circulation distinct from tides and include those set up by *wind drift* and *wind waves*. Wind drift imparts a drag on the ocean or lake surface and causes the movement of a thin top layer of water at velocities of about 3 per cent of the wind speed. This movement is called *Stokes drift*. Wind waves increase the roughness of the water surface: 10–40 per cent of the wind energy is transferred to the waves and about 5 per cent of the energy is lost to *whitecap,* or open-water breaker, generation. Rainstorms can increase surface movement considerably. Winds can also generate a more subtle circulation of surface water that causes lines or streaks of foam and surface debris (weed, flotsam) that are aligned as **windrows** parallel to wind direction. These are associated with corkscrew-like circulation systems set up in the surface water at right angles to wind direction. Looking downwind, water moves towards the windrow from the right and from the left. This pattern is called *Langmuir circulation* (and these cells are known as *Langmuir cells*).

Wind Waves and Their Properties

Many forces help shape coastal landforms, but the key erosional agents are wind-generated ocean waves. Most waves (not only in oceans, but also in seas and lakes) are generated by wind. Waves form when energy is transferred from moving air to water. Large waves form in water when the wind *velocity* is high, the wind *direction* is persistent, the wind *duration* is protracted, and the *fetch* (the distance over which the wind blows) is long. When conditions are favourable, the ocean's upper layer

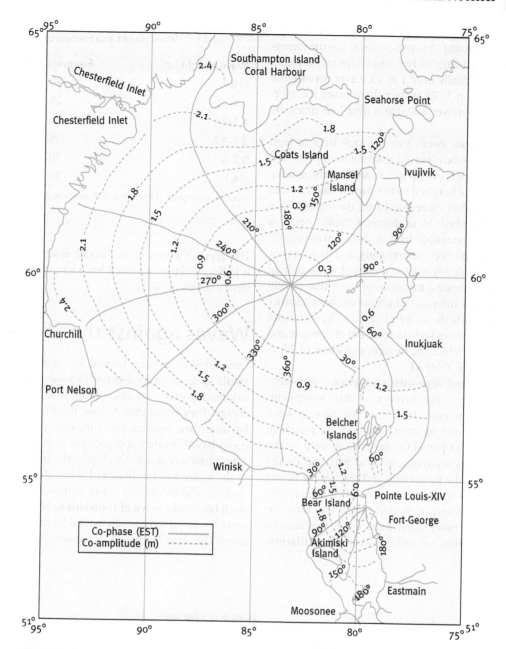

Figure 41.1 Cotidal chart of Hudson and James Bays, showing the amphidromic point from which tides rise and fall. The straight solid lines are cotidal lines, meaning the locations along these lines on either side of the amphidromic point experience the same rise in tide at the same time. The circular broken lines represent the maximum rise in tide (in feet) along these lines.

is stirred into long rolling waves, or **swells**, which can travel thousands of kilometres before they break against a shore. When conditions are less favourable (changing wind directions, for example), waves are generally smaller but may have a more complex result.

Once a series of swells are well developed and moving across open water, their properties can be observed. The **wave height** is the vertical distance between the *crest*, or top, of a wave, and its *trough*, or bottom (Figure 41.2). Wave height is important when a wave reaches the coast because a high wave will do more erosional work than a low wave. The **wave length** (Figure 41.2)

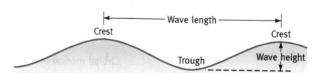

Figure 41.2 Wave height is the vertical distance between the wave crest and the wave trough. Wave length is the horizontal distance between two crests (or two troughs).

is the horizontal distance from one crest to the next (or from trough to trough). A wave's *period* is the time interval between the passage of two successive crests past a fixed point. Statistically only 1 in 23 waves is twice the average height, 1 in 1175 is over three times the average height, and 1 in over 300,000 is over four times the average height.

In the open ocean, swells may not look large or high because they cannot be observed against a fixed point. But they often reach heights of up to 5 m and lengths ranging from 30 m to several hundred metres. Storm waves tend to be much higher, often exceeding 15 m; the highest wave ever measured reached 34 m during a Pacific storm in 1933. Seemingly anomalous freak or giant waves over 20 to 30 m in height do occur infrequently, and these appear to be related to randomly moving groups of waves uniting and adding up to create a mountain of water that usually lasts less than two minutes. Observations from weather ships in the North Pacific indicate that 20 m waves are not uncommon. Such waves seem to come out of nowhere and are totally unpredictable. The frequency of waves of different sizes is shown in Table 41.1.

When swells travel across the open ocean, they seem to move the water in the direction of their movement. But this is not the case. In reality, the passing wave throws the water into an orbital motion. As shown in Figure 41.3, a water parcel (or particle) affected by the passing wave takes a circular, vertical path. When the wave approaches, the parcel rises and reaches the height of the crest. Then it drops to the level of the trough, coming back to where it started when the wave arrived. Waves that move water particles in this circular up-and-down motion are called **waves of oscillation**.

LINK

Table 41.1 Wave Height and Frequency	
Wave Height (m)	Frequency (%)
0–0.9	20
0.9–1.2	25
1.2–2.1	20
2.1–3.7	15
3.7–6.1	10
>6.1	10

Source: Thompson (1981), after Schumacher (1939).

The depth of a wave of oscillation, as seen in Figure 41.3, is half its length—if a swell has a length of 100 m, it will have a depth of 50 m.

Waves against the Shore

Once they have been formed by steady strong winds, swells (a series of long-period waves) may move across vast reaches of open ocean without losing their strength or energy. They retain their length, height, and period even far from their sources, and they can travel across entire ocean basins. As they approach the coastline, they usually enter shallower water. Obviously, the free orbital motion of the water will be disrupted when the wave begins to 'feel' (be affected by) the ocean bottom. At this point, the swell becomes a **wave of translation**. No longer do water particles in orbital motion return to their original positions. The wave has begun its erosional work.

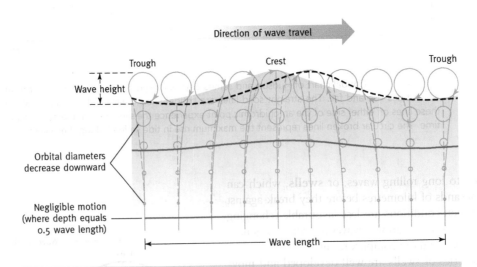

Figure 41.3 Orbital motion of water parcels within a wave of oscillation in deep water. To follow the successive positions of a water parcel at the surface, follow the arrows in the largest loops from right to left. This is the same as watching the wave crest travel from left to right. Parcels in smaller loops below have corresponding positions, marked by continuous, nearly vertical lines. Dashed lines represent wave forms and water parcel positions one-eighth of a period later.

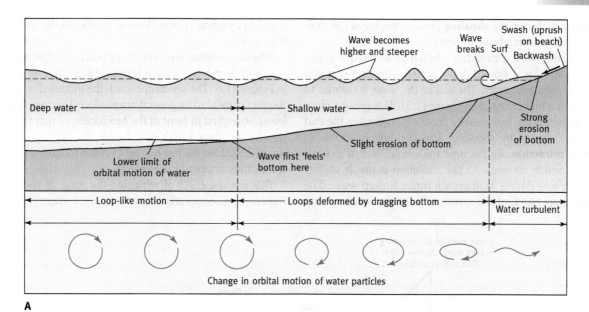

A

B

Figure 41.4 In the diagram (A), circles, ovals, and wave lengths are not drawn to scale with the waves on the surface. Waves are transformed as they travel from deep water through shallow water to shore along the coast of PEI, producing evenly spaced breakers as they approach the beach (B).

Because we know that the depth of a wave is half its length, we can determine where it will 'feel' bottom first. The wave in our example, with a length of 100 m, will begin to interact with the ocean bottom when the water depth becomes less than 50 m. There, the circular orbit of a water particle is compressed into an oval one (Figure 41.4A, bottom). Contact with the bottom also slows the wave down, so that the wave length is forcibly decreased. As the water becomes still shallower, the coastward-moving wave pushes water upward, increasing the wave height. Soon the wave becomes so steep that its crest collapses forward, creating a *breaker*. This happens along the breadth of the advancing wave, which is now capped by a foaming, turbulent mass of water.

From the beach one sees a series of approaching waves developing breakers as they advance towards the shore

(Figure 41.4B); such a sequence of breaking waves is referred to as the **surf**. When a wave reaches the shore, it finally loses its form and the water slides up the beach in a thinning sheet called **swash**. The dying wave still has some power, and the uprushing water carries sand and gravel landward. Then the last bit of wave energy is expended, and the water flows back towards the sea as **backwash**, again carrying sand with it. Along the shore, therefore, sand is continuously moved landward and seaward by wave energy.

Wave Refraction

When we look out across the surf from the top of a dune, it seems as though the surf consists of waves arriving parallel, or very nearly parallel, to the coastline. In actuality the parallel approach is quite rare, but the impression is produced during the **shoaling** process, the impact of shallow water on an advancing wave.

When a wave approaches a beach at an oblique angle, only part of it is slowed down at first—the part that first reaches shallow water. The rest of the wave continues to move at a higher velocity (Figure 41.5). This process obviously bends the wave as the faster end overtakes the end already slowed by shoaling. This bending is known as **wave refraction**. By the time the whole wave is in shallower water, its angle to the shoreline is much smaller than it was during its approach through deep water. The angled approach of the waves vis-à-vis the beach sets up

a littoral *longshore current* flowing parallel to the shoreline (Figure 41.5).

When a coastline has prominent headlands (promontories) and deep bays, wave refraction takes place as shown in Figure 41.6. The waves approach the indented coastline roughly parallel to its general orientation. They reach shallower water first in front of the headlands, so that they are slowed and their length is reduced. The segment of the wave headed for the bay has yet to reach shallow water, so it continues at open-water velocity.

This has the effect of refracting the wave as shown in Figure 41.6, concentrating its erosional energy on the

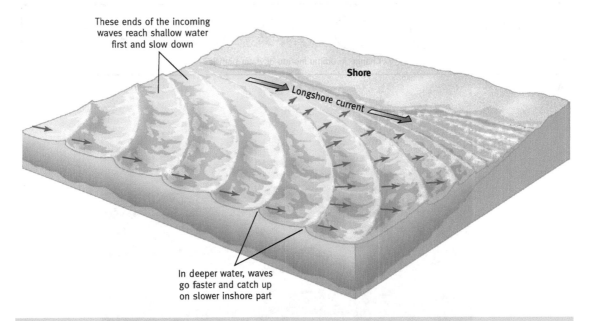

Figure 41.5   Refraction of incoming waves at the shoreline. Waves are bent, so their angle to the coastline is much smaller than in the deep water at the beginning of their approach. However, the inshore angle of the waves is still sufficient to produce a longshore current that flows parallel to the shoreline.

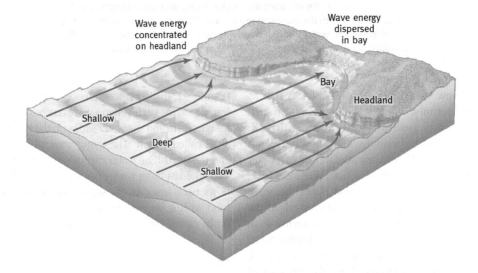

Figure 41.6   As the arrows indicate, the refraction of waves concentrates wave energy on headlands and dissipates it along bay shores. Note how, on the sea surface, the incoming waves are increasingly distorted as they approach the irregular coastline above a bottom that is deepest in front of the bay.

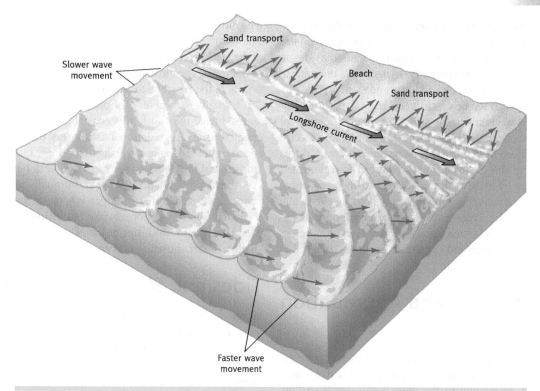

Slower wave movement

Sand transport

Beach

Sand transport

Longshore current

Faster wave movement

Figure 41.7 Longshore drift of sand at the water's edge. The larger process of beach drift is heightened by the longshore current in the surf zone. The net effect is to move the entire beach slowly downshore.

point of the headland. Rock material loosened from the promontory is transported towards the concave bends of the bays, where it forms a beach. Wave action, therefore, has the effect of straightening a coastline, wearing back the promontories and filling in the bays. Wave refraction is a crucial part of this process.

Longshore Drift

When a wave's swash rushes up the beach carrying sand and shingle (gravel), it does so at the angle of the arriving wave. But when the backwash (undertow) carries sand back seaward, it flows straight downward at right angles to the shoreline. The combined effect of this is to move sand along the beach, as shown in Figure 41.7.

This process, called **longshore** (or littoral) **drift**, can easily be observed on a beach. The movement seen in one area of swash and backwash is continuously repeated along the entire length of beach. The larger process of **beach drift** moves huge amounts of sand or shingle along the shore and sometimes becomes so powerful that it threatens to move the whole beach downshore. The amount of longshore drift on sandy beaches in the upper Great Lakes amounts to between 50,000 and 100,000 m³/yr. When that happens, engineers build **groynes** and other structures at an angle to the beach and out into the surf, hoping to slow the drift of beach sand (Figure 41.8). The building of groyne fields may conserve the beach, but erosion usually occurs where the groyne field ends. This is because the waves beyond the groyne field have expended little energy in sediment transport and thus have energy to erode the coast; that is, they

Figure 41.8 Groynes, extending into the surf at a 90-degree angle, mark the beaches of the resort hotels that line the Atlantic shore of Miami Beach. These structures prevent the excessive loss of sand by beach drift, which piles up on the upcurrent side of each groyne. The narrowness of the beach, however, indicates that this method is not very effective.

have the energy to gain sediment to transport. This process is called *terminal groyne scour* or *terminal groyne syndrome*. When this occurs, engineers either extend the groyne field or use rip-rap (**revetments**)—large rocks or concrete blocks—to slow down or stop further erosion.

While we can see beach drift occurring, longshore drift also affects materials in the surf zone where the waves of translation operate. We may not be able to observe it directly, but longshore drift in the breaker zone can create ridges of sand and shingle parallel to the shore. Those elongated ridges may interfere with the advance of the very waves that build them as they grow longer and wider, eventually rising above the water surface as **barrier islands**. As explained in Unit 42, such landforms may even grow across the mouths of rivers and bays, often creating ecological as well as economic problems.

Degradation and Aggradation by Waves

Waves are powerful erosional agents, but they also are capable of deposition. The above examples describe waves that, after developing in the open ocean, reach shallow water and lose their energy as they approach the shore. But the water does not always become so shallow near a coast. There are many places where the land descends steeply into the water, and where the water is hundreds of metres deep just a few metres offshore. In such places the waves advancing towards the land do not 'feel' bottom, are not slowed down, and do not form breakers and surf. Where this happens, of course, the full force of the onrushing wave strikes the coast.

The speed and weight of the water smashing against the vertical bedrock contribute to erosion by *hydraulic action*. Hydraulic action is especially effective where rocks are strongly jointed or otherwise cracked (for instance, along bedding planes). Air enters the joints and cracks; when the water pounds the rock face, this trapped air is compressed. Next the wave recedes, and the air expands almost explosively. This type of wave is called a *clapotis* and this process, repeated over thousands of years, can fracture and erode coastal rocks quite rapidly.

Like streams and glaciers, waves break pieces of rock from the surface being attacked, and these fragments enhance the waves' erosional effectiveness. This mechanical erosion process is known as **corrasion**. A wave loaded with rock fragments, large and small, erodes much more rapidly than water alone. Some coastal bedrock is also susceptible to chemical action by seawater. The breakdown of coastal bedrock by solution or other chemical means is referred to as **corrosion**. Unlike at inland sites, carbonate rocks such as limestones and dolostones are not attacked by solution as much as other rocks. This is because the seawater is saturated with $CaCO_3$ or $MgCO_3$.

Where offshore water is deep and coastal topography steep, the onslaught of waves produces a set of degradational landforms that tell us immediately what processes are going on. No gently sloping beaches or sandy offshore islands grace these high-relief coastlines (Figure 41.9). All of the evidence points towards the hardness and resistance of the rocks, the erosional force of the waves, and the exposure of the coastline to storms.

Alternatively, where offshore water is shallow and waves break into surf, the coastal landforms also are characteristic. Aggradational landforms dominate, and coastal relief is usually low: beaches, dunes, and sandy islands reveal the dominant processes at work here. Wherever they erode or deposit, waves continually move loose material about. Gradually, larger fragments are reduced to smaller ones in a process called **attrition**. We associate a beach with sand, but much of the material along a shallow-water shoreline is even more finely textured.

Tides and Shore Zone Currents

Waves do the bulk of the degradational and aggradational work along shorelines, but other kinds of water movements also contribute to the shaping of the coastal landscape.

Effects of Tides

The sea level rises and falls twice each day (see 'Perspectives' box). Again, the beach tells the story: what has been washed ashore during the *high tide* lies along the upper limit of the most recent swash, ready for beachcombing during *low tide*. Thus, the whole process of wave motion onto the beach, discussed previously, operates while the tides rise and fall. This has the effect of widening the sloping beach. During high tide, the uprushing swash reaches farther landward than during low tide; during low tide, the backwash reaches farther seaward than during high tide.

Along a straight or nearly straight shoreline, the **tidal range** (the average vertical distance between sea level at high tide and at low tide) may not be large, usually between about 1 and 4 m. But in partially enclosed waters, such as estuaries, bays, and lagoons, the tidal range is much larger. The morphology (shape) of the inlet and its entrance affect the range of the tide. Probably the world's most famous tides occur in the Bay of Fundy and Minas Basin on Canada's Atlantic coast; there the tidal range is 11–16 m, creating unusual problems for people living on the waterfront. The French Acadians who settled the area in the seventeenth century built dykes to create agricultural land from the low-lying salt marshes. High tidal ranges also occur in some long, narrow bays along the BC coast. Tides have erosional and depositional functions. In rocky, narrow bays, where the tidal range is great and tides enter and depart with much energy and power, tidal waters erode the bedrock by hydraulic action and corrasion. The changing water level associated with tides sets in motion *tidal currents*, which rush through the sandy entrances of bays and lagoons, keeping those narrow thresholds clear of blockage. Where the tidal current slows down, the sediment it carries is deposited in a fan-shaped, delta-like formation (we examine such tidal features in Unit 42).

From the Fieldnotes

Figure 41.9 *'On the advice of a Chilean colleague I took the coastal road north from Viña del Mar, and high relief evinces the submergence of this coastline as waves pound the promontories. The rocks themselves show ample evidence of the stresses imposed by tectonic-plate motion in the form of numerous fractures and faults, planes of weakness attacked by the waves. Much of South America's western coastline, from the cliffs of western Colombia to the fjords of southern Chile, reflects the forces of subduction; turn westward, and beneath those onrushing waves lies no gently sloping continental shelf. This is fast-changing scenery.'*

Tides occasionally take on the form of waves. A **tidal bore**, or eagre, is created when a rapidly rising high tide creates a wave front that runs up a river or bay. A dramatic example is sometimes seen in the lower course of Brazil's Amazon River, where the bore is called the *pororoca*. The tide here is known to rush in like a foamy breaker that never collapses forward. It is reported to start as a wall of water as much as 8 m high, moving upstream at a rate of 25 km/h. It loses its height as it advances upriver (4 m), but has been observed more than 400 km inland from the Atlantic coast. Many rivers draining into the Bay of Fundy exhibit this phenomenon. The Petitcodiac River (which runs through Moncton, NB) had the highest tidal bore in North America (>2 m) until bridge construction and silt deposition reduced its height. The tidal bore on the Shubenacadie River in Nova Scotia is ~1 m high and travels 20 km upstream at a speed of 14 km/h before dissipating. It occurs at all high tides but is especially large around the time of the equinoxes. The tidal bore in the Tsientang Kiang estuary in China is the world's largest. It occurs during spring tides and reaches 7.5 m high and has a velocity of 27 km/h.

Canadian Geographers in the Field

'*During a period of fieldwork studying coastal sand dunes on Iles de la Madeleine (Magdalen Islands), Quebec, in the Gulf of St Lawrence, I came across this excellent display of beach cusps on the coastline of Ile du Havre aux Maisons. The shore faces east and is on the leeward side of the island, protected from prevailing westerly winds. It is known that beach cusps develop best on gravel beaches with waves of consistent height and period approaching directly onshore. Those factors are all present here, and the regularity of the cusps is enhanced by the straightness of the beach.*'

Philip Giles is an Associate Professor in the Department of Geography at Saint Mary's University.

Shore Zone Currents

The water itself moves along the shore in the direction governed by the angle of the waves' approach. This water movement, parallel to the shore, is called a **longshore** (or littoral) **current**, and its generation and operation are shown in Figures 41.5 and 41.7. Longshore currents also can develop from tidal action and from storms along the coast. They are important agents because in total they move huge amounts of material. They are capable of erosion as well as deposition, creating lengthwise hollows and ridges in the surf zone. Moreover, they can erode beaches as well as build sand ridges across the mouths of rivers and bays.

Another type of current is the **rip current**. Rip currents occur where two opposing longshore currents collide. Even as the surf is surging landward, narrow stream-like currents cut across it, flowing from the shore seaward

Perspectives on the Human Environment

Tides and Their Behaviour

The Earth's envelope of water—the hydrosphere—covers more than 70 per cent of the planet. The surface of this layer of water unceasingly rises and falls in response to forces that affect its global distribution. This cyclical rise and fall of the sea level is known as the tide recorded at any given place in the world ocean. The tidal range is the vertical difference between sea levels at high tide and low tide.

Three principal forces control the Earth's tides: (1) the rotation of the planet, (2) the gravitational pull of the Moon, and (3) the gravitational pull of the Sun. The Earth's daily rotation has the effect of countering the gravitational pull of its own mass. The rotational velocity is greatest near the Equator and lowest at the poles, so that the layer of water bulges slightly outward towards the Equator. This is a permanent condition. But the Earth orbits around the Sun and is, in turn, orbited by the Moon. This means that the gravitational pulls of the Moon or the Sun come from different directions at different times.

Tidal levels at a coastal location rise and fall rhythmically based on the Earth's rotation and the 28-day lunar revolution, which produce two high tides and two low tides within a period slightly longer than 24 hours. When the Earth, Moon, and Sun are aligned, as shown in Figure 41.10A, the effects of terrestrial rotation, lunar attraction, and the Sun's attraction are combined, and the result is an unusually high tide, or spring tide. But when the Moon's pull works at right angles against the Sun's attraction and the rotational bulge, the result is a neap tide, the least extreme tide (Figure 41.10B).

Tides play a major role in coastal erosion. They can generate strong tidal currents that rush into and out of river mouths. They carry waves to higher coastal elevations during spring-tide extremes. And when a severe storm attacks a coastline in conjunction with a spring tide, substantial erosion may occur. The contribution of tides to shoreline erosion also is influenced by the coastal topography, both below the water (shallow and sloping or deep and steep) and above (long, narrow estuaries or wide, curving bays). Compared to the constantly pounding waves, tides are not prominent as coastal modifiers—but their impact is still significant.

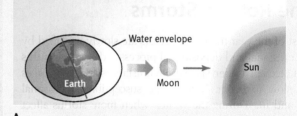

A

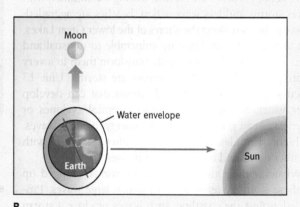

B

Figure 41.10 Schematic diagram of tides. (A) *Spring tide*: the Earth's rotational bulge and the gravitational pulls of both the Sun and the Moon combine to produce an unusually high tide. (B) *Neap tide*: the Moon's gravitational pull is at a right angle to the Sun's pull and the terrestrial rotation bulge, resulting in the least extreme tide. The Earth's water envelope and astronomical distances are strongly exaggerated.

(Figure 41.11A). These rip currents travel primarily in the surface layer of the water and can attain a high velocity, although they die out quickly beyond the surf zone. Rip currents have complex origins. They begin as small feeder currents in the shore zone, flowing parallel to the beach, sometimes behind low, surf-built sand ridges. At certain places along the beach, usually at fairly regular intervals, enough water gathers from these feeder currents to rush seaward, carrying a cloud of muddy sediment.

Because the rip current advances against the incoming surf, the breakers are interrupted where the rip current encounters them. Patches of mud carried by the rip current are visible against the less muddy surf (Figure 41.11B). Rip currents vary in strength. When the tide is high and waves are strong, rip currents are especially powerful. When the waves are lower, the rip current is weaker.

The erosional work of rip currents is limited but is still of geographical interest. One spatial peculiarity just mentioned is that they tend to develop at rather regular intervals along the beach. This seems to be related to the feeder channels that supply the water from two directions (Figure 41.11A). These longshore feeder currents hollow out their courses, so that the shore zone is marked by lengthwise depressions. Where the rip currents turn seaward, the beach surface is slightly lowered because the current carries much of its muddy sediment away from the beach. Thus, rip currents do have an erosional function, moving fine beach particles outward beyond the surf zone.

The Role of Storms

Most of the year the world's coasts are slowly modified by the erosional and depositional processes described in this unit. Except under special circumstances, these changes are slow to occur. Beaches are susceptible to seasonal cut and fill. During the winter, when more storms affect wave action, beaches are eroded. During the summer, with fewer storms and less wave action, beaches are aggraded. This can be seen along the shores of the lower Great Lakes. But virtually all coastlines are vulnerable to unusual and even rare events that can greatly transform them in a very short period of time. These events are storms. Unit 13 discussed the various kinds of storms that can develop over water. In the lower latitudes, tropical cyclones or hurricanes can generate enormous energy in ocean waves. At higher latitudes, storms are most often associated with weather fronts and contrasting air masses.

Whatever the source, the powerful winds whipped up in these storm systems, in turn, spawn large waves. Propelled against the coastline, such waves produce a **storm surge**, a combination of rising water and forceful wave action. During a storm surge, waves attack coastal-zone areas normally untouched by this kind of erosion.

One severe storm surge can break through stable, vegetation-covered barrier islands, erode dunes lying well above the normal swash zone, and penetrate kilometres of coastal plain (as in the case of Hurricane Katrina in 2005). When such a storm strikes the coast at the time of high tide, or during a spring tide, its impact is all the more devastating. Volcanic or earthquake activity also can cause surges in the form of tsunamis, as seen in the Boxing Day 2004 Indian Ocean tsunami. These dramatic events notwithstanding, physical geographers disagree as to the long-term geomorphological effects of severe storms. It is certainly true that much of the coast and shore will return to pre-storm conditions after the surge. But some effects of the storm may be long-lasting, if not permanent.

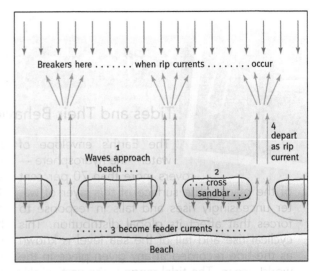

Figure 41.11 Rip currents are generated by small feeder currents in the shore zone that at regular intervals rush seaward directly into the oncoming waves (A). Rip currents die out beyond the surf zone, and swimmers caught in them can easily exit to the side. Rip currents have an erosional function, moving the beach particles outward beyond the surf zone. This can be seen in their usually muddy composition (B).

Crustal Movement

When we study coastal processes, we must be mindful not only of the many and complex marine processes discussed in this unit, but also of the vertical mobility of the Earth's crust. When we first observe a section of coastline, we classify it as a coast of erosion (degradation) or deposition (aggradation), depending on the dominant landforms we identify. That observation is based on the present appearance of the coast and the prevailing processes now at work.

Over the longer term, however, the coastal bedrock may be rising (relative to the sea level) or sinking. For instance, the Scandinavian Peninsula is undergoing isostatic rebound following the melting of the heavy ice sheet that covered it until recently. This means that its coasts are rising as well. Along the coastlines of Norway and Sweden, therefore, we should expect to find evidence of marine erosion now elevated above the zone where wave processes are taking place. In other areas the coast is sinking. The coastal zone of Louisiana and Texas shows evidence of subsidence, in part because of the increasing weight of the sediments of the Mississippi Delta, but probably for other reasons as well.

Add to this the rising and falling of the sea level associated with the Pleistocene Ice Age, and we can see that it is impossible to generalize about coasts—even over short stretches. Ancient Greek port cities built on the waterfront just 2500 years ago are now submerged deep below Mediterranean waters as a result of local coastal subsidence. But in the same area there are places built on the waterfront that are now situated high above the highest waves. Unravelling the marine processes and Earth movements that combine to create the landscapes of coastlines is one of the most interesting challenges of physical geography.

KEY TERMS

amphidromic points *page 588*
attrition *page 594*
backwash *page 591*
barrier island *page 594*
beach drift *page 593*
coast *page 588*
corrasion *page 594*
corrosion *page 594*
groynes *page 593*
gyres *page 588*
littoral zone *page 588*

longshore current *page 596*
longshore drift *page 593*
revetments *page 594*
rip current *page 596*
secondary currents *page 588*
shoaling *page 592*
shore *page 588*
storm surge *page 598*
surf *page 591*
swash *page 591*
swells *page 589*

tidal bore *page 595*
tidal range *page 594*
tide *page 588*
wave height *page 589*
wave length *page 589*
wave refraction *page 592*
waves of oscillation *page 590*
waves of translation *page 590*
windrows *page 588*

REVIEW QUESTIONS

1. Why is an understanding of coastal processes an important part of physical geography?
2. Under what environmental conditions do large waves develop?
3. Describe what happens as incoming waves enter shallow water.
4. What is longshore drift, and how is it generated?
5. What are tides? What are their controlling forces?

REFERENCES AND FURTHER READINGS

Bascom, W. 1980. *Waves and Beaches: The Dynamics of the Ocean Surface*, 2nd edn. Garden City, NY: Anchor/Doubleday.
Bird, E.C.F. 1984. *Coasts: An Introduction to Coastal Geomorphology*, 3rd edn. New York: Blackwell.
Carter, R.W.G. 1989. *Coastal Environments: An Introduction to the Physical, Ecological and Cultural Systems of Coastlines*. Orlando, Fla: Academic Press.
Charlier, R.H., and C. De Meyer. 1997. *Coastal Erosion: Response and Management*. New York: Springer-Verlag.
Davies, J.L. 1980. *Geographical Variation in Coastal Development*, 2nd edn. London/New York: Longman.
Davis, R.A., Jr, and D. Fitzgerald. 2002. *Beaches and Coasts*. Malden, Mass.: Blackwell.
Dean, C. 1999. *Against the Tide: The Battle for America's Beaches*. New York: Columbia Univ. Press.
Hansom, J.D. 1988. *Coasts*. London/New York: Cambridge Univ. Press.

Hardisty, J. 1990. *Beaches: Form and Process*. Winchester, Mass.: Unwin Hyman Academic.
Haslett, S. 2001. *Coastal Systems*. London/New York: Routledge.
Ketchum, B.H., ed. 1972. *The Water's Edge: Critical Problems of the Coastal Zone* Cambridge, Mass.: MIT Press.
King, C.A.M. 1966. *Beaches and Coasts*. London: Edward Arnold.
Leatherman, S.P. Annual. *America's Best Beaches*. Miami, at: <www.topbeaches.com>.
Lencek, L., and G. Bosker. 1999. *The Beach: The History of Paradise on Earth*. New York: Penguin Putnam.
McCann, S.B., ed. 1980. *Coastlines of Canada: Littoral Processes and Coastal Morphology*. Ottawa: Geological Survey of Canada, Paper 80–10.
National Geographic Society. 1991. *Canada's Incredible Coasts*. Washington: National Geographic Society.
Pethick, J.S. 1984. *An Introduction to Coastal Geomorphology*. London: Edward Arnold.

Schwartz, M.L., ed. 1982. *The Encyclopedia of Beaches and Coastal Environments*. Stroudsburg, Penn.: Dowden, Hutchinson & Ross.

Siever, R. 1988. *Sand*. New York: Scientific American Library.

Thompson, R.E. 1981. *Oceanography of the British Columbia Coast*. Ottawa: Department of Fisheries and Oceans, Fisheries and Aquatic Sciences, Special Publication No. 56.

Trenhaile, A.S. 1997. *Coastal Dynamics and Landforms*. New York: Oxford Univ. Press.

Viles, H., and T. Spencer. 1995. *Coastal Problems: Geomorphology, Ecology and Society at the Coast*. New York: Oxford Univ. Press.

WEB RESOURCES

co-ops.nos.noaa.gov NOAA's Center for Operational Oceanographic Products and Services maintains a web page that includes online tide information, predictions and observations, water-level data, and maritime navigation safety information.

www.nearctica.com/ecology/habitats/beaches.htm This site is a comprehensive list of links to beach erosion and formation. Both technical data and non-technical descriptive articles are available.

Coastal Landforms and Landscapes

Objectives

- To examine the characteristics of a beach.

- To relate beaches to the coastline's topographic and tectonic setting.

- To recognize related coastal landforms of aggradation, such as sand dunes, offshore bars, and barrier islands.

- To identify landforms typical of erosional coastlines.

- To relate erosional and depositional processes to a general classification of coastlines.

Unit 41 reviewed the numerous marine processes that contribute to the formation of coastal landforms and landscapes. This unit examines those features themselves. The landforms of shorelines and the landscapes of coasts reveal the dominant processes at work. Cliffs and caves suggest that erosional activity is paramount. On the other hand, beaches and barrier islands indicate deposition. Coastal landforms can therefore be divided into two groups—degradational and aggradational. However, most coastal landscapes display evidence of both erosion and deposition.

LINK

Degradational Landforms

LINK

Where wave erosion is the dominant coastal process, exposed bedrock, high relief, steep slopes, and deep water are key features of this terrain. If there are islands, they are likely to be rocky remnants of the retreating coast, not sandy embankments being built in shallow water. In Unit 41 we considered the processes of degradation by waves: hydraulic action, corrasion, corrosion, and the attrition of rock fragments. Just as a stream seeks to produce an equilibrium profile, so wave erosion works to straighten an indented, embayed coastline. Wave refraction concentrates erosional energy on the headlands that stick out into the water, while sedimentary material collects in the concave bends of bays, a process whose beginning was observed in Figure 41.6.

A possible sequence of events that follows is depicted in Figure 42.1. When headlands (A) are eroded by waves, steep **sea cliffs** develop (B). Waves vigorously erode the bottom part of the cliff, seeking out joints, layers of softer strata, and other weaknesses, excavating a wave-cut notch. In so doing, the waves often create **sea caves** near the base of the cliff, undercutting the cliff. Soon the overhanging part of the cliff collapses, so that wave action combines with mass movement to erode the coastal bedrock.

The cliff continues to retreat (Figure 42.1B and C). A **wave-cut platform** (also called an *abrasion platform*) develops at the foot of the cliff (B), marking its recession. Erosion starts with the waves and entrained sediment, carving out a *wave-cut notch* at the base of the cliff. These platforms are nearly flat bedrock surfaces that slope seaward. At low tide we can see pocket beaches with boulders and cobbles, broken from the cliff, laying on this platform. Soon the waves of a high tide (or a storm) will hurl these fragments back against the cliff face. Recently, it has been suggested that wave-cut platform development might be caused by a combination of slope and marine processes. As the headlands retreat, certain parts invariably prove to be more resistant than others (B and C).

Sections of the headlands survive as small islands, and as wave erosion continues, these islands are sometimes penetrated at their base and become **sea arches** (C) such

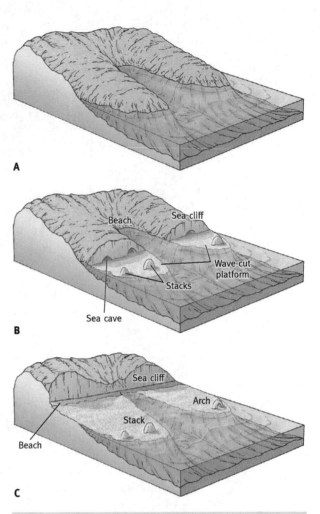

Figure 42.1 Hypothetical model of straightening of an embayed, indented coastline by wave erosion.

as at Percé Rock, Quebec; the Hole in the Wall on Grand Manan, NB; The Arches, north of Gros Morne National Park on the island of Newfoundland; and at the Hole in the Wall on the west coast of Vancouver Island. Other remnants of the headlands stand alone as columns called **stacks** (B and C), such as the Bird Islands off Cape Breton, NS; the Five Islands in the Minas Basin of Nova Scotia; Flowerpot Island off Tobermory, Ontario; and the Hopewell Rocks in the Bay of Fundy, NB. Arches and stacks (see opening photo, this unit) are typical of coastlines being actively eroded, but they are temporary features, and soon they, too, will be eroded down to the level of the wave-cut platform. Eventually the headlands may be completely removed, as are the beaches that lay at the heads of the bays. A nearly straight, retreating cliff then marks the entire coastal segment (Figure 42.1C), with a portion of the wave-cut platform, covered by sediment, at its base.

Cliffs can form in any coastal strata, ranging from hard crystalline rocks to soft and loose glacial deposits.

England's famous White Cliffs of Dover are cut from chalk (a very pure limestone). Tall cliffs in the Hawaiian Islands are carved from volcanic rocks. Cliff coastlines around the Mediterranean Sea are cut from layers of sedimentary rocks (see Figure 23.6). The speed of cliff retreat depends on a number of conditions, including the power of the waves and, importantly, the resistance of the coastal rocks. In the Point Grey area of Vancouver the coast is formed by glacial deposits, and this loose material retreats as much as 1 m per year. Along parts of the BC coast, deeper water and soft bedrock combine to produce an even faster rate of retreat, but in other segments of the same coast the hard crystalline rocks wear away at a much slower rate. Cliffs are widespread along the coasts of Canada; good examples are found at Conception Bay, Cape St George, Cape Spear, and Cape St Mary's in Newfoundland; Cape Blomidon and Joggins, Nova Scotia; around Cape Breton Island; along the Gaspé and north shore coasts of Quebec; along the west coast of Vancouver Island and the coast of mainland British Columbia; and in many locations on Prince Edward Island.

 ## Aggradational Landforms

Undoubtedly the most characteristic depositional landform along the coastline is a **beach**, or strand, defined as a coastal zone of sediment shaped by the action of waves and longshore currents. This means that a beach is much wider than the part of it we can see. On the landward side it begins at the foot of a line of dunes, a cliff, or some other feature, but on the seaward side it continues beneath the surf. Beaches are constructed from sand and other material, derived from both local and distant sources. Beach material in the coastal environment comes from a number of sources. When streams enter the ocean or a lake, the sediments they carry are deposited and transported along the shore by waves and currents. In addition, beach material may be produced locally: by the erosion of nearby sea cliffs and the physical breakdown

of those particles as they are moved along the shore. Material can be blown in from the land by wind. It can also be brought in from along shore and offshore. Some material has glacial provenance.

Beach Dynamics

The character of a beach reflects the nature of the material of which it is composed. Most beaches along the North American Atlantic coast are made of sand, their light colour a result of the quartz fragments that make up the material. In areas where dark-coloured igneous rocks serve as the source for beach material, as they do in parts of Hawaii, beaches are dark-coloured. Along the coasts of British Columbia, northern California, Oregon, and Washington, high-energy conditions usually prohibit sand from being deposited on the beach, and larger particles make up the beach fabric. The resulting gravel and pebble beaches are often called *shingle* beaches. It has been quite common to find berms of plastic bottles, food containers, six-pack rings, and other detritus on beaches around the world for some time, but some of the beaches around the southern coasts of England are so dominated by sand-sized plastic grains derived from this flotsam that they are now called 'microplastic' beaches.

A beach profile has several parts (Figure 42.2). The **foreshore** is the zone that is alternately water covered during high tide and exposed during low tide. This is the zone of beach drift and related processes. Seaward of the foreshore lies the **nearshore** (sometimes called *offshore*), which is submerged even during an average low tide. One or more **longshore bars** (a ridge of sand parallel to the beach) and associated troughs often develop in this zone, where longshore drift, currents, and wave action combine to create a complex and ever-changing topography. Landward of the foreshore lies the **backshore**, which extends from the high-water line to the dune line. As Figure 42.2 shows, the backshore consists of one or more sandy beaches called **berms**. These flat berms were laid down during storms and are beyond the reach of normal wave action.

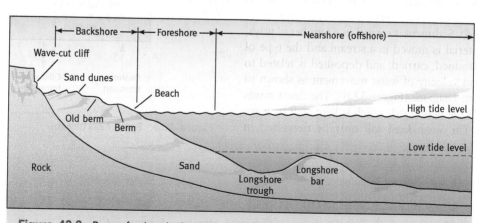

Figure 42.2 Parts of a beach shown in cross-sectional profile. The length of the profile is between 100 and 200 m. Vertical exaggeration is about double.

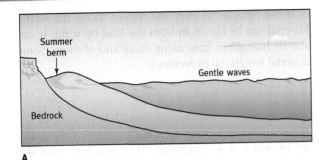

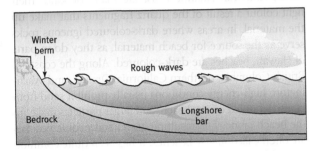

Figure 42.3 Seasonal variation in beach cut and fill. Gentle summer waves produce a wide berm that slopes gently landward (A). The rougher waves associated with winter storms produce a cold-season beach profile, which shows the summer berm eroded to a narrower, steeper-sloped remnant (B).

Beach profiles show a considerable amount of seasonal variation. Where seasonal contrasts in wave energy are strong, a beach will have one profile during the winter and another during the summer (Figure 42.3). The summer's long, steady, low waves carry sand from the nearshore zone onto the beach and create a wide summer berm that may develop a crest and slope gently landward. During the following winter, higher and more powerful storm waves erode much of the summer berm away, carrying the sand back to the nearshore zone and leaving a narrower winter berm. Thus a beach displays evidence of erosion as well as deposition.

Material is transported to and along a beach by various processes. Some material is carried dissolved in the water (solution load). Sediment is carried in a number of ways, much as material is moved in a stream and the type of sediment entrained, carried, and deposited is related to grain size and velocity of water movement as shown in the Hjulstrom Diagram (Figure 32.8). The finest muds are carried as the wash load, which is kept aloft by wave turbulence. The wash load will only be deposited in very tranquil water. Other fine material (clay to sand size) forms the suspended load, which again is kept in the water by turbulence. Heavier material is rolled or dragged along the seabed or beach by the current (traction load, shingle creep) or saltates along the bottom in a series of ballistic jumps. Another way material is moved is by seaweed or kelp rafting. Larger forms of kelp (e.g., *Macrosystis* sp.) attach themselves to the seabed by holdfasts, which hold onto shingle and other material. When the wave action or current increases, as in a storm, some of the kelp is detached from the seabed and carries some sediment with it (kelp dragging). The amount of sediment moved along the shore and onto the beach by kelp dragging and rafting appears to be site-specific: some beaches have major inputs by this process while on others it is a minor component of transport.

The entrainment, transport, and deposition of material are governed by the velocity and turbulence of the water and by the size and shape of the material. For example, shingle that is disc- or rod-shaped is transported the greatest distances.

Beaches are best viewed as open systems, characterized by inputs, outputs, and changes in storage. The size of the beach reflects the material in storage, and is therefore a measure of the balance between the availability of sediment and wave energy. The input of sediment is derived from local erosion, from offshore, and from upshore sections of the beach. Outputs of sediments can occur onshore (i.e., to the land), offshore, or downshore, and the width of the beach reflects the magnitude of the inputs and outputs.

Beach Mass Balance Figure 42.4 illustrates **beach mass balance**—that is, the balance between inputs and

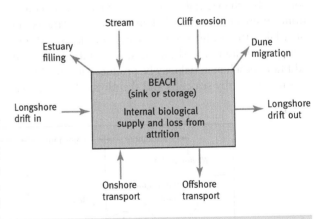

Figure 42.4 Beach mass balance.

Beach Mass Balance Equation:

$$L_I - L_O + O_I - O_O + S_I - E_O + C_I - D_O = O$$

| Longshore drift [in] | − | Longshore drift [out] | + | Onshore transport [in] | − | Offshore transport [out] | + | Stream input [in] | − | Estuary filling [out] | + | Cliff erosion [in] | − | Dune migration [out] | = O |

Table 42.1 Annual Mass Balance, Point Pelee (Cuspate Foreland), Ontario (All values m³ × 10³)

| | West Side | | | East Side | | |
	Offshore	Nearshore	Beach	Beach	Nearshore	Offshore
Year 1	134.1	130.0	28.7	−13.0	−338.7	−69.4
Year 2	−422.5	−173.7	13.5	55.3	89.1	−60.0
5 year avg.	240.7	−126.7	102.9	−432.9	−625.3	−246.6

Net movement of sediment over this period.

Source: Coakley (1972).

outputs. *Inputs* of material to a beach include longshore transport from upcoast, stream-supplied sediment, erosion of adjacent cliffs, and transport of material from offshore. *Outputs* from a beach take place by longshore drift to downshore, offshore transport, estuary filling, and finer material being blown off the beach into dune areas.

The mass balance varies seasonally, yearly, and over longer periods depending on the amount of inputs and outputs. If inputs equal outputs, there is a state of equilibrium every rare condition. If inputs are greater than outputs, there is a positive mass balance and the beach will grow. If outputs are greater than inputs, there is a negative balance and the beach will be eroding. As an example, see Table 42.1 and Figure 42.5.

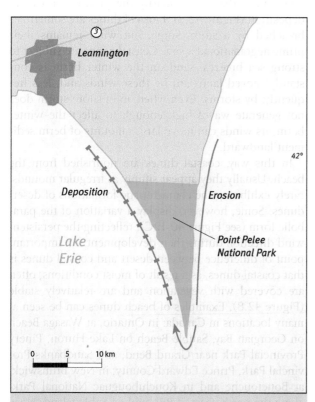

Figure 42.5 Point Pelee, Lake Erie. A cuspate foreland that is gradually moving westward because of erosion and deposition.

Two scenarios illustrate the behaviour of a beach. Temporary increases in wave energy, say, associated with a storm, promote temporary erosion (increased output to offshore zones). When wave energy conditions return to normal, offshore material is redeposited on the beach and it rebuilds to its former configuration. Long-term changes in sediment supply, however, can disrupt this general balance and produce substantial, and rather permanent, changes in the beach. Most often, coastlines experience a decline in sediment supply from streams because of upstream dams and reservoirs, groynes on shorelines upcoast, etc. Since the wave energy is not affected, the decreased sediment supply results in heightened beach erosion (Figure 42.6). Accordingly, the beach gets smaller as the storage of sediment decreases to reflect the lower inputs from streams or along shore it may even cause cliff erosion. In such cases rip-rap, or revetments, are placed to stop cliff erosion and artificial beach nourishment of coarser material may be used.

The location and distribution of beaches are therefore related to both sediment availability and wave energy. Where the coastal topography is being shaped by convergent lithospheric plate movement, coasts are steep, the wave energy is generally high, and beaches are comparatively few. On the mainland of North America, for example, beaches on the coast of the Pacific Northwest and in the Maritime provinces generally are discontinuous, short, and narrow ('pocket beaches'). Long Beach on the western shore of Vancouver Island is the exception and stretches for about 16 km; but the Gulf of Mexico and Atlantic coasts, from the Mexican border to New York's Long Island, are almost continuously beach-fringed, and beaches tend to be wide. Long, wide beaches (strands) are also found in southern Labrador, such as the 36-km-long Wonderstrands beach (described in two of the Icelandic sagas as Furdustrandir). The north coast of Prince Edward Island on the Gulf of St Lawrence also has extensive beaches (Figure 42.7). The continental shelves generally provide a good indication of the likelihood of beach development. Where shelves are wide, beaches usually are well developed. Along high-relief

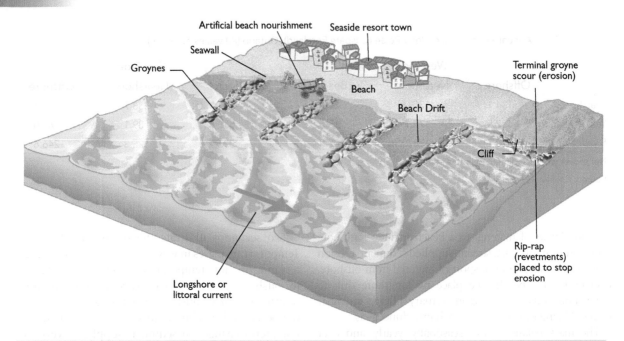

Figure 42.6   A groyne field designed to preserve a beach in front of a seaside resort. Erosion of the coast occurs down coast of the last groyne (terminal groyne scour). Rip rap, or revetments, are put in along the shore or more groynes are built to stop further erosion. Artificial beach nourishment (dumping of coarser beach material) can also be used to enhance the beaches.

coastlines, where shelves are frequently narrow, beach forms are generally restricted to more sheltered locations, and the material composing the beaches tends to be larger.

There is a general latitudinal zonation in terms of different types of beach sediments:

1. **Polar and subpolar regions**   Shingle beaches are characteristic and pure sand is present in long exposed beaches. Quartz and rock fragments dominate sand material.
2. **Temperate regions**   Quartz sand dominates. Rock fragments and feldspar are abundant in sand near stream mouths and along eroding bedrock coasts.
3. **Tropical regions**   Tropical beaches consist of carbonate sand composed of coral and algal fragments, shell, and carbonate precipitates. Quartz and rock fragments are common in sand, especially in areas of eroding bedrock and close to stream mouths.
4. **Oceanic islands**   Most beaches here have volcanic sands (normally black). In other places carbonate sands dominate.

Coastal Dunes
LINK

Wind is an important geomorphological agent in coastal landscapes, and many beaches are fringed by

sand dunes that are primarily the product of aeolian deposition (Figure 42.8). Lines of dunes are sometimes breached by a storm surge, but wind remains their prime aggradational agent. Coastal zones are subject to strong sea breezes; sand on the winter berm is constantly moved landward by these winds and, less frequently, by storms. Even when an offshore storm does not generate waves high enough to affect the winter berm, its winds can move large amounts of berm sediment landward.

In this way, coastal dunes are nourished from the beach. Usually they appear simply as irregular mounds, rarely exhibiting the characteristic formations of desert dunes. Some, however, display a variation of the parabolic form (see Figure 40.12C), reflecting the persistent wind direction during their development. An important point of difference between desert and coastal dunes is that coastal dunes, as a result of moist conditions, often are covered with vegetation and are relatively stable (Figure 42.8). Examples of beach dunes can be seen at many locations in Canada: in Ontario, at Wasaga Beach on Georgian Bay, Sauble Beach on Lake Huron, Pinery Provincial Park near Grand Bend, and Sandbanks Provincial Park, Prince Edward County; in New Brunswick, at Bouctouche and in Kouchibouguac National Park; along the north coast of PEI; and on Sable Island, Nova Scotia.

Figure 42.7 Aerial view of the white sandy beaches along the north coast of Prince Edward Island.

Figure 42.8 Dunes at Sandbanks Provincial Park on Lake Ontario near Picton, Ontario.

Sandspits and Sandbars

One of the most characteristic of the aggradational coastal landforms is the **sandspit**. When longshore drift occurs and the shifting sediment reaches a bay or a bend in the shoreline, it may form an extension into open water as shown (twice) in the central portion of Figure 42.9. In effect, the spit is an extension of the beach. It begins as a small tongue of sand and grows larger over time. It may reach many kilometres in length and grow hundreds of metres wide, although most spits have more modest dimensions. Two well-known sandspits are the Toronto Islands and Long Point in Lake Erie (Figure 42.10). The Toronto Islands are a recurved spit (Figure 42.12). Other examples are Sooke Harbour on Vancouver Island and Rebecca Spit, Quadra Island, BC.

Some sandspits are affected by two currents from different directions. This forms a cuspate foreland, as at Point Pelee near Leamington, Ontario (Point Pelee National Park), and Rose Point Spit, Naikoon Provincial Park, near Masset at the northern end of Haida Gwaii (Queen Charlotte Islands).

Some sandspits continue to grow all the way across the mouth of a bay and become **baymouth bars** (Figure 42.9, centre). The bay may simply be an indentation in the coastline, or it may be a stream estuary. At first, tidal currents may breach the growing bar and keep the bay open (where the tidal inlet is located to the right in Figure 42.9). But if the longshore drift is strong and sediment is plentiful, the bay will soon be closed off.

This has important consequences, because if the tidal action ceases, the bay is no longer supplied with cleansing ocean water. If the mouth of an estuary is closed off, the river that enters it will drop its sediments in the bay instead of the ocean. Thus, the bay becomes a lagoon, and its former saltwater environment changes as river water and sediment fill it. Behind the baymouth bar, the ecology of the new lagoon changes to that of a swamp or marshland (Figure 42.9). Examples of baymouth bars can be found at Hamilton, Ontario; at the Sandbanks at West Lake (Sandbanks Provincial

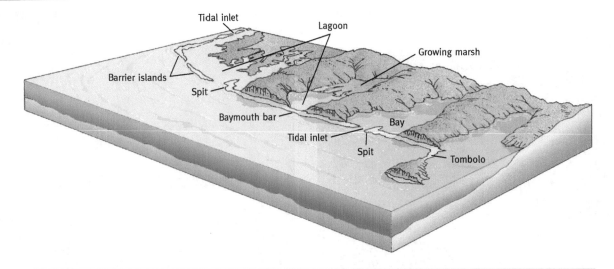

Figure 42.9 Common depositional landforms along a stretch of coastline.

Figure 42.10 Long Point, a 40-km-long sandspit that juts out into Lake Erie, Ontario, offers refuge and a stopover for migrating birds in fall and spring. It is recognized by the United Nations as a biosphere reserve.

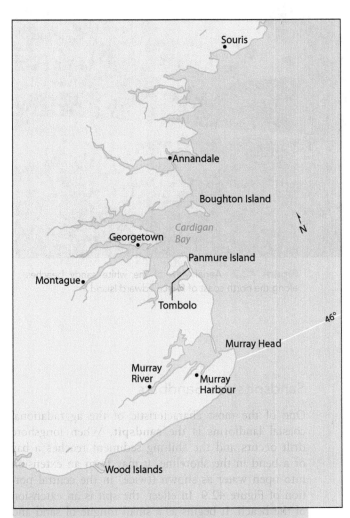

Figure 42.11 Map showing Panmure Island (Cardigan Bay, Prince Edward Island) attached to the mainland by a tombolo.

Park) and the bar at East Lake, both in Prince Edward County, Ontario; and at the *barachois*, or sand and gravel bars, at Channel-Port aux Basques and Bellevue Beach in Newfoundland. A growing sandspit also may form a link between an offshore island and the mainland, creating a landform called a **tombolo** (Figure 42.9, right front). These may be permanent features along lake coasts but only exposed at low tides along the sea coast. Examples of tombolos are in Pres'quile Provincial Park near Brighton, Ontario; Poverty Beach on

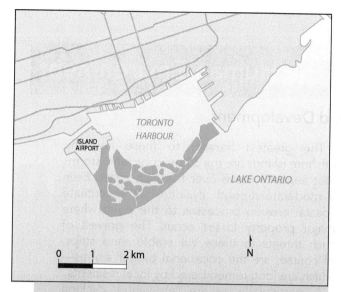

Figure 42.12 Map showing the Toronto Islands. Originally a recurved spit built from eroded material from the Scarborough Bluffs, the islands formed from dredging and infilling.

Panmure Island; Cardigan Bay, on the east coast of PEI; and at Percé Rock in Gaspé. Spits, bars, and tombolos can take on many different shapes as they bend, curve, and shift during their evolution (Figures 42.10, 42.11, and 42.12).

Offshore Bars and Barrier Islands

A sure sign of offshore aggradation is the *sandbar*, or **offshore bar**, which lies some distance from the beach and is not connected to land. We referred to longshore bars in connection with the beach profile (Figure 42.2), and such offshore bars can be observed to expand and contract depending on wave action and sediment supply. Once

formed, offshore bars interfere with the very waves that built them. Waves will break against the seaward side of a bar, then regenerate and break a second time against the shore itself (see Figure 42.3B). Some offshore bars become stable enough to attain permanence, rising above the water surface during low tide and being submerged only during high tide.

Along certain stretches of the Earth's coasts lie large and permanent offshore bars, appropriately called **barrier islands**. These islands are made of sand, but they reach heights of 6 m above sea level and average from 2 to 5 km in width. They can lie up to 20 km from the coast, but more commonly are half that distance from shore, and they often stretch for dozens of kilometres, unbroken except by tidal inlets. The offshore barrier island strip (known locally as the Outer Banks) that forms North Carolina's Cape Hatteras is a classic example, as are the barrier beaches along the north coasts of New Brunswick and Prince Edward Island.

Barrier islands may have had their origins as offshore bars during the last glaciation, when the sea level was much lower than it is today. As the sea level rose, these offshore bars migrated coastward, growing as they shifted. Since about 7000 years ago, when the sea level stopped rising rapidly, the barrier islands have moved landward slowly. In the meantime they have developed distinctive profiles. There is a gently sloping beach on the seaward side, a wind-built ridge of dunes in the middle, and a zone of natural vegetation (shrubs, marram grasses, mangroves) on the landward side (Figure 42.13). Finally, a lagoon almost always separates the barrier island from the mainland. Because barrier islands are breached by tidal inlets, however, tidal action keeps these lagoons from becoming swamps (Figure 42.9, left top).

Because of their recreational and other opportunities, which often attract intensive development (see Figure 41.8), barrier islands are of more than geomorphological interest. In fact, several large cities and many smaller towns have developed on these

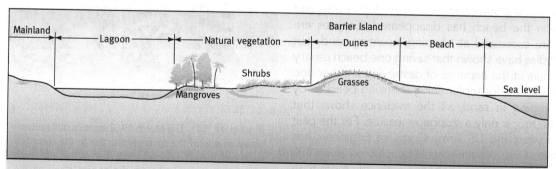

Figure 42.13 Cross-sectional profile of a barrier island and adjoining lagoon in a tropical or subtropical locale. Vertical exaggeration is about double.

Perspectives on the Human Environment

Hazards of Barrier Island Development

From Bar Harbor, Maine, to the mouth of the Rio Grande at Brownsville, Texas, more than 4000 km away, 295 barrier islands lie along much of the US Atlantic and Gulf of Mexico coastlines. Given Americans' love of the seashore—and the fact that more than half of them reside within an hour's drive of a coast—it should come as no surprise that most of these islands have witnessed the development of lengthy ocean-side strips of summer homes, resorts, high-rise condominiums, commercial and tourist facilities, fishing piers, and public beaches.

Barrier islands, as we know, are in constant motion, migrating slowly landward in response to increases in sea level (which have totalled about 30 cm over the past century along the eastern coast of the United States). The myriad structures built on loose sand atop these islands, therefore, are always threatened by erosional processes, which are strongest on the seaward side, directly facing the most desirable beach-front development sites.

To protect themselves, barrier island communities construct seawalls parallel to the beach and groynes or rock jetties perpendicularly outward into the surf (see Figure 41.8). They also spend lavishly to replenish beaches by pumping in massive amounts of new sand from offshore, deeper water sources (artificial beach nourishment). These measures, unfortunately, buy only a few years' time and may actually worsen erosion in the long run. Seawalls block the onrushing surf, but the deflected swash returns to the ocean so quickly that it carries with it most of the new sand that would otherwise have been deposited—and soon the beach has disappeared. Groynes are more successful at trapping incoming sand, but studies have shown that saving one beach usually occurs at the expense of destroying another one nearby. As for replenishing shrinking beaches by pumping in sand, all the evidence shows that this, too, is only a stopgap measure. For the past 30 years the US Army Corps of Engineers has shifted massive amounts of beach sand along 800 km of the eastern seaboard, with little more than a $10 billion expenditure to show for its herculean efforts.

The greatest hazards to these low-lying offshore islands are the 30 or so cyclonic storms that annually move over the east coast. Even a moderate-strength cyclone can accentuate coastal erosion processes to the point where major property losses occur. The gravest of such threats to these vulnerable sand strips, of course, are the occasional bigger storms—which are long remembered by local residents.

A particularly severe late-winter cyclone in 1962 smashed its way northward from Cape Hatteras to New England, leaving in its wake a reconfigured coastline (as the flooding ocean created new inlets across barrier islands) and nearly $1 billion worth of storm damage in today's US dollars (Figure 42.14). The worst devastation, however, is associated

Figure 42.14   The March 1962 storm is still remembered as one of the most destructive in the recorded history of the US Atlantic coast. This is the aftermath of that storm on Fire Island, the barrier island off the south-central shore of Long Island, about 80 km east of New York City.

with tropical cyclones. After Hurricane Camille (one of the most powerful of the past century) attacked the Louisiana and Mississippi Gulf coast in 1969, the United States was spared this kind of awesome damage for 20 years—until Hurricane Hugo roared across the South Carolina shoreline in 1989. Most importantly, this uncharacteristic lull of the 1970s and 1980s was accompanied by the largest coastal construction boom in history. Developed areas along the Gulf coast were decimated by Hurricanes Katrina (August 2005), Gustav (August 2008), and Ike (September 2008).

Only belatedly are the federal and state governments taking a hard look at all this development, and in many seaside locales a new consensus is emerging that it was a mistake to build in such unstable environments. The realization is dawning that nature is certain to win the battle of the barrier islands in the end—despite the best efforts of policy-makers, planners, and coastal engineers to manage the precarious human presence that has cost so many billions of dollars to put into (temporary) place.

In Canada, barrier islands are concentrated along the northern coasts of New Brunswick (which has the longest barrier coast in Canada, from Miscou Island to Cape Tormentine) and northern Prince Edward Island. They have not been developed in the same way as in the US. Many are located in national or provincial parks and they and most other barriers along the Canadian coasts have not been built upon. They have not been groyned to any great extent. These coasts are very sensitive to erosion and flooding caused by storm surges during winter storms (such as in January 2000, which caused $1 million in damages in PEI) and hurricanes (e.g., Hurricane Juan in 2003 caused $14 million in damage in PEI). These storms uproot trees, damage houses and boats, erode some barriers, and flood many coastal freshwater marsh areas important to breeding fish and bird species. They also cause the rapid migration of beaches and shift tidal inlets. Such low-lying areas are at very high risk in terms of rising sea levels resulting from global warming and the greater number and severity of storms and hurricanes stemming from this climatic change.

strips of sand, including Miami Beach, Galveston, and Atlantic City. Numerous long stretches of barrier islands extend from southern Texas to New York along the Gulf of Mexico and lower Atlantic coast of the United States. Between these islands and the mainland lies the Intracoastal Waterway, an important artery for coastal transport. Being low and exposed, the barrier islands are vulnerable to hurricanes, and severe storm waves can temporarily erase parts of them. In heavily developed areas the hazard is particularly obvious (see 'Perspectives' box).

Coastal Landscapes

The events described in regard to degradational coastal forces (Figure 42.1) constitute a possible model for the evolution of a shoreline from an initially irregular shape to a straight, uniform beach. The reason so few beaches resemble this model is that many coastlines have experienced marked fluctuations in the conditions that shape shoreline evolution. Simply put, most beaches are too recent to have achieved their equilibrium form. Recent sea-level fluctuations, as well as tectonic movements

along plate margins, continually disrupt the operation of coastal processes. With this in mind, it is convenient to distinguish between two general types of coastlines—*emergent* and *submergent* coasts.

Emergent Coasts

The landscapes of *uplifted* coasts, or **emergent coasts**, carry the imprints of elevation by tectonic forces. Some coastal zones have been uplifted faster than postglacial sea levels rose. The net effect of this is that such features as cliffs and wave-cut platforms are raised above (sometimes tens of metres above) the present sea level (Figure 42.16). When raised this way, a wave-cut platform is termed an **uplifted marine terrace**. Occasionally such landforms as stacks and arches still stand on the uplifted marine terrace.

Coasts where aggradational processes dominate also may be uplifted, but such depositional coastlines tend to lie in more stable lithospheric zones. There the evidence is more rapidly erased by erosional processes, because uplifted landforms—dunes, berms, bars, spits—are far less resistant than bedrock cliffs and wave-cut platforms. Sometimes cultural features reveal recent uplift. Stone structures of coastal settlements (including docks) may

From the Fieldnotes

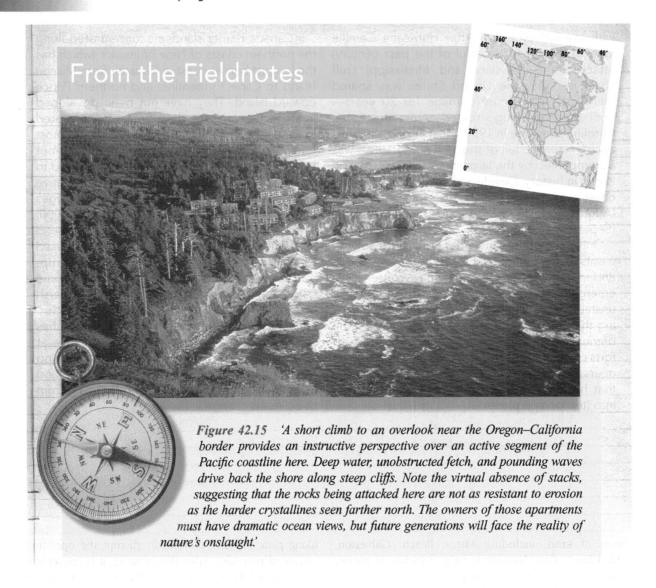

Figure 42.15 *'A short climb to an overlook near the Oregon–California border provides an instructive perspective over an active segment of the Pacific coastline here. Deep water, unobstructed fetch, and pounding waves drive back the shore along steep cliffs. Note the virtual absence of stacks, suggesting that the rocks being attacked here are not as resistant to erosion as the harder crystallines seen farther north. The owners of those apartments must have dramatic ocean views, but future generations will face the reality of nature's onslaught.'*

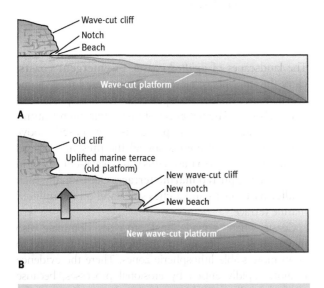

Figure 42.16 A wave-cut platform (A) is transformed into an uplifted marine terrace (B) when tectonic uplift elevates the coastal zone above the existing sea level.

survive longer than soft sedimentary landforms. When such settlements lie well above the water, we can conclude that uplift has occurred. Some Mayan buildings, constructed on the waterfront more than 1000 years ago, now lie elevated on uplifted segments of the Mexican and Central American coasts.

Submergent Coasts

More coastlines are **submergent coasts**, that is, *drowned* rather than uplifted. This submergence was caused in large part by the rise of the sea level over the past 10,000 years. At the beginning of the Holocene the sea level stood perhaps 100–120 m below its present average mark. This exposed large parts of the continental shelves (see Figure 2.6) that are now under water. Streams flowed across these areas of land as they do today across the coastal plain, eroding their valleys to the edge of the lowered ocean.

The courses of many such streams, in fact, can be traced from their present mouths across the continental shelf to their former outlets. When Holocene glacial melting raised global sea levels by many metres, these marginal areas were submerged and the stream valleys became submarine canyons. The water rose quite rapidly until about 7000 years ago. This was the time when the world's barrier islands formed and began to migrate landward. Over the past seven millennia the sea level has continued to rise, but so slowly that many coastlines have stabilized.

In the drowned stream mouths, it is possible to witness the effects of submergence. Streams often flow into these estuaries (or *rias*) and leave no doubt regarding their origins. Sometimes the tops of nearly submerged hills rise as small islands above the water within the estuary. If sea levels continue to rise because of global warming, the invasion of stream valleys by advancing ocean water will continue. However, the rise of the sea level had slowed sufficiently to permit longshore drift to form spits and bars across many estuaries.

Evidence of submergence also can be seen on tectonically active, high-relief coasts and in areas affected by glacial erosion that were adjacent to coastlines. A combination of crustal subsidence and rising sea levels produces very deep water immediately offshore (for instance, along the western coasts of North and South America). This exposes the coastal bedrock to the onslaught of powerful, deep-water waves not slowed by shoaling. Where fjords were carved by glaciers reaching the ocean, rising water has filled the U-shaped troughs above the level of the ice. Fjords, of course, are drowned glacial valleys, their waters deep, their valley sides sheer and often spectacular (see Figure 37.18C). Good examples can be seen in BC, Newfoundland and Labrador, and parts of Nova Scotia. Submergent coastlines, therefore, display varied landscapes, all resulting from rising water or subsiding crust, or both.

Living Shorelines

Living organisms, such as corals, algae, and mangroves, can shape or affect the development of shores and coasts. A **coral reef** is built by tiny marine organisms that discharge calcium carbonate. New colonies build on the marine limestone deposits left by their predecessors, and this process can create an extensive network of coast-fringing ridges. To grow, corals need clear water, warm temperatures, and vigorous cleansing wave action. This wave action does erode the reef, but it also washes the growing coral. Ideally, the coral is covered with water during high tide and exposed to the air during low tide.

Where conditions are favourable, wide, flat-topped coral reefs develop. Sometimes they are attached

to the shore; others lie offshore and create lagoons between shore and reef. Still other corals create atolls. **Atolls** are roughly circular reefs that surround a lagoon, but without any land in the centre. The round shape of atolls, many of which are found in the lower latitudes of the Pacific Ocean, was studied more than 150 years ago by Charles Darwin. He concluded that the corals probably grew on the rims of eroded volcanic cones. As the flattened volcano subsided (or the sea level rose), the corals continued to build upward (Figure 42.17).

Vegetation also influences the evolution of shorelines. In parts of West Africa, Southeast Asia, and the southeastern United States, mangroves and their elaborate root systems have become builders of shorelines. Once these unique plants have taken hold, the erosional power of waves and currents is harnessed by those root systems. As a result, a zone of densely vegetated mud flats develops, creating a unique ecological niche. As we have seen recently,

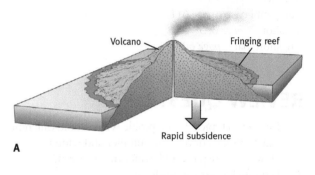

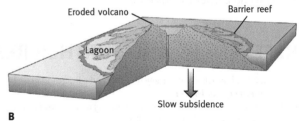

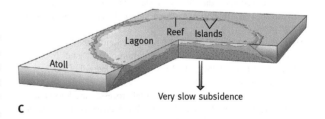

Figure 42.17 Relationship between coral atoll reefs and marine volcanoes. The coral reef originally develops around the rim of a subsiding volcanic cone (A). As the cone erodes, the corals continue to build upward, leaving a lagoon surrounded by a ring-like reef (B). When the cone has disappeared below the water, the circular atoll is the only feature remaining at the ocean surface (C).

the widespread removal of mangroves has worsened the effect of hurricanes (such as Katrina in 2005) and cyclones (Nargis in 2008), and the previous removal of both mangroves and coral reefs was a significant factor in the devastation caused by the December 2004 tsunami in South Asia.

The landforms and landscapes of coastlines are formed and modified by many processes and conditions. No two stretches of shoreline are exactly alike because the history of a coastal landscape involves a unique combination of waves, tides, currents, wind, sea-level change, and crustal movement.

KEY TERMS

atolls   *page 613*
backshore   *page 603*
barrier island   *page 609*
baymouth bar   *page 607*
beach   *page 603*
beach mass balance   *page 604*
berm   *page 603*
coral reef   *page 613*
emergent coast   *page 611*
foreshore   *page 603*
longshore bar   *page 603*

nearshore   *page 603*
offshore bar   *page 609*
sandspit   *page 607*
sea arch   *page 602*
sea cave   *page 602*
sea cliff   *page 602*
stack   *page 602*
submergent coast   *page 612*
tombolo   *page 608*
uplifted marine terrace   *page 611*
wave-cut platform   *page 602*

REVIEW QUESTIONS

1. Describe a typical beach profile. Why would different beach profiles develop in summer and winter?
2. How do sandspits and baymouth bars form?
3. How do barrier islands form?

4. Describe the processes by which irregular, embayed coastlines become straightened.
5. What has been the fundamental cause of the many submergent coastlines encountered throughout the world?

REFERENCES AND FURTHER READINGS

(Note: Additional references for this unit are listed in the References and Further Readings for Unit 41.)

Bird, E.C.F. 1993. *Submerging Coasts: The Effects of a Rising Sea Level on Coastal Environments*. New York: Wiley.

Coakley, J.P. 1972. 'Nearshore Sediment Studies in Western Lake Erie', *Proceedings of the 15th Conference on Great Lakes Research*. Madison, Wis.: International Association of Great Lakes Research, 330–43.

Davidson-Arnott, R.G.D., and H.E. Conliffe Reid. 1994. 'Sedimentary Processes and the Evolution of the Distal Bayside of Long Point, Lake Erie', *Canadian Journal of Earth Sciences* 31, 9: 1461–73.

———— and R. Kreutzwiser. 1985. 'Coastal Processes and Shoreline Encroachment: Implications for Shoreline Management in Ontario', *Canadian Geographer* 29, 3: 256–62.

Davis, R.A., Jr, and D. Fitzgerald. 2002. *Beaches and Coasts*. Malden, Mass.: Blackwell.

Dolan, R., and H. Lins. 1987. 'Beaches and Barrier Islands', *Scientific American* (July): 68–77.

French, P.W. 1997. *Coastal and Estuarine Management*. London/New York: Routledge.

————. 2001. *Coastal Defences: Processes, Problems and Solutions*. London/New York: Routledge.

Hooke, J.M., et al. 1996. 'Sediment Transport Analysis as a Component of Coastal Management—A UK Example', *Environmental Geology* 27, 4: 347–57.

Jolliffe, I.P. 1978. 'Littoral and Offshore Sediment Transport', *Progress in Physical Geography* 2, 2: 264–308.

McCann, S.B. 1982. 'Coastal Landforms', *Progress in Physical Geography* 6, 3: 439–45.

Shaw, J., et al. 1998. 'Potential Impacts of Global Sea-level Rise on Canadian Coasts', *Canadian Geographer* 42, 4: 365–80.

Shaw, J.R. 1986. *Beach and Offshore Changes at Point Pelee National Park, Lake Erie 1974–1981*. Canadian Technical Report of Hydrography and Ocean Sciences, Fisheries and Oceans, no. 76. Ottawa: Supply and Services.

Snead, R.A. 1982. *Coastal Landforms and Surface Features: A Photographic Atlas and Glossary*. Stroudsburg, Penn.: Dowden, Hutchinson & Ross.

Steers, J.A. 1971. *Applied Coastal Geomorphology*. Cambridge, Mass.: MIT Press.

Stevenson, W.J. 2000. 'Shore Platforms: A Neglected Coastal Feature', *Progress in Physical Geography* 24, 3: 311–27.

Time. 1987. 'Where's the Beach? America's Vanishing Coastline', 10 Aug., 38–47.

Trenhaile, A.S. 1987. *The Geomorphology of Rock Coasts*. London/New York: Oxford Univ. Press.

WEB RESOURCES

aczisc.dal.ca The website of the Atlantic Coastal Zone Information Steering Committee includes a guide to coastal information in Atlantic Canada and links to other coast-related sites.

disc.sci.gsfc.nasa.gov/geomorphology/GEO_6/GEO_CHAPTER_6. shtml NASA's geomorphology site provides descriptions of major coastal landforms, with graphics depicting worldwide distribution of tectonic coastlines and shelf types.

gsc.nrcan.gc.ca/marine/index_e.php This website has information about coastal processes and research in Canada.

gsc.nrcan.gc.ca/org/atlantic/index_e.php This is the website of the Geological Survey of Canada's Atlantic section. It includes information about the coastal information system, coastal map examples, dynamic segmentation, and references.

www.ec.gc.ca/inre-nwi/ The National Water Research Institute of Environment Canada provides information, research, and links to sites dealing with coastal and other water-related themes. The major NWRI facility is at the Canadian Centre for Inland Water in Burlington, Ontario.

PART FIVE
The Biosphere

Units

PART FIVE The Biosphere

Biosphere

The biosphere is the most recent of the Earth's great environmental realms, where lithosphere, hydrosphere, atmosphere, and cryosphere converge and interact in the formation and sustenance of all forms of life. Numerous systems and subsystems, processes, and cycles link lithosphere and biosphere, beginning with the weathering of rock and continuing through the evolution of terrestrial and marine ecosystems. The key component in this endless series is the development and deepening of soil, with its various properties reflecting the environmental regimes under which it evolved. Air, water, temperature, and other factors combine to transform rock into soil, and elements of the global climatic map are reflected in the soil regions recognized. In turn, these soil regions support particular combinations of plants, generating biomes that sustain life in literally countless forms. But global environments change, and biomes formed over thousands of years can be swept away in short order by climatic changes. Advancing glaciers can scrape the bedrock bare of soils and plants, and only after the planet warms up again can the whole process start over. Like all environmental maps, those of soils and biomes are but still pictures of an ever-changing planet.

Climate, Soil, Plants, and Animals

Objectives

- To expand our concept of physical geography by including biotic systems operating at the Earth's surface.

- To relate biotic systems to our understanding of global climates.

- To link physical geography to the more general topic of conservation.

Part Two focused on one major aspect of physical geography—climate. After examining the processes that take place in the atmosphere, it then concentrated on a geographical interpretation of the results—the Earth's present climate regions. (Figure 16.2 summarizes the global distribution of macroclimatic regions.) Part Two concluded with a discussion of the dynamics of human–climate interactions.

This section delves further into the physical geography (and with it, the natural history) of our planet. It should be remembered that processes and the resulting patterns are always changing. Just a few thousand years ago, leafy forests and green pastures stood where desert conditions prevail today; now-extinct animals roamed landscapes that are now empty and barren. A mere 10,000 years ago, enormous ice sheets were melting back after covering much of North America and Eurasia.

The news is now full of stories about other changes in our terrestrial environments. One such example is the change in climate caused by the burning of fossil fuels; another is the depletion of the atmosphere's ozone layer, especially above Antarctica. As we note in the 'Perspectives' box in Unit 6, this climate change may portend a future of greater health risks and untold unforeseeable effects on plants and animals. In short, maps of climates—as well as other elements of the environment—are still pictures of a changing world.

Part Five discusses several aspects of the environment that are closely related to climate. Geographers are most interested in interrelationships—between climate and soils, soils and plants, natural environments and human societies, and many other ecological connections. More often than not, the prevailing climate, past or present, is a key to our understanding of such relationships. Again and again, when studying the distributions of natural phenomena such as soils, plants, and animals, the importance of climate patterns can be seen.

Natural Geography

The study of soils, plants (*flora*), and animals (*fauna*) in spatial perspective is a branch of physical geography (see Figure 1.4), although this aspect of the discipline might be better designated *natural geography*—the geography of nature. The geography of soils is a part of the science of **pedology** (soil science), the name of which is derived from the ancient Greek word *pedon*, meaning ground. The geography of plants and animals defines the field of **biogeography**, a combination of biology and geography. Biogeography can be further divided into two subfields: **phytogeography**, the geography of plants, and **zoogeography**, the geography of animals.

Geography of Soils

The next two units (44 and 45) examine the development, properties, classification, and regionalization of

Figure 43.1 Leaf litter on the forest floor—a source of vital nutrients for the living plants.

soils. On the landmasses, soils and vegetation lie at the *interface* between the lithosphere and the atmosphere, at the plane of interaction between rocks and their minerals, on the one hand, and the air with its moisture and heat, on the other. Soil is the key to plant life, containing mineral nutrients and storing water. But the vegetation itself contributes to its own sustenance by adding decaying organic matter to the soil, which is absorbed and converted into reusable nutrients (Figure 43.1). The processes that go on at this interface are intricate and complicated.

Life would not exist on this planet without the presence of water. One reason is that without water there would be no soil. The Moon's lifeless surface of rock fragments and pulverized rubble holds no water—and therefore no soil. Water is the key to the chemical and physical processes that break down rocks, thus triggering the process of soil formation. As the soil develops or matures, water sustains its circulatory system, promotes the necessary chemical reactions, transfers nutrients, helps decompose organic matter, and ensures the continued decay and disintegration of rocks below the evolving soil layer. Some soils capable of supporting permanent vegetation can develop in a short period (between one and two centuries), but most soils require thousands of years to mature fully (Figure 43.2). Over this period of time the soil absorbs and discharges water, inhales and exhales air through its pore spaces, takes in organic matter and cycles nutrients, and is inhabited by organisms of many kinds. In every sense of the term, *the soil is a living entity*.

LINK

As with all living things, the soil's well-being can be threatened, and soils can actually die. When allowed to develop and mature, a soil will achieve a state of equilibrium with the prevailing climate, with the vegetation it supports (and that supports it), and with other elements of the surrounding environment. Many conditions can threaten a soil, some natural, others artificial. Climatic change also may lead to change in the natural vegetation,

Figure 43.2 A soil profile of a well-developed soil whose structure has evolved over thousands of years.

which, in turn, can expose a soil to increased erosion. Farming may overtax the soil, giving it insufficient time to recover from ploughing, planting, and harvesting year after year (Figure 43.3). Domesticated animals may trample vegetation and compact topsoil, thereby weakening the soil structure and subjecting it to erosion by water and wind.

The geographical study of soils involves learning about the development and maturation of this critical 'cloak of life', as well as about ways to protect and conserve it. When it comes to the components of the Earth's biosphere, the more we know about nature, the better prepared we are to help sustain it. Part Five, therefore, explores the development of a typical soil, looks at a mature soil in profile, and discusses the processes that go on within and between the soil layers. Next, soil classification is discussed, and from this classification emerges regionalization, the map of world soils (see Figure 45.15). A comparison of this map with other global maps in the text (such as climate [Figure 16.2], precipitation [Figure 11.16], and vegetation [Figure 47.1]) reveals some of the spatial relationships between soil regions and other elements of the natural environment. Moreover, comparing the soil map and a map of world population distribution (see Figure 2.5) indicates the critical importance of certain soil types for food production.

Biogeography

Another major topic, addressed in Units 46 to 48, is biogeography, or the geography of flora and fauna. Several of the world's climates are named after the vegetation that characterizes them (e.g., savanna, steppe, and tundra). When climate, soil, vegetation, and animal life reach a stable adjustment, vegetation constitutes the most visible element of the ecosystem. When you fly from the west coast of BC to Ontario or the Atlantic provinces you cross over a series of ecosystems ranging from west coast rainforest to prairie and boreal forest. You cannot always see the climate changing, nor can you clearly see the soil most of the way. But the vegetation tells the story: lush forest of the west coast gives way to different kinds of forest over the Rockies; on the leeward side of this huge mountain range the trees are gradually replaced by areas that were once grassland (the Prairies). The grassland changes to forest again east of Winnipeg, but this time it is boreal forest. The best indicator of the succession of prevailing ecosystems is vegetation (Figure 43.4).

In Unit 47, we will learn that the Earth's great vegetation assemblages consist not of just one or two, but of literally millions of **species**. Biologists suggest that there may be as many as 30 million species alive today, of which only about *1.7 million* have been identified and classified (see 'Perspectives' box). Geographers are especially interested in the distribution of the known species, as well as in the relationships between plant and animal communities and their natural environments. Biogeographers seek explanations for the distributions the map reveals. For example, why are certain species found in certain areas but not in others that also seem suitable for them? And why do species exist co-operatively in some places but competitively in others? What is the effect of isolation on species and their interrelationships?

The founder of biogeography as a systematic field of study was Alexander von Humboldt (1769–1859), who travelled much of the world in search of plant specimens. When von Humboldt reached South America's Andes, he recognized that altitude, temperature, natural vegetation, and crop cultivation were interrelated. After returning to Europe, he produced a monumental series of books that formed a basis not only for biogeography but also for many other fields of the natural sciences.

The separation of biogeography into phytogeography and zoogeography occurred after the appearance of von Humboldt's writings. Probably the most important book on zoogeography to appear during the nineteenth century was written by Alfred Russel Wallace (*The Geographical Distribution of Animals*, 1876). Wallace was particularly

From the Fieldnotes

Figure 43.3   *'About 16 km from the Kenyan town of Meru the landscape showed signs of severe erosion. We stopped to talk with the people of these homesteads and asked them about their crops. Yes, they knew that farming on slopes as steep as these would lead to "gullying", but they saw no alternative. You get a crop one or two years, and that's better than nothing, they said. Some neighbours whose village had lost most of its land this way had gone to the city (Nairobi), we were told, and now the place where they had lived was like a desert.'*

Figure 43.4   Vegetation boundaries on the Coast Mountains of British Columbia. Here the coniferous west coast rainforest gives way to the hardier tundra ecosystem above the treeline.

interested in the complicated distribution of animals in Southeast Asia and Australia. Australia is the last major refuge of the marsupials (animals whose young are born very early in their development and then carried in an abdominal pouch); the kangaroo, koala, and wombat are three Australian marsupials. While a few marsupials survive in other areas of the world (such as the Virginia opossum in North America and the yapok, or water opossum, of South America), Australia's fauna is unique, and Wallace wanted to establish the zoogeographical boundary line between Southeast Asia's very different animal assemblage and that of Australia. When he did his fieldwork, he discovered that Australian fauna existed not only in Australia itself but also in New Guinea and even on some eastern islands of what is today Indonesia. So Wallace drew a line between Kalimantan (Indonesian Borneo) and Sulawesi, and between the first island (Bali) and the second island (Lombok) east of Java (see Figure 48.3). *Wallace's Line* soon became one of the most hotly debated zoogeographic boundaries ever drawn. The debate continues to this day (Unit 48).

Zoogeography is a field of many dimensions and challenges. Vegetation regions can be seen from the air and can be mapped from remotely sensed data. But animals move and migrate, their *range* (area of natural occurrence) changes over time and even seasonally, and detection can present problems as well. Mapping faunal distributions for large animals is difficult enough; for smaller species it is often far more complicated.

Conservation and the Biosphere

The more that is learned about the Earth's biosphere, the more concern is voiced about the future. The overuse and erosion of soils are worsening global problems

(Figure 43.5). A large part of the sediment load carried oceanward by the world's great rivers comes from slopes where cultivation has loosened the topsoil, which is carried away by rainstorms. The destruction of tropical rainforests is accelerating in South and Central America, sub-Saharan Africa, and Southeast Asia. Botanists estimate that as many as one-quarter of all the presently living plant species may become extinct during the next 50–100 years. Animals large and small are also facing extinction, from the African elephant to tiny insects.

People pose many threats to animals. Among these threats are human invasion of the last refuges of wildlife and human-induced climate change. The horn of the African rhinoceros, for instance, is prized in Saudi Arabia as a dagger handle, and in East Asia its powdered form is regarded as an aphrodisiac. As a result, rhinos have been killed by poachers so quickly that relatively few remain. Recently, the price of powdered rhino horn on the Asian

Perspectives on the Human Environment

Biodiversity under Siege

Biodiversity, shorthand for biological diversity, refers to 'the number, variety, and variability of living organisms' (MacDonald, 2003). The cataloguing of those life forms according to species has proven to be the most practical approach (spatial variations are discussed in the 'Perspectives' box in Unit 46). A species may be defined as a population of physically and chemically similar organisms within which free gene flow takes place.

How many living species does the global environment contain? By 2003 approximately 1.7 million species had been identified and described. About 963,000 of these are insects, 270,000 are plants, 46,000 are vertebrate animals, and the remainder consists of invertebrates, fungi, algae, and micro-organisms. However, biologists unanimously agree that these subtotals constitute only a small proportion of the total number of terrestrial species. The renowned biologist Edward O. Wilson estimates that the total far exceeds the number of known species and lies somewhere between 5 and 30 million.

Biodiversity may be regarded as one of our planet's most important resources, and it is a rising concern today because it is under siege. As noted in Unit 17, tropical rainforests are especially threatened by the mass burning and cutting of trees, which annually removes a woodland area

just over three times the size of New Brunswick. These forests also are home to about 80 per cent of all living species, and the rate of loss is now about 100 species per day (36,500 per year). Other fragile biological communities are besieged as well, particularly in coastal zones and wetlands. The main cause of these exterminations is loss of habitat because of the expansion of such human activities as deforestation, agriculture, urbanization, and air and water pollution.

As these uses—and misuses—of the global environment multiply, there is growing evidence that decline in biodiversity may soon become a universal phenomenon. An ominous example is the decrease in field observation, since the mid-1980s, of more than 70 per cent of the bird species known to summer in eastern North America. This decrease is consistent with Wilson's finding that perhaps 20 per cent of all bird species have disappeared in modern times and another 10 per cent are endangered.

Although biodiversity is one of the newest research areas in life sciences, we already know enough to draw the following conclusion: as human technology continues to advance, it is increasingly accompanied by the largest extinction of natural species the world has undergone since the mass extinctions that occurred at the time the dinosaurs disappeared 65 million years ago.

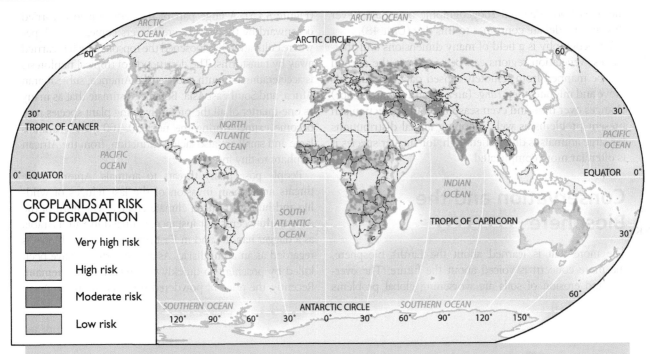

Figure 43.5 Croplands susceptible to degradation on the basis of climate, soil type, and human pressures. Such areas are most at risk where population densities are high. That risk is reduced, however, in countries where proactive measures to preserve soil resources are being pursued.

market has been four to five times higher by weight than that of gold! So Africa's rhinos are threatened less by competition from poor, land-hungry farmers than by the whims of the distant wealthy.

Whether we focus on soils, plants, or animals, our geographic perspective soon underscores the reality that the Earth's biosphere is under severe stress. All too often, the changes that take place are irreversible. Topsoil that has taken hundreds or thousands of years to develop is washed away in a few months. Plant species never even inventoried are lost forever, and it will never be known what role they might have played in combatting disease. As Africa's elephant herds dwindle in the face of ivory poachers, we are witnessing the extinction of a legacy of hundreds of millions of years. The explosive growth of the Earth's human population and the profligate spending behaviour of consumers in the world's wealthiest countries have combined to put the biosphere under stress as never before. From fishing grounds to mountain pastures, from rainforest to desert margin, the evidence is everywhere (Figure 43.6).

How can this tide of destruction be slowed or reversed? Knowledge and awareness are powerful allies in any such endeavour. For years after the Communists took power in China in 1949, Chinese leaders extolled the virtues of population expansion, at home and abroad, as a means of furthering their ideological objectives. Then China became aware that economic development would be stymied by the needs of so many millions of additional citizens, and its policies were changed (Figure 43.7). In the summer of 2004 the Chinese government announced that the country

was going to have millions more men than women because of this policy; the traditional cultural preference for male children has led to many abortions, infanticide of females, and disregard of the law. Not only population control but also soil conservation and reforestation programs were made high priorities. But the People's Republic of China, unlike India and many other countries, has a powerful, highly centralized government that can impose such

Figure 43.6 Signs of a forest in trouble. Three decades ago this section of forest in eastern Ontario was in good condition, but years of pollution from factories in the US and Ontario and acid precipitation have done much damage.

From the Fieldnotes

Figure 43.7 *'I walked from my hotel towards the main square of the city of Chengdu. On the opposite side of the square stood a huge billboard. At first I thought that it was merely an unusually large advertisement (of which in 1981 one sees rather more in southern China than in the north), but soon it became obvious that there was a message here, and it was clear enough. One child per couple is the official stipulation, and here that is proclaimed in Chinese as well as in English. A tough rule, but it will undoubtedly be enforced. Perhaps this will slow the land degradation and overuse we had observed on the way to Chengdu from Kunming.'*

measures rather effectively. Elsewhere, change must come through education and voluntary co-operation, which is far more difficult to achieve.

Although Part Five concentrates on the biosphere, it should be remembered that the principles and practices of conservation apply to more than soils, plants, and animals. **Conservation** entails the careful management and use of natural resources, the achievement of significant social benefits from them, and the preservation of the environment. For more than half a century, courses in conservation were a cornerstone of an education in geography.

One of the incentives behind this practice was the terrible experience of the 1930s, a phenomenon now known simply as the *dust bowl*. On the Great Plains of North America, where raising wheat was the mainstay of the re-

gion's farmers, below-average rainfall was recorded for several years running. Wheat had been sown on land that was only marginally suitable for grain cultivation, and when the rains failed, the loosened soil fell prey to the ever-present wind. Great clouds of dust soon blackened the skies as millions of tonnes of topsoil were blown away (Figure 43.8). Dunes formed, some more than 3 m high, and the landscape was transformed. Thousands of farmers abandoned their land and moved westward, hoping to make a new start in British Columbia, Alberta, or California. Nearly 200,000 migrated from the Prairie provinces and went further west during this period. The physical destruction of much of the Great Plains and the social dislocation that accompanied it made an indelible mark on North America (a struggle immortalized in John Steinbeck's classic novel

Figure 43.8 A massive dust storm southwest of Lakenheath near Assiniboia, Saskatchewan, during the height of the dust bowl of the 1930s.

The Grapes of Wrath), and the idea of conservation took hold. Since geographers study climates, soils, agriculture, and related topics, many students came to geography because of their interest in conservation.

The Roosevelt administration in the United States (1933–45) launched large programs to counter future dust-bowl experiences. The US Congress passed legislation in support of land-use planning and soil protection, and the federal government created several offices and agencies to implement these initiatives. The Soil Conservation Service was among these agencies, as were the Natural Resources Board and the Civilian Conservation Corps. One of the most important agencies to be founded during this period was the Tennessee Valley Authority (TVA), a massive regional project begun in 1933 to control destructive floods, assist farmers, improve navigation, and create electric power sources in the Tennessee River basin (Figure 43.9). The TVA, still operating today, includes parts of seven states: Alabama, Georgia, Kentucky, Mississippi, North Carolina, Tennessee, and Virginia. It has transformed the physical and human geography of a large region. No such large programs were initiated in Canada. The Conservative government of R.B. Bennett (1930–5) was reluctant to spend money on massive public works or relief payments. The Mackenzie King government that followed (1935–47) initiated the Prairie Farm Rehabilitation Administration (PFRA) in the late 1930s. This agency had the authority to rehabilitate devastated land and develop sustainable dryland farming practices that it would then demonstrate to the remaining farmers. Such practices were essential to the farmers' ability to make a living. For nearly a decade the PFRA's soil and water conservation and development practices had positive

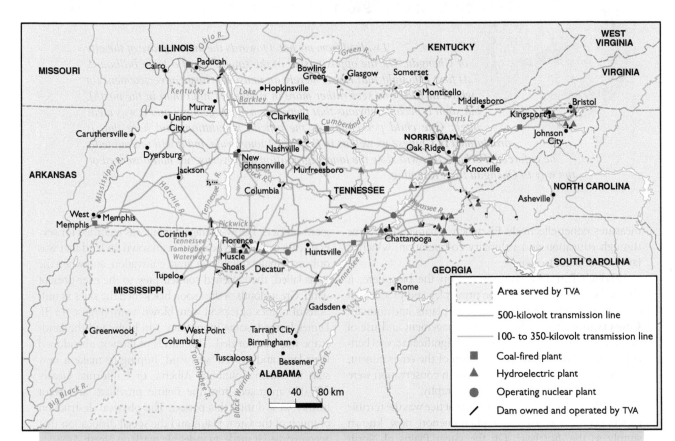

Figure 43.9 Region developed by the Tennessee Valley Authority (TVA), beginning in the mid-1930s.

results. New drought-resistant grasses were introduced and watering sites were supplied, transforming lifeless, wind-eroded land into productive pasture land.

The 1930s, which some have called the golden age of conservation in the United States, were followed by a period during which attention in the US was diverted to other causes: war and global strategic competition. In the meantime, urbanization was increasing in North America, and many farmers, unable to afford mechanization and other new technologies required to compete in the post-war marketplace, were forced to sell their land. Fortunately, some far-sighted people continued to support conservationist ideas and programs with their own money. Among privately funded conservation organizations were the US Conservation Foundation (founded in 1948), US Resources for the Future (1952), and the Canadian Audubon Society (1948). The latter is now called Nature Canada (2004). The Canadian Nature Conservancy was established in the early 1960s. Such organizations sponsored research and publications on conservation issues and practices and helped keep the conservation ethic before the North American people.

As environmental problems intensified not only at home but also abroad, the public interest in and concern over conservation matters was revived. The US government finally responded in 1970 by creating the Environmental Protection Agency (EPA). The EPA soon became a high-profile agency that addressed a wider range of conservation and environmental concerns than any of its predecessors. After a number of scandals and exposures of lax enforcement during the 1980s, under the Clinton administration in the 1990s the EPA—along with a reinvigorated US Department of the Interior—again played a major role in the conservation arena. Although that government-led effort substantially diminished during the tenure of George W. Bush in the first decade of the twenty-first century, the conservation movement continues—increasingly under the banner of **sustainable development**, which the World Commission on Environment and Development defines as 'development that meets the needs of the present without compromising the ability of future generations to meet their own needs'.

The government of Canada has led the way in terms of the establishment of national parks and ecological reserves in all ecological zones of the country. The Department of the Environment (Environment Canada) has established a two-prong approach to conservation: (1) a landscape approach that provides for the ecologically sound use of resources and environmental protection of all Canadian landscapes (terrestrial and marine); and (2) a national network of representative protected areas (national parks and reserves) within each of the ecological and/or landscape areas of Canada. The protected areas now occupy approximately 20 million hectares, or about 2 per cent of Canada's territory. However, many of these protected areas are too small to be ecologically self-sustaining. In western Canada, only four national parks (in the Rockies) are large enough to sustain resident populations of predators, such as cougars and wolves. Canada also led the way in the international environmental movement with the establishment of Greenpeace in 1971 (founding members included Patrick Moore, Bob Hunter, David McTaggart, and Paul Watson) to protest nuclear weapons testing in Alaska. This organization is now working in nearly 30 countries, and its 2.5 million members champion environmental conservation of all types. Some of the original members of Greenpeace have gone on to form other conservation groups, such as the Sea Shepherd Society. The reality of climate change has been brought home to a lot of people around the world by the work of former US Vice-President Al Gore Jr (Nobel Peace Prize 2007, with the Intergovernmental Panel on Climate Change [IPCC]), and especially by the movie based on his lectures about climate change, *An Inconvenient Truth* (Academy Award for Best Documentary, 2006, director Davis Guggenheim), which brought increasing awareness of climate change to the fore. The release of a series of reports by the UN's IPCC has also intensified interest in the subject. The rising cost of oil and food staples and increasing awareness of pollution and other environmental problems have made a lot more people think of using alternate energy resources (lowering their 'carbon footprint' and going 'green' in terms of food, energy, and other purchases).

Clearly, the geographic study of the biosphere is not just a theoretical exercise. It involves science as well as policy, research as well as application. To make decisions we need basic information, and each of the units in Part Five contains essential background to help us do so.

KEY TERMS

biodiversity *page 623*
biogeography *page 620*
conservation *page 625*
pedology *page 620*

phytogeography *page 620*
species *page 621*
sustainable development *page 627*
zoogeography *page 620*

REVIEW QUESTIONS

1. Which subjects are encompassed by *pedology* and by *biogeography*?
2. What are the major functions of soil?
3. In what way does physical geography help us understand problems of conservation?
4. Why was the Tennessee Valley Authority created in the 1930s?
5. What was the Canadian government's response to the dust bowl of the 1930s?

REFERENCES AND FURTHER READINGS

Bailey, R.G. 1996. *Ecosystem Geography.* New York: Springer-Verlag.

Bradbury, I.K. 1998. *The Biosphere,* 2nd edn. New York: Wiley.

Cutter, S.L., and W.H. Renwick. 1999. *Exploitation, Conservation, Preservation: A Geographic Perspective on Natural Resource Use,* 3rd edn. New York: Wiley.

Eblen, R.A., and W.R. Eblen, eds. 1994. *The Encyclopedia of the Environment.* Boston: Houghton Mifflin.

Gore, A.A., Jr. 2000, 2007. *Earth in the Balance: Ecology and the Human Spirit.* Boston: Houghton Mifflin, and Emmaus, Penn.: Rodale.

———. 2006. *An Inconvenient Truth: The Planetary Emergency of Global Warming and What We Can Do about It.* Emmaus, Penn.: Rodale.

Guggenheim, D., dir. 2006. *An Inconvenient Truth.* Los Angeles: Paramount Vantage/Paramount Home Entertainment DVD.

Hole, G.D., and J.B. Campbell. 1985. *Soil Landscape Analysis.* Totowa, NJ: Rowman & Allanheld.

Huggett, R.J. 1997. *Environmental Change: The Evolving Ecosphere.* London/New York: Routledge.

Huston, M.A. 1994. *Biological Diversity: The Coexistence of Species on Changing Landscapes.* New York: Cambridge Univ. Press.

Jefferies, M. 1997. *Biodiversity and Conservation.* London/New York: Routledge.

Lovelock, J. 1988. *The Ages of Gaia: A Biography of Our Living Earth.* New York: Norton.

MacDonald, G.M. 2003. *Biogeography: Introduction to Space, Time and Life.* New York: Wiley.

McMichael, A.J. 1993. *Planetary Overload: Global Environmental Change and the Health of the Human Species.* New York: Cambridge Univ. Press.

Pepper, D. 1995. *Modern Environmentalism: An Introduction.* London/New York: Routledge.

Raven, P.H., and L.R. Berg. 2004. *Environment,* 4th edn. Hoboken, NJ: Wiley.

Reaka-Kudla, M.L., D.E. Wilson, and E.O. Wilson, eds. 1997. *Biodiversity II: Understanding and Protecting Our Biological Resources.* Washington: National Academy Press.

Scientific American. 1970. *The Biosphere: A Scientific American Book.* San Francisco: Freeman.

Spellerberg, I.F., and S. Hardes. 1992. *Biological Conservation.* New York: Cambridge Univ. Press.

Steinbeck, J. 1939. *The Grapes of Wrath.* New York: Viking Press.

Trudgill, S.A. 1988. *Soil and Vegetation Systems,* 2nd edn. London/New York: Oxford Univ. Press.

Wallace, A.R. 1962 [1876]. *The Geographical Distribution of Animals; With a Study of the Relations of Living and Extinct Faunas as Elucidating the Past Changes of the Earth's Surface.* New York: Hafner.

Wilson, E.O. 1988. 'The Current State of Biological Diversity', in Wilson, ed., *Biodiversity.* Washington: National Academy Press, 3–18.

———. 1992. *The Diversity of Life.* Cambridge, Mass.: Belknap/Harvard Univ. Press.

 # WEB RESOURCES

www.sp2000.org/ A baseline data set is being created to outline all currently known species of plants, animals, fungi, and microbes to facilitate global biodiversity research. This project is still underway, and species now catalogued can be searched for in the growing database for scientific name, status, and classification.

The Formation and Physical Properties of Soils

Objectives

- To understand the components of soil.

- To outline the factors affecting soil formation.

- To introduce terminology used to describe soil characteristics.

- To define some important physical properties of soil.

- To illustrate the likely arrangement of soil characteristics in a hypothetical landscape.

*S*oil is regarded as a living system because it supports plants, the organisms responsible for plant decay, and a variety of other life forms. Using more formal terms, the Canadian System of Soil Classification defines **soil** as a 'naturally occurring body of animal, mineral, and organic constituents at the Earth's surface that is capable of supporting plant growth. It is differentiated into horizons of variable depth which differ from the material below and the parent material in morphological makeup, chemical properties and composition, and biological characteristics.' In this unit we will first examine the major controls governing soil formation, then we will turn to *weathering*, the chemical decay and physical disintegration of earth materials.

The term 'soil' actually means different things to different people. Agricultural scientists regard soil as the few top layers of weathered material in which plants root and grow. But geologists use the term to refer to all materials that are produced by weathering at a particular site. Using this definition, we can still consider as soil those soils that were produced thousands of years ago and are now covered by layers of other material, even though it is impossible to grow plants in them. Alternatively, civil engineers look upon soil as something to build on and, in general, as anything that does not have to be blasted away.

Soil is obviously located at the Earth's surface and in contact with the atmosphere. It is not, except in small quantities, found in the air, although when dry or unprotected, soil is subject to wind action. Nor is it naturally encountered in large quantities in streams, although erosion and transportation by water may put it there. The general location of soil is at the interface of the atmosphere, hydrosphere, biosphere, and lithosphere. The soil layer, in fact, constitutes one of the most active interfaces among these spheres of the Earth System.

So it is with soil. Soil is a renewable resource—it can be used and depleted, but it continues to regenerate. Renewable resources, however, are not inexhaustible. Damaged beyond a certain level, a soil may be lost to erosion and perhaps destroyed permanently. Farmers know the risks involved in cultivating steep slopes by the wrong methods. Terraces must be created, but more importantly, they must be *maintained* (Figure 44.1). Once neglected, a terraced slope is ripe for soil erosion; once gullies appear, the process may be irreversible (Figure 44.2).

The Formation of Soil

When the Earth first formed and molten rock began to solidify, there was no soil. The surface was barren, and not until an atmosphere and a biosphere evolved could any soil develop. Once the Earth acquired its layer of

moisture-carrying and heat-transferring air and organisms of various kinds, soil formation progressed—as it continues to do today. Material must have organic matter and include organisms to be classified as soil.

Soil Components

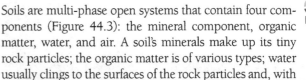

Soils are multi-phase open systems that contain four components (Figure 44.3): the mineral component, organic matter, water, and air. A soil's minerals make up its tiny rock particles; the organic matter is of various types; water usually clings to the surfaces of the rock particles and, with air, fills the intervening gaps.

The *mineral component* is made up of primary minerals, weathered rock fragments, and secondary minerals—for example, iron and aluminum oxides and clay minerals such as illite or kaolinite.

Another soil component is *organic matter*, the material that forms from living matter. Half of every handful of soil is made up of small animals, plants, and organic residues. In the upper layers of the soil, there is an accumulation of decaying and decayed remains of leaves, stems, and roots of plants. There are also the feces and dead bodies of various types of animals. The decay processes are carried out by an astronomical number of micro-organisms, such as bacteria and fungi. All of these contribute to the organic content of the soil, the most important product of which is called *humus*. Humus is the most active form of organic matter in terms of soil formation and plant growth. It is a colloid (like clay). A colloidal state occurs when microscopic particles (about 1 μm in size) are dispersed evenly throughout a material, liquid, or air. Two common examples of colloids are milk (tiny particles of milk solids dispersed in liquid) and cloud (water droplets dispersed in air).

Soil also contains life-sustaining *water*. There is an electrical attraction between the mineral particles and the water molecules surrounding them. Normally after a rainstorm, water fills much of the space between the soil particles. But even in very dry soils, the attraction is so persistent that there may be a thin film of water, possibly one or two molecules thick, around the mineral particles. The water is not pure, but exists as a weak solution of the various chemicals found in the soil. Without water, the many chemical changes that must occur in the soil could not take place. Soil water and air have a reciprocal relationship.

There are five types of soil water: surface runoff, gravitational, capillary, hygroscopic, and chemically combined (see Figure 44.4).

1. *Surface runoff* drains across the soil surface when the soil is frozen or saturated or if the intensity of rainfall is too high for *infiltration* to occur. As the water moves over the surface it erodes material from the soil surface. If infiltration occurs, water is absorbed into

From the Fieldnotes

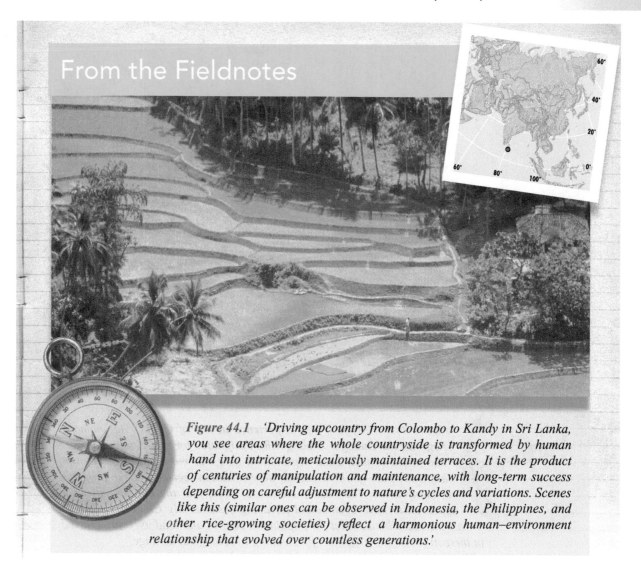

Figure 44.1 *'Driving upcountry from Colombo to Kandy in Sri Lanka, you see areas where the whole countryside is transformed by human hand into intricate, meticulously maintained terraces. It is the product of centuries of manipulation and maintenance, with long-term success depending on careful adjustment to nature's cycles and variations. Scenes like this (similar ones can be observed in Indonesia, the Philippines, and other rice-growing societies) reflect a harmonious human–environment relationship that evolved over countless generations.'*

the soil. The *infiltration rate* (I_r) is measured in depth per unit time (mm/hr). The rate is influenced by the texture and moisture content of the soil, the type of plant cover, and the duration and intensity of the rainfall. Over a relatively small area, infiltration rates can vary considerably, as shown in these examples from the York University campus, Toronto. When water

enters the soil through infiltration, it becomes one of the other types of soil water.

2. *Gravitational water* drains down through the soil to the groundwater table pulled by gravity. Its rate of movement is defined by soil permeability, and gravitational water is important in terms of leaching and lessivation.

3. *Capillary water* occurs as a thin layer on non-colloidal soil grains. It is held in place by tension. It moves in any direction from areas of excess to areas of deficit, and is important to plant growth and in terms of the up-profile movement of bases and salts.

4. *Hygroscopic (or imbibed) water* is adsorbed on the surface of colloidal grains because of a force between the grains and the water molecules. It forms an exceptionally thin, immobile layer that is not available to plants or for soil processes.

Table 44.1 Infiltration Rates, York University Campus

Landscape/Location	Infiltration Rate
Woodland on Oneida clay loam	500 mm/hr
Natural Vegetation on undulating terrain	70 mm/hr
Parkland on Oneida clay loam (grass with single trees or tree groups)	12 mm/hr
Parkland on Chinguacousy clay loam	4 mm/hr

From the Fieldnotes

Figure 44.2 'My first field experience in one of China's Autonomous Regions, the Guangxi-Zhuang A.R., designated for non-Han minorities, had mixed results. Land degradation here was more advanced than in any other part of China visited; desertification seemed to be in progress in many areas. The cause, overuse of land, and the collapse of what appeared to have been sound terracing systems. My Chinese colleague told me that China's rules for population control and land use were relaxed in these Autonomous Regions, often leading to ecological damage.'

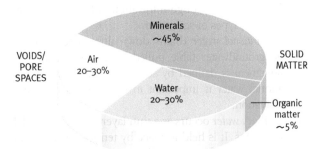

VOIDS/ PORE SPACES — Air 20–30%; Water 20–30%

SOLID MATTER — Minerals ~45%; Organic matter ~5%

Figure 44.3 Four major soil components and their relative percentages.

Soil air fills the spaces among the mineral particles, organic matter, and water. It is not exactly the same as in the atmosphere. Soil air contains more carbon dioxide and less oxygen and nitrogen than atmospheric air (Table 44.2). As water enters the soil during a rainstorm, air is displaced as water fills the pores. As the water drains down-profile, air replaces it in the vacated pores.

5. *Chemically combined water* is held within some minerals, such as silicon, iron, and aluminum. It is not available to plants or to soil processes as it is only released and evaporated at temperatures over 105°C.

LINK

Table 44.2 Soil Air and Atmosphere

	Atmosphere (%)	Soil Air (%)
Nitrogen	79	79–80
Oxygen	18–20.80	15–20
Carbon Dioxide	0.03	0.25–5

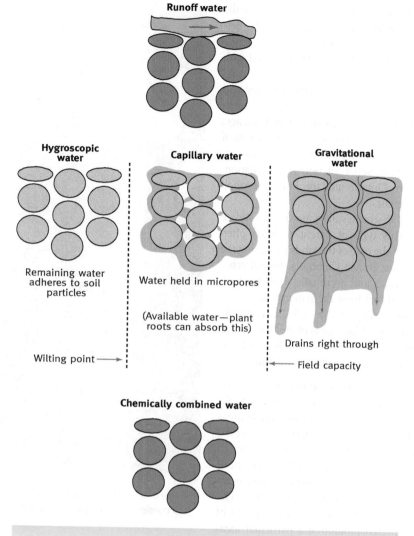

Figure 44.4 Types of soil water.

Various organisms use oxygen and respire carbon dioxide, so the supply of oxygen has to be constantly replenished. This is why adequate aeration is necessary for soil organisms and plant growth. The creation of a **tilth**—a well-aerated surface layer of soil—is very important to soil productivity. Earthworms are important to this process. Ploughing by farmers creates a tilth that is important to crop growth.

It is simple enough to deduce that the four soil components—minerals, organic matter, water, air—came from the other spheres of the Earth System. The more interesting task is to discover how. Five important factors will direct us to that understanding.

Factors of Soil Formation

Some of the factors of soil formation are obvious, whereas others are not so apparent. Rocks and the deposits formed from them are called the **parent material**. The atmosphere provides the water and air for the soil layer (and in high latitudes the cryosphere also plays a role where soil ice

dominates some permafrost soils). But the processes of the atmosphere vary across the Earth's surface, and therefore *climate* is a distinct soil-forming factor. Because of the presence of organic matter, vegetation and other organisms will be factors. Only close observation tells us that soils seem to vary with *topography*. The last factor is not obvious, but the formation of soils depends on *time*. Once the soil has started to develop, its character also will influence soil processes and development. Thus, soil (S) is a function of (f^1) parent material (P), climate (C), organisms (O), topography (To), time (Ti), and soil or:

$$S = f^1 (P, C, O, To, Ti, S)$$

How do these factors come into play?

Parent Material When a soil forms directly from underlying rock, the dominant soil minerals bear a direct relationship to the original rock. This simplest kind of soil formation gives rise to what is known as a **residual soil**. Thus, on the Canadian Shield, soils contain the insoluble residues of the iron oxides and aluminum silicates from the original rock. Such cases are quite common throughout the world. Yet even on the Shield there may also be soil differences resulting from the variation of climate.

In a second category of soil, known as **transported soil**, the soil may be totally independent of the underlying solid rock because the parent material has been transported and deposited by one or more of the gradational agents, often far from its original source. During the most recent ice age, large quantities of material were transported thousands of kilometres by ice sheets and deposited. These materials then formed the parent material for new soil formation. Many soils in southern Ontario and the Prairies formed from such parent materials.

Sediments deposited in stream valleys are another source of parent material. This type of parent material often creates fertile soils, as in the case of the lands bordering the Fraser River in southwest British Columbia. In still other instances, the wind carries and eventually deposits thick blankets of fine material that form the parent materials of new soil. Such windblown deposits are called **coversands** and loess (silt-rich deposits). Many areas of the Prairies and southern Ontario are underlain by coversands and loess, sometimes reaching up to several metres in thickness.

Climate   In parts of the Maritime provinces, Ontario, and Quebec, the soils have developed from granites. Yet the resulting soils are not the same because these areas have different climates. The warmer, moister climate of the Maritimes has caused a much more complete pattern of chemical change in the soils. As far as the development of soils is concerned, the important elements of climate are moisture, temperature, and to a lesser degree, wind. The amount of soil moisture is determined by the amount of precipitation and evapotranspiration at a particular location. Both moisture and higher temperatures accelerate the chemical reactions of the soil. Thus thicker, well-developed soils should be found in the lower, warmer latitudes. Wind is another factor in the formation of some soils. In certain areas, wind action is responsible for the accumulation of sediment that may become the parent material of soil. Elsewhere, especially in areas with sparse vegetation cover, wind may be responsible for soil erosion by deflation.

Organisms   Climate affects the types and amounts of vegetation and other organisms that are found in an area. Outside the tropics, usually the greater the amount of vegetation on the soil, the greater the amount of organic matter in the soil. Most of the organic activity takes place at or close to the surface in the **rhizosphere**, or root zone. Partially decomposed organic matter, called **humus**, forms a dark layer at the top of the soil (Figure 44.5). The most fertile soils are rich in humus. In many respects, humus and vegetation form a closed system. The substances that circulate through this system are plant foods—such as nitrogen compounds, phosphates, and potassium—collectively known as *plant nutrients*.

There are a number of ways that organic matter can enter a soil as *litter* to form various types of humus. *Mor humus*

Figure 44.5   Humus in the blackish layer at the top of the soil consists of decomposed organic matter.

is found under coniferous vegetation. It develops as a mat of twigs, cones, and other debris on top of the mineral soil. Because of the acidic conditions, earthworms are rare and there is not much mixing of organic and mineral layers. *Moder humus* is found under deciduous forest where the soil pH is less acidic. Conditions allow mixing of the organic and mineral components by various micro- and meso-fauna (especially earthworms).

A microscope would be needed to see the bacteria and fungi that are the key to this circulation. There are more bacteria in a tablespoon of soil than the entire population of the Earth. Decomposing micro-organisms continually change the nutrients into simpler compounds, which can enter plants through their roots. At the same time, other bacteria 'fix' atmospheric nitrogen so that it, too, can be absorbed. Plants use these nutrients to grow, and when they die the decomposing bacteria return the nutrients to the soil to continue the cycle. This system becomes open when erosion, humans, or animals remove the vegetation. Then the soil must often be balanced with artificial nutrients (fertilizers).

Figure 44.6 The earthworm aerates the soil, produces tilth, adds nutrients to the soil, and moves soil material around.

Figure 44.7 Termites are the most important animal in soil formation in the tropics.

Several macro- and meso-organisms living in the soil also act as biological agents of formation. While the most important animal in temperate-zone soils is the earthworm, the most important in the tropics is the termite. There are many different species of earthworm, but the most important in many areas is the dew worm, or night crawler (also called the rainworm—*Lumbricus terrestris* [Figure 44.6]). The importance of earthworms to the soil is threefold:

1. They burrow through the soil and create a *porosphere*, which increases aeration and drainage.
2. They produce a *tilth*—a suitable habitat for micro-organisms. As earthworms move through the soil, they mix mineral and organic soil components in their digestive systems. In doing so, they add nitrogen, potassium, organic matter, and 11 trace elements to the soil. They also add $CaCO_3$ from a calciferous gland situated on their skin near their heads. Earthworms also produce a lot of urine each day (60 per cent of body weight). They urinate through their skins. This adds ammonia to the soil.
3. They move soil around. Some species cast or defecate on the surface, while others defecate in the soil. Their castings can amount to 5,000–10,000 kg/ha/yr. It is estimated that there are approximately 1.5 million earthworms per hectare in southern Ontario (50 to 75 per cent of the soil animal biomass).

Termites (often mistakenly called red ants) are part of the family *Isoptera* (Figure 44.7). The top 2–3 m of soil in the tropics are derived from the erosion of above-ground termite nests (*termitaria*). Some of the larger species—for example, *Macrotermes* sp.—build mounds reaching up to 15 m high in some areas of Africa, although generally only 6 m (Figure 44.8). Each mound contains 2–4 tonnes of fine soil material, termite saliva, and feces. The soil

Figure 44.8 A termite hill, or termitaria, is both home to a large colony of termites and a source of soil material.

material is less than 1 mm in diameter (limited by the strength of a termite). Termitaria are built to maintain an internal temperature of 31–2°C. Openings in the nests can be closed or opened to change airflow to maintain the temperature. Some mounds have roofs to divert precipitation away from the termitaria. Erosion usually occurs once a colony moves out or dies.

Termites are important to tropical soils for these reasons:

1. They create a stone-free topsoil because the soil is derived from the erosion of the termitaria.
2. They bioturbate, or mix, the top 1.5 to 2.0 m of the soil as they tunnel through it.
3. They create a lack of vegetation and vegetable debris on the soil surface around their nests because they collect it and concentrate organic matter in their nests for their 'gardens'. They chew up organic matter to use to grow fungi (specific to termite gardens). They also 'herd' aphids in these gardens, which they 'milk' for nectar.

4. They speed up the breakdown of organic matter. Their digestive systems are more efficient than those of earthworms and have a symbiotic bacterium that can break down cellulose.

LINK

Topography   Another factor that affects the formation of a soil is its location with respect to the Earth's terrain. In the case of mountain climates, the aspect of a slope partially determines its receipt of radiation and moisture and therefore the amount of moisture evaporating from it. Windward and leeward slopes receive varying amounts of precipitation. Their steepness also affects runoff and thus the amount of moisture that penetrates to the lower layers of the soil. These phenomena, to a large degree, control the amounts of moisture and heat in a soil-forming area. A hillside might have a relatively thin layer of soil in part because of its efficient drainage and erosion. If the hillside faces away from the Sun, this is even more likely because both heat and moisture are minimized. In contrast, a less well-drained valley bottom, receiving a large amount of heat and moisture, is an optimal location for the chemical processes of soil formation. We could therefore expect a deep soil layer in a valley because of this and because of deposition of eroded material from upslope. It is normal to find a sequence of different soils on a slope (a *catena*) related to erosion and moisture drainage.

Time   Time is the only independent factor. Whether a soil is deep or shallow, it still may need a long time to form. The processes of soil formation are slow, and thus time becomes an important factor. An example of relatively rapid soil formation comes from the Indonesian volcanic island of Krakatau, which violently erupted in 1883. In its tropical climate, 35 cm of soil developed on newly deposited lavas and ash within 45 years. The same process often takes much longer in colder climates: some of the organic matter in Arctic soils in the Northwest Territories and the Yukon is still not thoroughly decomposed, even though it is nearly 3,000 years old. Often the first evidence of a layered soil develops in as little as a century, but a fully mature soil requires thousands of years. This shows how serious any damage to a soil can be. The destruction caused in a few years of careless farming (such as by overgrazing) can take centuries to repair.

Soil   The character of developing soil will influence the soil-forming processes and inevitably influence the long-term development of a certain type of soil.

A particular soil type at a specific location is a function of the dynamic interaction of the factors of soil formation. The factors can be divided into two groups based on their relation to energy:

1. Active (or energy-supplying) factors
   a) climate
   b) organisms
2. Passive (or energy-receiving) factors
   a) topography
   b) parent material
   c) time

The passive factors cannot form soil without the action of the active factors. Numerous combinations of factors are possible, hence the great many different soil types that are found.

Processes in the Soil

From the foregoing it may be concluded that soil formation results from a set of processes, all occurring simultaneously within the soil's developing layers. It is difficult to generalize about these processes. What goes on in evolving equatorial soils is very different from what happens in higher-latitude or high-altitude soils.

In 1959, the American soil scientist Roy Simonson published a general theory of soil formation that provides a useful framework for understanding what takes place within a developing soil. Simonson noted that certain processes occur in all soils during their formation, but that some very active processes present in some soils are nearly dormant in others. He further noted the lack of sharp boundaries between soils: soils tend to change gradually over space, and few **soil bodies** (geographical areas within which soil properties remain relatively constant) have distinct margins.

Soils also change vertically, but in a much more abrupt manner, so that we normally observe a sequence of layers, or horizons. It was concluded that the development of such layers in soils can be ascribed to four sets of processes (Figure 44.9):

1. **Additions** refer to the gains made by the soil when solar energy, water, gases, and organic matter from plant growth are added, or sometimes when loose sediments move downslope and come to rest on the soil. Many soils have a dark-coloured upper layer whose appearance results from the addition of organic material. Some soils even develop an entirely organic uppermost layer consisting of decaying vegetative matter (e.g., organic soils).

2. **Transformations** denote the weathering of rocks and minerals and the continuing decomposition (humification) of organic material in the soil. The breakdown of rocks and minerals proceeds throughout all the layers of a soil, but the processes of weathering tend to be more advanced in the upper layers. Near the base of the soil, chunks of yet unaltered rock still exist, but toward the top of the soil no trace of these can be found.

3. **Losses** result from the movement of dissolved soil components as they are carried downward by water (leached), and include the loss of other material in suspension as the water percolates through the soil from the upper towards the lower layers (lessivation). Some soil material is removed by water or wind at the soil surface. While the upper layers are thus depleted, the dissolved and suspended materials are redeposited lower down in the soil or downslope.

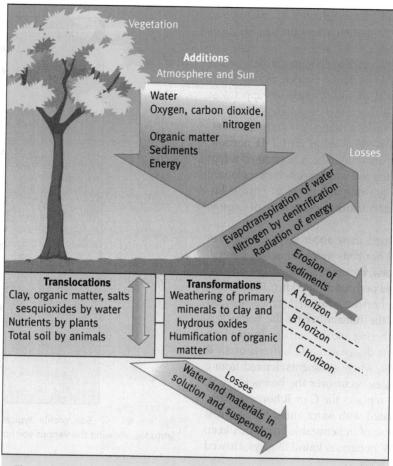

Figure 44.9 Diagrammatic representation of additions, losses, translocations, and transformations involved in soil formation. (After Millar, Turk, and Foth, 1965)

4. **Translocations** refer to the introduction of dissolved and suspended particles from the upper layers into the lower ones or vice versa. Nutrients are moved by plants and total soil by animals. In deep soils, for example, in equatorial and certain other tropical areas, the translocation processes redeposit these particles so deep into the soil that plant roots cannot reach them.

These fundamental processes take place within all soils, but not everywhere at the same rate or with the same degree of effectiveness. They depend on the soil-forming factors and on the conditions just discussed—parent material, climate, organisms, topography, and time. As they proceed, the soil is internally differentiated into discrete layers with particular properties (horizons).

Soil Profiles

Now that some information about the factors involved in soil formation and the major processes that go on within soils have been discussed, the time has come to dig a hole in the soil in a certain location to see what lies below the surface.

A hole or pit about 2 m deep has been excavated. Even before it was finished a major discovery was made: the soil consisted of a series of layers revealed by changes in colour and by the 'feel' or texture of the materials of which they are composed. Each of these soil layers is called a **soil horizon**, and the differentiation of soil into distinct layers is called *horizonation*. Some soils have quite sharply defined horizons; in others, horizons are difficult to identify. All the horizons, from top to bottom, are known as the **soil profile**. A soil profile is to a pedologist what a fingerprint is to a detective. Soil scientists, of course, cannot take the time to dig holes wherever they study soils, so they often use a device called a screw, or bucket, auger. The bucket auger is a hollow, sharp-edged pipe that is pushed into the soil and retrieves a sample of the upper horizons (or, in a shallow soil, the entire profile).

When looking at a 2-m profile of a well-developed soil, it is usually not difficult to identify the horizonation within it. Soil scientists for many years have used a logical scheme to designate each horizon in a model profile: they divided the profile into three sections designated alphabetically. Accordingly, the **A** horizon lies at the top (often darkened by organic material); the **B** horizon in the middle, often receiving dissolved and suspended particles from above; and the **C** horizon at the bottom, where the weathering of parent material proceeds.

This **A–B–C** designation has been in use for over a century, although it has undergone much modification. For instance, some soil profiles include an uppermost horizon—*above* the **A** horizon—consisting entirely of organic material in various stages of decomposition. Where this occurs, it is identified as an **L-F-H** horizon, an organic horizon separate from the **A** horizon on top of which it lies. Note that a soil with an **A** horizon coloured dark from vegetation growing in it is *not* an organic horizon; an **L-F-H** horizon consists exclusively of organic material.

As pedologists learned more about soil profiles, they found that individual horizons were themselves layered. Some upper **A** horizons, for example, are dark-coloured but turn light-coloured perhaps 30 cm down. Thus, these are designated an **Ae** horizon (eluviated, or leached). At the base of the soil, the horizon where the bedrock is breaking up and weathering into the particles from which soil is being formed is designated a **C** horizon or an **R** horizon (**R** for *regolith*, where sediments derived from a wide range of processes occur over the bedrock). A **W** (as in water) horizon replaces the **C** or **R** horizon where the soil is fully saturated with water either because it is under water or because of impermeable layers that keep water in the soil. A **W** horizon is found in gleys, thawed cryosols, and organic soils.

A typical soil profile, representing a soil found in the moist coastal area of a Maritime province, would look like the one shown in Figure 44.10. Note that the major horizons (**A**, **B**, etc.) are sometimes given secondary designations, such as **Ae** and **Bt**. The significance of these combinations will be identified as this diagram is studied.

The profile shown in Figure 44.10 contains master horizons marked by capital letters: **L-F-H**, **A**, **B**, **C**, and **R**. The organic matter at the soil surface is designated an **L-F-H** layer. These layers correspond to the degree of decomposition and humification of the organic matter. **L** stands for *litter*, **F** for *fermentation*, and **H** for *humus*. The litter layer is formed by largely unrotted leaves, twigs, fruit, cones, conifer needles, animal feces, and so on. The fermentation layer underlying it is undergoing decomposition. The humus layer contains the end product of the decomposition process, humus. Organic soils and gleys do not have the same kind of organic layers. In both of these types of soil there is water-logging, and they are generally found in areas with cooler temperatures. These conditions favour a greater production of decayable vegetation matter, and at the same time, inhibit the microbial breakdown, so that deep layers of decaying and decayed organic matter build up. This type of thick organic layer is designated an **O** horizon.

Immediately below this layer is the **A** horizon, the uppermost layer of the soil derived from the parent material below but coloured dark by the organic mat-

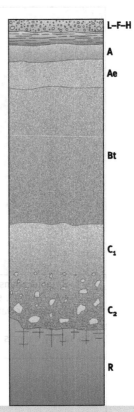

Figure 44.10 Soil profile typical of the humid mid-latitudes, showing the various soil horizons.

ter from above. Soon, however, the **A** horizon becomes lighter, and about 25 cm down it shows evidence of the removal by percolating water of material in solution or particles in suspension. It is now designated an **Ae** horizon (**e** standing for the process known as **eluviation**, the general term for removal; it means leached or 'washed out').

Below the **Ae** horizon comes the **B** horizon. When a soil is developing, it may not yet possess a clearly developed **B** horizon. Figure 44.11 shows the possible development of soil horizons on a sedimentary parent material. Note that a **B** horizon develops only in the second stage of soil evolution. Also note that when the **B** horizon first develops, it is not yet enriched by particles carried down from the **A** horizon; eluviation, too, is just beginning. Such weakly developed **B** horizons are marked **Bw**. But after enough time has elapsed, the soil displays an **A** and an **Ae** horizon, translocation is in full force, and the **B** horizon matures. The symbol **Bt** (**t** stands for translocated) is used to identify such a mature **B** horizon, and the term **illuviation** signifies the deposition of particles carried downward by percolating water. Thus eluviation from the **Ae** horizon is matched by illuviation in the **Bt** horizon.

The **Bt** designation reflects the common presence of calcium carbonate ($CaCO_3$) in the soil. For instance,

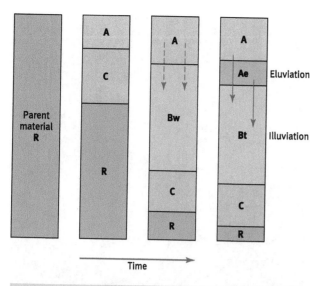

Figure 44.11 Possible 'stages' of soil horizon evolution on a sedimentary parent material.

The **C** horizon is the soil layer in which parent material is transformed by weathering into soil particles. The parent materials of soil range widely, of course, from already fragmented glacial sediments and river-deposited alluvium to hard bedrock. Figure 44.10 assumes a hard-bedrock parent material. Accordingly, the **C** horizon is divided into a lower zone (C_2), where pieces of bedrock still lie interspersed with weathered soil material, and an upper zone (C_1), where the weathering process is more advanced. If this layer is formed by in situ weathering of hard rock it is also called *saprolite*.

Soil Regimes

The soil profile represented in Figure 44.10 is only one of thousands of such profiles charted by soil scientists around the world. Imagine the range of possibilities: take the complex pattern of global geology, superimpose a map of climates much more intricate than the Köppen regionalization studied earlier, overlay this with the diversity of biogeography, add local variations of relief and slope, and insert the factor of time. The resulting soil map is infinitely complicated, and understanding it is quite a challenge.

The concept of **soil (pedogenetic) regimes** is used to explain the special patterns of soil formation. Even if the parent material remained the same throughout the world, soils would differ because they would form under different temperature, moisture, biogeographical, and other conditions. It is possible to imagine some of these regimes by recalling some information from Part Two. Among other things, it was learned that soils may form under various types of moisture and temperature conditions. Early in this discussion of soils it was learned that certain soils with particular characteristics prevail under certain regimes: calcium-rich soils under arid conditions in lower latitudes; silica-rich soils under somewhat more moist and much cooler environments in higher latitudes; and iron- and aluminum-rich soils under both warmer tropical and cooler temperate areas.

Different sets of factors can be grouped together, and the regimes can be divided according to these major controlling factors as follows:

1. Bioclimatic regimes (dominated by biogeographical and climatic factors)
   a) Podzolization regime
   b) Laterization regime
   c) Calcification regime
2. Hydromorphic regime (dominated by waterlogged conditions)
   a) Gleization regime
3. Geomechanical regimes (dominated by specific clay minerals and/or their reaction to freeze–thaw or wetting–drying)
   a) Vertisolization (cracking) regime

the sediments from which many soils of the Prairies are formed, consisting of rock processed and deposited by ice sheets, contain lime, as do tills in southern Ontario. When rainwater percolates downward through such lime-rich soils, the $CaCO_3$ is dissolved in the water (a process called *carbonation*) and carried away in a process called **leaching**. This eventually makes the topsoil acidic, which in turn stimulates mineral weathering. The result of this weathering is the release of ions of nutrients, which enter the soil solution and greatly contribute to soil fertility and plant growth (see 'Perspectives' box).

Another effect is the formation of microscopic clay particles. These clay particles, translocated by eluviation (lessivation) and illuviation from the **A** horizon into the **B** horizon, signal the maturing of the **Bt** horizon. The illuvial accumulation of clay particles transforms a weakly developed **Bw** horizon into a more fully developed **Bt** horizon.

What happens when the parent material contains little or no clay and there is little lime to set the clay-producing process in motion? There will be little clay illuviation into the **B** horizon, and no **Bt** horizon will develop. However, the decaying organic materials in the **L-F-H** layer will acidify rainwater, causing chemical reactions with aluminum (Al) and iron (Fe) in the upper soil. Oxides of Al and Fe are then mobilized and eluviated from the **Ae** horizon and illuviated into the **B** horizon, creating the red-coloured **Bhs** horizon of so many tropical and equatorial soils (**h** for humus; **s** for sesquioxides of aluminum and iron). In North America, soils with **Bhs** horizons occur in forested areas from Quebec to Florida, and they are more common in the tropical areas. Soils with such **B** horizons tend to be of low fertility and have a low water-retention capacity.

Bioclimatic Regimes

Podzolization Regime   The podzolization regime is common in areas with a positive moisture balance in mid- and high latitudes and at high elevations. The characteristic climate in the northern parts of North America and Eurasia has long cold winters with considerable snowfall. The annual precipitation ranges from 250 to 1000 mm/yr. Soils may freeze in the winter to a depth of 2 m. The summers are short but have long days and the average temperature of the warmest month is over 10°C. This regime also occurs on coarse granular materials and weathered acidic bedrock in a wide range of environments. *Podzols* are characteristic of the better-drained areas of the Canadian Shield, especially towards the top of catenas or slopes or on well-drained fluvioglacial materials. The temperatures are cold enough to inhibit the intense microbial breakdown of organic matter. The organic matter accumulates on the soil surface and forms a distinct mat of coniferous needles, cones, twigs, and so forth—mor humus. The climate is warm enough to support large coniferous or boreal forests. These forests require few bases, as they do not lose all of their leaves annually. The soil pH ranges from below 5 to 6. The most significant decomposing agents are fungi. The acidity of the plant litter and soil is not suitable for earthworms and most other soil organisms. Bases, colloids, and oxides are mobilized as the conditions become more and more acidic and are eluviated (leached), leaving a very diagnostic soil profile.

As stated above, the organic litter forms a discrete mat on top of the mineral soil (mor humus with **L-F-H** layers). Organic acids from this layer are washed down into the top of the **A** horizon, which is dark brown to black in colour as a consequence. The lower part of the **A** horizon is eluviated, is ash-grey coloured (albic or podzolic: Figure 44.12), and has a sandy texture (an **Ae** horizon). Many, if not most, of the bases and colloids have been leached out of this horizon, hence its pale colouration and sandy texture. Most of the materials that have been removed are flushed out of the soil column into the groundwater system. Some bases and colloids plus iron and/or aluminum oxides accumulate in the **B** horizon to form an illuviated (spodic) horizon—**Bfe** (iron-rich), **Bt** (translocated), **Bh** (humic), etc.—which is characteristically reddish brown in colour because of staining by the oxides and organic matter. The illuviated material may be diffused throughout the horizon or occur as nodules, along root holes or as a pan (placic horizon—iron-pan). The development of an indurated pan may cause the soil-forming processes to change. Pans can stop water drainage downprofile, which will ultimately lead to a change in processes affecting soil development and the character of the soil.

The podzol profile becomes less distinct as the climate becomes warmer and the vegetation changes towards the Equator or downslope. In Canada the luvisolic soil order is distinguished from the true podzols. Luvisolic soils are

Figure 44.12   The grey, ash-like colour of the **Ae** horizon is the signature of the podzolic soil type.

lessivated rather than leached. Luvisols are not excessively leached and have bases retained in the profile, but they are characterized by the translocation of clay particles downprofile (the old name for these soils was grey-brown podzols).

To the north of the podzol zone (or at higher elevations) the podzolization processes are retarded by colder temperatures and a lack of freely drained sites in permafrost areas.

Laterization Regime (Oxisolization or Ironstone Formation)   The term *laterite* is derived from the Latin word for brick. The name 'laterite' was first used by Dr Francis Buchanan (later Hamilton) in his 1807 publication, *A Journey from Madras through the Countries of Mysore, Canara and Malabar*. He described the local people either making adobe-like bricks out of a vesicular, mottled red-and-cream, iron-rich soil or cutting them out of the same kinds of materials. The bricks were used for houses and road surfaces. Many of the large ceremonial buildings in parts of India and Southeast Asia are built of laterite (e.g., Ankor Wat in Cambodia).

Laterite occurs in areas with seasonally heavy rainfall and warm temperatures (e.g., tropical and equatorial

Perspectives on the Human Environment

Exchange of Cations

Just how do mineral substances become nutrients for plants? How do mineral particles enter the water that percolates through the soil, and how do they leave these liquids to enter plant roots? We would need a powerful microscope to observe these exchanges in the soil. When minerals and humus break down, they disintegrate into tiny particles no larger than 0.1 micrometre (0.0000001 m) in diameter. Such tiny particles of humus and clay are called colloids, and they can be observed in suspension in the soil solution, making it look turbid.

The colloid surface is electrically charged, attracting other particles with an opposite charge. These other particles also result from the breakup of humus and minerals, but not into colloidal fragments. Rather, they result when mineral compounds dissolve in the soil water and form atoms or groups of atoms called ions. Calcite ($CaCO_3$), for example, breaks up into atoms of calcium and carbonate.

The ions resulting from the decomposition of minerals also are electrically charged. Positively charged ions, such as those of calcium (Ca^{2+}), are called **cations**. Negatively charged ions, such as the carbonates, nitrates, and phosphates, are known as **anions**.

A colloid particle with its negatively charged surface will attract (depending on its size) many positively charged ions. These cations come from plant nutrients such as calcium, potassium, magnesium, and sodium. The colloids hold these cations on their surfaces, but let them go when a stronger attraction pulls them into the roots of plants or downprofile. They are replaced by other cations in the soil solution (cation exchange). So the colloids function to make the nutrient-providing ions available to the plants growing in the soil. Without them, these nutrients would be quickly washed away.

---

areas with humid climates with a pronounced dry season). Precipitation ranges from 250 to 2000 mm/yr. Laterites occur under savanna and tropical forests of various kinds. Tropical rainforests are characterized by their lateritic and podzolic soils rather than by true laterites.

Vegetation production is high because of the conditions, but there is intense microbial breakdown of the litter and hence organic matter rapidly turns back into biomass. Consequently, there are few minerals and little humus in the soil. The environmental conditions also cause intense deep weathering of the bedrock and the removal of the weatherable minerals. These processes have gone on uninterrupted by glaciations, or anything else, for tens or even hundreds of millions of years. Much of the topsoil in these areas is washed in or blown in or is derived from the erosion of termite mounds, and bears no relation to the laterite layers. Because of this long-continued weathering even silica derived from quartz and silicate minerals has been rotted and removed. The solubility of silica can be seen by the amount of silica carried in *dissolved solid*, or solution, form by streams in these environments (e.g., the average amount of silica carried by all streams draining such deeply weathered

etchplain areas is in the order of 50 per cent of the dissolved solid load; this can be compared to the average silica content of all streams, which is 12 per cent). The mobilization and leaching of all the bases and even silica leaves a residual iron-rich or oxic horizon in kaolinite clay. Iron oxides are mobilized and are accumulated in the **B** horizon to form this layer. Once deposited, they are relatively insoluble because of the lack of organic acids. The iron-rich horizons can become vesicular, pisolitic, concretionary, slag-like, massive, or a mixture of more than one type. Some of these types may have been eroded and moved from one place to another (*remanie*). Sometimes two types of laterite can occur on top of each other. On exposure, the iron-rich layer may become indured to form a laterite or plinthite cuirasse (duricrust or ferricrust). If aluminum is the main mineral left in the soil, this residual layer is called *bauxite*. Bauxite is the most important ore of aluminum, and this soil layer is mined in places such as Jamaica and Guyana for export to North America and elsewhere.

The major problem with respect to the lateritic layer is its scale. In places it can reach up to 30 or 40 m in depth. Some scientists have argued that this amount of iron can only be accounted for by the erosion of a former iron-rich rock bed, but there is little evidence for the existence of such beds in areas close to where laterite is found. Others have suggested that the iron was deposited by bacterial action. According to prevailing wisdom, laterite forms because of the recycling of minute iron particles by termites that descend through the laterite to get material to build or repair their termitaria, and by so doing, bring iron material up to the soil surface. It has also been suggested that seasonal variations in the depth of the groundwater table lead to the deposition of iron onto the laterite layer from below. Iron is deposited during periods with a high water table. There is a pallid *lithomarge* layer under the laterite that looks very much like the *albic* layer in podzols, but the thickness is much, much greater (more than 20 to 30 m in places).

The laterite cuirasses or duricrusts are very important protectants of the landscape and underlie many savanna plateaus. The indurated ends of the laterite are exposed at the edges of the plateaus and 'breakaway' forest occurs on the eroded slopes of the lithomarge exposed on the slopes under the laterite, between different savanna levels.

In wetter and/or cooler areas the laterite layers are not as deep or as dominating, and the soils are called *lateritic* or *ferruginous soils*. Tropical or subtropical red soils developed on basalts or other *mafic* parent materials are called *krasnozems* (red earths), which do not generally exhibit strongly developed horizons.

Calcification Regime   The calcification regime occurs in arid and semi-arid areas with negative water balances where the lack of moisture means that there is little vegetation cover and lots of bare, exposed surface (Figure 44.13). These conditions supply little organic matter to the soil, and thus there is little humus available. Some minor leaching may occur down to

Figure 44.13 Calcified soils, characteristically light in colour, dominate California's Mojave Desert.

approximately 1 to 1.5 m below the surface and is related to sporadic infiltration from the surface. Calcium, magnesium, halite, and other bases remain in the soil and may cement the soil into dense structures. Evapotranspiration from the surface causes the capillary rise of groundwater into the soil column. This brings more calcium, halite, and so on into the soil as the water rises and is evapotranspired from the surface. Calcium and/or other salts may build up to form nodules in the **B** horizon or a diffuse layer. In some areas the salts form a surface crust, or *efflorescence*. In very arid areas the calcium may reach the surface layer, and when exposed by erosion this layer becomes a deep, indurated calcium or calcium-magnesium-rich surface horizon called a *calcrete* or *caliche*. This, like laterite, can protect more easily eroded strata and tops many buttes, mesas, and columns in areas of the southwestern United States. Less extreme examples of calcification are found in areas of short-grass prairie of Palliser's Triangle in southern Alberta and Saskatchewan.

In more moist areas where grasses can grow more luxuriantly, organic debris can build up because of limited microbial activity. The buildup of grass, leaf, and root debris tends to form a deep, dark-coloured *mollic* horizon (moder humus). This layer is essentially developed in situ and has not been subjected to mixing by soil organisms and micro-organisms such as earthworms. In many areas the major organisms found in this layer of the soil are arthropods (insects, spiders, centipedes, etc.). The calcium-rich horizon occurs deeper in the soil profile and is less well developed because there is more leaching and a shorter dry period. Instead of a calcium-rich horizon there may be calcium nodules, some shaped like dolls (*loess kinder*). There may also be rodent burrows (made by ground squirrels, gophers, etc.) that have been in-filled by fine (wind-blown) material from the surface. These are called *krotovinas*. All these features are diagnostic of *chernozems*. These soils are very common in the moister areas to the north and east of Palliser's Triangle and other more humid parts of the Great Plains. Chernozems are associated with the long-grass prairie region of Manitoba.

Under very arid conditions with little vegetation, and therefore not much organic material, excessive evaporation from the surface may leave a salt crust, or *efflorescence*, and halite in the topsoil (salinization). This process occurs in extremely dry areas, such as parts of the American Southwest, Australia, North Africa and the Middle East, and in the dry interior of British Columbia. In wetter areas the salt-rich horizon (salic horizon) occurs at greater depth. Salinization can also occur because of a saline parent material (e.g., saline soils developed on marine sedimentary rocks in the Peace Country of northeastern British Columbia near Fort St John). Some pedologists consider salinization to be another separate pedogenetic regime.

It is quite easy to see changes of soil type along environmental gradients of temperature and moisture that influence vegetation cover and soil processes within the calcification regime.

Hydromorphic Regime

Gleization Regime   Gleization is related to topography and soil drainage. Gleys (gleis) occur in waterlogged conditions associated with bogs or wetlands and slope-foot areas in cool or cold environments. Climate is not the limiting factor, however, except that there must be sufficient precipitation for this type of regime. This regime is common in marine, tundra, and humid continental–cool summer zones, but it is also widespread in certain situations in the wet and dry tropics and monsoonal areas. It is often developed on a wide range of Pleistocene and Holocene sediments and usually forms where the water table approaches or breaks the surface—in flat areas, in depressions, or at the base of slopes where there are high rates of vegetation production and low rates of microbial breakdown because of anaerobic (waterlogged) conditions and fairly cool or cold temperatures. This means that there is a buildup of decaying organic matter and the development of a deep organic horizon (**O** horizon). Moisture is the dominant influence on soil development and hence gleization is called a *hydromorphic* regime.

The organic layer may reach well over 10 cm deep. Because of the type of vegetation and groundwater or surface water chemistry, the sites are typically acidic. In time the organic matter may develop into a peat (organic soil). The gleying process occurs best with anaerobic bacterial activity in stagnant water. Over time a small amount of sticky blue-grey clay forms under the organic horizon. This material is derived from clays washed down through the thick organic mat.

This layer gives the regime its name. *Glei* is the Russian word for blue-grey. The colour of this horizon occurs because of internal weathering and the reduction of iron to the ferrous state in anaerobic conditions. Blue-grey mottling may occur in soils upslope from gley sites. The mottling is indicative of imperfect or seasonally imperfect drainage. Gleys form the lower wetter ends of many catenas in many areas.

Geomechanical Regime

Vertisolization (Cracking) Regime   This soil regime is also known by the Australian term *gilgai* and as a *grumusol*. It is restricted to sites with a specific soil mineral content and is characterized by the mechanical mixing and inversion of the upper 1 to 2 m of the soil because of cracking caused by the wetting and swelling and the drying and shrinking of *montmorillonitic clays*—

$Ca_{0.4}(Al_{0.3}Si_{7.7})Al_{2.6}(Fe^{3+}_{0.9} Mg_{0.3})O_{20}(OH)_4 nH_2O$. Typically these soils occur on flat or gently sloping sites in arid and semi-arid areas beneath tall grass or sclerophilous vegetation (thorn scrub). These types of vegetation are *fire disclimaxes*. Their greatest extent is in tropical and mid-latitude desert and steppe areas where leaching is minimal so that basic cations accumulate in the soil. This provides conditions favourable to the formation of this type of clay mineral. Drying and shrinkage occur in the dry season as the surface becomes dessicated. Cracks form and topsoil is blown and/or washed into the cracks. During the wet season the clays swell because of the presence of water, and the cracks close. The soil is inverted in this way. This type of regime is found in the arid and semi-arid areas of North America on montmorillonitic clay soils. In Canada these soils occur in the Palliser's Triangle area of the southern Prairies.

In cold permafrost areas the same process of cracking and closure of the soil surface occurs, but here it is not related to the presence of specific clay minerals. As the surface freezes, cracking takes place and surface material is blown and/or washed into the cracks. The cracks close up as thawing occurs. This process is associated with the development of ice wedges and patterned ground. This type of regime is common in the permafrost areas of northern Canada, Alaska, and northern Eurasia.

Sol and Ped

The terms **sol** and **ped** appear frequently in soil studies, either alone or in some combined form. We already have encountered both, as in luvisol and, of course, pedology, the science of soils. In examining the classification and regionalization of soils in Unit 45, it is possible to identify soil orders by means of a dominant characteristic followed by *sol* or *solic*. For example, soils forming in poorly drained areas are known as *gleysols* or *gleysolic*. Why 'sol'? Russian scientists were among the world's leading experts in this area and the Russian word for soil is *sol*.

The **solum** of a soil consists of the **A** and **B** horizons, and constitutes that part of the soil in which plant roots are active and play a role in the soil's development. Below the solum, in the **C** horizon, parent material is being weathered. Therefore, when it is reported that 'the solum is 1.5 m thick', the reference is to the zone where all the interacting processes of plant life and soil development are taking place.

The *ped* in pedology also appears in the term **pedon**, a column of soil drawn from a specific location, extending from the top of the surface horizon all the way down to the level where the bedrock shows signs of being transformed into **C** horizon material (Figure 44.14). In other words, a

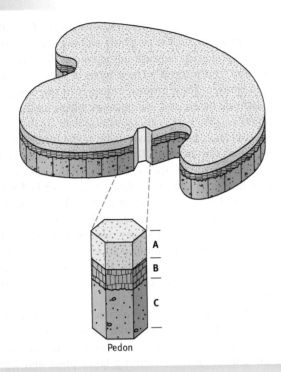

Figure 44.14 Complete soil column, or pedon.

pedon is the smallest three-dimensional area representing the entire soil type. In Canada all soil types have a type profile, or pedon. The term *ped* also is used by itself to identify a naturally occurring aggregate or 'clump' of soil and its properties. The discussion of this topic is deferred until later in the unit, when it is easier to understand why soils exhibit this property of forming natural peds.

Soil Texture

Descriptions of soils often contain terms such as sandy clay, loam, or silt. These terms are not just general descriptions of the character of soils. In fact, they have a very specific meaning and refer to the sizes of the individual particles that make up a soil (or one of its horizons). If you were to rub a tiny clump of soil between your thumb and forefinger, you would be left with the smallest grains that make up that part of the soil from which the clump came. These grains may be quite coarse and look or feel like sand, or they may be very fine, like dust on your fingertip. The size of the particles in soil, or its *texture,* is very important, because it has to do with the closeness with which soil particles can be packed together, the amount of space in the soil for air and water, how easily roots can penetrate, and other aspects of what it is and isn't good for.

Soils, of course, often exhibit several kinds of textures. For instance, that clump on your forefinger may contain some sandy and some much finer particles. In your field

notes, therefore, you might call it a *sandy clay*—a mostly fine-grained soil, but with some coarser particles in it. The coarsest grains in a soil are **sand** (not counting even larger gravel, which is sometimes found in soil as well). Sand particles range in size from 2 mm down to 0.05 mm. The next smaller particles are called **silt** (0.5 to 0.002 mm). There are still smaller grains than silt, namely, the **clay** particles (below 0.002 mm). The smallest of the clay particles are in the colloidal range and are less than a one hundred-thousandth of a millimetre in diameter (Figure 44.15).

A single soil may contain grains of all three size categories—sand, silt, and clay. Such a soil is called a loam if all three are present within specific proportions (Figure 44.16). Unlike sand, silt, and clay, therefore, loam refers not to a size category but to a certain combination of variously sized particles. The Soil Survey of Canada has established a standard system to ensure that such terms as sandy clay and silt loam have more than a subjective meaning (Figure 44.16).

When you rub some soil between your thumb and forefinger, you can tell that there are particles of different sizes in the clump—but you can only estimate in what proportions. An accurate determination of these proportions requires additional analysis. Figure 44.16 is a triangular chart that shows the percentages of all three components. A soil that is about one-third sand, one-third silt, and one-third clay falls in the clay loam area. To be called a silty clay, a typical soil would have 45 per cent silt, 45 per cent clay, and 10 per cent sand.

The soil texture is related to the parent material from which the soil was derived. Some types of bedrock yield sand-rich soils, whereas others give rise to clayey soils. Most soils contain some combination of various components. Texture is the critical factor determining the pore spaces in soil, and hence its capacity to hold (**porosity**) and to transmit (**permeability**) water. This is not difficult to imagine: the very term clay seems to imply a waterlogged soil, and sand is usually dry and light. Thus a sandy soil allows water to percolate downward under the influence of gravity, draining (and drying up) rapidly. Plants with roots in sandy soils do not have much opportunity to absorb water, because the soil is drained rapidly.

Clay, on the other hand, has a far greater **field capacity** (ability to hold water against the downward pull of gravity). But this characteristic produces a different problem for plants: the pore spaces in clay are so small that permeability (drainage) is poor, reducing the circulation of nutrient- and oxygen-carrying solutions. Furthermore, the close packing of clay particles may make it difficult for plant roots to penetrate deeply into the soil. Such texture-related properties must be considered when farmers plant crops. The potato plant, for example, handles the wetness and compactness of clayey soils well, but wheat should not be sown in these soils.

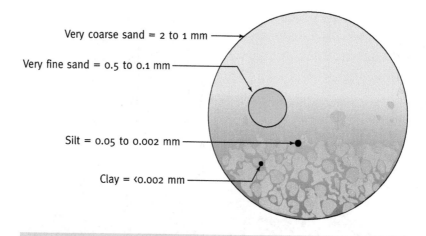

Figure 44.15 Soil particles.

Very coarse sand = 2 to 1 mm

Very fine sand = 0.5 to 0.1 mm

Silt = 0.05 to 0.002 mm

Clay = <0.002 mm

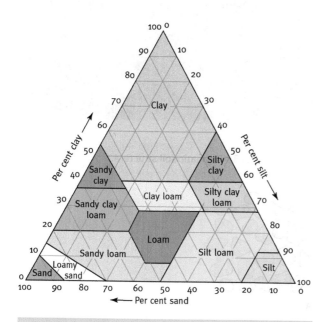

Figure 44.16 A ternary diagram of soil texture categories, defined by the percentages of sand, silt, and clay found in a soil sample.

Soil Structure

Earlier we referred to so-called peds, naturally occurring clumps of soil that tend to form and stay together unless they are purposely broken up. Again, you will discern this tendency in soil when you examine it: dislodge a bit of soil and notice that it does not disintegrate, like loose sand, but forms small clumps. Only when rubbed do these peds break up into the individual grains described previously. Peds develop because soil particles are sometimes held together by a thin film of clay, which is deposited during soil formation by

circulating solutions. Other peds may develop because of molecular attraction among the particles they contain. Either way, peds give soil its structure, and they are quite important because they affect the circulation of water and air throughout the soil. Soil structure—that is, the nature of its peds—affects the soil's vulnerability to erosion, its behaviour under cultivation, and its durability during dry periods when cohesive forces weaken.

Soils exhibit four basic structures: *platy, prismatic, blocky,* and *spheroidal* (Figures 44.17–44.20).

1. **Platy structure** (Figure 44.17), as the term suggests, involves layered peds that look like flakes stacked horizontally. A soil with a platy structure is immediately recognizable because the individual plates often are as much as 1 to 2 cm across, and occasionally even larger.

2. **Prismatic structure** (Figure 44.18) reveals peds arranged in columns, giving the soil vertical strength. In Unit 40 a wind-deposited material called *loess,* on which very fertile soils develop, is discussed. In their deep **B** horizons, loess soils have a well-developed prismatic structure and can form bluffs many metres high without collapsing. Individual peds in soils with prismatic structure range from 0.5 cm to as large as 10 cm.

3. **Blocky (angular) structure** (Figure 44.19) consists of irregularly shaped peds. These peds, however, have straight sides that fit against the flat surfaces of adjacent peds, giving the soil considerable strength.

4. **Spheroidal (granular or crumb) structure** (Figure 44.20) displays peds that are usually very small and often nearly round in shape, so that the soil looks like a layer of bread crumbs. Such soils are very porous, and with the peds so small and cohesion very weak, they are more susceptible to erosion.

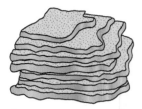

A

B

Figure 44.17 Platy soil structure.

A

B

Figure 44.18 Prismatic soil structure.

A

B

Figure 44.19 Blocky (angular) soil structure.

A

B

Figure 44.20 Spheroidal (granular) soil structure.

As noted, not only the shape of the peds (i.e., the structure alone) but also their size is important. Descriptions of soil structure include observations on whether the peds are coarse, medium, or fine. There are no hard rules governing these size categories, but previously reference was made to dimensions that range from a fraction of 1 cm to 10 cm (note the scale—the soil structure relative to the object shown—of each of the photographs in Figures 44.17–44.20).

Another indicator of soil properties is what pedologists call *soil consistence*. This is a rather subjective measure of a moist or wet soil's stickiness, plasticity, cementation, and hardness. It is a test done in the field by rolling some moist soil in the hand and observing its behaviour. After a bit of soil has been subjected to this test, some of it will have stuck to the skin (indicating its stickiness). The rolled-up soil may form a small rope and then break up, or it may attain a thin, twine-like shape, as moist clay would. This reveals its plasticity. The greater the clay content, the more tightly the soil particles bind together because of the cohesiveness of clay, and the longer the rope- or worm-like roll will be. Conversely, the greater the sand content, the more likely the soil is to crumble and fall apart. Soil hardness often varies downprofile as well. The soil may crumble easily in the **A** horizon, but parts of the **B** horizon may resist even a knife. All these attributes relate to soil consistence.

Soil Colour

Soils generally exhibit a range of colours. Only rarely are soils encountered that do not display some colour variation down their profile. Even a typical equatorial or tropical soil, dominated by the redness of iron and aluminum oxides, exhibits lighter and darker shades of red and orange. Soil colour is a most useful indicator of the processes that prevail. A dark brown to black upper layer reflects the presence of organic material, humus. A soil's colour may range from nearly black at the top of the profile to brown in the lower **A** and the **B** horizons to beige in the lower **B** horizon—indicating the decrease in humus content with depth.

The soil colour tends to change with the degree of wetness. Moisture causes soil colours to become much more vivid. Obviously the range of hues in soils is almost infinite, and soil scientists use the Munsell Soil Color Chart to describe soil colours objectively. This chart, which takes into account many possible conditions, contains hundreds of colours, each with a letter and number code. The colour of a sample of soil can therefore be codified. If we do the job carefully, we can be certain that a coded soil from the **B** horizon of a Prairie pedon is exactly the same colour as one from the **B** horizon in Ukraine without having to put the samples side by side.

Soil Acidity and Alkalinity

Soil colloids are associated with the presence of cations in the soil (see 'Perspectives' box). Hydrogen (H^+) cations are very common, and their dominance in the soil solution defines an *acid* condition. Conversely, a relative absence of H^+ cations and the presence of hydroxyl (OH^-) anions plus sodium (Na^+) and other associated cations make the soil *alkaline* (or basic) in nature. The acidity of soil is measured by its pH value. A pH value of 7.0 is considered neutral, which occurs when H^+ and OH^- ions are balanced and present at relatively low levels. Lower values (normally between 4.0 and 7.0) indicate acidic soils, whereas higher values (7.0 to 11.0) indicate alkaline soils.

The acidity of a soil is closely related to its fertility because acids are necessary to make nutrients available to plants. However, extreme acidity or alkalinity is detrimental to plant growth. In dry climate regimes, where alkaline soils often occur, one remedy is to treat them with compounds containing sulphur. Conversely, the most common treatment for too much acidity is to apply lime to the soil. Different plants and micro-organisms are adapted to varying degrees of acidity. The variation of acidity often bears a relationship to both climate and parent material, and is associated with the different soil-forming processes.

Soils of Hills and Valleys

Topography strongly influences soil formation. On gently undulating (rolling) countryside, soil profiles tend to develop fully and would look much like the profile shown in Figure 44.10. When the landscape flattens out, the soil reflects this by developing a thick **B** horizon. A flat surface promotes leaching, and a dense clay layer in the **B** horizon may be encountered. When the landscape becomes hilly, soils tend to become thinner. As a rule, hilltop soils have a thin **A** horizon, and the **B** horizon will be shallow as well. Rapid draining and exposure to surface erosion inhibit the development of soils on the crests of slopes. Where the land is poorly drained, as in meadows and bogs, the soil profile may show a lack of contrast between **A** and **B** horizons. The regional landforms, therefore, are an important guide to what types of soils occur.

Soils have a characteristic arrangement from the top to the bottom of a slope. As Figure 44.21 shows, lateritic soils and a capping of hard *laterite* are found on the top of the hill, as in Sudan in East Africa. Some of the soil particles washed downhill during overland flow (or wash) come to rest farther down the slope. They form a material called *colluvium*, and soils that develop from this are called *colluvial* soils. Most of the material brought down valleys by stream water ends up as *alluvium* on the valley floor, and *alluvial* soils may develop from it (these are often poorly

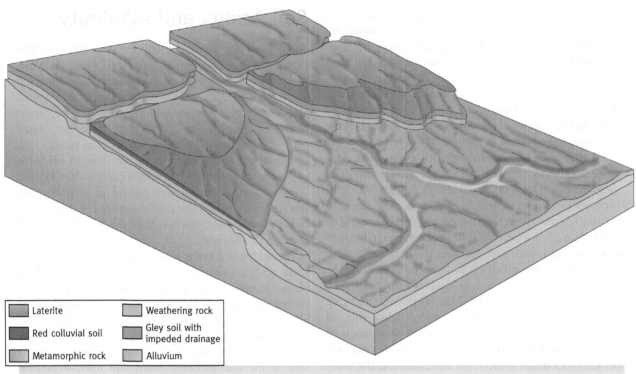

Laterite

Red colluvial soil

Metamorphic rock

Weathering rock

Gley soil with impeded drainage

Alluvium

Figure 44.21   Type of soil catena commonly found in southern Sudan.

drained). When the same parent material results in an arrangement of different soil types along a hillside slope, this is called a *catena*. This term comes from the Latin word meaning chain or series. A **soil catena** is usually defined as a sequence of soil profiles appearing in regular succession on landform features of uniform rock type. The differences in soil types reflect the erosion, transport, and deposition of soil material (which influences soil depth, soil texture, and horizonization), and soil drainage variations downslope.

The Soil-Development System

LINK

These main spheres of the Earth System are the starting point of the soil-development system (see Figure 44.22). Atmosphere and hydrosphere provide heat and moisture, whereas lithosphere and biosphere furnish the materials. Then a variety of chemical and physical weathering processes (enhanced by cryospheric processes at high latitudes and high altitudes) break down and transform the parent material and organic matter. The biosphere provides not only organic material, but also new chemicals, especially acids, resulting from the breakdown of this material. These can contribute to further weathering of the inorganic matter of the lithosphere. At the same time, the chemical and physical weathering processes can release nutrients to the plants of the biosphere. The interaction between the biosphere and the soil of the lithosphere is therefore both reciprocal and vital.

As a result of the weathering process and the decay of the plants of the biosphere, the soil system ends up with four ingredients. First there is *organic matter*. Second there is the *resistant residue* that cannot be altered in any way by the weathering processes; this often takes the form of silica, such as the quartz particles found in most soils, particularly sandy soils. Third there is a whole host of newly *altered chemical compounds*, such as oxides and carbonates. These include the various clay minerals, which by cation exchange react with the fourth component, the *soil solution* (water plus dissolved solids). The soil solution contains many of the minerals extracted from the original parent material.

These four components of the soil system are then subjected to various processes of dispersion, translocation, and aggregation. Some of the more important of these processes are the flow of water through the soil under the influence of gravity (leaching), the upward movement of water by capillary action, and the evapotranspiration of water from the soil surface. Water is clearly important. Although the diagram does not include such events as the carbon dioxide and nitrogen cycles (see Unit 5), the groundwater component of the hydrological cycle is illustrated. The final result of these and many more processes is usually the soil profile, with its distinctive horizons.

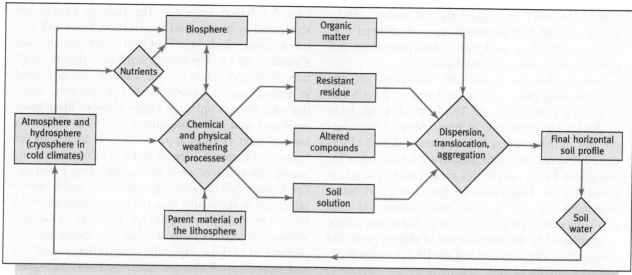

Figure 44.22 Structure and flows of the soil-development system.

All parts of the soil-development system often operate simultaneously. Soils are a particularly dynamic component of the physical world, and they also exhibit important spatial variations. These are considered in Unit 45, which focuses on the geography of soils.

The Human Impact on Soils

Soils are exploited for a wide range of uses:

- food and timber production;
- building materials and water supply;
- burying infrastructure (sewers, electricity cables, etc.);
- industrial raw materials (such as bauxite ores for aluminum refining and kaolinite for china production); and
- the burial of solid domestic waste and the biodegradation of liquid effluent from septic fields.

Soils are also important to trafficability over the terrain (roads, pipelines, airfields, railways, trails, etc.). They are also used for the disposal of the dead.

Clearly, humans have had a profound effect on soils. These effects have come from global warming, from accelerated soil erosion and soil degradation resulting from human activities, and from soil pollution caused by the use of chemical fertilizers, by large-scale animal production, by leakage from septic systems, by leakage from pipelines and from buried and above-ground tanks of various types, and by leachate from sanitary landfills.

 Global Warming

Most scientists now believe that humans have played a major role in the process of global warming through the Agricultural and Industrial Revolutions. Global warming affects soils in a number of ways. It changes soil temperatures and causes the thawing of permafrost in cryosolic soils. It affects the soil moisture regimes by causing drier or wetter conditions. These changes alter vegetative cover and animal communities at all scales. Global warming also affects the cycling of nutrients and atmospheric gases such as carbon, oxygen, and nitrogen.

Desertification

Desertification is the relatively rapid development of deserts or desert conditions caused by human activities in arid and semi-arid areas where rainfall is less than 600 mm/yr. Very arid areas are characterized by a rainfall of less than 250 mm/yr. Many of the areas affected border true deserts. A prime example is the Sahel zone south of the Sahara. The desertification process is caused by poor land-use practices, often accompanied and accelerated by drought conditions. Dryland vegetation is limited. It provides food for people and/or their livestock. On land used for farming, the native vegetation has been cleared for raising crops. If the crops fail, the land remains unplanted and can be eroded by the wind (deflated). In more arid areas, livestock eat more plant material because they need its supply of water, so this can also lead to the destruction of native vegetation cover.

The second most important factor in desertification is the decrease of soil fertility caused by the loss of topsoil rich in nutrients and organic matter. The third most important process is the loss of soil structure. In many cases a crust or cuirasse forms at the soil surface, inhibiting soil permeability and the infiltration of water into the soil and ultimately into the groundwater system. Instead of loss of some storm water into the ground more is available to runoff and erodes the soil surface. Similar results are found in numerous types of confined livestock areas (feedlots, stockyards) where compaction and puddling of the soil surface takes place.

Natural drought cycles are important to the desertification process. It is occurring in the US but is a major problem in the Third World. Large areas of the US are potentially at harm. Most of the western half of that country has an average rainfall of less than 500 mm/yr. It is estimated that 2.6 million km² (or just under 33 per cent of this area) is subject to severe desertification. This means the loss of desirable native vegetation, seriously increases soil erosion, and leads to a reduction in crop yields. The problems are caused or aggravated by the intensive use of surface water and overgrazing. The population of the US Southwest is rising very rapidly as more and more people migrate to the 'Sunbelt'. The impact of the population on this part of the US is modest so far because other areas can supply food and other necessities. Groundwater is being used for potable and irrigation water or it is supplied by the dams and reservoirs along the Colorado River. At the moment, erosion and sediment redistribution into the river systems is not very visible or important to the public. Similar problems exist in areas of Canada (e.g., the Okanagan Valley of BC and drier parts of the Prairies) but not to the same extent, as there are no extremely hot arid environments.

Desertification is a great concern because it effectively reduces the amount of cultivatable land on which food can be grown. It is estimated that over 600 million people worldwide now live in arid areas. All of these areas are vulnerable to desertification. In 2000, one-third of what was once productive semi-arid land was deemed useless because of desertification and soil deterioration (loss of fertility, pollution, etc.). The famines in Ethiopia, Somalia, and the Darfur region of Sudan were caused by drought but prolonged because of desertification due to the concentration of millions of people and their livestock. Major dust storms have increased tenfold in less than two centuries and these will continue to increase because of global warming. Atmospheric dust has increased because of deforestation, expanding cultivation, and desertification. Marginal agricultural land will be threatened by this process. Increasing aridity will cause vegetation to die and wind erosion will increase.

Soil Erosion by Running Water

The estimated soil erosion loss in the US is over 4 billion tonnes/yr. Worldwide, an estimated 75 billion tonnes/yr are lost. Soil erosion by running water takes its greatest toll in Asia, Africa, and Latin America. It is estimated that India alone loses 6.6 billion tonnes/yr while China loses 5.5 billion tonnes/yr. The rates of erosion are accelerated by farming and construction. Some 165 million hectares, or about 20 per cent of all cropland, are affected in the US. The average soil loss (sediment yield) from these agricultural areas is about 2 tonnes/hectare/yr. Erosion rates for construction areas are three times this rate. For example, the Upper Humber River basin north and west of Toronto during the 1970s and 1980s saw sediment yields of approximately 94 tonnes/km²/yr because of a combination of arable agriculture and intensive construction, while the neighbouring Etobicoke Creek watershed (agricultural in the north and relatively urbanized in the south) over the same period recorded rates of around 50 tonnes/km²/yr. The work of Gordon Wolman and others in the US has also shown the importance of land use, especially construction, to soil loss and river channel changes (see Figure 44.23). Again, the major problem is the loss of fertile (nutrient-rich) topsoil, which has to be replaced by using chemical fertilizers. Another related problem is sediment pollution caused by the eroded soil material being supplied to river systems, where it accumulates behind dams and along riverbanks, fills reservoirs, affects water quality, harms fish habitats, and decreases hydroelectricity production. The productivity of eroded land continues to drop and more chemical fertilizers are used to make up for the lost nutrients.

Soil Erosion in Canada

Soil erosion is the most widespread environmental problem in Canada. The rates of soil erosion vary widely because of the differences in climate, soil types, landforms, and land use. Soil loss of less than 5 tonnes/hectare/yr is actually hard to see, but depending on the soil type and depth, 5–10 tonnes/hectare/yr can cause long-term productivity problems. Any rates above the natural rate of soil formation (about 0.5–1.0 tonne/hectare/yr) will reduce soil quality. In the Peace River area of northeastern BC rates of 14 tonnes/hectare/yr have been measured on summer fallow (soils kept bare during the summer to control weeds). In Saskatchewan and Alberta, water erosion causes 40–50 per cent of total soil loss and affects about 5 million hectares of agricultural land. In Ontario, sediment damage to agricultural land is estimated to cost around $100 million/yr. On non-farmland the problem is just as significant and expensive. Water erosion in the province is most severe in southwestern Ontario, where agricultural yields may be cut by 40 per cent as a consequence. In Quebec, water erosion is a problem where row crops are grown on fine-textured soils on rolling terrain, as is the case in Estrie (the Eastern Townships). Soil losses in Atlantic Canada are the highest in the country, especially in potato-growing areas. In Prince Edward Island, for example, soil loss rates of up to 20 tonnes/hectare/yr are common.

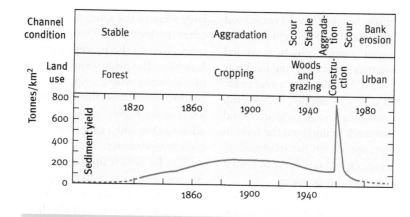

Figure 44.23 Land-use changes, sediment yield, and channel behaviour in a Piedmont region beginning prior to the advent of extensive farming and continuing through a period of construction and subsequent urban landscape. (After Wolman, 1967)

The problems caused by soil material in rivers and other waterways include the following:

- Silt accumulation reduces channel capacity (size) and may cause more floods.
- Fish habitat is damaged or destroyed.
- Plant and algal growth is accelerated because of an excess of nutrients (eutrophication).
- Pollution is caused by the buildup of heavy metals (e.g., mercury, lead, and cadmium), pesticides, and other toxins from industrial activity, large livestock operations, and the application of human sewage sludge to the fields.
- Recreational values decrease.
- Making water fit for human consumption becomes more costly.

LINK

Another major problem is **soil compaction**. This is a significant problem in such areas as the Lower Fraser Valley of BC and in parts of central and eastern Canada, as it is in other areas around the world. The estimated cost in Canada is between $68 million and $200 million/yr. It is caused by frequent field traffic under moist conditions and intensive tillage with heavy machinery. Confined livestock operations are also associated with this problem. Compaction causes a loss of permeability (puddling) and erosion of the soil surface by runoff. Clay soils and soils with low organic matter content are vulnerable to this process. Field crops (e.g., potatoes, corn, soybeans, and sugar beets) are often associated with compaction because they need a long growing season and must be planted in early spring and harvested in the fall. Both these times of year are associated with wetter conditions. Crop yields can decrease by up to 60 per cent when soils are severely compacted. When this happens it is difficult for plants to root, the root zone is restricted, and plants experience moisture and nutrient

stress. The compaction and churning of wet soil by vehicles or livestock can also break down the soil structure.

Acidification is another problem. Leached acidic soils are very common in Canada, especially in areas with high rainfall, acidic parent materials, and decomposing acidic plant residues. They also occur on sand and gravel spreads and landforms. Acid precipitation is not a contributing factor. The problem occurs when nitrogen- and sulphur-rich fertilizers are used. When these are employed the pH drops below 5.5 and crop yields decline, and so farmers use lime on their fields to raise the pH. Acidification causes the mobilization and leaching of iron and aluminum and bases such as calcium and magnesium. Most of the bases are flushed out of the soil column and into the groundwater system and have to be replaced by chemical fertilizers to maintain the pH for crop growth.

The loss of organic matter also takes place. As discussed earlier, organic matter, especially humus, is important to maintaining a stable, well-aggregated soil structure and enhances water infiltration and retention. It also aids in the production of a well-aerated rhizosphere and nutrient uptake by plants. Organic matter is also necessary to aid the bearing capacity of the soil for heavy agricultural machinery. In addition, it contributes nutrients to the soil and plants, adds to the cation exchange capacity of the soil, and reduces groundwater pollution because of its role in the cation exchange process.

When the Prairies were developed for agriculture it meant that the native grasslands were replaced with cereal production. This change has led to the export of a lot of nutrients (in the wheat, etc.) to the cities and abroad. The loss of these nutrients and erosion caused by tillage have contributed to an estimated decrease of 50 per cent of the original organic matter in the soils. In eastern and central Canada, intensive farming has decreased soil organic matter content by about 30–40 per cent since the 1960s. Until then the organic matter content remained constant by using a forage rotation system: the land was cropped for two or three years, lay fallow for a year or so, and then was sown with clover or another forage crop to add nutrients to the soil—the forage crop itself and the feces of the grazing livestock maintained the level of organic matter. Cultivation speeds up the oxidation of organic matter and if a forage crop rotation is not used it leads to the release of more greenhouse gases.

Dryland salinization is a natural process. It is important in arid and semi-arid environments such as the drier areas of western Canada (Palliser's Triangle and the central interior of BC). It occurs primarily on solonetzic and alkaline soils and on highly saline parent materials (as in northeastern BC). These soils cover 6–8 million hectares of the western provinces. There are also large areas of the same soil types in the western US and other dry areas of the world. Induced salinization is the term given to the process when it is caused by human activities. The prime example of this is the central valley of California where irrigation is used for the intensive production of vegetables and fruits. The parent materials here are highly saline, and as the irrigation water is added to the soil, evaporation takes place because of the high temperatures. This causes groundwater carrying salts to be drawn up into the soils by capillary action. As more and more water is applied to the crops the soils become increasingly saline. The same process is seen in some drier areas in Canada. It is estimated that about 2.2 million hectares (about 6 per cent of the agricultural land) is affected by induced salinity in central and southern Alberta and Saskatchewan and in some areas of southwestern Manitoba. This has caused an estimated loss in production of $104–$257 million/yr.

KEY TERMS

additions   *page 636*
anion   *page 641*
blocky (angular) structure   *page 645*
cation   *page 641*
clay   *page 644*
coversands   *page 634*
eluviation   *page 638*
field capacity   *page 644*
humus   *page 634*
illuviation   *page 638*
leaching   *page 639*
loam   *page 644*
parent material   *page 633*
pedon   *page 643*
peds   *page 643*
permeability   *page 644*
platy structure   *page 645*
porosity   *page 644*
prismatic structure   *page 645*

residual soil   *page 633*
rhizosphere   *page 634*
sand   *page 644*
silt   *page 644*
soil   *page 630*
soil bodies   *page 636*
soil catena   *page 648*
soil compaction   *page 651*
soil horizon   *page 637*
soil profile   *page 637*
soil (pedogenetic) regime   *page 639*
sol   *page 643*
solum   *page 643*
spheroidal (granular) structure   *page 645*
tilth   *page 633*
transformation   *page 636*
translocation   *page 637*
transported soil   *page 634*

REVIEW QUESTIONS

1. What are the four primary soil components?
2. What are the five major factors in soil formation?
3. What are the four processes of soil formation?
4. Describe the dominant characteristics of the **L-F-H, A, B, C,** and **R** soil horizons.
5. What is meant by the terms *sol* and *ped*?
6. Identify the size ranges for grains of sand, silt, and clay.
7. Define *field capacity*.
8. What is the difference between an acid soil solution and an alkaline soil solution?
9. What is a soil *catena*?
10. What is cation exchange and how does it work?

REFERENCES AND FURTHER READINGS

Amundson, R., et al., eds. 1994. *Factors of Soil Formation: A Fiftieth Anniversary Retrospective*. Madison, Wis.: Soil Science Society of America.

Ashman, M., and G. Puri. 2002. *Essential Soil Science*. Malden, Mass.: Blackwell.

Birkeland, P.W. 1999. *Soils and Geomorphology*, 3rd edn. London/New York: Oxford Univ. Press.

Brady, N.C., and R.R. Weil. 1999. *The Nature and Properties of Soil*, 12th edn. Upper Saddle River, NJ: Prentice-Hall.

Canada, Ministry of the Environment. 1991. *The State of Canada's Environment*. Ottawa: Government of Canada.

Charman, P., and B. Murphy, eds. 2000. *Soils: Their Properties and Management*, 2nd edn. New York: Oxford Univ. Press.

Cooke, R.U., and J.C. Doornkamp. 1990. *Geomorphology in Environmental Management*, 2nd edn. Oxford: Clarendon Press.

Daniels, R.B., and R.D. Hammer. 1992. *Soil Geomorphology*. New York: Wiley.

Diamond, J.M. 1997. *Guns, Germs and Steel: The Fates of Human Societies*. New York: Norton.

Ellis, S., and A. Mellor. 1995. *Soils and Environment*. London/New York: Routledge.

Fanning, D.S., and M.C.B. Fanning. 1989. *Soil: Morphology, Genesis, and Classification*. New York: Wiley.

Fitzpatrick, E.A. 1983. *Soils: Their Formation, Classification, and Distribution*. London/New York: Longman.

Foth, H.D. 1990. *Fundamentals of Soil Science*, 8th edn. New York: Wiley.

Gerrard, A.J. 1981. *Soils and Landforms: An Integration of Geomorphology and Pedology*. Winchester, Mass.: Allen & Unwin.

———. 2000. *Fundamentals of Soils*. London/New York: Routledge.

Jenny, H. 1981. *The Soil Resource: Origin and Behavior*. New York/Berlin: Springer-Verlag.

Loynachan, T.E., et al. 1999. *Sustaining Our Soils and Society*. Alexandria, Va: American Geological Institute, AGI Environmental Awareness Series, 2.

Millar, C.E., et al. 1965. *Fundamentals of Soil Science*. New York: John Wiley & Sons.

Parton, T.R., et al. 1996. *Soils: A New Global View*. New Haven: Yale Univ. Press.

Raven, P.H., et al. 1993. *Environment*. Fort Worth: Saunders College Publishing.

Ross, S. 1989. *Soil Processes: A Systematic Approach*. London/New York: Routledge.

Rowell, D.L. 1994. *Soil Science: Methods and Applications*. New York: Wiley/Longman.

Selby, M.J. 1993. *Hillslope Materials and Processes*, 2nd edn. Oxford: Oxford Univ. Press.

Simonson, R.W. 1953. 'Outline of Generalized Theory of Soil Genesis', *Soil Science Society of America, Proceedings* 23: 152–6.

Soil Science Society of America. 1984. *Glossary of Soil Science Terms*. Madison, Wis.: Soil Science Society of America.

US Government Printing Office. 1938. *Soils and Men: Yearbook of Agriculture, 1938*. Washington: US Department of Agriculture.

White, R.E. 1987. *Introduction to the Principles and Practice of Soil Science*, 2nd edn. New York: Wiley.

Wolman, M.G. 1967. 'A Cycle of Erosion and Sedimentation in Urban River Channels', *Geografiska Annaler* 49A: 385–96.

Young, A. 1972. *Slopes*. London: Longman.

 # WEB RESOURCES

english.uiuc.edu/maps/depression/dustbowl.htm Interesting text and images related to the American dust bowl.

history.cbc.ca/history/?MIval=EpisContent.html&series_id=1&episode_id=13&chapter_id=1&page_id=2&lang=E Canadian experiences of the 1930s dust bowl; information from CBC television *History of Canada* series.

news.nationalgeographic.com/news/2001/06/0601_chinadust.html China's dust storms raise fears of impending catastrophe.

pubs.usgs.gov/gip/deserts/desertification A very good website about desertification around the world.

soil.gsfc.nasa.gov/forengeo/secret.htm An overview of soil formation factors, and a description of instruments used to study soil and of what forensic geologists do. Links to other soil science pages and research materials are provided.

www.ec.gc.ca/soer-ree/english/default.cfm Environment Canada site on the state of environmental reporting and environmental indicators;

annual update of information on all aspects of the environment, including soil erosion.

www.livinghistoryfarm.org/farminginthe30s/water_02.html Extensive website about the dust bowl, with lots of text, images, and interviews with people who survived the period.

www.planetfriendly.net/ecoportal.html Environmental directories, portals, and networks; links to all major environmental organizations in Canada and some in the US and elsewhere.

www.sciencedaily.com/releases/2008/04/080430152030.htm Did dust storms make the 1930s drought worse?

www.soils.org The Soil Science Society of America's website, with soil degradation information, a glossary of terms, and links to soil science journals.

Unit 45

Classification and Mapping of Soils

Objectives

- To present a brief history of pedology and highlight problems in achieving a universal soil classification scheme.

- To outline the current Canadian System of Soil Classification (CSSC).

- To outline the current US Soil Taxonomy.

- To survey the 12 soil orders in the CSSC and examine their regional patterns on the North American and world map.

This unit takes a geographical perspective to describe how soils are distributed across North America and the rest of the world. Unit 16 points out the problems associated with the classification of climates and their spatial representation. It is necessary to establish criteria to distinguish climate types from one another—criteria not ordained by nature but established by scientists. Certainly there are justifications for those lines in Figure 16.2: climatologists found transition zones between different climate regimes that also were marked by vegetation changes and often by other modifications as well.

As noted at the beginning of Part Five, the map of world climates keeps re-emerging as soils, vegetation, and animal life are discussed. In many respects, classifying and regionalizing soils is even more difficult than classifying climates. A small area may contain a bewildering variety of soils of different profiles, thicknesses, textures, and structures. For more than a century, pedologists have been working to devise an acceptable system of classifying soils on which a map of world soil distribution could be based.

Classifying Soils

For more than a century the study of soils has been dominated by Russian and American scientists. Up to about 1850 soils were believed to be simply weathered parts of the underlying bedrock. A Russian scholar, Vasili Vasil'evich Dokuchaev (1846–1903), was the first pedologist to demonstrate what the famous scientist Mikhail Lomonosov had suggested a century before. This was that soils with the same parent material develop differently under different environmental conditions. Dokuchaev wrote a very significant book entitled *Ruskii Chernozem* ('Russian Blackearth', 1883) and began an elaborate survey and description of Russian soils based on their field characteristics (depth, profile development, colour, texture, structure, consistence, etc.). After 1870 he and his colleagues (e.g., Nikolai Sibirtsev and Konstantin Glinka) produced several successive soil classifications.

Soil mapping and classification were still very crude in North America during the early part of the twentieth century, even though pioneering work had been done by Eugene W. Hilgard (1833–1916), a German-American who had done a tremendous amount of fieldwork in the US Midwest around the time of the American Civil War and for quite some time after. Hilgard had even begun considering soils in much the same way as the Russian workers had, and towards the end of his life, in 1906, he published a very important book about soils, *Soils, Their Formation, Properties, Composition and Relations to Climate and Plant Growth in Humid and Arid Regions*.

The first soil survey in Canada was undertaken by A.J. Galbraith in southern Ontario, to the south and west of Kingston, in 1914. Galbraith used the US Bureau of Soils classification, which was largely based on the type of parent materials and soil texture. He recognized nine 'soil series' in this area. These were very broad areas that were

similar in scale to rock formations. In the early 1920s J.H. Ellis identified field system associations of soils based on parent material and topography in parts of Manitoba.

There was limited progress in terms of classification in Canada during the 1920s and 1930s. Soil surveys were established in Ontario, the Prairie provinces, and British Columbia by 1931, but by 1936 only 1.7 per cent of Canada had been surveyed. Soil classification was thus hampered by the fragmentary state of knowledge of soils in the country.

In 1914, Glinka (1867–1927) published a book, in German, on the work done on Russian soils (*Die Typen der Bilenbildung*). However, this book was unknown in the West until well after World War I. It was finally translated into English (*The Great Soil Groups of the World and Their Development*) in 1927 by Curtis F. Marbut, head of the US Department of Agriculture's Bureau of Soils. This book made a great impression on soil scientists in North America and elsewhere, informing them about Russian ideas concerning soil development, classification based on field properties, and the Russian soil taxonomic system. For years North American workers had been grappling with exactly the same kinds of problems faced by the Russians, and now they could adapt the Russian concepts. The Russians recognized three distinct groups of soils: *zonal*, *intrazonal*, and *azonal* soils. The characteristics of zonal soils reflected the influence of climate and vegetation (e.g., soils like chernozems and podzols). The characteristics of intrazonal soils were influenced by the dominance of topography, parent material, or drainage (e.g., solonetzs and gleis). Azonal soils were poorly developed soils because of age and/or their location in geomorphologically active sites or on fairly recently deposited parent materials, as would be found on steep, unstable slopes or on flood plains (e.g., regosolic soils).

Marbut (1863–1935) was the most important North American pedologist of the first half of the twentieth century. He laid the groundwork for the first genetic soil classification, using Russian ideas and terminology. The classification system devised by Marbut and his colleagues (the Marbut, or USDA, System) was published in 1938 and was frequently revised and modified during the 1940s. To arrive at this system, the American soil scientists superimposed the Russian classification onto a basic division of the soils of North America (outside of northern areas). The following soil types were recognized in this basic scheme (Figure 45.1):

1. **Pedocal soils** occurred west of 98°W longitude. These soils retained calcium in their profiles (hence the name pedo*cals*). They were unleached alkaline soils with pHs above 7. They occurred in areas where the precipitation was less than 600 mm/yr.

2. **Pedalfer soils** occurred east of 98°W longitude. These soils retained ferrous iron and aluminum in their **B** horizons (hence the name ped*alfers*). They occurred in wetter areas with more than 600 mm/yr precipitation, and the bases, such as Ca, had been leached out of the soil. The soils were acidic with pHs below 7.

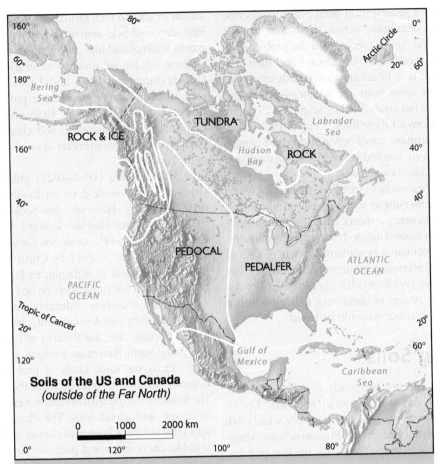

Figure 45.1 Soils of Canada and the United States, divided into two major classes determined by climate (after Marbut).

The Marbut classification, along with Ellis's ideas and other American developments, greatly influenced the development of soil classification in Canada. The USDA classification was used in Canada, although the concept of zonal soils was not very useful in eastern Canada, where parent material and topography dominated soil development in many areas. In 1940 the National Soil Survey Committee of Canada formed the Soil Classification Subcommittee (after 1970 the Canadian Soil Survey Committee) to co-ordinate soil surveys across Canada, increase research into soil characteristics, and use this improved knowledge to map and classify Canadian soils. In 1945 this committee adopted a field classification system of soils similar to the one proposed earlier by Ellis. The first real Canadian soil taxonomic system was published in 1955. This came about because of an increase in knowledge concerning Canadian soils, a desire to classify soils, and the development of a new system of classification in the United States.

In the United States it had been clear for some time that the Marbut classification had fundamental flaws that no amount of modification would solve. American soil scientists had a number of problems. Many soils had been altered from their natural state by either agricultural practices

or other events. Soil scientists felt that the Marbut system laid too much emphasis on the soils' origins—that is, on soil-forming factors and soil-forming processes. They believed that the characteristics of the soils—not the formation processes—should be classified. Thus, classification criteria must be stated in terms of the characteristics of the actual soils rather than in terms of the soil-forming factors, such as climate or topography. They also argued that the origin of a soil was sometimes unknown and that such a soil could not be classified genetically. The effort to build a new US soil classification was begun during the 1950s by the US Soil Conservation Service. The US Soil Survey staff had gathered an enormous mass of data on the soils of the United States, and now an attempt was made to create the first comprehensive classification based on soil field characteristics. This initial effort was followed by a series of revisions (called 'Approximations') until 1975, when the **US Soil Taxonomy** (see Appendix B) was finally released.

The 1955 Canadian classification system became the basis of the current **Canadian System of Soil Classification** (CSSC). Since 1955, more precise definitions and criteria for classification have been put in place. The Canadian developments were greatly helped by the American experience, and consequently the two systems are more closely associated than any other classifications. The CSSC was published in 1970 and has been revised a number of times. The last revision was in 1998. The main differences between the Canadian and American systems can be summed up as follows: (1) the Canadian system uses the entire soil profile to classify the soils, while the US taxonomy uses only the horizons below the plough level (this is because most soils in Canada will never be used for agriculture because of the climate and terrain); (2) the Canadian system is designed for use in Canada, while the US system has a global scope; and (3) the Canadian system is based on soil properties but, unlike the US system, has retained a genetic bias in the properties, or group of properties, and in the terminology used (e.g., the term *podzol* is used). Such terminology denotes not only the kind of properties of the soil but also the soil-forming processes that led to the development of the soil. The numbers of soil orders and other taxa have been revised periodically. Table 45.1 shows the number of levels of organization in the Canadian System of Soil Classification and the US Soil Taxonomy at present. Both systems are hierarchical—the *soil series* being the lowest level of classification and the *soil order* being the highest level of abstraction (see Table 45.1).

Some of the major soil types (orders) were encountered in Unit 44. A **soil order** is the highest level of classification

in both systems, but as can be seen in Table 45.1 the definition of what constitutes a soil order differs somewhat between the two taxonomies.

Soil Distribution on a Hypothetical Continent

The general distribution of soil orders can now be discussed. One way to approach soil classification is to consider the spatial distribution of soil orders on a simple hypothetical continent (Figure 45.2). The mapped contents of this model are somewhat familiar because climate is a soil-forming factor. Thus the southeastern region would be dominated by **mT** air masses, the northwestern area by **mP** air masses, and so forth (see Figure 12.14). Remembering what was learned about the soil-forming processes, it is possible to conclude that the warm, moist southeast would experience the kind of leaching that produces laterites, while the cool, moist, northwest would have soils that are leached or lessivated (podzols, luvisols).

Care is needed in drawing these conclusions. Whereas the regional climates might indicate such a distribution, parent materials could change the picture considerably. For the hypothetical continent, therefore, it is necessary

LINK

Table 45.1 Organization of the Canadian System of Soil Classification Taxonomy Compared with That of the US Soil Taxonomy

Level	CSSC Taxa Description	Level	US Soil Taxa Description
Order (10)	Differentiated on the basis of soil characteristics that reflect the nature of the total soil environment and the effects of the dominant soil-forming factors	Order (12)	Differentiated on the basis of the degree of horizon development, degree of weathering, gross composition, and presence or absence of specific horizons
This level of organization is not used in the CSSC		Suborder (96)	Differentiated on the basis of chemical and physical properties and formative and environmental factors
Great Group (31)	Differentiated on the basis of characteristics that reflect the differences in the strengths of dominant processes or a major contribution of an additional process	Great Group (230)	Same as the CSSC
Subgroup (221)	Differentiated on the basis of the kind and arrangement of horizons that reflect a conformity to the central concept of the great group, a gradation towards another soil order, or the presence of a special horizon	Subgroup (~1000)	Same as the CSSC
Family	Differentiated on the basis of the parent material characteristics (e.g., texture, mineralogy, depth, and/or reaction) and on differences in soil climatic factors	Family (~5000)	Same as the CSSC
Series	Groupings of pedons with similar arrangements of horizons, whose colour, texture, structure, consistence, thickness, reaction, and composition fall within relatively narrow, well-defined ranges	Series (~16,000)	Same as the CSSC

Source: Canadian System of Soil Classification

Source: US Department of Agriculture

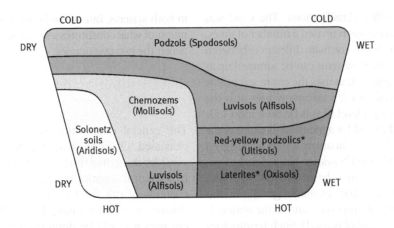

Figure 45.2 Distribution of soil order regimes on a hypothetical continent in the Northern Hemisphere. This figure uses Canadian soil order names, with US names in parentheses. Red-yellow podzolics and laterites are not included in the Canadian classification because they only occur outside of Canada.

Perspectives on the Human Environment

Soil Taxonomy—What's in a Name?

Science is based in part on classification systems. Biologists organize the living world into kingdoms. Chemists classify types of changes in matter and energy. Anthropologists identify types of kinship systems and family structures. New classification systems are constantly being put forward, yet not all survive.

What defines the difference between a useful system and one that does not stand the test of time? A useful system is flexible enough to accommodate new data and phenomena, yet rigid enough so that its underlying principles can be applied again and again. Because of the increasing internationalization of science, names should have some significance in a variety of languages. Finally, a system should organize its information in ways that show useful relationships.

How do the Canadian and US soil classifications surveyed in this unit measure up according to

these standards? The Canadian system uses a lot of terms that are borrowed from Russian and that carry a genetic bias—that is, the terms imply the processes or genesis of a particular soil. An example is *podzol*. The term implies that this soil developed through the podzolization process. When the US Department of Agriculture (USDA) first proposed the comprehensive soil taxonomy in the 1950s and 1960s, its major goals were to replace old terms, employ terms that suggest some properties of the soils, and use names that would have some meaning in the many world languages with words derived from Latin or Greek. The USDA employed classical scholars from the Universities of Ghent (Belgium) and Illinois to provide the Latin and Greek roots to match the soil characteristics. The etymologies of the names employed by both the Canadian and US systems are shown below in Table 45.3. This chart also shows the relationship between the Canadian and US soil orders.

to make some far-reaching assumptions, including the assumption of a uniform parent material (with calcareous and mixed-mineral content and a loam texture), gently rolling relief without groundwater in the soil profile, and a long period of soil formation (approximately 100,000 years). Given these idealized conditions, the generalized soil order map might look like the map in Figure 45.2, but it does make the hypothetical continent very simplified and at some distance from the complexities of the real world.

The Soil Orders

Before looking more closely at Figure 45.2, it is necessary to become acquainted with the properties of the Canadian soil orders in some detail (see 'Perspectives' box). These are listed, along with their great groups, in Tables 45.2 and 45.3.

1. **Brunisolic Order** These soils have the beginnings of a **B** horizon. **Brunisolic soils** (US: **inceptisols**) form rather quickly but are generally older than regosols. They have a weakly developed **B** horizon noted for its reddish coloration; this horizon lacks strong clay development and the accumulation of other compounds. But brunisols contain significant amounts of organic matter and/or evidence that the parent material has been weathered to some extent. Brunisols are generally found in humid climates, but they occur from the Arctic to the tropics and are often found in highland areas. These soils most frequently develop under forest cover, but they can also be found under tundra or grass (Figure 45.3).

2. **Chernozemic Order** These are found in climates that normally have dry seasons, but temperatures can range from microthermal to tropical. Rainfall may be sufficient to leach these soils, but calcification is far more common. **Chernozems** (US: **mollisols**) are the soils of the Canadian Prairies, the grass-covered steppes of south-central Russia, and the Great Plains that lend their name to the **BS** climatic zone. The dominant attribute of a chernozem is a thick, dark, humus-rich surface layer (Figure 45.4), high in alkaline content and at least 50 per cent saturated with basic cations (calcium, magnesium, potassium, sodium). This layer has a ratio of carbon to nitrogen of less than 17 per cent, and the stability of its structure is moderate to strong. Chernozems occasionally are found under water-loving plants or deciduous hardwood forests, but the vast majority are found under tall- or short-grass prairie. Chernozems are often associated with large-scale commercial grain production and livestock grazing. Corn is the grain of choice when precipitation is sufficient, but wheat is by far the predominant crop. Drought is the most common problem facing chernozems.

3. **Cryosolic Order** These are defined as high-latitude or high-altitude soils that have (1) permafrost within

Table 45.2 The Canadian System of Soil Classification: Soil Orders and Great Groups*

Soil Order	Great Group	Characteristics
Brunisolic	Melanic brunisol	**Ah** horizon greater then 10 cm
	Eutric brunisol	No **Ah** horizon
	Sombric brunisol	**Ah** horizon, dark coloration
	Dystic brunisol	No **Ah** horizon, has $CaCl_2$
Chernozemic	Brown chernozem	Calcium-rich soil with intermediate coloration
	Dark-brown chernozem	Calcium-rich soil with a darker colour
	Black chernozem	Calcium-rich soil with exceptionally dark coloration
	Dark-grey chernozem	Calcium-rich soil with eluviation; associated with forest vegetation
Cryosolic	Turbic cryosol	Evidence of cryoturbation; permafrost within 2 m of the surface
	Static cryosol	Formed in mineral soil; no major cryoturbation; permafrost within 1 m of the surface
	Organic cryosol	Formed primarily in organic materials; has permafrost within 1 m of the surface
Gleysolic	Humic gleysol	Has either an **Ah** horizon or an **Ap** horizon; 2% organic carbon in surface horizon
	Gleysol	Thick **O** horizon; thin blue-grey horizon below
	Luvic gleysol	Has a **Btg** horizon and usually an eluvial horizon
Luvisolic	Grey Brown luvisol	Has a forest mull **Ah** horizon and a mean soil temperature of >8°C
	Grey luvisol	Has either an **Ah** or **Ahe** horizon
Organic	Fibrisol	Formed in relatively undecomposed organic matter
	Misisol	Formed in organic matter in an intermediate stage of decomposition
	Humisol	Formed in organic matter in an advanced state of decomposition
	Folisol	Developed in upland organic (folic) materials; seldom saturated with water
Podzolic	Humic podzol	Has a **Bh** horizon
	Ferro-humic podzol	Has a **Bhf** horizon
	Humo-ferric podzol	Has a **Bfh** horizon
Regosolic	Regosol	Has an **Ah** horizon
	Humic regosol	Has layers below the **Ah** horizon
Solonetzic	Solonetz	Saline or alkaline soil
	Solodized solonetz	Has a thick **Ae** horizon
	Solod	Has an **Ae** horizon and a distinct **AB** or **BA** horizon
	Vertic solonetz	Has a slickenside horizon within 1 m of the surface
Vertisolic	Vertisol	Surface layer cracks when dry
	Humic vertisol	Darker coloration; cracks when dry

*Canadian System of Soil Classification, Agriculture Canada 2004

Table 45.3 Equivalency of Canadian and US Soil Orders and Derivation of Terms

The Canadian System of Soil Classification uses the whole soil profile to classify the soils. It is designed for use in Canada.			The US Soil Taxonomy uses only the soil horizons below the plough level to classify soils. It is designed for global usage.		
Canadian Soil Orders	Derivation of Canadian Term	% Area of Canada	US Soil Orders	Derivation of US Term	% Area of US
Brunisolic	French: *brun*—brown	8.8	Inceptisols, some psamments	Latin: *inceptum*—beginning	9.7
Chernozemic	Russian: *chernozem*—blackearth	5.1	Mollisols, borolls	Latin: *mollis*—soft	21.5
Cryosolic	Greek: *kryos*—icy, cold	45	Gelisols	Latin: *gelare*—to freeze	8.7
Gleysolic	Russian: *glei*—blue-grey	1.9	Aquic subgroups	Latin: *aqua*—water, wet	
Luvisolic	ELUViated	10.3	Alfisols, boralfs, and udalfs	Al (Aluminum) and Fe (Iron), PedALFEr	13.9
Organic	Organisms—living things	4.2	Histosols	Greek: *histos*—tissue	1.7
Podzolic	Russian: *podzol*—under wood ash	22.6	Spodosols, some inceptisols	Greek: *spodos*—wood ash	3.5
Regosolic	Greek: *regos*—blanket	1.3	Entisols	RecENT	12.3
Solonetzic	Russian: *solon*—salt	0.6	Aridisols, natric mollisols, and alfisols	Latin: *aridus*—dry Latin: *natric*—salty	8.3
Vertisolic	Latin: *verto*—to turn	0.2	Vertisols	Latin: *verto*—to turn	2.0
Soils found outside of Canada			Andisols	ANDesite—volcanic rock	1.7
			Oxisols	French: *oxide*—Iron	0.02
			Ultisols	Latin: *ultimus*—last	9.2

Figure 45.3 Profile of a brunisolic soil (inceptisol), exhibiting many physical properties described in the text.

1 m of the soil surface, or (2) *gelic materials* within 1 m of the surface and permafrost within 2 m. Gelic materials are mineral or organic soil materials that show evidence of cryoturbation (frost-churning) and/or ice segregation in the talik (seasonally thawing active layer) or the uppermost part of the permafrost just below it. In North America **cryosols** (US: **gelisols**) are found primarily in areas poleward of 60°N (Figure 45.5). Here they are often associated with such frozen-ground periglacial landforms as patterned ground and pingos (discussed in Unit 39).

4. **Gleysolic Order** These soils can occur in any waterlogged environment in cool or cold environments and elsewhere. The characteristic thick organic layer includes decomposing and decomposed vegetation that remains because of the slow rotting process undertaken by anaerobic micro-organisms. **Gleysolic soils** occur near to and upslope of organic soils and at the base of slopes where moisture collects. Their development is influenced by temperature, topography, and drainage collection.

5. **Luvisolic Order** These soils are found in moister, less-continental climatic zones than chernozems. They are high in mineral content and usually moist. As Figure 45.6 indicates, luvisols lack the dark surface

Figure 45.4 Profile of a chernozemic soil (mollisol), the dominant soil beneath the grass-lands of the Prairies.

Figure 45.5 A cryosolic soil, underlain by permafrost 38 cm below the surface. Such soil can be found on the foothills of the Mackenzie Mountains in the Northwest Territories. The irregular horizon boundaries result from cryoturbation (frost-churning) processes.

horizon of the chernozems, but they do exhibit note-worthy clay accumulation in the **B** horizon. **Luvisols** (US: **alfisols**) are usually found under higher-latitude mixed forests or middle-latitude deciduous forests, but occasionally can be found in areas of vegetation adapted to dryness. Areas of luvisolic soils are notable for having the most intensive forms of agriculture in North America. Luvisols are typical of highly produc-tive agricultural areas such as southern Ontario, parts of the Fraser Valley in British Columbia, and areas of the American Corn Belt. Market gardening, oats, soy-beans, and alfalfa are the main usage of these soils. A major area of luvisols lies in tropical Africa, within two wide zones (one in the Northern and one in the South-ern Hemisphere) between the moist equatorial region and the Sahara and Kalahari Deserts of the subtropical latitudes.

6. **Organic Order** Organic soils (US: **histosols**) are of-ten water-saturated for most of the year. They occur in muskeg, bogs, fens, and other wetlands. Organic material tends to dominate the **O** horizon and clay in the **C** horizon (Figure 45.7). Some organics are

Figure 45.6 Profile of a luvisolic soil, a soil associated with some of the most productive farming areas in southern Ontario and parts of the Fraser Valley, British Columbia.

mainly in more northerly latitudes of the Northern Hemisphere. They are characterized by a **Bf** (podzolic) horizon with an illuvial accumulation of sesquioxides (oxides with 1.5 oxygen atoms to every metallic atom). Usually this horizon shows rounded or subangular black or very dark brown, iron-rich pellets the size of silt, or a thin indurated iron pan may develop. A characteristic sandy, ash-grey or albic **Ae** horizon—the signature of silica, which, unlike other soil minerals, is resistant to dissolution by organic acids—often marks the lower part of the topsoil of podzols (see Figure 44.12) but is not itself a defining feature. Podzols are found only in humid regions, mostly with coniferous forest covers and/or on granular parent materials.

Because of the association of forest cover with podzols, lumbering is one of the most important human activities that takes place on these soils. Agriculture is minimal, although corn, wheat, oats, and hay are now being grown in upstate New York and other places where such soils occur.

8. **Regosolic Order** This order includes all the soils that do not fit into any of the other orders. Such soils tend to be of recent origin, often developed in unconsolidated material (alluvium, for example) and on hard bedrock. **Regosols** (US: **entisols**) have a thin **A** horizon overlying a **C** or **R** horizon; otherwise they show little development (Figure 45.8). Because there are numerous reasons for the absence of well-developed horizons, regosols are found in many different environments. Climate, therefore, is not a strong influence in their distribution.

9. **Solonetzic Order** These soils cover a large area of the world's land surface. **Solonetzic soils** are usually dry unless they are artificially irrigated. They are characterized by a thin, light-coloured horizon at the surface that is low in organic carbon. Moreover, these soils often contain horizons rich in calcium, clay, gypsum, or salt minerals, as shown in Figure 45.9. Large expanses of solonetzic soils are found in deserts such as northern Africa's Sahara and eastern Asia's Gobi. Areas with these soils can be used for grazing or intensive crop production with the aid of irrigation. Desert shrubs and grasses are the main form of vegetation, and overgrazing of the land is often a serious problem. The soil-forming process of calcification is common in solonetzic soils, which are similar but not equivalent to the US **aridisols**.

10. **Vertisolic Order** These are clay soils that develop large cracks in the dry season and swell with moisture when damp during the wet season (Figure 45.10). More than 35 per cent of their content is clay, especially montmorillonite. The clay particles are normally derived from the parent material, so **vertisols** (US: **same term**) are found where the clay-producing materials are available—in mesothermal or tropical climates with periodic dry and wet seasons. Their great groups are closely related to climatic divisions.

unique among the soil orders because they can be totally destroyed over time or altered by natural or artificial drainage. It is difficult to generalize about the geographical distribution of these soils because wetland areas are so widespread. Poor drainage in low- or flat-lying topographical areas explains their occurrence better than climate or prevailing vegetation. When they can be drained, intensive cultivation of cabbage, carrots, potatoes, and other root crops is possible (e.g., the Holland Marsh near Newmarket, Ontario).

7. **Podzolic Order** These soils result when organic soil acids associated with pine-needle decay cause the depletion of most **A** horizon minerals, like the soil in Figure 44.12. **Podzolic soils** (US: **spodosols**) develop

Figure 45.7 Profile of an organic soil near East Lansing, Michigan. Such soils can also be found in southwestern Ontario. In many parts of the world (e.g., Iceland and Ireland) such organic soil is dug up, cut into shoebox-sized pieces, dried, and used as fuel.

Figure 45.8 Dunes carry regosols (entisols), developed on recently deposited, unconsolidated materials and capable of supporting some adapted vegetation. But the materials are unstable, the soil is ephemeral, and the vegetation vulnerable, which is why many dune areas are protected and people are asked to keep off.

They are found in the drier parts of the Prairies and Great Plains as well as in Australia, India, and Sudan. Vertisols are hard to use for most human purposes, particularly construction. When they shrink and crack, fences and telephone poles may be thrown out of line. Pavements, building foundations, and pipelines can all be damaged by the movement of these 'turning' soils. They also occur in permafrost areas where the surface cracks as the soil freezes and the cracks close as the talik thaws in the spring and summer. These types of vertisolic soils are found in the permafrost areas of northern North America, northern Eurasia, and elsewhere.

Volcanic soils (US: **andisols**) occur on volcanic ash and other erupted materials. These weakly developed soils lie principally in the Pacific Ring of Fire (see Unit 24), Hawaii, the Pacific Northwest, and other volcanic zones (Figure 45.11). They occupy less than 1 per cent of the world's land surface and are so locally distributed that they cannot be seen on the small-scale maps employed later in this unit. Volcanic soils also contain much organic matter and hold water well; they are quite fertile.

LINK

Figure 45.9 Profile of a solonetzic soil. Such soils can be found in southwestern Saskatchewan.

Figure 45.10 The sequence of wetting and drying of this soil creates the cracks characteristic of vertisolic soils in some locations in the drier parts of the Prairies. The same features are created by freezing and thawing of the surface in permafrost areas in the northern part of North America and elsewhere.

Figure 45.11 Road cut on the island of Hawaii, revealing the profile of an andisol atop layered volcanic ash.

As noted in Unit 44, **laterite** soils (US: **oxisols**) are restricted to tropical areas with high rainfall. Organic matter is quickly destroyed, and downward-percolating water leaches the soil, leaving behind compounds of iron and aluminum. It is hard to distinguish the horizons in such soils. Laterites are therefore characterized only by a horizon with a large part of its silica, previously combined with iron and aluminum, removed or altered by weathering. This often produces a hard layer called an *oxic horizon*, which is bright red or orange in colour, caused by a high concentration of clay-sized minerals in the **B** horizon, mainly sesquioxides. The natural vegetation on most laterites is savanna, while tropical rainforest occurs over less well-developed lateritic soils. The soils tend to be of low fertility (as explained in Unit 44),

except where they develop from alluvial or volcanic deposits. These soils are found in Hawaii, Puerto Rico, other Caribbean islands, and in other areas of the world (Figure 45.12).

The low fertility of laterites has given rise to a pattern of *shifting* or *slash-and-burn (swidden) cultivation*. The land is farmed for only a year or two and is then left for many years to renew its nutrients naturally. Population pressures in some parts of the world, such as Nigeria and Amazonia, have altered this agricultural system, and the rapid deterioration of this soil's already limited fertility is usually the result.

Warmer, wetter climatic zones host **red-yellow podzolic soils**, distinguished by a **B** horizon with strong

From the Fieldnotes

Figure 45.12 'What should have been one day in Suva, the capital of Fiji, turned into a week due to schedule complications, and we had an opportunity to study Viti Levu's interesting human as well as physical geography. Driving through the interior was challenging because maps and reality seemed to differ; but homesteads and villages were interesting and welcoming. The island has some fertile soils, but much of the centre was dominated by laterites which, when fully developed, are deep (often dozens of metres) and characteristically red-coloured due to the preponderance of iron and aluminum in the oxic horizon. The upper part of this profile of a local laterite shows the virtual absence of humus in these soils. Note also the virtual absence of colour change from very near the top of the soil all the way down.'

LINK

clay accumulation (Figure 45.13). The native vegetation of these red-yellow podzolics (US: **ultisols**) may have been forest or savanna grassland. They contain at least a few minerals that may be subject to weathering. These soils may well be luvisols that have been subjected to greater weathering. In eastern North America, red-yellow podzolics lie to the south of the southern border of Pleistocene glaciation, and luvisols lie to the north. Therefore, red-yellow podzolics are older, some being pre-Pleistocene in origin, whereas luvisols are of Pleistocene age or younger. Red-yellow podzolics are often associated with the farming of cotton and peanuts.

The Spatial Distribution of Soils

It is now possible to return to the hypothetical continent shown in Figure 45.2 to model the distribution of Canadian soil orders. Note that between the laterites of the southeast, the solonetzic soils of the southwest, and the podzols of the north, there lie zones of chernozems, ultisols, and luvisols (the last developing under different climatic conditions in two separate areas).

Soils of North America

The distribution of soils in the real world is more complicated. Figure 45.14 shows the spatial pattern for North America. The climatic relationships are quite clear with soils such as podzols and solonetzic soils, but complications arise because other soils, such as regosols, are caused by different factors. Thus, Appalachian soils in Atlantic Canada, because of their highland environment, are poorly developed, whereas the regosols of the lower Fraser Valley are at an incipient stage of development because they occur on flood-plain sediments that are sporadically flooded. This fact accounts for their relatively recent age. Terrain can complicate the actual pattern even further. The Rocky Mountain region of Canada, for instance, is a complex mosaic of podzolic, regosolic, organic, and cryosolic soils. It is therefore difficult to place all the soil orders that are not directly related to climate on a map of this scale.

The World Soil Map

At the global scale there are many distinct relationships between soils and climate, but there are also some differences in detail, as Figure 45.15 demonstrates. The relationship between soils and climates is quite clear in central Eurasia. Soil types vary from south to north, changing from solonetzic soils to alfisols, then to podzols, and finally to cryosols. These variations parallel changes in climate from desert through steppe and microthermal to polar climates (see Figure 16.2). A similar progression may be observed in corresponding parts of North America. Perhaps the most obvious relationship at the global scale is that between the desert climates and the solonetzes and regosols. Notice, too, that in the world-scale classification of soils, rock-dominated mountain

Figure 45.13   Profile of red-yellow podzolic (ultisol), exhibiting a **B** horizon rich in clay.

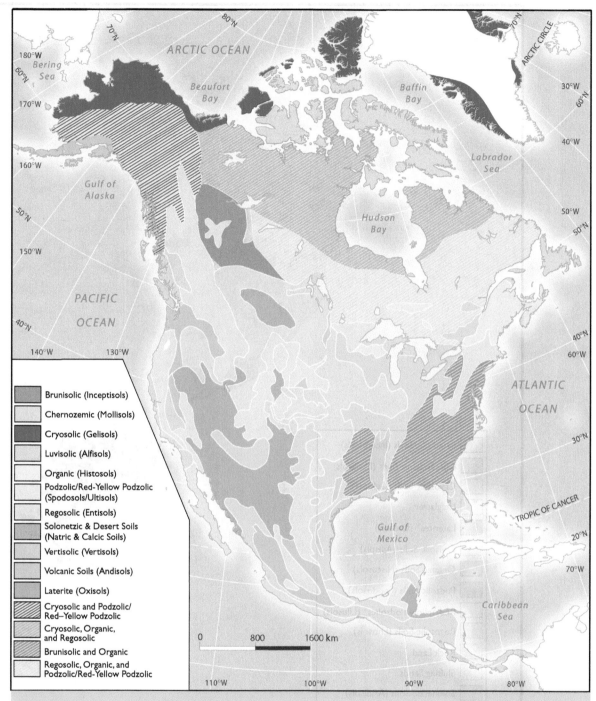

Figure 45.14 Generalized spatial distribution of soils in North America using the Canadian Soil Orders (US Soil Orders are in parentheses) and other general soil types (outside of Canada).

areas (as is also the case at the continental scale of Figure 45.14) and ice-covered terrain have been grouped into separate categories.

Despite the clear relationships between climate and soil types at this macro scale, similar climates do not always correspond to similar soil types. The humid subtropical climate (**Cfa**) is also a case in point. This climate type prevails in the southeastern parts of the five major continents (refer to Figure 16.2), but another look at Figure 45.15 shows that the soil types in these areas vary. Only in the southeastern United States and south-

eastern China do we find ultisols. Southeastern parts of South America around the Rio de la Plata exhibit chernozems, whereas southeastern Africa possesses alfisols. And east-central Australia, an area of predominantly humid subtropical climate, is also dominated by alfisols. If you continue to compare Figures 45.15 and 16.2, you will be able to pick out additional spatial discrepancies between climate and soils. This underscores that other factors in soil formation, such as parent material and the way people use soil, also help to determine the prevailing type of soil.

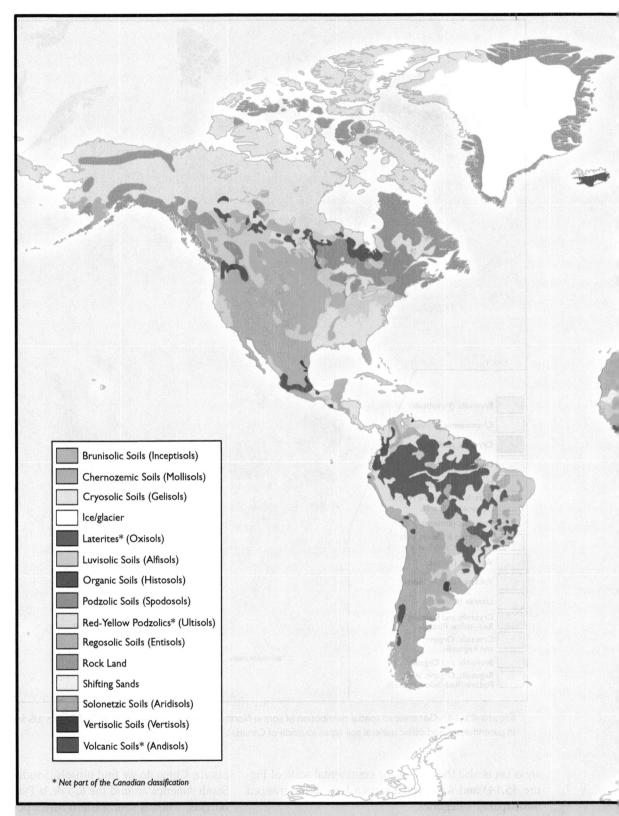

Brunisolic Soils (Inceptisols)

Chernozemic Soils (Mollisols)

Cryosolic Soils (Gelisols)

Ice/glacier

Laterites* (Oxisols)

Luvisolic Soils (Alfisols)

Organic Soils (Histosols)

Podzolic Soils (Spodosols)

Red-Yellow Podzolics* (Ultisols)

Regosolic Soils (Entisols)

Rock Land

Shifting Sands

Solonetzic Soils (Aridisols)

Vertisolic Soils (Vertisols)

Volcanic Soils* (Andisols)

Not part of the Canadian classification

Figure 45.15   Global distribution of soils.

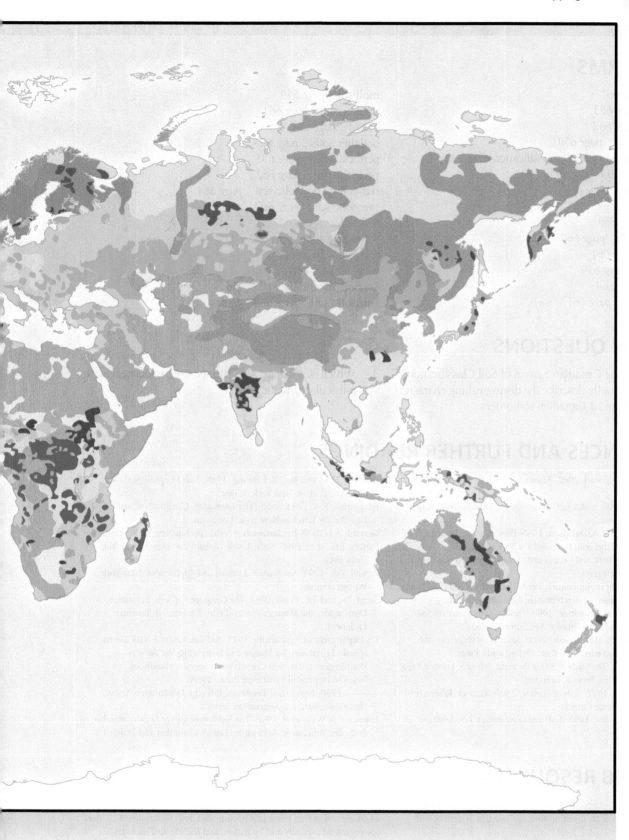

KEY TERMS

alfisol   *page 661*
andisol   *page 663*
aridisol   *page 662*
brunisolic soil   *page 659*
Canadian System of Soil Classification   *page 656*
chernozemic soil   *page 659*
cryosolic soil   *page 660*
entisol   *page 662*
gelisol   *page 660*
gleysolic soils   *page 660*
histosol   *page 661*
inceptisol   *page 659*
laterite   *page 664*
luvisolic soil   *page 661*

mollisol   *page 659*
organic soil   *page 661*
oxisol   *page 664*
pedalfer soils   *page 655*
pedocal soils   *page 655*
podzolic soil   *page 662*
red-yellow podzolic soil   *page 664*
regosolic soil   *page 662*
soil order   *page 657*
solonetzic soil   *page 662*
spodosol   *page 662*
ultisol   *page 666*
US Soil Taxonomy   *page 656*
vertisolic soil   *page 663*

REVIEW QUESTIONS

1. What is the Canadian System of Soil Classification?
2. List and briefly describe the distinguishing characteristics of the 12 Canadian soil orders.
3. Which Canadian soil orders are associated with particular climatic zones?

REFERENCES AND FURTHER READINGS

Ashman, M., and G. Puri. 2002. *Essential Soil Science*. Malden, Mass.: Blackwell.

Birkeland, P.W. 1999. *Soils and Geomorphology*, 3rd edn. New York: Oxford Univ. Press.

Bridges, E.M., and D.A. Davidson. 1986. *Principles and Applications of Soil Geography*, 2nd edn. London/New York: Longman.

Buol, S.W., et al. 1989. *Soil Genesis and Classification*, 3rd edn. Ames: Iowa State Univ. Press.

Canada Department of Agriculture. 1970. *The System of Soil Classification for Canada*. Ottawa: Research Branch, Agriculture Canada.

Canada Soil Survey Committee. 1998. *The Canadian System of Soil Classification*, 3rd edn. Ottawa: Agriculture Canada.

Charman, P., and B. Murphy, eds. 2000. *Soils: Their Properties and Management*, 2nd edn. New York: Oxford Univ. Press.

Clarke, G.R. 1971. *The Study of Soil in the Field*, 5th edn. London/New York: Oxford Univ. Press [Clarendon].

Clayton, J.S., et al. 1977. *Soils of Canada*, 2 vols. Ottawa: Research Branch, Agriculture Canada.

Ellis, S., and A. Mellor. 1995. *Soils and Environment*. London/New York: Routledge.

Fanning, D.S., and M.C.B. Fanning. 1989. *Soil: Morphology, Genesis, and Classification*. New York: Wiley.

Fitzpatrick, E.A. 1983. *Soils: Their Formation, Classification, and Distribution*. London/New York: Longman.

Gerrard, A.J. 2000. *Fundamentals of Soils*. London/New York: Routledge.

Parton, T.R., et al. 1996. *Soils: A New Global View*. New Haven: Yale Univ. Press.

Rowell, D.L. 1994. *Soil Science: Methods and Applications*. New York: Wiley/Longman.

Steila, D., and T.E. Pond. 1989. *The Geography of Soils: Formation, Distribution, and Management*, 2nd edn. Totowa, NJ: Rowman & Littlefield.

US Department of Agriculture. 1975. *Soil Taxonomy: A Basic System of Soil Classification for Making and Interpreting Soil Surveys*. Washington: USDA, Soil Conservation Service, Handbook No. 436 (reprinted by Krieger Publ., 1988).

———. 1998. *Keys to Soil Taxonomy*, 8th edn. Washington: USDA, Natural Resources Conservation Service.

Valentine, K.W.G., et al. 1998. *The Soil Landscapes of British Columbia*, 2nd edn. Vancouver: Agriculture British Columbia and Trafford.

 ## WEB RESOURCES

sis.agr.gc.ca/cansis/taxa/cssc3 This Agriculture Canada site has the online version of the most up-to-date Canadian System of Soil Classification.

soils.usda.gov/technical/classification/taxonomy The USDA-NRCS National Soil Survey has the second edition of *Soil Taxonomy, A Basic System for Soil Classification for Making and Interpreting Soil Surveys* available for download on this site.

www.itc.nl/~rossiter/research/rsrch_ss_class.html A compendium of online soil survey information, compiled by D.G. Rossiter. Materials are organized topically and by nation, and the site also includes a section on frequently asked questions.

Biogeographic Processes

Objectives

- To discuss the process of photosynthesis and relate it to climatic controls.

- To introduce the concept of ecosystems and highlight the important energy flows within ecosystems.

- To outline the factors influencing the geographic dispersal of plant and animal species within the biosphere.

The soil is located at the base of the biosphere. Not only is the soil itself a living, maturing entity, but life exists within the soil layer in many forms. This unit and the next look at the most obvious evidence of the Earth's 'life layer'—the natural vegetation. Biogeography, as noted in Unit 43, consists of two fields: *phytogeography* (plant geography) and *zoogeography* (animal geography). The plants are dealt with first.

Dynamics of the Biosphere

The story of the development of life on Earth parallels that of the formation of the atmosphere. The earliest atmosphere, about 4 billion years ago, was rich in gases such as methane, ammonia, carbon dioxide, and water vapour. A half-century ago, a scientist named Stanley Miller filled a flask with what he believed may have been a sample of this early atmosphere. He then subjected the contents to electrical discharges (to simulate lightning) and to boiling (much of the crust was volcanic and would have been red hot as it erupted). This resulted in the formation of amino acids, the building blocks of protein, which, in turn, are the constituents of all living things on Earth. Another scientist tried freezing the same components, and out of that experiment came organic material that forms one of the ingredients of deoxyribonucleic acid (DNA), a key to life. It is believed that these experiments replicated what actually happened on Earth about 4 billion years ago, events that led to the formation of the first complex molecules. The earliest forms of life—single-celled bacteria and algae—came from these molecules.

Photosynthesis

When the first bacteria colonized parts of the Earth's surface, a process could begin that would be essential to advancing life—**photosynthesis**. This process requires solar energy, carbon dioxide, and water. In those ancient bacteria, the first conversion of water (H_2O) and carbon dioxide (CO_2) under solar energy yielded *carbohydrates* (an organic compound and food substance) and oxygen (O_2). Starting about 2 billion years ago, photosynthetic organisms increased the oxygen content of the atmosphere from 1 per cent to 20 per cent. The atmosphere became sufficiently rich not only in oxygen but also in stratospheric ozone (O_3), and more complex life forms could now evolve as the intensifying ozone layer increasingly afforded protection from solar ultraviolet radiation. Organisms eventually evolved in the aquatic environment and colonized the landmasses. The first land plants colonized the Earth more than 400 million years ago and were followed by 'higher' forms of life (Figure 46.1).

A fundamental requirement for photosynthesis is a green pigment, *chlorophyll*, at the surface of the part of the plant where the process is taking place. The colour of this pigment in part ensures that the wavelength of light absorbed from the Sun is correct for photosynthesis. This produces the dominant green colour of plants. If photosynthesis required a different wavelength of light, the Earth's vegetated landscapes might look blue or orange! As to the need for light or solar energy, plants constantly compete for the maximum exposure to this essential ingredient of life. Some plants have adapted to survival in low-light environments, but mostly every leaf turns towards the Sun.

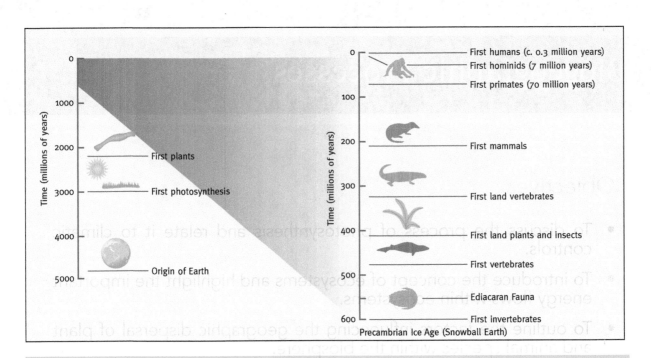

Figure 46.1 Development of the biosphere on Earth—the time scale of life.

Figure 46.2 A nearly continuous canopy of leafy vegetation marks the tropical rainforest as seen from the air (or the ground). The tall trees have spread their crowns until they interlock, competing for every ray of sunlight. This is an expanse of rainforest in eastern Bolivia.

Where solar energy arrives on Earth in the greatest quantities, the tall trees of the equatorial and tropical forests soar skyward, spreading their leafy crowns in dense canopies as they vie for every ray of the Sun (Figure 46.2).

Photosynthesis, therefore, is critical to life on Earth. It removes carbon dioxide from the atmosphere and substitutes oxygen. Humans could not live as they do in an oxygen-poor atmosphere, and had photosynthesis not altered the Earth's primitive envelope of gases, the evolution of life would have taken a very different course. Thus life depends on plants in a very direct way. If the tropical rainforests are destroyed, as is continuing to happen (see Unit 17), the atmosphere will sustain damage of a kind that cannot be accurately predicted.

One result of such destruction could possibly involve not only oxygen depletion but also, through the relative increase of carbon dioxide, a general warming of the planet—a further enhancement of the greenhouse effect. Photosynthesis also produces carbohydrates, which nourish plants and, consequently, animals and people. The natural production of organic food substances would cease entirely without photosynthesis. In addition, the fossil fuels (coal, oil, natural gas) were produced from carbohydrates originally formed during photosynthesis.

Limitations of Photosynthesis   Combining what we have learned about climatic patterns with what we know about photosynthesis, we can deduce where the process goes on most productively. Solar energy is most abundant in the tropical latitudes, and there, in general terms, photosynthesis is most active. However, some significant limitations must be recognized. In equatorial and tropical

latitudes, the high solar energy also generates heat, and heat increases the plants' rates of **respiration**. Respiration runs counter to photosynthesis because it breaks down available carbohydrates, combines them with oxygen, and yields carbon dioxide, water, and biochemical energy, which sustains life. When leafy plant surfaces become hot, therefore, heightened respiration diminishes the effectiveness of photosynthesis. The rate of photosynthesis is tied to temperature. A temperature of 10°C is needed before the process takes place. The rate doubles for every 10° rise up to an optimum temperature of 30°C. At temperatures of 35–40°C heat stress affects plants and may result in death.

Photosynthetic/Respiration Formula

Photosynthesis>

$$6CO_2 + 6H_2O \leftrightarrow C_6H_{12}O_6 + 6O_2$$

<Respiration

| **Carbon dioxide + Water** | Combined with Photons (light energy absorbed by chlorophyll) | **Heat** (2830J) (low-grade energy lost to the atmosphere or ecosystem) **Glucose** (sugars) **Carbohydrates** (starches) **Oxygen** (respired/lost to the atmosphere) |

Another limiting factor is the availability of water. Carbon dioxide from the atmosphere is not available for photosynthesis until it dissolves in water at the plant surface. Thus, continued photosynthesis requires moisture. Small holes in the leaf surface (*stomata*) are openings for the water that arrives from the roots and stem of the plant for **transpiration**. Oxygen is also degassed via the stomata. The more water there is at the stomata, the greater the amount of carbon dioxide that can be dissolved and the greater the production of plant food. Our knowledge of the map of moisture (see Figure 11.16) is an important aid in understanding the distributional pattern of photosynthesis.

Several other processes occur at or near the leaf surface as photosynthesis and respiration proceed. Obviously, when heat and moisture are present, evaporation will occur. Evaporation from the leaf surfaces has a drying effect, which in turn affects photosynthesis. Plants also lose moisture in the same way that humans do, through transpiration. These two processes in combination, as learned in Unit 11, are referred to as *evapotranspiration*. It was learned from that discussion that an intimate relationship exists between the amount of moisture lost in evapotranspiration (see Figure 11.15) and the production of living organic plant matter.

Phytomass   The total living organic matter produced in a given area is referred to as that area's **biomass**. Technically, biomass refers to all living organic things, including

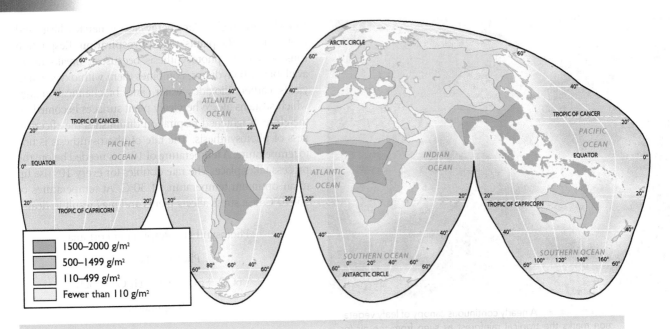

Figure 46.3 Global distribution of annual biomass productivity (in grams per square metre of dry biomass matter).

an area's fauna, so the plant matter should be called the **phytomass**. Biomass is expressed in terms of weight—that is, in grams per square metre—and the weight of plant matter is so dominant that the terms *biomass* and *phytomass* tend to be used synonymously. Figure 46.3 maps, in very general terms, the global distribution of annual biomass productivity. Note the overall similarities between certain climatic patterns and this configuration. Biomass productivity is greatest in humid equatorial and tropical lowlands; it is at a minimum in desert, highland, and high-latitude zones. But this is true only for the *natural* vegetation, not for cultivated crops. As the map suggests, forests contain the largest biomass. Replace the tropical forest with a banana plantation, and photosynthesis and biomass will decline precipitously.

To understand fully the dynamics of the biosphere, we must appreciate certain other concepts, capabilities, and limitations.

Concept of Environment or Habitat

To speak of environment or habitat is essentially a holistic approach that includes physical factors such as climate, geology, soil, topography, and also time and biotic factors. Biotic factors are caused by organisms. To a great extent the physiology of all organisms reflects the environment, even though certain growth processes (at times) are strictly genetically controlled, e.g., leaf aspect of some trees and other plants varies according to a *circadian cycle* of about 24 hours in length. Most other interactions are directly or indirectly affected by the relative availability of basic requirements such as water, heat, oxygen, carbon dioxide, and food or nutrients.

Concept of Tolerance

All organisms have **tolerance limits** beyond which they will not grow in a given environment or along an environmental gradient. These are controlled by the presence or absence of a certain requirement (*limiting factors*). These factors are highly complex as the various environmental gradients (water, heat, etc.) influence all plants and, consequently, all animals. Tolerance is a *hardiness factor* that enables plants to withstand harmful conditions. The reverse of tolerance is either *evasion* or *avoidance*.

There are two aspects of tolerance:

1. *Stress* is a deficiency or a surfeit of a factor that affects photosynthesis, e.g., light, low or high temperatures, carbon dioxide, water, nutrients, or high winds. Most stresses increase as the magnitude of an event increases—wind stress on a tree trunk, for example, increases with increasing wind speed.

2. *Disturbance* involves low-magnitude frequent and higher-magnitude infrequent catastrophic events, such as high winds, fire, snow, ice and ice storms, flooding, storm waves, slope instability, volcanic eruptions, human activities, etc. These events adversely affect the establishment, growth, and survival of the plant or plants, or destroys or damages the ecosystem.

Evasion and avoidance are attempts to prevent injury. Xerophytic plants may *evade* drought conditions by becoming dormant. Other plants (succulents, cacti) may *avoid* drought conditions by developing (through evolution) hard, thick cuticles on their leaves to reduce transpiration.

Adaptation

There are two types of adaptation. The first type, *acquired adaptation*, or morphological or physiological change to a plant or plants during their lifetime, usually is a response to disturbance or stress. These changes are not passed on to successive generations. A good example of this is bonsai, the Japanese art of pruning and binding a plant's roots to turn it into a miniature with a pleasing shape, so that a Japanese maple tree (*Acer palmatum*) that naturally grows to 6–10 m in height can be stunted to less than 1 m in height (Figure 46.4). The second type, *genetic adaptation*, involves morphological or physiological changes brought about by genetic mutations and passed on to succeeding generations (evolutionary change via the process of natural selection).

There are three main types of adaptation strategy. First, in *competition strategy* the more successful competitors are able to exploit resources for photosynthesis. This usually occurs in environments with low levels of disturbance and stress, for example, in tropical rainforests, which are characterized by dense communities with many different species. Many species of trees in these conditions grow quickly to exploit canopy openings (e.g., when a large tree dies and falls) and thereby maximize photosynthesis. These species, when mature, are very tall and have extensive (buttressed) root systems. Many species are shade-tolerant so as to survive in the low light conditions under the canopy and on the forest floor. The same strategy works in all types of forest communities.

Second, *stress-tolerance strategy* is characteristic of very active sites (i.e., in constant flux) with high levels of stress,

such as seashores, slopes, and agricultural land. There are two types of active sites:

1. Areas subjected to fires, grazing, browsing, and erosion. These processes kill plants or parts of plants and remove plant biomass from a habitat.
2. Areas subject to frost, ice, disease, and drought. These processes kill plants or parts of plants but do not remove biomass from the habitat.

Plants that survive under these conditions are called *ruderals*, and they have special structures or functions to be able to endure these environments. Some have adapted buds or nodes that enable them to regrow after a fire (e.g., grasses), flood, overgrazing, or even burial. Some species have seeds that can survive ingestion by animals; other species are fast-growing and can broadcast abundant seed before they are killed off.

The third type of adaptation strategy, *phenological adaptation*, occurs in response to constant or recurring natural phenomena or conditions especially related to climate and seasonality. The most important adaptations of this kind are:

1. *Annualism* (hence some plants are called 'annuals'). This adaptation is very common in the temperate zone. This life cycle has a seed dormancy phase during the high-stress season (usually winter). All other phases are completed in the spring and summer, including death. These plants exhibit very fast growth. They leave dormant seeds to over-winter.
2. *Ephemeralism.* This adaptation is found in arid areas, both in deserts and in the tundra. There is seed dormancy during extended dry or cold periods. The plants grow quickly, mature, flower, and set seed during the very short wet period when the 'desert blooms' or the very short warm period in the tundra.
3. *Xericism.* This habit is used by perennial desert plants adapted to drought (xerophytes). There are two main types of adaptation to drought:

   a) Adoption of a *succulent habit*, e.g., cacti (Figure 46.5). These types of plants have three traits: very few leaves with widely spaced stomata, or the stomata occur on the underside of the leaves (this reduces the loss of water vapour); thick fleshy bodies for water storage; extensive shallow root systems to exploit infiltration water from infrequent periods of rainfall.

   b) Some plants adopt a *deep rooting habit*, e.g., mesquite (*Prosopis* spp.), which has very long tap roots to utilize groundwater (Figure 46.6).

Figure 46.4 The acquired adaptation of this Japanese maple as a result of bonsai—a human intervention to create a 'miniature' tree—does not get passed to subsequent generations because the genetic makeup of the tree has not been altered.

Types of Range

All plants and animals have two types of species ranges: a *potential (tolerance) range* and an *actual (ecological) range*. The potential range is defined by the distribution of habitable conditions for that particular species and is governed

Figure 46.5 The desert cactus is a succulent with a shallow, extensive root system to access infiltration water when it rains.

Figure 46.6 The mesquite tree, common in the US Southwest and Mexico, has long tap roots—over 25 m—to reach groundwater.

by environmental factors such as climate, soils, and vegetation. The potential range is usually far more extensive than where the species is actually found. The actual range, on the other hand, is where the species is presently located.

This range is restricted in size by competition with other species, barriers—such as mountain ranges, seas, and deserts—and the migrational ability of the species. Most birds, for example, can fly and so they have a great deal of migrational ability. Thus, their actual ranges may be quite large. On the other hand, tortoises are quite slow, so their migrational ability is low and their actual ranges are small.

The same is true of plants. Plants that bear small and/or winged seeds are more likely to be able to distribute their seeds farther than other species because they can be transported in the wind or in the guts of birds or animals. Plants producing large seeds that cannot be windblown or survive being eaten by birds or animals will have a smaller range.

Ecosystems and Energy Flows

An **ecosystem** (from **eco**logical **system**) is a linkage of plants and animals to their environment in an open energy system: solar energy is absorbed, and chemical and heat energy are lost in several ways. You can observe part of an ecosystem in action in a sunlit freshwater pond (Figure 46.7). Energy from sunlight is taken up in photosynthesis by microscopic green plants called *phytoplankton* (you may be able to see these in the aggregate as a greenish sheen on the water), which in turn produce carbohydrate (the food substance). Such food-producing plants are called **autotrophs**, and they provide sustenance for small larvae and other tiny life forms in the pond, collectively called *zooplankton*. Zooplankton is eaten by small fish, and these fish are later consumed by larger fish. Meanwhile plants and animals die in the pond and are broken down by decomposers, thereby releasing chemicals back into the water to be used once more by autotrophs in the production of food. Thus food energy passes from organism to organism in the ecosystem represented by our pond, generating a food chain or, more correctly, a **food web**. Food chains or webs exist in all ecosystems, on land as well as in the oceans.

LINK

Ecological Efficiency

It is very difficult to measure precisely the production and consumption of energy in a food chain or web. Research has shown, however, that only a fraction of the food produced by autotrophs—as little as 15 per cent—is actually consumed by the next participants in the food chain. For example, the zooplankton in the pond consumes only about 15 per cent of the food energy yielded by the phytoplankton. A still smaller percentage of the zooplankton is eaten by the smallest fish. Each of these groups—phytoplankton, zooplankton, small fish, and larger fish—along the food chain or web is called a **trophic (feeding) level**. In the boreal forest, the autotrophs are the trees and other plants; at the next trophic level are the animals that eat (browse or graze) these plants, the **herbivores** such as various types of deer. In turn, the animals that eat herbivores (as well as other animals), the **carnivores**, form a still higher trophic level (cougars, wolves).

From the Fieldnotes

Figure 46.7 *'A pond like this is a crucial part of the local ecosystem. The Sun's energy reaches the surface of this lake in Britain's Lake District, where phytoplankton (microscopic green plants) convert it through photosynthesis into carbohydrate, a food substance. Tiny life forms, zooplankton, feed on this carbohydrate, and small fish eat the zooplankton. Larger fish feed on the smaller fish, and the food chain continues.'*

Central to the way the biosphere operates is the loss of chemical food energy at each trophic level. We have already noted that a mere 15 per cent of the food energy generated by the autotrophs in the pond is passed on to the herbivores (the zooplankton). Most of the primary production is not utilized by herbivores and is decomposed. Only 11 per cent of the zooplankton reaches the carnivores (the smallest fish), and just 5 per cent of these go on to the larger fish when they eat the smaller ones. Most of the energy is used for respiration and other metabolic processes or goes to waste (is voided as feces). These numbers indicate a very low efficiency, but they reflect efficiency at *each trophic level* in the pond. We also can estimate efficiency for entire ecosystems, averaging the efficiencies at different levels. Desert ecosystems have the lowest efficiency of all, with values of less than 0.1 per cent. Swamps in tropical areas have the highest, but even they average as little as 4 per cent.

Several important consequences arise from the various efficiencies in ecosystems. First there must always be a large number of **primary producers** to support smaller numbers of herbivores and even fewer carnivores. The masses of living material at each trophic level therefore stack up like a pyramid, as in Figure 46.8. Because only about 10 per cent of the energy produced in the form of food is passed from one stage to another, to obtain enough food the animals at the higher trophic levels must have large territorial areas that provide enough of the species at the lower trophic level. This explains why large carnivores such as lions require a wide territorial range.

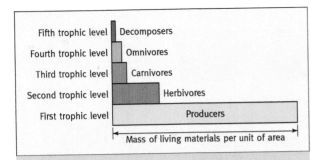

Figure 46.8 Mass of living materials per unit of area in different trophic levels of an ecosystem.

Another consequence is that because food and energy move along a chain or web in only one direction, the whole system collapses if earlier links of the chain are broken. Thus, the removal of the autotrophs (grass) by too many rabbits in Australia caused the breakdown of an entire ecosystem. A related consequence of the chain-like structure is the fact that undesirable materials can be passed along and concentrated by the ecosystem. The insecticide DDD was applied in Clear Lake, California, to kill gnats. It was sprayed onto the water at a concentration of 0.02 parts per million (ppm). The DDD density was 5 ppm in the plankton, 15 ppm in the herbivores feeding on the plankton, 100 ppm in the fish, and 1600 ppm in the grebes (birds) that ate the fish. The grebes died. It is therefore important to understand the nature of food-energy flow through ecological systems.

Food energy moves along two **trophic pathways** in any ecosystem:

1. a grazing pathway: autotroph → herbivore → carnivore → decomposers
2. a detrital pathway: autotroph → decomposers (Figure 46.9)

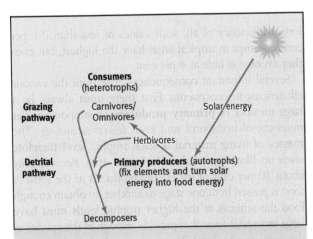

Figure 46.9 The two trophic pathways: grazing and detrital.

Biogeochemical Cycles

While energy moves through ecosytems along grazing and detrital pathways, biological, geological, and chemical materials are involved in numerous cycles from one point in an ecosystem to another. All cycles are themselves systems that are composed of reservoirs or storages (sinks) and flows (or fluxes). Biogeochemical cycles involve three different forms of interactions: biological, geological, and chemical.

LINK

Additions of nutrients into an ecosystem occur by:

1. The weathering of rocks, sediments, and soils
2. Atmospheric inputs such as in rainwater or snow and dust
3. Biological inputs from vegetation and animals
4. Fertilizer input by humans.

Outputs of nutrients from an ecosystem occur by:

1. Erosion
2. Leaching
3. Gaseous losses
4. The migration of vegetation, animals, and humans
5. The harvesting of crops and their export to cities and abroad.

Biogeochemical cycling in the soil is influenced by the decomposition of organic matter, the type and amount of soil nutrients, the type and amount of cation adsorption onto colloid surfaces, and the cation exchange process and cation exchange capacity of a particular soil.

There are five biogeochemical cycles: water (hydrologic), carbon, nitrogen, phosphorus, and sulphur. The water cycle has been discussed in Unit 11 (see Figure 11.6) and is intimately associated with another material cycle, the rock cycle, considered in Unit 23. The rock cycle is the major system in which the biogeochemical cycles take place (see Figure 23.11).

Water, carbon, nitrogen, phosphorus, and sulphur are very important to organisms because they make up essential chemical components of their cells. Carbon, nitrogen, and sulphur occur as solid and gaseous compounds in the environment, while water is found in all three phases (solid, liquid, and gas). The four cycles involving these minerals have components that move over great distances in the atmosphere. Phosphorus does not form a gaseous compound so it is cycled locally. Humans affect all of these cycles at both local and global scales by using various parts and/or products of the systems, e.g., fossil fuels, organic fertilizers.

The Carbon Cycle

Carbon is essential to life. It is contained in proteins, carbohydrates, and other molecules. All life is based on carbon (hence the term 'carbon-based units'). Carbon makes up about 0.04 per cent of the atmosphere as carbon dioxide (CO_2). It is also present in the ocean, where it occurs in several forms: as dissolved CO_2 (both inorganic and organic), and in carbonate and bicarbonate form. Carbon is also present in sedimentary rocks such as limestones, dolostones, and shales, and in the form of fossil fuels such as coal and petroleum. Plants, algae, and some forms of bacteria remove CO_2 from the air during photosynthesis or metabolism and fix it or incorporate it into chemical compounds such as sugars, which are then available to consumers when the plant or other organism is eaten. Plants use sugar to make other compounds. Thus, the fixing process incorporates abiotic carbon into the biological compounds of the primary producers. These compounds are usually used as fuel for *cellular respiration* for the primary producers, the consumers, and the decomposers. The process of cellular respiration returns CO_2 to the atmosphere. A similar **carbon cycle** occurs in aquatic ecosystems between aquatic organisms and CO_2 dissolved in the water (Figure 46.10).

Sometimes the carbon in biological molecules is not returned back to the abiotic environment for long periods, for example, a large amount of carbon is stored as tree wood where it stays for several hundreds of years. Another

such instance occurs when carbon is stored by the burial of partially decayed forests as vast coal beds for millions of years. Organic compounds of unicellular marine organisms entombed in sedimentary rocks probably gave rise to oil and natural gas deposits (fossil fuels), first discovered and produced in Canada at Oil Springs in southwest Ontario (Figure 46.11).

The carbon stored in fossil fuels is now being returned to the atmosphere by combustion (burning) in homes, factories, cars, ships, planes, etc. The process causes the organic molecules to rapidly oxidize and convert into CO_2 and water. The process also produces heat and light.

The carbon–silicate cycle occurs on a geological time scale over millions of years. It is formed by the interaction of the carbon and silicon cycles. Aspects of this cycle are discussed in the units on weathering (Unit 29) and karst processes (Unit 35). This cycle involves atmospheric CO_2 and the carbonation and solution processes. Hydrogen ions enter silicate-rich minerals such as feldspars and change their chemical composition and release calcium ions (Ca^{2+}). These ions, along with calcium bicarbonate ions, wash into groundwater and streams and make their way to

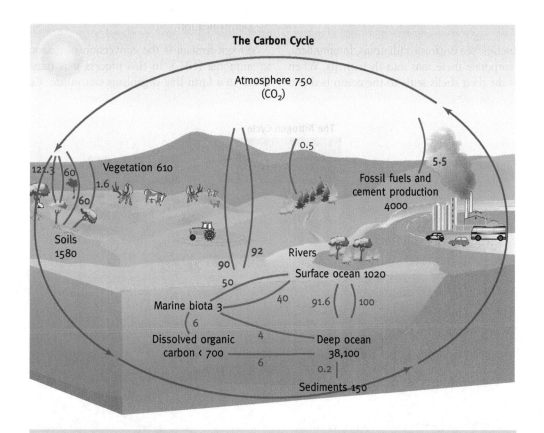

Figure 46.10 The carbon cycle is understood in terms of carbon storage in 'sinks' or 'reservoirs' and of fluxes, i.e., the carbon that is cycling within the system from land, water, biota, and human activities into the atmosphere and back again. The sinks (black numbers on diagram) are measured in gigatons (billions of tons); the fluxes (blue numbers) are gigatons/yr.

Figure 46.11 Oil production at Oil Springs, Ontario, c. 1870. The first commercial oil well in North America began producing here in 1858 after the discovery of oil in this area of Southwestern Ontario.

LINK

form oozes (e.g., globigerina ooze). The oozes are covered by sediments and are cemented to form very pure carbonate rock (chalk) beds several kilometres thick. Plate tectonics uplifts and exposes these rocks, and weathering returns CO_2 to the water and the atmosphere to be cycled again. Subduction may bury carbonate rocks and the heat and pressure caused by deep burial may partially melt the rocks, releasing CO_2 that is vented into the atmosphere in volcanic eruptions.

The Nitrogen Cycle

The **nitrogen cycle** (Figure 46.12) is crucial to all organisms because nitrogen is an essential part of biological molecules, especially proteins and nucleic acids. The atmosphere is composed of 78 per cent nitrogen gas (N_2). Atmospheric nitrogen is not stable and does not combine with other elements unless it is broken apart; only after this occurs can the nitrogen help to form proteins and nucleic acids. There are five steps in the nitrogen cycle between the abiotic environment and its use by organisms. Bacteria are exclusively involved in all of these except assimilation:

1. Nitrogen fixation
2. Nitrification
3. Assimilation
4. Ammonification
5. Denitrification

Nitrogen fixation is the conversion of gaseous nitrogen to ammonia (NH_3). In this process it is transformed or 'fixed' to a form that organisms can utilize. Combustion,

the sea. Microscopic sea organisms (diatoms, foraminifera, radiolaria) incorporate these ions into their shells. When the organisms die their shells settle to the ocean bed and

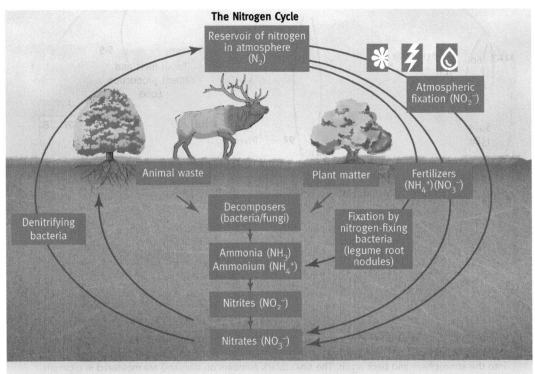

Figure 46.12 The nitrogen cycle.

lightning discharges, volcanicity, and industrial processes all break apart and fix considerable amounts of nitrogen. Nitrogen-fixing bacteria (including cyanobacteria) fix biological nitrogen in the soil and in aquatic environments. They use an enzyme called *nitrogenase* to split atmospheric nitrogen and combine the resulting atoms with hydrogen. Nitrogenase can only function in aerobic but wet conditions (with about 50 per cent of soil pore spaces filled with water). Some nitrogen-fixing bacteria live beneath layers of oxygen-excluding slime on the roots of certain plants while others, such as *rhizobium*, live inside nodules on the roots of leguminous plants (peas, beans, and some woody plants). Rhizobium and their hosts have a mutualistic relationship where the bacteria get carbohydrates from the host plants and the plants are supplied with a usable form of nitrogen by the bacteria. Some filamentous cyanobacteria have special oxygen-excluding cells that function as sites for nitrogen fixation.

Nitrification is the conversion of ammonia (NH_3) or ammonium (NH_4) (ammonium is formed when water reacts with ammonia) to nitrate (NO_3). Soil bacteria perform this conversion by a two-step process: (1) some soil bacteria convert ammonia or ammonium to nitrite (NO_2); then (2) other bacteria oxidize nitrite to form nitrate. This process supplies the nitrifying bacteria with energy.

Assimilation is where plant roots absorb the nitrate, ammonia, or ammonium and incorporate the nitrate in these molecules into plant proteins and nucleic acids. When animals eat the plants, they assimilate nitrogen by taking plant nitrogen compounds (amino acids) and converting them to animal proteins.

Ammonification is the conversion of biological nitrogen compounds into ammonia and ammonium ions. The process begins when organisms produce nitrogen-containing waste products such as urea in urine and uric acid (in bird droppings). Some nitrogen compounds are also released by the decay of organisms. Assimilation releases nitrogen into the abiotic environment as ammonia. This process is performed by ammonifying bacteria in the soil and aquatic sites. The ammonia produced enters the nitrogen cycle and is available for nitrification and assimilation processes.

Denitrification involves the reduction of nitrate (NO_3) to gaseous nitrogen. Denitrifying bacteria reverse the action of the nitrogen-fixing and nitrifying bacteria by returning nitrogen to the atmosphere. Denitrifying bacteria prefer oxygen-starved (anaerobic) environments deep in the soil near the groundwater table or wet environments such as wetlands or at the feet of slopes.

The Phosphorus Cycle

Phosphorus does not form compounds in a gaseous phase and does not appreciably enter the atmosphere (except during dust storms). **Phosphorus cycles** are local and occur between the land and the ocean. As water runs over phosphorus-containing rocks, such as those containing apatite and other phosphorus-rich minerals, it gradually wears away the surface and carries off inorganic phosphate molecules (PO_3). It releases phosphate-containing minerals to the soil, where they are absorbed by plant roots in the form of inorganic phosphates. Once in the plant cells the phosphates are incorporated into biological molecules such as nucleic acids and ATP (adenosine triphosphate). ATP is important in the energy transfer reactions in the cells. Animals obtain most of their required phosphate from food. In some areas, water, too, contains substantial amounts of organic phosphates. Phosphorus released by decomposers becomes part of the soil's pool of inorganic phosphates for plants to reuse. Like carbon, nitrogen, and other biogeochemical nutrients, phosphorus moves through the food web as one organism eats another.

Phosphorus cycles through aquatic environments in much the same way. Dissolved phosphorus enters aquatic communities by adsorption and assimilation by algae and plants. These are eaten by plankton and larger organisms, which in turn are predated by fish and molluscs. Ultimately, decomposers break down wastes and dead organisms and release inorganic phosphorus into the water, where it becomes available to aquatic primary producers again.

Phosphorus can be lost from the biological cycles. Streams carry some phosphate from the land to the ocean, where it is deposited on the ocean floor and can reside for millions of years. Geological uplift can expose these rocks to weathering and the erosion of phosphate once more. A small proportion of the phosphate in the aquatic food web finds its way back to the land through the action of sea birds. Birds such as white-breasted cormorants, pelicans, and white-breasted gannets catch and eat fish and other marine organisms and defecate as they roost on land. This process makes some phosphate minerals available to plant roots.

In some areas where the climate is arid great quantities of droppings (guano) built up over thousands of years (estimates suggest that each bird produces about 20 g of droppings/day). Some of the best areas were the islands off the coast and along the Pacific coastal areas of the Atacama Desert (now southern Peru and northern Chile). In many areas the guano was between 30 and 60 m deep. These deposits were very rich in both nitrogen and phosphorus. During the nineteenth century this guano was exported to England, Europe, and the United States and was considered to be the best form of fertilizer, although it was far more expensive than other forms of manure. In fact, the trade was so lucrative that exporters, shippers, and merchants became multi-millionaires and the salary of the president of Peru was twice that of the president of the US during the boom years of the 1840s. Between 1840 and 1880, 20 million tonnes of guano were exported. Later in the century, old beds of fossilized guano (called caliche or Chile nitrate) were found at inland sites and dug and exported for fertilizer. Guano financed the first railway built in South America (in Peru, between Lima and Callao, the major shipping port for the trade). Later in the century, guano and caliche deposits were two of the causes of the War of the Pacific (1879–83) fought between Peru, Chile, and Bolivia. Bolivia lost its Atacama coastal provinces in this war (the country still maintains a small navy on Lake Titicaca in the hope of winning back the lost coastal territory).

Towards the end of the nineteenth century guano and caliche became important to the production of explosives (as we have seen with more modern forms of fertilizers in recent years). The first major naval battle after the outbreak of World War I, 1 November 1914, was fought off Coronel, Chile, between the German Pacific Squadron and the British South Atlantic Squadron in an attempt to stop German ships from harassing cargoes of guano and nitrate bound for Britain for agricultural and munitions purposes. The British lost two large cruisers and 1654 officers and men in the action—the British navy's first defeat in 102 years. About a month later the Germans were defeated at the Battle of the Falkland Islands and there was no longer a threat to British access to the guano and caliche supplies in the Pacific. The Germans, who could not get supplies of these commodities, had to develop and use the Haber–Bosch chemical method to produce nitrogen-based fertilizers and explosives.

Along the British Columbia and Alaska coasts a lot of nutrients are added to the forests every year by bears and wolves catching migrating salmon and abandoning partially eaten carcasses in the adjacent forests or at the forest margins. Along a 250 m reach of one such stream it was estimated that over 80 kg of nitrogen and about 11 kg of phosphorus were added to the forest per month. This is significant in terms of nutrient supply and health of forest lands.

The Sulphur Cycle

The **sulphur cycle** (Figure 46.13) is not as well understood as the other cycles discussed. Scientists are still piecing it together. Most sulphur is buried underground in sedimentary rocks and in mineral form, e.g., gypsum and anhydrite. When exposed, these rocks and minerals can erode over time to release sulphur-containing compounds

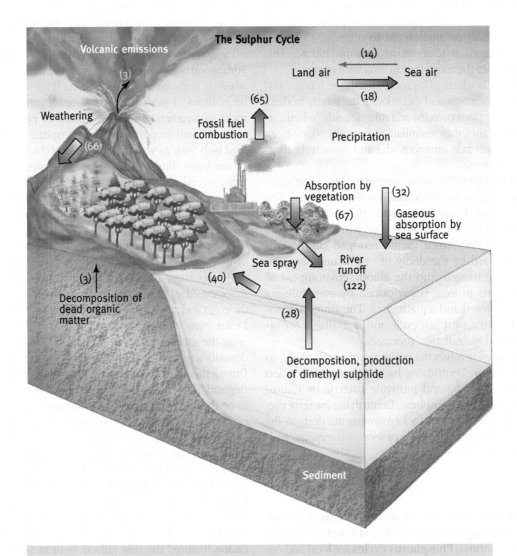

Figure 46.13 The sulphur cycle. The transfer rates, expressed as 10^9 kg of sulphur per year, include both human-caused and natural fluxes. Total fluxes today are more than twice what they were 100 years ago, principally a result of the burning of fossil fuels.

to the oceans. Sulphur gases enter the atmosphere from natural sources in both the oceans and on the land (volcanic eruptions are a major source). Sea spray delivers sulphates (SO_2) into the air, as do forest fires and dust storms (desert sediments and soils contain a lot of calcium sulphates [$CaSO_4$]). Volcanoes release hydrogen sulphide (H_2S, which smells like rotten eggs) and sulphur oxides (S_{ox}), including sulphur dioxide (SO_2), an acrid gas, and sulphur trioxide (SO_3).

LINK

Sulphur gases form a very minor part of the atmosphere and are not long-lived because they are very reactive. Hydrogen sulphide reacts with oxygen to form sulphur oxides, which react with water to form sulphuric acid (H_2SO_4), now known to be responsible for the formation of some caves and other 'karst' features (Unit 35), and acid precipitation, which is responsible for the acidification of many lakes and the degradation of many stone buildings, statues, and gravestones (see Units 17 and 29). Although the amount of sulphur in the atmosphere is small, the movement to and from the atmosphere is substantial. Sulphur occurs in tiny amounts in organisms and is an essential part of proteins. Plant roots absorb sulphate and incorporate it into cells. Animals consume plants and convert these proteins to animal proteins. In the ocean certain marine algae release large amounts of a compound that bacteria convert to dimethyl sulphide, or DMS (CH_3SCH^3). This is released into the atmosphere, where it is converted to sulphate and is involved in the condensation of water to form cloud droplets and may affect weather and climate.

Bacteria drive the sulphur cycle. In aerobic areas (wetlands, tidal flats, and water-logged soils) some bacteria convert sulphates to hydrogen sulphide gas, which is released ('burped') into the atmosphere or is converted into metallic sulphides. These are deposited in sediments and rocks. Some aerobic bacteria practise a primitive type of photosynthesis by using sulphide instead of water. In aerobic conditions other bacteria oxidize sulphur compounds to sulphates.

The next section discusses a vegetation system that changes, and we find once again that energy is crucial.

Plant Successions

The flow of energy through a food web illustrates the interconnectivity and dynamic nature of the biosphere. The vegetation layer, too, changes continuously and is as dynamic as the atmosphere, soil, and crust of the Earth. Some of the changes occur within a stable ecosystem, but sometimes one type of vegetation is replaced by another. This is called a **plant** (or **seral**) **succession**. There three types.

Primary succession occurs on new terrain, e.g., created by volcanic eruptions, a fall in sea level, or continental deglaciation. Soil and plant *seres* develop at the same time (over 500–1000 years). The plants themselves initiate changes in the land surface, which consequently cause vegetational changes. It is a linear process, i.e., the order of succession in any one place is not normally repeated. Figure 46.14

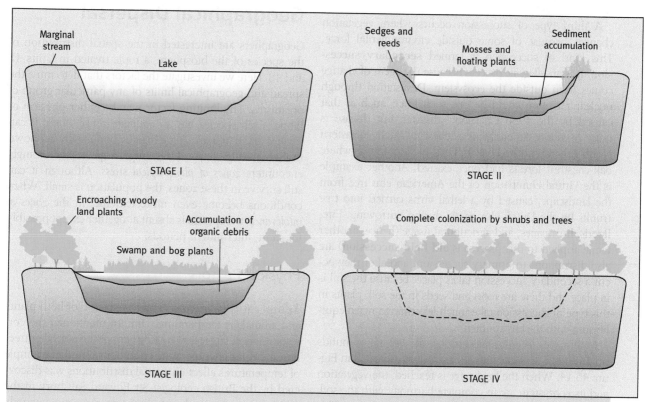

Figure 46.14 Idealized sequence of primary succession by which a lake is eventually colonized by shrubs and trees.

shows how the growth of vegetation in an area that has been a lake (Stage I) is a primary succession. As the lake gradually fills with sediments, the water becomes chemically enriched; mosses and sedges as well as floating rafts of vegetation build up (Stage II). Plant productivity increases in the lake, and other plants encroach around its edges (Stage III). After the lake has completely filled with organic debris, soil begins to form and dryland plants (pioneers) first appear. These are plants that can tolerate poor soil conditions and that can reach the site and colonize it before other species. These plants die and add their organic matter to the soil. In this way the plant community and the soil develop together; as the soil matures and the microclimate changes, these communities replace each other until longer-lived and more stable communities of trees finally take over (Stage IV: Climax).

Sometimes one kind of vegetation is replaced by another, which is in turn replaced by the first. Or possibly the original vegetation follows a series of two or three others. This is called **cyclic succession**. An example can be found at the northernmost limit of tree growth (near the treeline) in Canada, where permafrost (perenially frozen ground) lies beneath tundra vegetation of grasses, sedges, and bare ground. The permafrost melts to a sufficient depth in summer to allow colonization by willow scrub and later by spruce trees. Gradually this forest becomes denser and forms a layer of litter. The permafrost, thus insulated, gradually rebuilds. The forest degenerates and eventually gives way to the original tundra vegetation. The cycle is then complete and ready for another sequence. The above succession processes are *autogenic,* or caused by internal ecosystem changes

A third type of succession occurs where vegetation changes because of some outside environmental force. This kind of succession is termed **secondary succession.** It is an *allogenic* process because the agent of change comes from outside the ecosystem. Devastation through nuclear radiation could be one such force, such as that caused by the 1986 Chernobyl disaster, but disease is more common. An epidemic of chestnut blight in eastern North America created oak and oak-hickory forests where oak-chestnut forests had once existed. Another example is the virtual elimination of the American elm tree from the landscape, caused by a lethal virus carried into tree trunks by the Dutch elm beetle during burrowing. Fire, floods, hurricanes, and agricultural usage (hence, another name applied to this process is **old field succession**) are also disruptions to primary succession, and after they occur a secondary succession takes place. Because the soil is in place and there are roots and seeds in the soil, plants in this type of succession take much less time to reach equilibrium with the environment.

In all types of plant successions, the vegetation builds up through a series of stages (or *seres*), as indicated in Figure 46.14. When the final stage is reached, the vegetation and its ecosystem are in complete harmony with the soil, the climate, and other parts of the environment. This

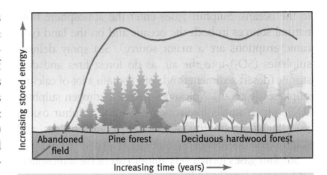

Figure 46.15 Increase in stored energy of the biomass in a typical secondary succession. In this case a deciduous hardwood forest takes over from an abandoned field over a period lasting about 175 years.

balance is called a **climax community**. If fire or disease interrupts this process and creates a different type of community, they are called fire or disease *disclimaxes* or *plagioclimaxes*. The major vegetation types, or *biomes* (described in Unit 47), all represent climax communities, which also are characterized by ecosystems with stable amounts of accumulated energy. Solar energy is taken in and energy is lost through respiration and other processes, but the stored energy of the biomass is relatively constant. During a plant succession, however, the amount of energy stored in the biomass increases, as Figure 46.15 shows. Input of energy must exceed losses for the plant succession to develop.

Geographical Dispersal

Geographers are interested in the spatial distribution of the species of the biosphere, a topic treated in Units 47 and 48. Here we investigate the factors that determine the spread and geographical limits of any particular group of organisms. The limiting factor may be either physical or biotic. Each species has an *optimum range* where it can survive and maintain a large healthy population, as shown in Figure 46.16. Beyond this range, a species increasingly encounters *zones of physiological stress*. Although it can still survive in these zones, the population is small. When conditions become even more extreme, in the *zones of intolerance*, the species is absent altogether except possibly for short, intermittent periods.

Physical Factors

Temperature A common limiting factor for both plants and animals is temperature. Unit 16 mentioned the correspondence, suggested by Köppen, of the northern treeline and certain temperature conditions. Another example of temperature's effect on spatial distributions was discovered by the British ecologist Sir Edward Salisbury in the 1920s. One species he studied was a creeping woody

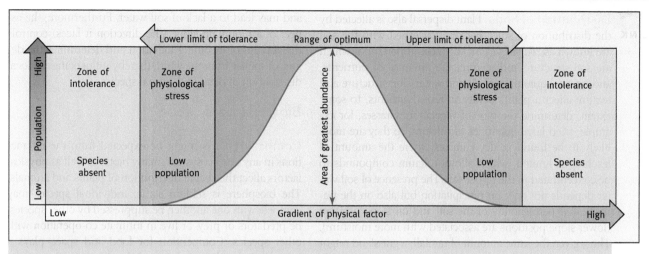

Figure 46.16 Model of population abundance in relation to the physical factors in the environment of a species.

plant known as the wild madder (*Rubia peregrina*). He found that the northern boundary of the wild madder in Europe coincided closely with the January 4.5°C isotherm. This temperature was critical because in January the plant formed new shoots, and lower temperatures would inhibit their development and subsequent growth. Indeed, temperatures play such a large role in determining plant distributions that plants are sometimes classified according to their propensity for withstanding heat. Plants adapted to heat are called *megatherms*; those that can withstand low temperatures are designated *microtherms*; and those with a preference for intermediate temperatures are called *mesotherms*.

Availability of Water Another vital factor—the availability of water—limits the spread of plants and animals throughout the physical world. Water is essential to photosynthesis and in other functions of plants and animals. Several plant classifications take water availability into account.

Plants adapted to dry areas are called *xerophytes*, and desert plants have evolved many adjustments to aridity. Stomata are deeply sunken into the leaf surface to reduce water loss by evapotranspiration. Some xerophytes only have stomata on the underside of leaves. Roots often reach 5 m or more into the ground in search of water, or more commonly spread horizontally for great distances to be able to use infrequent supplies of rainwater. Plants that live in wet environments are classified as *hygrophytes*, with rainforests, swamps, marshes, lakes, and bogs the habitats of this vegetation. The aquatic buttercup, a curious example of a hygrophyte, produces two kinds of leaves: it develops finely dissected leaves when in water and simple entire leaves when exposed to the air. Finally, plants that develop in areas of neither extreme moisture nor extreme aridity are called *mesophytes*. Most plants growing in regions of plentiful rainfall and well-drained topography fall into this category.

In tropical climates with a dry season, flowering trees and plants drop their leaves to reduce water loss during the dry season. This phenomenon spread to plants of higher latitudes, where the formation of ice in winter sometimes causes a water shortage. Trees and other plants that drop their entire leaf cover seasonally are called *deciduous*, and those that 'keep' their leaves year-round are called *evergreen*. These plants do lose their leaves but not en masse.

Other Climatic Factors Several other factors related to climate play a role in the dispersal of plants. These include the availability of light, the action of winds, and the duration of snow cover. The position of a species within a habitat shared by other species determines the amount of light available to it. It is possible to divide plants in terms of light tolerance into *heliophytes*, which grow best in strong sunlight, and *sciophytes*, which grow best in low light areas or in areas with daily or seasonal variations in sunlight, as in the mid-latitudes. For example, in deciduous forests of the middle latitudes, many low shrubs grow intensely in spring before the canopy of taller trees filters out light. The amount of available light is further determined by latitude and the associated length of daylight. Growth in the short warm season of humid microthermal (**D**) climates is enhanced by the long daylight hours of summer, and plants can mature surprisingly fast (see Figure 17.25). The struggle for light causes the *vertical stratification* of plants in a community. This is caused by a difference in light tolerance of various species, and is most dramatically seen in the tropical rainforest where the stratification includes emergents; canopy, middle, and lower tree layers; shrub/small tree layer; and ground vegetation levels.

Wind influences the spread of plants in several ways. It can limit growth or even destroy plants and trees in extreme situations; but it also spreads pollen and the seeds of many plants.

Distribution of Soils Plant dispersal also is affected by the distribution of soils. Factors concerned with the soil are known as *edaphic factors*, the most important of which are soil structure and texture, the presence of nutrients, and internal quantities of air and water. Soil structure and texture affect a plant's ability to root. Nutrients, to some extent, determine the type of vegetation. Grasses, for example, need large quantities of calcium, so they are more likely to be found in dry climates where the amount of leaching is limited, which allows calcium compounds to be concentrated in the upper soil. The presence of soil water depends not only on precipitation but also on the porosity and permeability of the soil and on slope position (lower slope positions are associated with more moisture). Thus, given the same amount of rainfall, a grassland might exist over permeable soils and a forest over less permeable soils.

Landforms The final physical factor, landforms, controls vegetation distribution in many ways. On a large scale, as shown in Unit 17, vegetation changes with altitude in much the same way as it does with latitude. On the flanks of Mount Kenya in East Africa (Figure 46.17), there is a transition from savanna grassland below 1650 m to alpine vegetation above 3650 m. A similar zonation (with very different types of vegetation) can be seen in the Coast and Rocky Mountains and elsewhere. Landforms have a small-scale effect as well. Steep slopes foster rapid drainage

and may lead to a lack of soil water. Furthermore, the aspect of a mountain slope (the direction it faces) controls the amount of incoming radiation and determines the degree of shelter from the wind, thereby influencing the local distribution of plant and animal species.

Biotic Factors

Competition As might be expected from the interactions in any one ecosystem, many biotic as well as physical factors affect the spatial distribution of plants and animals. The biosphere is seldom static: individual species may compete with one another, be suppressed by other species, be predators or prey, or live in intimate co-operation with other species. Competition for food and space plays a strong part in plant and animal distributions. Sometimes new species compete for resources so well that they eliminate old species. For example, in large areas of eastern North America, purple loosestrife (*Lythrum salicaria*) has invaded wetlands and moist soil areas, choking out up to 60 per cent of native plants (Figure 46.18). It is estimated that approximately 200,000 hectares/year are lost to purple loosestrife in Canada. This plant was introduced from Europe in the early 1800s. It now dominates many wetlands from the Maritime provinces to the Great Lakes. Distribution is spotty in western Canada; the most extensive infestations are in Manitoba and British Columbia. One plant can produce over 2 million seeds. Seeds can be

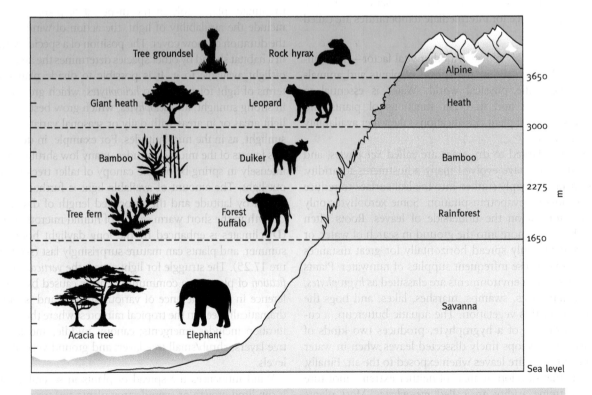

Figure 46.17 Zones of vegetation and animal life on the flanks of Mount Kenya in East Africa, which lies directly on the Equator.

Figure 46.18 Purple loosestrife (*Lythrum salicaria*), a European species, has taken over many wetlands in eastern North America and has choked out many native species.

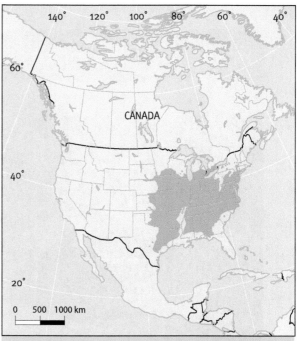

Figure 46.19 The black walnut tree (*Juglans nigra*) releases a toxin (juglone) from its root system that inhibits the growth of most plant species growing in its understory.

dispersed by air or water. Seedlings can float, so dispersal is very rapid.

Amensalism Another form of biological interaction, the inhibition of one species by another, is called **amensalism**. The black walnut (*Juglans nigra*) is a medium-sized deciduous tree (up to 35 m tall) that grows in the deciduous forests of eastern North America (Figure 46.19). It is a component of the Carolinian forest of southwestern Ontario. This species is known for its exquisitely coloured wood (once used for furniture) and its nuts, which have been used to dye cloth. The black walnut's roots (and those of other members of the *Juglans* genus) release a toxin (juglone) into the soil that inhibits most plant species from growing in its understory (under and around the tree).

Predation Anyone who saw the ravaged landscapes of Australia before rabbit control began (Figure 46.20) cannot doubt the efficiency of predation as a factor in the distribution of vegetation. (In 1950, Australia's estimated rabbit population was 600 million.) But examples of one species eating all members of another species tend to be rare. It is in the best interest of predators in balanced ecosystems to rely on a number of prey species so that their food will never be exhausted.

In this more natural situation, predation affects the plant distribution mainly by reducing the pressure of competition among prey species. In general, the presence of predators tends to increase the number of species in a given ecosystem. Charles Darwin suggested that ungrazed pasture in southern England was dominated by fast-growing tall grasses that kept out light. Consequently, the ungrazed areas contained only about 11 species whereas the grazed lands possessed as many as 20 in response to the opening up of more niches.

Figure 46.20 After their introduction and following the elimination of natural predators, the rabbit population of Australia exploded. States and individual landowners built fences to protect pastures and farmlands. The introduction of a rabbit-killing disease temporarily stemmed this tragic tide, but by the 1980s the rabbit population was back to its huge pre-disease numbers. Here rabbits are seen running along the rabbit-proof border fence between the states of South Australia (foreground) and New South Wales.

From the Fieldnotes

Figure 46.21 'Along the northern California coast you can see the competition between sagebrush and grass in progress, the grass losing out over time. The Mediterranean climatic regime, high relief, and thin soils give the better adapted sage a durable advantage.'

Mutualism Yet another biological interaction is termed **mutualism**, the coexistence of two or more species because one or more is essential to the survival of the other(s). Many examples of mutualism, or *symbiosis*, can be found in equatorial and tropical forests. When certain species in the rainforest are cut down and removed, their leaf litter and other organic remains no longer decay on the forest floor. Since equatorial lateritic soils are so infertile, this leaf litter keeps other plants supplied with nutrients. Remove them, and the remaining plants may die. Such human intervention, of course, reminds us that another species— *Homo sapiens*—can often significantly shape the geography of plants and animals as well.

Species Dispersal and Endemism Terrestrial and aquatic (freshwater and marine) plants, animals, and other biota (living organisms) are naturally present in specific geographic locations because of their adapta-

tion to local and/or regional environments. Ancestral species from which modern species evolved arrived in a given area by movement over land, swimming, rafting, or flying (**dispersal**)—or were carried along by plate mobility over tens of millions of years (**vicariance**). A good example of vicariance is the flora, fauna, and other biota on the island of Madagascar, which split off and moved away from the African continent with the breakup of Gondwanaland that began 160 million years ago (see Figure 24.1). As a result, Madagascar, other oceanic islands, and certain isolated (or once isolated) land areas contain a significant percentage of species of plants, animals, and other life forms that exist nowhere else on Earth. Biologists call such species *endemic*. Regions of high biotic **endemism** are particularly vulnerable to the extinction of endemic species because of environmental changes caused by human modification of the landscape (e.g., deforestation) or the intended or unintended

LINK

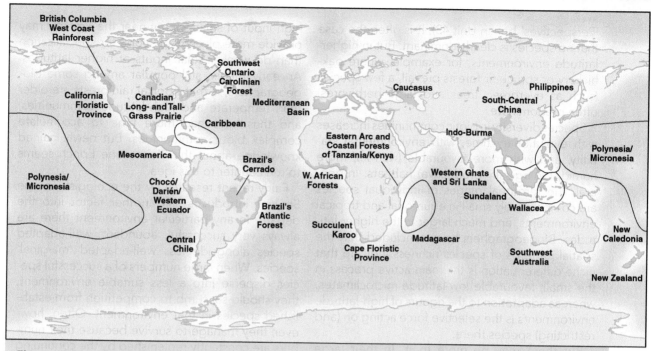

Figure 46.22 Global distribution of biodiversity 'hot spots'. These areas contain high concentrations of endemic species that are threatened by human activities.

introduction of other terrestrial and marine organisms (Figure 46.22).

Ever since humans began to travel beyond their home areas, they have brought plants, animals, and other biota with them. The process of dispersing species distant from their natural areas accelerated with long-distance sea voyaging. In more recent times, ships have been joined by aircraft and motor vehicles as agents of transfer of species from one region to another, thereby bypassing natural

barriers to the dispersal of species (e.g., oceans, inhospitable climates, and mountain ranges).

Although researchers have not been able to fully explain every major geographic variation (see 'Perspectives' box), these limiting physical and biotic factors contribute a great deal to our understanding of the distribution of plant and animal species. Unit 47 shows how the biogeographic processes discussed in this unit are expressed spatially on the world map of vegetative associations.

Perspectives on the Human Environment

A Biogeographic Puzzle—The Species-Richness Gradient

For over a century it has been known that the number of species per unit area decreases with latitude. A single square kilometre of tropical rainforest contains thousands of plant and animal species; a square kilometre of tundra may contain only a few dozen. This phenomenon is known as the **species-richness**

gradient, and many theories have been proposed to explain it.

Associated with the species-richness gradient is the relationship between the most abundant and important species and lesser species. This is the principle of species dominance. In tropical rainforest environments, where the number and the diversity of species are very large (see

'Perspectives' box in Unit 43), it is often the case that no species is clearly dominant. But in higher-latitude environments, for example, where oak-hickory or spruce-fir forests prevail, a few species (such as evergreen trees and large herbivores) often predominate.

Species diversity in biotic communities increases with evolutionary time, with environmental stability, and with more favourable (warmer, more humid, biologically productive) habitats. In general, the territorial ranges of individual species are comparatively small in equatorial and tropical environments, and much larger in the higher latitudes. Biogeographers have concluded that the spatial patterns of species richness indicate that niche differentiation is the main active process in the small, favourable low-latitude microclimates, whereas adaptation to the rigours of high-latitude environments is the selective force acting on (and restricting) species there.

But there may be more to it. In their large ranges at high latitudes, species must adapt to wide fluctuations in temperature and other environmental conditions. Animals roam far and wide; plants are hardy and durable. In tropical areas, however, species tend to be closely bound to a narrow set of environmental conditions; the mosaic of microclimates reflects the limited range of many species. Such species cannot adapt to even a small change in their environment. Plants may be fragile and vulnerable. Migrating animals quickly find themselves at a disadvantage.

The species-richness gradient may thus be explained in terms of adaptation, species success and dispersal, and environmental limitations. Some ecologists argue that biological resources can be shared more finely where the environment is relatively constant; specialization is more possible under such circumstances. Considering the relationship another way, we observe that the high input of solar energy near the Equator may provide more placement scope for specialization than do weaker solar inputs at higher latitudes. An early theory, still popular among some biogeographers, is that tropical rainforests are older than temperate and high-latitude communities, and thus have had more time to accumulate complex biotic communities. But newly gained knowledge about the Pleistocene Epoch seems to run counter to this idea.

Fairly recent research by the ecologist George Stevens introduces still another factor into the debate. In any particular environment there are always very successful, abundant, well-adapted species alongside less well-adapted 'marginal' species. When large numbers of a successful species disperse into a less suitable environment, they should succumb to competition from established species in that environment. Often, however, they manage to survive because their numbers are constantly replenished by the continuing stream of migrants. This is known as the rescue effect.

Migrants in small tropical microclimates quickly move beyond their optimal environmental niches (niches are discussed in Unit 48). But in high-latitude environments, where species' ranges are larger and where species are adapted to wider environmental ranges, dispersing individuals of successful species are much less likely to stray into unsuitable habitats. As Stevens points out, the rescue effect is much less influential in higher-latitude areas than in the tropics, contributing to the geographic pattern of the species-richness gradient.

Various theories combine different ideas about the species-richness gradient in various ways, but no single theory has won general acceptance. And so one of biogeography's grandest global designs continues to evoke discussion and debate.

KEY TERMS

REVIEW QUESTIONS

1. Which subjects are encompassed by *phytogeography* and *zoogeography*?

2. Describe the process of photosynthesis, including consideration of requirements, limitations, and related processes.

3. What are food chains or webs, and how efficient are they at transferring energy to higher trophic levels?

4. Describe how a lake might undergo primary succession.

5. Describe the physical and biotic factors that affect the geographic dispersal of plants and/or animals.

REFERENCES AND FURTHER READINGS

Bailey, R.G. 1996. *Ecosystem Geography*. New York: Springer-Verlag.

———. 1998. *Ecoregions: The Ecosystem Geography of the Oceans and Continents*. New York: Springer-Verlag.

Barbour, M.G., et al. 1980. *Terrestrial Plant Ecology*. Menlo Park, Calif.: Benjamin/Cummings.

Bown, S.R. 2005. *A Most Damnable Invention: Dynamite, Nitrates and the Making of the Modern World*. Toronto: Viking Canada.

Bradbury, I.K. 1998. *The Biosphere*, 2nd edn. New York: Wiley.

Cox, C.B., and P.D. Moore. 1993. *Biogeography: An Ecological and Evolutionary Approach*, 5th edn. Cambridge, Mass.: Blackwell.

Fitzpatrick, E.A. 1983. *Soils: Their Formation, Classification and Distribution*, 3rd edn. Harlow, UK: Longman.

Freeman, S., et al. 2005. *Biological Science*, 2nd edn. Upper Saddle River, NJ: Pearson Prentice-Hall.

Havelka, M. 2008. *Plants and Animals: The Diversity of Organisms*. New York: McGraw-Hill Primis.

Huggett, R.J. 1998. *Fundamentals of Biogeography*. London/New York: Routledge.

Jarvis, P.J. 1999. *Plant and Animal Introductions*. Malden, Mass.: Blackwell.

MacArthur, R.H. 1984. *Geographical Ecology: Patterns in the Distribution of Species*. Princeton, NJ: Princeton Univ. Press.

MacDonald, G.M. 2003. *Biogeography: Introduction to Space, Time and Life*. New York: Wiley.

McGinnis, M.V., ed. 1999. *Bioregionalism*. London/New York: Routledge.

Maurer, B.A. 1994. *Geographical Population Analysis: Tools for the Analysis of Biodiversity*. Cambridge, Mass.: Blackwell.

Myers, A.A., and P.S. Giller, eds. 1988. *Analytical Biogeography: An Integrated Approach to the Study of Animal and Plant Distributions*. New York: Chapman and Hall.

Raven, P.H., and L.R. Berg. 2004. *Environment*, 4th edn. Hoboken, NJ: Wiley.

Ricklefs, R.E., and D. Schluter, eds. 1993. *Species Diversity in Ecological Communities: Historical and Geographical Perspectives*. Chicago: Univ. of Chicago Press.

Skaggs, J.M. 1994. *The Great Guano Rush: Entrepreneurs and American Overseas Expansion*. New York: St Martin's Press.

Smil, V. 2002. *The Earth's Biosphere: Evolution, Dynamics, and Change*. Cambridge, Mass.: MIT Press.

Tivy, J. 1982. *Biogeography: A Study of Plants in the Ecosphere*, 2nd edn. London/New York: Longman.

Watts, D. 1971. *Principles of Biogeography: An Introduction to the Functional Mechanisms of Ecosystems*. London: McGraw-Hill.

Williams, R.S., Jr. 2000. 'A Modern Earth Narrative: What Will Be the Fate of the Biosphere?', *Technology in Society* 22: 303–39.

Wilson, E.O. 1992. *The Diversity of Life*. Cambridge, Mass.: Belknap/Harvard Univ. Press.

Zimmer, C. 2001. *Evolution: Triumph of an Idea*. New York: HarperCollins.

 ## WEB RESOURCES

www.nationalgeographic.com/wildworld Information and images for all 867 worldwide land-based ecoregions are available on this site, as well as data from Project Global 2000: priority areas for ecological conservation.

Unit 47

The Global Distribution of Plants

Objectives

- To briefly survey the principal terrestrial biomes.
- To describe the vegetation regions of North America.

The classification and mapping of climate posed many geographical challenges. It was necessary to establish a set of measures to form the basis for Figure 16.2, the map of world climates. That map shows the distribution of *macroclimates*—climatic regions on a broad global scale. Embedded within those macroclimates, as was noted, are local microclimates, which do not always conform to the established criteria. The global map, therefore, is only a general guide to what should be found in a particular place.

Mapping vegetation is in some ways an even more difficult problem. On one of your field trips, stop near any vegetated area and note the large number of plants you can identify, probably ranging from trees and grasses to ferns or mosses. Part of the local area you examine may be tree-covered; another part of it may be open grassland; some of it may be exposed rock, carrying mosses or lichens. How can any global map represent this intricate plant mosaic? The answer is similar to that for climates and soils: plant geographers (phytogeographers) look for the key to the largest units of plant association. In the case of climate, this can be done by analyzing temperatures, moisture, and seasonality. Soil orders (see Figure 45.15) are based on a determination of the most general similarities or differences in soil horizons and formative processes. In classifying the Earth's plant cover, biogeographers use the concept of the *biome* to derive their world map.

Biomes

A **biome** is the broadest justifiable subdivision of the plant and animal world, an assemblage and association of plants and animals forming a regional ecological unit of subcontinental dimensions. We can readily visualize the most general classes of vegetation—forest, grassland, desert, and tundra—but such a classification would not be useful to geographers. For example, there are tropical forests and high-latitude coniferous forests, and they are so different that grouping them within a single ecological unit would serve little or no purpose. However, if we subdivide forests into tropical, monsoon, temperate (mid-latitude), northern (coniferous), and Mediterranean, we have identified true biomes. At this level, the classification is quite useful.

Just as geographers continue to debate the merits of the global climatic map, so biologists are not in total agreement concerning the Earth's biomes. In fact, if we were to look at maps of biomes in biology textbooks, we would find quite a range of interpretations. Moreover, biologists include both *terrestrial* and *marine* biomes in their classifications (biogeography tends to concentrate on the terrestrial biomes). Even the identity of terrestrial biomes is not uniformly accepted, and thus Figure 47.1 should be viewed as one justifiable representation of the Earth's land biomes, but not as the only possible one.

Biomes are not so sharply defined regionally that their limits are clearly demarcated on the surface. The lines separating biomes on the world map, therefore, represent broad transition zones (biotones or ecotones). If you were to walk from one biome region to another, you would observe a gradual change as certain species thin out and vanish while others make their appearance and become established. To move from one fully developed biome to its neighbour might require several days of walking.

The distribution of biomes results from two major factors—climate and topography. Both climate and terrain are reflected on the map of global vegetation. The key *climatic factors* are (1) the atmosphere and its circulation

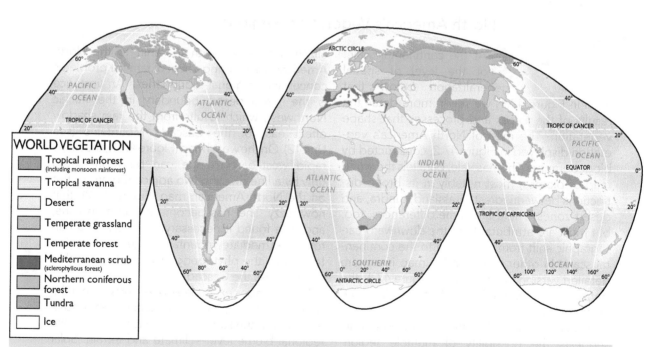

Figure 47.1 Global distribution of the principal terrestrial biomes.

systems, which determine where moisture-carrying air masses do (and do not) go, and (2) the energy source for those circulation systems, solar radiation. (The Sun's energy not only drives atmospheric movements, but also sustains photosynthesis and propels the endless march of the seasons.) The main *terrain factors* are (1) the distribution of the landmasses and ocean basins, and (2) the topography of the continents.

Some biomes that are widely distributed in the Northern Hemisphere hardly ever occur south of the Equator because the Southern Hemisphere does not include large landmasses at comparable latitudes. The varied topography and elevation of the landmasses disrupt much of the regularity the map might have shown had the continents been flatter and lower. Accordingly, the orientations of the Earth's great mountain ranges can clearly be seen on the world map of these biomes (Figure 47.1). Interestingly, many of these same patterns exist at the continental scale as well (see 'Perspectives' box).

It can be concluded that the latitudinal transition of biomes from the hot equatorial regions to the cold polar zones can also be observed along the slope of a high mountain. After all, mountain-slope temperatures decrease with altitude, and precipitation usually increases with altitude. Mount Kenya, in East Africa, stands with its foot on the Equator and is capped with snow. The same holds for Ecuador's Mount Chimborazo in northwestern South America. This mountain is remembered in this connection because it was there that Humboldt first recognized the relationships not only between vegetation and altitude, but also between altitude and latitude. These relationships, applied to the vertical sequencing of biomes, are illustrated in Figure 47.3. Note that it is not just mountains that have a **treeline**, a zone above which trees will not grow—the entire Earth exhibits a treeline, poleward of which the northern coniferous forests are replaced by the stunted plants of the frigid tundra.

Another way to gain a perspective on the factors influencing the global distribution of biomes is represented in Figure 47.4. In this scheme the latitude is increasing along the left side of the triangle and the moisture is decreasing along the base. Notice that forest biomes are generated within three latitudinal zones: tropical, temperate, and subarctic. Also note that the tropical forests develop more than one distinct biome before giving way to savanna and ultimately desert.

Perspectives on the Human Environment

North America's Vegetation Regions

At the continental scale, or the level of spatial generalization below that used in Figure 47.1, we see in more detail the results of the forces and processes that shape vegetation. The map of North America's vegetation displayed in Figure 47.2, constructed by biogeographer Thomas Vale, parallels the world map of biomes, most notably in its broad distinctions between forest, grassland, tundra, and desert zones. There are some differences, too, but most are attributable to the downward cartographic shift from the global to the continental scale. In other words, Vale's map is a more detailed version of a portion of Figure 47.1, the detail made possible by the larger scale of the North American map.

This comparison of spatial frameworks again suggests the possibility of multiple regionalization schemes, with the shift to the North American scale raising a host of familiar problems concerning regional boundaries. An instance is the forest–desert boundary in the Pacific Northwest, which results from the rain shadow effect east of the Cascade Mountains (see Unit 12). On the world map (Figure 47.1), that fairly rapid west–east change can be represented only by a line dividing two adjacent biomes. But on the North American map (Figure 47.2), that now fuzzy 'line' has become a transition zone, and Vale found it necessary to introduce a narrow, intermediate mountain vegetation region to contain the phytogeographical changes that occur across the Cascade Range.

The Cascades example also reminds us that the geography of vegetation on the continental scale results from the same factors that operate at the regional biome level—climate and terrain. Solar radiation and atmospheric circulation patterns are again the key climatic factors. Accordingly, much of the North American map can be related to the actions of processes discussed in Part Two, especially those shaping north–south temperature gradients and east–west moisture variations.

Terrain differences markedly influence vegetation as well, and such major topographic features as the Coast and Cascade Mountains and the ranges of the Rocky Mountains in the western third of North America are prominently visible in Figure 47.2. To the east, topography appears to play a lesser role, but the southwestward-pointing prong of the mixed coniferous–deciduous forest region near the central northeastern seaboard clearly reflects the presence of the Appalachian Mountains. It also suggests the existence of yet another embedded mosaic of vegetation regions at the next lower level of spatial generalization.

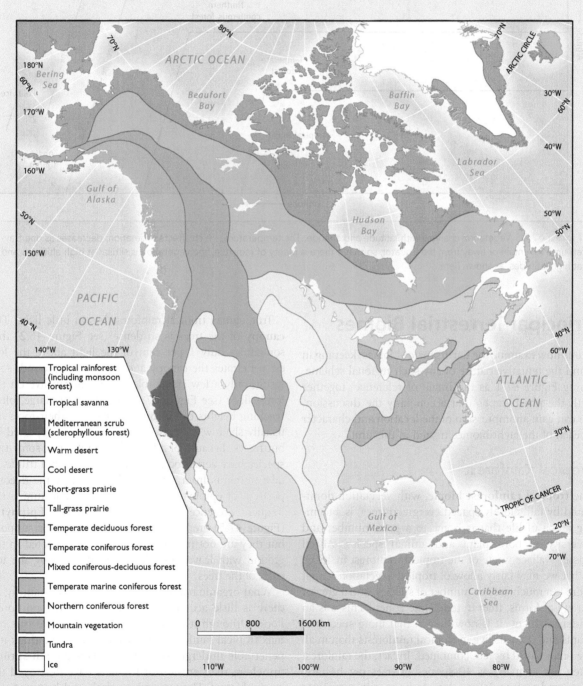

Figure 47.2 Distribution of natural vegetation in North America.

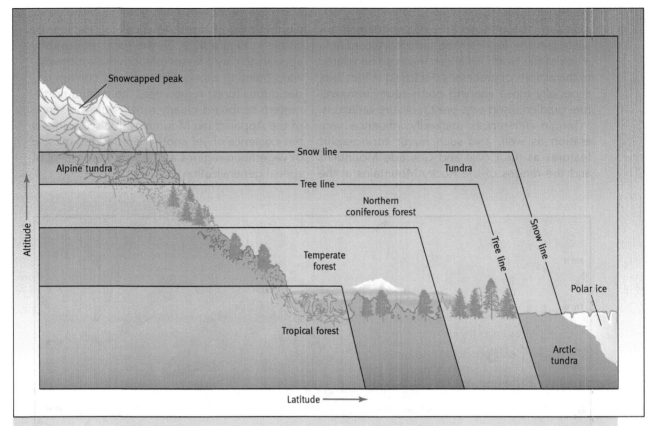

Figure 47.3 Vegetation changes with latitude and altitude. The temperature, which affects vegetation, decreases as one travels up a mountain or away from the Equator, so that if there is plenty of moisture, the vegetation is similar at high altitudes and at high latitudes, as shown here.

Principal Terrestrial Biomes

Let us now examine the Earth's major biomes, keeping in mind the tentative nature of any such regional scheme. Using Figure 47.1 as the frame of reference, together with the photographs that accompany the discussion, we can gain an impression of the location and character of each of the eight biomes treated in this unit.

Tropical Rainforest

The **tropical rainforest biome**, with vegetation dominated by tall, closely spaced evergreen trees, is a teeming arena of life that is home to a great number and diversity of both plant and animal species. Alfred Russel Wallace wrote of the tropical rainforest in 1853: 'What we may fairly allow of tropical vegetation is that there is a much greater number of species, and a greater variety of forms, than in temperate zones.' This was an understatement. It is now known that more species of plants and animals live in tropical rainforests than in all the other world biomes combined. In fact, the rainforest often has as many as 40 species of trees per hectare, compared to 8 to 10 species per hectare in temperate forests.

True climax tropical rainforest lets in little light. The **canopy** of the trees is so dense (see Figure 46.2) that sometimes only 1 per cent of the light above the forest penetrates the canopy and reaches the ground. As a result, only a few shade-tolerant plants can live on the forest floor (see Figure 17.2). The trees are large, often reaching heights of 40 to 60 m. Because their roots are usually shallow, the bases of the trees are supported by buttresses. Because of a lack of soil nutrients, some tree species have aerial roots on their branches and trunks to take nutrients from soil mats developed by the decomposition of epiphytes, ferns, etc. Another feature is the frequent presence of epiphytes and lianas. **Epiphytes** (Figure 47.5) are plants that use the trees for support, but they are not parasites; *lianas* are vines rooted in the ground with leaves and flowers in the canopy, the top parts of the trees.

What organic matter there is decomposes rapidly, so there is little accumulation of litter on the rainforest floor. Although it is easy to walk through the true climax tropical rainforest, many areas contain a thick impenetrable undergrowth (jungle). This growth springs up where river erosion or humans have destroyed the original forest. The areas where slash-and-burn agricultural practices (Figure 47.6) are common are especially

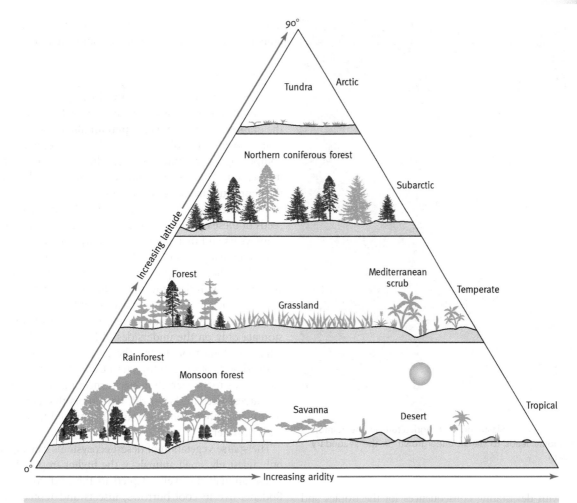

Figure 47.4 Simplified scheme of the major terrestrial biomes, arranged along gradients of increasing aridity at different latitudes, illustrating the dominant influence of moisture and temperature on the structure of plant communities.

Figure 47.5 An epiphyte uses a tree for support but is not a parasite.

likely to exhibit such secondary growth. It has been estimated that most of the true tropical rainforest may disappear by the middle of this century. Moreover, where

natural vegetation is cleared from the lateritic soils of this biome, hardpans frequently develop through the extreme leaching of the upper soil, which produces high concentrations of iron and aluminum compounds. Agriculture is difficult and minimally productive in such untillable soil.

Monsoon rainforests are included in this biome, even though they differ slightly from tropical rainforests. Monsoon rainforests are established in areas with a dry season and therefore exhibit less variety in plant species. This vegetation is lower and less dense, and it also grows in layers or tiers composed of species adjusted to various light intensities.

Until recently, tropical rainforests covered almost half the forested area of the Earth (Figure 47.1). The largest expanses are in the Amazon River Basin in northern South America and the Congo River Basin in west-equatorial Africa. A third area includes parts of southeastern Asia, northeastern Australia, and Indonesia. Human destruction of rainforests (see Unit 17) continues at an alarming

Figure 47.6 Slash-and-burn agriculture in the rainforest biome leads to dense undergrowth in the secondary growth.

rate—with devastating consequences for the tropics and possibly far beyond.

Tropical Savanna

The **savanna biome** encompasses a transitional environment between the tropical rainforest and the desert, consisting of tropical grassland with widely spaced single trees or groups of trees (Figure 47.7). Thorn forests, characterized by dense, spiny, low, fire-resistant trees, predominate, and bulbous plants are abundant. The most common trees of the savanna are deciduous, dropping their leaves in the dry season. These include fire-resistant *Brachystegia* and *Isoberlinia* trees in wetter areas and acacia (*Acacia* spp.) and the curious water-storing, fat-trunked baobab tree (*Adansonia digitata*) in more arid environments. Grasses in the savanna are usually tall and have stiff, coarse blades. The grasses can withstand fire and intensive grazing because they can regrow from a leaf growth node (meristematic tissue) very close to the soil surface.

Savanna vegetation has developed primarily because of the seasonally wet and dry climate (**Aw**) in large areas of Africa, South America, northern Australia, and India as well as in parts of Southeast Asia. However, periodic burning plays a significant role in limiting tree growth, as does grazing. In some places, the grasses form a highly flammable straw mat in the dry season. This can be ignited through lightning, but humans may also set fire to it. Typical of the food web of this biome are large migrating herds of grazing animals—zebras, gnu, Cape buffalo, and antelope.

Desert

The **desert biome** is characterized by sparse vegetation or even its complete absence (see Figure 17.7). Whereas the grasses of the savanna are **perennials**, persisting from year to year, many of the desert plants are **ephemerals**, completing their entire life cycle during a single growing season. These ephemerals often grow quickly after the short but intense seasonal rains, covering open sandy or rocky areas in a spectacular display (Figure 47.8). The seeds of these ephemerals often lie dormant in the soil for many years and then germinate rapidly after a rainstorm. The perennial plants in the desert biome, such as cactuses and euphorbias (spurges), are dormant much of the year. Some, with fleshy water-storing leaves or stems, are known as *succulents*. Others have small leathery leaves or are deciduous. Some plants have very few stomata or have stomata only on the undersides of leaves. Woody plants have very long roots to tap the groundwater. Mesquite, in the deserts of the southwestern US and Mexico, for example, has roots over 25 m deep (most plants, including the largest trees in the world, have roots that are 1–2 m deep), and other woody plants are restricted to localized areas of water.

The sparse vegetation of desert ecosystems can support only relatively small animals at the higher trophic levels. These animals are well adapted to the arid conditions. Rodents live in cool burrows; insects and reptiles have waterproof skins that help them retain water. There are many *fossorial* animals that spend the heat of the day below the surface. Some species have evolved special mechanisms to cope with the aridity. For example, recent studies have found that the sand gazelle (*Gazella subgutturosa*) of the Sahara and Arabian deserts and the arid areas of central Asia decreases the size of its heart and other internal organs to cut down the need for water, and also cuts down water loss from sweating during very dry periods. In some areas it does not produce liquid urine but deposits urine crystals. The desert biome, of course, coincides with areas of arid (**BW**) climates. Pedocal and regosolic soils are the most common soil orders associated with the desert biome.

Temperate Grassland

The **temperate grassland** (or parkland) **biome** generally occurs over large areas of continental interiors. Perennial and sod-forming grasses like those shown in Figure 47.9 are dominant. This biome, like the savanna, has historically been inhabited by herds of grazing animals such as bison and saiga antelope and their predators. In North America, the short-grass prairie of the Prairies and Great Plains gradually gives way towards the east to the moister, richer, tall-grass prairie (Figure 47.2). This transition in vegetation is accompanied by a transition in the soil types from calcic soils to cher-

From the Fieldnotes

Figure 47.7 *'The East African savanna is sometimes called a "parkland" savanna because trees are widely spaced and give the landscape a regularity that seems cultivated, not wild. The umbrella-like acacia tree is an ally of wildlife and human traveller alike, as I can attest—its shade made many a hot day bearable. The savanna feeds grazing animals as well as browsers because it offers grasses as well as leaves to its migrants; the flat-topped acacia tends to be trimmed at around 5 m by giraffes, which are able to strip leaves from the thorniest of branches. And, as this photo shows, the acacia supports other species as well, as the large and occupied eagle's nest confirms.'*

nozems and then luvisols (see Figure 45.14). As in the savanna biome, fire was important in limiting the invasion of trees.

This biome has been highly susceptible to human influence. Large areas have been turned over to crop and/or livestock farming in the interior areas of North America, the pampas grasslands of Argentina, and the steppes of southern Russia, where the biome is most widespread (see Figure 47.1). Temperate grasslands maintain a delicate ecological balance, and mismanagement or climatic change quickly turns them into temperate forests or deserts.

Temperate Forest

There are several varieties of temperate forest. The **temperate deciduous forest biomes** occur in eastern North America (Figure 47.10), Europe, and eastern China. These forests of broadleaf trees are shared by herbaceous plants, which are most abundant in spring before the growth of new leaves on the trees. An outstanding characteristic of temperate deciduous forests is the similarity of plants found in their three locations in the Northern Hemisphere. Oak (*Quercus* spp.), beech (*Fagus* spp.), birch (*Betula* spp.), walnut (*Juglans* spp.), maple (*Acer* spp.), ash (*Fraxinus* spp.), and chestnut (*Castanea* spp.) trees are all common. As with the temperate grasslands, large areas of this forest type—the Carolinian forest in southern Ontario, for example—have been cleared and converted to agricultural production.

From the Fieldnotes

Figure 47.8   '*A field trip through Arizona desert country reminded us that the desert biome encompasses rich and diversified vegetation. Despite the often thin and unproductive solonetzic and other desert soils prevailing under desert climatic conditions, the infrequent and scant rainfall recorded here is enough to sustain a wide range of plant species as well as a varied fauna.*'

Figure 47.9 Canadian Prairie grasses in Alberta.

Figure 47.11 Lush, old-growth Douglas fir forest in British Columbia's coastal rainforest.

Figure 47.10 Deciduous trees in the Carolinian Forest in southern Ontario.

Temperate evergreen forest (temperate west coast rainforest) biomes are found on western coasts in temperate latitudes where abundant precipitation is the norm. In the Northern Hemisphere they take the form of needle-leaf forests. The coastal redwoods and Douglas firs of the northwestern coast of North America are representative (Figure 47.11). Some of the tallest and oldest trees on Earth are located in the coastal areas of British Columbia and the US Pacific Northwest: Sitka spruce (*Picea sitchensis*), Douglas fir (*Pseaudotsuga menziesii*), western hemlock (*Tsuga heterophylla*), California redwood (*Sequoia sempervirens*), giant redwood (*Sequoiadendron giganteum*), and, in the interior just to the east, sequoias that reach over 100 m in height and 3 m in diameter over a thousand-year lifespan. Only a few relatively small areas

still contain primary redwood and sequoia forests because of the high demand for such wood as a building material. The podocarps of the temperate evergreen rainforest on the western coast of New Zealand exemplify the broadleaf and small-leaf evergreen forests of the Southern Hemisphere. All these forest types, too, are subject to periodic natural fire, which cleans out built-up fallen debris, opens areas for new growth, and adds nutrients to the soil.

Mediterranean Scrub (Sclerophyllous Forest)

The Mediterranean climate (see Unit 17) is characterized by hot dry summers and cool moist winters. Such climates prevail along the shores of the Mediterranean Sea, along the coast of southern California, in central Chile, in South Africa's Cape Province, and in southern and southwestern Australia (see Figure 16.2). The **Mediterranean scrub** (sclerophyllous forest) **biome** corresponds to these **Csa** and **Csb** climates. The vegetation of this biome consists of widely spaced evergreen or deciduous trees (pine and cork oak) and often dense, hard-leaf evergreen scrub. Thick waxy leaves are well adapted to the long, hot, dry summers.

Mediterranean vegetation creates a very distinctive natural landscape (Figure 47.12). Even though this biome's regions are widely separated and isolated from each other, their appearance is quite similar. In coastal California, the Mediterranean landscape is called *chaparral*; in the Mediterranean region of southern Europe, it is referred to as *maquis* (French) or *macchia* (Italian); in Chile it is known as *mattoral*; and in South Africa it is called *fynbos*. All of these areas are adapted to sporadic burning, hence the spectacular fires seen most years in southern California.

Mediterranean regions are among the world's most densely populated and most intensively cultivated.

From the Fieldnotes

Figure 47.12   *'Mediterranean physical and cultural landscapes coexist in a distinctive way. Where human activity has encroached on even the steepest slopes, Mediterranean vegetation somehow survives. Italy's Amalfi coast, south of Naples, provides an example.'*

Human activity has profoundly altered the Mediterranean biome through the use of fire, grazing, and agriculture. Today vineyards and olive groves have replaced countless hectares of natural landscape. Great stands of trees have been removed, and many species of fauna have been driven away or made extinct. Before the rise of ancient Greece, the hills of the Greek peninsula were covered with oaks and pines that had adapted to this climatic regime. Only a few of the legendary cedars of Lebanon now survive. The cork oak, another example of adaptation, still stands in certain corners of the Mediterranean lands. From these remnants it can be deduced that the Mediterranean biome has been greatly modified, but it has not lost its regional identity.

Northern Coniferous Forest

The upper mid-latitude **northern coniferous forest biome** has many different names. In North America it takes a Latin name to become the **boreal forest**. In Russia it is called the *snowforest* or *taiga*. The most common coniferous (cone-bearing) trees in this biome are spruce (*Picea* spp.), hemlock (*Tsuga* spp.), fir (*Abies* spp.), and pine (*Pinus* spp.). These needle-leaf trees can withstand the periodic drought resulting from long periods of freezing conditions, fast-draining, and base-poor podzolic soils. The trees are slender and grow to heights of 12 to 18 m; they generally live less than 300 years but grow quite densely (Figure 47.13). Depressions, bogs, and lakes hide among the trees. In such areas, low-growing bushes with leathery leaves, mosses, and grasses rise out of the waterlogged soil. This type of growth assemblage, combined with stunted and peculiarly shaped trees, is known as *muskeg*.

Some coniferous species need fire (heat or flame) to open their cones so that their seeds can be distributed—for example, Jack pine (*Pinus banksiana*) in eastern North America and Lodgepole pine (*Pinus contorta var. latifolia*) in the northwestern forests of North America, both of which have resin-covered cones that require flame or heat to open them and release the seeds.

All the biomes discussed here could be differentiated even more precisely. For instance, the boreal forest of Canada can be divided into three subzones: (1) the main boreal forest, which is characterized by a continuous canopy; (2) the open boreal woodland, marked by patches where the trees are broken up by open spaces of grass or muskeg; and (3) a mixture of woodland in the valleys and tundra vegetation on the ridges, called forest tundra, which is found along the polar margins of this biome (near the treeline).

Tundra

The **tundra biome** is the most continuous of all the biomes, and it occurs almost unbroken along the poleward margins of the northern continents (see Figure 47.1). It is also found on the islands near Antarctica and in alpine environments

Figure 47.13 A river meanders across a taiga (snowforest) landscape on the eastern side of the Ural Mountains in Siberia. It is the Russian midsummer, and the water level is relatively low.

above the treeline on mountains at every latitude. Only cold-tolerant plants can survive under harsh tundra conditions in seasonally frozen cryosolic soils. The most common are mosses, lichens, sedges, and sometimes, near the forest border, dwarf trees (see Figure 17.29). The dwarf trees are affected by both low temperatures and the wind and have a ground-hugging habit (**Krummholz**). Ephemeral plants are rare; the perennial shrubs are pruned back by the icy winter winds and seldom reach their maximum height. Nor can plant roots be extensive in this biome because the top of the permafrost is seldom more than 1 m below the surface. The permafrost also prevents good surface drainage.

During the short summer, shallow pools of water at the surface become the home of large insect populations. In the Northern Hemisphere, birds migrate from the south to feed on these insects. The fauna is surprisingly varied, considering the small biomass available. It consists of such large animals as reindeer (caribou), muskox, and polar bear and such small herbivores as hares, lemmings, and voles. Carnivores include foxes, wolves, bears, hawks, falcons, owls, and, of course, people.

This survey of the Earth's principal terrestrial biomes has concentrated on the vegetation that dominates their landscapes. A biome, however, consists of more than plants; the animals that form part of its biological community also must be considered. Unit 48 looks at the geography of fauna—zoogeography. Although the focus is on the larger animals, it should be kept in mind that fungi, bacteria, and other types of biota that coexist with plants and animals are also integral parts of the Earth's terrestrial and marine ecosystems.

KEY TERMS

biome   *page 693*
boreal forest   *page 703*
canopy   *page 696*
desert biome   *page 698*
ephemeral plant   *page 698*
epiphytes   *page 696*
Krummholz   *page 703*
Mediterranean scrub biome   *page 701*
northern coniferous forest biome   *page 703*

perennial plant   *page 698*
savanna biome   *page 698*
temperate deciduous forest biome   *page 700*
temperate evergreen forest biome   *page 701*
temperate grassland biome   *page 698*
treeline   *page 694*
tropical rainforest biome   *page 696*
tundra biome   *page 703*

REVIEW QUESTIONS

1. What is a biome?
2. What climatic and terrain features influence the distribution of terrestrial biome regions?

3. List and briefly describe each of the Earth's eight principal terrestrial biomes.

REFERENCES AND FURTHER READINGS

Archibold, A.W. 1995. *Ecology of World Vegetation*. New York: Chapman and Hall.

Barbour, M.G., and W.D. Billings. 2000. *North American Terrestrial Vegetation*, 2nd edn. London/New York: Cambridge Univ. Press.

Collinson, A.S. 1988. *Introduction to World Vegetation*, 2nd edn. Winchester, Mass.: Unwin Hyman.

Hengeveld, R. 1990. *Dynamic Biogeography*. London/New York: Cambridge Univ. Press.

Kellman, M.C. 1980. *Plant Geography*, 2nd edn. New York: St Martin's Press.

Küchler, A.W., and I.S. Zonneveld, eds. 1988. *Handbook of Vegetation Science 10: Vegetation Mapping*. Hingham, Mass.: Kluwer.

MacDonald, G.M. 2003. *Biogeography: Introduction to Space, Time and Life*. New York: Wiley.

Maurer, B. 1994. *Geographical Analysis of Biodiversity*. Cambridge, Mass.: Blackwell.

Morin, N., chief ed. 1992–2004. *Flora of North America North of Mexico*, 14 vols. New York: Oxford Univ. Press.

Nadkarni, N.M. 1985. 'Roots That Go out on a Limb', *Natural History* 94, 2: 43–8.

Orme, A.R., ed. 2002. *The Physical Geography of North America*. New York: Oxford Univ. Press.

Sauer, J.D. 1988. *Plant Migration: The Dynamics of Geographic Patterning in Seed Plant Species*. Berkeley, Calif.: Univ. of California Press.

Vale, T.R. 1982. *Plants and People: Vegetation Change in North America*. Washington: Association of American Geographers, Resource Publications in Geography.

Vankat, J.L. 1979. *The Natural Vegetation of North America: An Introduction*. New York: Wiley.

Vavilov, N.I. 1992. *Origin and Geography of Cultivated Plants*. New York: Cambridge Univ. Press.

Walter, H. 1985. *Vegetation of the Earth and Ecological Systems of the Geo-Biosphere*, 3rd edn. New York: Springer-Verlag.

Woodward, F.I. 1987. *Climate and Plant Distribution*. New York: Cambridge Univ. Press.

 ## WEB RESOURCES

www.geocities.com/RainForest/2498/bsghome1.htm The homepage for the Biogeography Specialty Group of the Association of American Geographers (AAG). This page has biogeography and ecology links, information about student paper session opportunities, the *Biogeographer* newsletter, and links to other AAG information.

www.worldbiomes.com This site provides background information about each distinct type of biome, a list of reference reading, and a discussion board for the wildlife ecology unit.

Unit 48

Zoogeography: Spatial Aspects of Animal Populations

Objectives

- To briefly outline the theory of evolution and related principles such as natural selection, which led to the present-day spatial distribution of animals.

- To give a brief history of zoogeography.

- To relate zoogeography to the larger context of environmental conservation.

The principal terrestrial biomes discussed in Unit 47 are based primarily on the distribution of dominant vegetation. But the distribution of fauna (animals) is closely associated with plants and with soils that sustain the flora. A biome, therefore, actually is an interacting set of ecosystems that extends over a large area of the Earth. Its establishment and maintenance depend not only on climate and soils but also on plants and animals—animals ranging from the tiniest bacteria to the largest mammals.

Processes of Evolution

To appreciate the work of zoogeographers we should take note of some aspects of the theory of evolution. This theory has led to our understanding that both variety and order mark life on this planet. Basic to evolutionary theory is the concept of *natural selection* within a single species. Natural selection stems from reproductive processes: genetic information (*genes*) from each parent joins in such a way as to combine a small degree of randomness (chance) with a high degree of specification (stability). Thus a human child may have blue or green eyes, but very likely only two arms and two legs.

The mechanism of speciation (which confers continuity on the species) sometimes breaks down, and when this happens, the exact message of heredity is not passed on. The result is a **mutation** (an inheritable change in the DNA of a gene), and a new species may originate from such an occurrence. Another important part of evolutionary theory holds that a species will produce more offspring than can survive to reproduce. In all species, many immature individuals die by accident, disease, or predation. We encountered this idea in studying food chains, where we saw that autotrophs are eaten by herbivores and herbivores are consumed by carnivores. But while individuals are often killed, the entire population continues to evolve. No matter how many antelope are eaten by lions on the African plains, as long as the herds maintain a sustainable population, they will continue to survive.

An important related principle has to do with the place where a species can best sustain itself and thrive. This is referred to as its **ecological niche** (or, in the zoogeographic context, simply *niche*), the environmental space within which an organism operates most efficiently. Some niches are very large, perhaps coinciding with entire biomes or continental parts of biomes. The ecological niche of the South American jaguar is a substantial part of the Amazonian rainforest. Other niches are very small. A specialized (or very small) niche reduces competition from other species, but it also increases the risk of total annihilation, perhaps resulting from a change in the natural environment. A large niche may overlap other niches, causing competition, but it has the advantage of permitting adjustment in the event of environmental change.

Zoogeography focuses mainly on the larger ecological niches. These are so complex that they are better termed habitats. The **habitat** of a species is the environment it normally occupies within its geographic range. A habitat usually is described in quite general terms, such as grassland, seashore, or alpine. Obviously each of these habitats contains many smaller ecological niches.

Now we come to a zoogeographical-evolutionary principle of great importance. Some offspring are better adapted to their habitat or niche than others. One familiar example of this idea is the evolution of the giraffe's long neck, first proposed by Darwin. We start with the assumption that neck length varied in previous giraffe populations. The animals with the longest necks could reach higher into the trees and thereby obtain more food than giraffes with shorter necks. Shorter-necked individuals had to compete for food near the ground with several other species. These shorter-necked giraffes were less successful, and over time the longer-necked giraffes came to prosper, breed successfully, and dominate the species (Figure 48.1). Recent studies have suggested that giraffes may have developed necks greater than 2 m long and weighing up to 90 kg to win mates. In battles over the females, the male giraffes use their necks against their competitors. The giraffe with the longer and heavier neck generally wins. This implies, then, that better adapted organisms are more likely to survive and reproduce, whether they are giraffes or camouflaged insects. Through their genes, they pass on favourable aspects of their adaptation to successors.

The environment changes over time and places differing demands on species populations. There is a great deal of variation within a species (e.g., humans: tall and short people; fat and thin people; different skin, hair, and eye coloration). Some individuals are better fitted to a certain kind of environment and remain to breed and pass on their DNA, while other, less well-suited individuals die. The process is endless, and the evidence exists everywhere in the natural landscape.

A good example of complex adaptations to a shared habitat is the Serengeti Plain of East Africa, an area of savanna grassland grazed and browsed by many species. The herbivores are so finely adapted that they use different portions of the Serengeti's vegetation at different times. During part of the year, mixed herds graze on the short grass, satisfying their protein requirements without having to use too much energy in respiration while obtaining the food. Eventually the short grass becomes overgrazed. Then the largest animals, the zebras and buffalo, move into areas of mixed vegetation—tall grasses, short grasses, and herbs. Zebras and buffalo eat the stems and tops of the taller grasses, and trample and soften the lower vegetation. The wildebeests (or gnus) can then graze the middle level of vegetation, trampling the level below. Next the Thomson's gazelles move into the softened area to eat the low leaves, herbs, and fallen fruit at ground level.

LINK

From the Fieldnotes

Figure 48.1   *'Safari in Tanzania, March 1984. Spent a morning watching a small herd of giraffes as they browsed together, dispersed in the bush, reconvened, were briefly joined by a small herd of zebras, then separated again. In the competitive evolution of East Africa's herbivores, these longer-necked animals had advantages, notably their access to food beyond the reach of others, that led to larger numbers of offspring—who passed the genetic information involving the long neck to later generations.'*

The pastoral indigenous people of the Serengeti have long been part of this well-balanced ecosystem. Some scientists conclude that their regular use of fire, as well as naturally occurring fire, has helped to maintain the short grass best adapted to the native animals. In its totality, the Serengeti ecosystem perfectly illustrates the arrangement of plants and animals that has developed under the rules governing both energy flow and natural selection. An understanding of these rules can explain both the nature of species and their geographical spread throughout the biosphere.

Emergence of Zoogeography

The field of zoogeography began to develop following the publication of works by Humboldt (1769–1859) and Charles Darwin (1809–1882). Humboldt's maps and drawings of plants in their environmental settings and of animals encountered on his explorations formed the first hard evidence for early zoogeographical theories. Darwin's momentous 1859 work on evolution, *The Origin of Species*, spurred ideas about environment and adaptation. Through his remarkable field studies, Darwin focused attention on some unique zoogeographical areas that have remained at the centre of research ever since, especially the Galapagos Islands in the Pacific off Ecuador. Here lay a diversity of habitats for a number of different species of finches, with each having different types of beaks and feeding habitats suitable for the particular environment of an individual island. During the middle part of the nineteenth century, information about the distribution of species and ideas about habitats and food chains began to crystallize quite rapidly.

As more became known about animals and plants in places distant from the centres of learning, urgent zoogeographical questions presented themselves. One of the most interesting involved the transition of fauna from Southeast Asia to Australia. Somewhere in the intervening Indonesian archipelago, the animals of Southeast Asia give way to the very different animals typical of Australia. Australia is the Earth's last major refuge of *marsupials*, animals whose young are born very early in their development and are then carried in a pouch on the abdomen—kangaroos, wallabies, wombats, and koalas (Figure 48.2) are among Australia's many marsupials. Australia is also the home of the only two remaining egg-laying mammals (monotremes), the platypus and the echidna. Marsupials are found in New Guinea and on islands in the eastern part of Indonesia, but non-marsupial animals (such as tigers, rhinoceroses, elephants, and primates) prevail in western Indonesia. Where, then, lies the zoogeographical boundary between these sharply contrasting faunal assemblages?

One answer to this still debated question was provided by Alfred Russel Wallace in an important work published in 1876, *The Geographical Distribution of Animals*. Wallace mapped what was then known about the animals of Indonesia. He showed how far various species had progressed eastward along the island stepping stones between mainland Southeast Asia and continental Australia; he also mapped the westward extent of marsupials. On the basis of these and other data, Wallace drew a line across the Indonesian archipelago, a zoogeographical boundary between Southeast Asia's and Australia's fauna (Figure 48.3). **Wallace's Line** lay between Borneo and Sulawesi, and between the first and second islands (Bali and Lombok) east of Java. This line became one of the most hotly debated zoogeographical boundaries ever drawn, and to this day it remains one of the more intensely discussed lines in all of physical geography.

As more evidence was gathered concerning the complex fauna of the Indonesian archipelago, other zoogeographers tried to improve on Wallace's Line. In the process they proved how difficult the problems of regional zoogeography can be. The zoologist M.C. Weber argued that Wallace's Line lay too far to the west. His alternative line (see Figure 48.3) was placed just west of New Guinea and north-central Australia, making virtually all of Indonesia part of the Southeast Asian faunal region. The substantial distance between Wallace's Line and **Weber's Line**, now known as Wallacea, underscores the fact that zoogeographical data can be interpreted differently.

Many biogeographers would agree that the delimitation of vegetative regions presents fewer problems than faunal regions do. It is one thing to draw maps of stands of rainforest, an expanse of desert, or the boundary between taiga and tundra, but to do the same for African lions, American jaguars, or Indian tigers is quite another matter. Animals move and migrate, their range (region of natural occurrence) varies, and they may simply be difficult to locate and enumerate.

The Earth's Zoogeographical Realms

A global map of zoogeographical realms, based on Wallace's pioneering work, is an exercise in generalization, but it does reflect evolutionary centres for animal life as well as the work of natural barriers over time (Figure 48.4). Note that zoogeographical realm boundaries in several areas coincide with high mountains (Himalayas), broad deserts (Sahara, Arabian), deep marine channels (Indonesia), and narrow land bridges (Central America).

By many measures, the *Paleotropical (Ethiopian) realm* contains the Earth's most varied fauna, an enormously rich assemblage of animals, many of which are unique to this realm. Some species, however, have relatives in other realms. For example, the lion and the elephant also occur in the *Indomalayan (Oriental) realm*. Nevertheless, the Indomalayan realm has a less diverse fauna. The fauna of the island of *Madagascar*, shown on the map as a discrete realm, differs quite strongly from that of nearby Africa. While Madagascar is home to the lemurs, a group of small

From the Fieldnotes

Figure 48.2 *'Moving slowly and quietly through a eucalyptus forest in New South Wales, Australia, I was rewarded with this extraordinary sight, a koala resting in a tangle of branches. The koala "bear" is part of Australia's unique fauna; it is a marsupial and carries its offspring in its pouch for as long as seven months. It eats about 1.3 kg of eucalyptus leaves daily, but only a particular kind and quality of leaf; in the wild its lifespan averages 20 years. The koala has diminished in number from an estimated several million to perhaps 150,000, and the population continues to decline as humans encroach on its natural habitat and diseases take their toll.'*

primates, the island has nothing to match East Africa's herd animals, lions, or even poisonous snakes.

The faunal assemblage of the *Australian realm* exhibits the consequences of prolonged isolation and separate evolution. This is the realm of marsupials, such as the kangaroo and the wombat, of the platypus and the thylacine, or Tasmanian 'tiger'. While some biogeographers include New Zealand in the Australian realm, others map *New Zealand*, like Madagascar, as a discrete realm. There is ample geographical reason for doing so: New Zealand's native fauna includes no mammals, very few terrestrial vertebrates of any kind, and nothing to match the assemblage of Australia—except when it comes to birds. New Zealand has a rich variety of bird life, with a number of flightless species like the kiwi.

The *Neotropical realm* also has a rich and varied faunal assemblage, which includes such species as the tapir, the jaguar, sloths, and the boa constrictor. In both plants and animals, biogeographers can discern evidence of the

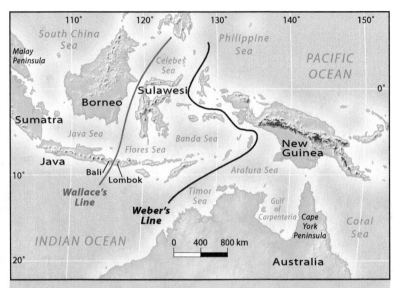

Figure 48.3 Wallace's Line across the Indonesian archipelago. This controversial boundary between the faunal assemblages of Southeast Asia and Australia was challenged by others, including Max C. Weber, who placed his alternative Weber's Line much closer to Australia and New Guinea. The faunal area between the two lines is now known as Wallacea.

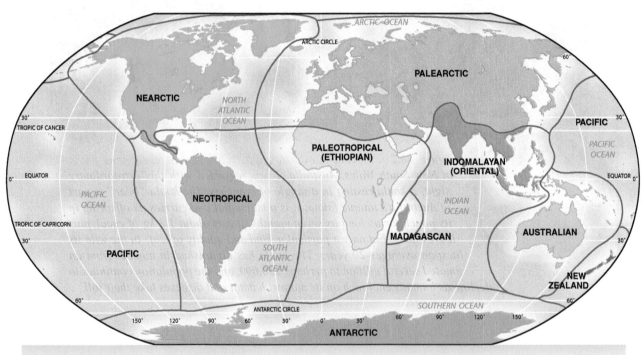

Figure 48.4 World zoogeographical realms.

theory of **convergent evolution**, which holds that organisms in widely separated biogeographical realms, though descended from diverse ancestors, develop similar adaptations to measurably similar habitats.

The two remaining realms, the *Nearctic* and the *Palearctic*, are much less rich and much less diverse than the other major zoogeographical realms. Some biogeographers prefer to map these together as a single realm, but

evidence of long-term isolation (the Beringia land bridge notwithstanding) is much stronger in the North American Nearctic than in the Eurasian Palearctic realm. Remarkable adaptations exist, such as the polar bear (both realms), the Siberian tiger and giant panda (Palearctic), and the bison and grizzly bear (Nearctic).

Figure 48.4 presents the global zoogeographical map at a high level of generalization, and it should

LINK

be remembered that this is a map of *realms*. Embedded within each realm are numerous subdivisions, or zoogeographical *regions*. Consider the Australian realm: the fauna of mainland Australia, despite commonalities with the nearby large island of New Guinea, nonetheless differs sufficiently to make New Guinea and Australia separate zoogeographical regions within the Australian realm.

Further Studies in Zoogeography

As interest in zoogeography grew, new kinds of studies were undertaken. After 1900 zoogeography became more ecological and less cartographic. Zoogeographers became concerned with changing environments, past faunal migration routes, and present migratory habits, such as the flight paths of birds between summering and wintering grounds. This change in the field can be seen by comparing Wallace's book, published more than a century ago, with a volume by Philip J. Darlington Jr, carrying a very similar title and published in 1957, *Zoogeography: The Geographical Distribution of Animals*. Darlington posed four questions for zoogeographers: (1) What is the main pattern of animal distribution? (2) How has this pattern been formed? (3) Why has this pattern developed as it has? (4) What does animal distribution—past and present—tell us about lands and climates? Note that the first question is only the beginning, not the entire objective, as was the case in Wallace's work.

By the time Darlington did his research, much more was known about ice ages, crustal mobility, and changing sea levels than was known in Wallace's time. It was not long before **ecological zoogeography**, the study of animals as they relate to their total environment, became a leading theme. A book published in 1965, *The Geography of Evolution*, by G.G. Simpson, deals with such topics as adaptation, competition, and habitats. By the 1990s, as their titles indicate, ecological zoogeography had expanded to encompass books on *Geographical Analysis of Biodiversity* by B. Maurer and *Plant and Animal Introductions* by P.J. Jarvis.

Island Zoogeography

Biologists believe that there may be as many as 30 million species of organisms on our planet, of which only 1.7 million have been identified and classified. Obviously, many species live in the same habitat, often sharing ecological niches or parts of niches. What determines how many species can be accommodated in a specific, measured region? This is a central question in modern zoogeography. Where ranges and niches overlap, as on large landmasses, it is not practical to calculate the number of species an area can sustain because there are no controllable boundaries. But an island presents special opportunities.

A small island can be inventoried completely, so that every species living on it is accounted for. When zoogeographers did this work, their research had some expected and some unexpected results. In 1967 R.H. MacArthur and E.O. Wilson determined that the number of species living on an island is related to the size of that island. Given similar environmental conditions, the larger the island, the larger the number of species it can accommodate. This might have been anticipated, except that the larger island does not have a wider range of natural environments, so that it is the size, not the internal variability that might come with it, that affects the species total. Moreover, it was discovered that an island of a given size can accommodate only a limited number of species. New species may arrive, brought by birds from far away or entering via debris washing up onshore. If the island already has a stable population, these new species will not succeed unless another species first becomes extinct.

This conclusion, that an island's capacity to accommodate species has a numerical limit, was tested on some small mangrove islands off the coast of Florida over a period of two years. Zoogeographers counted the species of insects, spiders, crabs, and other arthropods living on each island. Then they took the rather radical step of spraying the islands with pesticides, wiping out the entire population. After a few years, the islands were reinhabited. The same number of species had returned to them, although the number of individuals was proportionately different. That is, while there were crabs and spiders before the extinction, now there were more crabs and fewer spiders. This indicates not only that a certain number of species is characteristic of an island in a certain environment, but also that the kinds of species making up this number vary and may depend on the order in which they arrived to fill the available ecological niches.

Biogeographers can also learn about niches and habitats when new land is formed—for example, following the formation of a volcanic island. In 1883 the volcanic island of Krakatau in western Indonesia exploded, leaving small island remnants and creating a wholly new and barren landscape. Soon new soil began to form on the fertile lava base, and plant seeds arrived by air, sea, and via birds. New vegetation could be seen within a few years (Figure 48.5), and soon animal repopulation began. The arrival of new species was monitored, adding to our knowledge about the occupation of available niches and habitats. Such knowledge permitted optimistic predictions about the revegetation and recovery of Mount St Helens in the state of Washington following its destructive eruption of 1980. Just three years after this eruption, 90 per cent of the plant

From the Fieldnotes

Figure 48.5 *'We drove across an expanse of lava formed from a recent fissure eruption in Tanzania—so recent that virtually no vegetation had yet taken hold on it. Research has shown that plants manage to establish themselves quite soon (a matter of years, not generations or centuries) after new rocks are created by volcanic eruptions. This lava must therefore be quite young, but the process is clearly at work. A seed found a way to sprout in a crack in the rock, where weathered particles and some moisture supplied the essentials for growth.'*

species that originally inhabited the devastated slopes had already re-established themselves.

What has been learned about island zoogeography also applies to other isolated places, such as the tops of tepuis (in South America), buttes, and mesas (see Figure 33.7) where steep slopes act as barriers to invasion. The stable populations atop such landforms resemble island populations in some ways, but in other ways they relate more closely to the surrounding ecosystems. By studying these hilltop faunal assemblages, zoogeographers come still closer to an understanding of the complex relationships that characterize habitats and niches in general. The next section looks at how the distribution of animal life is influenced by humans, who, even by their inadvertent actions (see 'Perspectives' box), can produce widespread negative consequences.

Zoogeography and Conservation

Research in zoogeography often has important implications for the survival of species. Knowledge of the numbers, range, habits, and reproductive success of species is crucial to their effective protection. The explosive growth of the Earth's human population and the destructive patterns of consumption by prospering peoples have combined to render many species of animals extinct, endangered, or threatened. Awareness of the many threats to the remaining fauna has increased in recent decades, and some species have been saved from the brink of extinction. But for many others hope is fading.

Animal Ranges

An important zoogeographical contribution to research in support of species conservation lies in detailed studies of the spatial properties of **animal ranges**. This concept is discussed in Unit 46, and the ranges of four North American mammals are mapped in Figure 48.6. It is not just the size of a range, however, but also its geographical pattern that will determine whether a species can be expected to survive. The case of the spotted owl in the Pacific Northwest is a good example. What this owl needs is old forest, not secondary growth after logging. It needs soft and rotting wood so that it can establish nests in the trunks; neatly reforested slopes do not have such old decaying trees. The range of the spotted owl is therefore restricted to the dwindling stands of older forest, and the map that conservationists need will show where those patches of remaining old forest are located. The pattern of these patches—how large

they are, how densely forested, how close together—will reveal more about the prospects of the spotted owl than any estimate of the total size of its range.

Human Impact on Animal Habitats

The effect of human encroachment on animal habitats is another important sphere of zoogeographical study. In many parts of the world—in the foothills of the Himalayas, on the plains of East Africa, in the forests of tropical South America—people and animals are competing for land. Not long ago, substantial parts of India teemed with herds of wild buffalo and many kinds of antelope and deer, as well as their predators, lions and tigers, and large numbers of elephants and rhinoceroses. The South Asian human population explosion, together with a breakdown in the conservation programs, has destroyed one of the Earth's great wildlife legacies. The Indian lion is virtually extinct; the great tiger is endangered and survives in only small numbers in remote forest areas. In East Africa, population pressure in the areas surrounding the major wildlife reserves, along with poaching, is decimating the fauna. In the Amazon Basin, rainforest habitat destruction (see Unit 17) threatens the survival of many species of animals as well as plants.

All this is reminiscent of what happened to the wildlife of North America following the arrival of the Europeans. The North American conservation effort over the past century has concentrated on the salvageable remnants of this realm's wildlife, and there have been successes as well as setbacks. The protection of wildlife poses complex problems. Special-interest groups such as hunters sometimes demand the right to shoot particular species, endangering what may be a delicate balance in the ecosystem. Others object to closing wilderness areas to the public for any purpose, even sightseeing, when this is necessary to allow an endangered area or animal species to recuperate. And because wildlife is mobile, it may move beyond the boundaries of a wildlife refuge or national park, thus becoming endangered. The protection of birds, whose migratory habits may carry them across the length of the continent, is made especially difficult by their mobility. At the same time, regulatory regimes were first established nearly a century ago by Canada and the US for migratory birds, the Yellowstone to Yukon protected area initiative seeks to create a lengthy corridor to preserve wildlife, and hunter groups such as Ducks Unlimited have been instrumental in conserving wildlife habitat from human encroachment.

Preservation Efforts

Conservationists in North America have learned a great deal about the most effective methods of wildlife preservation. This is not simply a matter of fencing off an

Perspectives on the Human Environment

The African Stowaways*

Around 1929 a few African mosquitoes arrived in Brazil. They had probably stowed away aboard a fast French destroyer in the West African city of Dakar. Once in Brazil, the immigrants established a colony in a marsh along the South Atlantic coast. Although the residents of a nearby town suffered from an unusual outbreak of malaria, nobody seemed to notice the presence of the foreign mosquitoes for a long time. Meanwhile, the insects settled comfortably in their new environment, and during the next few years they spread out along about 320 km of the coast. Then, in 1938, a malaria epidemic swept across most of northeast Brazil. A year later the disease continued to ravage the region; hundreds of thousands of people fell ill, and nearly 20,000 died.

Brazil always had malaria-carrying mosquitoes but none quite like the new African variety. Whereas the native mosquitoes tended to stay in the forest, the foreign pests could breed in sunny ponds outside the forest, and they quickly made a habit of flying into houses to find humans to bite. With the mosquito transplantation problem finally understood, the Brazilian government, aided by the Rockefeller Foundation, hired more than 3000 people and spent over $2 million to attack the invaders. After studying the ecological characteristics of the 'enemy', they sprayed houses and ponds. Within three years the battle wiped out the African mosquitoes in South America. Brazil also initiated a quarantine and inspection program for incoming aircraft and ships to keep out unwanted stowaways.

High-speed transportation developed by humans has inadvertently carried many plants and animals to other continents. In their new environment, the immigrants may react in one of three ways: they may languish and die; they may fit into the existing ecosystem structure; or they may tick away like a time bomb and eventually explode like the African mosquitoes.

Another accidental African arrival that could not be controlled in Brazil, the so-called African killer bee, threatens parts of North America today. These bees escaped from a Brazilian research facility in 1957 and have been slowly spreading out across the Americas ever since. By 1980 the bees had entered the Central American land bridge and were steadily progressing northward. By the early 1990s they had crossed all of Mexico and penetrated Texas across the Rio Grande. Today they are present in 13 southern and southwestern states. Although joint US–Mexican efforts to slow the advance of the bees were moderately successful in the late 1980s, the US Department of Agriculture was forced to abandon hope that the invaders could be repelled, and the USDA is still testing strategies to cope with this spreading pest on American soil.

*The source for most of this box is Elton (1971).

area where particular species exist, but involves the management of the entire habitat, the maintenance of a balance among animals and plants—and, sometimes, people. A series of legislative actions and commissions during the late twentieth century served to facilitate and implement the newly developed conservation practices. There have been several successes, including the revival of the bison, the wild turkey, and the wolf as well as the survival of the grizzly bear and the bald eagle.

In European countries, as well as in the countries of the former Soviet Union to the east, the story of conservation efforts is largely one of remnant preservation. Europe's varied wildlife fell to the pressure of human expansion centuries ago. Conservation is an expensive proposition, afforded most easily by the wealthier developed countries. European colonial powers carried the concept to their colonies, where they could carve wildlife refuges from tribal lands with impunity. In many areas of Africa and Asia, the Europeans

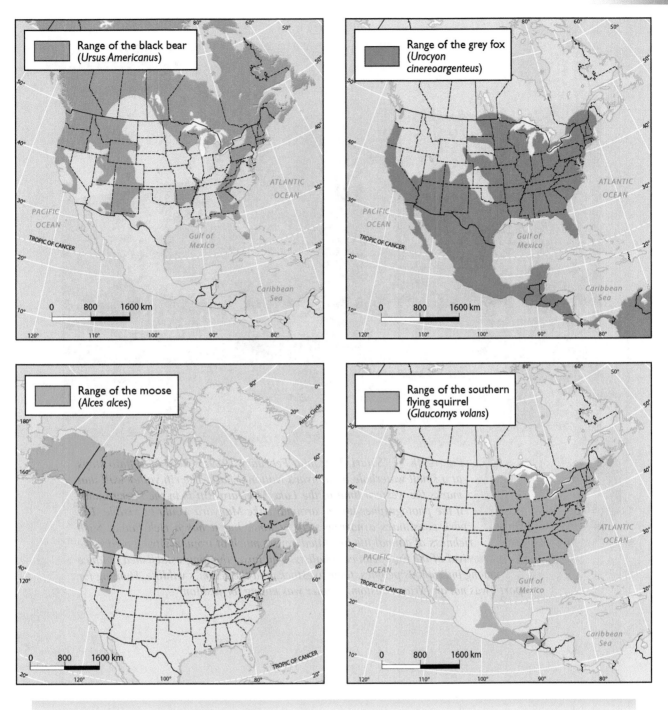

Figure 48.6 Ranges of some North American mammals.

found the indigenous population living in harmonious balance with livestock and wildlife. The invaders disturbed this balance, introduced the concept of hunting for profit and trophies, and then closed off huge land tracts as wildlife reserves with controlled hunting zones (Figure 48.7). That the African wildlife refuges have for so long survived the period of decolonization (some are now in danger) is testimony to a determination that was not present when orgies of slaughter eliminated much of North America's wildlife

heritage. North Americans may have advanced knowledge of conservation theory and management practices, but they are in no position to proselytize.

Zoogeography, therefore, has many theoretical and practical dimensions. The spatial aspects of ranges, habitats, and niches require research and analysis. The results of such investigations are directly relevant to those who seek to protect wildlife and who make policy to ensure species survival.

From the Fieldnotes

Figure 48.7 *'Safari, Tanzania, February 1989. A herd of buffalo stops at a small waterhole in Manyara National Park. The rift valley wall that marks the western limit of the Lake Manyara Rift is in the background; if the photographer turned around, Lake Manyara would be visible. The park constitutes a narrow strip of land, but it has a rich fauna. Such richness of animal life prevailed across much of tropical Africa before the arrival of the European colonialists, who upset the long-established balance among indigenous peoples, their livestock, and the realm's wildlife. Hunting for "sport" was not an African custom; neither was killing for fashion.'*

KEY TERMS

REVIEW QUESTIONS

1. What is an *ecological niche* and how is it related to a habitat?

2. How were Alexander von Humboldt and Alfred Russel Wallace instrumental in developing the field of zoogeography?

3. In what ways are animal and plant conservation similar?

4. In what ways do animal and plant conservation differ?

5. What have biogeographers learned about ecological niches and habitats from their fieldwork on islands and land newly emerged from the sea?

REFERENCES AND FURTHER READINGS

Anon. 1997. 'How the Giraffe Got Its Neck', *Discover Magazine* 18, 3 (Mar.): 14.

Banfield, A.W.F. 1974. *The Mammals of Canada*. Toronto: Univ. of Toronto Press and Natural Museums of Canada.

Briggs, J.C. 1995. *Global Biogeography*. Amsterdam: Elsevier.

Burt, W.H., and R.P Grossenheider. 1976. *A Field Guide to Mammals: North America North of Mexico*, Peterson Field Guide. Boston: Houghton Mifflin.

Darlington, P.J., Jr. 1957. *Zoogeography: The Geographical Distribution of Animals*. New York: Wiley (reprinted by Krieger, 1980).

Dasmann, R.F. 1984. *Environmental Conservation*, 5th edn. New York: Wiley.

Daws, G., and M. Fujita. 1999. *Archipelago: The Islands of Indonesia*. Berkeley: Univ. of California Press.

Elton, C.S. 1971. 'The Invaders', in T.R. Detwyler, ed., *Man's Impact on Environment*. New York: McGraw-Hill, 447–58.

Illies, J. 1974. *Introduction to Zoogeography*. New York: Macmillan.

Jarvis, P.J. 1999. *Plant and Animal Introductions*. Malden, Mass.: Blackwell.

MacArthur, R.H., and E.O. Wilson. 1967. *The Theory of Island Biogeography*. Princeton, NJ: Princeton Univ. Press.

MacDonald, G.M. 2003. *Biogeography: Introduction to Space, Time and Life*. New York: Wiley.

Maurer, B. 1994. *Geographical Analysis of Biodiversity*. Cambridge, Mass.: Blackwell.

Newbigin, M.I. 1968. *Plant and Animal Geography*. London: Methuen.

Nowak, R.M. 1999. *Walker's Primates of the World*. Baltimore: Johns Hopkins Univ. Press.

Quammen, D. 1996. *The Song of the Dodo: Island Biogeography in an Age of Extinctions*. New York: Scribner.

Simpson, G.G. 1965. *The Geography of Evolution: Collected Essays*. Philadelphia: Chilton Books.

Wallace, A.R. 1962. *The Geographical Distribution of Animals; with a Study of the Relations of Living and Extinct Faunas as Elucidating the Past Changes of the Earth's Surface*. New York: Hafner (reprint of 1876 original).

Whitmore, T.C. 1981. *Wallace's Line and Plate Tectonics*. London/New York: Oxford Univ. Press [Clarendon].

 ## WEB RESOURCES

animals.about.com/cs/conservation A page of wildlife conservation links, including the National Wildlife Federation and the Living Planet.

www.ultimateungulate.com/ Authoritative website about the ungulates of the world (deer, etc.).

www.worldwildlife.org/science/ecoregions/item1847.html Background information on world ecoregions, as well as maps and information about conservation programs.

REVIEW QUESTIONS

REFERENCES AND FURTHER READINGS

WEB RESOURCES

Appendix A   SI and Customary Units and Their Conversions

Appendix A provides a table of units and their conversion from older units to Standard International (SI) units.

Length

Metric Measure

1 kilometre (km)	= 1000 metres (m)
1 metre (m)	= 100 centimetres (cm)
1 centimetre (cm)	= 10 millimetres (mm)

Nonmetric Measure

1 mile (mi)	= 5280 feet (ft)
	= 1760 yards (yd)
1 yard (yd)	= 3 feet (ft)
1 foot (ft)	= 12 inches (in)
1 fathom (fath)	= 6 feet (ft)

Conversions

1 kilometre (km)	= 0.6214 mile (mi)
1 metre (m)	= 3.281 feet (ft)
	= 1.094 yards (yd)
1 centimetre (cm)	= 0.3937 inch (in)
1 millimetre (mm)	= 0.0394 inch (in)
1 mile (mi)	= 1.609 kilometres (km)
1 foot (ft)	= 0.3048 metre (m)
1 inch (in)	= 2.54 centimetres (cm)
	= 25.4 millimetres (mm)

Area

Metric Measure

1 square kilometre (km²)	= 1,000,000 square metres (m²)
	= 100 hectares (ha)
1 square metre (m²)	= 10,000 square centimetres (cm²)
1 hectare (ha)	= 10,000 square metres (m²)

Nonmetric Measure

1 square mile (mi²)	= 640 acres (ac)
1 acre (ac)	= 4840 square yards (yd²)
1 square foot (ft²)	= 144 square inches (in²)

Conversions

1 square kilometre (km²)	= 0.386 square mile (mi²)
1 hectare (ha)	= 2.471 acres (ac)
1 square metre (m²)	= 10.764 square feet (ft²)
	= 1.196 square yards (yd²)
1 square centimetre (cm²)	= 0.155 square inch (in²)
1 square mile (mi²)	= 2.59 square kilometres (km²)
1 acre (ac)	= 0.4047 hectare (ha)
1 square foot (ft²)	= 0.0929 square metre (m²)
1 square inch (in²)	= 6.4516 square centimetres (cm²)

Volume

Metric Measure

1 cubic metre (m³)	= 1,000,000 cubic centimetres (cm³)
1 litre (l)	= 1000 millilitres (ml)
	= 0.001 cubic metre (m³)
1 millilitre (ml)	= 1 cubic centimetre (cm³)

Nonmetric Measure

1 cubic foot (ft³)	= 1728 cubic inches (in³)
1 cubic yard (yd³)	= 27 cubic feet (ft³)

Conversions

1 cubic metre (m³)	= 264.2 gallons (US) (gal)
	= 35.314 cubic feet (ft³)
1 litre (l)	= 1.057 quarts (US) (qt)
	= 33.815 fluid ounces (US) (fl oz)
1 cubic centimetre (cm³)	= 0.0610 cubic inch (in³)
1 cubic mile (mi³)	= 4.168 cubic kilometres (km³)
1 cubic foot (ft³)	= 0.0283 cubic metre (m³)
1 cubic inch (in³)	= 16.39 cubic centimetres (cm³)
1 gallon (gal)	= 3.784 litres (l)

Mass

Metric Measure

1000 kilograms (kg)	= 1 metric tonne (t)
1 kilogram (kg)	= 1000 grams (g)

Nonmetric Measure

1 short ton (ton)	= 2000 pounds (lb)
1 long ton	= 2240 pounds (lb)
1 pound (lb)	= 16 ounces (oz)

Conversions

1 metric tonne (t)	= 2205 pounds (lb)
1 kilogram (kg)	= 2.205 pounds (lb)
1 gram (g)	= 0.03527 ounce (oz)
1 pound (lb)	= 0.4536 kilogram (kg)
1 ounce (oz)	= 28.35 grams (g)

Pressure

standard sea-level air pressure	= 101.325 kilopascals (KPa)
	= 1013.25 millibars (mb)
	= 14.7 lb/in²

Temperature

To change from Fahrenheit (F) to Celsius (C)

$$°C = \frac{°F - 32}{1.8}$$

To change from Celsius (C) to Fahrenheit (F)

$$°F = °C \times 1.8 + 32$$

Energy and Power

1 calorie (cal)	= the amount of heat that will raise the temperature of 1 g of water 1°C (1.8°F)
1 joule (J)	= 0.239 calorie (cal)
1 watt (W)	= 1 joule per second (J/s)
	= 14.34 calories per minute (cal/min)

Appendix B   Orders and Suborders of the US Soil Taxonomy

Order	Suborder	Characteristics
1. Entisol	Aquent	Shows evidence of saturation at some season
	Arent	Lacks horizons because of ploughing or other human activity
	Fluvent	Formed in recent water-deposited sediments, as in floodplains
	Orthent	Occurs on recent erosional surfaces, such as high mountains
	Psamment	Occurs in sandy areas, such as sand dunes
2. Histosol	Fibrist	Occurs in poorly drained areas, slightly decomposed
	Folist	Occurs in poorly drained areas, mass of leaves in early stage of decomposition
	Hemist	Occurs in poorly drained areas, intermediate stage of decomposition
	Saparist	Occurs in poorly drained areas, highly decomposed
3. Vertisol	Torrert	Occurs in arid climates
	Udert	Occurs in humid climates
	Ustert	Occurs in monsoon climates
	Xerert	Occurs in Mediterranean climates
4. Inceptisol	Aquept	Wet with poor drainage
	Ochrept	Freely drained, light in colour
	Plaggept	Has a surface layer more than 50 cm thick resulting from human activity, such as manuring
	Tropept	Freely drained, brownish to reddish, found in the tropics
	Umbrept	Dark reddish or brownish, acidic, freely drained, organically rich
5. Gelisol	Histel	Previously included under entisol and inceptisol soil orders
	Turbel	Occurs at high latitudes (beyond treeline) and high altitudes
	Orthel	Underlain usually by permafrost, cryoturbation, patterned ground, and other periglacial landforms (e.g., pingos, solifluction lobes) are widespread
6. Andisol	Aquand	Occurs in wet areas
	Cryand	Occurs in cold areas, including high altitudes
	Torrand	Occurs in warm, arid climates
	Udand	Occurs in humid climates
	Ustand	Occurs in monsoon climates
	Vitrand	Formed in association with volcanic glass
	Xerand	Occurs in Mediterranean climates
7. Aridisol	Argid	Has an illuvial horizon where clays have accumulated to a significant extent
	Orthid	Has an altered horizon, a hard layer (called hardpan or duripan), or an illuvial horizon of water-soluble material
8. Mollisol	Alboll	Has a surface layer that covers a white horizon from which clay and iron oxides have been removed, and a layer of clay accumulation below
	Aquoll	Saturated with water at some time during the year
	Boroll	Cool or cold, relatively freely drained
	Rendoll	Occurs in humid climates, developed from parent materials rich in calcium
	Udoll	Not dry for as much as 60 consecutive or 90 cumulative days per year
	Ustoll	Occurs in monsoon climates
	Xeroll	Occurs in Mediterranean climates

Order	Suborder	Characteristics
9. Alfisol	Aqualf	Periodically saturated with water
	Boralf	Freely drained, found in cool places
	Udalf	Brownish to reddish, freely drained
	Ustalf	Partly or completely dry for periods longer than 3 months
	Xeralf	Occurs in dry climates
10. Spodosol	Aquod	Associated with wetness
	Ferrod	Has an iron-enriched sesquioxide horizon
	Hurmod	Has a humus-enriched sesquioxide horizon
	Orthod	Has significant amounts of humus and iron in the sesquioxide horizon
11. Ultisol	Aquult	Occurs in wet places
	Humult	Freely drained, rich in humus
	Udult	Freely drained, poor in humus
	Ustult	Occurs in warm regions with high rainfall but a pronounced dry season
	Xerult	Freely drained, found in Mediterranean climates
12. Oxisol	Aquox	Formed under the influence of water
	Perox	Always moist, with a high humus content
	Torrox	Occurs in arid climates, may have formed under a different climate from that now existing in that location
	Udox	Occurs in places with a short or no dry season, other than aquoxes
	Ustox	Occurs in humid climates with at least 60 consecutive dry days per year

Sources: US Department of Agriculture; Birkeland, 1999.

Student Exercises

PART ONE

A Global Perspective

1. One often needs to convert units (particularly distance) in geography. Try converting the following values:

   550 m = _____ km
   550,000 cm = _____ km
   200 g = _____ kg (grams to kilograms)
   20 g = _____ mg (grams to milligrams)
   5.5×10^6 m = _____ km
   650,000 W = _____ MW (watts to megawatts)

2. Working with a map's scale is an essential skill for a geographer. Use the textbook, and the referenced websites below to try the following questions:

   Given a map scale of 1:25,000, what ground distance is represented by:

   a) 0.5 mm on the map, and
   b) 2 cm on the map?
   c) How many cm on this map scale represent 1 km of ground distance?
   d) How would you express this scale (1:25,000) as a statement in words?
   e) Which is larger, a 1:20,000 scale or a 1:100,000 scale?
   f) What is the difference in area covered by two maps of the same dimensions, one at a scale of 1:20,000 and the other at a scale of 1:100,000? Which map will show the larger area?

3. Using an atlas, find each of the following cities and provide the latitude and longitude of each (try to be as accurate as possible):

   a) Halifax, Nova Scotia
   b) Moscow, Russia
   c) Sydney, Australia
   d) Cairo, Egypt
   e) Rio de Janeiro, Brazil

4. Using an atlas, identify the following cities from the given coordinates:

   a) 8°48'S   13°14'E
   b) 35°41'N   139°44'E
   c) 51°30'N   0°

5. You are at 10°N and 30°E; you move to a new location which is 25° south and 40° west of your present location. What is your new latitude/longitude position?

6. Latitude, longitude, and physical distances: Since the meridians of longitude converge towards the poles, the physical distance on the ground ('linear distance') between two degrees of longitude is greatest at the equator and diminishes to zero at the poles. The linear distance between degrees of latitude, however, varies only slightly. The table below compares the physical distance of a degree of latitude and longitude at selected latitudinal locations.

Table 1 Physical distances represented by degrees of latitude and longitude

Latitudinal Location	Latitude Degree Length (km)	Longitude Degree Length (km)
90° (poles)	111.70	0
60°	111.42	55.80
50°	111.23	71.70
40°	111.04	85.40
30°	110.86	96.49
0° (equator)	110.58	111.32

Source: Christopherson and Hobbs, 2003.

In general, the degree of latitude is equal to approximately 111 km. Given this distance, the distance between any given pair of parallels can be calculated (given that these are located due north–south of each other—therefore along the same meridian). For example, Denver is approximately 40° north of the equator (arc distance). The linear distance between Denver and the equator can be calculated as follows:

$$40° \text{ N to } 0° = 40° \times 111 \text{ km/}1° = 4440 \text{ km}$$

Using the same values for a degree of latitude and an atlas, calculate the linear distance in km between the following sets of points (along a meridian):

   a) Mumbai, India, and the Equator
   b) Edinburgh, Scotland, and the 5th parallel
   c) Cape Horn, Chile, and the Equator
   d) Singapore and Vientiane, Laos

7. a) If it is 8 p.m. Thursday in Winnipeg, Manitoba, Canada (97°W), what day and time is it in Harare, Zimbabwe (31° E)?

   b) If you depart Vancouver International Airport at 10 p.m. on Tuesday, what day and time will you arrive in Auckland, New Zealand (175°E), assuming a flight time of 14 hours?

8. Complete diagram 'A' below (assume a spherical earth) by showing:

   a) North and South Poles
   b) Circle of illumination
   c) Lightly shade day and night as they would exist at **vernal equinox**

9. Complete diagram 'B' above by showing conditions at the southern hemisphere's **winter solstice** by including:

   a) The equator
   b) The 45°N latitude
   c) The circle of illumination
   d) Arctic and Antarctic circles
   e) Day and night

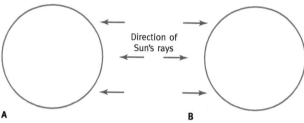

Useful Sources

Map Scale:

maps.nrcan.gc.ca/topo101/scale_e.php
www.nssgeography.com/canada9%20web/
   Unit%20Map%20Skills/Map%20Scale.htm
www.cartography.org.uk/default.asp?contentID=5747

Determining Latitude and Longitude:

www.nationalatlas.gov/articles/mapping/a_latlong.html
raider.muc.edu/~mcnaugma/Topographic%20Maps/
   latitude_and_longitude.htm

PART TWO

Atmosphere and Hydrosphere

1. Use Wien's Law (see p. 77) to answer the following question: The Sun has a surface temperature of 5770 K. At what wavelength is the Sun emitting most of its radiant energy? Show your calculations.

2. Use the surface energy balance (see p. 82) to determine the amount of energy reflected off a sandy surface with an albedo of 40% and incoming solar radiation of 1237 Wm^{-2}.

3. What would the net radiation be for a December, cloudless midday on a newly snow-covered surface at a temperature of −4°C (Q = 28 ly hr^{-1})? Will the bright sunshine cause snow to melt? Why or why not? (See p. 83.)

4. A winter day has a maximum temperature of 12°C and a minimum of −2°C. What is the mean daily temperature?

5. For one year at a hypothetical location, the mean monthly temperatures in degrees Celsius for January through December are: 2, 1, 2, 5, 13, 20, 22, 26, 21, 17, 11, and 4.

   a) Find the annual temperature range.
   b) How would you describe the variability of the annual temperature at this location?
   c) Where might this location be (in terms of a general latitudinal zone)?

6. On the Canadian Climate Data Centre and Archive website (www.climate.weatheroffice.ec.gc.ca/climate_normals/index_e.html), find an example of a location that shows a consistent wind direction for the entire year. Explain why this is the case for this location.

7. On the Australian Bureau of Meteorology website (www.bom.gov.au/climate/averages/wind/index.shtml), find a location that shows strong seasonal variation in wind direction. Explain why this is the case for this location.

8. Relative humidity can be calculated to express how close the atmosphere is to saturation at a given temperature. Determine the saturation mixing ratio of the air samples (from Table 1 on the next page) and the relative humidity of each.

Table 1 Saturation Mixing Ratio (g/kg) at Sea-Level Pressure as a Function of Dry-bulb Temperature (°C)

(°C)	(g/kg)	(°C)	(g/kg)
−4	2.852	20	14.956
−2	3.313	22	16.963
0	3.819	24	19.210
2	4.439	26	21.734
4	5.120	28	24.557
6	5.894	30	27.694
8	6.771	32	31.213
10	7.762	34	35.134
12	8.882	36	39.502
14	10.140	38	44.381
16	11.560	40	49.815
18	13.162		

Complete the following table using the equation below and data from Table 1.

Temperature (°C)	Saturation Mixing Ratio (g/kg)	Mixing Ratio (g/kg)	Relative Humidity (%)
14	10.140 (from table)	5	49.3 (using equation below)
14		9	
24		5	
24		2	
34		7	

Example: RH = [mixing ratio/saturation mixing ratio * 100%] = 5 g/kg / 10.140 g/kg * 100%] = 49.3%

9. An air mass can become saturated when air is cooled to its dew-point temperature. As an unsaturated air parcel rises, its temperature drops at the *dry adiabatic lapse rate* of approximately 10°C per km. Calculate the temperature of an air parcel at 100-metre increments as it is forced to rise from the Earth's surface, where the temperature is 32°C.

Height (m)	Temperature (°C)
1000	
900	
800	
700	
600	
500	
400	
300	
200	
100	
Surface	32

10. If the parcel of air cools to the dew-point temperature, it becomes saturated and clouds can form. The height at which this happens is called the *lifting condensation level* (LCL). If the air parcel continues to rise beyond this level, it cools at the wet adiabatic lapse rate (WALR), which ranges between 5 and 9°C per km. In the table below, the lifting condensation level is 1.5 km and the WALR is 5°C. Complete the table.

Height (km)	Temperature (°C)
5.0	
4.5	
4.0	
3.5	
3.0	
2.5	
2.0	
1.5	
1.0	
0.5	
Surface	26

11. Below are three unidentified climographs. Indicate the pattern of temperature and precipitation for each (e.g., maximum, minimum, range, variation over year). (Note: range = numeric value, variation = description.) What is the Köppen Climate Classification (full name and abbreviation) for each of these stations? Identify if the forest that would be found in that region would be a boreal forest, temperate broadleaf forest, or tropical monsoon forest.

a)

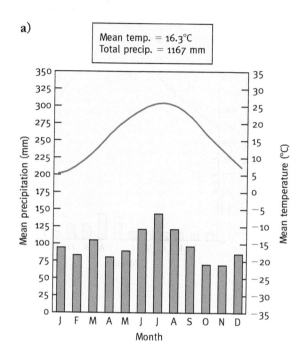

b)

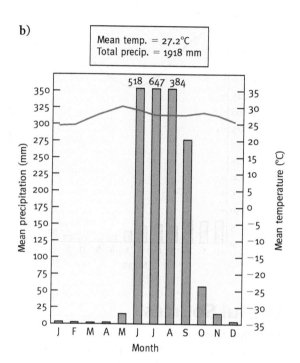

c)

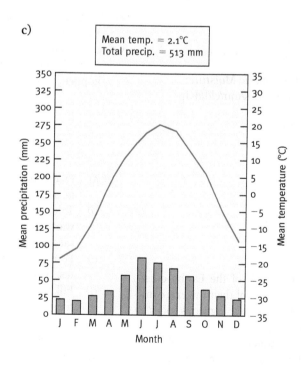

12. Indicate the pattern of temperature and precipitation for the climographs below (e.g., maximum, minimum, range, variation over year). What is the Köppen Climate Classification (name and abbreviation) for each station? In what hemisphere is each located?

a)

Mean temp. = 21.6°C
Total precip. = 243 mm

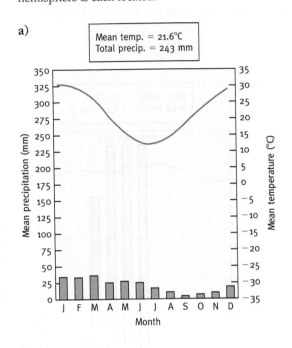

b)

Mean temp. = 13.4°C
Total precip. = 214 mm

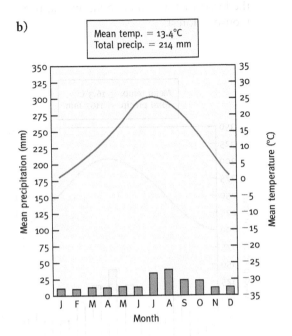

Useful Sources

Radiation Balance:

www.uwsp.edu/geo/faculty/ritter/geog101/textbook/energy/radiation_balance.html

www.physicalgeography.net/fundamentals/7i.html

Global Winds:

ogcuser.opengeospatial.org/node/31

www.rcn27.dial.pipex.com/cloudsrus/wind.html

Relative Humidity and Atmospheric Moisture:

ww2010.atmos.uiuc.edu/(Gh)/guides/mtr/cld/dvlp/rh.rxml

ohioline.osu.edu/aex-fact/0120.html

Adiabatic Lapse Rates:

www.uwsp.edu/geo/faculty/ritter/geog101/textbook/atmospheric_moisture/lapse_rates_1.html

www.metoffice.gov.uk/education/higher/lapse_rates.html

Global Climate/Köppen Climate Classification System:

www.blueplanetbiomes.org/climate.htm

www.marathon.uwc.edu/geography/100/koppen_web/koppen_map.htm

PART THREE

The Restless Crust

1. **Igneous Rocks.**

   Igneous rocks make up ~95% of the Earth's crust. They are classified on the basis of their mineral composition and texture. The texture of igneous rocks is related to the rate of cooling.

   A heated mixture of water and Epsom salts can be used as a model for magma. The mixture can be cooled at different rates to show the effect on crystal size.

   a) Predict how the rate of cooling will infuence crystal size.

   b) To create the 'magma' or 'melt', mix equal parts warm water and Epsom salts and stir until the salts are completely dissolved.

   c) Pour an equal amount of the 'magma' into three test tubes.

   d) Fill three large beakers with water at different temperatures. One with warm tap water, one with water at room temperature, and one with ice water.

   e) Place a test tube in one of the beakers.

   f) Leave for a day or so.

   g) Compare the crystal sizes in the three samples. Do they support your initial hypothesis (prediction)?

2. **Sedimentary Rocks and Structures.**

   Choose a bedrock geology map of part of Canada from your university map library (most are not available online). Select an area with sedimentary rocks—southern Ontario, Prairies, parts of BC, etc. Geological information for Canada and the provinces is available online from the Geological Survey of Canada and from provincial ministries of mines (geological survey departments, divisions, etc.). Draw a geological cross-section of an area of the map. The map contours can be used to construct the surface topography of the section (websites discuss how to do this). Information about the structure and the dip of the beds can be used to construct the subsurface geology. Use the geological column of the area to reconstruct past environments in which the sediments were deposited and the changes that occurred over time.

3. **Metamorphism.**

   Choose a bedrock geology map of part of Canada showing metamorphic rocks around an igneous intrusion. See Question 2 (above) for sources of maps and information. Two major areas with these kinds of structures are the Rocky Mountains and the Canadian Shield. Draw a geological cross-section across the igneous intrusion and the surrounding rocks (if the intrusion is very large just use one side of the structure). See how the intrusion has influenced the metamorphism and mineralization of the surrounding rocks (the metamorphic aureole/contact zone).

4. **Volcanism versus Meteoric Impact Cratering.**

   Compare and contrast the topography and features found around Mount Edziza and the Pingualuit Crater.

   Mount Edziza is a major eroded shield volcano in the Stikine Volcanic Belt in northwestern BC. Its last major eruption was ~4 million YBP. There has been flank crater and lava flow development during the Pleistocene and Holocene Epochs. See the Geological Survey of Canada's online Catalogue of Canadian Volcanoes (gsc.nrcan.gc.ca/volcanoes/cat/volcano_e.php) and National Topographic System map: 104/G10.

   The Pingualuit Crater (also known as Chubb Crater or Cratere de Nouveau Quebec) is an impact crater in Nunavik (northern Quebec). It was formed ~1.4 million YBP by an impact that had the force of 8500 Hiroshima-sized atomic bombs. See the University of New Brunswick's Earth Impact Database (www.unb.ca/passc/ImpactDatabase/) and (www.bivouac.com/MtnPg.asp?MtnId=4469), and NTS map: 35/H5.

   Construct topographic cross-sections across these landforms using the topographic maps to show how they differ in terms of major features. Label these features on the cross-sections. Discuss how they formed.

5. **Impactor versus Crater Size.**

   Table 1 gives data on the estimated size (diameter) of a selection of meteoric impacts and the diameter of the craters excavated. Most of the data are from B.M. French (1998) *Traces of Catastrophe: A Handbook of Shock-Metamorphic Effects in Terrestrial Meteorite Impact Structures* (Houston: Lunar and Planetary Institute, Contribution No. 954, 1998), available at: <www.lpi.usra.edu/publications/books/CB-954/CB-954.intro.html>. The Whitecourt data are from news reports in various scientific magazines.

Table 1 Impactors and Crater Size

Impactor Diameter	Crater Diameter	Comparable Terrestrial Event
~1 m	36 m	Whitecourt, Alberta, Crater: ~1100C^{14} YBP
2 m	35 m	Minimum damaging earthquake (magnitude = 5), largest chemical explosion, 'Snowball' Canada 1964
6 m	120 m	Hiroshima atomic bomb explosion 1945
23 m	450 m	'Typical' hydrogen bomb explosion (~ 1 MegaTon)
50 m	1 km	Wolfe Creek Crater, Australia (diameter = 0.875 km)
55 m	1.1 km	Barringer Meteor Crater, Arizona (diameter = 1.2 km), Tunguska explosion 1908, Mount St Helens, Washington 1981 lateral blast
90 m	1.8 km	San Francisco earthquake 1906 (magnitude = 8.4), largest hydrogen bomb detonation (68 MT)
155 m	3.1 km	Mount St Helens 1981 eruption (total including thermal energy)
250 m	5 km	Gardnos (Norway) and Goat Paddock (Australia) craters (diameter = 5 km and 5.1 km, respectively)
350 m	6.9 km	Largest recorded earthquake off Chile 1960 (magnitude = 9.6)
360 m	7.2 km	Krakatau eruption, Indonesia 1883 (total including thermal energy)

(Continued)

Table 1 (Continued)

Impactor Diameter	Crater Diameter	Comparable Terrestrial Event
500 m	10 km	Lake Mien (Sweden), Bosumtwi (Ghana), and Oasis (Libya) craters (diameter = 9 km, 10.5 km, 11.5 km, respectively)
600 m	12.2 km	Tambora eruption, Indonesia 1815 (total energy)
1 km	20 km	Haughton Dome, Nunavut, Rochechouart (France), and Ries (Germany) craters (diameter = 20.5 km, 23 km, 24 km, respectively)
1.5 km	31 km	Total annual energy release from the Earth (heat flow, seismic, and volcanic)
2.5 km	50 km	Montagnais (off Nova Scotia), Charlesvoix, Quebec, and Siljan (Sweden) craters (diameter = 45 km, 54 km, and 55 km, respectively)
5 km	100 km	Manicouagan, Quebec, and Popigai (Russia) craters (both diameter = 100 km)
10 km	200 km	Largest known terrestrial impact events (original diameters 200–300 km) Sudbury, Ontario, Vredefort (South Africa), and Chicxulub (Mexico)

a) Plot crater diameter against impactor diameter on log-log graph paper. Use 5 × 7 cycle log-log graph paper. Printable 5 × 6 cycle log-log graph paper is available at: <homepages.gac.edu/~wolfe/courses/graph-paper>. Click on 5 by 6 log-log pdf.

b) Draw in a line of best fit (by eye) through the plotted data.

c) Suggest what this line means in terms of the relationship between impactor and crater size.

6. **Earthquakes and Plate Tectonics.**

Table 2 gives selected seismic data for the Cascadia region, 47°N to 51°N Latitude, 121°W to 125°W Longitude, 1872 to 2006. The data is from the Pacific Northwest Seismic Network, University of Washington, Seattle.

Table 2 Seismic Data, Cascadia Region

Date	Longitude °W	Depth of Focus (km)	Moment Magnitude
1872	121.56	70	7.4
1918	123.75	30	7.0
1921	123.05	45	7.1
1925	122.30	55	7.6
1934	121.50	65	6.4
1940	124.10	10	4.1
1946	124.90	25	7.3
1949	122.60	60	7.1
1955	123.40	15	5.2
1960	124.50	10	4.0
1963	122.75	70	5.7
1965	122.40	60	6.5
1967	121.35	80	7.0
1969	123.60	45	6.2
1971	122.45	20	4.3
1972	122.65	25	6.0
1973	122.25	70	6.5
1975	125.00	10	3.8
1976	123.70	60	5.6
1979	122.30	80	6.1
1981	121.40	90	6.5

(Continued)

Table 2 (Continued)

Date	Longitude °W	Depth of Focus (km)	Moment Magnitude
1983	123.55	15	2.8
1985	124.80	30	7.0
1987	123.25	50	6.4
1989	121.30	75	6.8
1990	121.40	20	3.6
1990	121.90	65	7.4
1991	124.45	30	5.5
1992	121.00	75	8.0
1994	124.20	50	6.2
2001	122.72	51	6.8
2002	121.63	38	4.1
2003	123.25	50	4.8
2004	124.30	45	4.7
2005	121.15	<1	3.2
2005	122.13	0	4.0
2006	121.60	6	4.5

a)   Plot the seismic data (longitude, depth, and magnitude) from Table 2 on the chart below. Use symbols to indicate magnitude ranges (e.g., minor, major, and great events). Supply legend.

b)   What pattern of seismic activity is apparent?

c)   What mechanism or process could account for this pattern?

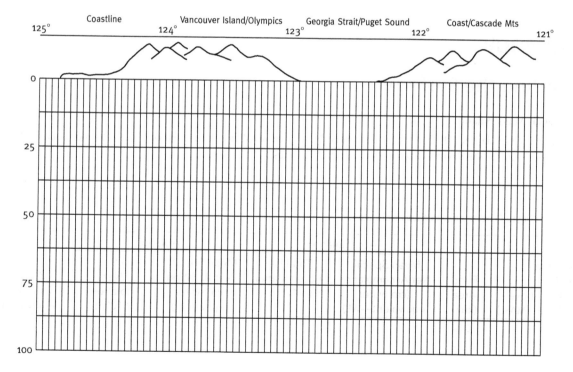

7.   **Volcanism.**

Use one or more of the following volcano websites to monitor events at a volcano of your choice. Record daily events in a log and after one month write a report about the activity:

United States Geological Survey, Volcano Hazards Program: volcanoes.usgs.gov

USGS Hawaiian Volcano Observatory: hvo.wr.usgs.gov

Cascades Volcano Observatory (Mount St Helens): vulcan.wr.usgs.gov/Volcanoes/MSH/

Volcanoes of Canada: gsc.nrcan.gc.ca/volcanoes/index_e.php (no active volcanoes, historic data)
Volcano World: volcano.oregonstate.edu
Montserrat Volcano Observatory: www.mvo.ms
Mount Vesuvius Volcano Observatory: www.vesuvioinrete.it (in Italian and English)

8. **Movement along the Queen Charlotte (BC)–Fairweather (Alaska) Transform Fault System, Pacific Northwest.**

Movement along any fault line can be gauged by looking at the displacement of rocks on either side of the fault and also studying the distribution and size or magnitude of seismic events along the margins of the fault. For the Queen Charlotte–Fairweather fault, maps and data are available from a number of websites. The most important are: Seismic Zones in Western Canada (earthquakescanada.nrcan.gc.ca/zones/westcan_e.php) and the Alaska Earthquake Information Centre (www.aeic.alaska.edu/maps/QueenCharlotteFairweather_fault.html).

Using a sample of data for a select period, suggest the rate of slip along the fault and the amount of fault movement for the largest seismic events. Also suggest what kind of movements the offset of the same rock beds on each side of the fault suggest.

9. **Plate Tectonics.**

Choose two continents (e.g., the eastern side of South America and the western side of Africa or Africa and the Indian subcontinent) and try to find out about the rate of spreading, the rock types and structures, fossils, etc. found. Do these data support the idea that these continents were once joined?

10. **Rocks, Minerals, and Weathering.**

Use dated historic church buildings (foundation stones) and gravestones/grave markers to study the weathering of different rock types and minerals. This approach was used by Sir Archibald Geikie in his classic study of weathering in Edinburgh graveyards in the nineteenth century. This project must be done tactfully and non-invasively. Permission must be asked from the church administration. These features are dated so that rates of weathering can be estimated. Rock types can be identified (in place) using a field guide (e.g., *Peterson Guide to Rocks and Minerals*) and the amount of estimated weathering can be graphed against time. If there are lots of dated historic buildings (dates are often on the cornerstone, which was ceremonially uncovered at opening or dedication of the edifice) in the area (bank buildings, federal, provincial, or municipal buildings, churches) these can be used with or instead of gravestones.

PART FOUR

Sculpting the Surface

1. **Glacial Mass Balance.**

Table 1 gives data for 150 m elevation bands, band area, total net accumulation, and total net ablation for one balance year for the Peyto Glacier in the Canadian Rockies.

Table 1 Peyto Glacier, Alberta, Statistical Data for One Year

Elevation Band (metres above sea level—MASL)	Band Area (km²)	Accumulation		Ablation		Net Budget (cm water equivalent)
		Mean Specific Net Accumulation (cm water equivalent—WE)	Total Net Accumulation ($\times 10^6$ m³)	Mean Specific Net Ablation (cm water equivalent)	Total Net Ablation ($\times 10^6$ m³)	
2895–3045	0.04		1.260		0.140	
2740–2895	0.38		3.923		0.658	
2590–2740	1.83		8.851		4.319	
2435–2590	4.23		5.299		7.564	
2285–2435	4.86		1.343		5.613	
2130–2285	1.77		0.125		1.165	
1980–2130	0.56		0.010		0.130	
Totals	13.67		20.811		19.589	

Note: Total net accumulation/ablation is the volume of ice accumulated or ablated. Mean specific net accumulation/ablation is the depth of ice accumulated/ablated in cm Water Equivalent (the depth of the meltwater produced by the ice sample accumulated or ablated).

a) Calculate the mean specific net accumulation/ablation in cm Water Equivalent (WE) for each band and enter the values in Table 1. Give one example of a calculation for accumulation or ablation.

b) Calculate the totals for mean specific accumulation and ablation in cm WE and enter in the table. Give one example.

c) Calculate the net budget for each elevation band and the glacier. Enter values in the table and give one example.

d) Draw a bar graph. Plot net budget as a curve and mean specific net accumulation/ablation as bars in cm WE against elevation. Round values up or down. Indicate the position of the following on the graph and label:
   i) equilibrium line
   ii) accumulation zone
   iii) ablation zone

2. **Drainage Density and the Constant of Channel Maintenance.**

These variables can be measured quite easily.

Equipment:

Canadian topographic map
Thread, fine string, or map measurer
Ruler
Calculator

Method:

Choose a topographic map.
Find a stream and outline its drainage basin.
Calculate the area of the drainage basin using the metric grid squares (1 square = 1 km²) to calculate the area in km².
Measure the length of all the streams of the drainage network using thread, fine string, or a map measurer. If a thread or string is used, measure these against a ruler and use the map scale to get the length of the stream channels.

Calculate: Drainage density

Drainage density = length of channels (km)/drainage basin area (km²)

The constant of channel maintenance is the reciprocal of drainage density.

Calculate: The constant of channel maintenance

Constant of channel maintenance = drainage basin area (km²) / length of channels (km)

3. **Meandering Streams and Drainage Networks.**

Random walk simulations can be used to generate meandering stream channels and drainage networks.

Equipment needed:

Graph paper
Set of playing cards
Pencil or pen

Meandering channel:

Take the jokers out of the pack of cards. Shuffle cards and place them face down in a pile. The lower cards are used for their numeric values. The royal cards are worth 11 (Jack), 12 (Queen), and 13 (King). Use black cards to indicate left and red cards to indicate right. Pick a random point along an edge of graph paper to start (at a grid intersection). Turn over the top card and find the value. Go down one square and left or right the number of squares indicated by the card. Put a dot or cross for each point. Continue until all the cards have been used or when the other edge of the graph paper is reached. Join the points with a curving line.

Drainage networks:

Use the same method but pick a number of random points along the edge of the graph paper. Draw cards as before except go from one line to the next in turn (left to right or right to left). When the other edge of the graph paper is reached join the points up with a curving line to form a drainage pattern.

4. **Sinuosity of River Channels.**

Table 2 on the next page shows the mean discharge, mean suspended sediment, and mean dissolved solid concentrations for two very different Canadian streams. The Sunwapta River is a braided stream draining from the Columbia Icefields in the Alberta Rockies and is a tributary of the Athabasca River. The Qu'appelle River rises in the Missouri Coteau and Sand Hills. It flows eastward along a meandering course across prairie and aspen parkland ecozones of the Saskatchewan Plain before joining the Assiniboine River. The Qu'appelle is re-excavating a valley in glacial and lacustrine deposits.

a) Plot the mean discharge, mean suspended sediment, and mean dissolved solid concentration data (as curves) over time for the two streams on separate graphs. The graphs should be the same size in terms of the months (x axis).

b) Describe and analyze the relationship between the three variables for both streams over the year.

c) Compare the two streams in terms of mean discharge, mean suspended sediment, and mean dissolved solid concentrations.

d) Find topographic maps of the two stream basins in the area of the gauging stations. Sunwapta River, Alberta: Map sheet 83C/6, 1:50,000 scale; Qu'appelle River near Lumsden, Saskatchewan: Map sheet 72I/10, 1:50,000 scale.

Table 2 Sunwapta and Qu'appelle Rivers: Mean Discharge, Mean Suspended Sediment, and Mean Dissolved Solid Concentrations

Sunwapta River

(Station 07AA007) (52°13'00"N Lat., 117°13'57"W Long.)
Near Sunwapta Pass, AB
Manual gauge, Natural flow. Drainage Area 29.8 km²

Month	Q m³/s	Concentration mg/L	
		Mean Suspended Sediment	Mean Dissolved Solids
January			
February			
March			
April			
May	0.6	52	203
June	3.1	122	115
July	4.0	291	98
August	4.3	348	84
September	1.8	76	107
October	0.8	60	192
November			
December			

Maximum recorded Q: 1,400,000 m³/s in August 1949
Minimum recorded Q: 0 m³/s – 6 months/year, most years

Qu'appelle River

(SaskWater Station No. 05JF001) (50°38'16"N Lat., 104°51'08"W Long.)
Lumsden SK, 1999
Recording Gauge, Regulated flow. Drainage Area: 18 300 km²

Month	Q m³/s	Concentration mg/L	
		Mean Suspended Sediment	Mean Dissolved Solids
January	37.76	23	841
February	32.69	17	868
March	160.34	53	319
April	227.56	147	308
May	343.43	261	294
June	375.40	295	251
July	314.75	210	268
August	187.91	171	418
September	127.03	87	543
October	53.17	55	739
November	30.93	41	824
December	33.63	20	853

n.b. Ice conditions November to early April.
Maximum recorded Q: 849.39 in June 1952
Minimum recorded Q: 0.67 on July 12 1990
Data: Personal communication Merle 'Reg' Moore of SaskWater

Measure the stream channel length (l_c) and valley length (l_v) of the Sunwapta and Qu'appelle Rivers along selected reaches using thread or fine string and a ruler. Measure channel length by following the twists and turns of the stream for the Qu'appelle and the midpoint of the braided channel downstream (remember that when braided channels flood, the streams fill the

Table 3 The Relationship Between Channel Sinuosity (P), Planform Geometry, Sediment Load, and Bed and Bank Materials

Channel Sinuosity Index (P)	Planform Geometry	Sediment Load (% granular)	Bed and Bank Material Silt/Clay (%)
1.0–1.2	Straight	>90	<45
1.3–1.5	Transitional	>90	>50
1.6–1.7	Regular Meanders	>90	>70
1.8–1.9	Irregular Meanders	<85	>80
>2.0	Tortuous Meanders-Anastomosing	<60	>85

Source: After Schumm, S.A. (1963). 'Sinuosity of Alluvial Rivers of the Great Plains'. Geol. Soc. Am. Bull. V74, 1089–99.

Table 4 Sediment Yields: Etobicoke Creek, Upper Humber River, Fraser River

Month	Etobicoke Creek (tonnes)	Upper Humber River (tonnes)	Fraser River (tonnes)
January	110	179	25,633
February	1,387	5,675	28,965
March	3,591	9,012	93,100
April	2,046	8,265	1,637,600
May	215	395	6,897,900
June	402	739	3,694,600
July	275	651	1,332,000
August	396	823	458,000
September	387	586	329,290
October	242	203	447,790
November	853	1,354	84,986
December	356	610	18,784
Annual Sediment Yield (tonnes/year)			

whole valley bottom). Measure the valley length using the midpoint of the valley all the way downstream.

e) Calculate the Channel Sinuosity Index (P) for these two streams and compare with the values in Table 3 above. The Channel Sinuosity Index (P) can be calculated as:

$$P = l_c/l_v$$

f) What does the Channel Sinuosity Index indicate about the planform geometries (the shape of the stream channels seen from above), the sediment loads carried by the streams, and their bed and bank materials?

5. **Sediment Yields from Drainage Basins.**

Compare the sediment yields for three drainage basins. The mean monthly suspended sediment yields (in tonnes) in 2006 for the drainage basins of Etobicoke Creek (gauged at the Queen Elizabeth Way bridge, Etobicoke/Mississauga, Ontario), the Upper Humber River (monitored at Elder Mills, Ontario), and the Fraser River (measured at Agassiz, BC) are shown in Table 4. The data are 30-year mean values. Elder Mills and Agassiz are both on the peripheries of large urban areas (Greater Toronto and Greater Vancouver).

a) Find the total annual sediment yield (t/yr) for each basin.

b) Why should there be so much variation in sediment yield? Based on the above data, what factors would influence erosion in the three basins?

c) Calculate the mean sediment yield per unit area for the three basins (t/yr/km²). Use the following formula:

$$\text{mean sediment yield per unit area (t/yr/km}^2) = \frac{\text{annual sediment yield (t/yr)}}{\text{basin area (km}^2)}$$

Basin Areas:

Etobicoke Creek Basin above the QEW: 204 km²
Upper Humber River Basin above Elder Mills: 303 km²
Fraser River Basin above Agassiz: 218,000 km²

d) What factors could account for the variation in mean sediment yield per unit area in these basins?

6. **Sediments and Contaminants.**

Contaminants such as lead, zinc, and mercury can enter a stream because of industrial, road, or rail accidents. Contaminants tend to be carried down a stream channel attached to suspended sediments. It is desirable to remove these sediments before they reach a lake or the sea where deposition will occur. Otherwise, pollutants will build up in the sediments, as is happening now at the mouths of many streams. Sediments can be removed by building settling ponds in the main stream channel. These ponds reduce the water velocity enough to allow some sediment to be deposited or captured. The sediment traps will fill up over time and require emptying.

Problem: A settling pond, or sediment trap, has been installed upstream of the mouth of Etobicoke Creek (on the border of Toronto and Mississauga). The trap has a surface area of 14,000 m² and an average depth of 2 m. It is 62% efficient (i.e., it captures 62 tonnes of every 100 tonnes of sediment). The volume of sediment moving down Etobicoke Creek per year can be calculated if the mass (sediment yield) and density of the sediment are known. The average density of the sediment is 1800 kg/m³:

volume of sediment (m³) = mass (kg)/density (kg/m³)

Given the data above, calculate (in years and decimals) how often the settling pond has to be cleaned out.

7. Focus on one Canadian glacier and find out its mass balance sequence for a 10- or 20-year period using the Internet, books, journals, etc. What are accumulation and ablation of ice on that glacier influenced by? Find out how it has been or will be affected by climate changes.

8. Research the Ice Age deposits in your area using the Internet and reports, journals, etc., and make up a chronological chart of the major events and sediments.

9. Use the Internet and reports, journals, etc. to look at how climate change (global warming) will affect the periglacial areas of Canada.

10. Choose a part of a Canadian coastline (ocean or lake) and look at the areas being eroded and aggraded. What are the beach mass balance inputs and outputs? What would happen to the beach if a groyne field was built? What other things could be done to conserve the beach and shoreline?

PART FIVE

The Biosphere

1. **Soil Texture.**

   The mineral component of soils is composed of three major textural sizes: sand, silt, and clay. This easy experiment gives you an indication of the textural composition of any soil sample.

   Equipment:

   Trowel
   Ruler
   Soil sample
   Strait-sided jar with tight seal (Mason jar)
   Powdered dishwasher detergent
   Calculator
   Soil texture triangle (see: p. 645 or www.pedosphere. com/resources/texture/triangle_us.cfm)

   Method:

   a) Use a trowel to take a sample of soil from ~10–20 cm below the surface. Fill a sandwich-size Ziplock bag with soil. Do not include stones or roots.

   b) Put 200 g (1 cup) of the soil sample in to a Mason jar with a lid. Fill the remaining ~two-thirds of the jar with clean cold water. Add 8 g (1 tbsp) of dishwasher detergent. Screw the lid on tightly.

   c) Shake the mixture for 10 minutes.

   d) Let stand for 2–3 days so that the various sizes of material fall out of suspension. Coarse sand should be at the bottom, then fine sand, with silt and clay on top. (This uses Stokes's Law.)

   e) Use a ruler to measure the total depth of the soil material in the bottom of the jar and record.

   f) Measure the depth of the individual layers of particles—coarse and fine sand, silt, and clay—and record.

   g) Express these as percentages of the total depth.

   h) This will indicate the percentage of these size grades in the soil sample.

   i) Use this to find this textural class of the sample on the soil texture triangle. Record.

   This technique can be used to see changes of texture down a soil profile if a number of samples are taken at regular measured depths.

2. **Soil Colour.**

   Soil colour is an important indicator of soil moisture and organic matter content. Soil colour can be scientifically classified using a 'Munsell Soil Color Chart'.

   Method:

   a) Use a trowel to take a 200 g soil sample of soil from ~10–20 cm below the surface.

   b) Weigh the sample and record the soil colour using the 'Munsell Soil Color Chart'.

   c) Spread the sample on a tray to dry in a warm room for about a day. Weigh sample and record.

   d) Determine colour using the 'Munsell Soil Color Chart'.

   e) Record results.

   This technique can be used to see changes of soil colour down a soil profile if a number of samples are taken at regular measured depths down the profile.

3. **Soil Porosity.**

   Soil porosity can be measured using the following technique:

   a) Take a 400 g sample of moist soil.

   b) Spread the sample out on a tray to dry in a warm room for a day or two.

c)   Weigh the dry sample and record.

Soil porosity can be found by subtracting the dry weight of the soil sample from the moist weight of the sample. Express the weight difference as a percentage. Record result(s).

Soil porosity (%) =

Moist weight (g) – Dry weight (g)

4. **Soil Catena.**

The above methods can be used to study a soil catena if sampling takes place at measured intervals down a slope. The depth of the soil at different slope positions can also be researched using a screw or bucket auger or by digging soil pits. The angle of the slope can be found using an Abney level or by calculation using a contour map (at a scale of 1:10,000, etc.) and finding the difference in height from the highest to the lowest point on the slope and the horizontal distance between those points and calculating the angle.

5. **Mapping Soils and Vegetation.**

Look at different types of vegetation cover in your area—forests, grasslands, etc. Study soil texture, type of litter accumulation, organic matter content, soil colour, and porosity. Record all the information. Identify the type of vegetation (coniferous, deciduous, or mixed forest, grassland, wetland, etc.). If it is a small area, map the different types of vegetation cover. Try to identify the main plant species. Take samples of leaves, seeds, cones, etc. and use a plant identification guide, e.g., *Peterson* guides to trees, flowers, or types of ecosystem, *Golden* guides, *The Native Trees of Canada*, or more academic works and online sources. Correlate the vegetation types and soils.

6. **Soil Capability.**

Soil capability is a part of land capability classification and mapping. Land capability is used to get an integrated environmental information base for project planning and developments of various types. Assessment is based on factor analysis. The technique allows for the pinpointing of problems and makes it possible to find solutions that might be used to mitigate them. The approach was first used in Canada for agriculture. It is quite easy to understand that a number of very different factors are important to the agricultural capability of a parcel of land. Soil type, climate, slope, drainage, and other physical properties are important, but so are markets for the production, proximity to those markets, and transport systems (rail, road) to get the crops or other products to the markets.

Land capability classification and mapping has also been used for forestry, outdoor recreation, wildlife (ungulates and waterfowl), and scenic resources in Canada. A major use is for various forms of development—housing (foundations), roads and other infrastructure (utilities, sources of aggregate), and the disposal of domestic waste from cottages and other homes using septic tank–weeping field systems. The engineering use of land capability classification was championed by the US Army Corps of Engineers and subsequent classifications were based on their manuals. Obviously, it is vitally important to determine the capability of soils for the safe disposal of liquid waste because the soil is used to biodegrade the effluent before it reaches and pollutes surface water or groundwater. The installation and working of septic systems are regulated by provincial building codes, technical guidelines on water quality, and risk assessment and environmental protection acts. The Ontario Environmental Protection Act of 1971 and its updates state that 'Sewage or effluent shall not emit, discharge, seep, leak, or otherwise escape from the sewage system, or any part thereof, into a piped water supply, well water supply, a watercourse, groundwater, or surface water.'

How a Septic Tank–Weeping System Works

A septic system uses both anaerobic microbial biogradation in the tank itself and aerobic biogradation in the weeping field (soil bacteria). A septic tank is made out of concrete, fibreglass, or polyethelene and is either composed of one or two compartments. The size of the tank used depends on the number of bedrooms and occupants in the house or cottage. A three-bedroom cottage with three occupants and no water-saving devices, for example, needs at least a 3785-litre (1000-gallon) tank (~3 m long, 2 m wide, and 1.5–2 m high). Larger households need bigger tanks. Residences with clothes washers, garburators, etc. also need larger tanks or for these appliances to discharge into holding tanks and not into the weeping field. The tank has to be buried. A 3785-litre tank used by four people during the summer months requires the sludge to be emptied by a 'honey wagon' or 'honeysucker' every three to four years.

The domestic waste water comes out of the cottage or house through a pipe into the septic tank. The heavier solids settle out and form a layer of sludge on the bottom. Above this is a layer of liquid waste with coliform bacteria, other microbes, and smaller solid particles. Over this there is a layer of scum composed of suds and fat. At the very top of the tank is a layer of gas: mainly methane (CH_4) and hydrogen sulphide (H_2S). Over time the layer of sludge builds up and the scum layer thickens. The liquid effluent is discharged through a filter into a pipe and to the weeping field.

The exit pipe takes the liquid effluent (which still contains coliform and other harmful bacteria) to a distribution box, which distributes it to the absorption bed or weeping field. The weeping field is a grid of permeable and perforated pipes (called 'tiles') laid down on top of a layer of gravel. The tile field is buried about 60 cm below the soil surface and the area backfilled. The tiles gradually release the effluent into the soil where the soil bacteria break down the pollutants. The tile has to be buried at this depth to stop bad odours and also to prevent effluent from bubbling up to the soil surface.

Two processes occur in the soil. (1) Some of the effluent is adsorbed to the surface of soil colloids (clays and organic matter). (2) The rest is broken down by aerobic soil bacteria.

It is very important to install these systems in optimal locations in deep, stone-free, fairly well-drained non-organic soils (loams and clay loams) on gentle slopes away from surface or groundwater (both horizontally and vertically). Once a septic system is installed it is necessary to take care of it. Domestic water use should be restricted, vehicles should not be driven or parked on the weeping field, buildings should not be erected over it, vegetable or fruit gardens should not be grown on it, and trees should not be planted on or close to the tank or the tile field.

The soil characteristics most important for the successful installation and functioning of these systems are listed below. The important parts of the legend of a soil map to refer to are indicated for each characteristic:

Checklist of Soil Characteristics

Depth to the Water Table

The presence of a permanent or seasonally high water table presents a severe limitation to the installation and functioning of septic tank–weeping systems. Builders may attempt to solve the problem by placing a layer of porous material over the area and then installing the system. This has not been very successful in terms of solving the problem of waste disposal. In wet soils, anaerobic conditions interfere with the absorption of waste products. During periods with high water table conditions, wastes may appear at the surface, where they constitute a health hazard. Pollution of groundwater or surface water will occur from the weeping field.

- Look at the Drainage Column in the Legend on the Soil Survey map. Good Drainage means a low water table.

Depth to the Bedrock

Shallow soils (<1 metre) over hard or slowly permeable bedrock have severe limitations and present sanitation problems. These soils increase the cost of excavation for septic tank and weeping installation. Their limited capacity for water storage causes overloading when they are used for septic systems. Soils with depths of 1 to 2 metres on bedrock may present moderate problems, while depths >2 metres usually have no limitations.

- Look at the Complex Legend & the Parent Material Column in the main Legend. If the soil is a Complex it is automatically rated Poor in terms of depth to the bedrock. No mention of bedrock in the description rates as Good.

Slope

Soils on more than gentle slopes (>5 degrees) have some limitations for septic field systems. On steeper slopes (>10 degrees) construction costs are higher because of installing the weeping field with the contours. Effluent is still likely to return to the surface downslope. Erosion is a severe hazard during installation.

- Look at the Topography Column in the Legend.

Soil Drainage

Permeability enables soils to transmit water and air. The biogradation process requires the waste material to have a certain residence time in the soil so that the micro-organisms can break down the effluent. If soil permeability is too good the water laced with effluent will drain through the soil too rapidly and pollute the groundwater system. If permeability is restricted effluent may remain in the soil and cause a pollution problem or it can reappear at the surface.

- Look at the Drainage & Parent Material columns in the Legend. If Drainage is rated Good and the soil is a loam, silt loam, or clay loam, drainage would be Good. If Drainage is rated Good but the soil is a sand or gravel drainage would be Poor.

Soil Texture

This is closely linked to Soil Drainage. Coarse sandy or gravely soils are often so permeable that effluent has too short a residence time for biodegradation to occur. Fine textured soils (clays) are often impermeable and effluent can be retained close to the surface. Organic soils (Muck, Marsh, and Peat) do not have a soil texture and are rated Poor. The best soils for waste disposal are those with intermediate permeability—loams, silt loams, and clay loams.

- Look at the Parent Material in the Legend.

Stoniness

Installation costs of septic tank – weeping field systems increase with the volume of stones, especially stones with diameters >10 cm. These have to be removed before the installation of the weeping tile. This is done to be able to install the pipe or tile correctly and also to remove any materials that might cause part of the weeping field to drain faster than the rest, causing pollution problems.

- Look at the Parent Material column in the Legend.

Use a soil survey map of a largely rural area of a province. Pick an area of that map with a variety of different soil types. Copy the outlines and symbols of the soil types in that area onto a sheet of paper or make a black-and-white photocopy.

Suitability of land for cottages using septic systems is influenced by a large number of factors, including accessibility, distance from urban areas, scenic resources, etc. However, these other factors will be excluded from consideration. Classification is based solely on soil and landscape factors. No mitigation of problems is possible. Soils must be used as they occur and no material can be shipped in and laid down over the surface. This type of study is a first step to find areas worth investigating in greater detail in the field at a later date.

A Checklist of Soil Characteristics should be used in conjunction with the legend of the chosen soil survey map to classify the capability of the selected area of the soil map. Generalization should be used employing the largest area of the soil type. For example, if 90% of the soil type is away from surface water and only 10% is close to either lakes or streams, use the larger area for classification purposes (e.g., assigning capability for depth to the water table). Do not 'sit on the fence'. There is no Fair-to-Good or Poor-to-Fair classification! Always take a conservative approach.

a) Draw up a classification chart (or rationale) for each characteristic in the Checklist. Refer to the legend on the soil map. The object is to make the fairly general Checklist applicable to the specific soil map and how it describes the various soil traits. The following capability classes should be used:

Good: no limitations, or slight limitations that are easy to overcome.
Fair: some limitations which can be overcome with careful planning (i.e., larger lot sizes).
Poor: severe limitations that are difficult and expensive to overcome.

See an example of part of the classification chart in the next column. This is for the soils of the Golden Lake area of Renfrew County, Ontario.

Capability Factor and Capability Classes	Remarks
Depth to the Water Table	**See Map and Legend**
Good	A long way from the water table, surface water, and wetlands horizontally and vertically. Indicated by Good Soil Drainage.
Fair	Water table at depth but not very far below the surface. Indicated by Imperfect Soil Drainage.
Poor	Water table at or above the surface, e.g., wetlands. Indicated by Poor Soil Drainage.
Depth to the Bedrock	**See Map and Legend**
Good	A very deep soil, in a depression or valley. No mention of bedrock in description in Parent Material Column in Legend.
Fair	Bedrock at depth.
Poor	Rock crops out at the surface.

b) Construct a Capability Matrix with the soil characteristics along the top and the soil types (listed alphabetically) found in the area of the soil map down the side. Look at all the factors independently and, using the classification system, assign capability classes to each soil type for each characteristic. Add up all the Good, Fair, and Poor ratings for each soil type to assign an Overall Capability Class to the soil types. If there are more Goods, then the overall capability will be Good; if there are more Fairs, the overall rating will be Fair; and if there are a majority of Poor ratings, the overall rating will be Poor. If there are three Goods and three Poors, the Overall rating will be Fair. See how the Capability Matrix is organized and filled in below: G = Good; F = Fair; P = Poor Capability.

Soil Capability Matrix/Chart for Septic Tank Systems								
Soil Series/ Complex Symbol	Soil Series/ Complex	Depth to the Water Table	Depth of Bedrock	Slope	Soil Drainage	Soil Texture	Stoniness	Overall Capability Class
As	A Soil	G	P	F	F	F	G	F
Bs	B Soil	P	G	F	G	G	F	G
Zs	Z Soil							

c) Map the overall soil capability classes on the copy of the map or a photocopy using different colours to represent Good, Fair, and Poor Capability.

7. **A Vegetation Transect Down a Slope.**

Use the above two techniques—soil mapping and vegetation mapping—to determine the relationship of a soil catena and the change in vegetation down a slope of your choice. Describe this relationship.

8. **Slope Aspect and Vegetation Cover.**

As in Question 7 above, but now look at the relationship of a number of slopes along a bluff, escarpment, or ridge and consider their aspect or relation to the Sun and/or dominant wind direction. To do this, a compass can be used to find out which

way the slope is oriented. Dominant wind direction can be ascertained by looking at the topography (e.g., valley versus plateau or mountain side) and regional weather patterns (dominant wind direction, pressure systems, etc.). Describe and chart your findings.

9. **Specific Ecosystems and Trophic Pathways.**

Research a specific ecosystem (e.g., coniferous forest, tropical rainforest, grassland, savanna, desert) and draw up both grazing and detrital pathway diagrams showing the major plants and animals.

10. **Biogeochemical Cycles and Human Intervention.**

Look at the major biogeochemical cycles outlined in the text and suggest how humans can decrease their 'ecological footprint' in all or any of them.

ANSWERS

Please visit our website for additional answers.

Part One

1.   0.550 km
     5.5 km
     0.2 kg
     20,000 mg
     5.5×10^3 km
     0.65 MW

3.   a) Halifax, Nova Scotia   44°N 63°W
     b) Moscow, Russia   55°N 37°E
     c) Sydney, Australia   34°S 151°E
     c) Cairo, Egypt   30°N 31°E
     d) Rio de Janeiro, Brazil   23°S 47°W

5.   15°S 10°W

7.   a) 4 a.m. on Friday
     b) Accounting for flight time, you will arrive at 2 p.m. Wednesday in Vancouver time. Converted to Auckland time, it will be 10 a.m. on Thursday.

Part Two

1. $\lambda_{max} = \dfrac{2898\ \mu mK}{5770\ K} = 0.50\ \mu m$

3.   • The albedo of fresh snow is approximately 95%: therefore $K\uparrow$ is 95% of the total (28 ly hr^{-1}): = 26.6 ly hr^{-1}

     • It is a cloudless day and therefore there will not be a reflected terrestrial radiation value $L\downarrow$

• Outgoing longwave radiation $L\uparrow$ can be solved using Stefan-Boltzmann Law
• Outgoing longwave radiation can be established as the Intensity of Energy Emitted, $E = \sigma T^4$

where σ has a constant value of 4.9×10^{-9} and T is the temperature of the emitting surface in °K (°K = °C + 273)

With a surface temperature of −4°C, this value can then be calculated as:

$0.49(-4 + 273)^4 = 0.49(2.69)^4 = 0.49 \times 53.36$
$$= 25.66$$
$Q = K\downarrow - K\uparrow + L\downarrow - L\uparrow$
$Q = 28 - 26.6 + 0 - 25.66 = -24.26$

Since the net radiation is a negative value, there is a deficit of radiation, meaning that there is insufficient energy to melt the snow.

5.   a) $T_{annual} = \dfrac{\Sigma T_{monthly}}{12}$

     $2 + 1 + 2 + 5 + 13 + 20 + 22 + 26 + 21 + 17 + 11 + 4 = 144/12 = 12°C$

     b) There is a large variability in the temperature with colder winter months and much warmer summer months: there is a distinct 'seasonality' to the annual temperature trends. This would not be a tropical or subtropical location given the seasonality of the temperature. It is not a high latitude location given the fact that temperatures do not dip below zero in the winter months.

     c) There are many places in the world where this could be: large areas of Europe have temperature patterns like this, the southeastern United States, and western North America, to name a few.

7. Numerous acceptable responses depending on the sites selected.

9.

Height (m)	Temperature (°C)
1000	22
900	23
800	24
700	25
600	26
500	27
400	28
300	29
200	30
100	31
Surface	32

11. a) **Cfa** (Humid subtropical—partial marks for mesothermal): maximum temp. ~27°C, minimum 5°C, range = 22°C. Seasonality observed. Maximum precip. ~150 mm, minimum 72 mm, slightly more precip. in summer months (or less in winter), no dry season. Biome = temperate broadleaf forest.

b) **Am** (Tropical monsoon): maximum temp. ~30°C, minimum 25°C, range = 5°C. Minimal seasonal variation throughout year; maximum precip. ~647 mm, minimum 0 mm. Very high precip. during summer months. Biome = Tropical monsoon forest.

c) **Dfb** (Humid continental—partial marks for microthermal): maximum temp. ~20°C, minimum −19°C, range = 39°C. Strong seasonality. Maximum precip. ~85 mm, minimum 20 mm. Higher precip. in summer months, no dry season. Biome = coniferous/evergreen forest.

Part Three

1. Answers will vary.

3. Answers will vary with area chosen.

5. a) and b):

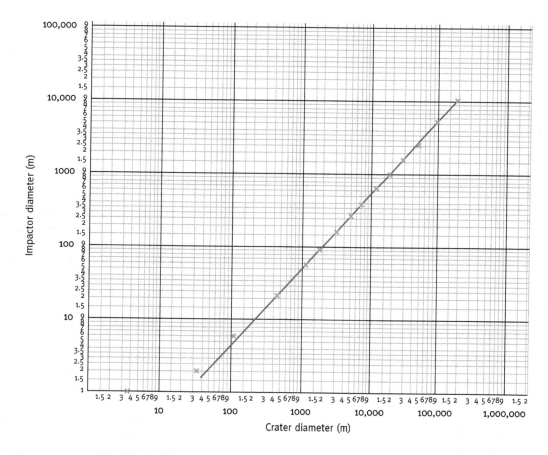

c) The line shows that there is a very close correlation between impactor (projectile or meteorite) and crater size. There is a consistent relationship between the amount of kinetic energy produced by an impact of any size (raindrop to huge meteorite/asteroid) and the mass and the terminal velocity of the bolide:

KE (projectile kinetic energy in joules) = ½ mass × terminal velocity²

The size of the crater may also be influenced by the rock type of the impact site and the composition of the meteorite (impactor).

7. Results will depend on the volcano and the period studied.

9. The answers will depend on the continents chosen and the parts of the continents studied.

Part Four

1. a)

Elevation Band (m above sea level)	Band Area (km²)	Accumulation		Ablation		Net Budget (cm water equivalent)
		Mean Specific Net Accumulation (cm water equivalent)	Total Net Accumulation ($\times 10^6\,m^3$)	Mean Specific Net Ablation (cm water equivalent)	Total Net Ablation ($\times 10^6\,m^3$)	
2895–3045	0.04	315.000	1.260	350.000	0.140	35.000
2740–2895	0.38	1032.368	3.923	173.158	0.658	859.210
2590–2740	1.83	483.661	8.851	236.601	4.319	247.060
2435–2590	4.23	125.272	5.299	178.817	7.564	−53.545
2285–2435	4.86	27.634	1.343	115.494	5.613	−87.860
2130–2285	1.77	7.062	0.125	65.819	1.165	−58.757
1980–2130	0.56	1.786	0.010	23.214	0.130	−21.428
Totals	13.67	152.238	20.811	143.299	19.589	8.939

$1\ km^2 = 1 \times 10^6\ m^2$
To find depth: depth = volume/area
For 2895–3045 MASL band – accumulation
Depth (cm WE) = $1.26 \times 10^6\ m^3 / 0.04 \times 10^6\ m^2 = 31.5\ cm \times 100 = 315\ cm\ WE$

b) The depth columns cannot be added to get the totals. The same formula has to be used as in the last question. The total area of the glacier and the totals for total net accumulation/total net ablation are used to calculate the figures.

c) For 2095–3045 MASL band: 315.000 cm WE − 350.000 cm WE = 35.000 cm WE.

d)

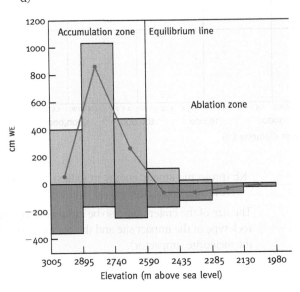

3. Results will vary.

5. a) Etobicoke: 10,260 t/yr; Upper Humber: 28,492 t/yr; Fraser: 15,048,648 t/yr
    b) It seems that the size of the drainage basin is important, as are the different climatic and topographic contexts of the three basins.
    c) Etobicoke Creek Basin above the QEW: 204 km²: 50.3 t/yr/km²
       Upper Humber River Basin above Elder Mills: 303 km²: 94.0 t/yr/km²
       Fraser River Basin above Agassiz: 218,000 km²: 69.0 t/yr/km²
    d) The sediment yield per year/unit area indicates something different from the conclusions in the answer to b). The Upper Humber River Basin has the highest sediment yield per unit area and it is right next door to the Etobicoke Creek Basin, which has the lowest sediment yield per unit area. The sediment yield/unit area for the Fraser Basin falls in between these two basins. The Upper Humber and Etobicoke Creek basins share the same kind of climate, topography, glacial history, soils, sediments, solid geology, etc., yet show very different amounts of sediment loss. The Fraser Basin is different in many respects: topography, glacial history, climate, vegetation cover, etc.

The difference in sediment yield per unit area in the neighbouring basins is related to land use. A large area of the Etobicoke Creek Basin was urbanized many years ago. The creek flows through the city of Brampton and then through Mississauga, passes Pearson International Airport, and then forms the boundary between Etobicoke and Mississauga until it reaches Lake Ontario. The Upper Humber River Basin was being urbanized or suburbanized during the period of measurement (2006). Large areas were under construction (with the clearing of vegetation, piling up of topsoil, surface compaction because of heavy construction vehicles, etc.), leading to more wind and water erosion. Other parts of the Upper Humber River Basin are used for the market gardening of vegetables (including corn) and fruit for the Greater Toronto area.

7. Answers depend on the glacier chosen and the years of record.

9. Answers will vary with areas and their specific characteristics.

Part Five

1.–10. For all the above questions there are numerous acceptable responses depending on the areas selected, etc.

Glossary

Aa   Angular, jagged, blocky shaped lava formed from the hardening of not especially fluid lavas.

Ablation till   Glacial material carried on the top of a glacier or ice sheet. The material is mainly supplied by slope and aeolian processes.

Ablation zone   Glacier's lower end where loss of mass occurs, such as from melting and evaporation.

Abrasion (glacial)   Glacial erosion process of scraping, produced by the impact of rock debris carried in the ice upon the bedrock surface below.

Abrasion (stream)   Erosive action of boulders, pebbles, and smaller sediment as they are carried along a stream channel. These fragments dislodge other particles along the stream bed and banks, thereby enhancing the deepening and widening process.

Absolute base level   Elevational level lying a few metres below sea level.

Abyssal plain   Large zone of relatively low-relief seafloor, constituting one of the deeper areas of an ocean basin.

Accretion   Process where bodies of rock, derived from other lithospheric plates, are attached to the margins of a shield-anchored continental landmass. These geologically consistent fragments can be regional in extent and are known as terranes.

Accumulation zone (névé)   The upper end of a glacier where precipitation (snow) exceeds loss from melting and evaporation and is turned into ice over a long period of time.

Acid precipitation   Abnormally acidic rain, snow, or fog resulting from high levels of the oxides of sulphur and nitrogen that exist as industrial pollutants in the air.

Active volcano   A volcano that has erupted in recorded human history.

Additions   Gains made by the soil when solar energy, water, gases, and organic matter from plant growth are added, or sometimes when loose sediments move downslope and come to rest on the soil.

Adiabatic   With air being a poor conductor of heat, a parcel of air at one temperature that is surrounded by air at another temperature will neither gain nor lose heat energy over a short period of time. When such non-transfer of heat occurs, the process is called adiabatic.

Advection   Horizontal movement of material in the atmosphere.

Aeolian   Related to wind.

Aerosols   Tiny solid or liquid particles suspended in the atmosphere.

Aggradation   Combination of processes that builds up the surface through the deposition of material that was removed from elsewhere by degradation; contributes to the lowering of relief by reducing the height differences between the high and low places in an area.

Air mass   Very large parcel of air (more than 1600 km across) in the boundary layer of the troposphere, which possesses relatively uniform qualities of density, temperature, and humidity in the horizontal dimension. It is also bound together as an organized whole, a vital cohesion because air masses routinely migrate for hundreds of kilometres as distinct entities.

Albedo   Proportion of incoming solar radiation that is reflected by a surface; the whiter the colour of the surface (albedo derives from the Latin word *albus*, meaning white), the higher its albedo.

Alfisol   One of the 12 soil orders of the US Soil Taxonomy, found in moister, less continental climate zones; characterized by high mineral content, moistness, and sizable clay accumulation in the **B** horizon. Canadian taxonomy: luvisolic soil order.

Alluvial fan   Fan-shaped deposit consisting of alluvial material located where a mountain stream emerges onto a plain or valley.

Alluvium   Material deposited by a stream composing its floodplain, made up of, from bottom to top in sequence, coarser material, sand and gravel, and clays and silts.

Alp   A higher area, with a stream-cut and rounded landscape, in a glaciated upland that has escaped ice erosion. This feature gave its name to the European Alps.

Alpine karst   Karst found at high altitude and characterized by sinks or sinkholes and karren (grooves and runnels); the sinks drain into deep cave systems.

Amensalism   Biological interaction in which one species is inhibited by another.

Amphidromic points   Hubs in the ocean (also called cotidal points), related to the Coriolis effect, around which tides rise and fall; at these points the tidal range is negligible.

Andisol   One of the 12 soil orders of the US Soil Taxonomy; established to include certain weakly developed, parent-material-controlled soils, notably those developed on volcanic ashes, which are locally distributed throughout the Pacific Ring of Fire, Hawaii, and the world's other volcanic zones. Canadian taxonomy: solonetzic soil order.

Animal range   The spatial extent and geographical pattern, including nesting habitat and food sources (grazing, prey, etc.), of the area in which a particular animal can survive and reproduce successfully.

Anion   Negatively charged ion, such as those of carbonates, nitrates, and phosphates.

Annual temperature cycle   Pattern of temperature change during the course of a year.

Annular drainage   Concentric stream pattern that drains the interior of an excavated geological dome.

Antarctic Circle   Latitude (66½°S) marking the northern boundary of the Southern Hemisphere portion of the Earth's surface that receives a 24-hour period of sunlight at least once each year.

Antarctic Icecap   Continental glacier that covers almost all of Antarctica, enabling the study of what conditions were like elsewhere in the world during much of the Pleistocene Ice Age.

Antecedent stream   Stream exhibiting transverse drainage across a structural feature that would normally impede its flow because the stream predates the structure and kept cutting downward as the structure was uplifted around it.

Anticline   Arch-like upfold with the limbs dipping away from its axis.

Anticyclone   Atmospheric high-pressure cell involving the divergence of air, which subsides at and flows spirally out of the centre. The isobars around an anticyclone are generally circular in shape, with their values increasing towards the centre. In the Northern Hemisphere, winds flow clockwise around an anticyclone; in the Southern Hemisphere, winds flow counterclockwise around an anticyclone.

Aphelion   Point in the Earth's orbit that occurs every 4 July, where the distance to the Sun is maximized (approximately 152.5 million km).

Aquiclude   Impermeable rock layer that resists the infiltration of groundwater; consists of tightly packed or interlocking particles, such as in shale.

Aquifer Porous and permeable rock layer that can at least be partially saturated with groundwater; a confined aquifer lies between two aquicludes and often obtains its groundwater from a distant area, while an unconfined aquifer obtains its groundwater from local infiltration; a perched aquifer is a pocket of groundwater above the local water table, often associated with karst areas.

Archipelago Group of islands, often elongated into a chain.

Arctic Circle Latitude (66½°N) marking the southern boundary of the Northern Hemisphere portion of the Earth's surface that receives a 24-hour period of sunlight at least once each year.

Arctic Oscillation (AO) Closely related to the North Atlantic Oscillation, occurring as a result of variations in air mass conditions at mid- and high latitudes in the Northern Hemisphere. The AO fluctuates between positive (warm) and negative (cold) phases, with the positive phase characterized by low pressure in the upper atmosphere over the polar region and high pressure over southern Canada and the United States, and the negative phase with high pressure in the upper atmosphere over the Arctic and low pressure in the upper atmosphere at lower latitudes.

Arête Knife-like, jagged ridge that separates two adjacent glaciers, glacial valleys, or cirques.

Arid (B) climates Dry climates where potential evapotranspiration always exceeds the moisture supplied by precipitation; found in areas dominated by the subtropical high-pressure cells, in the interiors of continents far from oceanic moisture sources, and in conjunction with rain-shadow zones downwind from certain mountain ranges.

Aridisol One of the 12 soil orders of the US Soil Taxonomy, and the most widespread on the world's landmasses; dry soil (unless irrigated) associated with arid climates, light in colour, and often containing horizons rich in calcium, clay, or salt minerals. Canadian taxonomy: chernozemic and solonetzic soil orders.

Arroyo Small, steep-sided, flat-floored gully, which has been cut into the surface of an alluvial fan and may continue onto the valley floor beyond. Found only in semi-arid and arid environments, these channels are usually dry but can contain ephemeral streamflow when intermittent local precipitation occurs.

Artesian well One that flows under its own natural pressure to the surface; usually associated with a confined aquifer that is recharged from a remote location where that aquifer reaches the surface.

Ash (volcanic) Solid, cinder-like fragments of lava or pyroclastic material, smaller than volcanic bombs, that are exploded into the air during an eruption. Most ash falls to the ground close to the erupting volcano.

Asteroids Small rocky bodies, also called planetesimals, that have been in the solar system since its beginning and have not been swept up and incorporated into planets. They range in size from a few km to tens of km in diameter (up to 1000 km). Most are found in the Asteroid belt between the orbits of Mars and Jupiter, but the orbits of some asteroids take them close to the Sun and across the paths of planets such as the Earth.

Asthenosphere Plastic layer of the upper mantle that underlies the lithosphere, which is able to move over it.

Atmosphere Blanket of air that adheres to the Earth's surface, which contains the mixture of gases essential to the survival of all terrestrial life forms.

Atolls Ring-like coral reefs surrounding lagoons; grew on the rims of eroded volcanic cones.

Atterberg limits Geotechnical engineering limits defining when an Earth material acts as a solid, plastic, or liquid; mainly influenced by the amount and type of clays and the amount of moisture.

Attrition Wave erosion process where larger rock fragments are reduced to smaller fragments as loose material is continuously moved about in churning water.

Aurora australis Name given to the aurora phenomenon that occurs in the Southern Hemisphere's upper middle and high latitudes.

Aurora borealis Vivid sheet-like displays of light in the nighttime sky of the upper middle and high latitudes in the Northern Hemisphere; caused by the intermittent penetration of the thermosphere by ionized particles.

Autotroph Organism that manufactures its own organic materials from inorganic chemicals. A good example is phytoplankton, food-producing plants that manufacture carbohydrates.

Avalanches (landslides) Forms of mass movement (snow, rock, debris) that travel downslope very rapidly. In effect, an avalanche is a collapse of a slope and does not need water as a lubricant (can be triggered by an earthquake, undercutting, glacial oversteeping as well as by human activities). The material travels as a turbulent density flow down the slope on a layer of compressed air and is preceded by a blast of air that can flatten trees, cause defoliation, etc.

Axis (Earth's) Imaginary line that extends from the North Pole to the South Pole through the centre of the Earth. The planet's rotation occurs with respect to this axis.

Azonal flow Meridional (north–south) flow of upper atmospheric winds (poleward of 15 degrees of latitude), particularly the subtropical and Polar Front jet streams. Periodic departures from the zonal (west-to-east) flow of these air currents are important because they help to correct the heat imbalance between polar and equatorial regions.

Backshore Beach zone that lies landward of the foreshore; extends from the high-water line to the dune line.

Backslope (dune) Windward slope of a sand dune.

Backwash Return flow to the sea of the thinning sheet of water that slid up the beach as swash undertow; also called undertow.

Bajada Coalesced assemblage of alluvial fans that lines a highland front (also known as alluvial apron); primarily a desert feature.

Barbed dendritic drainage Drainage pattern where tributaries enter the trunk stream at an obtuse angle, a result of drainage diversion or reversal caused by blockage of drainage systems by an ice sheet during the Pleistocene Ice Age.

Barchan Crescent-shaped sand dune with its points lying downwind. Convex side of this dune is the windward side.

Barometer Instrument that measures atmospheric pressure.

Barrier island Permanent offshore elongated ridge of sand, positioned parallel to the shoreline and separated from it by a lagoon; may have formed originally as an offshore bar during the last glaciation, migrated coastward, and grew as it shifted.

Basal ice Bottom ice layer of a glacier or ice sheet.

Basal (peripheral) sliding Lubrication and movement at the base or periphery (sides and base) of a glacier or ice sheet caused by the pressure melting of basal (or peripheral) ice. Only occurs in wet-based or temperate ice.

Basal (lodgement) till Till material that is carried englacially and subglacially and deposited under the ice.

Baseflow Stream discharge originating from groundwater, which in some cases is the source of most of a stream's discharge.

Base level Elevational level below which a stream cannot erode its bed. Ultimate base level is sea level.

Batholith Massive, discordant body of intrusive igneous rock (pluton), which has destroyed and melted most of the existing geological structures it has invaded.

Baymouth bar Sandspit that has grown all the way across the mouth of a bay.

Beach (strand) Coastal zone of sediment that is shaped by the action of waves; constructed of sand and other materials, derived from both local and distant sources.

Beach drift Process associated with longshore drift, which operates to move huge amounts of beach sand or shingle downshore in the direction of the longshore current.

Beach mass balance   The balance between material transported onto the beach (input) and material transported off of the beach (output). If input is greater than output, there is a positive mass balance; if output is greater, the balance is negative.

Bedding plane   Distinct junction between two sedimentary rock strata or beds.

Benioff zone   An inclined zone of earthquake foci associated with subduction, as in the Pacific Ring of Fire. The magnitude of the earthquakes increases with depth.

Berm   Beach ridge that lies in the backshore beach zone; deposited during storms and beyond the reach of normal daily wave action.

Bermuda High   The North Atlantic Ocean's subtropical high-pressure cell, which is generally centred over latitude 30°N, though it shifts somewhat north and south with the seasonal direction of the Sun; also known as the Azores High.

Biodiversity   *Biological diversity*; variety of the Earth's life forms and the ecological roles they play.

Biofilm   A thin coating of algae or bacteria covering a cave wall or other rock face, boulder, or tree.

Biogeography   Geography of plants (phytogeography) and animals (zoogeography).

Biological weathering   Decay and disintegration of rock minerals via biological means. Earthworms and plant roots are important in the development of soil, lichens contribute to the breakdown of rocks, and humans, of course, play various roles in the disintegration of rocks and the operation of soil-formation processes.

Biomass   Total living organic matter, encompassing all plants and animals, produced in a particular geographical area.

Biome   A major subdivision of the plant and animal world that is smaller than a biocycle (i.e., saltwater, freshwater, and terrestrial life forms) or a biochore (i.e. forest, savanna, grassland, steppe, and desert); an assemblage and association of plants and animals, which forms a regional ecological unit of subcontinental dimensions.

Biosphere   Zone of terrestrial life, the habitat of all living things; includes the Earth's vegetation, animals, human beings, and the soil layer.

Bioturbation   Mixing of the soil by animals or plants.

Black and white smokers   Submarine, mineral-rich hot water springs related to mid-oceanic ridge spreading sites. The seawater infiltrates the crust close to a magma body, becomes superhot, and melts some of the minerals in the crustal rock on the way back to the seabed. On release, the minerals are precipitated to form a chimney around the spring. The colour depends on the minerals involved. Also called hydrothermal vents.

Blizzard   Blowing snow with wind speeds of 40 km/h or more, drifting snow, and wind chill factors of up to −25°C, with a duration of at least four consecutive hours.

Blocky (angular) soil structure   Involves irregularly shaped peds with straight sides that fit against the flat surfaces of adjacent peds, thereby giving a soil considerable strength (see Figure 44.19).

Body waves   Seismic waves that travel through the interior of the Earth (**P** waves and **S** waves).

Boiling point (water)   Key setting in the calibration of the temperature scales. On the Celsius scale water boils at 100°C.

Bolides   Very large impactors of unknown type (asteroid, comet, or large meteorite).

Boreal forest   Upper mid-latitude northern coniferous forest; in Russia called taiga.

Bottomset beds   Finest deltaic deposits, usually laid down ahead of the delta, where the coastal water is quiet.

Boulder field   Slopes covered by blocky pieces of rock covering a large area, a result of gravity after large rocks are loosened from exposed surfaces by frost action.

Box canyon   Steep-sided gorge, usually in a desert area, where an arroyo occurs in the bottom of or leads out from; also called gulches or dry washes in the US or wadis in the Middle East.

Braided stream   Carries a high sediment load when in flood. The flow subdivides into many intertwined channels, reuniting some distance downstream. Sediment is deposited in bars and banks as the water flow decreases, giving the 'braided' appearance.

Breccia   Clastic sedimentary rocks where the pebble-sized fragments are angular and jagged.

Brunisolic soil   A Canadian soil order characterized by the weak development of a reddish brown **B** horizon lacking in clays and other compounds. The soils in this order are more developed than regosols. US taxonomy: inceptisol soil order.

Butte   Small, steep-sided, caprock-protected hill, usually found in dry environments; an erosional remnant of a plateau.

Caldera   Steep-walled, circular volcanic basin usually formed by the collapse of a volcano whose magma chamber emptied; can also result from a particularly powerful eruption that blows off the peak and crater of a volcano.

Calorie   One calorie is the amount of heat energy required to raise the temperature of 1 gram of water by 1°C; not the same unit as the calories used to measure the energy value of food (which are 1000 times larger).

Calving   When an ice sheet or glacier enters the sea, the repeated breaking away of the leading edge of that glacier into icebergs.

Canadian System of Soil Classification   The Canadian soil taxonomy.

Canopy   A canopy is formed by the inter-fingering of tree crowns in a forest, e.g., in a tropical rainforest.

Carbonation   Reaction of weak carbonic acid (formed from water and carbon dioxide) with minerals. Carbonic acid, in turn, reacts with carbonate rocks such as limestone in a form of chemical weathering that can be quite vigorous in certain humid areas, where solution and decay lead to the formation of karst landscapes.

Carbon cycle   The storage of carbon in 'sinks' or 'reservoirs' and the movement or flux of carbon within the Earth System, i.e., the carbon that is cycling within the system from land, water, biota, and human activities into the atmosphere and back again.

Carbon dioxide (CO_2) cycle   Dominated by exchanges occurring between air and sea. CO_2 is directly absorbed by the ocean from the atmosphere and is released during the photosynthesis of billions of small organisms known as plankton.

Carbon footprint   A measure of the impact human activities have on the environment in terms of the amount of greenhouse gases produced, measured in units of carbon dioxide; a way in which individuals and organizations can attempt to quantify their personal (or organizational) impact in contributing to global warming.

Caribbean karst   Rarest karst topography, associated with nearly flat-lying limestones; underground erosion dominated by the collapse of roofs of subsurface conduits, producing a characteristic sinkhole terrain.

Carnivores   Animals that eat herbivores and other animals.

Cartography   Science, art, and technology of mapmaking and map use.

Cation   Positively charged ion, such as those of calcium.

Cave   Any substantial underground chamber in bedrock large enough for an adult to enter.

Celsius scale   Metric temperature scale most commonly used throughout the world (except in the US). The boiling point of water is set at 100°C and its freezing point at 0°C.

Cementation   During the lithification process of compaction, as the grains of sediments are tightly squeezed together, water in the intervening pore spaces, which contains dissolved minerals, is deposited on the grain surfaces and acts as a glue to bond the grains together.

Channelled Scablands Area of eastern Washington state with some very unusual landscapes, including underfit streams, many dry valleys (or coulees), huge rectangular valleys, gorges with dry waterfalls cut into basalt bedrock, huge potholes (hence the 'Scablands' term), and erratic blocks weighing up to 250–300 tonnes, now believed to have been created by one or many immense floods from proglacial Lake Missoula 12,000–16,000 years before the present.

Chemical weathering Decomposition of rock minerals via chemical means. In any rock made up of a combination of minerals, the chemical breakdown of one set of mineral grains leads to the disintegration of the whole mass.

Chernozemic soil A Canadian soil order characteristic of the moister areas of the Prairies. Characterized by having a thick (mull) humus-rich **A** horizon over a calcium-rich **B** horizon. US taxonomy: mollisol (boroll) soil order.

Chinook wind Name given to the foehn winds that affect the leeward areas of mountain zones in the western plateaus of North America, e.g., Alberta.

Chlorofluorocarbons (CFCs) Ozone-depleting compounds that contain chlorine, fluorine, and carbon.

Cinder cone Volcanic landform consisting mainly of pyroclastics. Often formed during brief periods of explosive activity, they normally remain quite small.

Circle of illumination At any given moment on our constantly rotating planet, the boundary between the halves of the Earth that are in sunlight and darkness.

Circum-Pacific earthquake belt Aspect of the Pacific Ring of Fire, the lengthy belt of subduction zones that girdles the Pacific Basin. Here the heaviest concentration of earthquake epicenters as well as active volcanoes occurs.

Cirque Amphitheatre-like basin, high up on a mountain, that is cut by, and a source area of, an alpine glacier.

Cirrus clouds Cloud category that encompasses thin, wispy, streak-like clouds consisting of ice particles rather than water droplets; occur only at altitudes higher than 6000 m.

Clastic sedimentary rocks Sedimentary rocks composed of broken and fragmentary particles eroded from previously existing rocks.

Clay Smallest category of soil particles. Clay particles are smaller than 0.002 mm, with the smallest in the colloidal range possessing diameters of less than one micrometre. Clay minerals are a type of silicate material produced by weathering.

Cleavage Tendency of minerals to break in certain directions along bright plane surfaces, revealing zones of weakness in the crystalline structure, e.g., slate, shale.

Climate Long-term conditions (over at least 30 years) of aggregate weather over a region, summarized by averages and measures of variability; a synthesis of the succession of weather events we have learned to expect at any given location.

Climate change Regional variations in warming or cooling, and in storm activity, over a period of time; today, scientists believe that climate changes observed in recent years and decades are linked to global warming.

Climatic controls Features of the Earth's surface—such as the distribution of land and water bodies, ocean currents, and highlands—that shape the climate of an area by influencing its temperature and moisture regimes.

Climatology Geographical study of climates. This includes not only climate classification and the analysis of their regional distribution, but broader environmental questions that concern climate change, interrelationships with soil and vegetation, and human–climate interaction.

Climax community Achieved at the end of a plant succession. The vegetation and its ecosystem are in complete harmony (dynamic equilibrium) with the soil, the climate, and other parts of the environment.

Climograph Graph that simultaneously displays, for a given location, its key climatic variables of average temperature and precipitation, showing how they change monthly throughout the year.

Closed system Self-contained system exhibiting no exchange of energy or matter across its boundaries (interfaces).

Cloud Visible mass of suspended, minute water droplets or ice crystals.

Coast General reference to the strip of land and sea where the various coastal processes combine to create characteristic landscapes. The term 'shore' has a more specific meaning.

Cockpit karst In tropical karst areas, the sharply contrasted landscape of prominent karst towers and the irregular, steep-sided depressions lying between them. 'Cockpit' refers to the depressions.

Cold-air drainage Category of local-scale wind systems governed by the downward oozing of heavy, dense, cold air along steep slopes under the influence of gravity; produces katabatic winds (such as southeastern France's *mistral*) that are fed by massive pools of icy air that accumulate over such major mountain regions as the Alps and the Rocky Mountains.

Cold front Produced when an advancing cold air mass hugs the surface and displaces all other air as it wedges itself beneath the pre-existing warmer air mass. Cold fronts have much steeper slopes than warm fronts and thus produce more abrupt cooling and condensation (and more intense precipitation).

Cold (or polar) ice Ice that does not reach pressure melting point because it is in very cold areas or because it does not have sufficient mass. The ice is frozen to the ground. Movement is restricted to ice layers above the ice/ground interface.

Collapse doline Sinkhole in which the rock ceiling of an underground solution cavity has collapsed.

Collision-coalescence Process within clouds at temperatures above the freezing point through which larger droplets, which fall at a greater speed, collide and merge with smaller, slower-moving droplets, increasing in size to a point where they are large enough to fall to the Earth as precipitation.

Column (cave) Coalescence of a stalactite and a stalagmite that forms a continuous column from the floor to the roof of a cave.

Comets Bodies of rock and a considerable amount of volatile ices—from tens of km in diameter to greater than 100 km in diameter—that follow eccentric orbits about the Sun. As they move closer to the Sun these ices evaporate to form their characteristic tails.

Compaction Lithification process where deposited sediments are compressed by the weight of newer, overlying sediments. This pressure will compact and consolidate lower strata, squeezing their sediments tightly together. Usually occurs in conjunction with cementation.

Composite volcano Volcano formed, usually above a subduction zone, by the eruption of a succession of lavas, pyroclastics, and ash that accumulate as a series of alternating layers; the larger and more durable composite volcanoes are called stratovolcanoes.

Compressional stresses Stresses associated with the convergence of lithospheric plates. The lithosphere is forced to occupy less space and the rocks respond by breaking, bending, folding, sliding, and squeezing upward and downward and by crushing tightly together.

Concordant intrusion Intrusive magma that did not disrupt or destroy surrounding, existing geological structures but conformed to them.

Condensation Process by which a substance is transformed from the gaseous to the liquid state.

Condensation nuclei Small airborne particles around which liquid droplets can form when water vapour condenses; almost always present in the atmosphere in the form of dust or salt particles.

Conduction　Transport of heat energy from one molecule to the next.

Conglomerate　Coarse-grained sedimentary rock; a composite rock made of gravels, pebbles, and sometimes even boulders.

Conic projection　A map projection in which the transfer of the Earth grid is from a globe onto a cone, which is then cut and laid flat.

Conservation　Careful management and use of natural resources, the achievement of significant social benefits from them, and the preservation of the natural environment.

Constant gases　Atmospheric gases always found in the same proportions. Two of them constitute 99 per cent of the air: nitrogen (78 per cent) and oxygen (21 per cent).

Constant of channel maintenance　The reciprocal of drainage density, i.e., the area of drainage basin necessary to sustain part or all of a stream (km^2/km).

Contact metamorphism　Metamorphic change in rocks induced by their local contact with molten magma or lava.

Continent (geological)　Geologists define a continent as having granitic crust (SIAL) over basaltic crust (SIMA).

Continental drift　Notion hypothesized by Alfred Wegener concerning the fragmentation of Pangaea and the slow movement of continents away from this core supercontinent. Not the same as plate tectonics.

Continental effect (continentality)　Lack of the moderating influence of an ocean on air temperature, which is characteristic of inland locations; this produces hotter summers and colder winters relative to coastal locations at similar latitudes.

Continental glaciers　Huge masses of ice, also called ice sheets or icecaps, that bury large areas beneath them.

Continentality　Variation of the continental effect on air temperatures in the interior portions of the world's landmasses; the greater the distance from the moderating influence of an ocean (known as the maritime effect), the greater the extreme in summer and winter temperatures (northeastern Eurasia is the classic example of such extreme annual temperature cycles).

Continental rise　Transitional zone of gently sloping seafloor that begins at the foot of the continental slope and leads downward to the lower (abyssal) zone of an ocean basin.

Continental shelf　Gently sloping, relatively shallow, submerged plain just off the coast of a continent, extending to a depth of approximately 180 m; inundated part of a continent.

Continental shield　Large, stable, relatively flat expanse of very old rocks that may constitute one of the earliest 'slabs' of solidification of the primeval Earth's molten crust into hard rocks or formed by meteoric impact; forms the geological core of a continental landmass.

Continental slope　Steeply plunging slope that begins at the outer edge of the continental shelf (approximately 180 m [600 ft] below the sea surface) and ends in the depths of the ocean floor at the head of the continental rise.

Contouring　Representation of surface relief using isolines of elevation above sea level; an important basis of topographical mapping.

Convectional precipitation　Convection is the spontaneous vertical movement of air in the atmosphere. Convectional precipitation occurs after condensation of this rising air, e.g., related to a thunderstorm.

Convection cell　Rising column of air.

Convergent evolution　Organisms in widely separated biogeographic realms, although descended from diverse ancestors, develop similar adaptations to measurably similar habitats.

Convergent-lifting precipitation　Precipitation produced by the forced lifting of warm, moist air where low-level windflows converge; most pronounced in the equatorial latitudes, where the Northeast and Southeast Trades come together in the Inter-Tropical Convergence Zone (ITCZ), especially over the oceans.

Coral reef　Aggradational reef formed from the skeletal remains of marine organisms and living animals and plants.

Coriolis force　Force that, owing to the rotation of the Earth, tends to deflect all objects moving over the surface of the Earth away from their original paths. In the absence of any other forces, the deflection is to the right in the Northern Hemisphere and to the left in the Southern Hemisphere; the higher the latitude, the stronger the deflection.

Corrasion　Mechanical coastal-erosion process whereby waves break off pieces of rock from the surface under attack. The sediment-loaded water, now a much more powerful erosive agent, continues to be hurled against that surface.

Corrosion　Breakdown of coastal bedrock by solution or other chemical means.

Counterradiation　Longwave radiation emitted by the Earth's surface that is absorbed by the atmosphere and reradiated (also as longwave radiation) back down to the surface.

Coversands　Aeolian sands deposited during deglaciation.

Creep　Slowest form of mass movement; involves the slow, imperceptible motion of a soil layer downslope, as revealed in the slight downhill tilt of trees and other stationary objects.

Crevasse　One of the huge vertical cracks that frequently cut the rigid, brittle upper layer of a glacier or ice sheet.

Critical threshold　The point where stability and instability are finely balanced.

Cross-bedding　Consists of successive rock strata deposited not horizontally but at varying inclines. Like ripple marks on sand, this usually forms on beaches and in dunes.

Crustal spreading　Geographical term for seafloor spreading. Not all crustal spreading occurs on the ocean floor; on land, such spreading creates rift valleys.

Cryosolic soil　Canadian soil order distinguished by the presence of ice or permafrost in the profile. US taxonomy: gelisol soil order.

Cryosphere　Name for the ice system of the Earth, which constitutes one of the five subsystems of the total Earth System.

Crystalline rocks　Rocks composed of minerals that exhibit a regularly repeating molecular structure; can also be used generally to refer to igneous and metamorphic rocks as opposed to sedimentary rocks.

Cultural landscapes　Landscapes where human intervention dominates to such an extent that physical processes have been subordinated, such as urban areas; also, in cultural geography, landscapes that have been reshaped by human cultural activity, such as agriculture, forestry, the building of dykes, fences, houses, etc.

Cumulus clouds　Cloud category that encompasses thick, puffy, billowing masses that often develop to great heights; subclassified according to height.

Cycle of erosion (geographical cycle)　Model of landscape development suggested by W.M. Davis in the later part of the nineteenth century that postulated a short period of uplift followed by an extremely long (eons in length) period of erosion during which the landscape was worn down to a nearly flat surface (a peneplain). Now generally discounted.

Cyclic (autogenic) succession　Plant succession in which one type of vegetation is replaced by another, which in turn is replaced by the first, with other series possibly intermixed.

Cyclogenesis　Formation, evolution, and movement of mid-latitude cyclones.

Cyclone　Atmospheric low-pressure cell involving the convergence of air, which flows into and spirally rises at the centre. The isobars around a cyclone are generally circular in shape, with their values decreasing towards the centre. In the Northern Hemisphere, winds flow counterclockwise around a cyclone; in the Southern Hemisphere, winds flow clockwise around a cyclone.

Cylindrical projection   A map projection in which the transfer of the Earth grid is from a globe onto a cylinder, which is then cut and laid flat.

Daylight saving time   By law, all clocks in a time zone are set one hour forward from standard time for at least part of the year. In Canada, all provinces observe daylight saving time, with the exception of Saskatchewan.

Debris torrents   A hillslope process involving an excessively loaded channel flow containing rock, debris, and tree material, caused by the buildup of material in a mountain drainage basin and mobilization by intense rainfall and/or snow melt.

Deflation   Process whereby wind sweeps along a surface and carries away the finest particles.

Deflation hollow   A basin excavated by aeolian activity.

Deglaciation   Melting and receding of glaciers that accompanies climatic warming after the peak of a glacial period has been reached.

Degradation   A combination of processes that erode the landscape.

Degree   One three-hundred-sixtieth of a circle, such as the Earth's circumference.

Delta   Sedimentary deposit surrounding and extending beyond the mouth of a river where it empties into the sea or a lake; frequently assumes a triangular configuration, hence its naming after the Greek letter of that shape.

Deltaic plain   Flat, stable landward portion of a delta that is growing seaward.

Dendritic drainage   Tree-limb-like stream pattern that is commonly observed; indicates surface of relatively uniform hardness or one of flat-lying sedimentary rocks.

Denudation   Erosion of the landscape.

Deranged drainage   Drainage that is confused, i.e., many short sections of stream separated by intervening wetlands and lakes. Often characteristic of glaciated areas.

Desert biome   Characterized by sparse, xerophytic vegetation or even the complete absence of plant life.

Desertification   Process of desert expansion into neighbouring steppe lands as a result of human degradation of fragile semi-arid environments.

Desert pavement   A desert lag deposit of coarser material (gravel, stones) left behind as wind winnows the finer material and carries it away, and often covered by desert varnish; also called reg (Arabia), gibber plain (Australia), or gobi (central Asia).

Dew   Fine water droplets that condense on surfaces at and near the ground when saturated air is cooled. The source of this condensate is the excess water vapour beyond the saturation level of that air parcel, whose capacity to contain water decreases as its temperature drops.

Dew point   Temperature at which air becomes saturated and below which condensation occurs.

Diamicton   Technical term for till material or sediment left by a melted glacier composed of a wide range of sizes from very fine to very large.

Diffuse radiation   Proportion of incoming solar energy (22 per cent) that reaches the Earth's surface after first being scattered in the atmosphere by clouds, dust particles, and other airborne materials.

Dip   Angle at which a rock layer tilts from the horizontal.

Direct radiation   Proportion of incoming solar energy that travels directly to the Earth's surface; globally, this averages 31 per cent.

Discharge (stream)   Volume of water passing a given cross-section of a stream channel per unit of time; measured as average water velocity multiplied by the cross-sectional area (m^3/s).

Discordant intrusion   Intrusive magma that did not conform to but cut across or otherwise disrupted surrounding, existing geological structures.

Dispersal   Evolution of a modern species from an ancestral species that arrived in a given area by migration over land, swimming, rafting, or flying.

Distributaries   Several channels into which a river subdivides when it reaches its delta; caused by the clogging of the river mouth by deposition of fine-grained sediment as the stream reaches base level and water velocity declines markedly. Also used for channels of a braided stream.

Diurnal temperature cycle   Pattern of temperature change during the course of a day.

Doldrums   Equatorial zone of calm seas, unpredictable breezes, and sudden storms where the Northeast and Southeast Trades converge, roughly between the Tropics of Cancer and Capricorn; also called the 'horse latitudes'. The crews of sailing ships dreaded these waters because their vessels risked becoming stranded in this becalmed area.

Doline   A depression in karstic terrain caused by the collapse of a cave roof.

Dolomite (dolostone)   Soluble magnesium carbonate rock ($CaMg[CO_3]_2$), in addition to calcite-rich limestone, that can form karst topography.

Dormant volcano   Volcano that has not been seen to erupt but shows evidence of recent (i.e., prehistoric) activity.

Drag structures   Structures formed as a thawed soil moves down slope, 'pulling out' the underlying materials.

Drainage basin   Area occupied by a complete stream system formed by the trunk river and all its tributaries; also, the area from which all stream systems flow to a particular ocean, lake, wetland, or another stream system.

Drainage density   Total length of the stream channels that exist in a unit area of a drainage basin (km/km^2).

Driftless Area   Area in southwestern Wisconsin that was never covered by the continental ice sheets that repeatedly buried adjacent areas of the middle of North America.

Drifts   Term often used as a synonym for ocean currents when the rate of movement lags well behind the average speeds of surface winds blowing in the same direction. Currents are characterized by a slow and steady movement that rarely exceeds 8 km/h.

Drought   Below-average availability of water in a given area over a period lasting at least several months or years.

Drumlin   An asymmetrical whaleback or hogback hill, egg-shaped in plan, cut by subglacial mega-floods.

Dry adiabatic lapse rate (DALR)   Lapse rate of an air parcel not saturated with water vapor: $-1°C/100$ m.

Dune   Accumulation of sand that is shaped by wind action.

Dune crest   Top of a sand dune where the backslope and slip face meet.

Dust dome   Characteristic shape taken by the large quantities of dust and gaseous pollutants in a city's atmosphere.

Dynamic equilibrium   An equilibrium state where the fundamental controls vary over time, e.g., rainfall, temperature, etc.

Earthquake   Shaking and trembling of the Earth's surface; caused by sudden releases of stresses that have been building slowly within the crust.

Earth System   Shells or layers that make up the total Earth System range from those of the planet's deepest interior to those bordering outer space. This book focuses on the five key Earth layers: atmosphere, lithosphere, hydrosphere, cryosphere, and biosphere.

Easterly wave   Wave-like perturbation in the constant easterly flow of the Northeast and Southeast Trades, which produces this type of distinctive weather system. Westward-moving air is forced to rise on the upwind side (producing often heavy rainfall) and descend on the fair-weather downwind side of the low-pressure wave trough.

Ecological niche   The way a group of organisms makes its living in nature, or the environmental space within which an organism operates most efficiently.

Ecological zoogeography   The study of animals as they relate to their total environment.

Ecosystem   Linkage of plants or animals to their environment in an open system as far as energy is concerned; an ecological system.

Ecumene   Portion of the world's land surface that is permanently settled by human beings.

Eddies   Localized loops of water circulation in the ocean or streams detached from the mainstream of a nearby current, which move along with the general flow of that current.

Electromagnetic spectrum   Continuum of electric and magnetic energy, as measured by wavelength, from the high-energy shortwave radiation of cosmic rays to the low-energy longwave radiation of radio and electric power.

El Niño   Periodic, large-scale, abnormal warming of the sea surface in the low latitudes of the eastern Pacific Ocean that produces a (temporary) reversal of surface ocean currents and airflows throughout the equatorial Pacific. These regional events have global implications, disturbing normal weather patterns in many parts of the world.

Eluviation   'Washing out', referring to the soil process that involves removal from the **Ae** horizon and downward transportation of soluble minerals and microscopic, colloid-sized particles of organic matter, clay, and aluminum and iron oxides.

Emergent coast   Coastal zone whose landforms have recently emerged from the sea, through either tectonic uplift or a drop in sea level, or both.

Endemism   Biotic complex of an isolated (or once isolated) area, many of whose species of plants, animals, and other life forms exist nowhere else on Earth. The species in such places are particularly vulnerable to extinction through environmental changes introduced by humans, e.g., New Zealand and Australia.

ENSO   Acronym for El Niño–Southern Oscillation, the reversal of the flow of ocean currents and prevailing winds in the equatorial Pacific Ocean that disturbs global weather patterns.

Entisol   One of the 12 soil orders of the US Soil Taxonomy, which includes all the soils of recent origin. Canadian taxonomy: regosolic soil order.

Entrenched meanders   Meanders of a stream incised into hard bedrock from overlying floodplain topography; caused by the uplifting of the land or fall base level.

Entropy   The complete dissipation (usage and/or wastage) of energy.

Environmental lapse rate (ELR)   Non-adiabatic lapse rate at any particular time or place. The troposphere's (non-adiabatic) normal lapse rate averages $-0.64°C/100$ m.

Ephemeral plant   One that completes its life cycle within a single growing season.

Ephemeral stream   Intermittently flowing stream. Precipitation (and subsequent streamflow) is periodic, and when the rains end, the stream soon dries up.

Epicentre   Point on the Earth's surface directly above the focus (place of origin) of an earthquake.

Epiphyte   Tropical rainforest plant that uses trees for support, but is not parasitic.

Equal-area projection   A map projection in which all the areas mapped are represented in correct proportion to one another.

Equator   Parallel of latitude running around the exact middle of the globe, defined as 0° latitude.

Equatorial low   Inter-Tropical Convergence Zone (ITCZ) or thermal low-pressure belt of rising air that straddles the equatorial latitudinal zone; fed by the windflows of the converging Northeast and Southeast Trades.

Equilibrium line   A line that separates the accumulation zone from the ablation zone on a glacier or ice sheet.

Equinox   One of the two days (around 21 March 21 and 23 September) in the year when the Sun's noontime rays strike the Earth vertically at the Equator. In Northern Hemisphere terminology, 21 March is called the spring (vernal) equinox and 23 September is called the fall (autumnal) equinox.

Erg   Sand sea; large expanse of sandy desert landscape.

Erosion   Carrying away of weathered rock material and associated processes, where the Earth's surface is reshaped.

Escarpment (cuesta)   Long ridge formed by dipping rockbeds with a steep slope on one side and a gently dipping slope on the other.

Esker   Glacial outwash landform. A long ribbon-like ridge of sand and gravel in the landscape formed by the clogging of a river course within or under a glacier, the debris from which remains after the ice melts.

Etchplanation   The process of (deep) weathering and removal by erosional processes exposing a landscape.

Evaporation   Process by which water changes from the liquid to the gaseous (water vapour) state. It takes 597 calories of heat energy to change the state of 1 gram of water at 0°C from a liquid to a gas; also known as vaporization.

Evaporites   Rock deposits resulting from the evaporation of the water in which these materials were once dissolved; include halite (salt), epsomite, and gypsum.

Evapotranspiration   Combined processes by which water (1) evaporates from the land surface and (2) passes into the atmosphere through the leaf pores of plants (transpiration).

Exfoliation (spalling)   Kind of weathering that produces a joint pattern resembling a series of concentric shells, much like the layers of an onion. Following the release of confining pressure, the outer layers progressively peel away and expose the lower layers.

Exotic (suspect) terrane   Rocks possessing properties that sharply distinguish them from surrounding regional rocks; terrane consisting of a 'foreign' rock mass that is mismatched to its large-scale geological setting.

Extinct volcano   Volcano that shows no sign of life and exhibits evidence of long-term weathering and erosion.

Extratropical cyclone   A mid-latitude cyclone characterized by its circular windflow and low-pressure field as well as by the interaction of air of different properties; known as 'Wreckhouse winds' in southwest Newfoundland and 'Les Suêtes' among Acadians on Cape Breton Island.

Extrusive igneous rock   Rock formed from magma that cooled and solidified, as lava or ash, and pyroclastics on the Earth's surface.

Eye (hurricane)   Open vertical tube that marks the centre of a hurricane, often reaching an altitude of 16 km.

Eye wall (hurricane)   Rim of the eye or open vertical tube that marks the centre of a well-developed hurricane. The tropical cyclone's strongest winds and heaviest rainfall occur here.

Factor of safety (f)   An engineering way of determining the threshold angle of a slope and slope stability. The critical threshold is $f = 1$. $f > 1$ means stability, while $f < 1$ indicates instability.

Fall (autumnal) equinox   In Northern Hemisphere terminology, equinox that occurs when the Sun's noontime rays strike the Equator vertically around 23 September.

Fault   Fracture in crustal rock involving the displacement of rock on one side of the fracture with respect to rock on the other side.

Fault-line scarp   Scarp that originated as a fault scarp but was modified, perhaps even displaced, by erosion.

Fault plane   Surface of contact along which blocks on either side of a fault move.

Fault scarp Exposed cliff-like face of a fault plane created by geological action without significant erosional change.

Fault trace Lower edge of a fault scarp; line on the surface where a fault scarp intersects the surface.

Feedback A process that occurs in a system when an event causes a reaction that either retards (negative feedback) or enhances and accelerates (positive feedback) the original action.

Felsenmeer Area of loose rock fragments near their original location and formed from weathered rocks, as from frost wedging and karstic processes; rock sea.

Field capacity Maximum amount of water that a soil can hold by capillary tension against the downward pull of gravity.

Finger lake Elongated lake that fills much of an even longer, fairly narrow glacial trough.

Firn Granular, compacted snow.

Firn line Snow line; the boundary above which, at altitude, snow remains on the ground year-round.

Fjord A drowned glacial trough or the drowned lower end of a glacial trough.

Flatirons The triangular-shaped remnants left standing when stream erosion cuts through ridges or hogbacks.

Flood Episode of abnormally high stream discharge. Water overflows from the stream channel and temporarily covers its floodplain (which is built from the alluvium that is deposited by the floodwaters).

Floodplain Flat, low-lying ground adjacent to a stream that is flooded.

Flow regime Discrete region of outward ice flow in a continental ice sheet; possesses its own rates of snow accumulation, ice formation, and velocity.

Fluvial processes Degradation and aggradation related to running water; derived from Latin word for river, *fluvius*.

Fluvioglacial processes Related to meltwater streams flowing on, in, and under glacial ice and emerging from the margins of a glacier or an ice sheet, and the stratified material (usually sand and gravel) carried from glacier or ice sheet by these streams.

Fluviokarst Karstic formations, such as limestone pavement, caused by water flowing across the surface, i.e., karstic processes have been superimposed on a pre-existing fluvial landscape.

Focus (earthquake) Place of origin of an earthquake, which can be near the surface or deep inside the crust or upper mantle.

Foehn Rapid movement of warm dry air (caused by a plunge in altitude), frequently experienced on the leeward or rain-shadow side of a mountain barrier, whose moisture has mostly been removed via the orographic precipitation process. The name is also used specifically to designate such local winds in the vicinity of Central Europe's Alps; in western Canada these airflows are called chinook winds; in southern California they are the Santa Ana winds.

Fog Cloud layer in direct contact with the Earth's surface. Various types of fog—radiation, frontal, advection—are created by variations in the cooling/condensation process as warmer and cooler air meet.

Folding Bends or warps in layered rock.

Foliation Unmistakable banded appearance of certain metamorphic rocks, such as gneiss and schist; bands formed by minerals realigned into parallel strips during metamorphism.

Food web The cycling of energy in the form of food from organism to organism within an ecosystem; also known as food chain.

Foreset beds Sedimentary deposits built from the leading edge of the topset beds as a delta grows seaward. Later these beds are covered by the extension of the topset beds.

Foreshore Beach zone that is alternatively water-covered during high tide and exposed during low tide; zone of beach drift and related processes.

Fracture (mineral) When minerals do not break in a clean cleavage, they still break or fracture in a characteristic way. Obsidian, for example, fractures in an unusual shell-like (concoidal) manner that is a useful identifying quality.

Freezing Process by which a substance is transformed from the liquid to the solid state.

Freezing point (water) Key setting in the calibration of temperature scales. On the Celsius scale water freezes at 0°C.

Freezing rain Super-cooled liquid water drops larger than 0.5 mm in diameter that freeze on impact with the ground or other objects; freezing drizzle is similar, but composed exclusively of droplets of less than 0.5 mm in diameter.

Frictional force Drag that slows the movement of air molecules in contact with, or close to, the Earth's surface; varies with the 'roughness' of the surface. There is less friction with movement across a smooth water surface than across the ragged skyline of a city centre.

Front (weather) Surface that bounds an air mass, along which contact occurs with a neighbouring air mass possessing different qualities. This narrow boundary zone usually marks an abrupt transition in air density, temperature, and humidity. A moving front is the leading edge of the air mass built up behind it.

Frontal precipitation Precipitation that results from the movement of fronts whereby warm air is lifted, cooled, and condensed; also frequently called cyclonic precipitation.

Frost action Form of physical weathering in which water penetrates the joints and cracks of rocks, expands and contracts through alternate freezing and thawing, and eventually shatters the rocks.

Frost creep Movement of particles within the active layer (talik) above the permafrost under the influence of gravity. On the surface, soil will move downslope during the thawing phase.

Frost heaving Upward displacement of rocks and rock fragments within the active layer (talik) above the permafrost after they have been loosened by frost wedging; triggered by freezing of the ground that expands the total mass of rock materials.

Frost thrusting Horizontal movement of rocks and rock fragments within the active layer (talik) above the permafrost.

Frost wedging Forcing apart of a rock when the expansion stress created by the freezing of its internal water into ice exceeds the cohesive strength of that rock body.

Galaxy Organized, disk-like assemblage of billions of stars. Our solar system belongs to the Milky Way galaxy, which measures about 120,000 light-years in diameter.

Gelisol One of the 12 soil orders of the US Soil Taxonomy, found in cold, dry environments whose surfaces are underlain by permafrost. Such soils show evidence of cryoturbation (frost churning) and/or ice segregation in the seasonally thawing active layer (talik) that lies above the permafrost table. Canadian: taxonomy: cryosolic soil order.

General circulation Global atmospheric circulation system of wind belts and semi-permanent pressure cells. In each hemisphere, the former include the Trades, Westerlies, and Polar Easterlies. The latter include the Equatorial Low (ITCZ) and, in each hemisphere, the Subtropical High, Upper Mid-latitude Low, and Polar High.

Geographic information system (GIS) Assemblage of computer hardware and software that permits spatial data to be collected, recorded, stored, retrieved, manipulated, analyzed, and displayed to the user.

Geography Literally means 'Earth description'. As a modern academic discipline, it is concerned with the explanation of the physical and human characteristics of the Earth's surface.

Geological structure Landscape features originally formed by geological processes, which are sculpted by streams and other erosional agents into characteristic landforms.

Geological time scale Standard timetable or chronicle of Earth history used by scientists; sequential organization of geological time units, whose dates continue to be refined by ongoing research.

Geomorphology   Literally means 'Earth shape or form'; geography of landscape and its evolution, a major subfield of physical geography.

Geostrophic wind   Wind that results when the Coriolis and pressure-gradient forces balance themselves out. It follows a relatively straight path that minimizes deflection and lies parallel to the isobars.

Geosynchronous orbit   Orbit in which a satellite's revolution of the Earth is identical to the planet's rotational speed. Therefore the satellite is 'fixed' in a stationary position above the same point on the Earth's surface.

Glacial surge   An increase in the velocity of glacier flow caused by meltwater building up under the ice because of an increase in melting or damming of the glacier's plumbing system. This means that the ice is lubricated or floats on a layer of water, decreasing friction. Ends when most of the subglacial water discharges, often when a sediment or ice dam collapses, causing a jökulhlaup.

Glacial trough   Valley that has been eroded by a glacier; distinctively U-shaped in cross-sectional profile.

Glaciation   Period of global cooling during which continental ice sheets form and alpine glaciers expand.

Glacier   Body of ice, formed on land, which exhibits motion.

Gleysolic soil   A Canadian soil order characterized by water logging that restricts the microbial breakdown of organic matter, with a thick organic layer and a thin layer of bluish-grey (gley) clay (because of the reduction of iron) underneath. Generally occurs in wet sites at the base of slopes, or upslope from organic soils. US taxonomy: aquic soil subgroups.

Global Positioning System (GPS)   Constellation of more than two dozen linked orbiting satellites that broadcast signals to portable receivers anywhere on the Earth's surface. The simultaneous detection of these signals enables the person on the ground (or at sea or on an aircraft) to calculate precisely the latitude, longitude, and elevation of the receiver's location.

Global warming   The theory, now widely accepted by the scientific community, led by the Intergovernmental Panel on Climate Change, that anthropogenic fossil-fuel consumption is causing atmospheric warming that will melt glaciers, raise sea levels, and inundate low-lying coastal areas.

Gneiss   Metamorphic rock derived from granite that usually exhibits pronounced foliation.

Gondwanaland/Gondwana   Southern portion of the primeval supercontinent, Pangaea.

Graben   Crustal block that has sunk down between two fairly parallel normal faults in response to tensional forces.

Gradational processes   The wearing away of the geological materials built up on the Earth's landmasses.

Gradient (stream)   Slope of a stream channel as measured by the difference in elevation between two points along its course.

Gravity   Force of attraction that acts among all physical objects as a result of their mass (quantity of material of which they are composed).

Greenhouse effect   Widely used analogy describing the blanket-like effect of the atmosphere in the heating of the Earth's surface. Shortwave insolation passes through the 'glass' of the atmospheric 'greenhouse', heats the surface, is converted to longwave radiation, which cannot penetrate the 'glass', and thereby results in trapping heat that raises the temperature inside the 'greenhouse'.

Greenhouse gases   Various gases released to the atmosphere, especially carbon dioxide, and caused by human activity that contribute to the greenhouse effect.

Greenland Icecap   An icecap, about one-eighth the size of the Antarctic Icecap, that covers most of the surface of Greenland.

Green roofs   Roofs with a vegetated surface and substrate, which help to reduce the urban heat island effect and the amount of heat transferred through the roof during warm weather, lowering the energy demands of air-conditioning systems in the buildings.

Ground heat flow   Heat conducted into and out of the Earth's surface; also known as soil heat flow.

Ground moraine   Blanket of unsorted glacial till that was laid down at the base of a melting glacier or ice sheet; see basal (lodgement) till.

Groundwater   Water contained within the lithosphere. This water, hidden below the ground, accounts for about 25 per cent of the world's freshwater.

Groynes   Wooden or concrete structures built perpendicular to the shore, designed to retain beach material by stopping some beach and longshore sediment transport.

Gullies   Large erosional features cut into a slope by ephemeral streams that only run during and just after rainstorms and snowmelt.

Gyre   Cell-like circulation of surface currents that often encompasses an entire ocean basin. For example, the subtropical gyre of the North Atlantic Ocean consists of the huge loop formed by four individual, continuous legs—the North Equatorial, Gulf Stream, North Atlantic Drift, and Canaries currents.

Habitat   Environment a species normally occupies within its geographical range.

Hadley cell circulation   A simplified model of global atmospheric circulation, proposed by George Hadley in the eighteenth century, whereby circulation in the Northern Hemisphere is towards the south and in the Southern Hemisphere is towards the north.

Hail   Precipitation consisting of ice pellets of a half-centimetre or larger in diameter, which form in a cloud that has more ice crystals than water droplets; ice precipitation of smaller size is termed snow or sleet.

Hanging valley   Valley formed by a tributary glacier before it joins a trunk glacier. When the ice melts, the tributary valley floor usually is at a higher elevation and thus 'hangs' above the main valley's floor.

Headward erosion   Upslope extension, over time, of the 'head' or source of a river valley, which lengthens the entire stream network.

Heat-island intensity   Maximum difference in temperature between neighbouring urban and rural environments.

Heat wave   A period of more than three consecutive days of maximum temperature at or above 32°C.

Hemisphere   Half-sphere; used precisely, as in Northern Hemisphere (everything north of 0° latitude), or sometimes more generally, as in land hemisphere (the significant concentration of landmasses on roughly one side of the Earth).

Herbivore   Animal that lives on plants, or, more generally, the first consumer stage of a food chain.

Highland (H) climates   Climates of high-elevation areas that exhibit characteristics of climates located poleward of those found at the base of those highlands. The higher one climbs, the colder the climate becomes—even in the low latitudes. Thus **H** climate areas are marked by the vertical zonation of climates, as in South America's Andes.

Hillslope process   A slope process in which the debris is moved by flowing water or another agent.

Histosol   One of the 12 soil orders of the US Soil Taxonomy, an organic-based soil associated with poorly drained, flat-lying areas. Canadian taxonomy: organic soil order.

Hogbacks   Prominent steep-sided ridges with sharply dipping rockbeds.

Holocene   Current interglacial epoch, extending from 10,000 years ago to the present on the geological time scale.

Holokarst An array of closed surface depressions where water is routed underground, as in cave formation.

Holomictic lakes Lakes in which the entire water column is involved in the mixing process.

Horn Sharp-pointed, Matterhorn-like mountain peak that remains when several cirques attain their maximum growth by headward erosion into an upland area.

Horst Crustal block that has been raised between two reverse faults by compressional forces. See **Graben**.

Hot spot Place of very high temperatures in the upper mantle that reaches the surface as a 'plume' of extraordinarily high heat. A linear series of shield volcanoes can form on lithospheric plates moving over this plume, as happened in the case of the Anahim Volcanic Belt in BC or the Hawaiian island chain.

Hot springs Springs whose water temperature averages at least 8°C above mean air temperature; often emanate from a crustal zone that contains magma chambers near the surface.

Humidex A Canadian innovation used to describe how hot, humid weather feels to the average person. The humidex combines temperature and humidity into one number to reflect the perceived temperature.

Humid microthermal (D) climates Continental climates in the middle and upper latitudes far from the moderating influence of oceans, characterized by warm summers and frigid winters, with one or more months with mean temperatures above 10°C and a period averaging longer than a month when the mean temperature is below freezing (0°C).

Humification The process of turning organic matter into humus.

Humus Decomposed and partially decomposed organic matter that forms a dark layer at the top of the soil; a colloid; important to a soil's fertility.

Hurricane Tropical cyclone capable of inflicting great damage. A tightly organized, moving low-pressure system, normally originating at sea in the warm most air of the tropical atmosphere, exhibiting wind speeds in excess of 33 m per second. As with all cyclonic storms, it has a distinctly circular wind and pressure field.

Hydration Expansion in volume caused by the moistening and chemical change in minerals, which in turn results in the weathering of rock; a part of the hydrolysis-hydration process.

Hydraulic action Erosional work of running water in a stream or in the form of waves along a coast. In a stream, rock material is dislodged and dragged along the stream floor and sides; where waves strike a shoreline, the speed and weight of the water, especially when air is compressed into rock cracks by the power of the waves, this action can fracture and erode coastal rocks quite rapidly.

Hydrograph Graph of a river's discharge over time.

Hydrologic cycle Complex system of exchange involving water in its various forms as it continually circulates among the atmosphere, lithosphere, hydrosphere, cryosphere, and biosphere.

Hydrolysis Form of chemical weathering that involves moistening and the transformation of rock minerals into other mineral compounds associated with hydration; associated with hydration.

Hydrosphere Sphere of the Earth System that contains all the water that exists on and within the solid surface of our planet and in the atmosphere above.

Hypothetical continent Model of Earth's landmasses generalized into a single, idealized, shield-shaped continent of uniform low elevation.

Ice age Stretch of geological time during which the Earth's average atmospheric temperature is lowered; causes the expansion of ice sheets in the high latitudes and the growth of alpine glaciers in lower latitudes.

Icecap Regional mass of ice smaller than a continent-sized ice sheet (less than 50,000 km² in size). While the Laurentide Ice Sheet covered northern North America, the Cordilleran icecap covered the Rockies, the Interior Plateau, and the Coast Mountains. Name given to the ice cover of Greenland and of Antarctica.

Ice cores Cylinders of ice about 10 cm in diameter collected by drilling deep into a glacier or icecap. The cores are brought to the surface in lengths of approximately 3 m at a time and provide evidence of past climates.

Ice creep The internal deformation of glacial ice—a consequence of weight, slope, and gravity—with layers of crystals slipping over one another and causing the downslope movement of the glacier. This occurs in both wet-based and cold ice.

Ice shelf A sheet of ice that is a floating, seaward extension of a continental glacier, such as Antarctica's Ross Ice Shelf.

Ice wedge A ground ice feature formed by water freezing in a crack in the soil surface.

Ice-wedge casts 'Fossils' of ice wedges exhibiting infilling by finer soil material.

Ice-wedge polygons Polygonal features formed by the freezing and thawing of sediments that fill surface cracks caused by very cold winter temperatures in periglacial zones.

Igneous rocks Primary rocks that formed directly from the cooling of molten magma; igneous is Latin for 'formed from fire'.

Illuviation Soil process in which downward-percolating water carries soluble minerals and colloid-sized particles of organic matter and minerals from the **A** into the **B** horizon, where these materials are deposited in pore spaces and against the surfaces of soil grains.

Impact craters Large circular depressions on the Earth caused by the impact of meteors, which are classified, based on size, as simple craters, complex craters, and complex craters with central uplift, peak, or ring.

Impurities (atmospheric) Solid particles floating in the atmosphere whose quantities vary in time and space. Among other things, they play an active role in the formation of raindrops.

Inceptisol One of the 12 soil orders of the US Soil Taxonomy; forms quickly, is relatively young (though older than an entisol), has the beginnings of a **B** horizon, and contains significant organic matter. Canadian taxonomy: brunisolic soil order.

Infiltration Flow of water into the Earth's surface through the pores and larger openings in the soil mass.

Infiltration capacity/rate Rate at which a soil is able to absorb water percolating downward from the surface.

Inner core Solid, most inner portion of the Earth, consisting mainly of nickel and iron.

Inselbergs Rounded or sugar-loaf shaped residual bedrock hills left behind by the erosion of deeply weathered areas by slope and stream erosion; residuals on an etchplain.

Insolation Incoming solar radiation.

Intensity (earthquake) Size and damage of an earthquake as measured—on the modified Mercalli scale—by the impact on structures and human activities on the cultural landscape.

Interactive mapping In geographic information systems (GIS) methodology, the constant dialogue via computer demands and feedback to queries between the map user and the map.

Interception Blocking of rainwater through vegetation from reaching the ground. Raindrops land on leaves and other plant parts and evaporate before they can penetrate the soil below.

Interfluve Ridge that separates two adjacent stream valleys.

Interglacial Period of warmer global temperatures between deglaciation and the onset of the next glaciation.

International date line   An imaginary line for the most part antipodal to the prime meridian, following the 180th meridian in the middle of the Pacific Ocean, with Hawaii and Samoa on the eastern side of the date line, and Kiribati, Tonga, and New Zealand on the western side. The line, first recognized by Magellan's crew when they returned to Spain in 1522 and found the ship's log to be a day off, has been adjusted over the years for geopolitical reasons. Crossing the line towards the west involves skipping a day, whereas crossing the line towards the east means repeating a day.

Inter-Tropical Convergence Zone (ITCZ)   Thermal low-pressure belt of rising air that straddles the equatorial latitudinal zone, which is fed by the windflows of the converging Northeast and Southeast Trades.

Intraplate earthquake   An earthquake that occurs within one tectonic plate in the Earth's crust, as opposed to the more usual or predictable earthquakes caused by the shifting of two tectonic plates along a fault line.

Intrusive igneous rock   Rock formed from magma that cooled and solidified below the Earth's surface, e.g., granite.

Involutions   Patterns or structures in a soil or deposit caused by cryoturbation (freezing and thawing).

Ion   Atom or cluster of electrically charged atoms formed by the breakdown of molecules.

Ionosphere   An extension of the thermosphere representing less than 0.1 per cent of the total mass of the Earth's atmosphere where ionization takes place, producing two more belts that reflect radio waves.

Isarithmic (isoline) mapping   Commonly used cartographic device to represent three-dimensional volumetric data on a two-dimensional map; involves the use of isolines to show the surfaces that are mapped.

Island (volcanic) arc   Volcanic island chain produced in a zone where two oceanic plates are converging. One plate will subduct the other, forming deep trenches as well as spawning volcanoes that may protrude above sea level in an island-arc formation (Alaska's Aleutian archipelago is a classic example). Volcanic arc is used for a group of volcanoes associated with fold mountain belts (orogens).

Isobar   Line connecting all points having identical atmospheric pressure.

Isoline   Line connecting all places possessing the same value of a given phenomenon, such as 'height' above the flat base of the surface being mapped.

Isostasy   Derived from an ancient Greek term (*iso* = the same; *stasy* = to stand), the condition of vertical equilibrium between the floating landmasses and the asthenosphere beneath them. This situation of sustained adjustment is maintained despite the forces that constantly operate to change the landmasses.

Isotherm   Line connecting all points experiencing identical temperature.

Jet streams   Two concentrated, high-altitude, west-to-east flowing 'rivers' of air that are major features of the upper atmospheric circulation system poleward of latitude 15° in both the Northern and Southern Hemispheres. Because of their general occurrence above the subtropical and subpolar latitudes, they are respectively known as the subtropical jet stream and the Polar Front jet stream. A third such corridor of high-altitude, concentrated windflow is the tropical easterly jet stream, a major feature of the upper air circulation equatorward of latitude 15°N. This third jet stream, however, flows in the opposite, east-to-west direction and occurs only above the tropics of the Northern Hemisphere.

Jointing   Tendency of rocks to develop parallel sets of fractures without any obvious movement such as faulting.

Jökulhlaup (Icelandic)   A glacial burst flood.

Kame   Mound of glacial debris or stratified drift at the edge of a glacier or ice sheet; often found as deltaic deposits where meltwater streams flowed into temporary lakes near the receding ice front.

Karst   Distinctive landscape associated with the underground chemical weathering and erosion of particularly soluble limestone bedrock.

Katabatic winds   Winds that result from cold-air drainage; especially prominent under clear conditions where the edges of highlands plunge sharply towards lower-lying terrain.

Kelvin scale   Absolute temperature scale used by scientists, based on the temperature of absolute zero (−273°C). A kelvin is identical to a Celsius degree (°C), so that water boils at 373 K (100°C) and freezes at 273 K (0°C).

Kinetic energy   Energy of movement.

Köppen climate classification system   A descriptive classification of world climates based largely on plant life, first devised by Wladimir P. Köppen (1846–1940), which uses a shorthand notation of principal letter symbols—**A** (tropical), **B** (dry), **C** (mesothermal), **D** (microthermal), **E** (polar), and **H** (highland)—and secondary letter symbols (e.g., **Af** = tropical rainforest) to distinguish different characteristics of the major climates.

Krummholz   The ground-hugging habit of dwarf trees in tundra biomes.

Laccolith   Concordant intrusive igneous form in which a magma pipe led to a subterranean chamber that grew, domelike, pushing up the overlying strata into a gentle bulge without destroying them.

Lahar   A mudflow caused by a volcanic eruption (hot lahar); a mudflow caused by rainfall mobilizing a pre-existing blanket of volcanic ash (cold lahar).

Land breeze   Offshore airflow affecting a coastal zone, resulting from a nighttime pressure gradient that steers local winds from the cooler (higher pressure) land surface to the warmer (lower pressure) sea surface.

Landform   Single and typical unit that forms parts of the overall shape of the Earth's surface; also refers to a discrete product of a set of geomorphological processes.

Land hemisphere   The roughly one-half of the Earth that contains most of the landmasses (Northern Hemisphere); the opposite of the water (oceanic) hemisphere.

Landscape   Aggregation of landforms, often of the same type; also refers to the spatial expression of the processes that shaped those landforms.

La Niña   Lull or cool ebb in low-latitude Pacific Ocean surface temperatures that occurs between El Niño peaks of anomalous sea-surface warming.

Lapse rate   Rate of decline in temperature as altitude increases. The average lapse rate of temperature with height in the troposphere is −0.64°C/100 m.

Late Cenozoic Ice Age   Last great ice age that ended 10,000 years ago; spanned the entire Pleistocene epoch (1.8 million to 10,000 years ago) plus the latter portion of the preceding Pliocene epoch, possibly beginning as far back as 3.5 million years ago.

Latent heat of fusion   Heat energy involved in melting a solid into a liquid; a similar amount of heat is given off when a liquid freezes into a solid.

Latent heat of vaporization   Heat energy involved in the transformation of a liquid into a gas or vice versa.

Lateral moraine   Moraine situated along the edge of a mountain glacier, consisting of debris that fell from the adjacent valley wall.

Laterite (oxisol, lateritic)   Name sometimes given to a very hard iron oxide or aluminum hydroxide soil horizon that is reddish in colour (*later* is Latin for brick); found in wet tropical areas.

Latitude   Angular distance, measured in degrees north or south, of a point along a parallel from the Equator.

Laurasia   Northern portion of the supercontinent, Pangaea.

Laurentide Ice Sheet   Huge Late Cenozoic continental ice sheet that covered all of Canada east of the Rocky Mountains and expanded repeatedly to bury areas as far south as the Ohio and Missouri Valleys.

Lava   Magma that reaches and hardens on the Earth's surface.

Lava dome   A small volcanic mound, often formed inside a crater following an explosive eruption but also resulting when acidic lava (andesite, dacite) penetrates to the surface and oozes out without pyroclastic activity; usually much smaller than composite volcanoes.

Leaching   Soil process in which downward-percolating water dissolves and washes away many of the soil's mineral substances and other ingredients.

Leeward   Protected side of a topographical barrier with respect to the winds that flow across it; often refers to the area downwind from the barrier as well, which is said to be in the 'shadow' of that highland zone.

Legend (map)   Portion of a map where its point, line, area, and volume symbols are identified.

Lessivation (lessivated)   The process of washing clay particles down a soil profile from the **A** to the **B** horizon. 'Lessivated' is a term used for soils that have been affected by this process, e.g., luvisols.

Levee, artificial   Artificially constructed ridge built to reinforce a natural levee, most often along the lowest course of a river.

Levee, natural   River-edging ridge of alluvium deposited along some streams when they overflow their banks during a periodic flood. When the river contracts after the flood, it stays within these self-generated 'dykes' or levees. Debate exists about this feature based on the fact that humans have been fortifying stream channels for many thousands of years.

Lightning   An atmospheric discharge of electricity, which typically occurs during thunderstorms and sometimes during volcanic eruptions or dust storms; in thunderstorms, this results from the accumulation of positive charges towards the top of clouds and an accumulation of negative charges in the base of clouds.

Light-year   Distance travelled by a pulse of light in one year. Light travels at a speed of 300,000 km (186,000 miles) per second; a light-year thus involves a distance of 9.46 trillion km.

Limestone   Sedimentary rock formed from the respiration and photosynthesis of marine organisms in which calcium carbonate is distilled from seawater or from calcium with sediments or brine concentration. Finely textured and therefore resistant to weathering when exposed on the surface, it is susceptible to solution that can produce karst landscapes both above and below the ground.

Limnology   The study of lakes, lake sediments, and lake ecosystems.

Liquid limit   An Atterberg limit separating a plastic state from the liquid state. Dependent on moisture and clay content.

Lithification   Rock formation; the process of compression, compaction, and cementation whereby a sediment is transformed into a sedimentary rock.

Lithology   Rock type of a local area, which greatly influences its landform and landscape development.

Lithosphere   Outermost shell of the solid Earth, lying immediately below the land surface and ocean floor (*lithos* means rock); composed of the Earth's thin crust together with the solid uppermost portion of the upper mantle that lies just below.

Lithospheric plate   One of the fragmented, rigid segments of the lithosphere (also called a tectonic plate, which denotes its active mobile character). These segments or plates move in response to the plastic flow in the hot asthenosphere that lies just below the lithosphere.

Little Ice Age (Neoglacial)   Period of decidedly cooler global temperatures that prevailed from about 1450 to 1850 (averaging about 1.5°C lower than in the 1940s). During these four centuries, glaciers in most parts of the world expanded considerably.

Littoral zone   Coastal zone.

Loam   An agricultural term for soil containing grains of all three texture size categories—sand, silt, and clay—within certain proportions. The term refers not to a size category but to a certain combination of variously sized particles.

Local base level   Base level for a stream that flows into a lake at whatever altitude it may lie.

Loess   Deposit of very fine silt or dust laid down after having been blown some distance (perhaps hundreds of kilometres) by the wind; characterized by its fertility and ability to stand in steep vertical walls. Related to deserts (hot loess) or periglacial areas (cold loess).

Longitude   Angular distance, measured in degrees east or west, of a point along a meridian from the Prime Meridian.

Longitudinal dune   Long ridge-like sand dune that lies parallel to the prevailing wind.

Longshore bar   Ridge of sand parallel to the shoreline that develops in the nearshore beach zone.

Longshore current   Water current that runs along the shoreline similar to the longshore drift of sand, which is generated by the refracted, oblique-angled arrival of waves onshore; can also develop from tidal action and from coastal storms.

Longshore (littoral) drift   Movement of sand and shingle along the shoreline in the flow of water (longshore current) generated by the refracted, oblique-angled arrival of waves onshore.

Longwave radiation   Infrared radiation emitted by the Earth, which has much longer wavelengths—and involves much lower energy—than the solar (shortwave, higher energy) radiation emitted by the Sun.

Lower mantle   Solid interior shell of the Earth, which encloses the liquid outer core.

Luvisolic soil   A Canadian soil order, characterized by lessivated (washed) soils or soils that exhibit the translocation of particulate clays from the **A** to the **B** horizon. US taxonomy: alfisol soil order (boralfs, udalfs).

Magma   Liquid molten mass from which intrusive igneous rocks are formed.

Magnitude (earthquake)   Amount of shaking of the ground during an earthquake as measured by a seismograph.

Map   Any geographical image of the environment.

Map projection   Orderly arrangement of meridians and parallels, produced by any systematic method, that can be used for drawing a map of the spherical Earth on a flat surface.

Marble   Metamorphosed limestone. The hardness and density of this rock is preferred by sculptors for statues that can withstand exposure to the agents of weathering and erosion for millennia.

Marine geography   The study of coastlines and shores, beaches, river mouths, and other landscape features associated with the oceanic margins of the continents, including both physical geographical features and human geographical factors, such as maritime boundaries, the competition for marine resources, and the law of the sea.

Maritime effect   Moderating influence of the ocean on air temperature, which produces cooler summers and milder winters relative to inland locations at similar latitudes.

Mass balance   The inputs and outputs of mass in a system, such as a stream, glacier, or beach.

Mass movement   A slope process where the debris rolls or tumbles down slope because of gravity.

Meander   A bend or curve in a stream.

Meander scar   A dried-up oxbow lake, where a meander in a stream once existed.

Medial moraine Moraine—situated well away from a glacier's edges—formed by the intersection of two lateral moraines when a substantial tributary glacier meets and joins a trunk glacier.

Medieval Optimum The centuries prior to 1000 CE when sea levels were high and high-latitude areas such as Greenland, because of the milder climate, were amenable to permanent settlement; evidence suggests this was a global phenomenon and not restricted to the Northern Hemisphere.

Mediterranean scrub biome (sclerophilous forest) Consists of widely spaced evergreen or deciduous trees and often dense, hard-leaf evergreen scrub; sometimes referred to as chaparral or maquis. Thick waxy leaves are well adapted to withstanding the long, hot, dry summers and fire.

Mercalli scale (modified) Scale that measures earthquake intensity, the impact of a quake on the human landscape; ranges upward from intensity I to intensity XII.

Mercator projection Most famous of the cylindrical map projections, the only one on which any straight line is a line of true and constant compass bearing.

Meridian On the Earth grid, a north–south line of longitude. These range from 0° (Prime Meridian) to 180°E and W (180°E and W are the same line—the international date line—written simply as 180°).

Meromictic lakes Usually small pocket-shaped lakes with a deep basin in which the water column remains stratified, without mixing, over a long period of time.

Mesa Flat-topped, steep-sided upland capped by a resistant rock layer; normally found in dry environments.

Mesopause Upper boundary of the mesosphere, lying approximately 80 km above the surface of the Earth.

Mesosphere Third layer of the atmosphere, lying above the stratosphere. Here temperatures again decline with increasing elevation as they do in the troposphere.

Mesothermal (C) climates Moderately heated climates that are found on the equatorward side of the middle latitudes, where they are generally aligned as interrupted east–west belts; transitional between the climates of the tropics and those of the upper mid-latitudes where polar influences begin to produce harsh winters.

Mesozoic Era Era on the geological time scale, extending from 248 million to 65 million years ago.

Metabolic heat Heat produced by human and animal bodies (from the conversion of the chemical energy in the food they eat).

Metamorphic rocks Secondary rocks that were created from the transformation, by heat and/or pressure, of existing rocks.

Meteorites Solid bodies that have fallen to the Earth's surface (or the surface of any celestial body), varying in size from a grain of dust to a mass weighing several tonnes.

Meteorology Systematic, interdisciplinary study of the short-term atmospheric phenomena that constitute weather.

Microclimate Climate region on a localized scale.

Mid-oceanic ridge High submarine volcanic mountain range like the Mid-Atlantic ridge; part of a global system of such ranges.It is not always found in the central areas of the oceans. Here new crust is formed by upwelling magma. The crustal plates move away from here towards the margins of the oceans.

Midstream bar Midchannel sandbar that is deposited where sediment-clogged water of a stream significantly slows in velocity.

Milankovitch forcing The cyclical variability in Earth's axial tilt and orbit around the Sun that could cause climatic changes.

Mineral Naturally occurring inorganic element or compound having a definite chemical composition, physical properties, and, usually, a crystalline structure.

Model Creation of an idealized (somewhat simplified) representation of reality in order to demonstrate its most important properties.

Mohorovičić discontinuity (Moho) Contact plane between the Earth's crust and the mantle.

Mohs Hardness Scale Standard mineral-hardness measurement scale used in the Earth sciences; ranges from 10 (the hardest substance, diamond) down to 1 (talc, the softest naturally occurring mineral).

Mollisol One of the 12 soil orders of the US Soil Taxonomy, found in the world's semi-arid climate zones; characterized by a thick, dark surface layer and high alkaline content. Canadian taxonomy: chernozemic soil order.

Moment Magnitude Scale Most widely used measure of the severity of an earthquake's ground motion, which evolved from the Richter scale developed in the 1930s; based on the size of the fault along which a quake occurs and the distance the rocks around it slip.

Monadnock Prominent (not yet eroded) remnant of an upland on a peneplain in the cycle of erosion model.

Monsoon Derived from the Arabic word for 'season', a regional windflow that streams onto and off certain landmasses on a seasonal basis. The moist onshore winds of summer bring the *wet* monsoon whereas the offshore winds of winter are associated with the *dry* monsoon.

Moon Satellite that orbits a planet, probably originating from the clustering of planetesimals. All solar system planets except Mercury and Venus have such bodies. Our Moon orbits the Earth once every 27.3 days at an average distance of 385,000 km.

Moraine Ridge, mound, or sheet of glacial debris deposited during the melting phase of a glacier.

Mountain (alpine) glacier Rivers of ice that form in mountainous regions; confined in valleys that usually have steep slopes (valley or inlet glaciers).

Mudflow Flow form of slope process involving a stream of fluid, lubricated mud; most common where heavy rains strike an area that has long been dry and where weathering has loosened ample quantities of fine-grained material; also called earth flow.

Muskeg In the northern coniferous forest biome, the particular assemblage of low-growing leathery bushes and stunted trees that concentrate in the waterlogged soil bogs and lake-filled depressions.

Mutation Variation in reproduction in which the message of heredity (DNA) contained in the genes is imperfectly passed on and from which new species may originate.

Mutualism Biological interaction in which there is a coexistence of two or more species because one or more is essential to the survival of the other(s); also called symbiosis.

Natural disaster When a hazard triggers vulnerability and the damage is so extensive that the affected community cannot recover through the use of its own resources.

Natural hazard An endangerment in the environment—social, economic, or natural—that can affect anyone, anywhere. Hazards only become disasters when they interact with vulnerable communities in a way that overwhelms the communities' ability to cope, so that a flood or hurricane for one community might be a hazard but for another community it would be a disaster.

Natural landscapes Those areas of the planet still essentially subject to physical processes without the overwhelming shaping and forming created by human intervention.

Nearshore Beach zone that is located seaward of the foreshore, submerged even during an average low tide. Longshore bars and troughs develop here in this zone of complex, ever-changing topography.

Net radiation Amount of radiation left over when all the incoming and outgoing radiation flows have been tallied; totals about one-fourth of the shortwave radiation originally arriving at the top of the atmosphere.

Névé   Another name for the accumulation zone of a glacier.

Nitrogen cycle   The movement of nitrogen through the Earth System, chiefly through the activity of bacteria, in a five-stage process of nitrogen fixation, nitrification, assimilation, ammonification, and denitrification.

Nonclastic sedimentary rocks   Derived not from particles of other rocks, but from chemical solution by deposition and evaporation or from organic deposition.

Non-renewable resource   Natural resource that when used at a certain rate will ultimately be exhausted, such as metallic ores and petroleum.

Normal fault   Tensional fault exhibiting a moderately inclined fault plane that separates a block that has remained fairly stationary from one that has been significantly downthrown.

North Atlantic Oscillation (NAO)   Alternating pressure gradient between the North Atlantic Ocean's semi-permanent upper mid-latitude low-pressure cell (the Icelandic Low) and its semi-permanent subtropical high-pressure cell (the Bermuda High, especially its eastern segment—the Azores High) centred above the Azores Islands. Its fluctuations affect the warmth and moisture of windflows in Europe, and the NAO's complicated workings also involve the North Atlantic Drift ocean current, the sinking of warm water near Greenland and Iceland, the upwelling of cold water off northwest Africa, and many lesser components.

Northeast Trades   Surface wind belt that generally lies between the Equator and 30°N; the Coriolis force deflects equatorward-flowing winds to the right, thus recurving north winds into northeast winds.

Northern coniferous forest biome   Upper mid-latitude boreal forest (known in Russia as the snowforest or *taiga*); dominated by dense stands of slender, cone-bearing, needle-leafed trees, such as spruce, pine, and fir.

Northern Hemisphere   The half of the Earth located north of the Equator (0° latitude); the northernmost point is the North Pole (90°N).

Nuée ardente   Cloud of hot and noxious volcanic gas that races downslope following a spectacular explosion associated with unusually high pressures inside the erupting volcano; incinerates everything in its path.

Numerical weather prediction   Computer weather forecasting method used by Environment Canada and by the Atmospheric Environment Service in the US, based on projections by small increments of time up to 48 hours into the future.

Nunatak   Mountain peak that protrudes through the overlying glacier or ice sheet.

Occluded front   Surface boundary between cold and cool air in a mature mid-latitude cyclone; caused by the cold front undercutting and lifting the warm air entirely off the ground.

Ocean currents   Large-scale movements of water that form the oceanic counterpart to the atmospheric system of wind belts and semi-permanent pressure cells.

Offshore bar   Sandbar that lies some distance from the beach and is not connected to land. A longshore bar is an example.

Ogive   A dirt-band or sediment-rich layer in a glacier or ice sheet.

Old field succession   Another term for secondary succession, related to vegetation changes in an environment caused by external factors ranging from agricultural use to flooding and fire.

Open system   System whose boundaries (interfaces) freely permit the transfer of energy and/or matter across them.

Open wave   Early maturity stage in the development of a mid-latitude cyclone. Surface cyclonic air motion transforms the original kink on the stationary front into an open wave, around which cold and warm air interact in distinct ways.

Orders of magnitude   Sizes of geographical entities. Figure 1.7 shows the entire range of magnitudes, including those that geographers usually operate within.

Organic soil order   A Canadian soil order including all soils formed from rotting and rotted organic debris and associated with poorly drained sites. US taxonomy: histosol soil order.

Orogenic belt (Orogen)   Chain of linear fold mountain ranges.

Orographic precipitation   Rainfall (and sometimes snowfall) on the windward side of a mountain range or other highland zone produced by moist air parcels that are forced to rise over the topographic feature. Such air parcels move in this manner because they are propelled by both steering winds and the push of other air parcels piling up behind them.

Outer core   Liquid shell that encloses the Earth's inner core, the composition of which involves similar materials.

Oxbow lake   Lake formed when two adjacent meanders link up and one of the bends in the channel, shaped like a bow, is cut off. A slough is an oxbow lake that is partially infilled with sediment and organic matter.

Oxidation/reduction   The reaction of oxygen with a mineral (e.g., ferric iron). The removal of oxygen from a mineral (e.g., ferrous iron).

Oxisol   One of the 12 soil orders of the US Soil Taxonomy, not found in Canada but in tropical areas with high rainfall; heavily leached and usually characterized by pronounced laterite horizon, with red or orange colour.

Oxygen cycle   Oxygen is put back into the atmosphere as a by-product of photosynthesis, and is lost when it is inhaled by animals or chemically combined with other materials during oxidation.

Ozone hole   Seasonal depletion of ozone above the Antarctic region, which very likely is caused by the discharge of artificial chemical compounds called chlorofluorocarbons (CFCs). Evidence is mounting that a global thinning of the ozone layer is also taking place.

Ozone layer   Also known as the ozonosphere, the ozone-rich layer of the stratosphere that extends between 15 and 50 km above the surface. The highest concentrations of ozone are usually found at the level between 20 and 25 km.

Pacific Decadal Oscillation   Patterns of climatic variability that occur approximately every 20–30 years, primarily in the North Pacific, that can last for a decade or longer.

Pacific High   North Pacific high-pressure cell that shifts north and south with the seasonal location of the Sun; also called Hawaiian High.

Pacific Ring of Fire   Circum-Pacific belt of high volcanic and seismic activity, stretching around the entire Pacific Basin counterclockwise through western South America, western North America, Kamchatka, and Asia's island archipelagos (from Japan to Indonesia) as far as New Zealand.

Pack ice   Floating sea ice that forms from the freezing of ocean water.

Pahoehoe   Ropy-patterned lava; forms where very fluid lavas develop a smooth 'skin' upon hardening, which wrinkles as movement continues.

Paleozoic   Era of ancient life on the geological time scale extending from 570 million to 248 million years ago.

Pangaea   Primeval supercontinent, hypothesized by Alfred Wegener, that broke apart and formed the continents and oceans as we know them today; consisted of two parts—a northern Laurasia and a southern Gondwanaland.

Parabolic dune   Crescent-shaped sand dune with its points lying upwind. The concave side of this dune is the windward side.

Parallel   On the Earth grid, an east–west line of latitude. These parallels range from 0° (Equator) to 90°N and S (the North and South Poles, respectively, where the east–west line shrinks to a point).

Parent material   Rocks and deposits from which soils develop.

Patterned ground Periglacial rock and soil debris shaped or sorted by frost action in such a manner that it forms designs on the surface resembling rings, polygons, lines, and the like.

Pedalfer soils Acidic soils that are base-poor because of leaching but that retain iron and aluminum oxides in their profiles. Characteristic of the more humid areas of eastern North America.

Pediment Smooth, gently sloping bedrock surface that underlies the alluvial apron of a mountain front and extends outward from the foot of the highlands; primarily a desert feature.

Pediplain Surface formed by the coalescence of numerous pediments after a long period of erosion that has parallel slope retreat.

Pedocal soils Alkaline soils that retain calcium and other bases in their profiles. Characteristic of the more arid areas of western North America.

Pedology Soil science; study of soils.

Pedon Column of soil drawn from a specific location, extending from the soil surface all the way down to the level where the bedrock shows signs of being transformed into **C**-horizon material.

Peds Naturally occurring aggregates or 'clumps' of soil and their properties.

Peneplain (peneplanation) A nearly flat plain developed over an extremely long period of erosion and down-wearing of the landscape. The end result of the cycle of erosion model. Peneplanation is the process of developing a peneplain.

Perched water table Separate local water table that forms at a higher elevation than the nearby main water table; caused by the effects of a local aquiclude.

Percolation Downward movement of water through the pores and other spaces in the soil under the influence of gravity.

Perennial exotic stream A stream in a desert area with a continuous water flow throughout the year because its source is outside of the desert area, such as the Nile and Colorado Rivers; also called an exoreic stream.

Perennial plant A plant that persists for a long time.

Periglacial High-latitude or high-altitude environment on the perimeter of a glaciated area or with low temperatures.

Perihelion Point in the Earth's orbit, which occurs every 3 January, where the distance to the Sun is minimized (about 147.5 million km).

Permafrost Perennially frozen layer of subsoil (frozen for >2 years) that is characteristic of the colder portions of the **D** climate zone as well as the entire **E** climate zone; continuous permafrost in far northern Canada can exceed 300 m in depth; discontinuous permafrost is found at somewhat lower northern latitudes, and in some areas, such as at elevation on mountains, sporadic permafrost occurs.

Permeability The ability of a surface or Earth materials (soil, sediments, rock) to allow water or air to infiltrate and pass through it. Permeability is related to the connectedness and size of pores, root holes, and other voids in the material. Sands, gravels, and rocks such as limestone are permeable. Clays are porous but have low permeability.

Phanerozoic A unit of the geological time scale starting about 570 million years ago and characterized by rock units having visible fossils.

Phosphorus cycles The movement of phosphorus from a land environment to an aquatic environment and back again, which occurs at a local level because phosphorus does not form gaseous compounds and is not an appreciable part of the atmosphere.

Photosynthesis Process in which plants convert carbon dioxide and water into carbohydrates and oxygen through the addition of solar energy. Carbohydrates are a significant component of the food and tissue of both plants and animals.

Phreatic (magmatophreatic) eruption Extraordinarily explosive volcanic eruption involving the penetration of water into a superheated magma chamber. Such explosions of composite volcanoes standing in water can reach far beyond a volcano's immediate area.

pH scale Used to measure acidity and alkalinity of substances on a scale ranging from 0 to 14, with 7 being neutral. Below 7 increasing acidity is observed as 0 is approached, whereas above 7 increasing alkalinity is observed as 14 is approached.

Physical geography Geography of the physical world. Figure 1.4 diagrams the subfields of physical geography.

Physical (mechanical) weathering Disintegration of rocks by physical means through the imposition of certain stresses, such as freezing and thawing or the expansion of salt crystals (salt burst hydration).

Phytogeography Geography of flora or plant life; where botany and physical geography overlap.

Phytomass Total living organic plant matter produced in a given geographic area; often used synonymously with biomass, because biomass is measured by weight (plants overwhelmingly dominate over animals in total weight per unit area).

Phytoplankton Microscopic green autotrophic plants at the lowest rung of the food chain.

Pingo Mound-like, elliptical hill in a periglacial zone with a core consisting of ice rather than rock or soil.

Planar projection A map projection in which the transfer of the Earth grid is from a globe onto a plane, involving a single point of tangency.

Plane of the ecliptic Plane formed by the Sun and the Earth's orbital path.

Planet Dark solid body, much smaller in size than a star, whose movements in space are controlled by the gravitational effects of a nearby star.

Plant (seral) succession Process in which one type of vegetation is replaced by another.

Plasticity Index The relationship between the plastic and liquid Atterberg limits. The closeness of the limits indicates possible instability (the closer, the more unstable).

Plastic limit An Atterberg limit separating a solid state and plastic state, determined by moisture and clay content.

Plate tectonics Study of those aspects of tectonics involving the processes by which the lithospheric plates move over the asthenosphere.

Platy soil structure Layered peds that look like flakes stacked horizontally.

Pleistocene Epoch that extended from 1.8 million to 10,000 years ago on the geological time scale; includes the latter half of the last great (Late Cenozoic) ice age, which began about 3.5 million years ago, as well as the emergence of humans.

Plucking (quarrying) Glacial erosion process in which fragments of bedrock beneath the glacier or ice sheet are extracted from the surface as the ice advances.

Pluvial lakes Lakes that developed in presently dry areas during times of heavier precipitation associated with glaciations. Glacial Lake Bonneville, the (much larger) forerunner of Utah's Great Salt Lake, is a classic example.

Podzolic soil A soil order of the Canadian System of Soil Classification characterized by the leaching of bases and the retention of iron and aluminum oxides in the profile. US taxonomy: spodisols, some inceptisols.

Polar (E) climates Climates in which the mean temperature of the warmest month is less than 10°C (50°F). The tundra (**ET**) subtype exhibits warmest month temperatures between 0°C (32°F) and 10°C (50°F), whereas in the (coldest) icecap (**EF**) subtype the average temperature of the warmest month does not reach 0°C.

Polar Easterlies High-latitude wind belt in each hemisphere, lying between 60 and 90 degrees of latitude. The Coriolis force is strongest in these polar latitudes, and the equatorward-moving air that emanates from the Polar High is sharply deflected in each hemisphere to form the Polar Easterlies.

Polar Front Latitudinal zone, lying at approximately 60°N and S, where the equatorward-flowing Polar Easterlies meet the poleward-flowing Westerlies. The warmer Westerlies are forced to rise above the colder Easterlies, producing a semi-permanent surface low-pressure belt known as the Upper Mid-latitude Low.

Polar Front jet stream Upper atmosphere jet stream located above the subpolar latitudes, specifically the Polar Front; at its strongest during the half-year centred on winter.

Polar High Large semi-permanent high-pressure cell centered approximately over the pole in the uppermost latitudes of each hemisphere.

Polar orbit The longitudinal orbit of satellites operating at about 1100 km high, which pass close to the poles, so that they survey a different meridional segment of the surface during each revolution.

Pollutant Any substance that impacts an organism negatively.

Pollution (air) Air is said to be polluted when its composition departs significantly from its natural composition of such gases as nitrogen and oxygen.

Pollution plume When prevailing winds exceed 13 km/h, dust domes begin to detach themselves from the cities over which they are centred. The polluted air streams out as a plume above the downwind countryside.

Polythermal ice A glacier or ice sheet having both cold and wet-based ice.

Pools Deeper parts of a stream channel usually associated with meander bends.

Porosity Water-holding capacity of a soil or rock; the number of pores (i.e., the interstices of rock, sediment, or soil) per unit volume.

Potential evaporation Maximum amount of water that can be lost to the atmosphere from a land surface with abundant available water.

Precambrian Era that precedes the Paleozoic Era on the geological time scale, named after the oldest period of the Paleozoic, the Cambrian; extends backward from 570 million years ago to the origin of the Earth, now estimated to be about 4.6 billion years ago.

Precipitation Any liquid water or ice that falls to the Earth's surface through the atmosphere (rain, snow, sleet, and hail).

Pressure (atmospheric) Weight of a column of air at a given location, determined by the force of gravity and the composition and properties of the atmosphere at that location. Standard sea-level air pressure produces a reading of 760 mm on the mercury barometer. In terms of weight, it is also given as 1013.25 millibars (mb).

Pressure gradient force The difference in surface pressure over a given distance between two locations is called the pressure gradient. When that pressure gradient exists, it acts as a force that causes air to move (as wind) from the place of higher pressure to that of lower pressure.

Primary landform Structure created by tectonic activity.

Primary pollutant Gaseous or solid pollutant that comes from an industrial or domestic source or the internal combustion engine of a motor vehicle.

Primary producers The first trophic level in an ecosystem, composed of autotrophs (plants on land, algae in water).

Primary succession Process that occurs on new terrain, e.g., created by volcanic eruptions, a fall in sea level, or continental deglaciation, where soil and plant seres develop at the same time (over 500–1000 years), with plants initiating changes in the land surface, which consequently cause vegetational changes. It is a linear process, i.e., the order of succession in any one place is not normally repeated. Also called linear autogenic succession.

Prime Meridian North–south line on the Earth grid, passing through the Royal Observatory at Greenwich, London, defined as having a longitude of 0°.

Prismatic soil structure Involves peds arranged in columns, giving a soil vertical strength.

Proglacial Close to glaciers.

Proglacial lake A lake impounded between the snout of a glacier or a margin of an ice sheet and higher ground such as a terminal moraine or an escarpment, e.g., Glacial Lake Agassiz.

Proterozoic The last Pre-Cambrian geological era between the Archaean and Palaeozoic Eras (1.6 Ga to 570 Ma). Includes the Varangian and Ediacarian Periods.

Proxy climatic data Indirect evidence of past climatic change; found all over the natural world, such as in seafloor sediment deposits and the concentric annual growth rings of trees.

Psychrometer Instrument consisting of two thermometers. The bulb of one is swaddled in a wet cloth or sock, the other is not, so that both 'wet-bulb' and 'dry-bulb' temperatures are recorded. It is used to measure relative humidity, specific humidity, and the mixing ratio.

Pyroclastics Collective name for the pre-existing rock and lava fragments that are erupted explosively from a volcano.

Quartzite Very hard metamorphic rock that resists weathering; formed by the metamorphosis of sandstone (made of quartz grains and a silica cement).

Radial drainage Stream pattern that emanates outward in many directions from a central mountain or dome area.

Radiation Transmission of energy in the form of electromagnetic waves. A wide range of energy occurs within the electromagnetic spectrum.

Radiosonde Radio-equipped weather instrument packages that are carried aloft by balloon.

Rain shadow effect Dry conditions—often at a regional scale as in western North America—which occur on the leeward side of a mountain barrier that experiences orographic precipitation. The passage of moist air across that barrier wrests most of the moisture from the air, whose adiabatic warming as it plunges downslope sharply lowers the dew point and precipitation possibilities, e.g., Interior Plateau of British Columbia and Alberta.

Rainsplash erosion The preferential erosion of fine material caused by the impact of raindrops on a bare soil surface on a slope.

Rawinsonde High-altitude radar tracking of radiosonde balloons, which provides information about wind speed and directions at various vertical levels in the atmosphere.

Recessional moraine Morainal ridge marking a place where glacial retreat was temporarily halted.

Rectangular drainage Stream pattern dominated by right-angle contacts between streams and tributaries, but not as pronounced as in trellis drainage.

Red-yellow podzolic soil A well-developed luvisolic soil found to the south of the margins of the Pleistocene ice sheets in North America. They are characterized by a strongly developed clay-rich **B** horizon. US taxonomy: ultisol.

Regelation A process involving melting, entrainment, movement, and refreezing whereby debris is added to the basal sediment load of wet-based glacial ice and transported.

Regional subsystem Particular interconnection, at any given place within the total Earth System, of the five spheres or subsystems (atmosphere, hydrosphere, cryosphere, lithosphere, biosphere).

Regolith Weathered, broken, loose material overlying bedrock, usually derived from the rock below (then called saprolite), but sometimes transported to the area. First stage in the conversion of bedrock to soil; located at the base of the soil in the **R** horizon (**R** for regolith).

Regosolic soil A Canadian soil order composed of recently or poorly developed soils in areas that are geomorphologically active or recently deposited. US taxonomy: entisol soil order.

Relative humidity   Proportion of water vapour present in a parcel of air relative to the maximum amount of water vapour that air could hold at the same temperature.

Relaxation   The undergoing of change or adaptation to current environmental conditions, e.g., slope failures.

Relief   Vertical distance between the highest and lowest elevations in a given area.

Remote sensing   Technique for imaging objects without the sensor being in immediate contact with the local scene.

Renewable resource   One that can regenerate as it is exploited.

Residual soil   Simplest kind of soil formation in which a soil forms directly from underlying rock. When this occurs, the dominant soil minerals bear a direct relationship to that original rock.

Respiration   Biological term for the chemical combination of oxygen and other materials to create new products (chemists call this process oxidation). Heat increases the plants' rates of respiration; respiration runs counter to photosynthesis because it breaks down available carbohydrates and combines them with oxygen.

Reverse fault   Result of one crustal block overriding another along a steep fault plane between them; caused by compression of the crust into a smaller horizontal space.

Revetments   Blocks of concrete put along a stream bank or a coast to stop or slow down erosion; rip-rap.

Revolution   One complete circling of the Sun by a planet. It takes the Earth precisely one year to complete such an orbit.

Rhizosphere   The root zone of a soil.

Rhumb lines   Any straight lines drawn on a cylindrical Mercator map projection, which are automatically lines of true and constant compass bearing.

Richter scale   Open-ended numerical scale, first developed in the 1930s, which measures earthquake magnitude; ranges from 0 to 8+, and has evolved into the Moment Magnitude Scale.

Riffles   Faster flowing shallower parts of a stream channel found between pools and associated with straightaways.

Rift   Opening of the crust, normally into a trough or trench, that occurs in zone of plate divergence or spreading.

Rift valley   Develops in a continental zone of plate divergence where tensional forces pull the crustally thinning surface apart. The rift valley is the trough that forms when the land sinks between parallel faults in strips.

Rill, rilling   A micro-channel cut into a slope that can be eliminated by ploughing or bulldozing; a hillslope process where rills are eroding a slope.

Rip current   Very strong, narrow, short-distance, stream-like rapid current that moves seaward from the shoreline cutting directly across the oncoming surf.

Roche moutonnée   Landform created by glacial smoothing and plucking; asymmetrical rock mound that results from abrasion to one side (the side from which the glacier advanced) and plucking on the leeward side.

Rock   Any naturally formed, firm, and consolidated aggregate mass of mineral matter, of organic or inorganic origin, that constitutes part of the planetary crust.

Rock cycle   Cycle of transformation that affects all rocks and involves all parts of the Earth's crust. Plutons form deep in the crust, uplift pushes them to the surface, weathering and erosion wears them down, and the sediments they produce become new mountains.

Rock flour   Very finely ground-up debris carried downslope by a mountain glacier; when deposited, it is often blown away by the wind. Rock flour remains suspended in water causing the characteristic aquamarine colour of streams and lakes in the Canadian Rockies and Coast Mountains, for example.

Rock glacier   In high-relief periglacial areas, a tongue of boulder-like rock debris that has slowly moved downslope as a unit; may have been consolidated by a since-eroded matrix of finer sediments, or cemented together by long-melted ice.

Rock sea   Area of large blocky rock fragments formed when weathered rocks—particularly from frost wedging—remain near their original location (also called blockfield, felsenmeer, and boulder field).

Rock steps   Step-like valley profile (in the postglacial landscape) often created as alpine glaciers move down valley.

Rossby wave   The largest of wavelike flows of air in the upper atmosphere of mid-latitude regions, of which there are typically three to seven circulating the globe in relatively fixed positions. These waves fluctuate according to the seasons, with higher frequencies and strongest winds associated with their presence in winter, which can have a significant impact on weather conditions.

Rotation   Spinning of a planet on its axis, the imaginary line passing through its centre and both poles. It takes the Earth one calendar day to complete one full rotation.

Runoff   Removal—as overland flow or the network of streams—at the land surface of the surplus precipitation that does not infiltrate the soil or accumulate on the ground through surface retention.

Saltation   Transportation process that entails the bouncing of sand- and gravel-sized fragments along the bed of a moving stream or in the nearshore zone, or coarser sand grains moved by wind.

Salt crystal (salt burst) hydration   Form of physical weathering in arid regions, also called haloclasty. Salt crystals behave much like ice in the process of frost action, entering rock joints dissolved in water, staying behind after evaporation, growing and prying apart the surrounding rock, and weakening the internal structure of the host landform.

Sand   Coarsest grains in a soil. Sand particles range in size from 2 to 0.05 mm.

Sandspit   Elongated extension of a beach into open water where the shoreline reaches a bay or bend; built and maintained by littoral or longshore drift.

Sandstone   Common sedimentary rock possessing sand-sized grains.

Sandur (Icelandic, plural: sandar)   A glacial outwash plain.

Santa Ana wind   Hot, dry, foehn-type wind that affect southern California, sometimes spreading wildfires into human-inhabited areas. Its unpleasantness is heightened by the downward funnelling of this airflow from the high inland desert through narrow passes in the mountains that line the Pacific coast.

Saturated air   Air that is holding all the water vapour molecules it can possibly contain at a given temperature.

Saturated (wet) adiabatic lapse rate (SALR)   Lapse rate of an air parcel saturated with water vapor in which condensation is occurring; unlike the dry adiabatic lapse rate (DALR), the value of the SALR is variable, depending on the amount of water condensed and the latent heat released. A typical value for the SALR at 20°C is −0.44°C/100 m.

Savanna biome   Transitional vegetation of the environment between the tropical rainforest and the subtropical desert; consists of tropical grasslands with widely spaced trees and is subject to sporadic burning.

Scale   Ratio of the size of an object on a map to the actual size of the object it represents.

Scarp   Cliff; steep face of a cuesta or escarpment.

Schist   Common metamorphic rock so altered that its previous form is impossible to determine; fine-grained, exhibits wavy bands, and breaks along parallel planes (but unevenly, unlike slate).

Sea arch   Small island penetrated by the sea at its base. Island originated as an especially resistant portion of a headland that was eroded away by waves.

Sea breeze   Onshore airflow affecting a coastal zone, resulting from a daytime pressure gradient that steers local winds from the cooler (higher pressure) sea surface onto the warmer (lower pressure) land surface.

Sea cave   Cave carved by undercutting waves eroding the base of a sea cliff.

Sea cliff   Especially steep coastal slope that develops when headlands are eroded by waves.

Seafloor spreading   Process wherein new crust is formed by upwelling magma at the mid-oceanic ridges, and then continuously moves away from its source towards the margins of the ocean basin; crustal spreading.

Seamount   Undersea abyssal-zone volcanic mountain reaching over 1000 m above the ocean floor.

Secondary currents   Ocean circulation distinct from tides, including currents caused by wind drift and wind waves.

Secondary landform   Landform that is the product of weathering and erosion.

Secondary pollutant   Produced in the air by the interaction of two or more primary pollutants or from reactions with normal atmospheric constituents.

Secondary succession   Vegetation changes within an environment because of some outside environmental force, such as agriculture, insect infestation, or fire.

Sedimentary rocks   Secondary rocks that formed from the deposition and compression of rock and mineral fragments or precipitation of material in solution.

Sediment cores   Core samples drilled from the ocean floor that reveal the conditions on that part of the planet many years ago; a 40 m ocean sediment core spans 12,000 years of Earth history.

Sediment yield   Measurement of the total volume of sediment leaving a drainage basin (t/yr).

Seiche   See-sawing motion or oscillation on the surface of a lake or the sea.

Seismic waves   Pulses of energy generated by earthquakes that can pass through the Earth. Love waves radiate out from the epicentre, like waves caused by a rock being thrown into a pond, and cause disruption of the surface and infrastructure; Rayleigh waves are surface waves that radiate out from the epicentre in a snaking motion.

Seismograph   Device that measures and records the seismic waves produced by earthquakes.

Sensible heat flow   Environmental heat we feel or sense on our skins.

Sere, seral   An assemblage of plants; relating to an assemblage of plants.

Shale   Soft, finest-grained of the sedimentary rocks; formed from compacted mud, mud rock.

Shear strength   Forces that act against downslope movement, e.g., cementation, cohesion, friction, weight, normal stress.

Shear stress   The force acting to move material downslope, influenced by weight and gravity.

Sheet erosion   Erosion produced by sheet flow as it removes fine-grained surface materials.

Shield volcano   Formed from fluid basaltic lavas that flow in sheets, which are built up gradually by successive eruptions. In profile their long horizontal dimensions peak in a gently rounded manner that resembles a shield (the main island of Hawaii has some of the world's most active shield volcanoes).

Shoaling   Near-shore impact of ever shallower water on an advancing, incoming wave.

Shore   More specific than 'coast'; the narrower belt of land bordering a body of water, i.e., the most seaward portion of a coast (the 'shoreline' is the actual contact border).

Shortwave radiation   Radiation coming from the Sun, which has much shorter wavelengths—and involves much higher energy—than the terrestrial (longwave, lower energy) radiation emitted by the Earth.

SIAL   Derived from the chemical symbols for the minerals *si*licon and *al*uminum; refers to the generally lighter-coloured, less dense rocks of the continents, which are dominated by granite or granitic rocks.

Sill   Concordant intrusive igneous form in which magma has inserted itself as a thin layer between strata of pre-existing rocks without disturbing those layers to any great extent.

Silt   Next smaller category of soil particles after sand, the coarsest variety. Silt particles range in size from 0.5 to 0.002 mm.

SIMA   Derived from the chemical symbols for the minerals *si*licon and *ma*gnesium; refers to the generally darker-coloured rocks of the ocean floors, which are dominated by basalt.

Slate   Metamorphosed shale; a popular building material, it retains the characteristic of shale to break along parallel planes.

Slip face   Leeward slope of a sand dune.

Slope-creating processes   Processes responsible for slope formation, e.g., tectonism, stream incision, wave erosion.

Slope-modifying processes   Hillslope processes that cannot form slopes but can modify slopes, e.g., wash, rilling.

Slump   Type of mass movement in which a major section of regolith, soil, or weakened bedrock comes down a steep slope as a backward-rotating slump block.

Smog   Poor-quality surface-level air lying beneath a temperature inversion layer in the lower atmosphere; derived from the contraction of 'smoke' and 'fog'.

'Snowball Earth'   A glacial period that affected most if not all of the Earth during part of the Late Proterozoic Era (1.6 billion years ago to 600 million years ago).

Snow line   High-altitude boundary above which snow remains on the ground throughout the year; also called firn line.

Soil   Mixture of fragmented and organic matter and weathered grains of minerals and rocks with variable proportions of air and water. The mixture has a fairly distinct layering, and its development is influenced by climate and living organisms.

Soil bodies   Geographical areas within which soil properties remain relatively constant.

Soil catena   A sequence of soil profiles appearing in regular succession on landform features of uniform rock type.

Soil compaction   Pressing down on soil, as by heavy equipment, frequent field traffic, or intensive livestock operations, that makes the soil of greater density, less porous, and less permeable, which results in puddling, surface runoff, and erosion.

Soil components   These are four in number: minerals, organic matter, water, and air.

Soil formation factors   These are five in number: parent material, climate, organisms, topography, and time. These influence the type of soils developed in an area.

Soil geography   Systematic study of the spatial patterns of soils, their distribution, and the interrelationships with climate, vegetation, and humankind.

Soil horizon   Soil layer. The differentiation of soils into layers is called horizonation.

Soil order   In soil taxonomy, the broadest possible classification of the Earth's soils into one of several major categories (in Canada: 10; in the US: 12); a very general grouping of soils with broadly similar composition, the presence or absence of certain diagnostic horizons, and similar degrees of horizon development, weathering, and leaching.

Soil profile   Entire array of soil horizons (layers) from the surface to the bottom.

Soil (pedogenetic) regimes   The special patterns in soil formation related to differences in the dominance of one or more soil-forming factors that influence the additions, losses, transformations, and translocations that occur in the soils, so that even if their parent material remained constant all over the world, soils would differ because they would form under varying temperature, moisture, biogeographic, and other conditions.

Sol   Russian word for soil (Russians were pioneers in the modern science of pedology); used as a suffix for some soil types in the Canadian System of Soil Classification and all soil types in the US Soil Taxonomy.

Solar elevation   Number of degrees above the horizon of the noontime Sun, the position at which the solar rays strike the surface at their highest daily angle; also called 'angle of incidence'.

Solar system   Sun and its nine orbiting planets (plus their orbiting satellites). In order of increasing distance from the Sun, these planets are Mercury, Venus, Earth, Mars, Jupiter, Saturn, Uranus, Neptune, and Pluto.

Solifluction (gelifluction)   The flow of super-saturated soil that has reached its liquid limit. Gelifluction is this process in an area of frozen ground or permafrost.

Solonetzic soil   A Canadian soil order including saline and alkaline soils. US taxonomy: no equivalent at the order level.

Solstices   The times of year (22 June and 22 December) when 'the Sun stands still', before rising or sinking in the sky; the solstices mark the two days of the year with the shortest (winter) and longest (summer) daytime periods of sunlight.

Solum   Consists of the **A** and **B** horizons of a soil, that part of the soil in which plant roots are active and play a role in soil development. Mainly used in the US.

Solution (stream)   Transportation process where rock material is dissolved and carried within a stream.

Solution (suffusion) sinkhole (doline)   In karst terrain, a funnel-shaped surface hollow (with the shaft draining the centre) created by solution when an overlying layer of unconsolidated material is left unsupported. Ranges in size from a bathtub to a stadium.

Solution weathering   The weathering and removal of the weathered minerals in a dissolved state or in solution.

Source region   Extensive geographical area, possessing relatively uniform characteristics of temperature and moisture, where large air masses can form.

Southeast Trades   Surface wind belt that generally lies between the Equator and 30°S. The Coriolis force deflects winds flowing towards the Equator to the left, thus recurving south winds into southeast winds.

Southern Hemisphere   The half of the Earth located south of the Equator (0° latitude); the southernmost point is the South Pole (90°S).

Southern Oscillation   Periodic, anomalous reversal of the pressure zones in the atmosphere overlying the equatorial Pacific, associated with the occurrence of the El Niño phenomenon. As the sea surface temperatures change and water currents reverse, corresponding shifts occur in the windflows above.

Spatial   Pertaining to space on the Earth's surface; synonym for geographic(al).

Species   Population of physically and chemically similar organisms within which free gene flow takes place.

Species-richness gradient   Phenomenon involving the general decline over distance in the number of species per unit area, as one proceeds from the equatorial to the higher latitudes.

Speleothems   Unique cave features of calcium carbonate deposits resulting from chemical solution of limestone, such as stalactites, stalagmites, cave straws, etc.

Spheroidal (granular) soil structure   Involves peds that are usually very small and often nearly round in shape, so that the soil looks like 'a layer of bread crumbs'.

Spheroidal weathering (spalling)   Product of the chemical weathering process of hydrolysis. In certain igneous rocks such as granite, hydrolysis combines with other processes to cause the outer shells of the rock to flake off in what looks like a small-scale version of exfoliation.

Spillway channels   Channels carved out by the overflow or breaching of proglacial lakes.

Spodosol   One of the 12 soil orders of the US Soil Taxonomy, which develops where organic soil acids associated with pine needle decay cause the depletion of most **A** horizon minerals. That **Ae** horizon is characterized by an ash-grey colour, the signature of silica that is resistant to dissolving by organic acids. Canadian taxonomy: podzolic soil order.

Spring (water)   Surface stream of flowing water that emerges from the ground.

Spring (vernal) equinox   In Northern Hemisphere terminology, the equinox that occurs when the Sun's noontime rays strike the Equator vertically on or around 21 March.

Stability (of air)   Parcel of air whose vertical movement is such that it returns to its original position after receiving some upward force. However, if an air parcel continues moving upward after receiving such a force, it is said to be unstable.

Stack   Column-like island that is a remnant of a headland eroded away by waves.

Stalactite   Rock formation composed of dripstone hanging from the roof of a cave.

Stalagmite   Upward tapering, pillar-like rock formation composed of dripstone standing on the floor of a cave.

Standard parallel   Parallel of tangency between a globe and the surface onto which it is projected.

Stationary front   Boundary between two stationary air masses.

Steady-state system   System in which inputs and outputs are in equilibrium.

Stefan-Boltzmann Law   The total energy radiated by an object across all wavelengths is proportional to the fourth power of its absolute temperature; an equation for explaining the growth in energy intensity as temperature increases.

Steppe   Transitional semi-arid area between fully developed desert conditions and the subhumid climates; in western Canada, the short-grass prairie.

Storm   Organized, moving atmospheric disturbance.

Stormflow runoff   Stream discharge supplied by rainfall or snowmelt.

Storm surge   Wind-driven wall of water hurled ashore by the approaching centre of a hurricane, which can surpass normal high tide levels by more than 5 m; often associated with a hurricane's greatest destruction.

Straightaways   The parts of stream channels between meander bends; associated with riffles.

Stratification   Layering.

Stratigraphy   Order and arrangement of rock strata (layers).

Stratopause   Upper boundary of the stratosphere, lying approximately 52 km above the surface.

Stratosphere   Atmospheric layer lying above the troposphere. Here temperatures are either constant or start increasing with altitude.

Stratus clouds   Cloud-type category encompassing layered and fairly thin clouds that cover an extensive geographic area; subclassified according to height.

Stream capacity Maximum load of sediment that a stream can carry at a given discharge (volume of water).

Stream piracy Capture of a segment of a stream by another stream.

Striations Scratches made in bedrock as a boulder or pebble at the base of a glacier or ice sheet was dragged along; they often are metres long and centimetres (but more often millimetres) deep, and are useful in indicating the direction of the ice flow.

Strike Compass direction of the line of intersection between a rock layer and a horizontal plane.

Subduction Process that takes place when an oceanic plate converges head-on with a plate carrying a continental landmass at its leading edge. The lighter continental plate overrides the denser oceanic plate and pushes it downward.

Subglacial Material carried under a glacier or ice sheet. Subglacial meltwater streams flow in tunnels under a glacier or ice sheet.

Subglacial cavity A ice cave under a glacier.

Sublimation Process where a solid can change directly into a gas. The reverse process is also called sublimation (or deposition). The heat required to produce these transformations is the sum of the latent heats of fusion and vaporization.

Submergent coast Drowned coastal zone, more common than uplifted, emergent coasts; submergence caused in large part by the rise in sea level (about 120 m) of the past 10,000 years.

Subpolar gyre Oceanic circulation loop found only in the Northern Hemisphere. Its southern limb is a warm current steered by prevailing westerly winds, but the complex, cold returning flows to the north are complicated by sea-ice blockages and the configuration of landmasses vis-à-vis outlets for the introduction of frigid Arctic waters.

Subsidence Vertical downflow of air towards the surface from higher in the troposphere; ground subsidence or sinking can occur because of solutional weathering or because of melting of permafrost, which creates thermokarst topography.

Subsystem Component of a larger system. It can act independently, but operates within, and is linked to, the larger system.

Subtropical gyre Circulates around the Subtropical High located above the center of the ocean basin; dominates the oceanic circulation of both hemispheres, flowing clockwise in the Northern Hemisphere and counterclockwise in the Southern Hemisphere.

Subtropical High Semi-permanent belt of high pressure found at approximately 30 degrees of latitude in both the Northern and Southern Hemispheres. The subsiding air at its centre flows outward towards both the lower and higher latitudes.

Sulphidic cave A cave formed by sulphidic bacterial action.

Sulphur cycle The movement of sulphur through the Earth System, as with the burning of fossil fuels and subsequent acid precipitation.

Summer solstice Each year, day of the poleward extreme in the latitude where the Sun's noontime rays strike the Earth's surface vertically. In the Northern Hemisphere that latitude is 23½°N (the Tropic of Cancer) and the date is 22 June; in the Southern Hemisphere that latitude is 23½°S (the Tropic of Capricorn) and the date is 22 December.

Sunspots Storm areas on the surface of the Sun that affect the amount of solar radiation reaching the Earth and that may affect terrestrial weather.

Supercontinent cycle The growth and breakup of supercontinents such as Pangaea. Also called a Wilson cycle.

Supraglacial Carried on the top of a glacier or ice sheet, such as ablation till.

Surf Water zone just offshore dominated by the development and forward collapse of breaking waves.

Surface creep Rolling or dragging movement of small rock fragments by the wind that pushes them along the ground, especially during windstorms.

Surface retention Water that collects on the surface in pools and hollows, bordered by millions of tiny natural dams, during a rainstorm that deposits more precipitation than the soil can absorb.

Suspension (stream) Transportation process whereby very fine clay- and silt-sized sediment is carried within a moving stream. Material is kept aloft by flow turbulence.

Sustainable development Inexact term made popular by the World Commission on Environment and Development in its 1987 report, *Our Common Future*, and used widely by social scientists and policy-makers; generally understood to mean development that meets the needs of the present without compromising the ability of future generations to meet their own needs.

Swash Thinning sheet of water that slides up the beach after a wave reaches shore and has broken.

Swells Long rolling waves that can travel thousands of kilometres across the ocean surface until they break against a shore.

Syncline Trough-like downfold with its limbs dipping towards its axial plane.

Synoptic weather chart Map of weather conditions covering a wide geographical area at a given moment in time.

System Any set of related objects or events and their interactions; usually connected by a flow of energy, water, or material.

Talik Soil above the permafrost table, which is subject to annual thawing and freezing, i.e., the active layer in permafrost areas.

Talus cone Steep accumulation of weathered rock fragments and loose boulders that have rolled downslope in free fall.

Tarn Small, usually circular lake on the floor of a cirque basin.

Temperate deciduous forest biome Dominated by broadleaf trees. Herbaceous plants are also abundant, especially in spring before the trees grow new leaves.

Temperate evergreen forest biome Dominated by needleleaf trees; especially common along western mid-latitude coasts where precipitation is abundant.

Temperate grassland biome Occurs over large mid-latitude areas of continental interiors. Perennial and sod-forming grasses are dominant.

Temperate karst Marked by disappearing streams, jagged rock masses, solution depressions, and extensive cave networks; forms more slowly than tropical karst.

Temperature Index used to measure the kinetic energy possessed by molecules; the more kinetic energy they have, the faster they move. Temperature, therefore, is an abstract term that describes the energy (speed of movement) of molecules.

Temperature gradient Horizontal rate of temperature change over distance.

Temperature inversion Condition in which temperature increases with altitude rather than decreases—a positive lapse rate. It inverts what we, on the surface, believe to be 'normal' temperature change with increasing height.

Temporary base level Temporary limitation on further upstream channel incision, as when a stream that erodes downward reaches an especially hard, resistant rock barrier, perhaps in the form of a dyke.

Tephra Loose assemblage of pyroclastics; volcanic ash.

Terminal moraine Rock debris, carried in and just ahead of the leading front of a glacier, and deposited as an irregular ridge when the ice's forward progress stops. These ridges are important because they mark the farthest extent of an ice lobe.

Terraces Higher lying remnants of an old floodplain that stand above the bluffs lining the newer floodplain of a rejuvenated river.

Terrane Geological region of 'consistent' rocks in terms of age, type, and structure. Mismatched subregions can occur and are known as suspect terranes.

Thermohaline circulation Describes the deep-sea system of oceanic circulation, which is controlled by differences in the temperature and salinity of subsurface water masses.

Thermokarst Areas where ground ice or permafrost has melted and created depressions (often water-filled) that look like landforms related to limestone solution.

Thermometer Instrument for measuring temperature. Most commonly these measurements are made by observing the expansion and contraction of mercury inside a glass tube.

Thermosphere Fourth layer of the atmosphere, above the troposphere, stratosphere, and mesosphere. In this layer, temperatures increase as altitude increases.

Threshold angle The angle at which mass movements stop on a slope; the angle of repose or stability.

Thrust fault Compressional fault in which the angle of the fault plane is very low; sometimes called overthrust fault.

Thunderstorm Local storm dominated by thunder, lightning, heavy rain, and sometimes hail; exhibits a definite life cycle involving developing, mature, and dissipation stages.

Tidal bore (eagre) A wall of water that moves up a coastal reach of a stream caused by an incoming tide. The incoming water moves upstream over the downstream-flowing stream water. The wall of water can be a few cm to many metres high.

Tidal range Average vertical difference between sea levels at high tide and low tide.

Tide Cyclical rise and fall of sea level controlled by the Earth's rotation and the gravitational pull of the Moon and Sun. Daily two high tides and two low tides occur within a period slightly longer than 24 hours.

Tills Two types of glacial material—ablation till and basal till; solid material (ranging in size from boulders to clay particles) carried by a glacier that is deposited as an unsorted mass as the ice melts back.

Tilth Aerated, mixed, humus-rich top soil formed by earthworms and other soil organisms. Ploughing fields produces a tilth.

Tolerance limits Limits related to various environmental factors, such as temperature range, precipitation, food supply, and stressors, beyond which organisms will not grow in a given environment or along an environmental gradient.

Tombolo Sandspit that forms a link between the mainland and an offshore island.

Topset beds Horizontal layers of sedimentary deposits that underlie a deltaic plain.

Torino Impact Hazard Scale Scale devised (and later modified) by MIT researcher Richard Binzel and others to rank the possibility of near-Earth object impact using a 10-point scale, named after the site of an International Astronomical Union conference in Turin, Italy, which adopted it in 1999.

Tornado Small vortex of air, averaging 100 to 500 m (330 to 1650 ft) in diameter, that descends to the ground from rotating clouds at the base of a severe thunderstorm, accompanied by winds whose speeds range from 50 to 130 m/s. As tornadoes move across the land surface, they evince nature's most violent weather and can produce truly awesome destruction in the natural and cultural landscapes.

Tower (karst) In tropical karst landscapes, a cone-shaped, steep-sided hill that rises above a surface that may or may not be pocked with solution depressions.

Traction Transportation process that involves the sliding or rolling of particles along a riverbed.

Transcurrent fault Transverse fault in which crustal blocks move horizontally in the direction of the fault; also known as a strike-slip fault because movement at a transcurrent fault occurs along the strike of the fault.

Trans-Eurasian earthquake belt Second in the world only to the Circum-Pacific belt, a belt of high earthquake incidence that extends east–southeast from the Atlantic Ocean across the Mediterranean Sea to southwestern and southern Asia to join the Circum-Pacific belt off Southeast Asia.

Transformation Soil-layer formation process involving the weathering of rocks and minerals and the continuing decomposition of organic material in the soil. Weathering is most advanced in the upper soil layers.

Transform fault Special case of transcurrent faulting in which the transverse fault marks the boundary between two lithospheric plates that are sliding past each other. California's San Andreas Fault is a classic example.

Translocation Movements of material in solution or in particulate form down a soil profile (e.g., the leaching of bases), up a soil profile (e.g., salts brought up into the soil by groundwater under capillary action), or moved horizontally within the soil (e.g., water moving clay-sized material downslope through the soil mass).

Transpiration Passage of water into the atmosphere through the leaf pores (stomata) of plants.

Transported soil When a soil is totally independent of the underlying solid rock because the parent material has been transported and deposited by one or more agents, often far from its source area.

Transport-limited slopes A slope form that is influenced to a great extent by erosional processes rather than weathering. Weathered material builds up to cover the slope.

Transverse dune Ridge-like sand dune positioned at a right angle to the prevailing wind; usually straight or slightly curved.

Treeline The latitudinal or altitudinal limit of tree growth (mainly because of cold temperatures and/or the lack of soil).

Trellis drainage Stream pattern that resembles a garden trellis; flows only in two orientations, more or less at right angles to each other; often develops on parallel-folded sedimentary rocks.

Tributaries In a stream system, the smaller branch streams that connect with and feed the main artery (trunk stream); terminology also applies to glacier systems.

Trophic (feeding) level Position in an ecosystem based on energy or food flow; the trophic levels are primary producer, consumer (herbivore, carnivore), and decomposer.

Trophic pathways The two routes—grazing and detrital—along which food energy moves through an ecosystem.

Tropical (A) climates Dominated by warmth (due to low-latitude location) and moisture (from the rains of the Inter-Tropical Convergence Zone); contained within a continuous east–west belt astride the Equator, varying latitudinally from 30 to 50 degrees wide.

Tropical deforestation Clearing and destruction of tropical rainforests to make way for expanding settlement frontiers and the exploitation of new economic opportunities.

Tropical depression Easterly wave of increased intensity, but exhibiting wind speeds of less than 21 m/s. Its low-pressure trough has deepened and begun to assume a rotating, cyclonic organization. Further intensification of the depression would next transform it into a tropical storm.

Tropical gyre Narrow, low-latitude oceanic circulation loop, in both the Northern and Southern Hemispheres, comprised of the equatorial currents and returning countercurrents; reinforced by the converging winds of the Northeast and Southeast Trades.

Tropical karst Dominated by steep-sided, vegetation-covered hill terrain; solution features are larger than in slower-forming temperate karst landscapes.

Tropical rainforest biome Vegetation dominated by tall, closely spaced evergreen trees; a teeming arena of life that is home to a greater number and diversity of plant and animal species than any other biome.

Tropical storm   Intensified tropical depression, exhibiting a deep central low-pressure cell, rotating cyclonic organization, and wind speeds between 21 and 33 m/s. Further intensification would transform the system into a tropical cyclone (hurricane).

Tropic of Cancer   Most northerly latitude (23½°N) where the Sun's noontime rays strike the Earth's surface vertically (on 22 June, the day of the Northern Hemisphere summer solstice).

Tropic of Capricorn   Most southerly latitude (23½°S) where the Sun's noontime rays strike the Earth's surface vertically (on 22 December, the day of the Northern Hemisphere winter solstice).

Tropopause   Upper boundary of the troposphere along which temperatures stop decreasing with height.

Troposphere   Bottom layer of the atmosphere in which temperature usually decreases with altitude.

True flows   Hillslope processes in which the sediment is carried in a viscous state.

Truncated spurs   Over-steepened hillsides that have been cut by a glacier, straightening the glacially eroded valley.

Trunk stream   Main stream in a drainage network, which is fed by all the tributary streams.

Tsunami (harbour wave)   Seismic sea wave, set off by a crustal disturbance (earthquake, volcanic eruption), which can reach gigantic proportions.

Tundra biome   Microtherm plant assemblage of the coldest environments; dominated by perennial mosses, lichens, and sedges.

Ultisol   One of the 12 soil orders of the US Soil Taxonomy; usually quite old, not particularly fertile, and located in warm subtropical environments with pronounced wet seasons. Red-yellow podzolic/lateritic soils not in the Canadian taxonomy.

Ultraviolet radiation   High-energy, shortwave radiation associated with incoming solar energy.

Unconformity   Gap in the geological history of an area as found in the rock record, owing to a hiatus in deposition, followed by erosion of the surface, with further deposition continuing later; more specifically, can also refer to the contact between the eroded strata and the strata of resumed deposition.

Underfit stream   Small stream lying in a large river valley that seems incapable of having sculpted that valley. Stream piracy is one cause.

Uniclinal shifting   The movement of a stream or stream network, which erodes the least resistant rock strata down the dip of the rocks. This leaves a low ridge with one fairly steep slope (scarp) and another very gentle one (dip).

Universe   The entity that contains all of the matter and energy that exists anywhere in space and time.

Uplifted marine terrace   In an emergent coastal zone, a wave-cut platform that has been exposed and elevated by tectonic uplift or a lowering of sea level (or both).

Upper mantle   Viscous interior shell of the Earth, which encloses the solid lower mantle. The upper part of this area is plastic (the asthenosphere), but the very uppermost part of the upper mantle is solid, and this zone, together with the crust that lies directly above it, is called the lithosphere.

Upper Mid-latitude Low   Semi-permanent surface low-pressure belt, lying at approximately 60°N and S, where the Polar Easterlies flowing towards the Equator meet the poleward-flowing Westerlies. At this sharp atmospheric boundary, known as the Polar Front, the warmer Westerlies are forced to rise above the colder Easterlies.

Upwelling   Rising of cold water from the ocean depths to the surface; affects the local climatic environment because cold water lowers air temperatures and the rate of evaporation.

Urban heat island   Form taken by an isotherm representation of the heat distribution within an urban region. The central city has higher temperatures than the surrounding areas.

US Soil Taxonomy   The comprehensive soil classification system developed and used in the United States. It is designed as a global classification system.

Uvala   In karst terrain, a large surface depression created by the coalescence of two or more neighbouring sinkholes.

Variable gases   Atmospheric gases present in differing quantities at different times and places; three are essential to life: carbon dioxide, water vapour, and ozone.

Varves   Paired layers of alternating finer and coarser sediments caused by seasonal variations in deposition on a lakebed.

Velocity (stream)   Rate of speed (m/s) at which water moves in a stream channel. This rate varies within the stream and over time.

Vent   Opening through the Earth's crust from which lava erupts. Most eruptions occur through pipe-shaped vents that build volcanic mountains, but fissure eruptions also occur through lengthy cracks that exude sheets of lava (flood basalts).

Venturi effect   Restriction of a pipe or stream cross-section causes an increase in the velocity of water (or air) flow; occurs because of riffles in a stream.

Vertical zonation   Characteristic of **H** climates, the distinct arrangement of climate zones according to altitudinal position. The higher one climbs, the colder and harsher the climate becomes.

Vertisolic soil   A soil order the Canadian System of Soil Classification characterized by surface cracking and swelling because of dessication and moisture or freezing and thawing. Fine material is blown into the cracks when open, exposing a lower layer at the surface. The soil material is inverted in this way, hence the name. US taxonomy: vertisol soil order.

Vicariance   Modern species evolved from an ancestral species that arrived in a given part of the world after being carried along as landmasses parted over tens of millions of years.

Volcanic Explosivity Index   A classification of volcanic eruptions based on criteria such as energy release, the volume of ash erupted, etc.

Volcanism   Eruption of molten rock at the Earth's surface, often accompanied by rock fragments and explosive gases.

Volcano   Vent in the Earth's surface through which magma, solid rock, debris, and gases are erupted. This ejected material usually assumes the shape of a shield or a conical hill or mountain.

Wadi   An Arabic term for a canyon or gorge.

Wallace's Line   A.R. Wallace's controversial boundary line that purportedly separates the unique faunal assemblage of Australia from the very different animal assemblage of neighbouring Southeast Asia. Wallace's line, suggested over a century ago, is still the subject of debate today. Wallacea is a faunal transition zone spanning the area between Wallace's Line and Weber's Line.

Warm front   Produced when an advancing warm air mass infringes on a pre-existing cooler one. When they meet, the lighter, warmer air overrides the cooler air mass, forming the gently upward-sloping warm front (producing far more moderate precipitation than that associated with steeply sloped cold fronts).

Wash (sheetwash, slopewash)   A hillslope process in which a sheet of water pulses over a slope.

Water balance   The measurement of the inflow (precipitation), outflow (evapotranspiration, fog, stream discharge), and net annual surplus or deficit of water at a given location.

Water (oceanic) hemisphere   The roughly one-half of the Earth that contains most of the surface water (Southern Hemisphere); the opposite of the land hemisphere.

Water resources   Subfield of physical geography involving its intersection with hydrology; systematic study of the surface and subsurface water supplies potentially available for human use.

Waterspout   Tornado that forms and moves over a water surface.

Water table   Top of the (phreatic) zone of saturation; does not lie horizontally, but follows the general profile of the land surface above.

Water vapour   Invisible gaseous form of water; the most widely distributed variable gas of the atmosphere.

Wave-cut platform   Abrasion platform that develops at the foot of a sea cliff, marking its recession. Its nearly flat bedrock surface slopes seaward.

Wave height   Vertical distance between wave crest (top) and wave trough (bottom).

Wave length   Horizontal distance between one wave crest (or wave trough) and the next.

Wave of translation   Swell nearing shore that has 'felt' the rising ocean bottom so that its internal water motion (as a wave of oscillation) begins to be affected by it; the wave's erosional work has begun.

Wave refraction   Nearshore bending of waves coming in at an oblique angle to the shoreline. Shoaling slows part of the wave, which progressively bends as the faster end 'catches up'.

Waves of oscillation   Waves that move water particles in a circular up-and-down path. Their depth is one-half their length.

Waves of transition   Swell nearing shore that has 'felt' the rising ocean bottom and whose internal water motion (as a wave of oscillation) begins to be affected by it; the wave's erosional work has begun.

Weather   Immediate and short-term conditions of the atmosphere that impinge on daily human activities.

Weather advisory   Announcement through the media from Environment Canada that actual or expected weather conditions may cause general inconvenience or concern but are not serious enough to warrant a warning.

Weathering   Chemical alteration and physical disintegration of Earth materials by the action of air, water, and organisms; more specifically, the breakdown of rocks in situ, and their disintegration and decomposition without distant removal of the products.

Weathering-limited slopes   A slope form that is greatly influenced by weathering rather than erosional processes. The slope form is not covered by regolith and is closely related to the characteristics of a particular rock type.

Weathering zone   The weathered material (saprolite) lying above unweathered rock.

Weather modification   Changes in local and regional weather patterns resulting from human activity, especially intentional, purposive efforts to alter weather such as to create or to mitigate precipitation.

Weather stations   Government-designated observation posts, of which there are more than 2000 in Canada, for observing and recording data about surface weather conditions with instrumentation including thermometers, barometers, rain gauges, hygrometers (to measure the moisture of the air), weather vanes (to indicate wind direction), and anemometers (to measure wind speed).

Weather systems   Organized phenomena of the atmosphere—with inputs and outputs and changes of energy and moisture but of a more transient and secondary nature than the semi-permanent pressure cells and windflows of the general circulation. Recurring weather systems make up our daily weather.

Weather warning   Public announcement from Environment Canada informing the public that severe weather is occurring or that hazardous weather is highly probable.

Weather watch   Announcement through the media from Environment Canada alerting the public to conditions favourable for the development of severe weather.

Weber's Line   A line, just west of New Guinea and north-central Australia, demarcating the Southeast Asian faunal region from that of Australia, devised by zoologist M.C. Weber, who argued that Wallace's Line lay too far to the west. The area between Weber's Line and Wallace's Line is called Wallacea.

Westerlies   Two broad mid-latitude belts of prevailing westerly winds, lying between approximately 30° and 60° in both hemispheres. These winds are fed by the poleward windflow from the Subtropical High, which is deflected by the Coriolis force.

Wet-based (temperate) ice   Ice that can reach pressure melting point because it occurs in warmer climates than cold ice or it has more mass to cause basal melting. It is mobile and therefore can erode the ground below.

Wien's Law   Identifies the wavelength at which maximum energy is emitted, on the basis of an object's temperature.

Wind   Movement of air relative to the Earth's surface. Winds are always named according to the direction from which they blow.

Wind abrasion (sandblasting)   Erosion of rock surfaces by wind-borne sand particles.

Wind chill temperature index   Index that tells us subjectively how cold we would feel under given combinations of wind speed and air temperature.

Windrows   Lines or streaks of foam and surface debris (weed, flotsam) in a body of water that are aligned parallel to wind direction.

Windward   Exposed, upwind side of a topographic barrier that faces the winds that flow across it.

Winter solstice   Day each year of the poleward extreme in latitude *in the opposite hemisphere* where the Sun's noontime rays strike the Earth's surface vertically. In the Northern Hemisphere, that date is 22 December when the Sun is directly above latitude 23½°S (the Tropic of Capricorn); in the Southern Hemisphere, that date is 22 June when the Sun is directly above latitude 23½°N (the Tropic of Cancer).

Wisconsinan glaciation   Most recent glaciation of the Pleistocene Ice Age, consisting of early and late stages.

Yardang   Desert landform shaped by wind abrasion in the form of a low ridge lying parallel to the prevailing wind direction; most common in dry sandy areas underlain by soft bedrock.

Younger Dryas   A return of glacial conditions during deglaciation in Europe between about 12 ,900 and 11,500 years ago and thought to have been caused by the discharge of glacial meltwater from Lake Agassiz and the Great Lakes into the North Atlantic. It had a very rapid onset. Named after an alpine-tundra wildflower (*Dryas sp.*).

Zenith   Point in the sky directly overhead, 90° above the horizon.

Zonal flow   Westerly flow of winds that dominates the upper atmospheric circulation system poleward of 15 degrees latitude in each hemisphere.

Zone of aeration   Upper of the two subterranean zones that contain groundwater; lies above the water table and is normally unsaturated, except during heavy rainfall; also known as vadose zone.

Zone of saturation   Lower of the two subterranean zones that contain groundwater; lies below the water table and is also known as the phreatic zone.

Zoogeographical (Wallace's) realms   Largest and most generalized regional units for representing the Earth's fauna; reflect evolutionary centres for animal life as well as the influence of barriers over time.

Zoogeography   Geography of animal life or fauna; where zoology and physical geography overlap.

Zooplankton   Microscopic animal life forms that float in the ocean and freshwater bodies; eaten by small fish, which in turn are eaten by larger fish.

Credits

Credits for Line Art and Tables

Unit 1 Fig. 1.7: Fig. 1.1, p. 19, from *Geography: A Modern Synthesis*, 3rd edn, by Peter Haggett. Copyright © 1983 by Peter Haggett, reprinted by permission of Pearson Education, Inc.

Unit 3 Fig. 3.4: Reproduced with the permission of Natural Resources Canada, 2008, courtesy of the Centre for Topographic Information. Fig. 3.5: From Norman J.W. Thrower, *Maps and Man*, 1st edn, 1972, p. 153, reprinted by permission of Pearson Education, Inc. Fig. 3.8: After Arthur Robinson et al., *Elements of Cartography*, 5th rev. edn, 1984, p. 99, published by John Wiley & Sons. Fig. 3.12: Adapted with permission from Alberta Agriculture, Food, and Rural Development. Figs 3.13, 3.14: Adapted from Brian J. Skinner and Stephen C. Porter, *Physical Geography*, John Wiley & Sons, 1987, pp. 715, 711.

Unit 4 Fig. 4.2: Adapted from *National Geographic Atlas of the World*, 6th rev. edn, 1992, plate 119, © National Geographic Society. Fig. 4.3: After I. Gass et al., *Understanding the Earth*, 1971, p. 65, published by The MIT Press, © The MIT Press. Fig. 4.11: Adapted from Environment Canada, 2004. Fig. 4.13: Adapted from Smithsonian Meteorological Tables, 6th rev. edn, by Robert J. List, published by Smithsonian Institution Press, this edition © 1971 Smithsonian Institution.

Unit 5 Fig.5.3: After C.D. Keeling et al., *Geophysical Monitoring for Climate Change*, National Oceanic and Atmospheric Administration (NOAA), 1988. Fig. 5.5: Adapted from *Understanding Our Atmospheric Environment*, by Morris Neiburger et al., copyright © 1973 by W.H. Freeman and Company. Fig. 5.8: Project HEX.

Unit 6 Fig. 6.3 Hugo Ahlenius, UNEP/GRID-Arendal, 2008, International Polar Year educational posters, <http://maps.grida.no/go/graphic/climate-change-ice-and-snow-and-the-albedo-effect>. Fig. 6.5: After J.G. Lockwood, *World Climatology: An Environmental Approach*, 1974, p. 43, published by Edward Arnold (Publishers) Limited, © Edward Arnold (Publishers) Ltd. Fig. 6.6: After M.I. Budyko (trans. I. Stepanova), *The Heat Balance of Earth's Surface*, US Department of Commerce, Office of Technical Services, 1958. Figs 6.7, 6.8: After M.I. Budyko, 'The Heat Balance of the Earth', Soviet Geography: Review and Translation, Vol. 3, No. 5, May 1962, pp. 7, 9, published by the American Geographic Society. Table 6.1: After W.D. Sellers, *Physical Climatology*, 1965, pp. 32, 47, published by The University of Chicago Press, © The University of Chicago Press.

Unit 7 Fig. 7.5: Fig. 3.14, p. 61, from *Geography: A Modern Synthesis*, 3rd edn, by Peter Haggett, copyright © 1983 by Peter Haggett, reprinted by permission of Pearson Education, Inc. Figs 7.7, 7.8: Adapted from Environment Canada, 2004. Fig. 7.9: From *Urbanization and Environment* by Thomas R. Detwyler and Melvin G. Marcus, © 1972 by Wadsworth Publishing Company, Inc. Fig. 7.10: From Roger G. Barry and Richard J. Chorley, *Atmosphere, Weather and Climate*, Methuen (Routledge), 5th rev. edn, pp.24–5, © 1987 by Roger G. Barry and Richard J. Chorley. Table 7.1: From Frederick K. Lutgens and Edward J. Tarbuck, *The Atmosphere: An Introduction to Meteorology*, 2nd edn, © 1982, p. 58, published by Prentice-Hall, Inc.

Unit 8 Fig. 8.2: From Roger G. Barry and Richard J. Chorley, *Atmosphere, Weather and Climate*, Methuen (Routledge), 2nd rev. edn, pp. 8, 43, © 1987 Roger G. Barry and Richard J. Chorley. Figs 8.4,
8.5: Frederick K. Lutgens and Edward J. Tarbuck, *The Atmosphere: An Introduction to Meteorology*, 8th edn, © 2001, p. 168, reprinted by permission of Pearson Education, Inc. Fig. 8.10: Adapted from Brian J. Skinner and Stephen C. Porter, *The Blue Planet: An Introduction to Earth System Science*, John Wiley & Sons, 1995, p. 351. Table 8.1: © Her Majesty the Queen in Right of Canada, Environment Canada, 2008, reproduced with the permission of the Minister of Public Works and Government Services Canada.

Unit 9 Fig. 9.1: From Roger G. Barry and Richard J. Chorley, *Atmosphere, Weather and Climate*, Methuen (Routledge), 2nd rev. edn, p. 43, © 1987 Roger G. Barry and Richard J. Chorley, reproduced by permission of Taylor & Francis Books UK. Figs 9.5, 9.6: After J.G. Lockwood, *World Climatology: An Environmental Approach*, 1974, pp. 146, 151, published by Edward Arnold (Publishers) Limited, © Edward Arnold (Publishers) Ltd.

Unit 10 Fig. 10.1: Peter N. Schweitzer, 1993, 'Modern Average Global Sea-Surface Temperature', US Geological Survey Digital Data Series DDS-10, US Geological Survey, Reston, Virginia, courtesy of the US Geological Survey. Fig. 10.3: Adapted from the Museum of Natural History (Halifax, NS) website. Fig. 10.4: From *Oceanography: An Introduction to the Marine Sciences* by Jerome Williams, copyright © 1962 by Little, Brown and Company. Fig. 10.7: Same source as Fig. 3.13, p. 382. Fig. 10.10: © Nick Mantua, reprinted by permission.

Unit 11 Fig. 11.3: ICSCR. Fig. 11.6: Same source as Fig. 3.13, p. 241. Fig. 11.8: Adapted from Environment Canada, 2004. Fig. 11.9: © Her Majesty the Queen in Right of Canada, Environment Canada, 2008, reproduced with the permission of the Minister of Public Works and Government Services Canada. Fig. 11.14: After W.D. Sellers, *Physical Climatology*, 1965, p. 84, published by the University of Chicago Press, © The University of Chicago Press.

Unit 12 12.1: Dr Nolan Atkins, reprinted by permission. Fig. 12.6: From S. Petterssen, *Introduction to Meteorology*, © 1958 McGraw-Hill, Inc. Fig. 12.8: After K. Hindley, 'Learning to Live with Twisters', Vol. 70, 1977, p. 281, published by New Scientist. Fig. 12.10: © Her Majesty the Queen in Right of Canada, Environment Canada, 2008, reproduced with the permission of the Minister of Public Works and Government Services Canada.

Unit 13 Fig. 13.1: After J.G. Lockwood, *World Climatology: An Environmental Approach*, 1974, p. 96, published by Edward Arnold (Publishers) Limited, © Edward Arnold (Publishers) Ltd. Figs 13.7, 13.8A: © Dr Michael Pidwirny, Okanagan University College.

Unit 14 Fig. 14.2: NOAA. Fig. 14.4: National Weather Service. Fig. 14.8: *The Cape Cod Times*.

Unit 15 Fig. 15.3: Courtesy of DataStreme Project, American Meteorological Society. Fig. 15.9: After map of World Weather Extremes, Geographic Sciences Laboratory, US Army Engineer Topographic Laboratories, Ft Belvoir, VA, n.d.

Unit 16 Fig. 16.3: Frederick K. Lutgens and Edward J. Tarbuck, *The Atmosphere: An Introduction to Meteorology*, 8th edn, Prentice Hall, 2000.

Unit 17 Fig. 17.3: Adapted from press release map, © 1985 National Geographic Society. Fig. 17.19: © M.D. Benett.

Unit 18   Fig. 18.3: Barnola, J.-M., D. Raynaud, C. Lorius, and N.I. Barkov, 'Historical CO$_2$ Record from the Vostok Ice Core', Carbon Dioxide Information Analysis Center, Oak Ridge National Laboratory, US Department of Energy, <http://cdiac.ornl.gov/trendco2/vostok .html>. Fig. 18.4: National Oceanic and Atmospheric Administration, with data from A. Berger and M.F. Loutre, 1991, 'Insolation Values for the Climate of the Last 10 Million Years', *Quaternary Science Reviews* 10: 297–317 and K. Kawamura et al, 2007, 'Northern Hemisphere Forcing of Climatic Cycles in Antarctica Over the Past 360,000 Years', *Nature* 448: 912–16. Fig. 18.6: Reprinted by permission of Paul Ward. Fig. 18.7: Same source as Fig. 8.10, p. 364 (based on NCAR sea-level temperature records). Fig. 18.9: After *Understanding Climate Change: A Program for Action*, National Academy Press, Washington, DC, 1975. Fig. 18.11: From *The Weather Machine* by Nigel Calder, copyright © 1975 by Nigel Calder. Fig. 18.12: Based on data from the World Resources Institute.

Unit 19   Figs 19.2, 19.3: From L.P. Herrington, 'Biophysical Adaptations of Man Under Climatic Stress', *Meteorological Monographs*, Vol. 2, No. 8, pp. 30–34, © 1954 by the American Meteorological Society. Fig. 19.6: From *Urbanization and Environment* by Thomas R. Detwyler and Melvin G. Marcus, © 1972 by Wadsworth Publishing Company, Inc. Fig. 19.7: From Stanley A. Changon, Jr, 'Recent Studies of Urban Effects on Precipitation in the United States', in *Urban Climates*, paper no. 254, pp. 325–41, © 1971 by World Meteorological Organization.

Unit 23   Fig. 23.4: Adapted from Brian J. Skinner and Stephen C. Porter, *The Dynamic Earth: An Introduction to Physical Geology*, John Wiley & Sons, 3rd rev. edn, 1995, p. 427. Table 23.1: Reproduced with the permission of Natural Resources Canada, 2008.

Unit 24   Fig. 24.2: Photo Archive Submitter/National Geographic Image Collection. Fig. 24.3: Data from the US Coast and Geodetic Survey and NOAA. Fig. 24.12: Same source as Fig. 3.13, p. 490. Figs 24.6, 24.15: Dr Ron Clowes, LITHOPROBE and Earth & Ocean Sciences, University of British Columbia, Vancouver, Canada.

Unit 25   Fig. 25.10: © Her Majesty the Queen in Right of Canada, Environment Canada, 2004, reproduced with the permission of the Minister of Public Works and Government Services Canada.

Unit 26   Fig. 26.6: Data from US Coast and Geodetic Survey. Fig. 26.7: After NOAA, n.d. Tables 26.1, 26.2: From *The Way the Earth Works*, by P.J. Wyllie, published by John Wiley & Sons, copyright © John Wiley & Sons, Inc.

Unit 27   Figs 27.2, 27.5, 27.10, 27.12, 27.13: Same source as Fig. 3.13, pp. 416, 417, 424, and 426.

Unit 28   Fig. 28.4: Same source as Fig. 3.13, p. 293.

Unit 30   Figs 30.7, 30.9, 30.10, 30.12: Same source as Fig. 3.13, p. 323. 30.11: After US Geological Survey, professional paper 950, n.d. 30.14: After Arthur Bloom, *The Surface of the Earth*, © 1969, p. 90, published by Prentice-Hall, Inc. 30.15: From Léo F. Laporte, *Encounter With the Earth*, Canfield Press, p. 97, © 1975 by Léo F. Laporte.

Unit 31   Fig. 31.2: After *Physical Geography: Earth Systems*, Scott Foresman & Co., Glenview, Illinois, 1974, © John J. Hidore. Fig. 31.6: After J.P. Bruce and R.H. Clark, *Introduction to Hydrometeorology*, Pergamon Press, Elmsford, New York, 1966, © J.P. Bruce and R.H. Clark. Fig. 31.12: Adapted from Brian J. Skinner and Stephen C. Porter, *The Dynamic Earth: An Introduction to Physical Geology*, John Wiley & Sons, 1989, p. 199. Fig. 31.13: From Léo F. Laporte, *Encounter With the Earth*, Canfield Press, p. 249, © Léo F. Laporte. Fig. 31.15: Adapted from *Introduction to Physical Geography*, 2nd edn, by H.M. Kendall, R.M. Glendinning, C.H. McFadden, and R.F. Logan, copyright © 1974 by Harcourt Brace Jovanovich, Inc.

Unit 32   Fig. 32.2: Adapted from Environment Canada, 2004. Fig. 32.10: Same source as Fig. 31.12, p. 221. Fig. 32.12: Same source as Fig. 3.13, p. 279.

Unit 34   Figs 34.2A, 34.11: Same source as Fig. 3.13, pp. 274, 287, and 290. Fig. 34.13b: Adapted from Environment Canada, 2004.

Unit 35   Fig. 35.4: Same source as Fig. 3.13, p. 256.

Unit 36   Fig. 36.2: Same source as Fig. 3.13, p. 345. Fig. 36.3: After NASA, n.d. Fig. 36.8: Same source as Fig. 31.12, p. 270.

Unit 37   Fig. 37.4: From J.F. Lovering and J.R.V. Prescott, *Last of Lands . . . Antarctica*, Melbourne University Press, 1979, data from Gordon and Goldberg, 'Circumpolar Characteristics of Antarctic Waters', American Geographical Society, Antarctic Map Folio Series, 1970, and Kort, 'The Antarctic Ocean', *Scientific American*, Vol. 207, 1962. Figs 37.6, 37.11: Adapted from Richard Foster Flint, *Glacial and Pleistocene Geology*, John Wiley & Sons, 1957, pp. 227 ff., copyright © Harrison L. Flint. Fig. 37.19: After Armin K. Lobeck, *Geomorphology*, McGraw-Hill Book Company, 1932. Fig. 37.22: Same source as Fig. 31.12, p. 268. Table 37.4: From P.F. Karrow, *Pleistocene Geology of the Scarborough Area*, © Queen's Printer for Ontario, 1967, reproduced with permission.

Unit 38   Fig. 38.8: Adapted from Richard Foster Flint, *Glacial and Pleistocene Geology*, John Wiley & Sons, 1957, pp. 227 ff., copyright © Harrison L. Flint. Fig. 38.9: Adapted from William D. Thornbury, *Principles of Geomorphology*, John Wiley & Sons, 2nd rev. edn, 1969, p. 399.

Unit 39   Fig. 39.4: Same source as Fig. 3.13, p. 361.

Unit 40   Figs 40.6, 40.11, 40.12: Same source as Fig. 3.13, pp. 316, 322, and 324. Fig. 40.15: After US Bureau of Reclamation, 1960.

Unit 41   Figs 41.2, 41.5, 41.7: After Keith Stowe, *Essentials of Ocean Science*, 1987, pp. 84, 87, and 124, published by John Wiley & Sons, copyright © 1987 by John Wiley & Sons, Inc. Figs 41.3, 41.4A, 41.6: Same source as Fig. 3.13, pp. 385, 386, and 387.

Unit 42   Figs 42.2, 42.9: Same source as Fig. 3.13, pp. 392, 393. Fig. 42.16: Same source as Fig. 31.12, p. 297. Fig. 42.17: Same source as Fig. 8.10, p. 302. Table 42.1: J.P. Coakley, 1972, 'Near Shore Sediment Studies in Western Lake Erie', Proceedings of the 15th Conference on Great Lakes Research, International Association of Great Lakes Research, pp. 330–43.

Unit 43   Fig. 43.5: Adapted from Paul Harrisson and Fred Pearce, eds, *AAAS Atlas of Population and Environment*, University of California Press, 2000, pp. 76–7. Fig. 43.9: Adapted from 'Water', *National Geographic* Special Edition, November 1993, p. 61, © 1993 National Geographic Society.

Unit 44   Fig. 44.14: From *Fundamentals of Soil Science*, 8th rev. edn, by Henry D. Foth, copyright © John Wiley & Sons, Inc. Fig. 44.16: After USDA, Soil Conservation Service, n.d. Fig. 44.21: From S.R. Eyre, *Vegetation and Soils: A World Picture*, Aldine, 1963, p. 259, © S.R. Eyre. Fig. 44.22: From Daniel H. Yaalon, *Transactions of the International Congress of Soil Science*, Vol. 4, V. 16, p. 120, © 1960 by the International Society of Soil Science.

Unit 45   Fig. 45.2: After USDA, n.d. Table 45.1: Soil Classification Working Group, 1998, *The Canadian System of Soil Classification*, Research Branch, Agriculture and Agri-Food Canada, Publication 1946, 3rd edn 1998, reproduced with the permission of the Minister of Public Works and Government Services, 2009.

Unit 46   Fig. 46.1: From Léo F. Laporte, *Encounter with the Earth*, Canfield Press, p. 120, © 1975 by Léo F. Laporte, reprinted by permission of the author. Fig. 46.3: After H. Lieth and E. Box, *Publications in Climatology*, C.W. Thornthwaite Laboratory of Climatology, Vol. 25, No. 3, 1972, p. 42. Fig. 46.8: Fig. 5.8b, p. 108, from *Geography: A Modern Synthesis*, 3rd edn, by Peter Haggett, copyright © 1983 by Peter Haggett, reprinted by permission of Pearson Education, Inc. Fig. 46.14: Smog Formation (a), p. 186, from *Geography: A Modern Synthesis*, 3rd edn, by Peter Haggett, copyright © 1983 by Peter Haggett, reprinted by permission of Pearson Education, Inc. Fig. 46.12: Reprinted with permission from the Hach Company, Loveland, CO. Fig. 46.15: Adapted from *Fundamentals of Ecology*, 3rd edn, by Eugene P. Odum, copyright © 1971 by Saunders College Publishing. Fig. 46.16: © *Biol. Bull.*, Vol. XXI, No. 3, pp. 127–51, and Vol. XXII, No. 1, pp. 1–38. Fig. 46.17: After C.B. Cox et al., *Biogeography*, 1973, p. 61, © Blackwell Scientific Publications Ltd. Fig. 46.22: From Carl Zimmer, *Evolution: Triumph of an Idea*, © 2001 by WGBH Educational Foundation and Clear Blue Sky Productions., used by permission of HarperCollins Publishers.

Unit 47   Fig. 47.2: Adapted from *Planets and People*, Resource Publication of the Association of American Geographers, Thomas R. Vale, 1982. Figs 47.3, 47.4: Adapted from *Environmental Science*, 3rd edn by Jonathan Turk, Amos Turk, and Karen Arms, copyright © 1984 by Saunders College Publishing.

Unit 48   Fig. 48.6: After *Guide to the Mammals of Pennsylvania*, by Joseph F. Merritt, published by the University of Pittsburgh Press, © 1987 by the University of Pittsburgh Press.

Credits for Photographs

Part One   *Opener*: Laguna Design/Science Photo Library.

Unit 1   *Opener*: Kevin A. Horgan/Science Photo Library. Fig. 1.2: BBC. Fig. 1.3: © James Gurney/National Geographic Image Collection. Fig. 1.5: Archives of Ontario, F 443, R-C(U), AO 1541. Fig. 1.6: H.J. de Blij. Fig. 1.8: © AbleStock Photos.

Unit 2   *Opener*: Zephyr/Science Photo Library. Fig. 2.6: Tibor G. Toth/National Geographic Image Collection.

Unit 3   *Opener*: H.J. de Blij. Fig. 3.1A: © The Trustees of the British Museum. Fig. 3.17: © 1995 Canadian Space Agency, image received by the Canada Centre for Remote Sensing, processed by MacDonald, Dettwiler and Associates Ltd.

Part Two   *Opener*: Steve Percival/Science Photo Library.

Unit 4   *Opener*: Detlev Van Ravenswaay/Science Photo Library. Fig. 4.1: © Dr Scott Nielsen/DRK PHOTO. Fig. 4.4: © 2001 by Fred Espenak, <www.MrEclipse.com>. Fig. 4.7: Mike Grandmaison/Firstlight.

Unit 5   *Opener*: Detlev Van Ravenswaay/Science Photo Library. Fig. 5.2: Bill Lowry/Ivy Images. Fig. 5.9: Ivy Images.

Unit 6   *Opener*: David Nunuk/Science Photo Library.

Unit 7   *Opener*: NASA/Science Photo Library. Fig. 7.1: Time Life Pictures/Getty Images. Fig. 7.6: Dick Hemingway.

Unit 8   *Opener*: John Mead/Science Photo Library.

Unit 9   *Opener*: K. Jayaram/Science Photo Library. Fig. 9.7: © Geospace/Science Photo Library.

Unit 10   *Opener*: Peter Scoones/Science Photo Library.

Unit 11   *Opener*: © Httin/Dreamstime.com. Fig. 11.5: Science Source/Photo Researchers. Fig. 11.10: H.J. de Blij. Fig. 11.11: *Cirrus*: © Iofoto/Dreamstime.com; *Cirrocumulus*: © iStockphoto. com/Ekspansio; *Cirrostratus*: © Pzake/Dreamstime.com; *Altocumulus*: © iStockphoto.com/rotofrank; *Altostratus*: © Hypermania/ Dreamstime.com; *Cumulus*: © iStockphoto.com/asiseeit; *Cumulus with development*: © iStockphoto.com/Avery Photography; *Stratus*: © Paha_l/Dreamstime.com; *Cumulonimbus*: © iStockphoto.com/ Dave Raboin. Fig. 11.12: The Canadian Press/Jonathan Hayward.

Unit 12   *Opener*: Detlev Van Ravenswaay/Science Photo Library. Fig. 12.5: JSC/NASA. Fig. 12.7: H.J. de Blij. Fig. 12.9: Library and Archives Canada/PA-116389.

Unit 13   *Opener*: NASA/Science Photo Library. Fig. 13.4: RCAF.

Unit 14   *Opener*: Eric Nguyen/Science Photo Library. Fig. 14.1: Space Science and Engineering Center. Fig. 14.3: The Canadian Press/Jacques Boissinot. Fig. 14.5: Graham Owen. Fig. 14.6: © Chris White/Fotolia.com. Fig. 14.7: © Warren E. Faidley/DRK PHOTO. Fig. 14.10: The Canadian Press/Dave Martin. Fig. 14.12: NASA/ MODIS Rapid Response Team. Fig. 14.13: © Jim Zuckerman/Corbis. Fig. 14.14: The Canadian Press/Jeff McIntosh.

Unit 15   *Opener*: Patrik Lindqvist/Getty Images. Fig. 15.1: Courtesy of The Weather Network. Figs 15.4, 15.5, 15.6, 15.7: Environment Canada, data courtesy of NOAA (28 July 2004). Fig. 15.8: Environment Canada, data courtesy of NOAA (29 July 2004). Fig. 15.11: Environment Canada, data courtesy of NOAA (1 October 2008).

Unit 16   *Opener*: Peter Falkner/Science Photo Library.

Unit 17   *Opener*: © zastavkin/Big Stock Photo. Figs 17.1, 17.2: H.J. de Blij. Fig. 17.6: © Wolfgang Kaehler/Corbis. Fig. 17.7: © John Moss/Photo Researchers, Inc. Fig. 17.12: © Steve McCurry/Magnum Photos. Fig. 17.17A: © Richard A. Cooke/Corbis. Fig. 17.17B: © IFA/ Peter Arnold, Inc. Fig. 17.25: © Doug Wilson/Corbis. Fig. 17.26: Winston Fraser/Ivy Images. Fig. 17.29: © Robert Glusic/Getty Images. Fig. 17.33: H.J. de Blij.

Unit 18   *Opener*: Bjorn Svensson/Science Photo Library. Fig. 18.1: © Tom Bean/Corbis. Fig. 18.2: Eric Calais. Fig. 18.5: David Vaughan/ Science Photo Library. Fig. 18.10A: Science Photo Library. Fig. 18.10B: NASA/Science Photo Library.

Unit 19   *Opener*: Ria Novosti/Science Photo Library. 19.4: Francis Lépine/Valan Photos. Fig. 19.8: © Bettmann/Corbis. Fig. 19.9: NASA. Fig. 19.10: China Photos/Stringer/Getty Images.

Part Three   *Opener*: Science Photo Library.

Unit 20   *Opener*: Science Photo Library. Fig. 20.1: Mark E. Gibson/ DRK PHOTO. Figs 20.7, 20.10, 20.11: H.J. de Blij. Fig. 20.9: Dr Ron Clowes, LITHOPROBE and Earth & Ocean Sciences, University of British Columbia, Vancouver, Canada. Fig. 20.14: © Tom and Susan Bean, Inc./DRK PHOTO. Fig. 20.15: © Richard Bergmann/ Photo Researchers Inc.

Unit 21   *Opener*: Reproduced with the permission of Natural Resources Canada, 2009, courtesy of the Geological Survey of Canada (Photo 2002-348 by Isabelle McMartin). Fig. 21.2: H. Raab. Fig. 21.3: The Planetary and Space Science Centre, University of New Brunswick, Canada. Figs 21.4, 21.5: The Planetary and Space Science Centre, University of New Brunswick, Canada. Fig. 21.6: NASA.

Unit 22   *Opener*: Sheila Terry/Science Photo Library. Fig. 22.2: © Mickey Gibson/Earth Scenes. Fig. 22.3A: © Phillip Hayson/Photo Researchers, Inc. Fig. 22.3B: © E.R. Degginger/Earth Scenes. Figs 22.5, 22.6: H.J. de Blij. Fig. 22.7: © Kevin Schaefer/Peter Arnold, Inc.

Unit 23   Opener: Gary Irving/PhotoDisc. Figs 23.1, 23.3, 23.5, 23.6, 23.10: H.J. de Blij. Fig. 23.7: © Dominique Braud/Earth Scenes. Fig. 23.8: Tom Bean/Corbis.

Unit 24   *Opener*: Bernhard Edmaier/Science Photo Library. Figs 24.4: Tibor G. Toth/National Geographic Image Collection. Fig. 24.11: © John S. Shelton. Fig. 24.14: Al Harvey/The Slide Farm. Fig. 24.16: H.J. de Blij. Fig. 24.17: © C. Montheath/Earth Scenes. Fig. 24.20: © Earth Satellite Corporation/Science Photo Library/Photo Researchers. Fig. 24.21: © Carson Baldwin, Jr/Earth Scenes.

Unit 25   Fig. 25.1: © Krafft/HOA.QUI/Photo Researchers Inc. Fig. 25.2: Bernhard Edmaier/Science Photo Library. Fig. 25.3: Bernhard Edmaier/Science Photo Library. Fig. 25.7: © Steve Raymer/National Geographic Image Collection. Fig. 25.8A: Dave Harlow, USGS. Figs 25.9, 25.13, 25.16: H.J. de Blij. Fig. 25.11: © E.R. Degginger/Earth Scenes. Fig. 25.14A: Tibor G. Toth/National Geographic Image Collection.

Index

Edwards Brothers Malloy
Ann Arbor MI. USA
August 29, 2016